HANDBOOK OF PHYSIOLOGY

SECTION 2: The Cardiovascular System, VOLUME IV, PART 1

HANDBOOK OF PHYSIOLOGY

A critical, comprehensive presentation of physiological knowledge and concepts

---

SECTION 2: **The Cardiovascular System**

Formerly SECTION 2: Circulation

VOLUME IV.

Microcirculation, Part 1

Volume Editors: EUGENE M. RENKIN
C. CHARLES MICHEL

Executive Editor: STEPHEN R. GEIGER

American Physiological Society, BETHESDA, MARYLAND, 1984

Library of Congress Catalog Card Number 79–10144

International Standard Book Number 0-683-07202-1

Printed in the United States of America by Waverly Press, Inc., Baltimore, Maryland 21202

Distributed by The Williams & Wilkins Company, Baltimore, Maryland 21202

Preface

Three hundred and fifty years ago, the microcirculation was a hypothesis, a necessary link between the arteries and veins in Harvey's theory of the circulation of the blood. Although capillaries were observed by Malpighi three years after Harvey's death, two centuries elapsed before the cellular nature of the capillary wall was conclusively demonstrated. Since the middle of the nineteenth century, knowledge of the structure and function of small blood vessels has steadily increased, and the pioneering work of Müller, Poiseuille, Ludwig, Cohnheim, Starling, and Krogh has been sustained and developed by their many notable successors.

Although hemodynamics and transport in the minute blood vessels have always been recognized as topics of major importance, it is only recently that large numbers of investigators have been attracted to work on the microcirculation. Since publication of the first edition of the *Handbook of Physiology* on circulation more than twenty years ago, societies and journals dedicated to the microcirculation have proliferated, and the subject has become one of the most active and challenging areas of cardiovascular research.

Modern study of the microcirculation is an interdisciplinary exercise. It has long been a field where physical principles have been broadly and fruitfully applied, and at times the search for physical explanations of observed phenomena has led to the discovery of new physical relationships. For example, Poiseuille discovered a law that forms the basis of our understanding not only of microvascular flow but also of transport through porous membranes such as the capillary wall. Until twenty years ago, physical principles had been successfully applied to the microcirculation by only a few outstanding physiologists. In the mid-1960s, however, an influx of engineers and mathematically inclined biologists imparted a strong biophysical character to the field. This did much to enhance theoretical developments, particularly in the areas of rheology and transport. Somewhat earlier, electron microscopists had turned their attention to the microcirculation, and their contributions continue to increase. The early advances are admirably described by Majno in volume III of the first edition of the *Handbook* on circulation, but subsequent developments have drastically altered our ideas about the relationships between structure and function. Most recently there has been an upsurge of interest in the cellular biology of endothelium, and this promises to be one of the most important stimuli for further advancement.

Preparation of this edition of the *Handbook of Physiology* on the cardiovascular system has provided an opportunity for consolidation of essential concepts and new developments of microvascular physiology. Each chapter introduces the scope and principles of the topic it describes and offers to more experienced investigators a critical assessment of the status of current ideas and techniques. It is also hoped that this volume will help cardiovascular physiologists to correlate phenomena at the macrocirculatory and microcirculatory levels.

The volume begins with a historical review of the contributions of Poiseuille to our understanding of microvascular flow. This is followed by two chapters on the structure of the microcirculation, a chapter on endothelial cell biology, and one on microvascular growth and adaptation. The next two chapters are devoted to microcirculatory dynamics of blood and lymph. Six chapters on material transport in and around the microcirculation cover the mechanics and thermodynamics of transport, movement of fluid, movements of small solutes and of macromolecules, transport in the interstitium, and transport modeling. A chapter on control of the microcirculation and exchange forms a bridge between these chapters and the rest of the volume. The next eight chapters describe microcirculation and exchange in selected organs and organ systems: liver and spleen, heart, gastrointestinal system, lungs, synovial joints, adipose tissue, brain, and eye. Finally there are chapters on capillary portal circulations and on disseminated intravascular coagulation. We have not covered all the topics that might have been included, nor have we covered certain topics to the extent that some readers and authors might desire. However, this volume is larger than we originally expected, and an end had to be made somewhere.

We are grateful to the many contributors to this volume for their time and effort.

EUGENE M. RENKIN
C. CHARLES MICHEL

Contents

Part 1

1. Contributions to microvascular research of Jean Léonard Marie Poiseuille
   J. R. PAPPENHEIMER 1
2. Architecture
   MARY P. WIEDEMAN 11
3. Ultrastructure of the microvascular wall: functional correlations
   MAYA SIMIONESCU
   NICOLAE SIMIONESCU 41
4. Physiology and biochemistry of the vascular wall endothelium
   DAVID SHEPRO
   PATRICIA A. D'AMORE 103
5. Development of microcirculation: capillary growth and adaptation
   O. HUDLICKÁ 165
6. Blood flow in small tubes
   SHU CHIEN
   SHUNICHI USAMI
   RICHARD SKALAK 217
7. Pressure-flow relations in blood and lymph microcirculation
   BENJAMIN W. ZWEIFACH
   HERBERT H. LIPOWSKY 251
8. Mechanics and thermodynamics of transcapillary exchange
   FITZ-ROY E. CURRY 309
9. Fluid movements through capillary walls
   C. CHARLES MICHEL 375
10. Capillary permeability to small solutes
    CHRISTIAN CRONE
    DAVID G. LEVITT 411
11. Exchange of macromolecules across the microcirculation
    AUBREY E. TAYLOR
    D. NEIL GRANGER 467
12. The interstitium and microvascular exchange
    JOEL L. BERT
    RICHARD H. PEARCE 521
13. Modeling in the analysis of solute and water exchange in the microvasculature
    JAMES B. BASSINGTHWAIGHTE
    CARL A. GORESKY 549

Index xi

Part 2

14. Control of microcirculation and blood-tissue exchange
    EUGENE M. RENKIN 627
15. Microcirculatory events in the liver and the spleen
    CARL A. GORESKY
    ALAN C. GROOM 689
16. Interactions between capillary exchange, cellular entry, and metabolic sequestration processes in the heart
    COLIN P. ROSE
    CARL A. GORESKY 781
17. Microcirculation of the gastrointestinal tract and pancreas
    OVE LUNDGREN 799
18. Pulmonary microcirculation and exchange
    RICHARD M. EFFROS 865

19. Blood flow and mass transport in synovial joints
J. R. LEVICK 917
20. Microcirculation and transport in adipose tissue
SUNE ROSELL 949
21. Blood-brain barrier
JOSEPH D. FENSTERMACHER
STANLEY I. RAPOPORT 969
22. Circulation in the eye
ANDERS BILL 1001
23. Capillary beds and portal circulations
J. R. HENDERSON
P. M. DANIEL 1035
24. Microcirculation in disseminated intravascular coagulation induced by endotoxins
HENRY Z. MOVAT 1047
Index xi

CHAPTER 1

Contributions to microvascular research of Jean Léonard Marie Poiseuille

J. R. PAPPENHEIMER | *Department of Physiology, Harvard Medical School, Boston, Massachusetts*

CHAPTER CONTENTS

Mercury Manometer and Measurement of Arterial Pressure
Pressures and Flow in the Venous System
Microcirculation
Poiseuille's Law: the Flow of Liquids in Glass Capillary Tubes
 Variations in tube diameter and ellipticity
 Temperature
 Pressure
Characterization of Membrane Permeability by Hydrodynamic Flow (Poiseuille's Law) and Diffusion (Fick's Law)

POISEUILLE'S LAW of viscous flow through cylindrical tubes is included in almost every introductory course in physics or medical physiology, but few scientists are aware of the meticulous experimental measurements that underlie the basic law and its application to hydrodynamics, physical chemistry, regulation of circulation, and capillary permeability. Nor is it generally known that Poiseuille was the first to use a mercury manometer for the measurement of blood pressure, to describe axial flow of red cells in the microcirculation, and to measure and correctly interpret the changes in central venous pressure that occur during breathing. These fundamental contributions to the physiology of the peripheral circulation were made between 1828 and 1841, and Poiseuille may well be considered the first major contributor to the modern field of microvascular research. It seems appropriate to introduce this *Handbook* volume on microcirculation with a historical essay bringing some of the most interesting and significant aspects of Poiseuille's work to the attention of contemporary students of the cardiovascular system.

Jean Léonard Marie Poiseuille (Fig. 1) was born in Paris on April 22, 1797; he was the son of Jean Baptiste Poiseuille, a carpenter, and Anne Victoire Caumont. Little is known of Poiseuille's personal life or even of his professional career. From 1815 to 1816 he studied at the École Polytechnique, where he presumably trained as an engineer. Subsequently he transferred to medicine, but we are ignorant of the reasons that led him to study medicine and experimental physiology. His doctoral thesis on arterial pressure (see Fig. 2) was a landmark in the history of cardiovascular physiology, and from then until 1868 Poiseuille continued to publish original work. Much of his work was conducted on animals, including horses and dogs as well as fish and Amphibia. However, we do not know where the work was done or what position, if any, he held at the university. The apparatus he constructed for experimental work was elaborate and expensive (see Fig. 4), and his work on large animals must have required considerable space and technical assistance. There are no records, however, that reveal the source of his financial support. According to Joly (18), Poiseuille maintained interests in medicine, particularly in diseases of the lung. Sachaile's book of 1845, *The Physicians of Paris* (42), lists Poiseuille's office hours as 7–10, but a note dated 1867 in Poiseuille's dossier at the department of primary schools states that he did not practice medicine after 1844. The question remains, therefore, as to how Poiseuille could afford to pursue his elaborate, expensive, and time-consuming research. In 1829 he married the daughter of M. Panay de Lorette, Chief Engineer of Roads and Bridges, and it may be that this alliance made it possible for Poiseuille to devote so much time to experimental work.

Poiseuille presented most of his work in the form of oral communications to the Academy of Sciences, followed by summaries in the Academy's *Comptes Rendus*. He presented the laws of flow through cylindrical tubes in three such communications during the winter of 1840–1841 and was awarded many prizes for both his physiological and physical studies. In 1842 he was elected to the Academy of Medicine, and he was also an active member of the Société Philomatique. Yet despite public acclaim for his work on hydrodynamics and the esteem with which Magendie and other noted physiologists regarded Poiseuille's physiological studies, he was never elected to the Academy of Sciences.

FIG. 1. Jean Léonard Marie Poiseuille (1797–1869). Original of this photograph is in the library of the Academy of Medicine in Paris and has been reproduced previously (4, 18). A drawing based on this photograph graces the Poiseuille Gold Medal Award of the International Biorheological Society (6, 7).

Poiseuille's most important contributions may be considered under four main headings.

1. 1828: Mercury manometer and measurement of pressure in the arteries (*Recherches sur la force du coeur aortique*).
2. 1830: Pressures and flows in the venous system (Les causes du mouvement du sang dans les veines).
3. 1833–1835: Microcirculation (Les causes du mouvement du sang dans les vaisseaux capillaires).
4. 1840–1846: Poiseuille's law (Le mouvement des liquides dans les tubes de très-petits diamètres).

RECHERCHES SUR LA FORCE DU COEUR AORTIQUE

In 1733 Hales published his famous *Essay on Hemastaticks* (14) in which he described the first measurements of arterial blood pressure. Considering the importance of these measurements, it may seem surprising that no further observations of blood pressure were made until Poiseuille took up the problem almost 100 years later. However, as Poiseuille points out in his thesis, the methods used by Hales were not suited to systematic investigations. In Hales's experiments the carotid arteries of horses and dogs were cannulated with brass pipes, the free ends of which were connected by flexible tubing (the trachea of a goose) to a vertical glass tube. It took time and loss of blood to fill the glass tube, and the blood clotted before systematic studies could be made in any one animal. Moreover there were large oscillations in the level of blood in the tube because of the respiratory movements of the struggling animals.

Poiseuille devised the U-tube mercury manometer to avoid dealing with a column of blood 10–12 ft high. He solved the clotting problem by using saturated $NaHCO_3$ to connect the artery with the mercury; presumably the carbonate precipitated the Ca^{2+} in blood, thus preventing coagulation. The U-tube mercury manometer is taken for granted by physiologists today, but the physical principles involved were by no means obvious to Poiseuille's contemporaries. He had to explain the physics of the instrument, including corrections for the varying column of bicarbonate-blood mixture in one limb of the U tube, the effects of

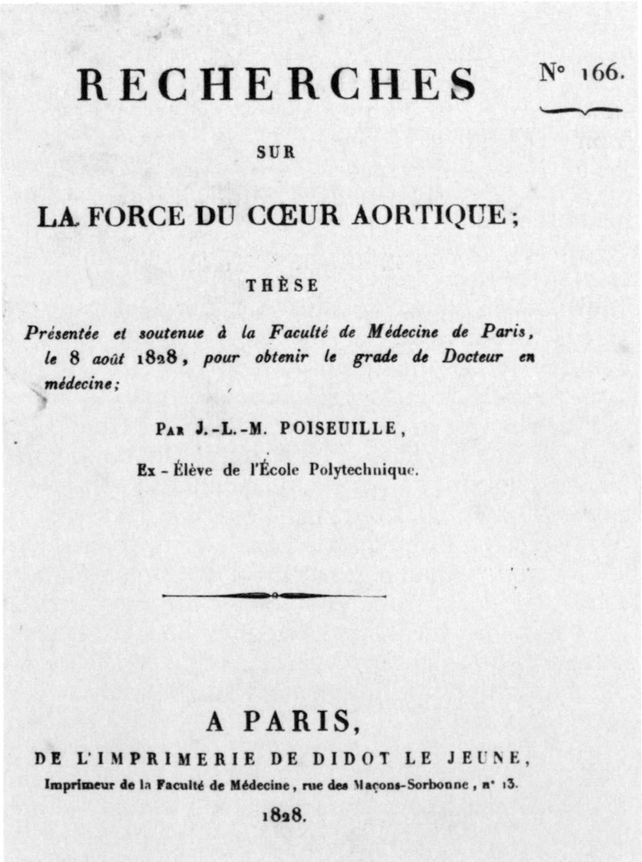

RECHERCHES N° 166.

SUR

LA FORCE DU CŒUR AORTIQUE;

THÈSE

Présentée et soutenue à la Faculté de Médecine de Paris, le 8 août 1828, pour obtenir le grade de Docteur en médecine;

PAR J.-L.-M. POISEUILLE,

Ex-Élève de l'École Polytechnique.

A PARIS,

DE L'IMPRIMERIE DE DIDOT LE JEUNE,

Imprimeur de la Faculté de Médecine, rue des Maçons-Sorbonne, n° 13.

1828.

FIG. 2. Title page of Poiseuille's doctoral thesis containing the first description of the mercury manometer and its application to the measurement of pressure in large and small arteries. [From Poiseuille (28).]

temperature on the density of mercury, the effects of slight inequalities in the diameters of the two limbs of the U tube, and the importance of maintaining the manometer in a vertical position. Poiseuille called his instrument the hemodynamometer, but it must be said that he failed to consider its dynamic properties and some of his reported oscillatory pressures must have reflected the inertial characteristics of the system. Addition of a float and recording stylus to the Poiseuille mercury manometer was first described by Ludwig in 1847 (22), and a detailed description of the recording hemodynamometer, with full credit to Poiseuille, is given in the 1861 edition of Ludwig's textbook (23). In the ensuing 100 years, until the 1960s, the Poiseuille-Ludwig hemodynamometer was used by hundreds of thousands of medical students and scientists. In recent years, however, the mercury manometer has been largely replaced by the electrical strain gauge even in the teaching laboratory. Today's students, adjusting the sensitivity of electrical pressure transducers, are unlikely to appreciate, as did Poiseuille, the physical meaning of force per unit area.

Poiseuille first used his hemodynamometer to investigate pressure gradients in the arterial circulation. It seemed obvious a priori that the pressure of blood would diminish with distance from the heart. However, Poiseuille's very first experiments to test this hypothesis (ref. 28, p. 23) "showed, to our astonishment, that two tubes (hemodynamometers) applied simultaneously to two arteries at different distances from the heart gave perfectly equal readings." Thus the average of nine successive readings of mean pressure in the carotid artery of an unanesthetized horse was 146.7 mmHg, whereas the mean pressure measured simultaneously in a small artery of the leg was also 146.7 mmHg. Yet the cross-sectional area of the leg artery was only 1⁄50 that of the carotid. Similarly precise comparisons were made between the mean pressures in many different arteries in dogs and horses, leading Poiseuille to generalize that *the mean pressure of blood is the same throughout the arterial system.*

Where, then, was the pressure drop in the circulation? In order to investigate this problem Poiseuille turned first to a study of pressures in the venous system and subsequently to a study of the microcirculation.

RECHERCHES SUR LES CAUSES DU MOUVEMENT DU SANG DANS LES VEINES

Hales (14) had already measured positive pressures in the external jugular veins of horses, sheep, and dogs, but Poiseuille was the first to insert tubes from the external jugular into the chest and so to record negative pressures with his U-tube manometers. For quiet breathing he found pressures ranging from −8 cmH_2O (saturated $NaHCO_3$ anticoagulant) during inspiration to −1.4 cmH_2O during expiration. When respiratory efforts were intensified, pressures ranged from −25 cmH_2O to +20 cmH_2O. In contrast, pressures measured in the abdominal vena cava or in peripheral veins were always positive and there were no respiratory fluctuations at locations protected from reflux of blood by valves. When the chest was opened and the lungs were artificially ventilated, pressures in the thoracic veins were always positive with respect to atmosphere.

Although these facts seem elementary and obvious today, it must be remembered that many of Poiseuille's contemporaries thought that blood was normally aspirated into the heart by suction caused by inspiratory muscles or by dilatation of the heart itself (3). Poiseuille established beyond doubt that the respiratory pump is only an accessory aid to venous return of blood and that the primary and most important force is the arterial pressure driving blood through the capillaries to the veins and heart. The above pioneer measurements and Poiseuille's clear interpretation of their significance were communicated to the Academy on September 27, 1830, and they were subsequently published in detail (29).

RECHERCHES SUR LES CAUSES DU MOUVEMENT DU SANG DANS LES VAISSEAUX CAPILLAIRES[1]

Under the conditions of Poiseuille's experiments the mean blood pressure in the arterial tree from the aorta to vessels 2 mm in diameter was about 150 mmHg, whereas peripheral venous pressures were only 5–10 mmHg. Thus the main pressure drop occurs in small blood vessels. Although Poiseuille did not state this explicitly, one may surmise that this conclusion led him to a study of the microcirculation. To this end he made microscopic observations of arterioles, capillaries, and venules in fish, amphibians, reptiles, birds, and small mammals. It was during the course of this work that Poiseuille noted the axial velocity gradient of red cells in arterioles and venules. He writes (30):

> at the center the speed is at its maximum; it diminishes as one approaches the walls: very near the walls one can distinguish a transparent space which is ordinarily occupied only by serum; this space has a width of about 1⁄8th to 1⁄10th that of the diameter of the vessel.

Poiseuille gives credit to Haller and to Spallanzini for prior descriptions of the clear layer of plasma at the walls of small blood vessels, but unlike Poiseuille, neither of his two distinguished predecessors under-

[1] The original paper of this title was communicated to the Academy of Sciences on December 28, 1835, but it was not published in detail in *Memoires des Savants Étrangers* (30) until 1841. The Section on Medicine and Surgery of the Academy awarded Poiseuille an emolument of 700 francs for this work.

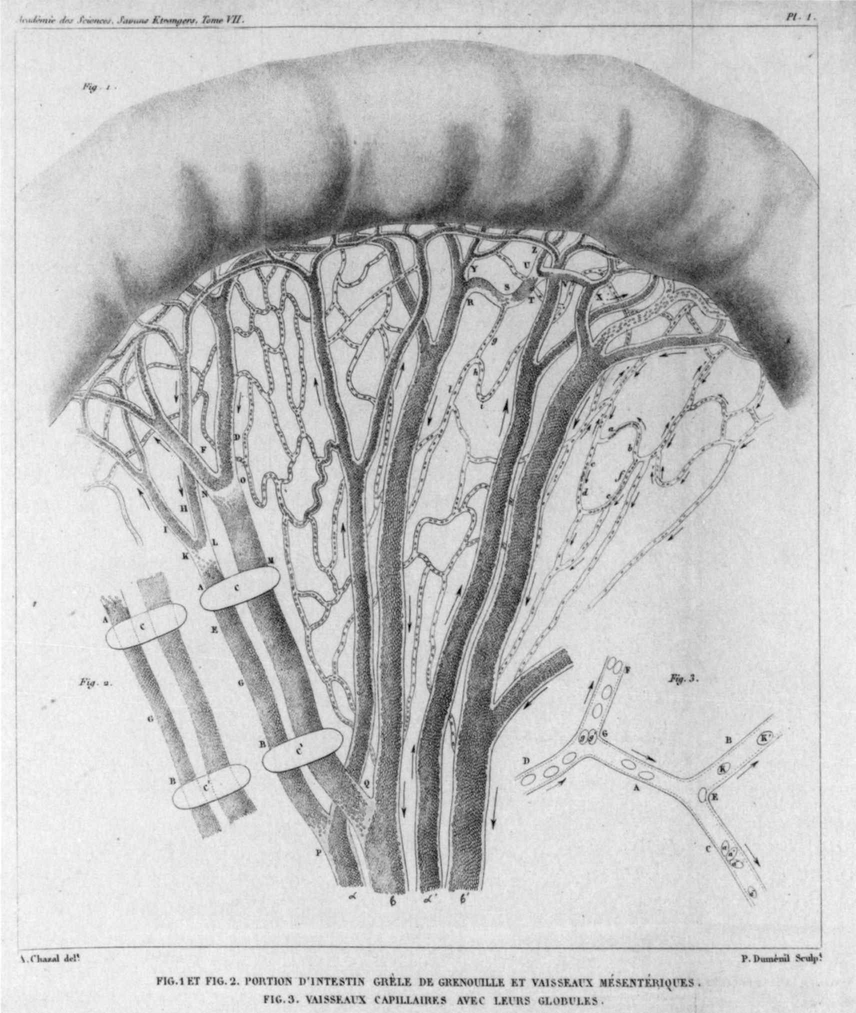

FIG. 3. Poiseuille's illustration of the microcirculation in frog mesentery. The *couche claire*, or plasma layer, is clearly seen at the walls of arterioles and venules. Occlusion of vessels by platinum weights at c and c′ prevented flow-dependent axial concentration of red cells. *Inset at right,* plasma skimming at branching junctions of arterioles and capillaries. [From Poiseuille (30).]

stood that this was a manifestation of an axial velocity gradient.

Figure 3 reproduces Poiseuille's illustration of the microcirculation in the mesentery of a frog. The clear layer of plasma is shown in pairs of arterioles and venules. Platinum weights were placed on a pair of vessels, and it is apparent that the plasma layer disappeared in the absence of flow. Plasma skimming at branching junctions of arterioles and capillaries is shown clearly in the inset at the right. The tendency of white cells to stick to the walls in the stagnant layer is also described in Poiseuille's paper (30).

Poiseuille subsequently performed an ingenious experiment to show that there is a sleeve of stagnant fluid at the walls during the flow of pure liquids through glass tubes (4). For this purpose he coated the walls of a glass tube with a thin layer of rough varnish and then measured the hydrodynamic resistance to flow of water through the tube. The rough coat of varnish was then polished by gentle heating but the resistance to flow was unaltered within the accuracy of measurement (better than 0.1%). This led to the conclusion that, in general, fluids flow on a thin, immobile layer of fluid at the walls of the tube.

Poiseuille's observations on axial flow of blood in arterioles and venules were of seminal importance to the field of hemorheology, being the forerunner of such classic contributions as those of Hess (16), Krogh (19), Fåhraeus and Lindqvist (9), and Whittaker and Winton (43). Modern hemorheology (see the chapter by Chien et al. in this *Handbook*) has its roots in this pioneer paper of 1841. Nevertheless Poiseuille's observations of the microcirculation failed to reveal the site of the main resistance to flow in the circulation, and it was not until the direct micropuncture studies of Landis (20, 21) that the main pressure drop was localized and attributed to the arterioles. Yet it was Poiseuille's failure to solve the problem in vivo that led him to study the flow of liquids in glass tubes of dimensions approximating those of blood vessels in the microcirculation.

RECHERCHES SUR LE MOUVEMENT DES LIQUIDES DANS LES TUBES DE TRÈS-PETITS DIAMÈTRES

The hydraulic engineers can perhaps afford to neglect the flow of liquids through tubes of small diameter but this is not true of the physiologists who have to consider the passage of liquids through tubes of about 0.01 mm in diameter.

With these words Poiseuille introduced his first paper on the laws of viscous flow to the French Academy of Sciences in 1840. During 1840–1841 he communicated four papers on this subject to the Academy. The first dealt with the flow of water through glass tubes as a function of pressures of up to 8 atm, and subsequent papers considered the effects on flow of tube length, tube diameter, and temperature. Each of these communications was published in the form of a short paper in the *Comptes Rendus de l'Académie des Sciences*, but for purposes of assigning priority it is important to note that they were deposited in a sealed packet with the Academy in 1839 and that preliminary results on the effects of pressure and of tube length had been reported orally to the Société Philomatique as early as 1838 (31). Full experimental details were not reported in communications to the Academy, but the stated results were considered so important that the Academy appointed a commission to investigate the validity of Poiseuille's claims. The commission members met during 1842 and actually repeated some of Poiseuille's experiments by using his basic apparatus fitted with different tubes. In 1843 they published their report in *Annales de Chimie et Physique* (5), fully confirming Poiseuille's claims: "en conséquence la Commission a l'honneur de proposer a l'Académie de donner son approbation au travail du M. Poiseuille et d'ordonner que son Mémoir soit inserrée parmi ceux des Savants Étrangers." Publication in extenso finally occurred in 1846 (35). It is indeed interesting that full publication of Poiseuille's great work should have been delayed in this way for several years until an elite committee of the Academy could approve the work.[2]

Poiseuille established his law of flow within a standard error of 0.1% in glass tubes ranging from 0.65 to 0.013 mm in diameter and over a pressure range of a few millimeters of water to 8 atm. This required meticulous experimental techniques and the wit to identify and incorporate a great many second-order correction factors. Indeed the historical interest in this phase of Poiseuille's work resides as much in contemplation of his exemplary experimental measurements as in his enunciation of Poiseuille's law, especially since the latter can be derived theoretically from first principles as was first done by Hagenbach in 1860 (13). In the words of Millikan (24), Poiseuille's papers of 1840–1846 "constitute one of the classics of experimental science. They are frequently quoted as a model of careful analysis of sources of error and painstaking investigation of the effects of separate variables."

The apparatus utilized by Poiseuille is shown in Figure 4. The heart of the apparatus, the viscometer bulb and tubing, are barely visible within the water bath CDEF and are therefore shown separately in Figure 5. The viscometer bulb and related "protective" gadgetry are connected via stopcock and four-way junction to a force pump capable of generating 10 atm of air pressure, a 60-liter buffer air reservoir capable of withstanding 20 atm of pressure, and mercury or water manometers via lead tubing. All scales and menisci were equipped with either optical magnifiers and/or vernier scales. The first 27 pages of the 1844 treatise are devoted mainly to the second-order corrections that eventually gave an accuracy of better than 0.2% in the prediction of flow rates as a function of pressure drop, tube dimensions, and temperature. Some of these factors are described briefly here.

Variations in Tube Diameter and Ellipticity

Since flow rate turned out to be a function of the fourth power of tube diameter, it was necessary to determine dimensions with great accuracy. Hundreds of tubes were examined and discarded in search of those having unusually uniform dimensions. Dimensions were measured both optically and from the weight of mercury as a function of length along the tube. After measurements of flow were completed on selected tubes, the tubes were sectioned, the ends ground flat, and the diameters of the hole in each section measured at high magnification to the nearest 0.5 μm. For example, in a tube of length 4.9375 cm, the maximum and minimum diameters at one end of the tube were listed as 0.01145 and 0.01125 cm; at the opposite end the diameters were 0.01142 and 0.01122 cm.

Similarly, precise measurements were made on many tubes of different lengths and diameters. To correct for ellipticity Poiseuille assumed that the equivalent tube radius would be that of a circle of cross-sectional area equal to the area of the measured ellipse, which in the above example is not significantly different from the algebraic mean of 0.01135 cm at the large end and 0.01132 cm at the small end of the tube. The equivalent radius was then taken as 0.011335 cm for this tube. This method of correcting for ellipticity and for changes in diameter with length is theoretically incorrect (see ref. 1 for laws of flow through elliptical tubes), but it sufficed to yield values for viscosity of water that did not vary by more than 0.15% over a wide range of tube sizes.

Temperature

Poiseuille determined the viscosity of water at temperatures ranging from 0°C–45°C, but most of his measurements were carried out at 10°C. At this temperature, viscosity varies 2.8%/°C, and in order to

[2] An earlier preprint of this paper was published in its entirety in 1844. The origin of this preprint is unknown, but it appears to be identical with the official 1846 edition except for the title page and the pagination. The 1846 edition is generally cited (see refs. 1, 2, 21), but Poiseuille himself in 1868 (39) refers to pagination of the 1844 preprint. A copy of this rare preprint is available in the rare books collection of the Health Sciences Library of the College of Physicians and Surgeons, Columbia University, New York.

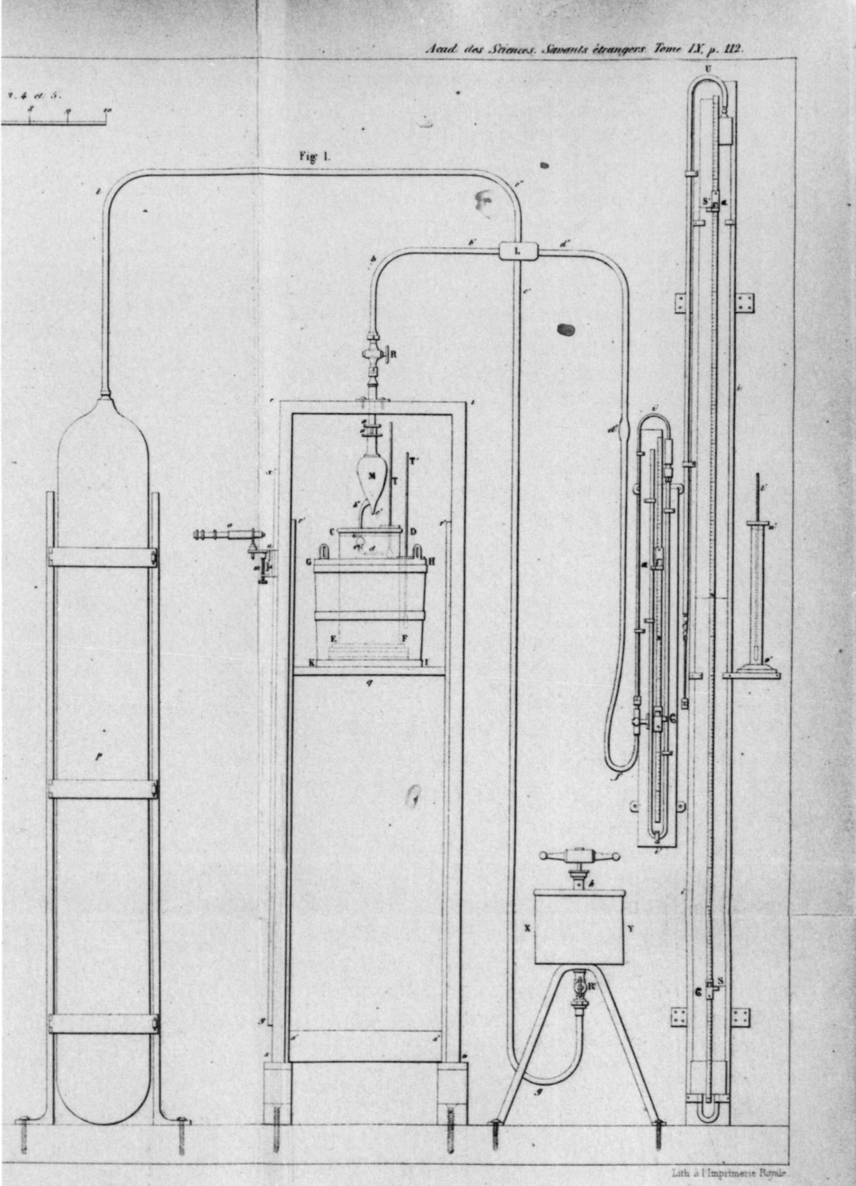

FIG. 4. Poiseuille's apparatus for measuring flow in glass capillary tubes as a function of pressure and temperature. The viscometer itself is barely visible in the water bath (CDEF) and so is shown separately in Fig. 5. The viscometer is connected via a particle separator (M) and stopcock (R) to a 4-way joint (L) leading to *1*) a force pump (XY) capable of generating 10 atm air pressure, *2*) a 60-liter buffer air reservoir (P) capable of withstanding 20 atm, and *3*) mercury or water manometers [via lead tubing (df)]. [From Plate I of Poiseuille's 1844 treatise (35).]

achieve consistency of results within 0.2% it was therefore necessary to set and control the temperature of the flow system within 0.1°C. This level of accuracy must have been exceedingly difficult to achieve in 1840 without the benefit of electrical methods for heating, cooling, stirring, and automatic thermostating. Poiseuille does not explain how he was able to cool and maintain the water bath at 10°C ± 0.05°C; he merely states that he took care to measure the temperature within 0.05°C and to make second-order corrections for temperature variations. These corrections included the temperature coefficient of expansion of glass. In one case the measured volume of the glass viscometer bulb changed from 13.341 ml at 10°C to 13.472 ml at 45°C, thus necessitating a 1% correction in calculating rate of flow. At the same time the diameter of the flow tube (also calculated from the coefficient of expansion of glass) changed from 0.1411 mm at 10°C to 0.1412 mm at 45°C, and a 0.3% correction was used in accordance with the fourth-power law. Other second-order temperature corrections were made to take into account changes in temperature (and hence density) of the water and/or mercury columns in the manometers.

Pressure

Second-order corrections to the pressures indicated by the U-tube manometers included *1*) the height of the column of liquid in the measuring bulb, which diminished from the top to the bottom meniscus during the course of the experiment; *2*) the pressure of water at the outflow orifice relative to that in the manometer; *3*) the capillarity (surface tension) in the

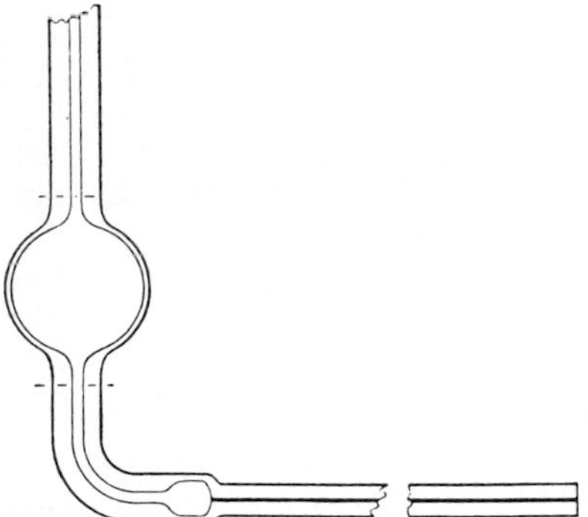

FIG. 5. Poiseuille viscometer. Poiseuille found that he could not obtain consistent flow measurements through small tubes if the efflux emerged to air. Consequently he submerged the entire bulb and flow tube in a water bath (CDEF, Fig. 4) and measured flow rate from the time taken to empty the bulb in the manner shown. Volume of each bulb was determined by weight of mercury, and corrections were made for varying counterpressures due to surface tension at bulb walls and for temperature effects on bulb volume and diameter of capillary tubing. [From Barr (1).]

capillaries of the measuring bulb and at the walls of the bulb itself (the latter correction was complex because of the changing diameter of the liquid surface within the bulb during the course of each experiment); and *4*) the differences in weight of air (atmospheric pressure) at the surface of each limb of the U-tube manometers, taking into account the change in density of air in the high-pressure limb of the manometer. It may seem surprising that the variation of barometric pressure with altitude is sufficient to have a significant effect on the determination of pressure in a simple vertical U-tube manometer, yet such is the case. The correction at an indicated pressure difference (column height) of 2019.6 mmH_2O was −2.9 mmH_2O in one example described by Poiseuille. At higher pressures, when mercury is used instead of water, this interesting correction is negligible.

The numerical examples here provide some insight into the meticulous, quantitative thinking underlying the experimental work leading to the discovery of Poiseuille's law. The law was stated explicitly by Poiseuille in the following equation

$$Q = K \frac{\Delta P \times D^4}{L} \quad (1)$$

where ΔP is the pressure difference (mmHg at 10°C), D is the mean equivalent diameter of the tube (mm), L is the length (mm), and Q is the volume flow rate (mm^3/500 s).

The K in Equation 1 is proportional to what is now defined as fluidity, or the reciprocal of viscosity. However, the units that Poiseuille used to calculate K are not readily converted to cgs units. I have therefore carried out the conversion shown in Table 1, utilizing the original data for pressure, flow, and tube dimensions for each of the seven tubes described in chapter III, p. 513–520 of the 1846 treatise (35). More complete tables based on Poiseuille's data from 40 different

TABLE 1. *Viscosity of Water Calculated From Poiseuille's Original Data*

Tube	Radius, cm × 10^3	Length, cm	Flow Resistance*, $dyn \cdot s \cdot cm^{-5}$	Viscosity†, $dyn \cdot s \cdot cm^{-2}$ (P)
F	32.608	38.383	1.132	0.01309
A	7.080	5.110	67.872	0.01311
B	5.670	2.357	76.015	0.01309
C	4.275	2.440	2.435×10^2	0.01309
D	2.187	2.517	3.671×10^3	0.01309
E	1.469	2.310	16.352×10^3	0.01309
M	0.697	1.850	26.056×10^4	0.01305
Mean				0.013087
SD				0.000018
SE				0.000007

Original data converted to cgs units assuming that 1 mmHg at 10°C in Paris = 1,331 dyn/cm^{-2}. * Flow resistance = $\Delta P/Q \times 10^6$. † Viscosity calculated from $\eta = \pi r^4 \Delta P / 8QL$. Units $dyn \cdot s \cdot cm^{-2}$ are poises (P). [From Poiseuille's 1844 treatise (35).]

tubes (or segments of the tubes listed in Table 1) are available in appendix D of Bingham's monograph (2). The standard error for viscosity of water calculated from the data on each of the seven tubes was only 0.053% of the mean, despite the fact that the ratio of the fourth power of the tube radii varied by almost 5,000,000 and hydrodynamic resistance varied by almost 250,000-fold. Indeed one must pay tribute to Poiseuille's experimental skill and the refinement of his correction factors.

Poiseuille determined the variation of fluidity as a function of temperature with equal refinement, obtaining the relationship

$$K = 1836.7\ (1 + 0.033681T + 0.00221T^2) \quad (2)$$

The absolute value of viscosity of water at 10°C (calculated as in Table 1 from the mean of seven tubes) was 0.013087 ± 0.000007 $dyn \cdot s \cdot cm^{-2}$. This value is within 0.1% of the value based on the work of Bingham (2) and given in the *Handbook of Chemistry and Physics* (15).

The calculations of viscosity summarized in Table 1 do not include corrections for the pressure required to accelerate fluid down the tubes (kinetic energy corrections); indeed Poiseuille did not take accelerative forces into account. Nevertheless he did note the related fact that in any given tube there was a critical length below which there were increasing deviations from his law, and he found that this critical length was related in some unspecified way to increasing tube diameter. For this reason he only used tubes that were longer than the critical length, and the data of Table 1 show no indication of systematic errors that could be accounted for by kinetic energy corrections.

Poiseuille formulated Equation 1 to fit his copious and accurate experimental data, but he was an experimental scientist rather than a theoretician and failed to understand the fundamental physics of his system. It was not until 1860 that E. Hagenbach (13) derived Poiseuille's law from first principles by using Newton's definition of viscosity and elementary calculus. Hagenbach derived the flow equation in the form it is seen today, and he generously suggested that the equation be named after Poiseuille "wir werden die obigen Formel die Poiseuille'schen Formel nennen." It is evident from Hagenbach's paper that he had studied Poiseuille's work in detail and indeed he utilized the latter's data to calculate the coefficient of fluidity or reciprocal viscosity (*Zähigkeit*) from his theoretically derived equation. Since Poiseuille was still alive and active at the time of Hagenbach's publication, it seems strange that no correspondence or records exist to indicate that Poiseuille acknowledged Hagenbach's important theoretical contribution with its generous and laudatory treatment of Poiseuille's own work.

In 1875 Ostwald (25) questioned the propriety of naming the flow law after Poiseuille on the grounds that a German physicist, G. Hagen, published a similar law prior to Poiseuille. It is true that Hagen published an empirical law of flow through tubes in 1839 (12). The metal tubes used by Hagen were shorter and had larger diameters than the glass capillaries used by Poiseuille. Consequently the kinetic energy term, proportional to the square of flow velocity, was important and Hagen clearly recognized this factor in stating that

$$P = k_1Q + k_2Q^2 \tag{3}$$

where P is pressure and Q is volume flow rate.

Hagen showed that k_2 (the kinetic energy component) depends on density but not directly on temperature, whereas k_1 (proportional to what is now defined as viscosity) is very sensitive to temperature. The measurements made by Hagen on three tubes were not comparable to those of Poiseuille in terms of precision or range of pressures, flows, and tube dimensions. Moreover Ostwald (25) was in error when he stated that Poiseuille first published his law of flow in 1843. Ostwald had cited the 1843 report (5) of the committee assigned to evaluate Poiseuille's published communications to the Academy of 1840–1841, but in fact Poiseuille first reported his results to the Société Philomatique in 1838 (31) as has already been noted. There seems very little justification, therefore, for the insistence of Ostwald (25) and later by Prandtl and Tietjens (40) that the law of flow should be renamed for Hagen. It is strange, nevertheless, that neither Poiseuille nor the select committee of the Academy ever referred to Hagen's paper (12), which was published in the principal German journal of physics and chemistry.

In addition to extensive measurements of the fluidity of pure water, Poiseuille carried out some interesting and important experiments on solutions, including electrolytes (24) and alcohol (33, 35). The latter measurements are of particular interest to physical chemists because they clearly distinguished density and surface tension from viscosity, and they foreshadowed fundamental discoveries of the relationship between viscosity and intermolecular forces in solution. Poiseuille found that pure alcohol, despite its low density and surface tension, was actually more viscous than pure water. Yet addition of water to alcohol increased the viscosity still further until it reached a maximum at an alcohol concentration of about 45% (w/w). This value was more than 3 times greater than that of pure water. To anyone who has watched sherry drain slowly down the side of a glass, this observation may not be surprising; a priori one might suppose, however, that viscosity would be related to density or surface tension. Certainly the discovery of a maximum viscosity in a binary mixture more than threefold that of either of the pure components was a remarkable and unexpected one.

Poiseuille was led to his precise measurements of the flow of liquids through capillary tubes because of his interest in factors controlling the flow of blood in the living microcirculation; yet the extreme accuracy of his measurements in vitro was quite unnecessary. The non-Newtonian behavior of whole blood and the geometrical complexity of branching vessels in the microcirculation introduce factors that render Poiseuille's law inapplicable except as a first approximation and a valuable teaching aid. Nonetheless the quantitative features of Poiseuille's research eventually found important application to microcirculatory physiology, namely to the measurement of capillary permeability.

CHARACTERIZATION OF MEMBRANE PERMEABILITY BY HYDRODYNAMIC FLOW (POISEUILLE'S LAW) AND DIFFUSION (FICK'S LAW)

Proportionality between flow rate, pressure drop, and fluidity (reciprocal viscosity) is characteristic of flow through porous media, including artificial or biological membranes containing aqueous channels of ultramicroscopic dimensions. As early as 1872 Guérot (11) proposed that the flow permeability of membranes might be characterized in terms of an "equivalent" membrane containing homogeneous cylindrical pores of diameter and number giving a hydrodynamic resistance corresponding to that defined by Poiseuille's law. Thus any membrane having a measurable hydrostatic or osmotic flow per unit pressure drop could be defined in terms of an equivalent membrane having N cylindrical pores of radius r and length Δx (thickness of membrane)

$$\frac{Q}{\Delta P} = \frac{N\pi r^4}{8\eta\Delta x} = \frac{A_p r^2}{8\eta\Delta x} \tag{4}$$

where A_p is the total cross-sectional area of the pores and η is the viscosity.

In artificial membranes of known thickness Δx the value of A_p can be estimated experimentally by the ratio of wet to dry weight or by electrical conductivity (17). It is then a simple matter to solve for the number and radii of cylindrical pores, which would offer the same resistance to flow as the unknown membranes. This technique, with variations, has been widely used for the calibration of artificial membranes of graded pore size (for reviews see refs. 8, 41).

In living membranes neither the pore area A_p nor the membrane thickness Δx can be determined as in artificial membranes. However, their ratio $A_p/\Delta x$ can be deduced from Fick's law of diffusion (7)

$$\frac{A_p}{\Delta x} = \frac{\dot{n}}{D\Delta c} \qquad (5)$$

where $\dot{n}$ is the measured rate of diffusion of an appropriate tracer through the membrane, D is its coefficient of free diffusion, and Δc is the concentration difference across the membrane. Combination of Equation 4 with Equation 5 yields the equivalent pore radius

$$r = \sqrt{\frac{8\eta D\Delta c}{\dot{n}} \times \frac{Q}{\Delta P}} \qquad (6)$$

Equation 6 was first derived by Pappenheimer et al. (26) in 1950 and was used to characterize the permeability of capillary walls in mammalian muscle (27) and in artificial membranes (41). The results and discussions of the many correction factors that must be considered for this application of Poiseuille's law to living capillaries are taken up in the chapters by Curry, Michel, and Crone and Levitt in this *Handbook*.

The treatise on flow of liquids in glass tubes (1846) was Poiseuille's last important work, although he continued to publish in *Comptes Rendus* on such diverse topics as the ventilation of ships (34), a theory of breathing (36), and the concentrations of glucose (37) and urea (38) in the blood of vertebrates. His last publication, dated one year before his death in 1869, was an inconsequential note on arterial blood pressure (39).

In 1858 Poiseuille applied for a position in the Paris public school system and in 1860 obtained a relatively menial position as Inspector of School Sanitation in the district of the Seine. The dossier on Poiseuille in the city files reveals that he was not well suited for this position, which indeed seems most inappropriate for a distinguished contributor to the Academy of Sciences and member of the Paris Academy of Medicine. The reasons that led Poiseuille at the age of 61 to apply for this position—his first "professional" job—are uncertain. It is known that in his application of 1858 Poiseuille stated that he was born in 1799, placing his age at 59 and thus making him eligible for the position and eventually a retirement income. In fact, Poiseuille was born in 1797, as attested by his birth certificate and certificate of matriculation at the École Polytechnique in 1815. Perhaps some personal disaster occurred in 1858 making it necessary for Poiseuille to seek employment for the first time at such a late age. It is a curious fact that in 1860 and again in 1868 Poiseuille withdrew his name as candidate for election to the prestigious Academy of Sciences to which he had aspired throughout his career. In his letter of withdrawal addressed to the President of the Academy he writes, "je pense, néanmoins, dans les circonstances présentes, devoir retirer ma candidature." One wonders what circumstances led to this unusual request for withdrawal from such a desirable candidacy.

In the seventeenth century, Isaac Newton defined viscosity in fundamental terms, and it is a fair guess that the inventor of calculus could easily have derived Poiseuille's law had there been any special reason for him to be interested in the flow of fluids through cylindrical tubes. It remained instead for Poiseuille, 170 years later, to discover the law by experiment. Poiseuille was a superb experimentalist with an intense and lifelong interest in the physiology of the circulation. We have seen how his interest led to invention of the mercurial manometer, systematic explorations of pressures in the arteries and veins, pioneering studies on axial flow in the living microcirculation, and finally to classic experiments on flow of liquids in glass capillary tubes. Surely, we can think of Poiseuille as one of the first great pioneers in the field of microvascular research, to which the present volume is dedicated.

I am indebted to R. Taton, Centre Alexandre Koyré, Écoles des Hautes Études en Sciences Sociales, Paris, for providing copies of notes pertaining to Poiseuille's life and professional career. Karen Hall, librarian at the College of Physicians and Surgeons in New York City, was most helpful in locating and providing copies of some of Poiseuille's publications. I am especially grateful to Prof. Ralph H. Kellogg for reading the manuscript and making many pertinent suggestions based on his own studies of Poiseuille's publications.

J. R. Pappenheimer is a Career Investigator of the American Heart Association.

REFERENCES

1. BARR, G. *A Monograph of Viscometry.* Oxford, UK: Oxford Univ. Press, 1931, chapt. III, p. 64–66.
2. BINGHAM, E. C. Measurements of Poiseuille. In: *Fluidity and Plasticity.* New York: McGraw-Hill, 1922, app. D, p. 331–339.
3. BRADLEY, S. Splanchnic circulation. In: *Circulation of the Blood: Men and Ideas*, edited by A. P. Fishman and D. Richards. Oxford, UK: Oxford Univ. Press, 1964.
4. BRILLOUIN, M. Poiseuille. *Ann. Phys. Paris* 15: 411–417, 1931.
5. Commission of the French Academy of Sciences Evaluation of Poiseuille's papers of 1840–1841. *Ann. Chim. Phys.* 7: 50–74, 1843.
6. COPLEY, A. L. Presentation of the Poiseuille Award. In: *Hemorheology*, edited by A. L. Copley. Oxford, UK: Pergamon, 1968, p. 35–36.

7. COPLEY, A. L. Biorheology: past, present and future. *J. Biophys. Med. Nucl.* 4: 125–132, p. 30, 1980.
8. ELFORD, W. J., AND J. D. FERRY. The calibration of graded collodion membranes. *Br. J. Exp. Pathol.* 16: 1–14, 1935.
9. FÅHRAEUS, R., AND T. LINDQVIST. The viscosity of the blood in narrow capillary tubes. *Am. J. Physiol.* 96: 562–568, 1931.
10. FICK, A. Über Diffusion. *Ann. Phys. Leipzig* 94: 59–86, 1855.
11. GUÉROT, M. Sur les dimensions des intervalles poreaux des membranes. *C. R. Acad. Sci.* 75: 1809–1812, 1875.
12. HAGEN, G. Über die Bewegung des Wassers in engen cylindrischen Röhren. *Ann. Phys. Chem. Poggendorf.* 46: 423–442, 1839.
13. HAGENBACH, E. Über die Bestimmung der Zähigkeit einer Flüssigkeit durch den Ausfluss der Röhren. *Ann. Phys. Chem. Poggendorf.* 109: 385–426, 1860.
14. HALES, S. *Statical Essays: an Account of Some Hydraulick and Hydrostatical Experiments Made on the Blood and Blood-Vessels of Animals.* London: Innys & Manby, 1733.
15. *Handbook of Chemistry and Physics* (30th ed.). Cleveland, OH: CRC, 1948.
16. HESS, W. R. Reibungswiderstand des Blutes und Poiseuillesches Gesetz. *Z. Klin. Med.* 71: 421–427, 1910.
17. HITCHCOCK, D. I. The size of pores in collodion membranes. *J. Gen. Physiol.* 9: 745–762, 1926.
18. JOLY, M. Notice biographique sur J. L. M. Poiseuille. In: *Hemorheology*, edited by A. L. Copley. Oxford, UK: Pergamon, 1968, p. 29–31.
19. KROGH, A. The flow of blood in the microscopic vessels. In: *The Anatomy and Physiology of the Capillaries.* New Haven, CT: Yale Univ. Press, 1922, chapt. I.
20. LANDIS, E. M. The capillary pressure in frog mesentery as determined by micro-injection methods. *Am. J. Physiol.* 75: 548–570, 1926.
21. LANDIS, E. M. The capillary pressure in mammalian mesentery as determined by the micro-injection method. *Am. J. Physiol.* 93: 353–362, 1930.
22. LUDWIG, C. Beiträge zur Kenntnis des Einflusses der Respirationsbewegungen auf den Blutlauf im Aortensystem. *Arch. Anat. Physiol. Wiss. Med.* 6: 242–302, 1847.
23. LUDWIG, C. *Lehrbuch der Physiologie des Menschen* (2nd ed.). Leipzig, Germany: Wintersche Verlagshandlung, 1861, vol. I, p. 122.
24. MILLIKAN, R. A., D. ROLLER, AND E. C. WATSON. *Mechanics, Molecular Physics, Heat and Sound.* Boston, MA: Ginn, 1937, p. 452.
25. OSTWALD, W. Über die Geschwindigkeits-Funktion der Viscosität in dispersen Systemen. *Kolloid Z.* 36: 99 (note 1), 1925.
26. PAPPENHEIMER, J. R., E. M. RENKIN, AND L. M. BORRERO. Filtration and molecular diffusion from the capillary circulation in muscle, with deductions concerning the number and dimensions of ultramicroscopic openings in the capillary walls. In: *Proc. Int. Congr. Physiol., 18th, Copenhagen*, 1950, p. 384–385.
27. PAPPENHEIMER, J. R., E. M. RENKIN, AND L. M. BORRERO. Filtration, diffusion and molecular sieving through peripheral capillary membranes: a contribution to the pore theory of capillary permeability. *Am. J. Physiol.* 167: 13–46, 1951.
28. POISEUILLE, J. L. M. Recherches sur la force du coeur aortique. Paris: Didot le Jeune, 1828. Dissertation.
29. POISEUILLE, J. L. M. Recherches sur les causes du mouvement du sang dans les veines. *J. Physiol. Exp. Pathol.* 10: 277–295, 1830.
30. POISEUILLE, J. L. M. Recherches sur les causes du mouvement du sang dans les vaisseaux capillaires. *C. R. Acad. Sci.* 6: 554–560, 1835 [and *Memoires des Savants Étrangers.* Paris: Académie des Sciences, 1841, vol. VII, p. 105–175].
31. POISEUILLE, J. L. M. *Écoulement des Liquides: Société Philomatique de Paris. Extraits des Procès-Verbaux des Séances Pendant l'Année 1838.* Paris: Rene et Cie, 1838, p. 1–3, 77–81.
32. POISEUILLE, J. L. M. Recherches expérimentales sur le mouvement des liquides dans les tubes de très-petits diamètres (Commun. Acad. Sci.) *C. R. Acad. Sci.* 11: 961–967, 1041–1048, 1840 [and 12: 112–115, 1841].
33. POISEUILLE, J. L. M. Écoulement des liquides de nature différente dans les tubes de verre de très-petits diamètres. *C. R. Acad. Sci.* 16: 61–63, 1843.
34. POISEUILLE, J. L. M. Ventilation des navires. *C. R. Acad. Sci.* 21: 1427–1432, 1845.
35. POISEUILLE, J. L. M. Recherches expérimentales sur le mouvement des liquides dans les tubes de très-petits diamètres. In: *Memoires presentés par divers savants à l'Académie Royale des Sciences de l'Institut de France*, 1846, vol. IX, p. 433–544.
36. POISEUILLE, J. L. M. Recherches sur la respiration. *C. R. Acad. Sci.* 41: 1072–1076, 1855.
37. POISEUILLE, J. L. M. De l'existence du glycose dans l'organisme animal. *C. R. Acad. Sci.* 46: 565–568, 677–679, 1858.
38. POISEUILLE, J. L. M. Recherches sur l'urée. *C. R. Acad. Sci.* 49: 164–167, 1859.
39. POISEUILLE, J. L. M. Sur la pression du sang dans le système artériel. *C. R. Acad. Sci.* 51: 238–242, 1860 [and 66: 886–890, 1868].
40. PRANDTL, L., AND O. G. TIETJENS. *Applied Hydro- and Aeromechanics.* New York: McGraw-Hill, 1934, chapt. III.
41. RENKIN, E. M. Filtration, diffusion and molecular sieving through porous cellulose membranes. *J. Gen. Physiol.* 38: 225–243, 1954.
42. SACHAILE, C. *Les Médicins de Paris.* Paris: 1845.
43. WHITTAKER, S. R. F., AND F. R. WINTON. The apparent viscosity of blood flowing in the isolated hindlimb of the dog and its variation with corpuscular concentration. *J. Physiol. London* 78: 339–368, 1933.

CHAPTER 2

Architecture

MARY P. WIEDEMAN†

Department of Physiology, Temple University School of Medicine, Philadelphia, Pennsylvania

CHAPTER CONTENTS

Historical Background
  Microscope
  Terminology
Skeletal Muscle
  Cremaster muscle
  Tenuissimus muscle
  Gracilis muscle
  Extensor hallucis proprius muscle
  Spinotrapezius muscle
Cardiac Muscle
Cat Mesentery
Intestinal Microcirculation
Hamster Cheek Pouch
Bat Wing
Cutaneous Microcirculation
Cerebral Circulation
Summary
Lymphatic Vessels

IN THE TWO DECADES since the patterns of arteriovenous pathways were reviewed in the *Handbook of Physiology* (87), new sites for microscopic observation of terminal vascular beds have been introduced. In addition new instruments have been designed for measuring blood pressure, velocity of flow, and diameters of vessels in the terminal vasculature. Equally important are advances in microscopic equipment, including the basic design of the microscope. Improved objectives and eyepieces allow a wider range of optical magnification with better resolution and light sources for transillumination. These technical advances have fostered an accelerated accumulation of information, both anatomical and functional, about the microvascular pathways in certain tissues and organs. Some areas, such as brain, cochlea, conjunctiva, and urinary tract, remain neglected.

HISTORICAL BACKGROUND

Microscope

The accumulation and advance of scientific knowledge are inextricably linked with the development of technology. An excellent example is the existence of the postulated hairlike blood vessels connecting arterial and venous vessels, which was not revealed until the science of optics advanced to permit their visualization. In retrospect the development of the microscope seems painfully slow.

In the eighth century BC, the Egyptians were using rock crystal and quartz to make jewelry and the art of glassmaking was developed. Certain characteristics of glass were recognized, such as its ability to converge the sun's rays to produce heat that could ignite wood. Pliny wrote of cauterizing wounds by placing a crystalline sphere in the sun's rays. By the end of the thirteenth century, lenses were used for magnification to correct presbyopia. Knowledge of optics was not too advanced at this time, but a clear crystal lens that was curved had been shown to magnify objects. Pope Leo X (1518) was painted by Raphael with a magnifying glass in his hand.

The development of the magnifying lens as a simple microscope continued and reached its greatest usefulness in the hands of Anton van Leeuwenhoek (1632–1723), who lived in Delft and made more than 250 microscopes. The compound microscope seems to have originated in Holland, which was the major source of lenses for spectacles and telescopes. It is thought that Hans Janssen and his son, some time between 1590 and 1609, first combined lenses to gain greater magnification. This microscope was built like a telescope with three tubes, one as a holder for the other two tubes; one of these held an eye lens and the other an objective lens. During this time Galileo was experimenting with telescopes and made a microscope in 1610 that consisted of a biconvex objective and a biconcave eye lens. Although the Dutch were the most accomplished in the manufacture of optical equipment, the application of the telescope and the microscope for scientific discovery was being done mostly in Italy. The Italian scientists contributed significantly to the development of both the telescope and the microscope. In 1661 Malpighi described small vessels connecting arterial and venous vessels in frog's lungs. In instructions to his friend Borelli, Malpighi suggested examining an expanded frog lung with a microscope consisting of one flea lens exposed against

† Mary P. Wiedeman died on April 4, 1982.

the horizontal sun. The flea-lens microscope was a single-lens microscope, so named because its low magnifying power made it suitable for examining insects, most commonly fleas. Malpighi suggested another method: place the lung on a plate of crystal illuminated from below by the light of a lamp through a tube and look at it through a microscope of two lenses. He told Borelli that he could then see movement of blood through the vessels and that with different degrees of light he would see other things, which were not possible to describe. In 1665 Robert Hooke, one of the great English scientists, published a book entitled *Micrographia* that included 60 descriptions of various objects such as the edge of a razor, blue mold on leather, numerous insects, and types of hairs. He also described his microscope and lens-grinding machine. Hooke preferred the compound microscope but knew the advantages of the single-lens microscope, particularly the absence of the high degree of chromatic aberration that was a disturbing factor in the compound-lens system. Van Leeuwenhoek continued to use the single-lens microscope; although not educated as a scientist, he made many exciting observations that he described at length and in great detail primarily in the form of letters to fellow scientists and to the Royal Society in England. Although he shared what he saw through the microscope, he was less willing to share his methods of making microscopes and kept his best microscopes for himself.

From the eighteenth century until the middle of the nineteenth century, many advances were made in the mechanical improvement of microscopes, primarily in England. Owning a microscope was considered fashionable, but the microscope was not popular for scientific investigations. Results of research with the microscope were referred to as "microscopical deception." The microscope was thought of as a toy, best suited for recreation and amusement. During this time, however, great improvements resulted in higher magnification with greater resolution. The achromatic lens was developed, the mechanical stage and focusing by fine adjustment were introduced, and the art of preparing material for study was advancing. By the end of the nineteenth century, the optical system in microscopes was excellent. The demands of World War I led to mass production of numerous instruments, microscopes included. Undoubtedly competition among manufacturers accelerated the development of the myriad mechanical and physical features of modern microscopes. Perhaps for many of us the microscope is still an instrument for recreation and enjoyment.

The material presented in this chapter describes the architecture and characteristics of vascular beds most commonly used in microscopy in vivo for investigations concerned with control of blood flow in exchange vessels, the interrelationship between the macrocirculation and the microcirculation in maintaining systemic blood pressure, and the influence of the architectural pattern on hemodynamics. If universal acceptance of terminology for the blood vessels and a recognition of the common features of their behavior in the numerous beds can be achieved, major discrepancies in descriptive material currently in the literature would disappear. There is a great deal of uniformity in the pattern, the structure, and the function of microvascular beds in most of the tissues studied, and this survey of information that has accumulated in the past two decades demonstrates this uniformity by comparing the microvascular beds in various organs and tissues.

Terminology

There is a lack of uniformity in the definition of terms used to designate the blood vessels generally acknowledged to be included in the microcirculation. Some discrepancies occur because of rather loose definitions of the words used to identify vessels, and confusion arises when functional and anatomical characteristics are merged. The most commonly accepted definitions are presented here in an attempt to make the descriptive material that follows more understandable.

The arterial vessel that marks the entrance into the microcirculation is called an arteriole. This arteriole serves as the parent vessel for the next branching order of arterial vessel, the terminal arteriole. The parent arteriole is invested in vascular smooth muscle, and its vasomotor activity is determined primarily by sympathetic vasoconstrictor efferent fibers. The terminal arteriole, which originates from the arteriole, is also invested proximally in vascular smooth muscle that gradually decreases until a single smooth muscle cell, spirally wrapped, marks the end of the muscular investment. This final smooth muscle cell has been named the precapillary sphincter (67). The terminal arteriole is easily identified as the last vessel of the arteriolar distribution because it terminates in a capillary network, does not form arcades with any other arterial vessel, and does not anastomose with any arterial or venous vessel. The terminal arteriole and precapillary sphincter are not innervated (30).

The capillary vessels are also easily identified because they are pure endothelial tubes. Their pattern in any tissue is a result of their conformation to the structural features of the tissue in which they lie. When one capillary converges with another, the vessel formed is designated a postcapillary venule. Postcapillary venules are slightly larger than capillaries and are usually devoid of any smooth muscle. They join to form venules that are most often paired with the arterial vessel serving the microvascular bed. An example of this configuration is seen in the bat wing vasculature (67).

The metarteriole is a structure often mentioned but

not thought to appear in most vascular beds. The term was introduced by Chambers and Zweifach in 1944 (12) to describe the most proximal portion of a central or thoroughfare channel that traverses the rat mesentery from an arteriole to a venule. Precapillary vessels, which become capillaries, branch off of the metarteriole and are encircled with muscle cells called precapillary sphincters. The metarteriole is not a common feature of microvascular beds (5), and the precapillary sphincter may vary in position in different tissues. The original use of the term *metarteriole* is discussed in more detail by Wiedeman, Tuma, and Mayrovitz (92).

Wiedeman et al. (91) suggested that the position of the precapillary sphincter is not limited to a branch site but rather should be considered as the final smooth muscle cell guarding the entrance to the capillary network; therefore it is the "gatekeeper" or final control site for blood flow into the exchange area. The definition first proposed by Nicoll and Webb (66) in 1945 must be considered the most useful, the most flexible, and the most adaptable to fit any microvascular bed regardless of the architectural pattern, which is determined by the tissue or organ to be served. It should not matter whether the precapillary sphincter controls flow into numerous capillaries simultaneously, as it does in the tenuissimus muscle, or if it controls flow into one capillary, as it does in the mesentery.

SKELETAL MUSCLE

The most assiduously studied tissue in the recent past has been various skeletal muscles in a number of small animals.

Cremaster Muscle

The cremaster muscle was used by Majno, Palade, and Schoefl (56, 57) in 1961 for studies on inflammation with histological and electron-microscopic techniques. It was first used for in vivo microscopy in 1964 by Grant (32), who presented the following descriptive material. Rats weighing 100 g were found to be most suitable because the scrotal subcutaneous tissue is thin and the muscle is easily dissected when spread for viewing. The larger arteries and veins have diameters ranging from 50 to 100 μm. The arteries, which are straight, and their arteriolar branches anastomose with each other. Arteriovenous anastomoses are not seen. Terminal arterioles, capillaries, and venules with diameters ranging from 5 to 10 μm lie between the muscle bundles with small arteries branching into arterioles, terminal arterioles, and capillaries that are arranged like candelabra. Capillary flow is intermittent. Thoroughfare vessels that have blood flow when the interior of the muscle is ischemic were found in the cleavage planes of the muscle. A subsequent paper in 1966 by Grant (33) dealt primarily with the nerve supply to the muscle and the effects of denervation but provided no additional information regarding vascular architecture.

In 1969 Baez (3) reported measurements made of inside and outside radii to determine wall thickness of pre- and postcapillary vessels in the rat cremaster and mesentery. There were more microvessels in a given area in skeletal muscle than in the mesentery, and the precapillary sphincter area in the muscle was different. Baez explains that in cremaster muscle a metarteriole gives rise to a short muscular vessel (ID 2.5–4.0 μm) that abruptly divides into four to six endothelial capillaries; he calls this short muscular "vessel" a sphincter. Baez describes a primary arteriole that bifurcates into two secondary arterioles only slightly smaller than the parent vessel. These secondary arterioles terminate by forming an arcade or by breaking up into capillaries. Metarterioles arise from terminal arterioles or arteriolar arcades; they then give rise to endothelial capillary side branches and divide into 8–10 capillaries. According to Baez, endothelial capillaries can originate as a side branch of the metarteriole or as the final ramification of either the metarteriole or a terminal arteriole. A cluster of muscle cells at the origin of a capillary branching from a metarteriole is also referred to as a precapillary sphincter. Baez describes some endothelial capillaries with diameters of 8.6 μm; however, these larger vessels may be designated as postcapillary venules by other investigators. The vessels of the cremaster muscle were smaller than similar vessels in the mesentery of rats. Baez suggests that the difference may occur because the cremaster muscle represents a three-dimensional or thick tissue, whereas the mesentery is a flat or thin tissue.

In 1970 Smaje, Zweifach, and Intaglietta (76) reported the basic microscopic anatomy of the rat cremaster vascular system and determined capillary filtration coefficients, microvascular pressures, and capillary blood flow velocity.

The cremaster muscle is supplied with blood by branches from the external spermatic artery, which enters the muscle as a single artery from which transverse vessels arise. The artery has an accompanying vein and the two vessels continue as paired structures through four to five branching orders together. Arterial and venous vessels form arcades in their separate circuits. Arteriovenous anastomoses do not appear. Capillaries run parallel to muscle fibers and have a length of 615 ± 194 μm with cross-connections about every 200 μm. The average internal diameter of the capillaries is 5.8 μm; the average weight of the rats is 80 g. The dimensions of the muscle were not given.

Postcapillary venules with a mean diameter of 12 μm were about one-half as long as the capillaries. Figure 1 is a diagram of the vascular pattern with the mean values of the measured parameters.

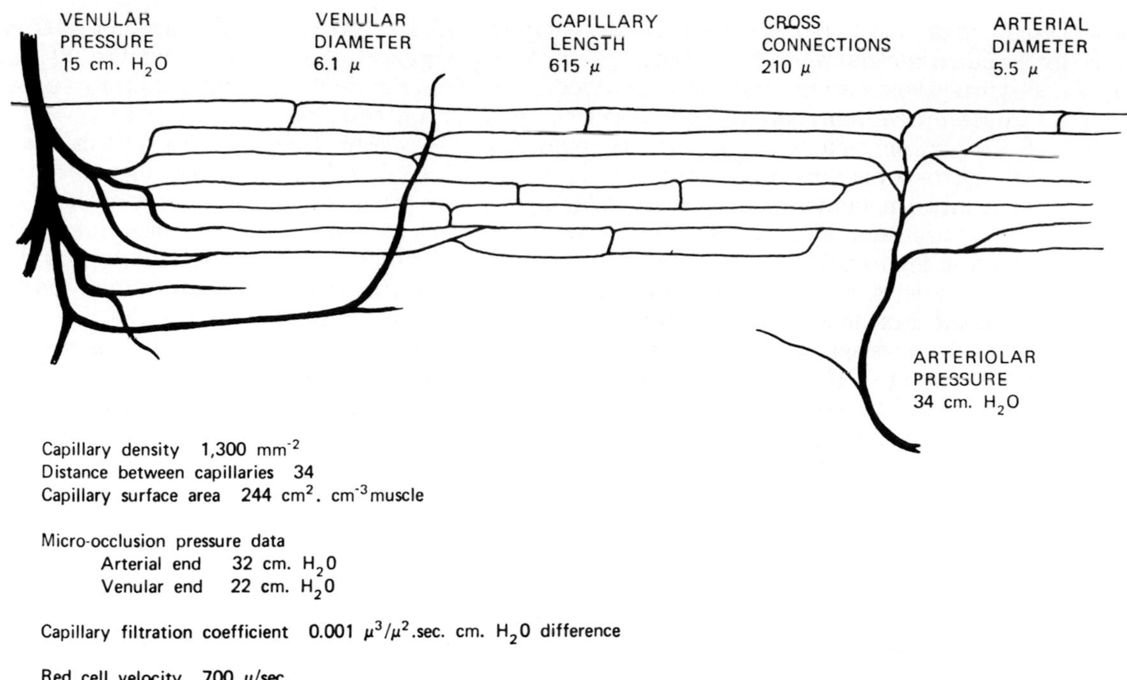

FIG. 1. Vascular pattern of rat cremaster muscle with mean values of measured parameters. [From Smaje et al. (76).]

Most of the capillaries showed an active flow that was intermittent. The velocity of flow varied from 200 to 1,200 μm/s (mean 700 μm/s). Capillary length, density, surface area, and cross-connections of this muscle are similar to those in other mammalian muscles as reported by Krogh (49) in 1922.

In a discussion of the technique for preparation of the open cremaster muscle, Baez (4) describes a single paired artery and vein occupying the medial region of the spread muscle, which is ~2.7 cm in diameter in a rat weighing 80–100 g. The arterial diameter is 120 μm, the venous diameter is 150 μm, and the muscle thickness varies between 167 and 183 μm. The arterial distribution from the main artery goes through orders of branching to fourth-order arterioles and metarterioles that break up into 8–10 endothelial capillaries. The metarteriole is said to occasionally continue as a thoroughfare channel and become a collecting postcapillary venule. Arteriovenous anastomoses are not seen, but arteriolar vessels do interconnect. Capillaries run parallel to muscle fibers and often cross-connect. Intermittent flow in capillaries was attributed to dynamic changes in arterioles and precapillary sphincters.

Hutchins et al. (46) in 1973 presented the arteriolar vessels as branching orders from first order to fourth order, with spontaneous contractile activity most prominent in fourth-order vessels. The following year he used a different nomenclature (44). The major arterial vessel entering the muscle was seen to parallel the muscle fibers and give rise to vessels branching off obliquely or at right angles to traverse the muscle. These vessels are called transverse arterioles and are parent vessels for branches called terminal arterioles. The terminal arterioles are defined as vessels that empty directly into capillaries. In addition metarterioles branch from major arterial vessels; although not defined here, they are presumably vessels that go directly to a venous vessel. Vessels originating from metarterioles are called precapillary sphincters. Vasomotion was seen in all these arterial vessels.

In a study designed to observe the reflex response of skeletal muscle arterioles (45), occlusion of the common carotid artery caused the transverse distribution arterioles, with the smallest initial diameters (<20 μm) to constrict to the greatest extent. This resulted in a sixfold increase in resistance to blood flow. The transverse arterioles were considered to be the primary vessels responsible for regulation of systemic arterial blood pressure. This implies that the strongest neurogenic control of diameter is found in these vessels, which are parent vessels to terminal arterioles, and this would be in agreement with Wiedeman (90) and Furness and Marshall (30) about the most distal point of central nervous control. Local control would determine the vascular size of terminal arterioles and precapillary sphincters and therefore the flow into the capillary bed. The average control diameters of the different vessels given by Hutchins et al. (45) show that precapillary sphincters, terminal arterioles, and metarterioles, which all branch from transverse distribution arterioles, are essentially the same. There are two classifications for these transverse arterioles, with one group more than twice as large as the other.

Morff and Granger (59) presented evidence that the

vasculature of the cremaster preparation can be considered to be in a normal physiological state, unaltered by the surgical procedure needed to expose the tissue for continuous microscopic observation. Their conclusion was based on measurements of total tissue blood flow to the undisturbed cremaster, to the biceps brachia, and to the gastrocnemius of the rat determined by the radioactive-microsphere technique. Blood flow to all three muscles, ~9.5 $ml \cdot min^{-1} \cdot 100\ g^{-1}$, was not statistically different, nor was flow to the cremaster altered when the muscle was prepared for observation. However, these investigators emphasize the need for careful maintenance of the artificial environment relative to pH, partial pressure of oxygen (P_{O_2}), partial pressure of carbon dioxide (P_{CO_2}), osmolarity, temperature, and ionic concentration.

In summary, the cremaster muscle, composed of two layers of muscle that run at oblique angles to one another, is served by a paired arterial and venous vessel that runs parallel to the upper layer of muscle fibers. From the major arterial vessel, right-angle or oblique-angle branches traverse the muscle. These transverse distributing arteries (or transverse arterioles) give rise to metarterioles, to vessels designated as precapillary sphincters, and most frequently to terminal arterioles. The diameters of these vessels vary from study to study. All of the investigators agree that *1)* no arteriovenous anastomoses are seen, *2)* the arterial vessels exhibit spontaneous contractile activity that produces intermittent capillary flow, and *3)* capillary diameters average ~5.1 μm.

Tenuissimus Muscle

In 1972 Brånemark and Eriksson (10) introduced a new site for microscopic observation of skeletal muscle blood flow. The tenuissimus muscle was selected because it is thin and because its middle portion can be easily dissected and transilluminated in situ. The preparation was found to be stable for up to 8 h and the entire vascular tree could be visualized because of the distribution of blood vessels. It was possible to measure muscle fiber diameter as well as the diameters and lengths of all vessel segments. Cats and rabbits were used as experimental animals.

The microvascular dimensions and red blood cell velocities were presented in a paper by Eriksson and Myrhage (21) in 1972. They reported that the average number of muscle fibers in a cross section of the muscle is 1,375 and the average diameter of the fibers is 44 μm. There are ~62% red fibers and 38% white fibers in a tenuissimus muscle that is 3–5 mm wide and 0.3–0.6 mm at its thickest part. One artery (avg ID 110 μm) and one or two veins (avg ID 165 μm) separated from each other by ~25 mm enter the muscle and give rise to a central artery (avg ID 72 μm) and central vein (avg ID 89 μm) accompanied by a nerve. These vessels and nerves parallel the muscle fibers. Central arteries are parent vessels for transverse arterioles (avg ID 22 μm) that branch off at angles of 45°–90°. The authors arbitrarily selected 50 μm as the diameter size that separates arteries and arterioles in the tenuissimus muscle of the cat. (To name a vessel according to its size is usually a poor policy.) Transverse arterioles appeared about every 650 μm. The transverse venule (avg ID 40 μm) varied considerably in its location from the nearest arteriole. The transverse arterioles had an average of 11 branches, which then divided dichotomously through several generations. The last division of the smallest arterioles marks the beginning of the capillaries that run parallel to the muscle fibers. Figure 2 illustrates the way in which a small arteriole divides into capillaries. The average capillary is ~1,015 μm long with a diameter of 4.7 μm at the arteriolar end and 5.9 μm at the venular end. The total number of capillaries in a cross section of the cat tenuissimus muscle is given as 1,310, giving a capillary-to-fiber ratio of 0.95. The muscle fibers were surrounded by 3.5–3.8 capillaries, the capillary surface area was 0.8 $mm^2/100\ mm^3$, and the average velocity of flow in the capillaries was 0.5 mm/s. Eriksson and Myrhage (21) saw no spontaneous changes in the diameter of arterioles, venules, or capillaries under resting conditions. They state that all capillaries in the muscle are always open to flow even though the flow velocity varies markedly. The flow stops temporarily due to blockage by a white blood cell. Eriksson and Myrhage, defining the precapillary sphincter as the last smooth muscle cell on a terminal arteriole [as previously stated by Wiedeman (87)], did not observe any distinct precapillary sphincter activity. In addition arteriovenous anastomoses were very rare, and no vessel resembling a metarteriole could be identified. Although precapillary sphincters were not seen, capillary flow was intermittent, with great variation in flow rate.

Eriksson and Lisander (19) previously presented evidence that arterioles with diameters of 10–30 μm can act as precapillary sphincters, that stimulation of sympathetic constrictor fibers evokes intermittent contraction and relaxation, and that topical epinephrine causes arterioles to constrict. In another study (17) electron micrographs revealed that 20-μm transverse arterioles close to the central artery have one or two continuous layers of smooth muscle cells and that in the middle segments, where the diameter of the transverse arteriole decreases to 12 μm, there is a single, often discontinuous layer of smooth muscle. At its most distal portion, where the diameter was <10 μm, there were no muscle cells. Two rather important points regarding nomenclature and definitions should be made here. *1)* A vessel with a diameter of <10 μm that is devoid of smooth muscle cells should not be designated as an arteriole. *2)* This discontinuous single layer of smooth muscle on the distal segment of the 12-μm-diameter arteriole (after which there is no more muscle) certainly satisfies the definition of precapillary sphincter. Unfortunately these investigators state very explicitly that no evidence for the presence of

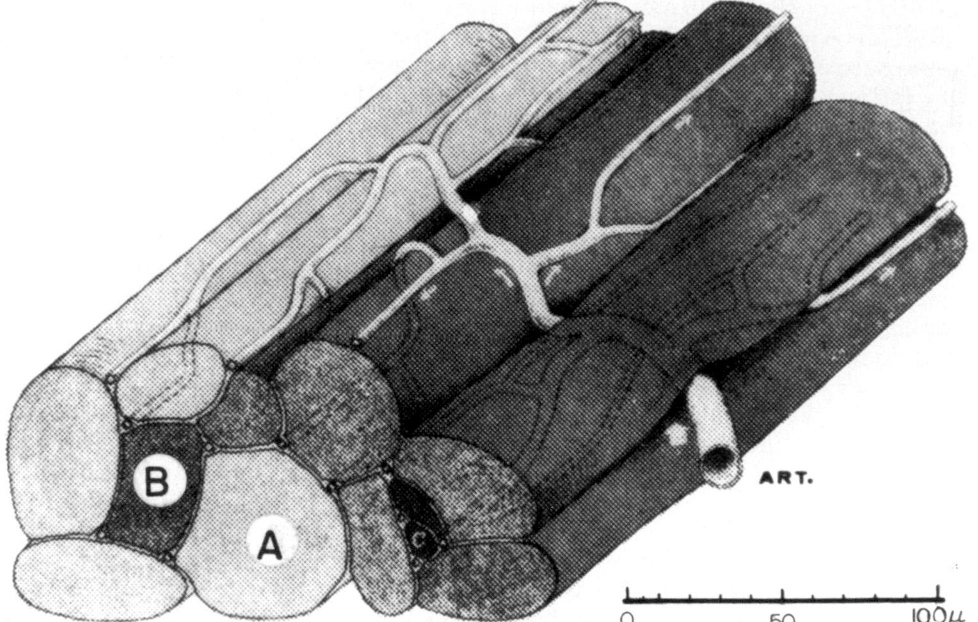

FIG. 2. Capillaries branch from small arteriole to supply blood to muscle fibers. [From Eriksson and Myrhage (21).]

precapillary sphincters could be obtained. Without a close analysis of their descriptive material, a reader would tend to accept this statement. Figure 3 summarizes the vascular dimensions of the tenuissimus muscle presented by these investigators.

A third paper in 1972 from the same group dealt with changes in precapillary resistance in this muscle caused by graded vasoconstrictor fiber stimulation, vasoactive drugs, and surgical denervation (20). Capillaries running parallel to the muscle fibers were seen to be interconnected every 200 μm by vessels 5 μm in diameter. Dramatic variations of flow in individual capillaries were seen. Sometimes these variations were caused by plugging of the vessels by white cells. Stimulation of sympathetic vasoconstrictor fibers caused the transverse arterioles, also called end arterioles, to close completely. The authors state that these arteriolar sections (30-μm-diam vessels) function effectively as proximally placed precapillary sphincter regions. Each sphincter has an influence on a group of capillaries rather than on a single capillary. Eriksson and Lisander (20) and Ericson and Eriksson (16) also studied the response of blood vessels in the tenuissimus muscle to aortic compression and hemorrhage resulting in low flow states. Transverse arterioles were seen to dilate, resulting in a 40% increase in diameter during aortic compression. These same vessels constricted initially and dilated after hemorrhage.

Myrhage and Eriksson (61) compared the tenuissimus with other muscles in the hindlimb of the cat and found that a basic vascular unit in the biceps, gastrocnemius, and soleus was similar to the whole vascular tree in the tenuissimus.

The tenuissimus muscle of cats was selected by Fronek and Zweifach (25) to study pressure distribution in the microvasculature of skeletal muscle. They found that blood pressure in the central artery (diam 70–100 μm) was within 90%–95% of systemic blood pressure. The branches from the central artery (transverse arterioles) had diameters ranging from 70 to 20 μm and subdivided into 20- to 10-μm-diameter offshoots. A transverse arteriole may branch directly into five to eight capillaries running parallel to the muscle fibers. They believe that the vascular pattern and long capillaries of this muscle differ from other skeletal muscles (trapezius and cremaster) because the feeding or central artery has such a high pressure as a result of direct branching from the femoral artery.

Fronek and Zweifach (26, 27) also studied the blood flow distribution in the cat tenuissimus muscle. Comparisons with numerous other investigators using different tissues and species show the flow velocity rate in the tenuissimus muscle presented by Fronek and Zweifach to be in general agreement. They stated that a capillary density of 1,000/mm^2 of skeletal muscle is a realistic estimate. All capillaries do not contain active flow simultaneously, only ~30%–35% being perfused at one time. Precapillary vasomotion, observed consistently, caused changes in velocity and diameter of arteriolar vessels. The average diameter of the capillaries was 5–6 μm.

Lindbom et al. (50) studied influences of oxygen on the number of capillaries perfused and on red cell velocity. They reported that capillaries originating from the same terminal arteriole were located in groups. In addition these capillary groups had similar flow patterns that often differed from those of adjacent groups. Although not designated in this paper,

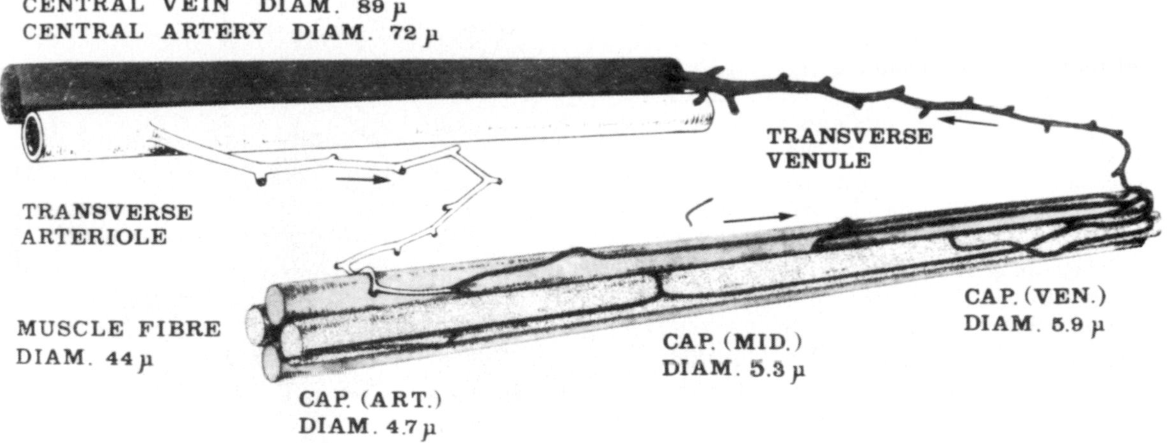

CAP. LENGTH 1015 µ
" " BETWEEN TWO ANASTOMOSES 200 µ
CAP./MUSCLE FIBRES 0.95
CAP. SURFACE AREA 0.9 M^2/100 CM^3 OF MUSCLE TISSUE
RED CELL VELOCITY 0.5 MM/SEC.

FIG. 3. Vascular dimensions in tenuissimus muscle. [From Eriksson and Myrhage (21).]

the terminal arteriole is presumably the muscular arteriole that branches from the transverse arteriole and finally gives rise to capillaries. The mean number of perfused capillaries (capillary density) varied with different oxygen tensions. Red cell velocity in the capillaries averaged 0.29 mm/s. Variations in environmental oxygen tension caused constriction of the first part of the terminal arteriole, which was a considerable distance from the branching points of the capillary network. Arterioles were considered to be responsible for the alterations in both the number of perfused capillaries and capillary flow velocity. Tuma et al. (82) had found a capillary velocity of 0.38 mm/s in the tenuissimus muscle. Flow periodicity was similar in all capillaries originating from the same terminal arteriole and was synchronous with vasomotion seen in the terminal arteriole. The authors state that their results do not support the existence of precapillary sphincters controlling the perfusion of capillaries. This statement applies when a precapillary sphincter is defined as an encircling muscle at the origin of each capillary. This kind of arrangement would be most inefficient for blood flow control in the vascular pattern displayed by the tenuissimus muscle.

Gracilis Muscle

Honig et al. (43) used the gracilis muscle of rats to study neural control of capillary density (perfused capillaries) and resistance. They report that capillaries were most frequently 400–500 μm long and that the mean capillary density was 240/mm^2 with a range of 220–2,943/mm^2. The presence of a capillary apparently was determined by visible blood flow. The flow was seen to be intermittent and it was concluded that precapillary sphincters were actively contracting, an event that occurred in denervated as well as innervated preparations. Denervation did not change the number of perfused capillaries, and it was concluded that in this muscle the precapillary sphincters are not controlled by vasoconstrictor fiber activity.

In a more recent study Honig (42) found that blood flow per gram of gracilis muscle was the same in rats and dogs, although oxygen extraction in the rat gracilis was much higher and more comparable to heart muscle. Capillary density is usually greater in small animals, and Honig states that this could compensate for the relatively low muscle blood flow that is characteristic of small animals.

Capillaries in the gracilis muscle that arise from one arteriole run parallel to one another and join a common venule. They seldom anastomose with capillaries from adjacent arterioles. Honig (42) likens this arrangement to that described by Eriksson and Myrhage (21) in the cat tenuissimus muscle. Rhythmic flow in the capillaries was ascribed to the activity of precapillary sphincters or their functional equivalents. Capillary diameter in the gracilis is assumed to be the same as that in the tenuissimus (5.3 μm). Few if any intrinsic nerves were seen in relation to precapillary sphincters, and Honig therefore believes that the sphincters are under metabolic control.

In 1978 Henrich and Hecke (41) presented some diameter measurements obtained from the rat gracilis muscle. The prepared muscle was hemodynamically isolated with its blood supply intact, a fact considered to be important by the investigators.

The muscle is made up of red and white fibers, supplied with blood by the great saphenous vein and the femoral artery, and innervated by the obturator nerve. Average capillary red cell velocity was found to be 0.26 mm/s in the resting muscle, which had a capillary density of 26.8 ± 7.2/mm^2. This must refer to functional rather than anatomical density. Capillary diameter was not given, but the smallest precapillary arterioles had a diameter of ~19 μm, their parent vessels (terminal arterioles) were nearly 25 μm, and the next upstream vessel was 34.5 μm in diameter. The vascular pattern was not described.

Extensor Hallucis Proprius Muscle

Myrhage and Hudlická (62) described the extensor hallucis proprius muscle of the rat. The dissection needed to expose and arrange the muscle for microscopic observation is shown in Figure 4. This muscle was selected for several reasons. They sought a muscle whose primary function was locomotion, one small enough so its total capillary network could be studied and reasonably accessible for microscopic observation. One objective was to determine the total capillary surface area in the muscle.

The muscle in 140-g rats is ~13 mm long and 2.0 mm wide, weighing ~14 mg. It is innervated by the peroneal nerve and its blood supply comes from the anterior tibial artery. The muscle generally has a central artery and vein with transverse arterioles and venules; its capillaries, which run parallel to the muscle fibers, are interconnected to form the familiar ladderlike pattern seen in most skeletal muscle capillary beds. Terminal arterioles with inside diameters of 8–12 μm were seen to be parent vessels of three to four capillaries ~535 μm in length. The internal diameter varied between 4.0 and 4.5 μm, with the smallest diameter at its arterial end (Fig. 5). The flow in these vessels was intermittent; at times no flow was seen for short periods (<1 min), although no vascular constriction was seen at the junction of capillaries and their parent arterioles. This suggests that the muscular investment responsible for the intermittent capillary flow is some distance upstream rather than at the arteriole-capillary junction, as has been reported for the tenuissimus muscle. It is not stated whether the terminal arterioles were seen to contract.

The capillary-to-fiber ratio was 1.01–0.93, the higher value for the proximal part of the muscle where the total number of fibers was 2,347. The number of capillaries was 1,347 ± 53/mm^2 at the proximal end and 1,043 ± 64/mm^2 at the distal end. The average surface area of individual capillaries was 7,980 μm^2, calculated from values of the average capillary radius and length. The total capillary surface area (S) was

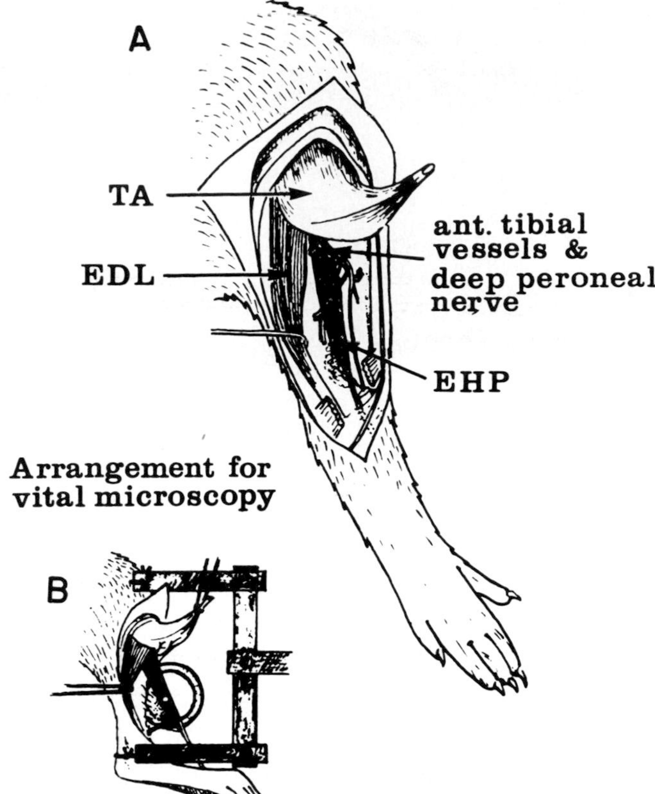

FIG. 4. Method of exposing rat extensor hallucis proprius (EHP) for microscopic observation. Tibialis anterior (TA) and extensor digitorum longus (EDL) are shown for orientation. [From Myrhage and Hudlická (62).]

calculated by the formula

$$S = S_c \frac{l_m}{l_c} \left(\frac{n_p + n_d}{2} \right)$$

in which S_c is the average surface area of individual capillaries, l_m is the total muscle length, n_p is the number of capillaries per square millimeter at the proximal end, and n_d is the value at the distal end of the muscle. The average total capillary surface area for this muscle was found to be 1.6 mm^2/mm^3 of tissue.

Spinotrapezius Muscle

The spinotrapezius muscle of rats was described by Zweifach and Metz in 1955 (97, 98). The capillary network originated from metarterioles that came off at right angles from arteriolar vessels and terminated as one or two capillaries disposed directly on the surface of the small muscle bundles. Each muscle bundle was surrounded by a network of arterial and venous vessels that interconnected with each other in the connective tissue separating the bundles. The capillaries were long and straight, running the length of the muscle. Zweifach and Metz also reported metarterioles along the free margins of the muscle that went

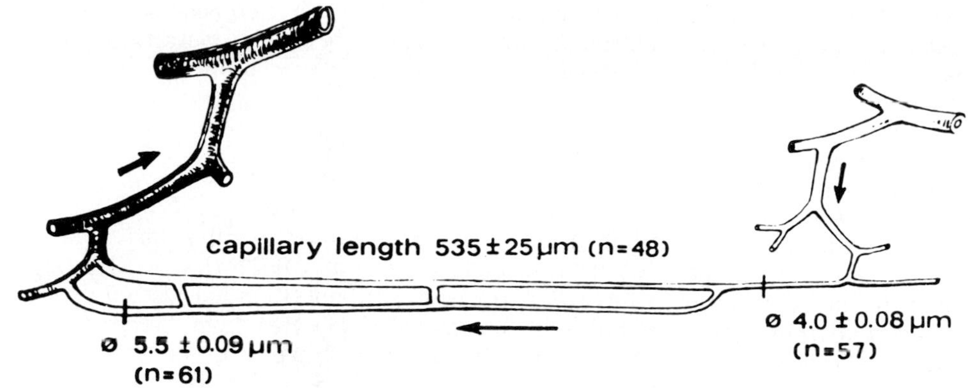

average surface area of individual capillaries 7980µm²

number of cap./crossection area (cap./mm²):

proximal end —— 1347±53 (n=3)

distal end —— 1043±64

muscle length 13.0±0.5mm (n=8)

muscle weight 14.3±0.5mg (n=18)

FIG. 5. Measurements of EHP capillaries in vivo with capillary surface area and capillary density at proximal and distal ends. [From Myrhage and Hudlická (62).]

directly to a venous vessel and therefore represented preferential pathways delivering blood rapidly from the arterial to the venous side. Spontaneous vasoconstriction was intense enough at the level of the precapillary sphincters to stop blood flow.

The muscle was used by Gray (34) to study the effect of hypertonic Ringer's solution on vessel diameters in the terminal vascular bed. The average diameters given for six vessel types from small artery to vein in 80- to 130-g rats were as follows: *1*) small artery, 40–90 µm; *2*) arteriole, 15–40 µm; *3*) precapillary sphincter, <15 µm; *4*) venule, 15–50 µm; *5*) small vein, 50–75 µm; and *6*) vein 75–135 µm. In 1972 Gray (35) reported that the anatomical pattern of the vessels of the spinotrapezius muscle permitted the passage of blood from arterial to venous vessels through direct pathways that bypass much of the capillary bed. The direct pathways appeared to be metarterioles and large capillaries, and they were connected to the capillaries that surrounded the muscle fibers. Spontaneous vasomotion was seen in arterial vessels during artificially induced hypotension. Precapillary vascular sections that control blood flow through the capillary network were noted. The numerous excellent photographs of the vasculature of the spinotrapezius muscle in this paper indicate a pattern of vascular architecture typical of other skeletal muscles used for in vivo microscopic studies. Gray and Renkin (36) subsequently determined capillary fiber ratios and capillary densities for the rabbit gastrocnemius, tibialis, and soleus muscles.

Additional information regarding the vasculature of rat spinotrapezius muscle was published in 1976 by Stingl (77–79), who dealt with three specific features: precapillary arterioles, preferential channels, and precapillary sphincters. Observations were made with light microscopy from an in vivo preparation and in vitro preparation in which the vessels were injected with India ink in gelatin, and the vessels were also studied from electron micrographs (77). In preparations in vivo and in vitro, a central artery and vein ran parallel to the muscle fibers down the center of the ventral strip of muscle. From these terminal arterioles, precapillary arterioles with a diameter of 25 µm branched dichotomously to form vessels of capillary size. These precapillary arterioles ran parallel to the muscle fibers and delivered blood into one or several wide capillaries and onto a postcapillary venule. According to Stingl, the well-filled vessels connecting the precapillary arteriole with the postcapillary venule would fit the definition of a preferential channel.

Electron microscopy showed that the precapillary arterioles had a lumen of ~3.5–5.0 µm and that the wall of these vessels was made up of one to three endothelial cells. Smooth muscle cells with no nerve fibers nearby were seen on the endothelium. Farther along the vessels had an internal diameter of 3.0–3.5 µm; the wall was formed of only endothelial cells, characteristic of a true capillary. As the pathway progressed toward a postcapillary venule, the lumen of the vessel became larger, ~4–5 µm. No nerve fibers were seen, but pericytes were observed. Branches joined to form a postcapillary venule with a diameter of 10–15 μm. Stingl concluded that vessels that appear in vivo to be preferential channels have the characteristics of true capillaries and cannot be regarded as morphologically specialized structures. No structures identifiable as precapillary sphincters were found. In a second paper, Stingl (78) noted that it had not been decided whether precapillary arterioles with a diameter of <20–30 μm, acting to regulate blood flow into the capillaries, are considered to be preferential channels, metarterioles, or precapillary sphincters of the classic type. (This classic type refers to smooth muscle at the branch site of a capillary from its parent arteriole or metarteriole.) His study was intended to determine the ultrastructure of this precapillary arteriole. Its length and diameter at three sites are shown in Figure 6. At the origin of the precapillary arteriole from the central artery, the vessel diameter is 20–25 μm; the wall consists of endothelium with one or two layers of smooth muscle cells and three to four bundles of axons. When the diameter is 10–20 μm, there is only one layer of smooth muscle cells with nerve fibers mostly above the nuclear area of these cells. When the diameter is ~9 μm, the distance between the smooth muscle cells increases. No lateral branching to true capillaries was observed, and nerve fibers were not seen to touch the muscle cells or penetrate their surface. Stingl concluded that these precapillary arterioles are not the same as metarterioles or preferential channels but act as sphincters to regulate blood flow through numerous capillaries. In a third paper (79) dealing with the area of precapillary arterioles it is stated that when the arterioles reach a diameter of 4 μm, only isolated smooth muscle cells appear and

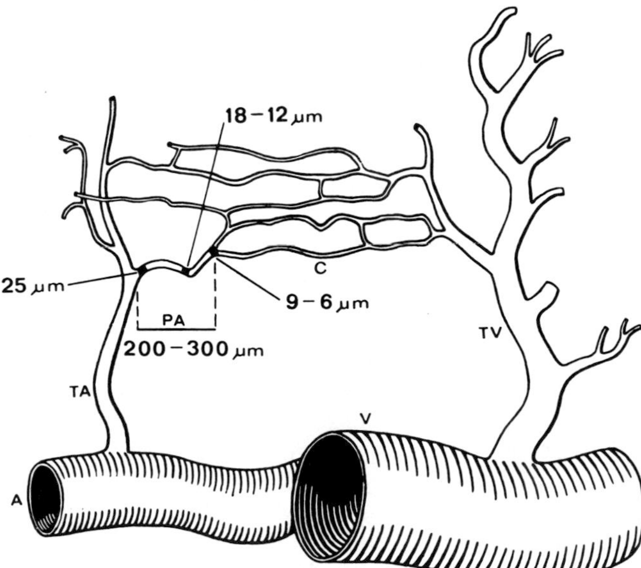

FIG. 6. Terminal vasculature of spinotrapezius muscle. PA, precapillary arteriole; A, central arteriole; V, central venule; TA, terminal arteriole; TV, terminal venule; C, capillary. [From Stingl (77).]

nerves are absent. The vessels then become true capillaries or pure endothelial tubes. No metarteriole type of vessel or isolated precapillary sphincters were seen.

CARDIAC MUSCLE

Martini and Honig (58) in 1969 used stop-motion photography to determine intercapillary distances in the beating heart of a rat. Capillaries on the right ventricular free wall were observed microscopically to a depth of 20 μm with reflected light. Movies were taken of the beating heart, and the focused frames were analyzed. Capillaries were seen lying parallel to muscle fibers, but it was not possible to differentiate arterial or venous ends of the vessels or the direction of flow. Capillaries seen carrying blood had a density of 4,400/mm^2, which was ~50% of the estimated anatomical capillary density in the rat heart. Mean intercapillary distance was 19.5 μm. Myers and Honig (60) had previously described gradients of capillary density from base to apex and from epicardium to endocardium in the dog heart and had concluded that the activity of precapillary sphincters determines the number of perfused capillaries. Martini and Honig (58) had observed sphincters contracting and relaxing in isolated perfused hearts.

Tillich et al. (80) measured red cell velocity in the microcirculation of the cat heart in situ by using transillumination of the left atrium. At a heart rate of 160 beats/min, capillary red cell velocity was 112 μm/s in capillaries with a diameter of 5.3 μm.

Tillmanns et al. (81) used both turtle heart and dog heart to study the pattern of the microcirculation and determine red cell velocity in capillaries, arterioles, and venules of the ventricle during the cardiac cycle. Their method for microscopic observation of the heart showed ingenuity. Transillumination was accomplished by inserting a 20-gauge light-transmitting needle (by use of a light pipe) just underneath the superficial layer of the myocardium. Frame-to-frame analysis of red cell movement was made from 16-mm color film taken at a rate of 400 frames/s. A system called a floating focus keeper maintained the focal distance between the moving heart and the microscope objective by having the objective of the microscope move in unison with the cardiac surface. With this method arterioles could be easily differentiated from venules because of the direction of flow at bifurcations. Prior to the confluence of capillaries and postcapillaries to form a venule, the vascular network became denser, the meshes shorter, and the cross bridges more frequent. The intraluminal diameter in dog arterioles was 15–29 μm during systole and increased to 20–36 μm during diastole. Mean red cell velocity in the capillaries was greatest during systole, whereas in the arterioles the maximum velocity occurred in diastole. Ventricular capillaries were observed lying on either side of the muscle fibers, running parallel to them with cross bridges between capillaries. These intercapillary anastomoses formed interconnecting loops of different lengths, permitting blood to flow in opposite directions in adjoining capillaries.

Red cell velocity in capillaries was found to be ~3,150 μm/s in systole and 1,428 μm/s in diastole, whereas red cell velocity in arterioles was 1,168 μm/s in systole and 3,391 μm/s in diastole. The velocity was about the same in venules and capillaries in the two phases. Capillary intraluminal diameters in the dog were ~4.1 μm in systole and ~6.3 μm in diastole.

Bassingthwaighte et al. (6) studied the microvasculature in the left ventricle of dog hearts perfused with a silicone elastomer and cleared in ethanol and methyl salicylate. Vessel identification can always be challenged in such a preparation, a fact that may be more important than changes in the vascular diameters produced by the technical procedures. In the elastomer-filled specimens of dog hearts, capillaries with functional lengths of 500–1,000 μm ran parallel to muscle fibers. Capillaries were linked by cross-connections. There were 2–4 times as many venules draining capillary networks as there were arteriolar vessels supplying them. Diameters in capillaries considered maximally dilated were ~5.6 μm. This value is thought to be larger than myocardial capillaries in vivo. Capillary densities in muscle groups were 3,100–3,800/mm^2 with intercapillary distances of 17.5–19.0 μm. Capillary surface area was estimated to be 500 cm^2/g of myocardium.

Grayson et al. (37) also studied the coronary microvasculature in dog hearts after the vessels were perfused with silicone rubber. The distribution of arteries and arterioles showed subepicardial networks giving rise to vessels that formed subsidiary networks of anastomosing vessels arranged parallel to the surface of the heart. Precapillary structures formed from these vessels ended in capillaries that supplied the outer portion of the myocardium. A second set of vessels went vertically down through the myocardium after branching off the subepicardial network. In the endocardium, branches of perforating vessels ~20 μm in diameter are long vessels that give off precapillary vessels. Capillaries arranged in parallel appeared to form sheets of anastomosing vessels (see Fig. 7). Arteriovenous anastomoses were not seen. Postcapillary venules are very short and quickly converge to form large veins. Superficial veins drain all thicknesses of the myocardial wall.

In 1976 Henquell et al. (40) measured capillary diameter in rat hearts from stop-motion photomicrographs and reported mean diameters of 4.41 μm for the whole cardiac cycle, 4 μm during systole and 5 μm during diastole. Capillaries were usually identified by the presence of red blood cells, although in the nonbeating heart capillaries could be identified by the optical properties of their endothelial cells. These investigators state that 99% of the capillaries in the beating rat heart are smaller than the mean diameter of the red cell, which easily traverses the small capillary during diastole because of red blood cell deformability. In 1978 the site of capillary control in coronary vessels was studied by investigators from this same laboratory (22). In the rat heart, capillaries (vessels <7 μm in diam) were divided into segments ~350 μm long by short perpendicular anastomoses. These cross-connections are more frequently called cross bridges or interconnecting bridges and are responsible for the ladderlike appearance of capillary networks described in most skeletal muscle. Conclusions drawn from this study were that the site for control of blood flow to capillaries in the heart occurs distal to the arteriole and is presumably at the precapillary sphincter. Complete closure of arterioles does not occur in the unstressed heart, and arterioles and precapillary sphincters are believed to function independently of one another.

Rakusan et al. (72) in 1980 compared the regional capillary supply in a normal rat heart to that of a hypertrophied heart. The capillaries were observed in fixed tissue. The midwall region and the subendocardial region were analyzed, and no significant difference was found between the two. The number of muscle fibers was reported as ~3,200/mm^2 with ~3,500 cap/mm^2. The ratio of fibers to capillaries was close to 0.9, and the diffusion distance was 8.4 μm. The authors state that the average diffusion distance in skeletal muscle is much greater—more than double that of a heart muscle. Figure 8 shows a scanning electron micrograph of heart muscle.

CAT MESENTERY

Johnson and Wayland (48) used an isolated cat mesentery preparation to study blood flow in single capillaries, and Johnson (47) later used the same preparation to study red cell separation in these mesenteric vessels.

A thoroughfare channel, observed in 50% of 15 networks, was often judged to be shorter than the distal capillaries.

Richardson and Zweifach (73) noted some features in the microvascular bed of the cat mesentery in a study to determine intravascular pressures at various levels of the macro- and microcirculation. Three or four large arteries and veins, the major supply vessels, give rise to smaller arterial branches (150–300 μm) and collecting veins (200–400 μm). Arterioles and venules originate from these vessels. Two or more capillaries join to form the earliest nonmuscular venous vessels, which are ~10 μm in diameter, and merge with similar vessels to join a venule 20–40 μm in diameter. Artery-to-artery and vein-to-vein anastomoses were abundant. Capillaries of 6–10 μm were

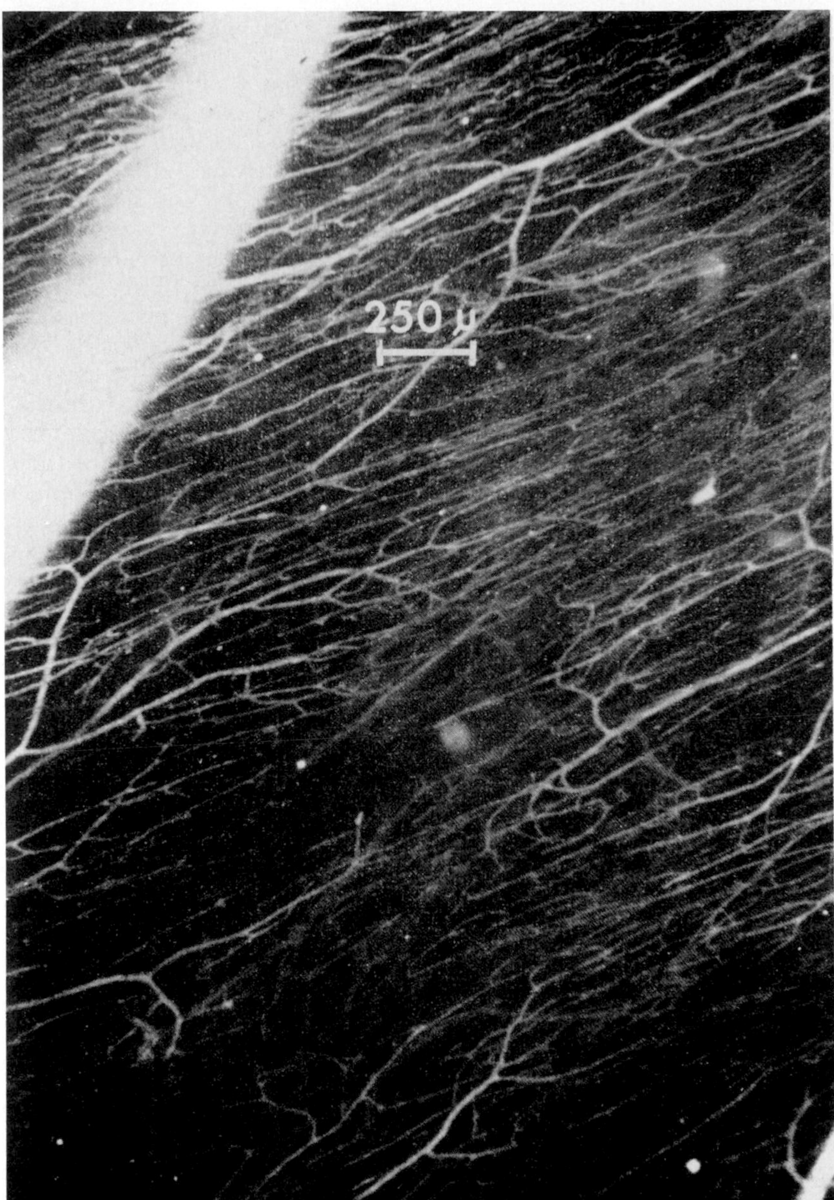

FIG. 7. Capillaries in subendocardium seen running parallel to muscle fibers. [From Grayson et al. (37).]

usually distributed at right angles from either terminal arterioles 20–30 μm in diameter or thoroughfare channels 10–12 μm in diameter. The capillaries interconnected freely to form a complex network. Pressure recording revealed pulsatile pressure in precapillary vessels down to the arteriole level and also in some small venules. Pressure measurements in pre- and postcapillary vessels showed that mean capillary pressure was ~30% of arterial input pressure and that the major resistance to blood flow in the cat mesentery occurs in precapillary vessels 10–30 μm in diameter. Pressure differences between some arterial and venous vessels indicated the presence of wide arteriovenous shunts. A wide range of pressures during lowering of arterial pressure indicated that active adjustments occurred in the microvasculature (autoregulation). Precapillary sphincter contraction is mentioned, and it is concluded that autoregulation of pressure rather than of flow occurs in this bed.

Frasher and Wayland (24) studied the repeating modular organization of the microcirculation in the cat mesentery. The module was described as an area of membrane surrounded by a small artery with an average diameter of 28 μm and by a small vein with an average diameter of 40 μm. The size of the enclosed area varied from 0.9 to 12.5 mm^2. Figure 9 shows a portion of mesentery from an injected specimen, providing a general view of the larger vascular pattern.

Lipowsky and Zweifach (51) presented a detailed analysis of the network of vessels in the cat mesentery.

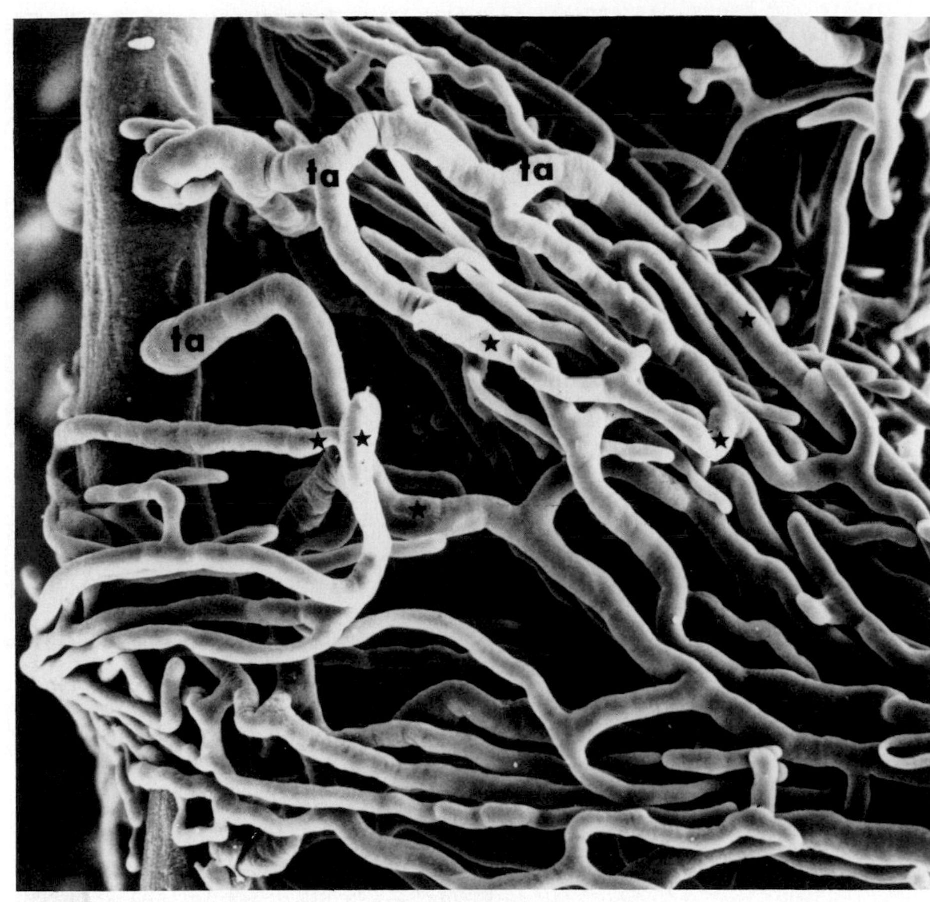

FIG. 8. Scanning electron micrograph of subepicardial myocardium prepared from corrosion cast. Terminal arterioles (*ta*) give rise to capillaries (*stars*). × 950. (Courtesy of Dr. R. S. Tomanck.)

According to the definitions of Frasher and Wayland (24), the first-order vessels are the large artery–vein pair distributed radially from the posterior line of attachment toward the bowel. The arteries range in diameter from 150–300 μm. These paired vessels bifurcate to form pairs of vessels that run parallel to the bowel and supply it with blood. This vascular distribution forms a triangular sector containing the second order of branching. Second-order artery-vein pairs with diameters of 20–40 μm traverse the interior and form a continuous interarcading network. This vascular pattern forms the modules described by Frasher and Wayland (24). Several geometric shapes are formed by the individual modules. Lipowsky and Zweifach (51) point out that an artery-vein pair may have such small diameters (15–20 μm) that they should be considered interior modular vessels; however, their connection with another first-order pair requires them to be designated as perimeter vessels of contiguous modules. The interior of each module is described as being made up of a network of pre- and postcapillary vessels that may number 165. True capillaries had diameters of 6–8 μm (avg 7 μm).

In 1977 Schmid-Schoenbein et al. (75) and Zweifach and Lipowsky (96) presented data regarding the geometrical characteristics of the microvessels in several tissues, including the cat mesentery. Lymphatic vessels were also examined. Because of its thinness and the absence of vessel superimposition, the mesentery is considered a two-dimensional structure. A module of the cat mesentery showed paired arcading arterial and venous vessels that supplied the capillary network through four or five metarterioles. The capillary network empties into three or four postcapillaries to return blood to the peripheral venule. Schmid-Schoenbein et al. (75) have classified the blood vessels according to their diameter, which is unfortunate because of possible inaccuracies. The identification of the end of the arteriole and the beginning of the capillary was based on the observation that the feeding arteriole decreased in diameter with successive branching and that the capillary began at the point where the diameter remained constant. This determinant for the beginning of the capillary makes some of the measurements suspect. The mean value found for capillary diameter was 7.4 μm, average length was 265 μm, and capillary volume per unit tissue area was 0.17 $\mu m^3/\mu m^2$.

INTESTINAL MICROCIRCULATION

In 1959 Baez (2) described the microcirculation in rat small intestine based on microscopic observations

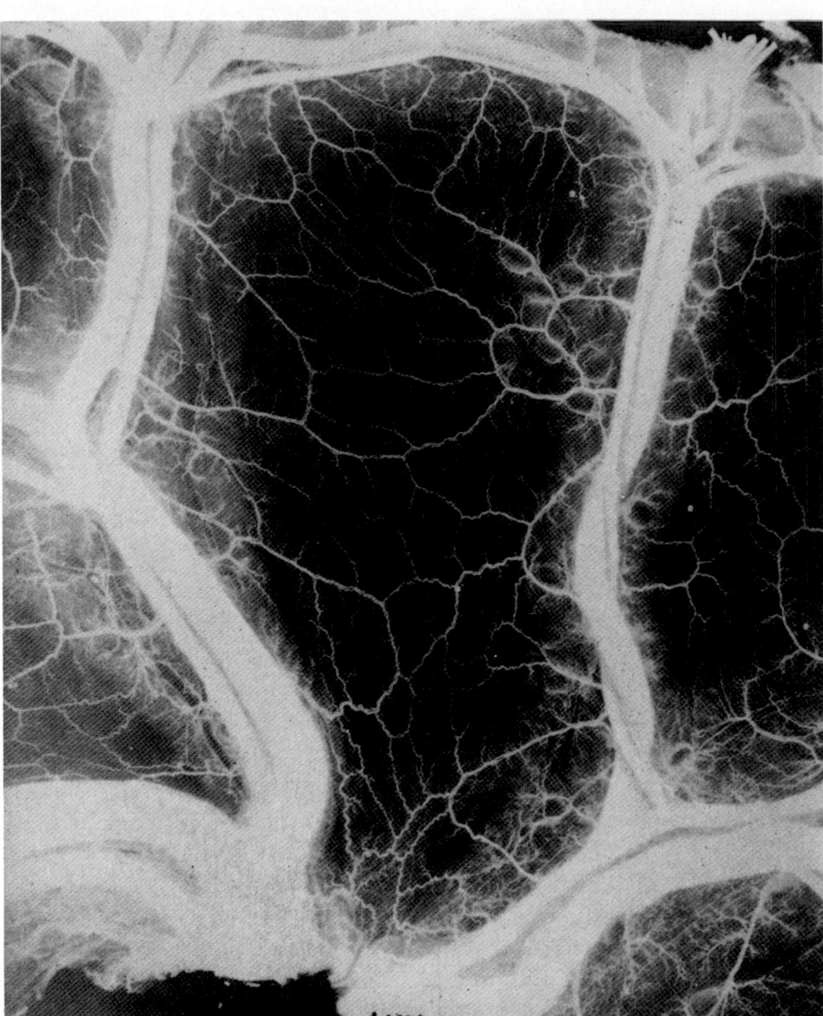

FIG. 9. Cat mesentery section bordered by paired arterioles and venules forming an arcade (*top*). [From Frasher and Wayland (24).]

in the living animal. The material was included in a review of arteriovenous pathways and more recently appeared with minor changes in an article by Baez (5) on gastrointestinal microvascular morphology. The descriptions presented here are confined to the muscular and mucosal layers of the gut. Baez found that vessels supplying the muscular coat arise from the proximal end of mucosal arteries far from secondary arcades in the submucosa. Most of the vessels are metarterioles 10–14 μm in diameter that extend to the plane of cleavage between the circular and longitudinal muscle layers and run in this area transverse to the long axis of the intestine. After reaching the intermuscular septum, two sets of capillaries in groups of three or four arise from the metarterioles. The first group supplies the circular muscle bundles and runs in the same plane as the parent vessels, whereas the second group supplies the longitudinal bundles and runs between the muscularis and the serosa farther out. These capillaries (some with precapillary sphincters) run parallel ~40–60 μm apart between the muscle fibers and have cross-connections approximately every 200–240 μm. The main arteriole or metarteriole is 500–1,000 μm in length and may divide into two vessels or become a small venule when it reaches the submucosa. The metarterioles and precapillary sphincters exhibit spontaneous contractile activity that produces intermittent capillary flow. They are considered the most reactive in the vascular elements in the intestine. Endothelial capillaries have an inside diameter of 4.5–6.2 μm and are 700–950 μm in length. This length entitles them to be classified with capillaries in skeletal muscle as being among the longest capillaries in the body.

The mucosal artery that supplies the arteriole to the muscular coat continues toward the muscularis mucosa and gives off one or two short arteriolar branches (14–18 μm) that immediately branch into 3–6 capillaries. The capillaries are interconnected and arranged in a semicircle. The capillaries surround an area of tissue 40–60 μm in diameter and enclose nerve cell aggregates and lymphatic channels. The mucosal arteries anastomose with one another deep in the submucosa and give off one or two lateral branches

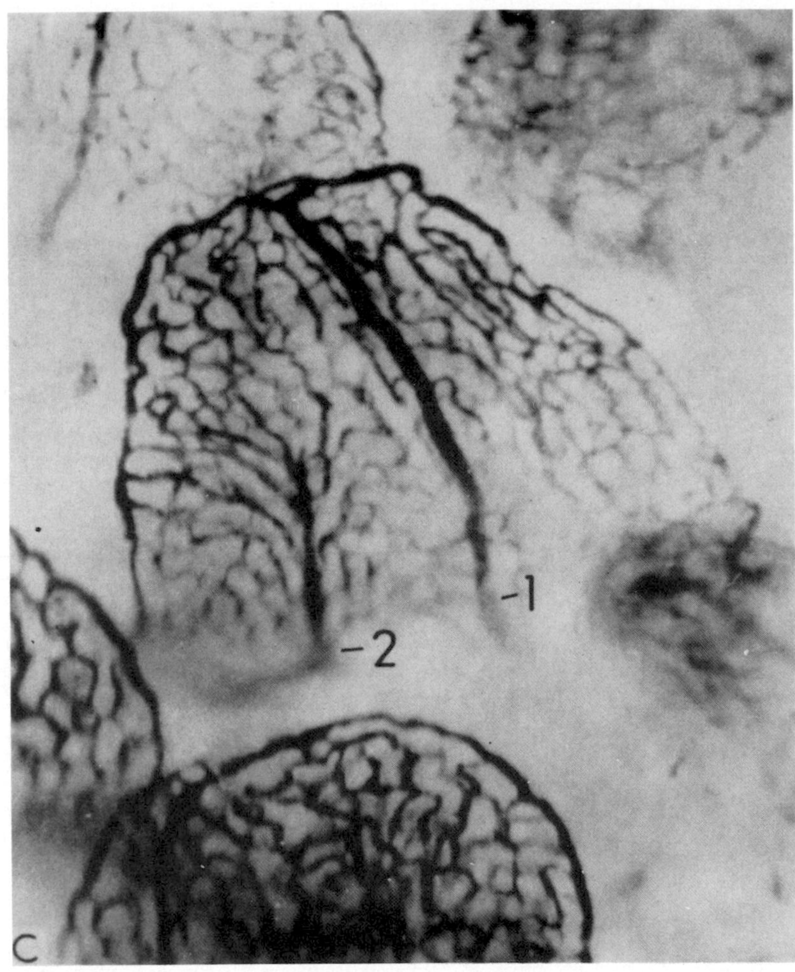

FIG. 10. Villus of the ileum injected with India ink. Ascending arteriole (*1*) gives rise to capillaries. Venule (*2*) drains blood from villus. [From Baez (5), © 1977, University Park Press, Baltimore, MD.]

that break into 6–8 endothelial capillaries. The mucosal artery becomes reduced and penetrates the villi as a single- or double-branched vessel.

Baez, observing an everted segment of ileum, describes the mucosal arteriole (14–18 μm) penetrating a villus, where it ascends toward the apex as a single trunk with numerous capillary side branches. When it reaches the apex, it divides into two arterioles or into 8–10 capillaries. The capillaries in the ascending and descending portion of the villus interconnect to form a meshwork as depicted in Figure 10.

Baez (5) states that the "architectural module" of the outer smooth muscle coat of the intestine is very similar to the pattern seen in skeletal muscle. Both have parallel endothelial capillaries that are cross-connected at intervals, and both form oblong meshes around terminal arterioles. No direct arteriovenous shunts are seen.

Further descriptions of in vivo preparations are given by Bohlen, Gore, and co-workers (7–9, 31). The microvessels of intestinal muscle described by Gore and Bohlen (31) in 1975 were identified by numerical classification, with the largest arterioles and venules as the first-order vessels. The first-order vessel is a branch of a small artery in the mesentery, and it immediately penetrates both muscle layers to run in the submucosa. Second- and third-order arterioles are given off, and the third-order vessels go through the submucosa to become the central arterioles of the villi. Fourth-order arterioles ascend through the muscle layers to supply fifth-order arterioles of the inner circular and outer longitudinal muscle layers. The fifth-order vessels run perpendicular to the muscle fibers and give rise to capillaries that run parallel to the fibers. The capillaries converge to form venules (fourth-order vessels) and continue to converge, forming larger venules until they empty into a small vein. A diagram of the vascular pattern is shown in Figure 11. Measurements of capillary pressures were reported as 30–34 mmHg in the mesenteric capillaries when systemic blood pressure was ~107 mmHg, whereas capillary pressure averaged 22–24 mmHg in the intestinal muscle and 13–15 mmHg in mucosal villi.

In 1975 Bohlen et al. (9) published results of experiments to determine the degree of neural and local vascular control in the intestinal mucosa by observing microvessels of the villi. The viability of the preparation was determined in part by the appearance of

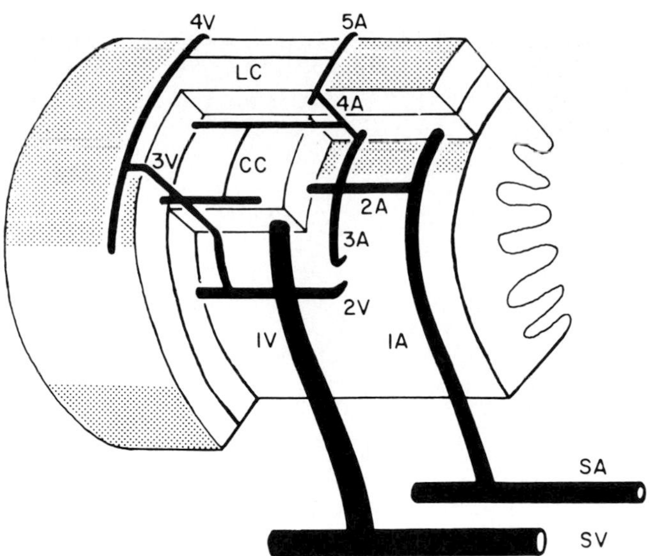

FIG. 11. Rat intestinal muscle and submucosal microcirculation. SA, small artery; SV, small vein; 1A–5A, major arteriolar branches; 1V–4V, major venular branches. Circular muscle layer (CC) and longitudinal muscle layer (LC) have capillaries that run parallel to the muscle fibers. [From Bohlen and Gore (7).]

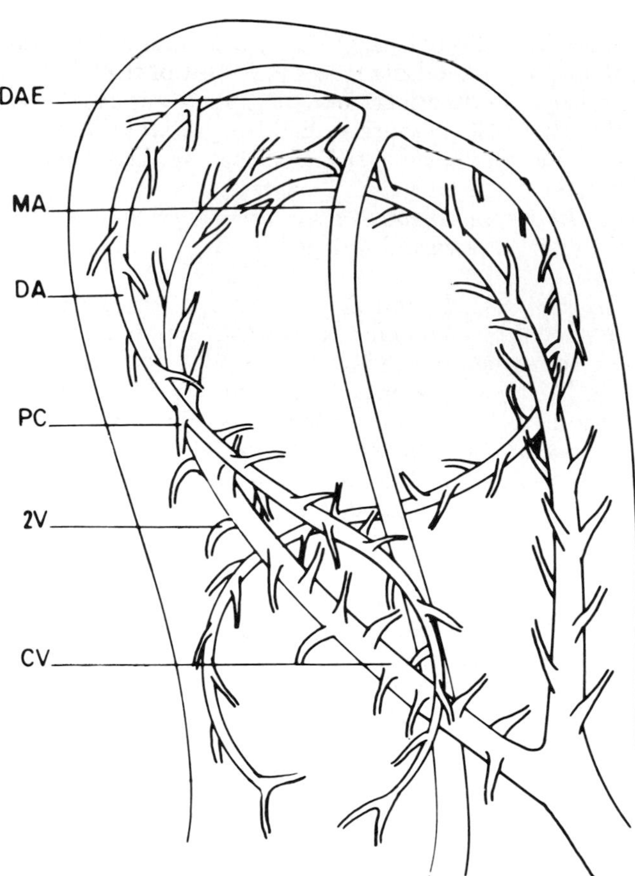

FIG. 12. Microvessels within a villus. DAE, distributing arteriole entrance; MA, main arteriole; DA, distributing arteriole; PC, precapillary sphincter; 2V, second-order venule; CV, collecting venule. [From Bohlen et al. (9).]

spontaneous activity (vasomotion) of arteriolar and venular vessels. The vasculature of a villus was seen to originate from a single arteriole that ran from the base to the apex and branched into two smaller arterioles designated as distributing arterioles. After a brief length devoid of any branches, capillaries were given off and the initial segment of each capillary was encircled by a single smooth muscle cell identified as a precapillary sphincter (Fig. 12). Denervation had little effect on the diameters of the main arteriole, the distributing arteriole, or the precapillary sphincter, whereas certain venous vessels appeared smaller than control values after denervation.

The following year Bohlen and Gore (7) presented data showing the diameters and pressures of the microvessels in intestinal muscle and the mucosa (Table 1). Of the total blood flow, 30% went to the intestinal muscle and 69% went to the mucosal circuit.

In 1977 Bohlen and Gore (8) compared pressures and diameters in innervated and denervated rat intestine and included additional information regarding the vascular arrangement in the intestine. The first-order arteriole that runs in the upper surface of the submucosa gives rise to 3–5 second-order arterioles, which in turn give off 16–18 third-order arterioles. Each third-order arteriole gives rise to a fourth-order vessel that ascends through the muscle layer and supplies blood to fifth-order arterioles in the circular and longitudinal muscle layers. Denervation caused a significant dilatation of small arterioles (third and fifth order) and of venules (first, second, and fourth order).

TABLE 1. *Micropressure and Diameter Distributions in Rat Intestinal Muscle and Mucosal Microcirculation*

	n	Pressure, mmHg	Inside Diam, μm
Muscle circuit			
First-order arteriole	16	44.6 ± 1.6	52.6 ± 1.8
Second-order arteriole	11	44.6 ± 2.9	29.6 ± 2.3
Third-order arteriole	14	32.4 ± 2.5	12.2 ± 0.6
Fifth-order arteriole	11	26.7 ± 2.0	8.4 ± 0.5
Capillary	8	23.8 ± 1.5	5.0 ± 0.5
Fourth-order venule	20	15.2 ± 1.2	9.9 ± 0.8
Second-order venule	10	15.7 ± 1.2	28.3 ± 5.4
First-order venule	11	10.1 ± 0.4	60.4 ± 3.6
Mucosal circuit			
Distributing arteriole	14	30.5 ± 1.7	8.3 ± 0.3
Capillary	11	13.8 ± 2.2	4.3 ± 1.1
Second-order venule	8	12.8 ± 1.5	9.3 ± 0.6

Values are means ± SE. Systemic arterial pressure was 100–110 mmHg. [From Bohlen and Gore (7).]

HAMSTER CHEEK POUCH

The description of microcirculation in the hamster cheek pouch presented in 1963 (87) was garnered from papers by Fulton et al. (28, 29), Lutz and Fulton (53, 54), and Poor and Lutz (69). No details of the vascular pattern were described, but the pouch was more vascular than rat mesentery, had no preferential channels, but did have a rich network of anastomoses between both venous and arterial vessels. Arterioles exhibited spontaneous vasomotion, and precapillary sphincters contracted independently of adjacent vessels.

In 1948 Priddy and Brodie (70) had reported that the pouch (0.4–0.05 μm thick) was composed of stratified squamous epithelium, dense connective tissue of equal thickness, a muscular layer in the proximal portion that was almost 3 times as thick, and a layer of loose areolar connective tissue. The most recent additional information regarding the anatomy of the cheek pouch is in a paper by Duling (15) published in 1973. The blood supply to the pouch comes from four branches of the external carotid artery called sacular arteries. The pouch has been characterized as cutaneous tissue but has no visible lymphatic vessels, no mucous cells, and a very diffuse network of nerves. Duling designates the vessels as artery, large arteriole, small arteriole, terminal arteriole, and precapillary sphincter. Arterial and venous vessels are parallel down to the level of the small arterioles. Spontaneous contractile activity is common in the arteriolar vessels. In 1973 Ausprunk et al. (1) described both adrenergic and cholinergic nerve fibers in the walls of arterioles with diameters of 35–50 μm, which would be first- and second-order vessels. This kind of dual innervation has not been demonstrated in microcirculatory beds of most mammalian tissues.

Vascular dimensions can be found in descriptive material by Wiedeman, Tuma, and Mayrovitz (92) and in the diagram of the vascular pattern shown in Figure 13. Examination of the pouch at low-power magnification gives the impression of a profuse distribution of arterial vessels with numerous small branches that have no distinct pattern. Many venous vessels of various sizes are prominent. The average diameter of one of the major arteries is 76.7 μm, and its branches average 29.8 μm in diameter. Arterioles that branch from the second-order vessels show a wide range in diameter, between 9.0 and 22.5 μm (avg 15.2 μm). Terminal arterioles are ~7.5 μm and capillaries are ~4.5 μm.

BAT WING

Descriptions of the architecture and characteristics of the vasculature of the bat wing presented by Nicoll and Webb (66, 67, 85) are comprehensive and definitive. These investigators discussed the arrangement

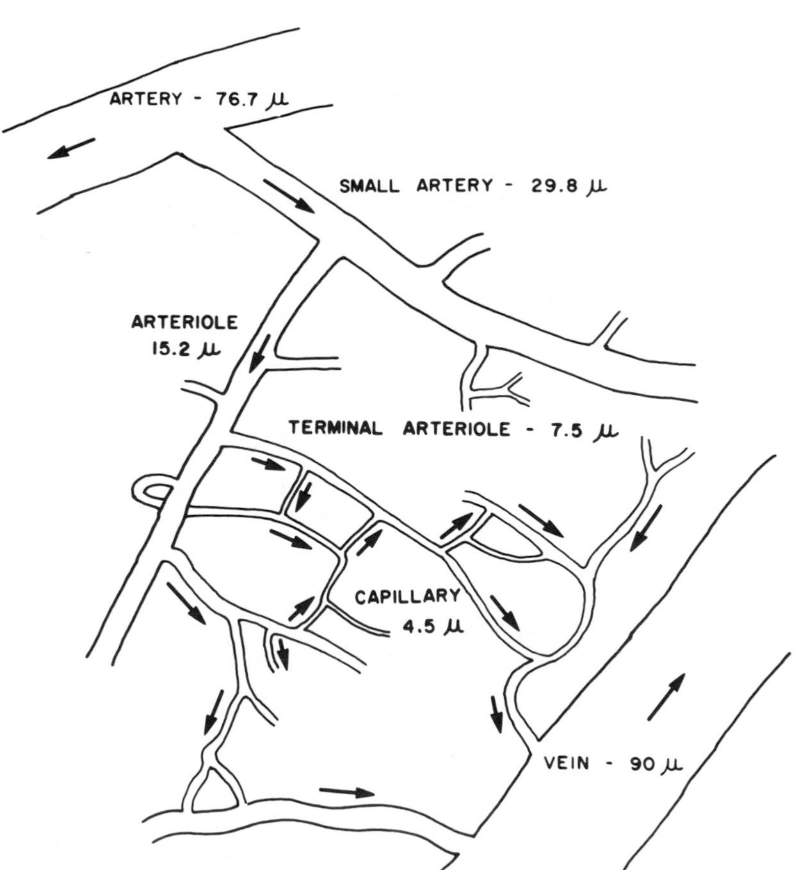

FIG. 13. Typical vascular pattern in hamster cheek pouch. [From Wiedeman et al. (92).]

of vascular smooth muscle down to the precapillary sphincter, the obstruction of capillary flow by leukocytes, the angle of branching of arterial vessels, the arcuate system or arcades, the vasomotion in arterial and venous vessels, and the spontaneous contractile activity of terminal arterioles as a determinant of capillary flow. These papers are reviewed in the 1963 edition of the *Handbook* on circulation (87).

In 1963 Wiedeman (86) reported vessel lengths, diameters, and the number of branches from each order of vessel of a total vascular bed in the bat wing from a major distributing artery to its accompanying vein (Table 2). The calculated total cross-sectional area in the bat wing vessel was found to be less at the capillary level than at the level of the postcapillary venule. This observation did not coincide with earlier measurements, notably Green's modification of Mall's data derived from fixed material from dog mesentery (38). The discrepancy was caused by differences in the diameter of the capillary, which was generally assumed to be 8 μm but actually measured an average 3.7 μm.

Nicoll (63) in 1964 discussed the structure and function of minute vessels involved in autoregulation. He divided the subcutaneous vessels in the bat wing into three sections and noted that no interconnecting shunts or arteriovenous anastomoses were present. The arteries and veins serve as high or low conduits, respond to nerve excitation, and show loss of tonus after denervation. Capillaries are exchange vessels, and the muscle cells of the terminal arterioles determine flow and pressure within these vessels. Nerve stimulation or denervation does not directly affect the smooth muscle cells of these vessels, which show spontaneous contractile activity. The venules have muscle cells that respond to local conditions and are included with the terminal arterioles as participants in autoregulation.

Nicoll (64) made direct pressure measurements in arterial vessels in the wing of the unanesthetized bat at locations indicated in Figure 14, which is a diagram of the arterial distribution. Along one of the two major arteries entering the wing at the shoulder, a pressure gradient was shown going from an average of 63 mmHg at the most proximal portion to 52 mmHg at the most distal portion. Nicoll found no correlation between diameter and pressure. The average diameter of the major artery (calculated from only 3 readings) was 71 μm at the proximal end and 49 μm at the distal end. Measurements along branches from the major vessel showed no correlation between either location or vessel size and pressure. He concluded that pressure in the microcirculatory bed showed local and cyclic variations unrelated to conditions in the macrocirculation. A detailed analysis of microvascular blood velocity and pressure distribution in the bat wing has been presented by Mayrovitz, Tuma, and Wiedeman (58a).

Wiedeman (88) studied the influence of intraluminal pressure changes on contractile activity and found that arteriolar vessels in the bat wing show a widely variable spontaneous contractile activity, contracting independently of one another with no similarity in frequency or duration of individual contractions. The terminal arterioles of fourth-order vessels in this bed had an average diameter of 7 μm. These precapillary arterioles showed augmented contractile activity in response to an increase in intraluminal pressure. The augmented contractile activity was directly related to the pressure increments. Denervation of the blood vessels of the bat wing resulted in an increase in diameter of the larger arterial vessels but a decrease in resting diameter and an increase in contractile activity of the distally located precapillary arterioles.

In a description of the architecture of the terminal vascular bed, Wiedeman (89) compared the vascular arrangement of arterial and venous vessels. Postcapillary venules were twice as large as the capillaries that converged to form them. Venules formed from convergence of the postcapillary venules were 3 times bigger in diameter than their accompanying arterioles and formed twice as many small veins as the small arteries in the same vascular bed. A diagram of the two systems showing the relative number of vessels and their diameters is shown in Figure 15.

The effect of surgical and chemical denervation on diameters of arterial vessels in the bat wing was reported in 1968 by Wiedeman (90). Surgical denervation produced a 40% increase in diameter in the major artery, a 15% increase in the first-order vessels, a 20% increase in the second-order vessels, an 8% decrease in the third-order vessels, and a 22% decrease in the fourth-order vessels. All the changes were statistically

TABLE 2. *Dimensions of Blood Vessels in Bat Wing*

	Avg Length, mm	Avg Diam, μm	Avg No. of Branches	No. of Vessels	Total Cross-Sectional Area, μm^2	Capacity, $mm^3 \times 10^3$	% of Capacity
Artery	17.0	52.6	12.3	1	2,263*	38.4	10.1
Small artery	3.5	19.0	9.7	12.3	4,144	14.4	3.8
Arteriole	0.95	7.0	4.6	119.3	5,101	4.7	1.2
Capillary	0.23	3.7	3.1†	548.7	6,548	1.5	0.39
Postcapillary venule	0.21	7.3		1,727.0	78,233	16.4	4.3
Venule	1.0	21.0	5.0	345.4	127,995	127.9	33.7
Small vein	3.4	37.0	14.1	24.5	27,885	94.7	25.0
Vein	16.6	76.2	24.5	1	4,882	81.0	21.4

* Avg of individual areas. † Calculated. [From Wiedeman (86), by permission of the American Heart Association, Inc.]

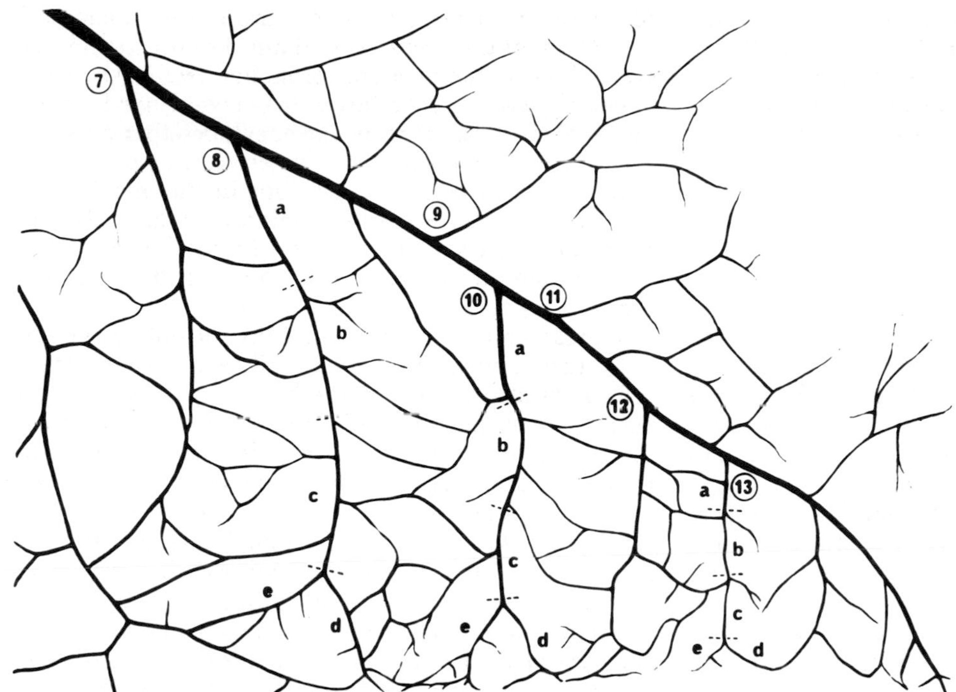

FIG. 14. Major vessels in bat wing membrane. Major arterial branches are numbered *7–13*, and letters indicate areas where pressure measurements were made. [From Nicoll (64). In: *Microcirculation: A Symposium*, © 1969. Courtesy of Charles C Thomas, Publisher, Springfield, Illinois.]

significant. Diameter changes caused by agents that block α-adrenergic receptors and ganglions showed the drugs to be less effective in altering vessel size. It was concluded that the contractile activity of the fourth-order terminal arterioles and of their final muscular investment, the precapillary sphincter, is independent of sympathetic vasoconstrictor impulses and is based on myogenic factors.

Harris et al. (39) and Longnecker and Harris (52) presented studies of the effects of various anesthetic agents on bat wing vessels showing that pentobarbital had a relaxing effect on arterial and venous vessels, whereas thiopental did not change vascular diameters but evoked an increase in venous vasomotion. Halothane produced arterial dilatation at a concentration lower than that required for venous dilatation.

Pressure measurements of microvessels, lymphatics, and interstitial tissue of the bat wing were presented by Wiederhielm and Weston (93) in 1973. The nomenclature of the blood vessels was taken from the classification used by Chambers and Zweifach (12) in 1944. The term *metarteriole* is used, although the location of this vessel in the bat wing vasculature is not identified. Cardiac pulsations were recorded in terminal arteries (ID 100 μm) and arterioles (ID 70–80 μm); irregular changes in pressure associated with vasomotion of these vessels were also recorded. Metarterioles (ID 10–20 μm) had pressures ranging from 50–75 mmHg. Mean pressure in arterial capillaries was 32 mmHg and varied considerably around the mean due to precapillary sphincter activity. Pressure in the tissue space averaged 1.3 mmHg, whereas lymphatic pressures averaged 1.2 mmHg in the relaxed state.

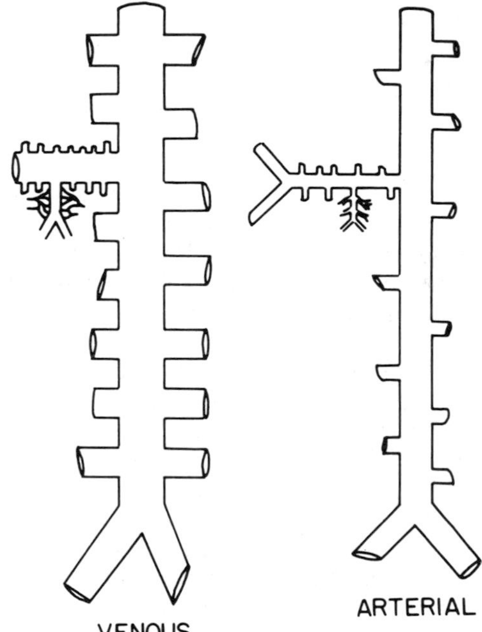

FIG. 15. Diagram of venous and arterial vessels comparing number of vessels and their relative sizes in a complete circuit from arterial to venous side. Data derived from measurements of vessels in wing of live bat. [From Wiedeman (89).]

CUTANEOUS MICROCIRCULATION

Eriksson et al. (18) developed an in vivo preparation of the ear of the homozygous hairless mouse that provided detailed information about the microvasculature of the skin.

The mouse ear is described as a large, prominent appendage representing ~6% of the body's total surface area. It consists of two layers of skin separated by a thin skeleton of elastic cartilage. With the exception of sweat glands and subcutaneous fat, it contains all of the components of human epidermis and dermis.

The vascular network originates from three pairs of arterioles and venules that enter at the base of the ear. Four branching orders of arterial vessels were observed, from the original first-order entering arteriole to the fourth-order precapillary arterioles. The inside diameter of the first-order arterioles was found to be 35 μm. Second- and third-order diameters were not given, but fourth-order arterioles had a diameter of 8–9 μm, whereas capillary diameters measured 6–7 μm. The precapillary arterioles, capillary loops, and postcapillary venules formed a network. Numerous arteriovenous anastomoses 10–12 μm in diameter were observed to have intermittent flow (Fig. 16). Capillary loops were organized around the empty hair follicles and occurred in areas some distance from the follicles. Intermittent flow in the capillaries was as normal as frequent reversal of flow. The authors state that no measurable vasomotion was seen in either arterioles or venules. It is difficult to explain intermittent flow or reversal of flow in the capillaries without contractile activity of pre- or postcapillary vessels altering the pressure relationships within the network to produce flow changes.

CEREBRAL CIRCULATION

The brain tissue does not lend itself to in vivo microscopic observations necessary to reveal the pattern formed by the microvasculature of the blood flow through it. Studies with the pial circulation offer little in descriptive material of microvessels because the major portion of these smaller vessels is beneath the visible arterial vessels, including the penetrating arterioles and their accompanying venous vessels. The microvessels are deep in the brain tissue and thus are obscured by both superficial vessels and tissue.

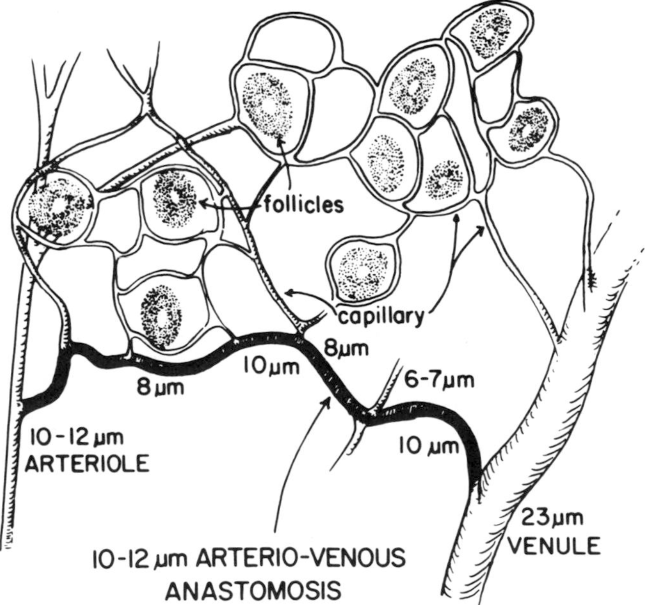

FIG. 16. Capillary pattern formed around follicles in hairless mouse ear. [From Eriksson et al. (18).]

The diameters of six branching orders of arterial and venous vessels and the velocity of blood flow in the cerebral microvessels in the rat were measured in 1974 by Ma et al. (55). A burr hole in the skull was drilled to expose the cerebral surface supplied by the parietal branches of the middle cerebral artery and the superior cerebral venous tributaries. The dura mater was removed to expose the superficial pial vessels. No parallel distribution of arterial and venous vessels was seen, and venous vessels were more numerous than arterial vessels. Capillaries had diameters between 7.23 and 3.13 μm, with a blood flow velocity of 4.6 ± 0.69 mm/s.

In a study by Wiederhold et al. (94), a three-dimensional reconstruction of brain capillaries was made from frozen serial sections that resulted in a visualization of the spatial arrangement of capillaries in the cat cerebral cortex and other information about capillary dimensions. The model included the pial surface and three layers immediately beneath it (Fig. 17).

Projected photographs of the capillaries were magnified × 200. Capillary diameter was 4.78 ± 0.11 μm, with a total capillary length of 41.60 ± 4.12 cm/mm^3. The volumetric density of the capillary network became greater with increasing depth into the cortex, the third layer having the greatest density. Wiederhold et al. (94) believe that the fourth layer of the cat cerebral cortex may have the greatest capillary density, although this was not determined in their study. The capillaries form an asymmetrical net arrangement.

An in vivo microscopic study of blood flow in the cerebral cortex of cats was conducted by Pawlik et al. (68) in 1981. Transillumination of the brain was achieved by adapting the system used for visualization of coronary microvessels in cardiac muscle. This procedure involves inserting, at a depth of 500 μm, a needle carrying an optical glass fiber that transmits light from a xenon source. Arterioles with diameters ranging from 318 to 681 μm were found to exhibit a spontaneous random vasomotion. Arterioles were seen to dilate during hypercapnia and to respond to minimal doses of vascular smooth muscle blockers and activators.

Intracortical capillaries formed a dense, asymmetric, three-dimensional anastomotic network. Capillaries formed smooth curves, short straight segments, loops, and junctions (Fig. 18). Capillary diameters did not change during the observation, and usually 90%

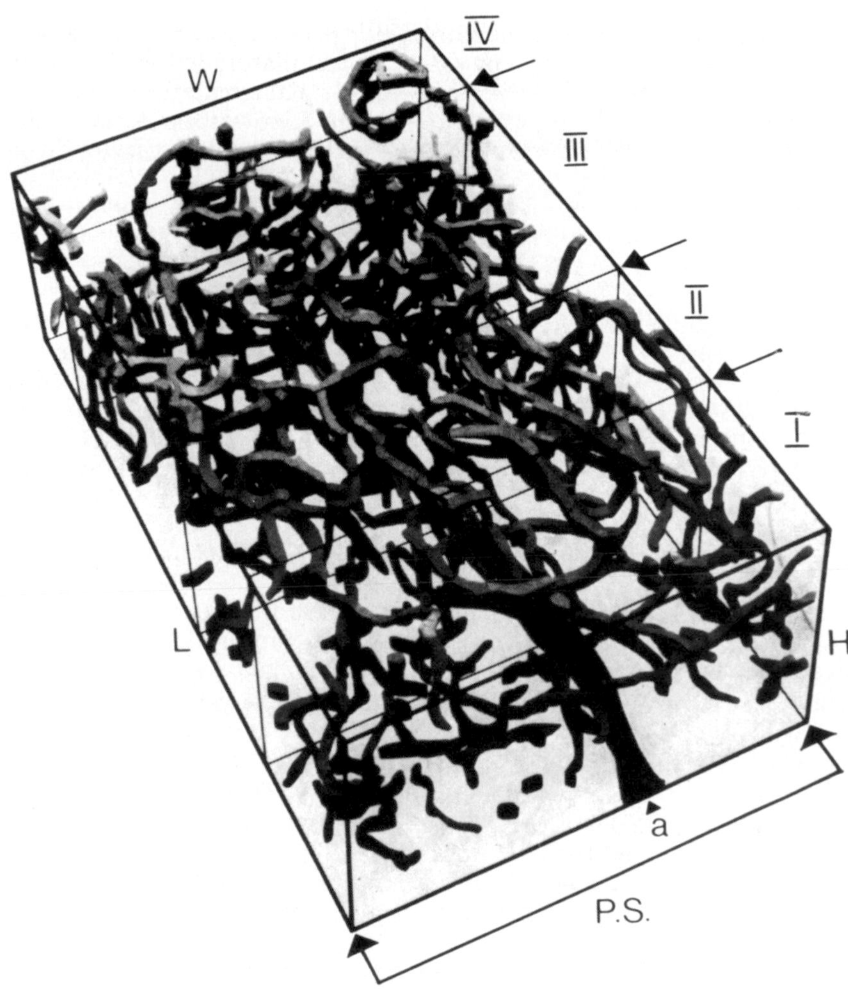

FIG. 17. Three-dimensional model of cat cerebral cortex vessels. a, Artery; PS, pial surface; I, molecular layer; II, external granular layer; III, external pyramidal layer; IV, parts of internal granular layer. [From Wiederhold et al. (94).]

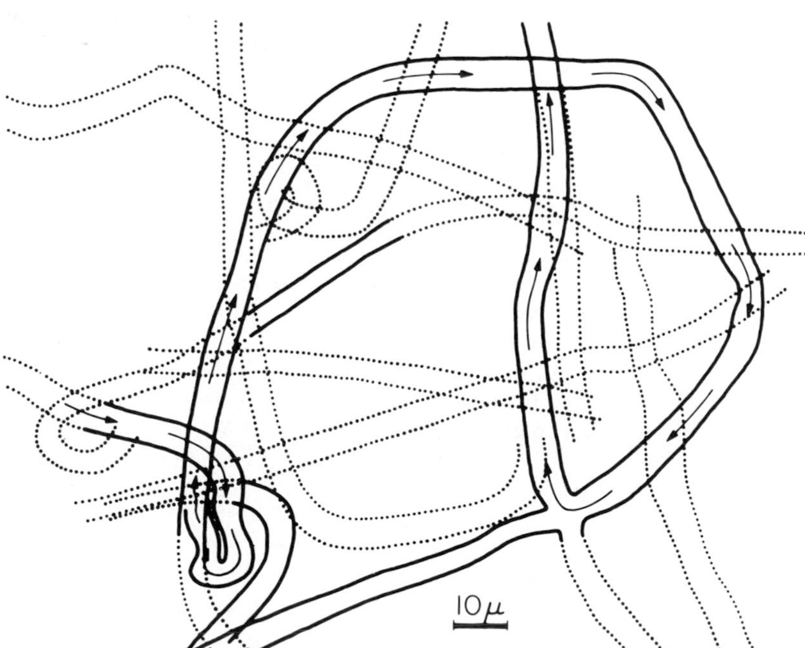

FIG. 18. Diagram of capillary vessels in cerebral cortex of cat drawn from an in vivo microscopic preparation. [From Pawlik et al. (68).]

of the visible capillaries were perfused with blood. Flow was generally unidirectional, but a complete stop or reversal of flow was occasionally seen. Flow velocity in capillaries was highly variable, ranging from 400 to 3,900 μm/s, with an overall median of 1,500 μm/s.

The authors reported capillary diameters of 5.1 ± 0.54 μm, total capillary lengths per tissue volume of 939 ± 338.2 mm/mm^3, total capillary surface areas of 13.3 ± 3.2 mm^2/mm^3, and intercapillary distances of 16.5–41.0 μm (mean 26.8 μm).

Capillary surface density per volume of tissue represents the main area of exchange between blood and tissue; for the cerebral cortex this value is within the same range as that of the extensor hallucis proprius muscle reported by Myrhage and Hudlická (62). Pawlik et al. (68) state that a fundamental characteristic of the intracortical cerebral capillary network is its irregularity, which affects the blood flow.

SUMMARY

It is apparent from the descriptions presented here that there are numerous similar anatomical and behavioral features in these microvascular beds in various tissues of different animals. For example, capillary diameters fall within the range of 4–5 μm, and capillary density in muscle, with the exception of cardiac muscle, is ~1,000/mm^2. Spontaneous contractile activity and intermittent flow are common to most beds, and precapillary sphincters are identified in most of them. Four of the five skeletal muscle beds observed have a central artery and vein; arterioarterial anastomoses and venovenous anastomoses (the means by which arcades are formed) are frequently seen in all beds, but arteriovenous anastomoses are not common. The ratio of capillaries to muscle fibers is essentially the same in the tenuissimus, the extensor hallucis proprius, and the heart, but capillary density in the heart is almost 3 times that of the other two muscles. The data from all of the vascular beds included in this survey are listed in Tables 3 and 4.

Characteristics of terminal vascular beds that are increasingly uniform are now being found. Intermittent flow in capillary networks was observed in 7 of the 10 beds examined, and spontaneous contractile activity of vessels was reported in 6 of the beds. Apparently it is necessary for these two characteristics to be coupled and to occur only together. Whether precapillary sphincters are reported as present seems to depend on the definition for the sphincter. The term has been defined in a number of ways: as an area of peripheral resistance upstream from the capillary bed, as a vessel, and as the muscular investiture at the point where a capillary branches from its parent vessel. The latter is the most restrictive definition and precludes designating a precapillary sphincter in vascular beds where the capillaries may originate as a

TABLE 3. *Architectural and Flow Characteristics of Capillary Beds*

Tissue	Species	Diam, μm	Length, μm	Density cap/mm^2	Surface Area, mm^2/mm^3	Flow Velocity, mm/s	Blood Flow, ml·min^{-1}·100 g^{-1}	Vessel/Fiber	Ref.
Cremaster	Rat	5.0–5.8	615 ± 194	1,300		0.70			76
					24.4		9.5		59
						0.21			
Tenuissimus	Cat	4.7–5.9	1,015	625	9.0	0.50		0.95	21
	Rabbit	5.0–6.0		1,000					26
						0.29			50
						0.38			82
Gracilis	Rat, dog		400–500	220–2,943					43
		5.3					5.6		42
	Rat					0.26			41
Extensor hallucis proprius	Rat	4.0–4.5	535	1,347 ± 53	1.6			0.93–1.01	62
Spinotrapezius	Rat	3.0–5.0							78
Heart muscle	Cat	5.3				0.112			80
	Dog	4.1				3.150			81
			100–500	3,100–3,800	50.0				6
	Rat			3,500				0.9	72
Mesentery	Cat	6–10							73
		7							51
		7.4	265						75
						0.5			48
Intestine	Rat	4.5–6.2	700–950						5
Cheek pouch	Hamster	4.5							92
Wing	Bat	3.7	230						86
Brain	Rat	4.23 ± 0.23				4.63 ± 0.69			55
	Cat	5.1			13.3	1.5			68

TABLE 4. *Components and Characteristics of Various Microvascular Beds*

Tissue	Species	No. of Cap/Arterioles	Central Artery	Transverse Arterioles	Intermittent Flow	Precapillary Sphincters	Metarterioles	Arteriovenous Anastomosis	Spontaneous Contractions	Ref.
Cremaster	Rat				Yes			No		32
		4–6	Yes		Yes	Yes	Yes	No		2, 4
		8–10								
			Yes	Yes	Yes		Yes	No		76
			Yes	Yes		Yes	Yes		Yes	44, 46
Tenuissimus	Cat		Yes	Yes	Yes	No	No			21
			Yes	Yes	Yes	No			Yes	25, 27
				Yes	Yes	No				50
Gracilis	Dog				Yes	Yes				42, 43
	Rat									
Extensor hallucis proprius	Rat	3–4	Yes	Yes	Yes					62
Spinotrapezius	Rat	1–2				Yes	Yes		Yes	97, 98
						No	No		Yes	35
			Yes			No	No			77–79
Cardiac muscle	Rat				Yes	Yes			Yes	57
Mesentery	Cat				Yes	Yes	Yes	Yes		73
Intestine	Rat				Yes	Yes	Yes		Yes	5
		3–6			Yes	Yes	Yes		Yes	8
Cheek pouch	Hamster				Yes	Yes	No		Yes	88
Wing	Bat	4			Yes	Yes	No	No	Yes	86
Ear	Mouse				Yes		No	Yes	No	18

burst of simple endothelial vessels from a single arteriole. The precapillary sphincter is the last contracting smooth muscle cell of the single arteriole that determines the flow of blood through the numerous distally located capillaries. Thus it is recommended that the precapillary sphincter be redefined as the final smooth muscle cells on the terminal arterioles that supply blood to the pure endothelial vessels that originate from them (91). The term *metarteriole* was originally used to designate a vessel that had a gradually decreasing muscular investment as it progressed from the arterial to the venous side of the network, giving off capillaries along the way. The metarteriole does not seem to be universally recognized and is described in only 3 of the 10 vascular beds discussed here.

There is a lack of uniformity in the use of the term *capillary density*. In some instances it refers to the number of capillaries that are perfused and therefore has a functional meaning; capillary density changes when blood flow through the tissue changes. The anatomical definition of capillary density describes the actual number of capillaries present in a tissue, which should be a stable figure.

A previously used method of identifying vessels by the diameter has been abandoned. Obviously the vessels in fixed preparations had only a small possibility of retaining their most usual in vivo dimensions. Selection of a diameter size in blood vessels of a living animal is difficult, especially in the autoregulating arterial vessels, because of the constant change in diameter. More important, the diameter of a small arteriole in one specific vascular bed may be quite different from that in the same tissue of a different animal. A vessel does not qualify as part of the microvasculature because it is observed through a microscope but rather because of its anatomical location in the vascular bed.

LYMPHATIC VESSELS

The stepwise accumulation of knowledge of the lymphatic vessels began with the recognition of the vessels as anatomical structures and ended with an understanding of the purpose of the lymphatic system several thousand years later. The abbreviated history of the discovery of lymphatics and lymph circulation presented here is based on a book by Rusznyak et al. (74) published in 1967 and one by Yoffey and Courtice (95) in 1970.

The discovery of lymphatic vessels is attributed to Asellius in Italy in 1622. During exposure of structures in the abdomen of a living dog, he noticed numerous vessels filled with a white fluid in the mesentery. He mistakenly thought the vessels were nerves. Later during the dissection when actual nerves became apparent, he punctured one of the structures and saw the milklike fluid in the vessel pour out. He performed the same surgery the following day and was greatly disappointed not to find the vessels filled with milky fluid. He reasoned that visible vessels were absent in the second dog because the dissection was done before the dog had been fed, so he repeated the procedure on a third dog that had been fed only a few hours before. His conjecture was correct, and once again he saw the milk-white vessels.

Between 1650 and 1653, Bartholinus in Copenhagen and Rudbeck in Uppsala independently discovered that the lymph vessels form a system. When Rudbeck began his studies in 1650, it was thought that the lymphatic vessels observed in the intestine were the only pathway for food absorption and that the vessels emptied their contents into the liver. Rudbeck disproved this theory and continued his investigations, which included the discovery of the thoracic duct, the presence of valves in the lymphatic vessels, and the fact that lymph coagulated like blood. Rudbeck was unaware until later that the thoracic duct had already been described. He expressed no opinion, however, about the function of the lymphatic system. In 1652 while traveling through Uppsala, Queen Christine of Sweden honored Rudbeck by inviting him to present his findings.

In 1653 Rudbeck went to Germany where he became acquainted with the work on lymphatic vessels by Bartholinus, a professor of anatomy in Copenhagen. Bartholinus, like Rudbeck, had determined that chyle vessels do not empty into the liver nor is the liver a center for blood production. Unfortunately a dispute arose about which of the two scientists had first learned the true nature of the lymphatic system. Bartholinus, who had published his findings a few months earlier than Rudbeck, published a second edition of his work including data to prove that he had recognized the hepatic peripheral lymphatics before Rudbeck. However, Rudbeck is given credit for being the first to describe the lymphatic system as a whole, referring to the vasa serosa, and had earlier presented his observations at the University in the presence of the court and foreign physicians, which at that time was equivalent to publication. Bartholinus, who named the vasa serosa "lymphatics," accused Rudbeck of plagiarism. However, Rudbeck's innumerable dissections (said to be at least 400) equipped him with a great depth of knowledge and the ability to make very precise drawings of the lymphatic system, making plagiarism out of the question. Rudbeck is acknowledged as the first to recognize the lymphatic vessels as a system for moving fluid to the arterial and venous systems. However, it was 100 years before the correctness of Rudbeck's observations was accepted. The technique of injecting the lymphatic vessels to make them more visible was developed, and by the end of the eighteenth century the topography of the major lymph trunks and lymph vessels had been documented. The origin of the smaller lymph vessels inside organs and the origin of lymphatic fluid were yet to be determined.

Bartholinus and Rudbeck made their observations after Harvey postulated in 1628 that the arterial and venous vessels were connected by capillaries. Then in 1661, Malpighi actually observed these capillaries through his magnifying lenses, which constituted the first microscope. By the end of the seventeenth century the fact that blood passed from the heart through arteries, capillaries, and veins back to the heart was known and accepted by most scientists. Studies on the lymphatic vessels continued, but their purpose remained unknown, although the suggestion had been made that the lymphatic vessels were absorbing vessels not only in the mesentery but over the entire body. Not until the end of the nineteenth century, however, did more useful information emerge. In 1862 von Recklinghausen demonstrated by staining with silver nitrate that lymphatic vessels were lined with endothelial cells. Ludwig had learned how to collect lymph from different parts of the body and proposed that lymph was a filtrate of blood. Starling showed the relationship between the hydrostatic pressure in capillaries and the colloid osmotic pressure of proteins in the plasma, thus introducing the Starling hypothesis.

A few publications in the early 1900s were concerned with movement of lymph by contraction of lymphatic vessels. Papers by Florey (23) in 1927, Clark and Clark (13) in 1932, and Webb (83) in 1933 dealt with the propulsion of lymph through the vessels. On viewing rat mesenteric vessels, Webb concluded that lymph is propelled by segmental contractions that occur in sections of vessels between valves at a rate of 12–18 times/min. The valves in the lymphatic vessels act passively, closing to prevent the backflow of lymph.

In 1935 Pullinger and Florey (71), using the ears of small albino mice as an observation site, injected a suspension of carbon particles into the lymphatic vessels to make them visible and reported that the lymphatic vessels did not respond to epinephrine, pituitrin, or mechanical stimulation. The lymphatic vessels were stretched by injecting fluid and were seen to be distended easily and then to recoil quickly when pressure was released. More informative in this paper, however, is the explanation for the observed sustained dilatation of lymphatic vessels in edematous areas. From histological sections prepared from ears made edematous by various methods, it was concluded that "as the connective tissue fills with edema-fluid and swells, tension on fibers attached to the lymphatic capillaries cause their walls to be drawn apart, their dilatation thus being passive."

Webb and Nicoll (84) had discovered the clarity with which blood and lymphatic vessels could be seen in the wing membrane of the bat and published their observations on the behavior of the lymphatics in this structure in 1944. The main interest in their study is the description of the contractile activity of the lymphatic vessels. The bats were anesthetized, and the authors state that direct comparison had shown that no important change in lymphatic behavior was introduced by light anesthesia. All types of rhythmical activity were recorded on movie film. A line drawing made to the exact scale of the lymphatic distribution in a typical region of the bat wing is shown in Figure 19. The lymphatic vessels were divided into three categories: *1*) transporting lymphatics, *2*) collecting lymphatics, and *3*) lymphatic capillaries.

The lymphatic vessels accompanying the larger blood vessels were called transporting lymphatics. The diameter of these vessels was often the same as the adjacent arterial vessel. Localized contractions caused the walls to be irregular and constantly changing. The transporting lymphatics have valves that divide the vessel into segments. The valves are in enlarged areas of the vessel that the authors called bulb-shaped sinuses. These areas appear to be the origin of a segmental type of contraction characteristic of the transporting channels. The contractile pattern of the segments was analyzed from consecutive frames of a motion picture film and was not considered to be peristaltic.

The collecting lymphatic originates where one or more lymphatic capillaries join and eventually empties into a transporting lymphatic. The sinus portion or bulb at the valve sites of the collecting lymphatics is large and prominent, with the bulbs connected by an irregular thin-walled channel. These vessels usually accompany venules. The sinus areas were seen to have a marked capacity for independent contraction, a powerful activity that completely closed that portion of the vessel, leaving the connecting portions showing only mild and irregular twitches. The lymphatic vessels were anchored to surrounding structures by fine strands of connective tissue that resulted in movement of tissues in the immediate area when the lymphatic vessels contracted.

The lymphatic capillaries are the most distal and begin as immense bulbs. The bulbs vary in shape from the spherical form of terminal bulbs to a more oval shape seen in a chain of bulbs. Measured by an optical micrometer, the size of a bulb was 720 by 450 μm. Its diameter was considerably greater than that of either the collecting or the transporting lymphatics and many times larger than that of the capillaries of the vascular system. The rhythmical contraction of the capillary bulbs is more pronounced than that of any other vessel in the lymphatic system. The chain contracts in a sequence that moves the fluid forward.

For all types of lymphatics the rate of contraction is variable and unrelated to respiratory rate, heart rate, or to the similar contraction observed in veins. Lymph flow is intermittent, and the active contractions in converging vessels are independent of one another and out of phase. Cliff and Nicoll (14) in 1970 reiterated some of the findings of the 1944 paper by Webb and Nicoll (84) and introduced some new information on the structure and function of lymphatics in the bat wing. The terminal bulbs, described as wide sacs, were found not to be contractile. They form

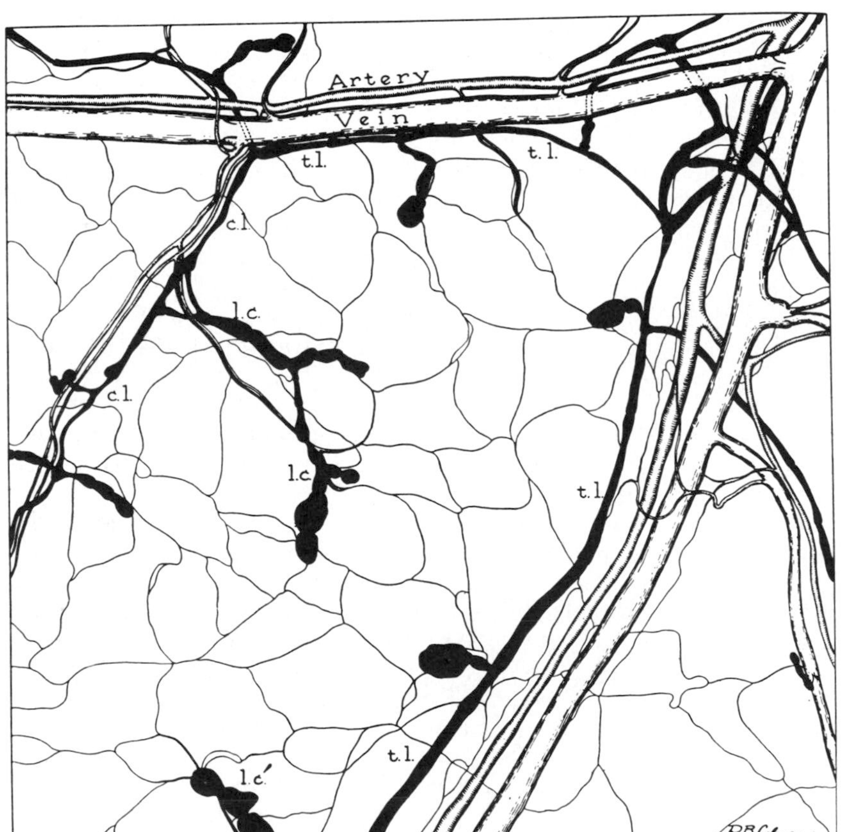

FIG. 19. Lymphatic distribution in typical region of bat wing. t.l. Transporting lymphatic; c.l., collecting lymphatic; l.c., lymphatic capillary. [From Webb and Nicoll (84).]

straight or branched chains of three to seven bulbs and are connected to the system of collecting and transporting lymphatics. The end bulb was the largest in each chain, and the bulbs became irregularly smaller as the chain approached the collecting duct. A diagram of the arrangement and the sizes of the various bulbs is shown in Figure 20. Each bulb opens into the one proximal to it through an opening that acts as a valved junction and promotes movement of fluid toward the adjoining collecting duct. The bulbs appear to be involved in the uptake of particles and extravasated blood cells. Material that enters the terminal bulbs moves proximally along the chain of bulbs and enters the contractile collecting ducts. The collecting ducts are narrow compared with the chain of bulbs and contract rhythmically at a rate of ~10 times/min. This contractile activity is unrelated to the vasomotion of neighboring blood vessels. The authors attribute the contractile activity to the smooth muscle in the wall of the lymphatic vessels, and the absence of innervation of the smooth muscle cells suggests that the contractions result from a myogenic response.

Wiederhielm and Weston (93) measured microvascular, lymphatic, and tissue pressure in unanesthetized bats and found that the rhythmic contraction of lymphatics raises the lymphatic pressure by ~5 mmHg and causes the lymph to move centripetally. These authors concluded from their studies that the lymphatic vessels appeared to be anatomically and physiologically an extension of the interstitial space. This was based on the observation that fluid, electrolytes, proteins, particulates, and cellular elements freely entered the lymphatic capillaries.

Zweifach and Prather (99) also measured pressure in the lymphatic vessels by using the mesentery of cats and rats, as well as rabbit omentum, as the experimental site. Zweifach and Prather note that the terminal ramifications of the lymphatic system have not been examined and described in the same detail as the blood capillary network. Although the same nomenclature is used for lymphatic vessels and blood vessels (despite marked differences in size and anatomical arrangement), the smallest lymphatics are 5–8 times as wide as blood capillaries, and the terminal lymphatic network has no regular pattern in its anatomical arrangement. Because the diameters of the microscopic lymph channels are larger than the largest collecting venules, Zweifach and Prather believe that the term *capillary* ("hairlike") is inappropriate. Although Casley-Smith (11) uses "initial" lymphatics for the vessels that make up the beginning of the system, Zweifach and Prather prefer "terminal" lymphatics for all of the lymphatic vessels involved in the uptake of materials from the interstitium and "collecting lymphatic channels" for the vessels that become confluent and begin to show the presence of valves. This nomenclature is the same as that of Cliff and Nicoll (14).

The terminal lymphatics in the cat mesentery were seen to form an interconnecting network that tended to parallel the arcuate pattern formed by the arteries and veins. The vessels appeared flattened and had an uneven contour with diameters of 25–50 μm. The walls of vessels appeared to consist of a thin and delicate endothelial membrane without discontinuities. A small number of blind lymphatic endings, appearing as bulbous structures, were seen in the interstitium of the mesentery. These structures formed no distinctive pattern, were seen to lie in an area away from blood

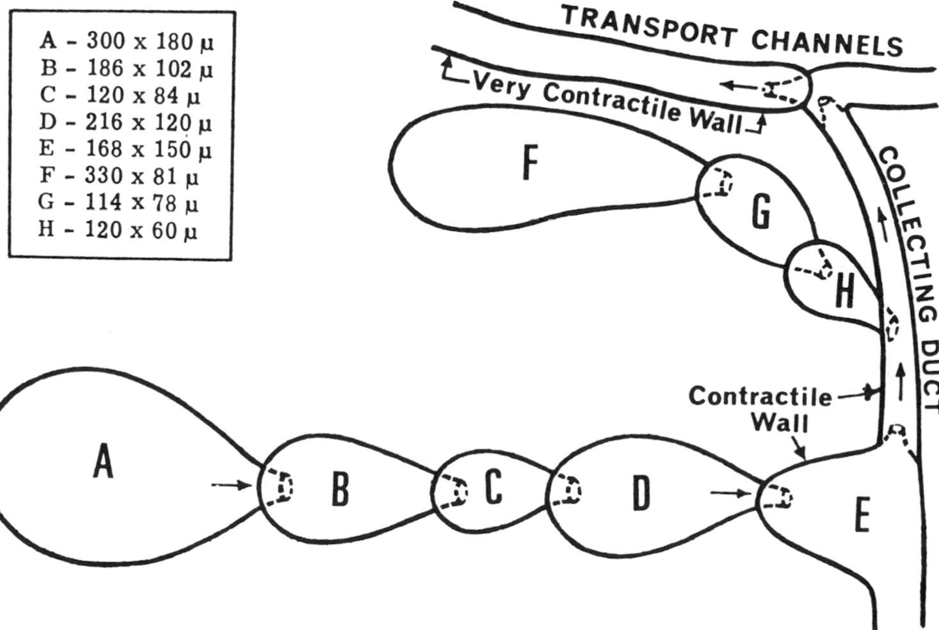

FIG. 20. Diagrammatic representation of chains of lymphatic bulbs as seen in bat wing. [From Cliff and Nicoll (14).]

vessels or with the rounded portion of the bulb touching a small venule, and always had a clearly visible endothelial wall.

The terminal lymphatics with their well-defined endothelial lining converge to form collecting channels 30–40 μm in diameter with valves. The collecting channels may become 200 μm wide and have a very prominent wall several microns thick. Valves in these channels occur at intervals of 400–1,500 μm with no consistent pattern except that they are always present where two collecting channels become confluent. The valves, which appear to be very fragile, can oppose retrograde pressures of up to 20 mmHg. The collecting lymphatics are muscular and show spontaneous contractile activity. The contractions range from a partial narrowing of the vessel to complete obliteration of the vessel lumen. This spontaneous vasomotion was seen in the mesentery of the rat and the guinea pig but not in the mesentery of the cat and rabbit or in the rabbit omentum. The pressures in cat mesentery terminal lymphatics ranged between 0 and 3.5 cmH_2O, with an average of 1.6 ± 2 cmH_2O. Collecting lymphatics had pressures as high as 12–18 cmH_2O. A composite drawing of a terminal lymphatic network in the mesentery is shown in Figure 21.

Two general review articles on lymph and lymphatic vessels appeared in 1977. One paper, written by Casley-Smith (11), discusses lymph and lymphatics; the second paper, written by Nicoll and Taylor (65), discusses lymph formation and flow.

The article by Casley-Smith restates general information regarding the structure of the terminal and collecting lymphatics. The terminal (most peripheral) lymphatics are 0.5 mm long, are irregular in shape,

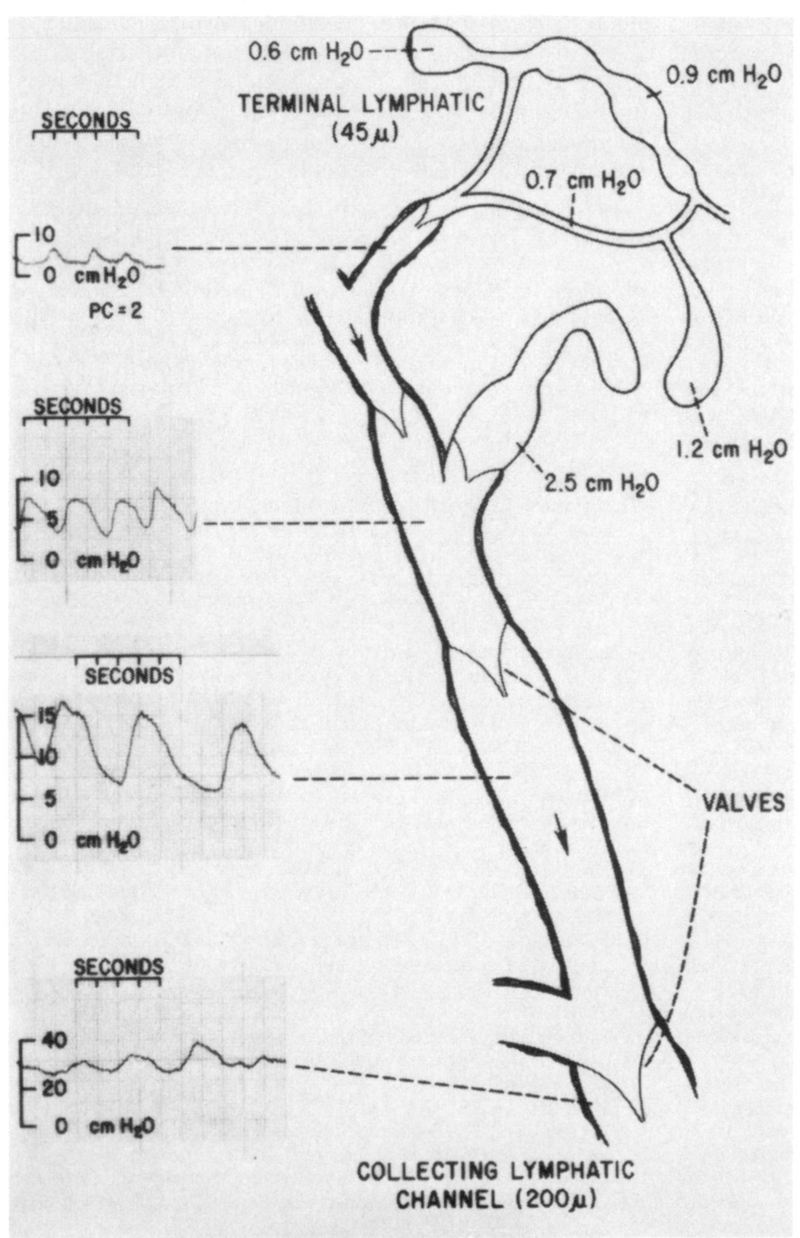

FIG. 21. Composite drawing of terminal lymphatic network in cat mesentery showing pressures in various areas. [From Zweifach and Prather (99).]

and have maximal diameters of 15–75 μm when completely filled. They are lined with endothelium and a variable amount of basement membrane. The collecting lymphatics also have an internal elastic lamina, smooth muscle cells, and connective tissue. They also have many centrally dilated valves. The paper deals with the filling and emptying of lymphatic vessels, postulates how these events are accomplished, and presents a mathematical model that fits the hypothesis. Evidence indicating that intravascular pressure change influences contractile activity is presented, but the role of the myogenic response is not developed.

Nicoll and Taylor (65) summarize the studies on bat wing lymphatics, noting that the lymphatic system is made up of three functional divisions, each with characteristic structures and activities. The first is the enlarged bulbous capillaries where lymph is formed; the second is a complex network of relatively narrow collecting ducts, which are interspaced at junctions by enlarged sinuses with valves that prevent retrograde flow; the third is the transport channels that receive lymph from the collecting ducts and empty into the axillary region.

To easily visualize lymphatic vessels in an area of the wing, one can infuse a few cubic microns of saline solution (260–280 mOsm, pH 7.2–7.4), which sufficiently hydrates the area and promotes movement of fluid from blood vessels into lymphatic capillaries that become filled and active. Lymph flow out of the area is markedly increased. The contraction of the lymphatic vessels, especially the bulb areas, causes movement in the surrounding area because of the numerous anchoring filaments attached to the lymphatics that run into the interstitial regions. The contractile activity of the lymphatic vessels is associated with the presence of smooth muscle in the walls of the vessels. The muscle cells mostly respond like vascular smooth muscle but there are some differences. As is the case with vascular smooth muscle, the contractions are spontaneous rather than nerve dependent. No nerves are present. Some mesenteric lymphatic vessels do not respond the same to various autonomic drugs as do blood vessels nor are these mesenteric lymphatics markedly sensitive to specific ion concentrations.

The ultrastructure of lymphatic vessels is discussed in the chapter by Simionescu and Simionescu in this *Handbook*, and the formation and movement of lymph are covered in other chapters.

REFERENCES

1. AUSPRUNK, D. H., H. J. BERMAN, AND W. F. MCNARY. Intramural distribution of adrenergic and cholinergic nerve fibers innervating arterioles of the hamster cheek pouch. *Am. J. Anat.* 137: 31–46, 1973.
2. BAEZ, S. Microcirculation in the intramural vessels of the small intestine in the rat. In: *The Microcirculation*, edited by S. R. M. Reynolds and B. W. Zweifach. Urbana, IL: Univ. of Illinois Press, 1959, p. 114–129.
3. BAEZ, S. Simultaneous measurements of radii and wall thickness of microvessels in the anesthetized rat. *Circ. Res.* 25: 315–329, 1969.
4. BAEZ, S. An open cremaster muscle preparation for the study of blood vessels by in vivo microscopy. *Microvasc. Res.* 5: 384–94, 1973.
5. BAEZ, S. Skeletal muscle and gastrointestinal microvascular morphology. In: *Microcirculation*, edited by G. Kaley and B. M. Altura. Baltimore, MD: University Park, 1977, vol. 1, p. 69–74.
6. BASSINGTHWAIGHTE, J. B., T. YIPINTSOI, AND R. B. HARVEY. Microvasculature of the dog left ventricular myocardium. *Microvasc. Res.* 7: 229–249, 1974.
7. BOHLEN, H. G., AND R. W. GORE. Microvascular pressures in innervated rat intestinal muscle and mucosa. In: *Microcirculation*, edited by J. Grayson and W. Zingg. New York: Plenum, 1976, vol. 1, p. 325–326.
8. BOHLEN, H. G., AND R. W. GORE. Comparison of microvascular pressures and diameters in the innervated and denervated rat intestine. *Microvasc. Res.* 14: 251–265, 1977.
9. BOHLEN, H. G., P. M. HUTCHINS, C. E. RAPELA, AND H. D. GREEN. Microvascular control in intestinal mucosa of normal and hemorrhaged rats. *Am. J. Physiol.* 229: 1159–1164, 1975.
10. BRÅNEMARK, P.-I., AND E. ERIKSSON. Method for studying qualitative and quantitative changes of blood flow in skeletal muscle. *Acta Physiol. Scand.* 84: 284–288, 1972.
11. CASLEY-SMITH, J. R. Lymph and lymphatics. In: *Microcirculation*, edited by G. Kaley and B. M. Altura. Baltimore, MD: University Park, 1977, vol. 1, p. 423–502.
12. CHAMBERS, R., AND B. W. ZWEIFACH. Topography and function of the mesenteric capillary circulation. *Am. J. Anat.* 75: 173–205, 1944.
13. CLARK, E. R., AND E. L. CLARK. Observations on living preformed blood vessels as seen in a transparent chamber inserted into the rabbit's ear. *Am. J. Anat.* 49: 441–477, 1932.
14. CLIFF, W. J., AND P. A. NICOLL. Structure and function of lymphatic vessels of the bat's wing. *Q. J. Exp. Physiol.* 55: 112–121, 1970.
15. DULING, B. R. The preparation and use of the hamster cheek pouch for studies of the microcirculation. *Microvasc. Res.* 5: 423–429, 1973.
16. ERICSON, L., AND E. ERIKSSON. Morphological aspects of intra- and extravascular phenomena in cat skeletal muscle at low flow states. *Adv. Microcirc.* 5: 72–79, 1973.
17. ERICSON, L., E. ERIKSSON, AND B. JOHANSSON. Morphological aspects of the microvessels in cat skeletal muscle. *Adv. Microcirc.* 5: 62–72, 1973.
18. ERIKSSON, E., J. V. BOYKIN, AND R. N. PITTMAN. Method for in vivo microscopy of the cutaneous microcirculation of the hairless mouse ear. *Microvasc. Res.* 19: 374–379, 1980.
19. ERIKSSON, E., AND B. LISANDER. Changes in precapillary resistance in skeletal muscle vessels studied by intravital microscopy. *Acta Physiol. Scand.* 84: 295–305, 1972.
20. ERIKSSON, E., AND B. LISANDER. Low flow states in the microvessels of skeletal muscle in cat. *Acta Physiol. Scand.* 86: 202–210, 1972.
21. ERIKSSON, E., AND R. MYRHAGE. Microvascular dimensions and blood flow in skeletal muscle. *Acta Physiol. Scand.* 86: 211–222, 1972.
22. FELDSTEIN, M. L., L. HENQUELL, AND C. R. HONIG. Frequency analysis of coronary intercapillary distances: site of capillary control. *Am. J. Physiol.* 235(*Heart Circ. Physiol.* 4): H321–H325, 1978.
23. FLOREY, H. Reactions of and absorption by lymphatics with special reference to those of the diaphragm. *Br. J. Exp. Pathol.* 8: 479–491, 1927.
24. FRASHER, W. G., JR., AND H. WAYLAND. A repeating modular organization of the microcirculation of cat mesentery. *Microvasc. Res.* 4: 62–76, 1972.
25. FRONEK, K., AND B. W. ZWEIFACH. Microvascular pressure distribution in skeletal muscle and the effect of vasodilation.

Am. J. Physiol. 228: 791–796, 1975.

26. FRONEK, K., AND B. W. ZWEIFACH. Distribution of blood flow in microcirculation in cat tenuissimus muscle. In: *Microcirculation*, edited by J. Grayson and W. Zingg. New York: Plenum, 1976, vol. 1, p. 365–367.
27. FRONEK, K., AND B. W. ZWEIFACH. Microvascular blood flow in cat tenuissimus muscle. *Microvasc. Res.* 14: 181–189, 1977.
28. FULTON, G. P., AND R. G. JACKSON. Cinemicroscopy of normal blood circulation in the cheek pouch of the hamster. *Science* 105: 361–362, 1947.
29. FULTON, G. P., R. G. JACKSON, AND B. R. LUTZ. Cinemicroscopy of normal blood circulation in the cheek pouch of the *Cricetus auratus* (Abstract). *Anat. Rec.* 96: 537, 1946.
30. FURNESS, J. B., AND J. M. MARSHALL. Correlation of the directly observed responses of mesenteric vessels of the rat to nerve stimulation and noradrenaline with the distribution of adrenergic nerves. *J. Physiol. London* 239: 75–88, 1974.
31. GORE, R. W., AND H. G. BOHLEN. Pressure regulation in the microcirculation. *Federation Proc.* 34: 2031–2037, 1975.
32. GRANT, R. T. Direct observation of skeletal muscle blood vessels (rat cremaster). *J. Physiol. London* 172: 123–137, 1964.
33. GRANT, R. T. The effects of denervation on skeletal muscle blood vessels (rat cremaster). *J. Anat.* 100: 305–316, 1966.
34. GRAY, S. D. Effect of hypertonicity on vascular dimensions in skeletal muscle. *Microvasc. Res.* 3: 117–124, 1971.
35. GRAY, S. D. Microscope observations of skeletal muscle vascular responses to vasopressors during severe hemorrhagic hypotension. *J. Trauma* 12: 147–180, 1972.
36. GRAY, S. D., AND E. M. RENKIN. Microvascular supply in relation to fiber metabolic type in mixed skeletal muscles of rabbits. *Microvasc. Res.* 16: 406–425, 1978.
37. GRAYSON, J., J. W. DAVIDSON, A. FITZGERALD-FITZ, AND C. SCOTT. The functional morphology of the coronary microcirculation in the dog. *Microvasc. Res.* 8: 20–43, 1974.
38. GREEN, H. D. Circulation: physical principles. In: *Medical Physics*, edited by O. Glasser. Chicago, IL: Year Book, 1944.
39. HARRIS, P. D., L. F. HODOVAL, AND D. E. LONGNECKER. Quantitative analysis of microvascular diameters during pentobarbital and thiopental anesthesia in the bat. *Anesthesiology* 35: 337–342, 1971.
40. HENQUELL, L., P. L. LACELLE, AND C. R. HONIG. Capillary diameter in rat heart in situ: relation to erythrocyte deformability, O_2 transport, and transmural O_2 gradients. *Microvasc. Res.* 12: 259–274, 1976.
41. HENRICH, H. N., AND A. HECKE. A gracilis muscle preparation for quantitative microcirculatory studies in the rat. *Microvasc. Res.* 15: 349–356, 1978.
42. HONIG, C. R. Hypoxia in skeletal muscle at rest and during the transition to steady work. *Microvasc. Res.* 13: 377–398, 1977.
43. HONIG, C. R., J. L. FRIERSON, AND J. L. PATTERSON. Comparison of neural controls of resistance and capillary density in resting muscle. *Am. J. Physiol.* 218: 937–942, 1970.
44. HUTCHINS, P. M., R. F. BOND, AND H. D. GREEN. Participation of oxygen in the local control of skeletal muscle microvasculature. *Circ. Res.* 34: 85–93, 1974.
45. HUTCHINS, P. M., R. F. BOND, AND H. D. GREEN. The response of skeletal muscle arterioles to common carotid occlusion. *Microvasc. Res.* 7: 321–325, 1974.
46. HUTCHINS, P. M., J. GOLDSTONE, AND R. WELLS. Effects of hemorrhage shock on the microvasculature of skeletal muscle. *Microvasc. Res.* 5: 131–141, 1973.
47. JOHNSON, P. C. Red cell separation in the mesenteric capillary network. *Am. J. Physiol.* 221: 99–104, 1971.
48. JOHNSON, P. C., AND H. WAYLAND. Regulation of blood flow in single capillaries. *Am. J. Physiol.* 212: 1405–1415, 1967.
49. KROGH, A. *The Anatomy and Physiology of Capillaries.* New Haven, CT: Yale Univ. Press, 1922.
50. LINDBOM, L., R. F. TUMA, AND K.-E. ARFORS. Influence of oxygen on perfused capillary density and capillary red cell velocity in rabbit skeletal muscle. *Microvasc. Res.* 19: 197–208, 1980.
51. LIPOWSKY, H. H., AND B. W. ZWEIFACH. Network analysis of microcirculation of cat mesentery. *Microvasc. Res.* 7: 73–83, 1974.
52. LONGNECKER, D. E., AND P. D. HARRIS. Dilatation of small arteries and veins in the bat during halothane anesthesia. *Anesthesia* 37: 423–429, 1972.
53. LUTZ, B. R., AND G. P. FULTON. The use of the hamster cheek pouch for the study of vascular changes at the microscopic level. *Anat. Rec.* 20: 293–302, 1954.
54. LUTZ, B. R., AND G. P. FULTON. Smooth muscle and blood flow in small blood vessels. In: *Factors Regulating Blood Flow*, edited by G. P. Fulton and B. W. Zweifach. Washington, DC: Am. Physiol. Soc., 1958, p. 13–24.
55. MA, Y. P., A. KOO, H. C. KWAN, AND K. K. CHENG. On-line measurement of the dynamic velocity of erythrocytes in the cerebral microvessels in the rat. *Microvasc. Res.* 8: 1–13, 1974.
56. MAJNO, G., AND G. E. PALADE. Studies on inflammation. I. The effect of histamine and serotonin on vascular permeability: an electron microscopic study. *J. Biophys. Biochem. Cytol.* 11: 571–605, 1961.
57. MAJNO, G., G. E. PALADE, AND G. K. SCHOEFL. Studies on inflammation. II. The site of action of histamine and serotonin along the vascular tree: a topographic study. *J. Biophys. Biochem. Cytol.* 11: 607–626, 1961.
58. MARTINI, J., AND C. R. HONIG. Direct measurement of intercapillary distance in beating rat heart *in situ* under various conditions of O_2 supply. *Microvasc. Res.* 1: 244–245, 1969.

58a. MAYROVITZ, H. N., R. F. TUMA, AND M. P. WIEDEMAN. Relationship between microvascular blood velocity and pressure distribution. *Am. J. Physiol.* 232(Heart Circ. Physiol. 1): H400–H405, 1977.

59. MORFF, R. J., AND H. J. GRANGER. Measurement of blood flow with radioactive microspheres in the intact and surgically exposed rat cremaster muscle. *Microvasc. Res.* 19: 366–373, 1980.
60. MYERS, W. W., AND C. R. HONIG. Number and distribution of capillaries as determinants of myocardial oxygen tension. *Am. J. Physiol.* 207: 653–660, 1964.
61. MYRHAGE, R., AND E. ERIKSSON. Vascular architecture in different skeletal muscles in the cat. *Bibl. Anat.* 13: 149–150, 1975.
62. MYRHAGE, R., AND O. HUDLICKÁ. The microvascular bed and capillary surface area in rat extensor hallucis proprius muscle (EHP). *Microvasc. Res.* 11: 315–323, 1976.
63. NICOLL, P. A. Structure and function of minute vessels in autoregulation. *Circ. Res.* 15: 245–253, 1964.
64. NICOLL, P. A. Intrinsic regulation in the microcirculation based on direct pressure measurements. In: *Microcirculation: A Symposium*, edited by W. L. Winters, Jr., and A. N. Brest. Springfield, IL: Thomas, 1969, p. 89–101.
65. NICOLL, P. A., AND A. E. TAYLOR. Lymph formation and flow. *Annu. Rev. Physiol.* 39: 73–95, 1977.
66. NICOLL, P. A., AND R. L. WEBB. Blood circulation in the subcutaneous tissue of the living bat's wing. *Ann. NY Acad. Sci.* 46: 697–711, 1946.
67. NICOLL, P. A., AND R. L. WEBB. Vascular patterns and active vasomotion as determiners of flow through minute vessels. *Angiology* 6: 291–308, 1955.
68. PAWLIK, G., A. RACKL, AND R. J. BING. Quantitative capillary topography and blood flow in the cerebral cortex of cats: an in vivo microscopic study. *Brain Res.* 208: 35–58, 1981.
69. POOR, E., AND B. R. LUTZ. Functional anastomotic vessels of the cheek pouch of the hamster. *Anat. Rec.* 132: 121–126, 1958.
70. PRIDDY, R. B., AND A. F. BRODIE. Facial musculature, nerves and blood vessels of the hamster in relation to the cheek pouch. *J. Morphol.* 83: 149–180, 1948.
71. PULLINGER, B. D., AND H. W. FLOREY. Some observations on the structure and functions of lymphatics: their behaviour in local oedema. *Br. J. Exp. Pathol.* 16: 49–61, 1935.
72. RAKUSAN, K., J. MORAVEC, AND P. Y. HYATT. Regional capillary supply in the normal and hypertrophied rat heart. *Microvasc. Res.* 20: 319–326, 1980.
73. RICHARDSON, D. R., AND B. W. ZWEIFACH. Pressure relationships in the macro- and microcirculation of the mesentery.

Microvasc. Res. 2: 474–488, 1970.
74. RUSSNYAK, I., M. FOLDI, AND G. SZABO. History of the discovery of lymphatics and lymph circulation. In: *Lymphatics and Lymph Circulation.* New York: Pergamon, 1967, p. 15–24.
75. SCHMID-SCHOENBEIN, G. W., B. W. ZWEIFACH, AND S. KOVALCHECK. The application of stereological principles to morphometry of the microcirculation in different tissues. *Microvasc. Res.* 14: 303–317, 1977.
76. SMAJE, L., B. W. ZWEIFACH, AND M. INTAGLIETTA. Micropressures and capillary filtration coefficients in single vessels of the cremaster muscle of the rat. *Microvasc. Res.* 2: 96–110, 1970.
77. STINGL, J. Fine structure of precapillary arterioles of skeletal muscle in the rat. *Acta Anat.* 96: 196–205, 1976.
78. STINGL, J. Ultrastructure of the skeletal muscle microcirculation. I. The area of the precapillary sphincters. *Folia Morphol. Prague* 24: 252–256, 1976.
79. STINGL, J. Ultrastructure of the skeletal muscle microcirculation. II. On the problem of the existence of preferential channels in skeletal muscle. *Folia Morphol. Prague* 24: 257–263, 1976.
80. TILLICH, G., L. MENDOZA, H. WAYLAND, AND R. J. BING. Studies of the coronary microcirculation of the cat. *Am. J. Cardiol.* 27: 93–98, 1971.
81. TILLMANNS, H., S. IKADA, H. HANSEN, S. JONNALAGEDOR, M. SARMA, J. M. FAUVEL, AND R. J. BING. Microcirculation in the ventricle of the dog and turtle. *Circ. Res.* 34: 561–569, 1974.
82. TUMA, R. F., L. LINDBOM, AND K.-E. ARFORS. Dependence of reactive hyperemia in skeletal muscle on oxygen tension. *Am. J. Physiol.* 233 (*Heart Circ. Physiol.* 2): H289–H294, 1977.
83. WEBB, R. L. Observations on the propulsion of lymph through the mesenteric lymphatic vessels of the living rat. *Anat. Rec.* 57: 345–350, 1933.
84. WEBB, R. L., AND P. A. NICOLL. Behavior of lymphatic vessels in the living rat. *Anat. Rec.* 88: 351–367, 1944.
85. WEBB, R. L., AND P. A. NICOLL. The bat wing as a subject for studies in homeostasis of capillary beds. *Anat. Rec.* 120: 253–263, 1954.
86. WIEDEMAN, M. P. Dimensions of blood vessels from distributing artery to collecting vein. *Circ. Res.* 12: 375–378, 1963.
87. WIEDEMAN, M. P. Patterns of the arteriovenous pathways. In: *Handbook of Physiology. Circulation*, edited by W. F. Hamilton. Washington, DC: Am. Physiol. Soc., 1963, sect. 2, vol. II, chapt. 27, p. 891–933.
88. WIEDEMAN, M. P. Contractile activity of arterioles in the bat wing during intraluminal pressure changes. *Circ. Res.* 19: 559–563, 1966.
89. WIEDEMAN, M. P. Architecture of the terminal vascular bed. In: *Physical Bases of Circulatory Transport: Regulation and Exchange*, edited by E. B. Reeve and A. C. Guyton. Philadelphia, PA: Saunders, 1967, p. 307–312.
90. WIEDEMAN, M. P. Blood flow through terminal arterial vessels after denervation of the bat wing. *Circ. Res.* 22: 83–89, 1968.
91. WIEDEMAN, M. P., R. F. TUMA, AND H. N. MAYROVITZ. Defining the precapillary sphincter. *Microvasc. Res.* 12: 71–75, 1976.
92. WIEDEMAN, M. P., R. F. TUMA, AND H. N. MAYROVITZ. *An Introduction to Microcirculation.* New York: Academic, 1981.
93. WIEDERHIELM, C. A., AND B. V. WESTON. Microvascular, lymphatic, and tissue pressures in the unanesthetized mammal. *Am. J. Physiol.* 225: 992–996, 1973.
94. WIEDERHOLD, K. A., W. BIELSER, JR., U. SCHULZ, M. J. VETEAU, AND O. HUNZIKER. Three-dimensional reconstruction of brain capillaries from frozen serial sections. *Microvasc. Res.* 11: 175–180, 1976.
95. YOFFEY, J. M., AND F. C. COURTICE. Development, structure and organization of the lymphatic system. In: *Lymphatics, Lymph and the Lymphomyeloid Complex.* London: Academic, 1970, p. 1–28.
96. ZWEIFACH, B. W., AND H. H. LIPOWSKY. Quantitative studies of microcirculatory structure and function. III. Microvascular hemodynamics of cat mesentery and rabbit omentum. *Circ. Res.* 41: 380–390, 1977.
97. ZWEIFACH, B. W., AND D. B. METZ. Regional differences in response of terminal vascular bed to vasoactive agents. *Am. J. Physiol.* 182: 155–165, 1955.
98. ZWEIFACH, B. W., AND D. B. METZ. Selective distribution of blood through the terminal vascular bed of mesenteric structures and skeletal muscle. *Angiology* 6: 282–289, 1955.
99. ZWEIFACH, B. W., AND J. W. PRATHER. Micromanipulation of pressure in terminal lymphatics in the mesentery. *Am. J. Physiol.* 228: 1326–1335, 1975.

CHAPTER 3

Ultrastructure of the microvascular wall: functional correlations

MAYA SIMIONESCU
NICOLAE SIMIONESCU
Institute of Cellular Biology and Pathology, Bucharest, Romania

CHAPTER CONTENTS

Tissue Components of Microvascular Wall
- Endothelium
  - General structure
  - Cell surface biochemistry: differentiated domains
  - Growth and regeneration
  - Endothelium as tissue: intercellular junctions
  - Differentiations of microvascular endothelium
- Basal lamina, subendothelial matrix, and pericytes
- Smooth muscle cells
- Connective tissue
  - Elastic fibers
  - Connective tissue cells
  - Nerves

Microvessels
- Arterioles
- Capillaries
  - Continuous capillaries
  - Fenestrated capillaries
  - Discontinuous capillaries (sinusoids)
- Venules
  - Pericytic (postcapillary) venules
  - Muscular venules
- Arteriovenous anastomoses

Structural Correlations in Basic Processes of Microvascular Endothelium
- Synthetic and metabolic activities
- Endocytosis and transcytosis: traffic of membranes
  - Endocytosis
  - Transcytosis: dissipative/convective
- Permeability
  - Lipids and lipid-soluble molecules
  - Water and water-soluble molecules

LARGE VESSELS such as arteries and veins are anatomical entities, whereas microvessels (arterioles, capillaries, venules, and arteriovenous anastomoses) are structurally and functionally part of the tissue they supply. The internal medium within tissues is confined to three compartments separated by semipermeable boundaries: the blood (contained in microvessels), the interstitial fluid (filling the matrix and intercellular spaces), and the lymph (which drains part of the interstitial fluid and its movable cells via the blindly ending lymphatic capillaries). Another compartment, the intracellular fluid, is continuously exchanged with the interstitial medium. Each fluid circulates within and across the boundaries of its own compartment.

Microvascular wall components are dynamic features capable of many physiological activities: permeability, uptake, transport, synthesis, and metabolism of many substances. Some functions may be particularly developed and differentiated in a given organ. The diverse activities of the microvascular wall are paralleled by structural modulations of its constituents, the functional correlates of which are only partially understood.

The organization of the microvascular wall, like the organization of the entire vascular system, is based on *1*) concentric layered arrangement of tissues and *2*) segmental differentiation of these components according to various functions prevailing in one or another part of the system (363).

1. Blood is separated from the vascular wall (or tissues) by a semipermeable, thin, continuous layer of squamous epithelial cells of mesenchymal origin, the endothelium. As in other epithelia, the endothelial cells rest on a basal lamina (basement membrane) that they produce. The relatively high pressure under which blood reaches the arterioles is associated with the occurrence in the arteriolar wall of tissues capable of active contraction (smooth muscle cells) and elastic tension (internal elastic lamina). The vessel wall also contains connective tissue, the components of which fulfill a complex role: support (fibrils), diffusion regulation (ground substance), production of local vasoactive mediators (mast cells), and defense (macrophages, plasma cells, eosinophils). The initial lymphatics originate in the perivascular connective tissue, and, with large local variations, nerve bundles and their terminals may be found here.

2. Influenced by various physiological factors, the concentric layers of the microvascular wall undergo segmental differentiations that characterize each type of vessel: some features of the basic plan are accen-

tuated, diminished, or omitted, or some additional structures are introduced. Two groups of physiological factors have influenced the segmental differentiations of the microvascular wall: *1*) mechanical factors, primarily the blood hydrostatic pressure that acts essentially on arterioles and determines the amount and arrangement of the elastic and muscular constituents of the arterioles; *2*) metabolic factors related to the local metabolic needs of tissues and reflected in the structural peculiarities of vessels involved in the blood-tissue exchanges (e.g., capillaries and pericytic venules).

Two physical conditions are necessary before blood enters tissues: *1*) upstream, a relatively high pressure should be maintained to ensure sufficient quantities of blood to tissues; *2*) downstream, blood should enter the capillary network under low pressure to protect the capillary walls, which are necessarily thin to allow an extensive and rapid exchange. This double effect is accomplished in arterioles, which have a narrow lumen surrounded by a relatively thick muscle layer and constitute the major resistance to and regulator of the blood flow.

Within tissues and organs, the magnitude, speed, and nature of the blood-tissue exchanges require a thin, semipermeable partition: at this level the microvascular wall is virtually reduced to the endothelium and its basal lamina, which is true for the capillaries and the immediately postcapillary vessels, the pericytic venules. In the muscular venules, which mark the beginning of return circulation, the blood circulates slowly and under low pressure, which explains the relative scarcity of muscular tissue and elastic elements in these vessels.

For descriptive purpose the layers of the microvascular wall are classified into three tunics: intima (endothelium, pericytes, basal lamina, internal elastica), media (smooth muscle cells), and adventitia (the rest of the wall, mainly connective tissue elements).

In addition to the segmental modulations that are routinely defined as arterioles, capillaries, and venules, the microvascular wall and especially the endothelium have several more refined degrees of structural differentiation closely related to the functional peculiarities of the host tissue.

Until recently the structural-functional correlations of microvascular wall (e.g., endothelium) were largely equated with the morphological equivalents of capillary permeability. Persuasive information acquired on cellular processes has extended the interest in structural correlates to other physiological activities occurring in the microvascular wall, such as biosynthesis, metabolism, endocytosis, exocytosis, and transcytosis.

Endothelia differ in structure and function not only between different organs and parts of the same organ but also along the sequential segments of a single microcirculatory loop. Thus any generalization concerning the endothelium is meaningless unless the physiological variations detected are referred to their dynamic morphological substrate.

TISSUE COMPONENTS OF MICROVASCULAR WALL

Endothelium

GENERAL STRUCTURE. The lining of small vessels in vertebrates consists of a single layer of simple, squamous epithelial cells, highly attenuated (~0.1–0.5 μm thick) (Fig. 1) and joined by intercellular junctions. Scanning electron microscopy of the luminal surface of microvessels shows that the endothelial cells are polygonal (~10–15 μm wide by ~25–40 μm long). The

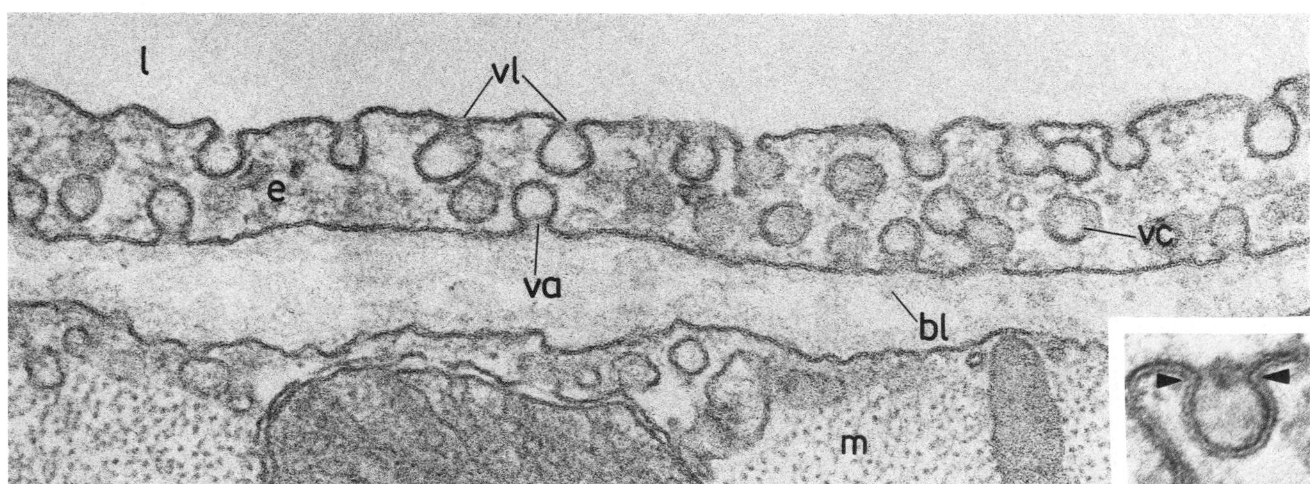

FIG. 1. Capillary endothelium of continuous type (rat diaphragm). Flattened endothelial cell (*e*) contains numerous plasmalemmal vesicles open on cell fronts (*vl*, *va*) or apparently free in cytoplasm (*vc*). *Inset*: vesicle opening on cell surface is marked by a relatively sharp bending at the fusion line (*arrowhead*) and is closed by a thin diaphragm with a central knob. *bl*, Basal lamina; *l*, lumen; *m*, muscle cell. × 95,000. *Inset*: × 157,000.

cells and their elongate, prominent nuclei are oriented in the long axis of the vessel, presumably because of the longitudinal vector fields generated by shearing effects of the blood flow. Abnormal conditions or inadequate preparative techniques change this pattern easily, resulting in numerous fingerlike projections, ballooning, craterlike defects, etc.

The endothelial cell is uniquely positioned: one face (luminal front) is directly exposed to the blood; the opposite face (abluminal front) is bathed by the interstitial fluid while attached to the basal lamina, which mediates contact with the surrounding tissues. The endothelial cell may establish close contact at its abluminal surface with the neighboring pericytes (in capillaries and pericytic venules) or with adjoining smooth muscle cells (in arterioles and muscular venules). Four parts are arbitrarily described in the endothelial cell: the nuclear region, the organelle region, the peripheral zone, and the parajunctional zone (348).

Plasma membrane. At the luminal front the endothelial cell membrane displays a fuzzy coat ~10–20 nm thick as revealed by ruthenium red staining. This coat usually extends into vesicles and continues down through intercellular spaces, being excluded from intercellular junctions proper. Based on indirect evidence (staining with ruthenium red, alcian blue, and ionic lanthanum), this coat was called the "endocapillary" (226) or "endoendothelial" layer (85), and it was assumed to consist of mucopolysaccharides (205, 226, 340), glycoproteins (213, 214), or an adsorbed film of fibrin or fibrinogen (85, 397). As detected by immunochemistry, cationized ferritin, lectins, and digestion with various enzymes, this cell coat appears to be made up primarily of glycosaminoglycans (353, 357, 374) secreted by the endothelial cell (47, 48), oligosaccharide moieties of cell membrane glycoproteins and glycolipids (25, 38, 354, 357, 358, 391), and sialoconjugates (100, 102, 214) (see CELL SURFACE BIOCHEMISTRY: DIFFERENTIATED DOMAINS, p. 52). The coat persists after vessels are washed out of blood. In vivo a certain amount of plasma proteins have been demonstrated or assumed to be adsorbed on the endothelial surface: α_2-macroglobulin (a protease inhibitor) (15), lipoprotein lipase (269), fibrin or fibrinogen (85), heparins (166), and albumin (24). According to Loudon et al. (223, 224) and Michel (253, 254), the slow labeling of surface-bound vesicles with ferritin (frog mesenteric capillaries) might be due to the endocapillary layer, which is presumed to behave as a diffusion barrier.

Generally both the circulating blood cells and the endothelial surface have a negative charge, thus repelling each other, but the anionic sites of the endothelial cell surface appear to have a more refined minute distribution (see *Anionic sites: distribution and partial characterization*, p. 52). Because of its charge, molecular composition, and metabolic activities, the intact endothelial cell membrane does not attract blood cells and therefore is nonthrombogenic.

Coated pits and coated vesicles. In rodents in the continuous capillary endothelium (276) and in pancreatic and intestinal fenestrated capillaries (353, 357, 359, 363, 375), coated pits and coated vesicles were observed on both endothelial cell surfaces, being generally more numerous on the luminal front (Fig. 2). The general configuration of endothelial cell coated pits and coated vesicles is similar to that in other eucaryotic cells: ~80–120 nm in diameter, with a geo-

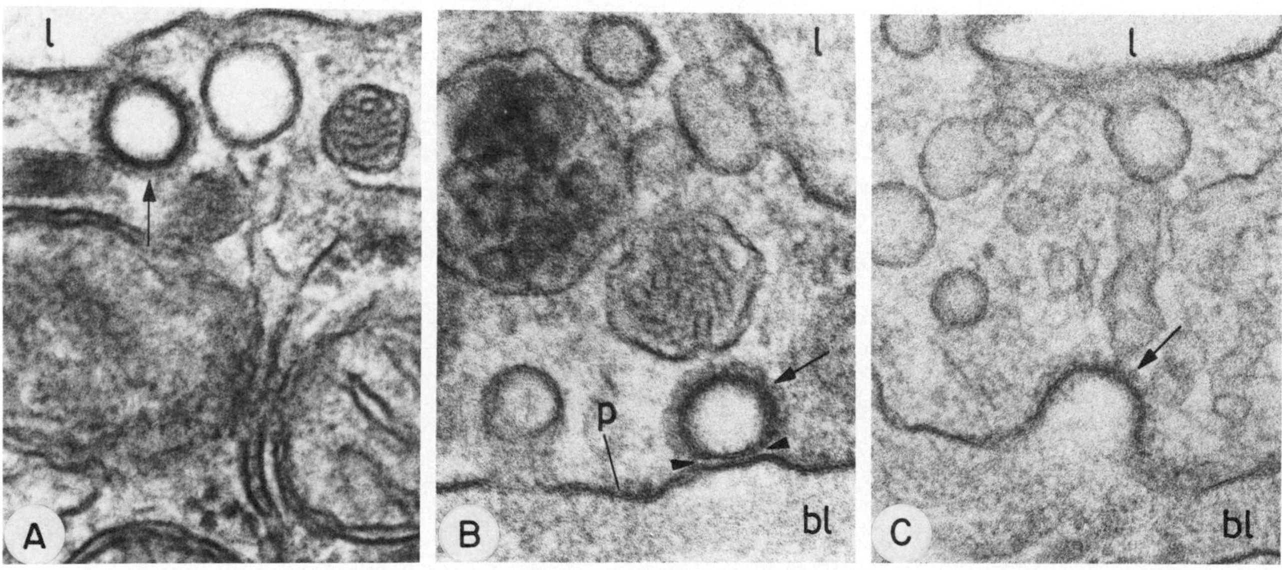

FIG. 2. Microvascular endothelium (rat diaphragm). *A*: coated vesicle (*arrow*) probably just closing its communication with vascular lumen (*l*). *B*: coated vesicle (*arrow*) approaching plasmalemma (*p*) of the abluminal cell front; at this level the clathrin basket has been eliminated (*arrowheads*). *C*: coated pit (*arrow*) on abluminal cell surface of endothelium. *bl*, Basal lamina. × 140,000.

desic basketwork of clathrin on their cytoplasmic aspect (281). In thin sections the radiating projections are ~20 nm long and are spaced by 20–25 nm. Coated pits and coated vesicles are particularly numerous in the endothelial cells of hepatic (446) and bone marrow sinusoids (100–102), and in steroid-secreting endocrine tissues (e.g., adrenal cortex, corpus luteum, interstitial tissue of testicle, and brown adipose tissue). In the vasa vasorum of the rat aorta, coated pits and coated vesicles recently have been implicated in the receptor-mediated endocytosis of specific macromolecules such as low-density lipoproteins (420) through a process largely similar to that described in human fibroblast (5). In the sinusoids of the rat bone marrow, large coated vesicles rapidly take up intravenously injected particles of carbon black (101). The polyene antibiotic filipin binds specifically to membrane cholesterol: the resulting complexes can be detected both in chemically fixed and thin-sectioned specimens (111) and in freeze-fracture preparations. Montesano et al. (259) previously reported the absence of filipin-cholesterol complexes from coated pits in fibroblasts. The same results were obtained in endothelial cells [Fig. 16*B*, *C*; (359a)], but this does not necessarily imply the absence of cholesterol from coated pits and vesicles.

Plasmalemmal vesicles. Microvascular endothelial cells are rich in spherical membranous vesicles of relatively uniform size of ~60–80 nm outer diameter. They appear either open on one of the endothelial cell fronts or free in the cytoplasm. The membrane of surface-bound vesicles is continuous with the plasmalemma, which explains why they are called plasmalemmal vesicles (275–277).

Other proposed names have a static connotation, e.g., *caveolae* (315, 380, 381), or functional implications, e.g., *cytopemptic* (17), *pinocytotic*, and *transport vesicles* (312). Vesicles open on the cell surface are generally flask shaped, with a short neck and a stomatal opening ~20–40 nm in diameter. Most of these stomata are closed by a thin diaphragm (6–8 nm thick) often provided with a central knob (Fig. 1). A short-lasting retardation in ferritin access to vesicles (43) and a declining tracer concentration within vesicles

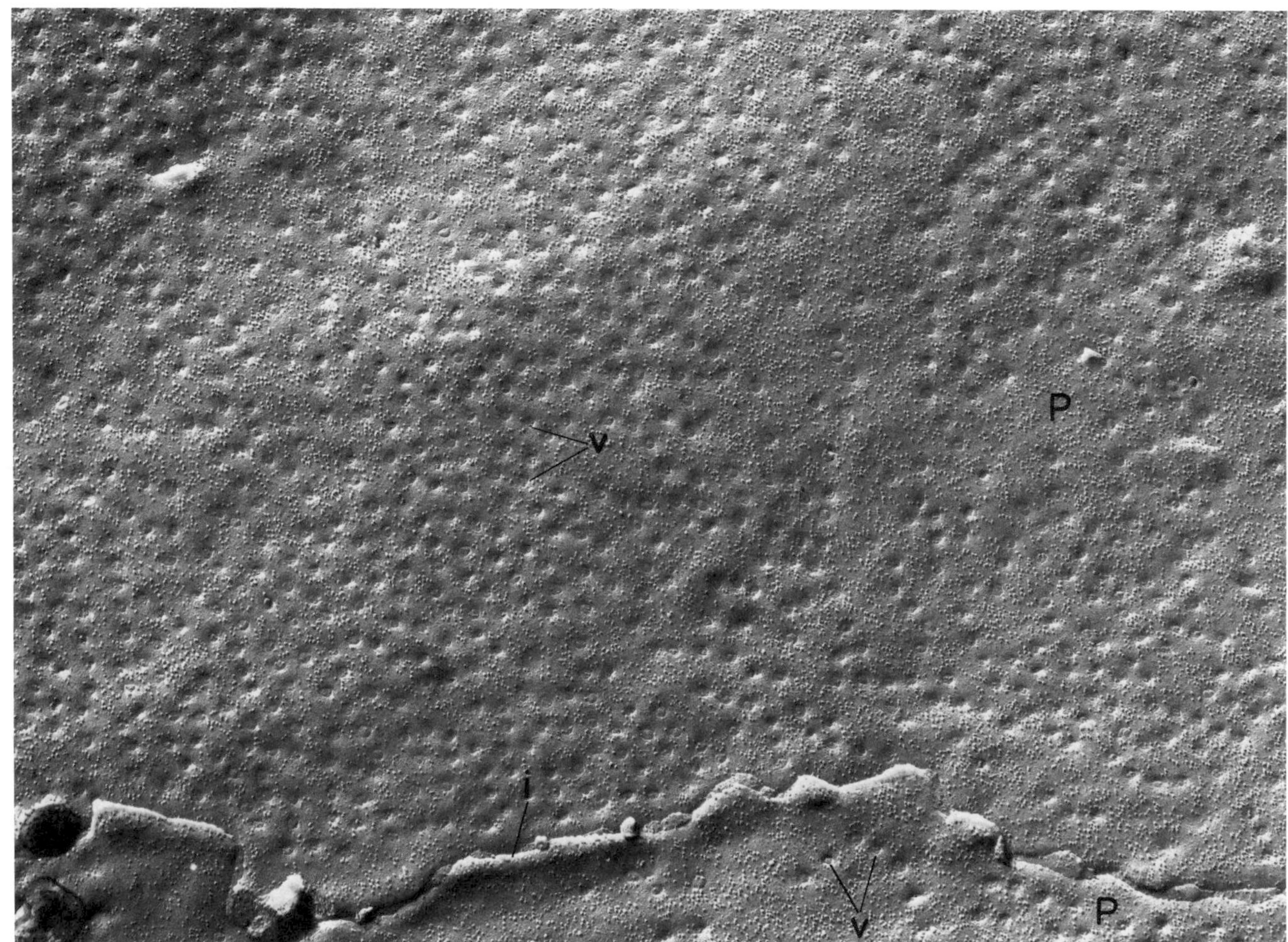

FIG. 3. Freeze-fracture preparation of a myocardium capillary (rat). The cleavage plane exposed the protoplasmic (*P*) face of endothelial cell membrane on which a high frequency of vesicle openings (*v*) can be seen. *i*, Intercellular line. × 54,000.

located at increasing distance from the labeling site (luminal front or abluminal front) (78) suggest that vesicle loading with macromolecules occurs by diffusion. The high number of vesicles (Fig. 3) almost doubles the actual surface of capillary endothelium. Concomitantly the diffusion pathway across endothelial cytoplasm is substantially reduced, and the chance of vesicle fusion and formation of transendothelial channels is increased. More detailed values for vesicle density are available for only a few endothelia: e.g., myocardium and skeletal muscle (60, 61, 187, 372, 384). Vesicle density varied significantly in sequential segments of the same microvascular unit [Table 1; (372)]. Compared with systemic capillaries, vesicle density is smaller (131 vesicles/μm^3) in the lung capillaries (144, 145) and has the lowest values in brain capillaries (39, 294). The frequency of vesicle openings on endothelial surface of several types of capillaries is given in Table 2. The wide spectrum of recorded appearances suggests that plasmalemmal vesicles are able to undergo sequential membrane fusion-fission with plasmalemma or vesicles of the same kind. The steps in these events are considered stages of a vesicular cycle during which vesicles pinch off from the surface, move through the cytoplasm, undergo fusion and fission while attached to the opposite plasmalemma, and discharge their content in the adjoining extracellular compartment (238, 275, 277, 409). This process is considered instrumental in the transport of water and water-soluble molecules across the endothelium, as indicated by experiments with a variety of macromolecular tracers (see TRANSCYTOSIS: DISSIPATIVE/CONVECTIVE, p. 79) (43, 59, 182–185, 222, 275, 324–327, 343, 360, 362, 364, 366, 370, 373, 436, 438). However, Bundgaard, Frøkjaer-Jensen, et al. (46, 136) regard the endothelial vesicles as a sessile, immobile system of cell membrane invaginations. They based their conclusions on tridimensional reconstruction of serial sections of endothelial cell profiles of frog mesenteric capillaries.

The occurrence of transitional forms suggests that vesicles are generators of transendothelial channels and possibly fenestrae (278, 279, 343, 357, 359, 366). The transition from vesicle (or vesicular neck) to plasma membrane proper—at least in chemically fixed specimens—is usually marked by a sharp bend (Fig. 1, *inset*). These bends resemble the creases developed in artificial liposomes, in which the lipids have undergone phase separation [Papahadjopulous, cited by Palade, Simionescu, and Simionescu (279)]. The vesicle shape is possibly maintained by either some stabilizing factor(s) or the vesicle membrane and the cell membrane do not mix freely, but a certain phase separation between the two membranes may exist. Recent studies with filipin have shown that this transitional form between vesicle opening and plasma membrane is particularly rich in cholesterol and is the first to develop filipin-cholesterol complexes after exposure

TABLE 1. *Density of Plasmalemmal Vesicles in Peripheral Zone of Endothelial Cells (Mouse Diaphragm)*

Microvascular Segments	Endothelial Thickness, μm	Vesicles/μm^3 of Endothelium
Arteriole	0.4 ± 0.2	187 ± 14
Capillary regions		
Arteriolar	0.25 ± 0.1	912 ± 114
Middle	0.25 ± 0.1	956 ± 89
Venular	0.17 ± 0.07	1,171 ± 98
Pericytic venule	0.2 ± 0.07	645 ± 72
Muscular venule	0.3 ± 0.1	297 ± 31

Values are means ±SE; 160–180 vascular profiles examined for each segment. Endothelial length varied from ~10 to 20 μm; areas of endothelial sections determined by planimetry. [Adapted from Simionescu, Simionescu, and Palade (373).]

TABLE 2. *Frequency of Vesicle Stomata and Fenestrae on Endothelial Surface of Capillaries (Rat)*

	Muscular Capillary		Visceral Capillary	
	Diaphragm	Myocardium	Pancreas	Jejunal mucosa
Aggregated area examined, μm^2	87.8	122.5	80.5	91.8
Vesicular stomata,* avg/μm^2				
Luminal front	59	67	32	11
Abluminal front	97	110	21	9
Fenestrae per μm^2			15	26

SD values not included. Freeze-fracture preparations. Replicas of 12–14 capillaries examined for each organ tissue. * Entire endothelial surface except for parajunctional zones. [Adapted from Simionescu, Simionescu, and Palade (348).]

of endothelial cells to this antibiotic [Fig. 16*A*; (359a)]. Although several biochemical dissimilarities have been reported recently between vesicle membrane and cell membrane (see CELL SURFACE BIOCHEMISTRY: DIFFERENTIATED DOMAINS, p. 52), the extent to which vesicle membrane has a special chemical makeup is still unclear.

Plasmalemmal vesicles seem to be a relatively stable population unaffected by anoxia, metabolic inhibitors, hypertension (400), change in temperature (34, 181, 290, 444), or labeling with macromolecules (346, 359). Vesicle number in lung capillaries was reportedly increased by high hydrostatic pressure and hemodynamic edema (70, 104, 143) with frequent development of large vacuoles or blisters. Vesicle involvement in endocytosis, transcytosis, and their presumed traffic across the endothelial cell is described in *Endocytosis and transcytosis: traffic of membranes*, p. 78.

Transendothelial channels. Single plasmalemmal vesicles or chains of two or more fused vesicles can open simultaneously on both endothelial fronts to form a patent transendothelial channel (366). At its fusion points a channel exhibits strictures ~20–40 nm in diameter and diaphragms morphologically similar

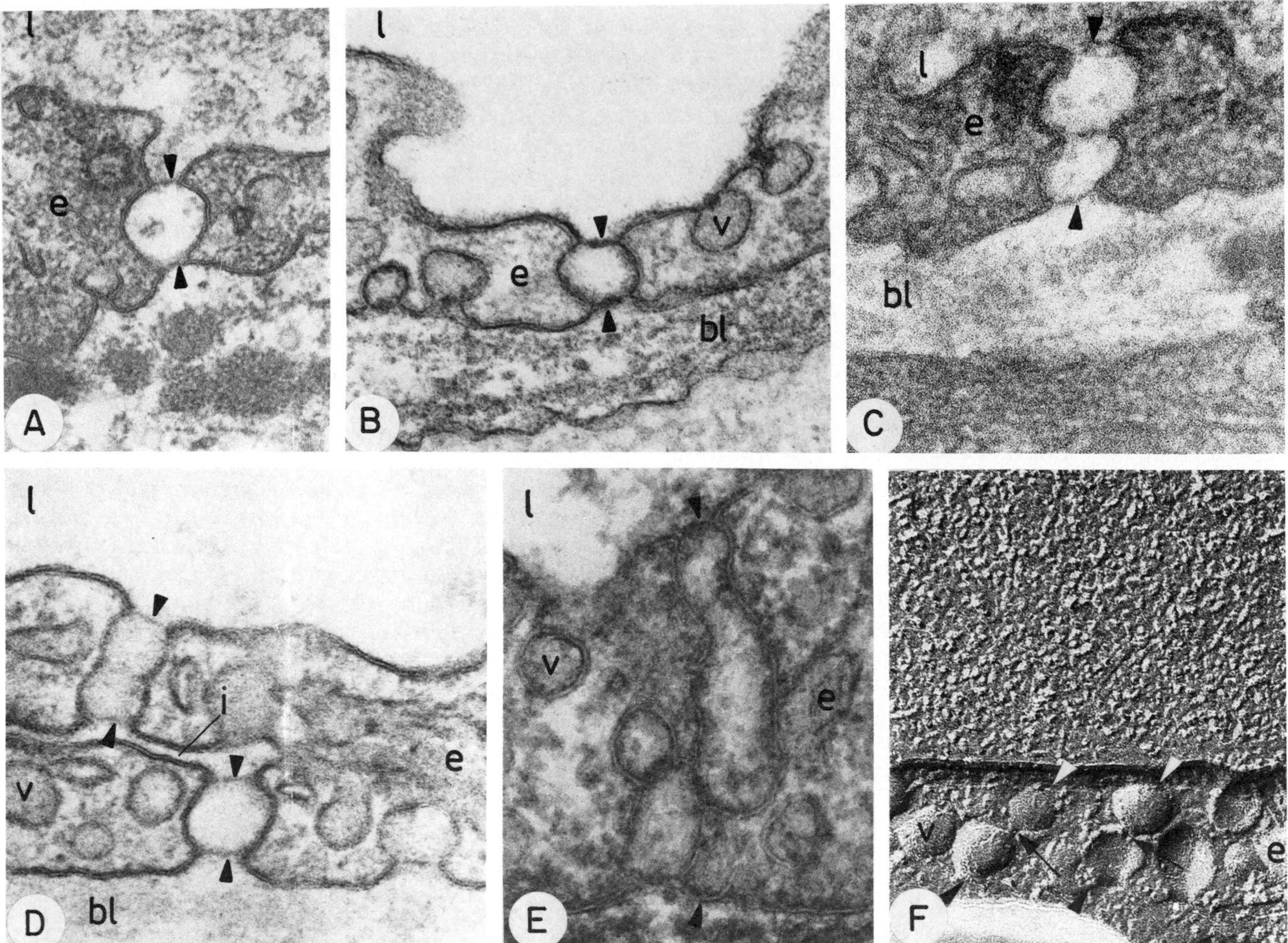

FIG. 4. Microvascular endothelium. Gallery of transendothelial channels (*arrowheads*) made up of a single vesicle (*A* and *B*), 2 fused vesicles (*C*), or a chain of several vesicles (*E*). *D*: 2 channels concomitantly open in the intercellular space (*i*). *F*: 2 channels (*arrowheads*), each with an intermediary stricture (*arrows*) as seen in freeze-fracture preparations. *bl*, Basal lamina; *e*, endothelium; *l*, lumen; *v*, vesicle. × 100,000. [*A*, *C*, and *F* from Simionescu (343).]

to the stomatal diaphragms of vesicles (Fig. 4). Electron micrographs illustrating transendothelial channels appear sporadically in the literature (161, 206, 256, 332, 451, 456). Detection of transendothelial channels often requires, in addition to large sampling, specimen tilting in the electron microscope and graphic analysis of the emerging micrographs (366). Despite their transitory nature and the remote chance of cutting a thin section along the full length of a channel, since 1975 (366) researchers have identified transendothelial channels in several endothelia (39, 87, 143, 144, 182, 186, 222, 357, 362, 371–373, 410, 432). These channels have been inferred as likely pathways that could explain some characteristics of capillary permeability to macromolecules (44, 77, 136, 144, 145, 242, 243, 252, 272, 273, 296, 299, 307, 393).

Single vesicle channels are frequently encountered in fenestrated endothelia (Figs. 4, 10); they appear to occur more often in venular segments of capillaries (372), but their numerical density remains to be established. Bundgaard, Crone, and Frøkjaer-Jensen (45) reported an extreme rarity of such channels in frog mesenteric capillaries, and other investigators failed to detect them (57, 144, 447, 448).

Transendothelial channels were identified in noninjected specimens and after the intravenular administration of macromolecular tracers such as dextran (343) and hemepeptides (357, 366, 370, 372, 373) or after the injection into the muscle interstitia of hemeundecapeptide (369) or horseradish peroxidase (182). The channels are presumed to behave like dynamic hydrophilic pathways (362) that can function as either small pores (366) or large pores (136, 343, 357) because of their transient and modulating size-limiting structures (strictures, diaphragms). Future work is needed to determine whether the density of the transendothelial channels fits the physiological data postulated for the two pore systems.

In abnormal conditions such as ischemia and inflammation the endothelium can be spanned by chains of fused large vacuoles ~100–200 nm wide (58, 143, 353).

Fenestrae. The endothelium of visceral capillaries, in addition to vesicles and channels, contains in its thin part a relatively large population of transcellular circular openings ~60–80 nm in diameter, the fenestrae (17, 55, 56, 75, 134, 135, 138). The fenestrae cut across the endothelium without affecting the continuity of the plasma membrane (Fig. 5).

Fenestrae often occur in clusters (Fig. 6) and usually are closed by a thin 6- to 8-nm single-layered diaphragm structurally similar to the diaphragms of vesicles and channels. Fenestrae have a central knob, 10–15 nm wide, from which a fine fibrillar feltwork appears to extend radially to the fenestral rim in chemically fixed specimens (112, 134, 135, 225, 246) and freeze-etched endothelia (M. Simionescu, unpublished observations). This rim is marked by a sharp bend in the plasma membrane. Fenestrae have given their name to a special type of capillary. In some locations the endothelial fenestrae are completely devoid of diaphragms (e.g., glomerular capillaries). Occasionally the endothelia of pericytic venules display fenestrae. Their frequency varies from one microvascular bed to another (22, 56, 134, 135, 348): some comparative values are given in Table 2. Fenestrae in mouse intestinal villi are ~12 times more numerous at venous ends of capillaries (56). Evidence indicates that they are rather labile structures that disappear in cultured endothelial cells isolated from adrenal cortex (129). Fenestrae lack a lipid bilayer (75, 225). Recent evidence indicates that fenestral diaphragms contain heparan sulfate–proteoglycan, which imparts to these structures a high net negative charge, unlike vesicle and channel diaphragms (353, 357–359, 361, 374, 375) (see *Anionic sites: distribution and partial characterization*, p. 52).

Based on the existence of the suggested structural intermediaries between vesicles and channels and between channels and fenestrae, it is generally assumed that vesicles, channels, and fenestrae belong to the same modulating system, with vesicles the key to the system. In this system the fenestral diaphragms are the single remaining diaphragm of a collapsed transendothelial channel (279). In the light of the differences described, the two types of diaphragms may be considered as either morphogenetically different or as having a common source with subsequent biochemical modification (e.g., acquiring of sulfated glycosaminoglycans by the fenestral diaphragms).

The role of fenestral diaphragms in permeability is discussed in *Permeability*, p. 81.

Cytoskeleton: endothelial contractility. Contractile proteins, which form a microtrabecular lattice, are a common constituent of the vascular endothelium, including capillary endothelium. Although there are re-

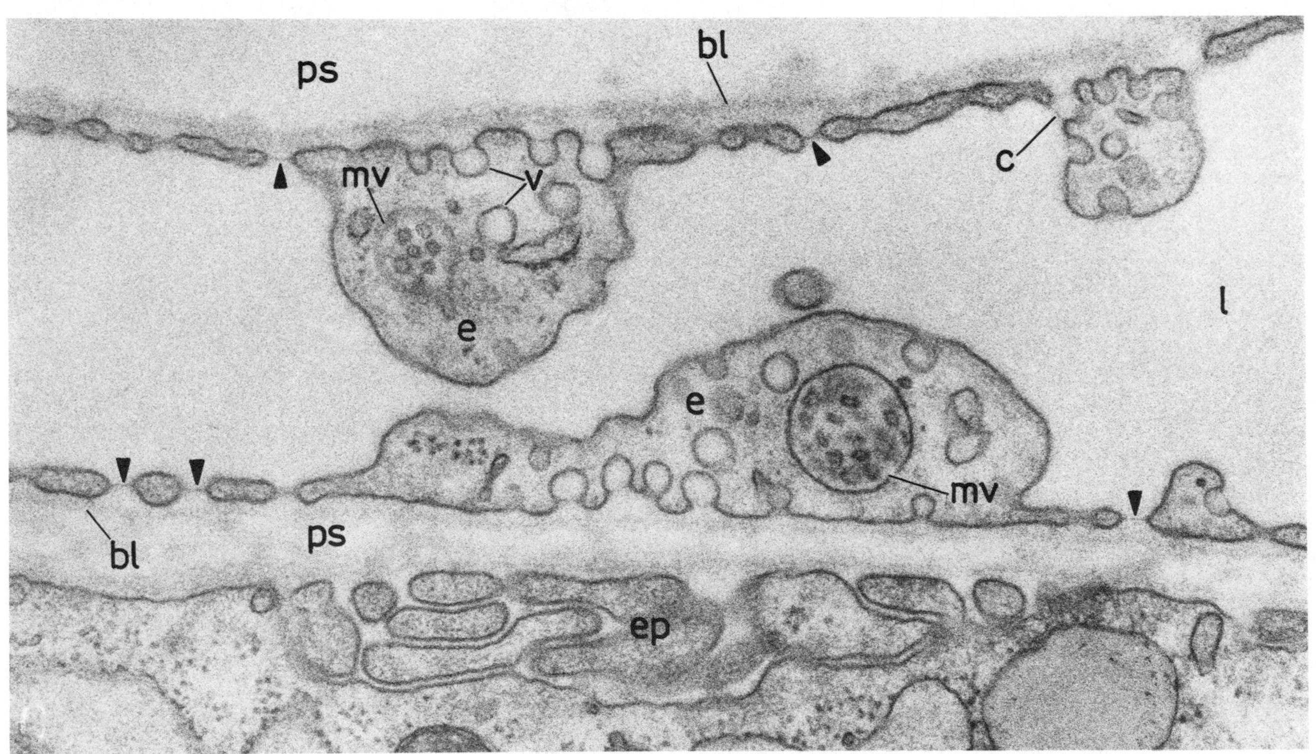

FIG. 5. Fenestrated capillary (rat thyroid). Endothelial cells (*e*) display numerous openings or fenestrae (*arrowheads*) closed by a thin diaphragm. *bl*, Basal lamina; *c*, single vesicle transendothelial channel; *ep*, epithelium; *l*, lumen; *mv*, multivesicular body; *ps*, pericapillary space; *v*, plasmalemmal vesicles. × 40,000.

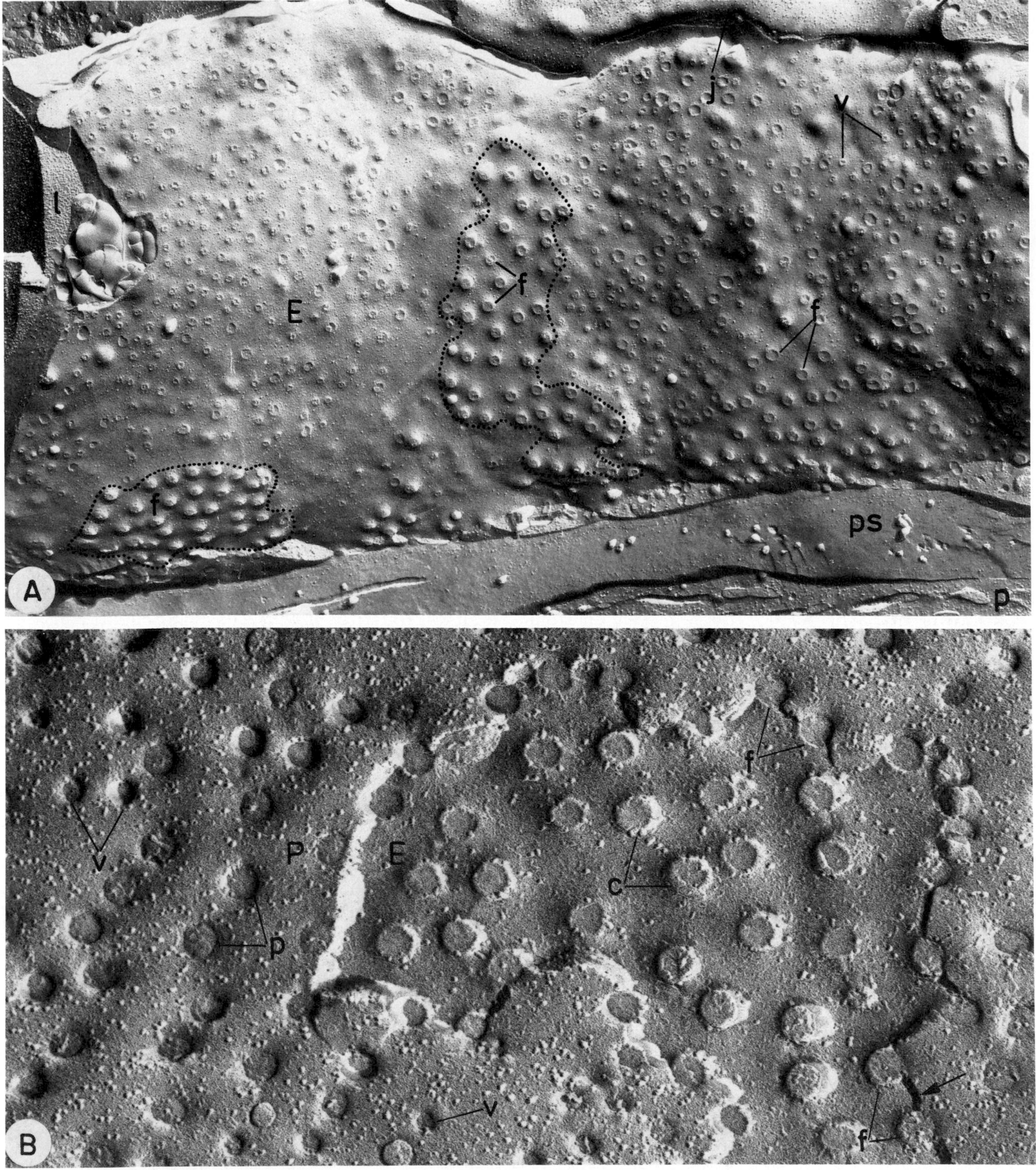

FIG. 6. Freeze-fracture preparation of fenestrated capillaries (rat pancreas). *A*: at low magnification fenestrae (*f*) often appear in clusters. × 30,000. *B*: at higher magnification fenestrae appear as papillae (*p*) on the protoplasmic (*P*) face and as craters (*c*) on the external (*E*) face of the cleaved membrane of the endothelial cell. Along fracture line (*arrow*), fenestrae appearance changes from crater to papilla. *f*, Fenestrae; *j*, junction; *l*, lumen; *ps*, pericapillary space; *v*, vesicle openings. × 80,000.

gional variations from one microvascular bed to another, cytoplasmic filaments are often concentrated around the nucleus and close to the abluminal cell membrane or in the parajunctional zone (Fig. 7). The cytoskeleton generally is more developed in the arteriole and venule endothelium than in capillary endo-

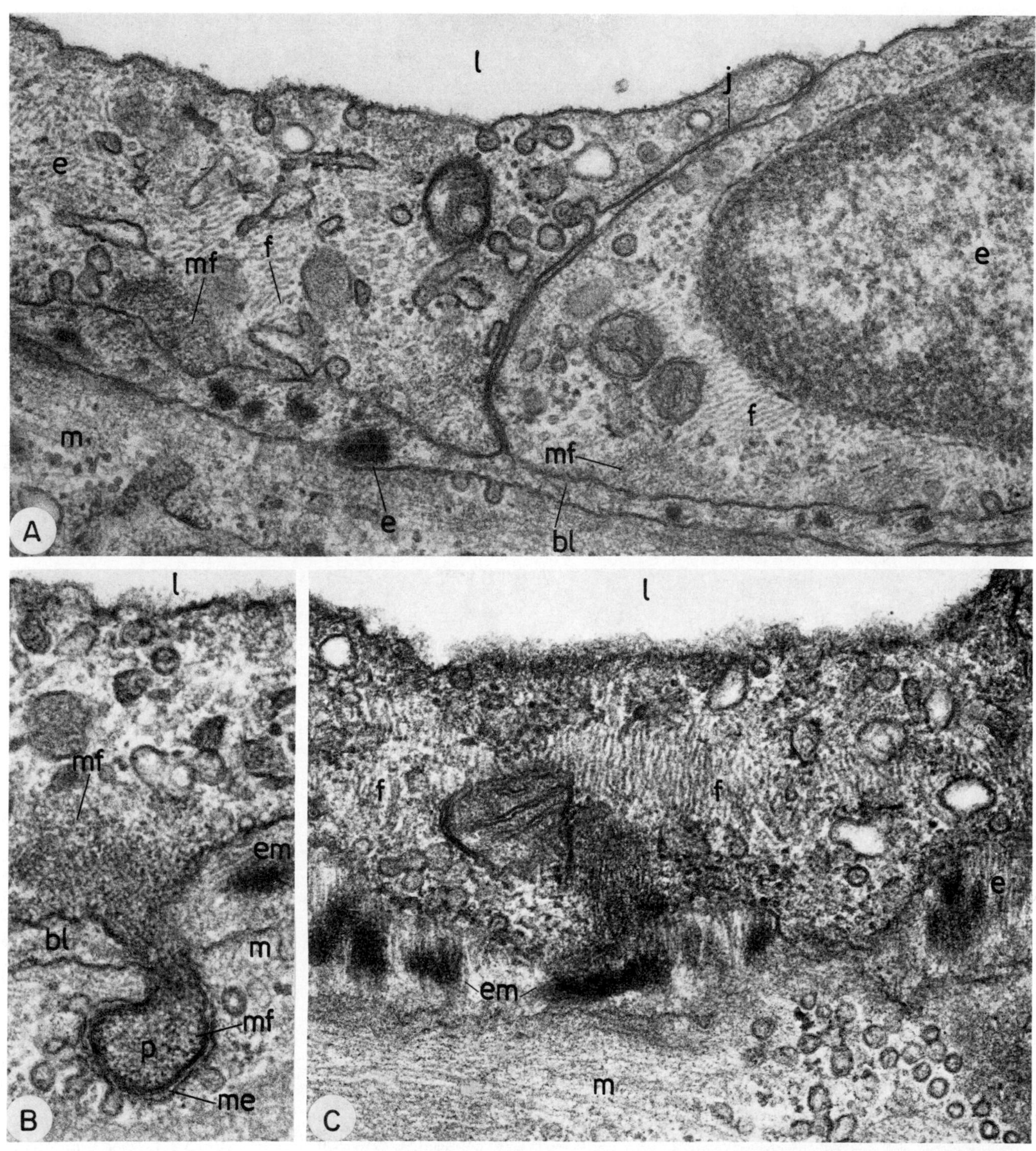

FIG. 7. *A*: metarteriole (rat diaphragm). Two endothelial cells (*e*) connected by an intercellular junction (*j*). Cytoplasm is rich both in 10-nm filaments (*f*) and microfilaments (*mf*). *B*: microfilaments frequently accumulate in the basal part, representing the main constituent of basal processes (*p*), which establish myoendothelial junctions (*me*). *C*: orientation of 10-nm filaments (*f*) is often in phase with that displayed by elastic microfibrils (*em*) occurring in the subendothelium. *bl*, Basal lamina; *l*, lumen; *m*, muscle cell. × 50,000.

thelium of the same microvascular unit. The number of contractile filaments within endothelial cells is relatively smaller than that in adjoining pericytes.

There is now evidence for the existence in the endothelial cells of at least four cytoskeletal components: *1*) the intermediate (~10-nm) filaments (29–31, 65), *2*) the actin (6-nm) filaments, *3*) the myosin-like filaments, and *4*) the microtubules.

1. In contrast to many other eucaryotic cells, endothelial cells in culture arrange most of their 10-nm filaments into a perinuclear ring. Unlike other microfilament bundles and cytoplasmic microtubules that disassemble and reassemble during mitosis, these 10-nm filaments cleave into symmetrical crescents that enter the daughter cells (3, 29). As distinguished by immunological procedures, endothelial cells contain several subclasses of intermediate-sized filaments (7–11 nm); the predominant type is the vimentin subclass, the typical filaments found in mesenchymal cells (133).

2. Thin actin filaments (6 nm) have been detected in brain capillaries and postcapillary venules by immunocytochemistry (270, 271) and by specific decoration with heavy meromyosin (216).

3. Thick filaments (~15 nm) have been identified as myosin by their appearance and size, especially in endothelial cells of arterioles (16). Immunofluorescence microscopy has shown that rabbit antisera to

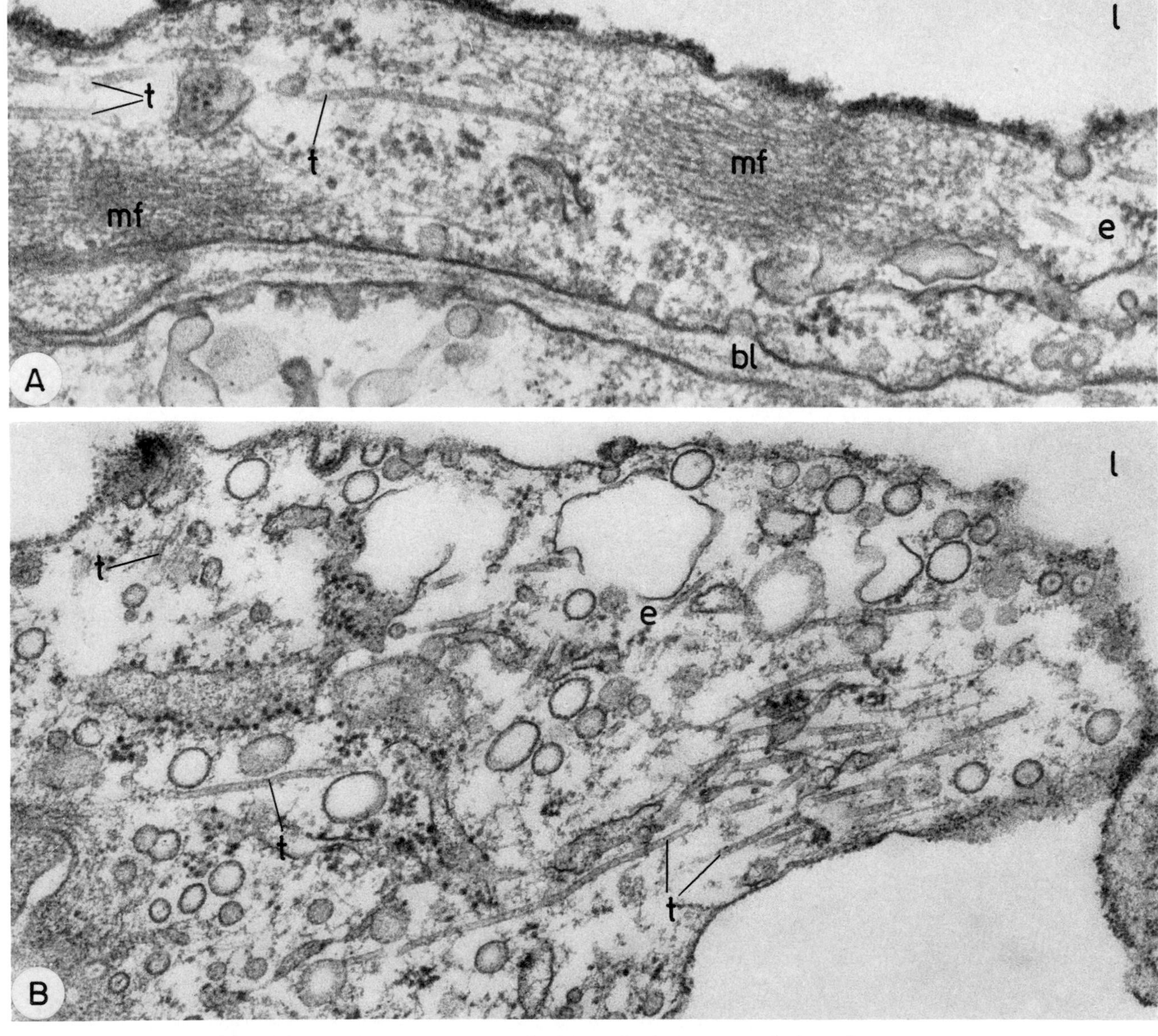

FIG. 8. *A*: arteriolar endothelium (metarteriole) of mouse diaphragm displaying accumulations of microfilaments (*mf*) alternating with microtubules (*t*) oriented parallel to the cell surface. × 48,000. *B*: venular endothelium (tangential section). Microtubules are preferentially oriented along the axis of the endothelial cell (*e*). Plasmalemma labeled with cationized ferritin. *bl*, Basal lamina; *l*, lumen. × 42,000.

human thrombostenin (platelet actomyosin) reacted with endothelial cells of arteries, arterioles, veins, venules, liver sinusoids, capillaries of heart, and capillaries of skeletal muscle (14–16, 99, 260, 271).

4. Microtubules are only sporadically mentioned, although their occurrence in endothelial cells is an established fact (Fig. 8).

Bundles of cross-striated fibrils with a periodicity of 0.6–0.7 μm are described in the endothelium of rat myometrial arterioles (310), cerebral arteries and arterioles (142), and aorta (138). Periodic banding is enhanced in contracted vessels, which suggests a role for these fibrils in vasoconstriction.

Based on ultrastructural modification (nuclear pinching, cellular shortening, and development of large intercellular gaps), it has been proposed that histamine-type mediators cause endothelial cells to contract, primarily in venules (188, 232, 234, 237). New findings on endothelial cytoskeleton and endothelial cell localization of receptors for histamine (163) support the notion of endothelial contractility and its important role in inflammation. Arguments against this role are presently irrelevant (160).

Other organelles. The common set of organelles is encountered in endothelial cells, usually concentrated next to the nucleus in the organelle region. In addition to the routinely fixed and thin-sectioned specimens, the endothelial cell organelles can be examined in negatively stained whole cells (291).

A well-developed rough endoplasmic reticulum is clearly a main characteristic of secretory cells. An increasing body of data indicates that endothelial cells are able to produce and secrete a large spectrum of products. However, most of these observations from studies on cultured endothelial cells of large vessels may not apply to microvessels. Endothelial cells have relatively little rough endoplasmic reticulum in physiological conditions. An increase in rough endoplasmic reticulum occurred during the healing phase after various tissue injury (341), in the capillary sprouts of inflamed tissues (328), in tumor angiogenesis (9, 64), in uterine capillaries after estrogen administration (158), and in hyperplastic thyroid glands (114). A few cisternae of smooth endoplasmic reticulum can also be detected, as well as free ribosomes, Golgi apparatus, some mitochondria, glycogen particles, and centrosphere regions with two centrioles.

The lysosomal apparatus is present as primary and secondary lysosomes of various dimensions (50–200 nm), dense residual bodies, and multivesicular bodies marked by the cytochemical reaction for arylsulfatase B (E. Constantinescu, unpublished observations). The implication of the endothelial lysosomal system in endocytosis and its relation with membrane traffic is discussed in ENDOCYTOSIS, p. 78.

Characteristic rod-shaped granules, ~0.1 μm thick and ~3 μm long, made of several parallel tubules (~15 nm diam) embedded in a relatively dense matrix (Fig. 9) have been described by Weibel and Palade in arterial endothelia of humans, rodents, and amphibians and later encountered in other vessels and species (19, 320, 394). These rod-shaped granules are particularly well developed in the fish, occupying as much as 70% of the cell volume (50, 320). Although well represented in the arteriolar endothelium (Fig. 9), the Weibel-Palade bodies are less numerous in venules and commonly absent in capillary endothelia. Despite several hypotheses (50, 320) the significance of these organ-

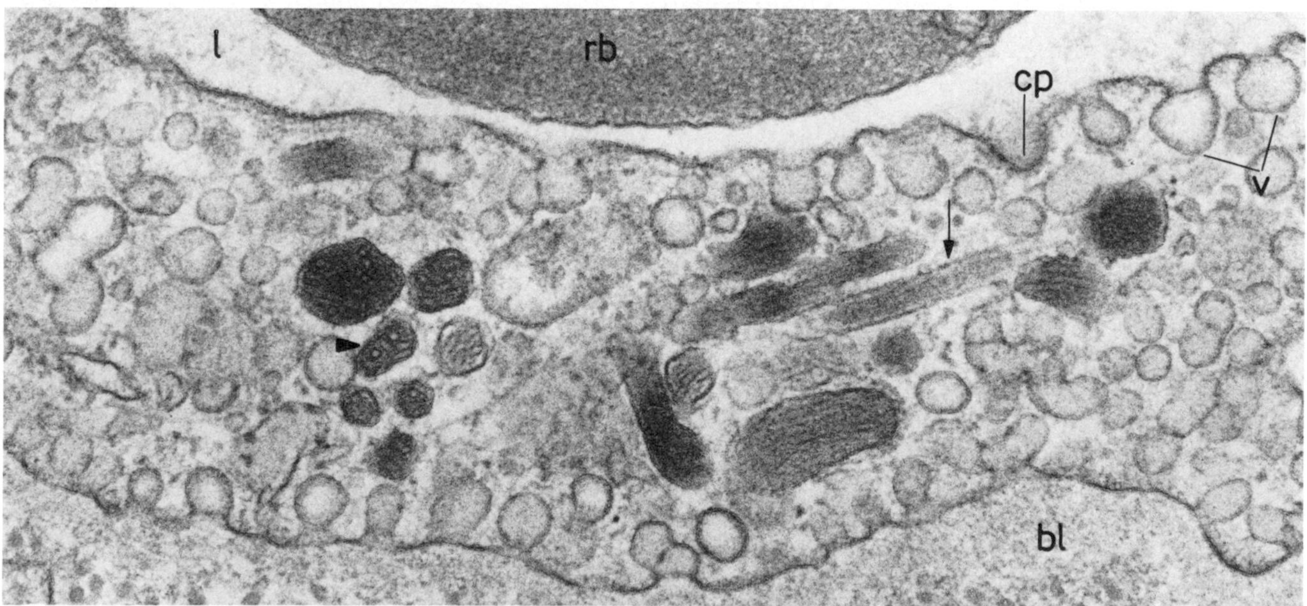

FIG. 9. Arteriolar endothelium (rat thyroid) displaying numerous Weibel-Palade bodies in longitudinal (*arrow*) and transverse section (*arrowhead*). *bl*, Basal lamina; *cp*, coated pit; *l*, lumen; *rb*, red blood cell; *v*, plasmalemmal vesicle. × 96,000.

elles is still unknown; however, they have been used as a reliable tag for the identification of isolated endothelial cells (147, 177, 347).

CELL SURFACE BIOCHEMISTRY: DIFFERENTIATED DOMAINS. Recent observations indicate that endothelial cell membrane and its associated features (vesicles, channels, and fenestrae) contain differentiated microdomains generated by a preferential distribution of the anionic sites, some glycosaminoglycans, sialoconjugates, and monosaccharide residues. These microdomains may be responsible for some physiological peculiarities of the capillary endothelium because they involve mainly the structures implicated in permeability.

Anionic sites: distribution and partial characterization. Electrophysiological studies (321) and experiments with charged tracers showed that the surface of endothelial cells has an overall negative charge in situ (98, 322, 377, 378) and in culture (282). In vivo or in situ detection of the acidic groups with polycations of large size (cationized ferritin, M_r 480,000, mol diam ~11 nm) and small size (alcian blue, M_r 1,300, estimated mol diam ~2 nm) demonstrated the existence of differentiated domains on the blood front of the fenestrated endothelium in pancreatic and jejunal capillaries. The highest concentration of high-affinity (low-pK) anionic sites appears on fenestral diaphragms. Coated pits (and coated vesicles) have the next highest binding affinity for the cationic probes, followed by the plasma membrane, with labeling that is often discontinuous. In contrast, plasmalemmal vesicles open on the luminal front, the transendothelial channels, and the stomatal diaphragms of both structures do not bind the cationic probes [Fig. 10; (353, 357, 358, 361, 375)]. In the continuous endothelium of lung capillaries, cationized ferritin usually fails to label vesicles open on the blood front even when they do not have a detectable stomatal diaphragm.

These findings indicate that although morphologically identical, the three categories of diaphragms have a different electrical charge: fenestral diaphragms are negatively charged; vesicle and channel diaphragms are neutral. The possible physiological implications of these differences in the electrical charge of the structures involved in endothelial permeability are further discussed in *Search for pores: electron microscopy and tracer experiments*, p. 84. Differences in cationized ferritin binding to coated pits and fenestrae of the myeloid sinusoidal endothelium as a function of the pH of the buffer used and treatment with neuraminidase were recently reported (100, 102).

Perfusion in situ with specific hydrolases (neuraminidase, hyaluronidase, chondroitinase ABC, heparinase) indicates that the anionic sites of the fenestral diaphragms are contributed primarily by heparan sulfate and/or heparin, although those of the plasma membrane proper are of mixed chemical nature. Heparinase removes almost completely the anionic sites of fenestral diaphragms and only partially (often in patches) those of the plasmalemma [Fig. 11; (353, 357, 358, 374)]. The heparinase treatment and mild digestion with proteases of broad spectrum (trypsin, papain, pronase) usually leave behind a structurally recognizable diaphragm or diaphragm remnant, which suggests that the fenestral diaphragms consist basically of a proteic core to which proteoglycans (mostly rich in heparan sulfate) are attached (353, 359). Cationized ferritin-free patches on plasmalemma increase in frequency after heparinase treatment. These patches may be preferential sites for plasmalemmal vesicle fusion to or detachment from the cell membrane. The complete removal of anionic sites with proteases of broad spectrum (pronase, papain) suggests that anionic sites of capillary endothelium are provided by glycosaminoglycans, acidic glycoproteins, and probably acidic glycolipids.

In mouse pancreas, after detachment of basal lamina by perfusion with collagenase, with or without cysteine, the interstitially injected cationized ferritin labels the anionic sites of the abluminal front of capillary endothelium. The distribution of these anionic sites is generally similar to that recorded on the luminal front, except for fenestral diaphragms, which lack anionic sites (Fig. 12, inset). These structures may contain heparan-rich proteoglycans only on their luminal aspect. Endothelial processes extending toward pericytes were particularly rich in anionic sites, except for the attachment sites. Basal lamina meshwork contains two parallel, polyanionic interfaces (toward the abluminal front of the endothelium and stroma) formed by clusters of anionic sites almost regularly spaced at 80–100 nm. These sites are particularly abundant on the lamina rara externa. Calcium

FIG. 10. Pancreatic capillaries (mouse). Distribution of cationized ferritin (CF) at different time intervals after administration. *A*: after 2 min, CF bound to plasma membrane (*p*) with a high density on coated pits (*cp*) and especially on fenestral diaphragms (*f, inset*), whereas it is absent from vesicles (*v*), channels (*c*), and their associated diaphragms. × 100,000. *B*: after 10 min CF binding is restricted mostly to fenestral diaphragms (*f*), which appear to be relatively stable structures. × 100,000. *C*: coated vesicle (*cv*), still communicating with cell surface, has a dense labeling with CF, in contrast to plasmalemmal vesicles (*v*) and their diaphragms (*d*), which lack CF decoration. × 120,000. *D*: At 20 min, CF (*arrow*) occurs primarily within the matrix of multivesicular bodies (*mb*). × 72,000. *bl*, Basal lamina; *l*, lumen. [*C* from Simionescu, Simionescu, and Palade (375). *D* from Simionescu (359).]

ions are not required for cationized ferritin binding. As revealed by polymyxin experiments, anionic phospholipids are a minor contributor to the negative charge of cell surface. Anionic sites of the abluminal front of the endothelium and basal lamina, not markedly affected by neuraminidase, were removed by hep-

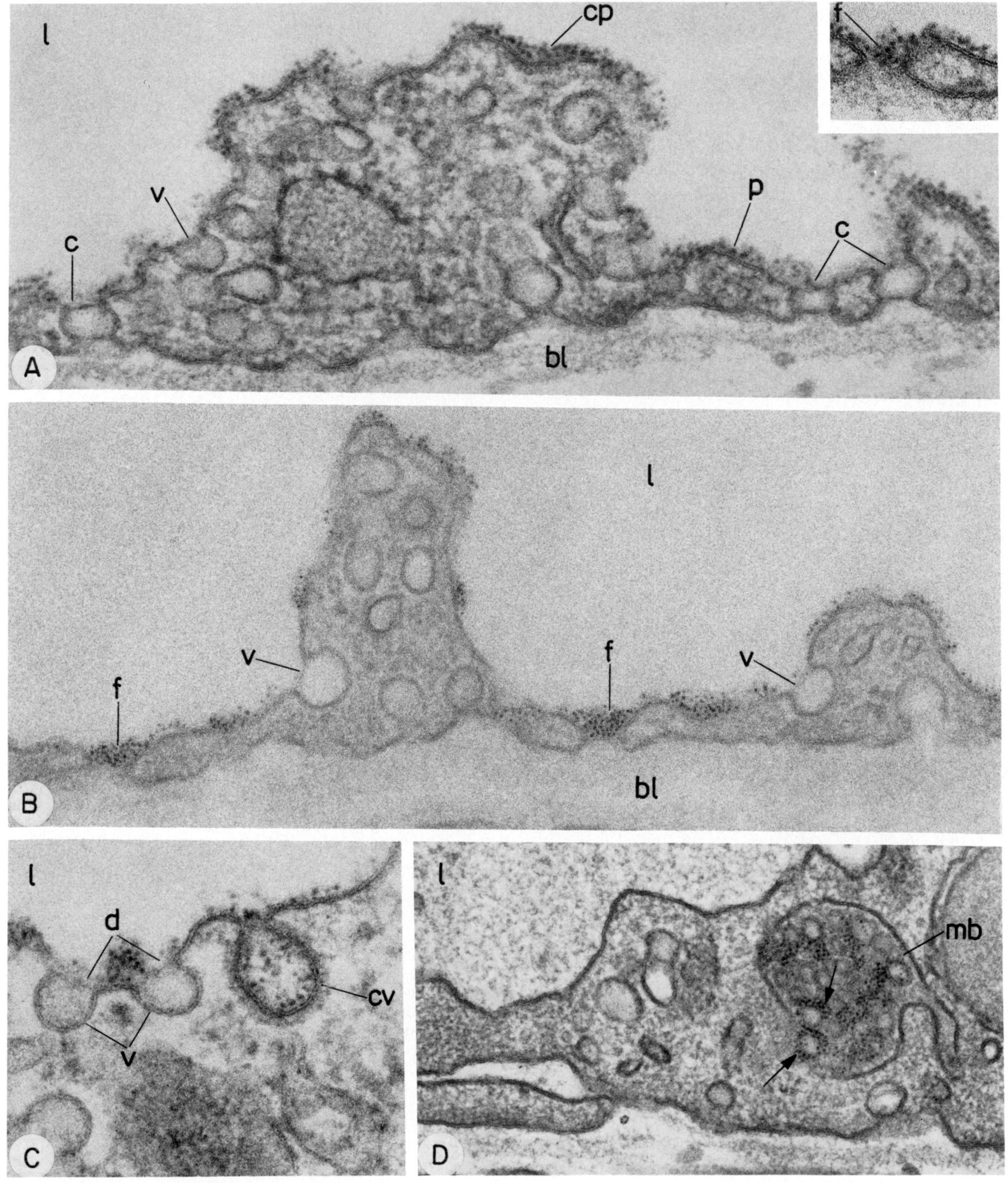

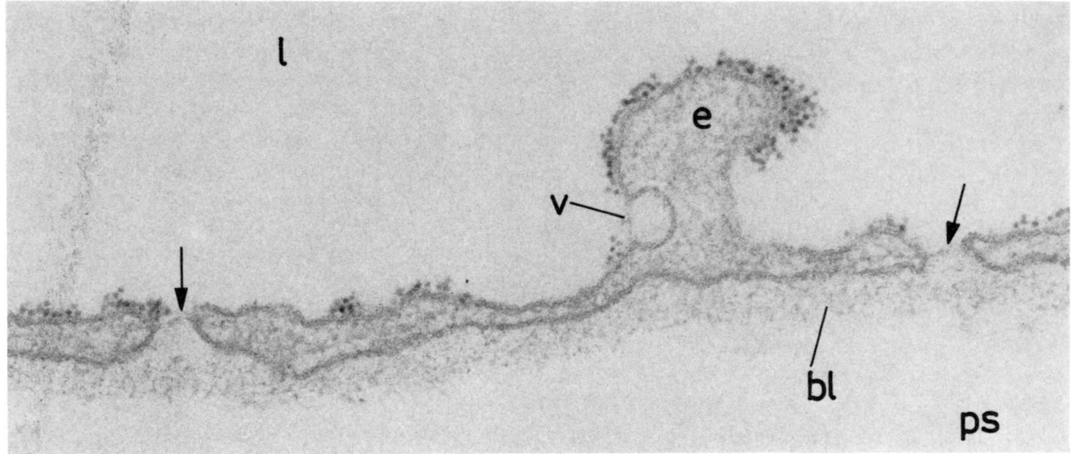

FIG. 11. Pancreatic capillary (mouse). Distribution of CF after previous perfusion with heparinase: fenestral diaphragms are devoid of CF binding sites (*arrows*). *bl*, Basal lamina; *e*, endothelium; *l*, lumen; *ps*, pericapillary space; *v*, plasmalemmal vesicle. × 90,000. [From Simionescu (359).]

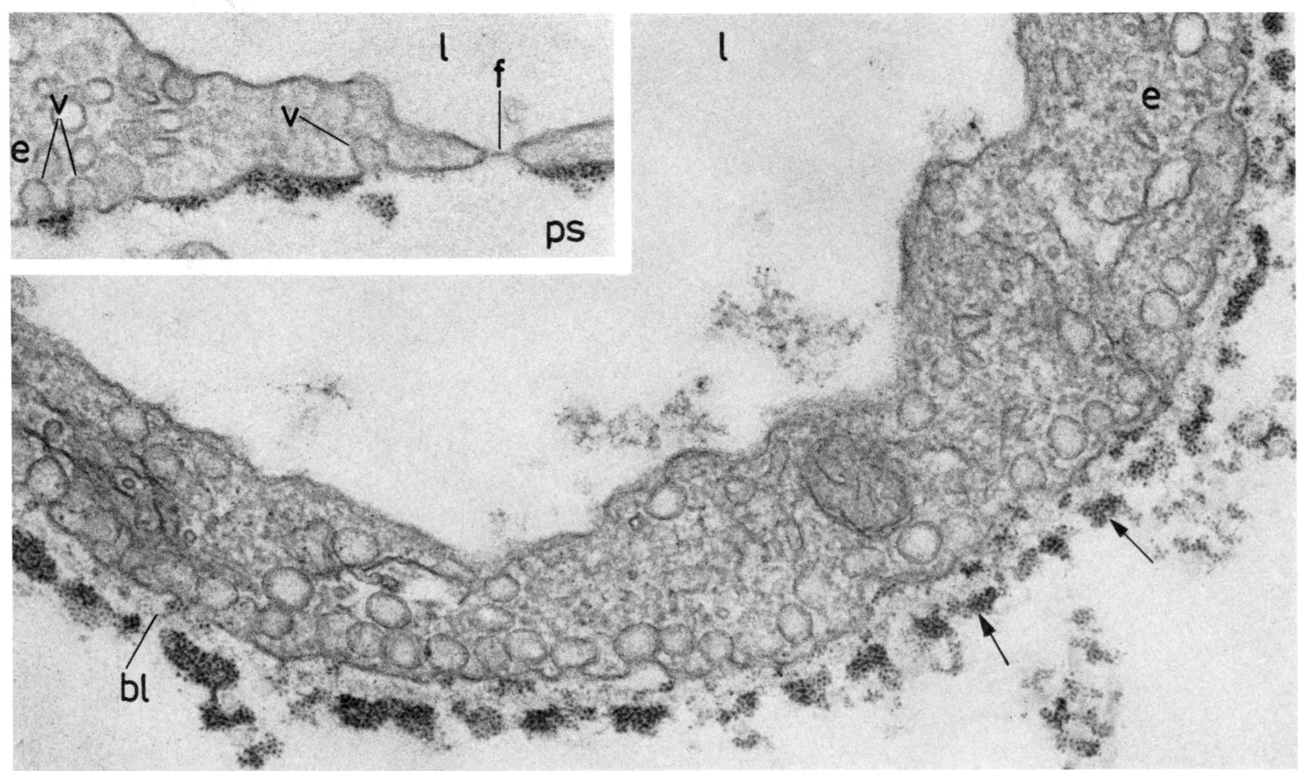

FIG. 12. Pancreatic capillary (mouse). Interstitially microinjected CF decorates anionic sites of basal lamina (*bl*) by forming clusters (*arrows*) almost periodically distributed at ~60–100 nm spacing. × 62,000. *Inset*: CF interstitially injected after basal lamina digestion with collagenase labels abluminal plasmalemma of endothelial cell (*e*) but is absent from vesicles, their diaphragms (*v*), and the abluminal aspect of fenestral diaphragms (*f*). *l*, Lumen; *ps*, pericapillary space. × 54,000.

arinase and fully digested by papain. The capillary wall appears to be a complex, heterogeneous, multilayered charge barrier composed of electrochemically distinct microdomains that can monitor the passage of macromolecules also according to their charge (355).

Glycoproteins: monosaccharide residues. Localization of some monosaccharide moieties on the endothelial cell surface of microvessels was detected in the lung (25), kidney glomeruli (38), heart (391), pancreas, and jejunum (354, 357, 358) by using lectin-peroxidase or lectin-ferritin conjugates. The lectins used have a reported specificity for terminal nonreducing residues: e.g., α-N-acetyl-D-galactosaminyl (soybean lectin), β-D-galactosyl (peanut agglutinin and *Ricinus communis* agglutinin-120), α-L-fucosyl (*Lotus tetragonolobus* lectin), α-D-glucosyl and α-D-mannosyl (concanavalin A), and β-N-acetyl-D-glucosaminyl and sialic acid (wheat germ agglutinin). The findings showed that the lectin-binding sites are relatively homogeneously distributed on plasma membrane, except for *Lotus tetragonolobus* lectin and concanavalin A, which frequently appear in patches. Plasmalemmal vesicles, transendothelial channels, and their stomatal diaphragms are particularly rich in β-D-galactosyl and β-N-acetyl-D-glucosaminyl (Fig. 13), whereas the fenestral diaphragms (known to contain a relatively large amount of heparan sulfate) had few or no monosaccharides. The high affinity of wheat germ agglutinin for vesicle diaphragms (which lack anionic sites) suggests that they do not have a significant amount of sialic acid and that on the capillary endothelial cell surface, wheat germ agglutinin sites for β-N-acetyl-D-glucosaminyl and neuraminic acid are different (354, 357, 358).

Biochemically differentiated microdomains involve mostly the features that participate in transcytosis. Although fenestral diaphragms have a net negative

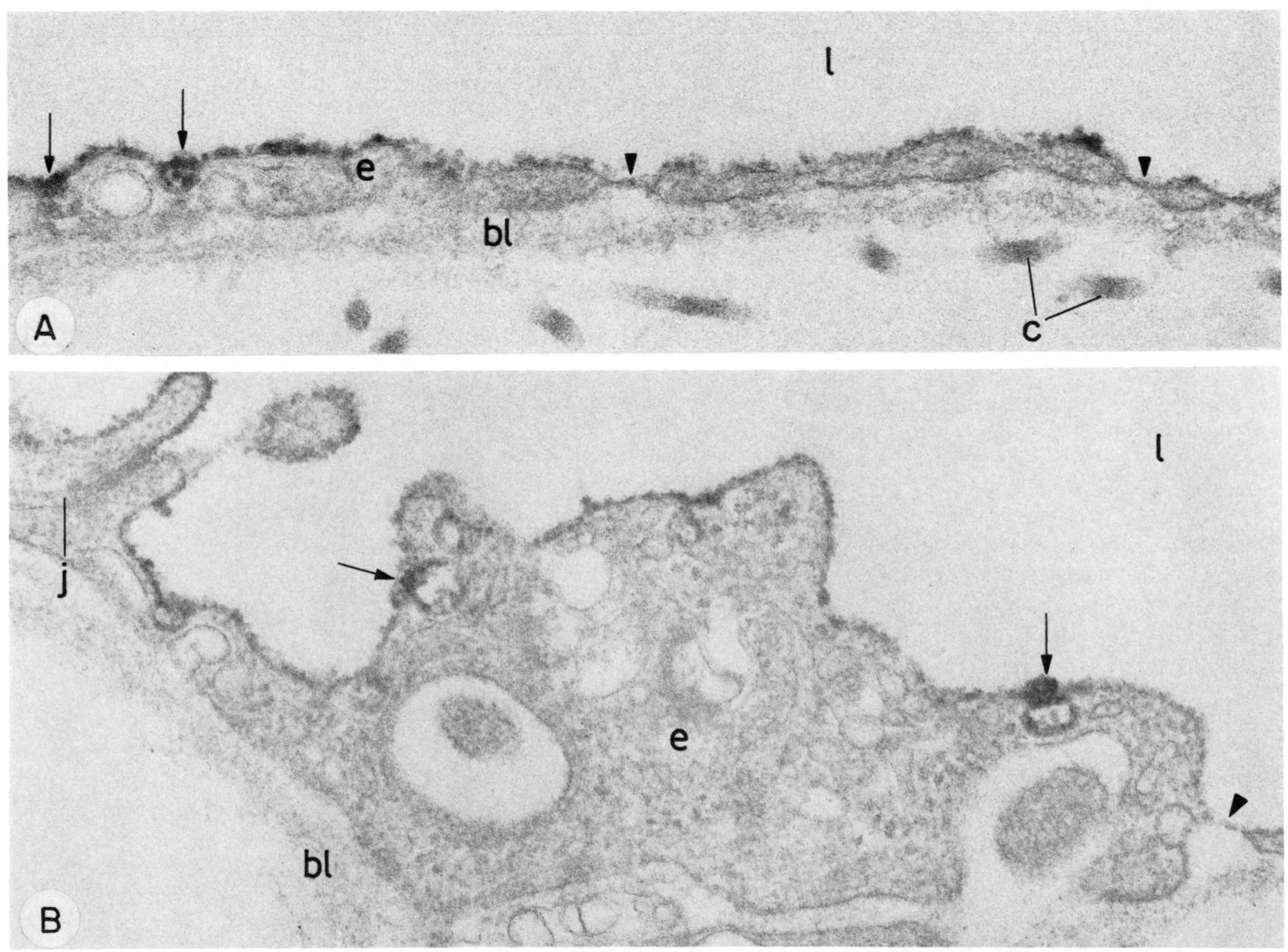

FIG. 13. *A*: pancreatic capillary (mouse). Peanut agglutinin–peroxidase conjugate is preferentially distributed on vesicle membrane and its associated diaphragm (*arrow*) and practically absent on fenestral diaphragm (*arrowhead*). × 90,000. *B*: pancreatic capillary (mouse). Distribution of wheat germ agglutinin–peroxidase conjugate. Heavy reaction product on vesicle diaphragms (*arrows*) in contrast with absence on fenestral diaphragms (*arrowhead*). × 90,000. *bl*, Basal lamina; *c*, collagen; *e*, endothelium; *j*, endothelial junction; *l*, lumen. [From Simionescu (359).]

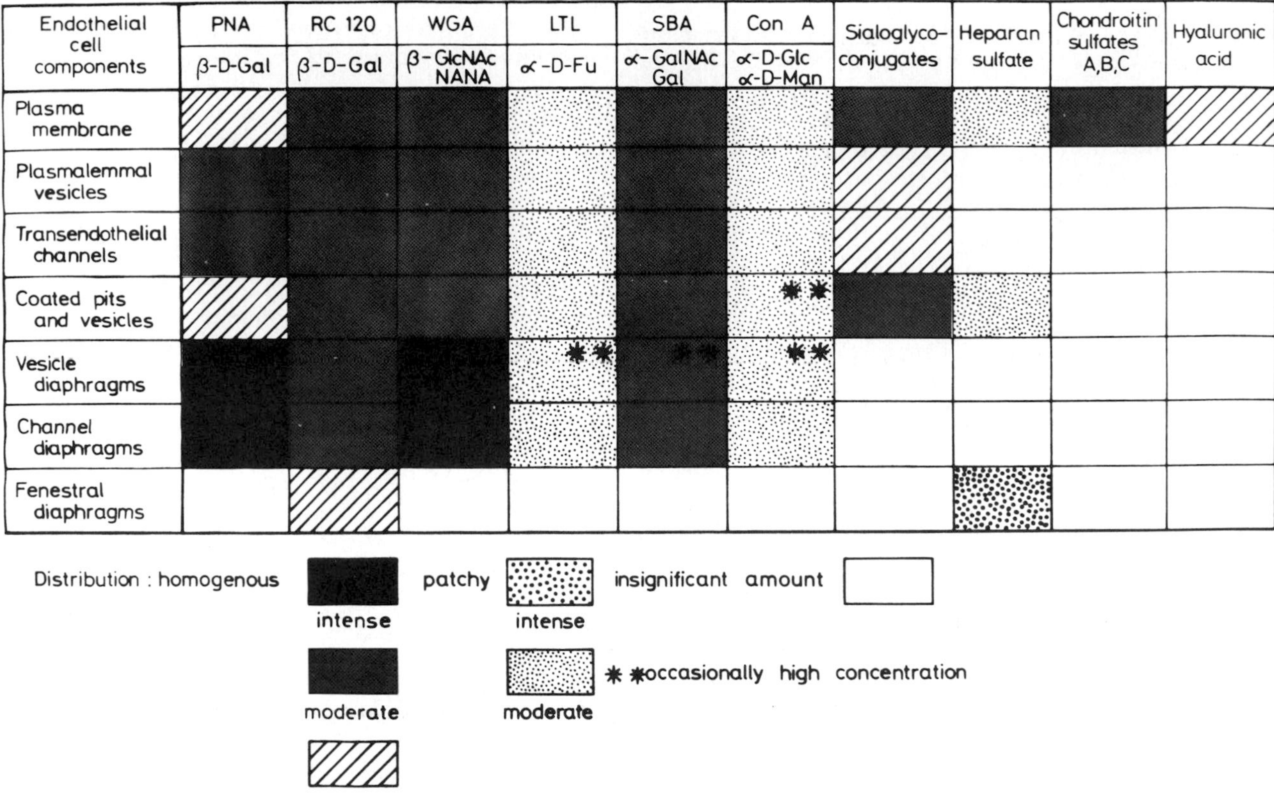

FIG. 14. Distribution of some glycoconjugates on cell surface of fenestrated endothelium (pancreatic capillaries). [From Simionescu and Simionescu (362).]

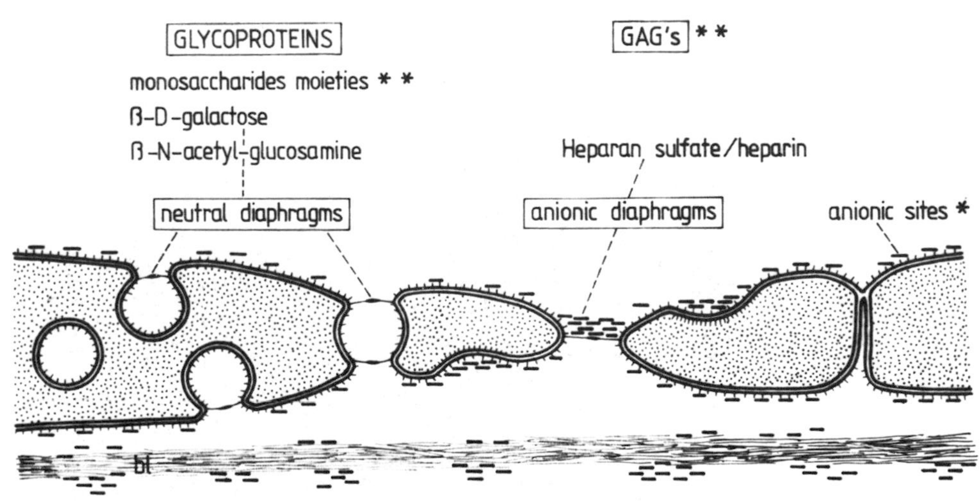

FIG. 15. Distribution of anionic sites and microdomains of glycoconjugates on cell surface of capillary endothelium and basal lamina (*bl*); *bl* is purposely depicted detached from endothelium. GAG, glycosaminoglycan; NANA, neuraminic acid; ChS, chondroitin sulfates A, B, C; HAc, hyaluronic acid; β-D-Gal, β-D-galactose; β-D-GlcNAc, β-*N*-acetyl-D-glucosaminyl; β-D-GalNAc, β-*N*-acetyl-D-galactosaminyl; Hs, heparan sulfate; α-D-Fu, α-D-fucose; α-D-Man, α-D-mannose; α-D-Glc, α-D-glucose. [Adapted from Simionescu, Simionescu, and Palade (369).]

charge contributed mostly by heparan sulfate, the stomatal diaphragms of vesicles and channels appear to be electrically neutral and to contain particularly glycoproteins rich in galactosyl and β-*N*-acetyl-D-glucosaminyl (Figs. 14 and 15). Thus it is expected that these features select permeant molecules not only depending on their size but also according to molecular charge.

Lipid domains: cholesterol and anionic phospholipids. Endothelial cells are able to synthesize sterols, which presumably are partly incorporated into the cell membrane (115, 124, 292, 379). Recent data derived from the perturbation of free fatty acid and from fluorescent lifetime heterogeneity of diphenylhexatriene indicate the existence of lipid domains in cell membrane of bovine aortic endothelial cells (204, 286).

It has been demonstrated that polyene antibiotics react specifically with membrane sterols (105, 267) and produce discrete complexes that can be detected in thin-sectioned specimens and in freeze-fracture preparations (111, 308).

The distribution of sterols and acidic lipids in the cell membrane of microvascular endothelium (mouse pancreas, diaphragm, thyroid) was investigated with filipin and polymyxin B, which reportedly have binding specificity for free 3-β-hydroxysterols and anionic phospholipids, respectively. Experiments were carried out at 37°C, 22°C, or 18°C. Short exposure (10 min) to filipin (≤100 μM) resulted in the initial appearance of a ring of characteristic filipin-sterol complexes within the rim surrounding the plasmalemmal vesicle stomata and fenestrae (Fig. 16). After longer exposure filipin-sterol complexes labeled randomly the rest of the plasma membrane (except for coated pits and interstrand areas of junctions) and also marked most plasmalemmal vesicles. The latter seemed to have fewer filipin-sterol complexes than an equivalent area of the cell membrane. The annuli of these complexes displayed mostly on the protoplasmic (P) face consist at their full development of 6–8 units around vesicle stomata and 10–12 units around fenestrae. At their level the intramembranous particles and the anionic sites are virtually excluded, and—as revealed by the location of polymyxin B–induced protrusions—the anionic phospholipids are scarce or absent. The annuli of the filipin-sterol complexes are lacking around the opening of coated vesicles; such rings did not occur in other regions of plasmalemma. Because the annuli are present around fenestrae (relatively stable structures where no ongoing fusion occurs), cholesterol molecules in these locations may be important contributors to the stabilization and, possibly, phase separation at the level of this unusually sharp bending on plasma membrane (359a).

Receptors. Because of its continuous and extensive exposure to all circulating substances, predictably the vascular endothelium should be richly endowed with specific binding sites or receptors for molecules to be metabolized by the endothelial cell itself or selectively transported to the subjacent tissues (10).

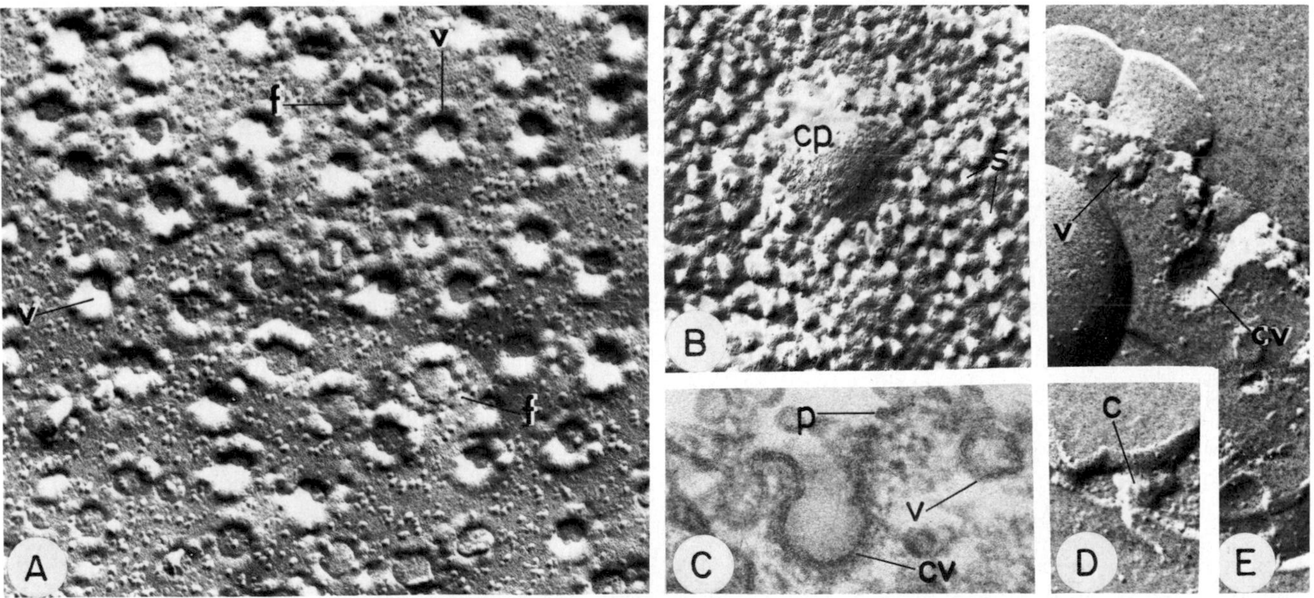

FIG. 16. *A–C*: pancreatic capillary (rat) after treatment with filipin. *A*: in freeze-fracture preparations, filipin-sterol complexes first appear around openings of plasmalemmal vesicles (*v*) and fenestrae (*f*), forming characteristic peristomatal rings. × 72,000. *B* and *C*: coated pits (*cp*) and coated vesicles (*cv*) are devoid of filipin-sterol complexes (*s*), which at high dose decorate plasma membrane (*p*) extensively. × 84,000. *D* and *E*: unlike coated vesicles, plasmalemmal vesicles and transendothelial channels (*c*) are marked by filipin-sterol complexes. × 50,000.

Physiological and pharmacological experiments indicate the existence of endothelial receptors; most of these experiments were performed on cultured endothelial cells usually obtained from large vessels (e.g., human umbilical vein, bovine or rabbit aorta) (293, 421). According to these data, several metabolic activities of the endothelia imply mechanisms mediated by receptors such as those for low-density lipoproteins (169, 293, 392, 421), angiotensin (219, 306), insulin (12, 147), epinephrine (α-adrenergic receptors) (20), norepinephrine, acetylcholine, serotonin (5-hydroxytryptamine), histamine (7, 49, 84, 127, 270, 411), kinins (pulmonary artery) (315–319), and thrombin (220, 221). Rapid binding of thrombin to the endothelial cell surface (cultures of human umbilical vein) behaves quantitatively like a classic ligand-receptor system (220), but the effects of thrombin on arachidonate metabolism in endothelial cells are not mediated by a high-affinity receptor (221). Although information about the nature and localization of endothelial receptors in microvessels is scarce, there are indications of the existence of surface receptors on microvascular endothelium.

Angiotensin II. Histochemical detection of angiotensin II coupled to horseradish peroxidase or cytochrome *c* showed that this conjugate binds to the capillary endothelium membrane in the kidney, liver, diaphragm, choroid plexus, and lungs. Richardson and Beaulnes (306) suggest that the receptor signal may be further transmitted through the myoendothelial junctions to the adjacent smooth muscle cells.

Serotonin and norepinephrine. Radioautography (398) demonstrated the uptake of serotonin by pulmonary endothelial cells (96); a similar process was also detected in cultures of bovine aortic endothelium (337, 338) and in isolated microvessels obtained from rat fat-pad and cardiac muscle. The activity appears to be also preserved in Triton X-100 lysate of freshly isolated endothelial cells (338).

Serotonin is almost completely removed in a single passage through the pulmonary circulation (139, 189, 190, 406). The process seems to occur by uptake and degradation via monoamine oxidase both in laboratory animals and in anesthetized patients (125, 146). Radioautography and fluorescence histochemistry (11, 146) have identified the endothelial cells of microvessels as the sites for removal of both serotonin and norepinephrine. The sites for removal of serotonin and norepinephrine are different, and in some respects their primary reaction with the endothelia is of ligand-receptor type (249, 250, 411).

Histamine. The distribution and properties of histamine receptors as defined for several cells, tissues, and organs, including blood vessels, are primarily based on the target responses to either histamine alone or histamine associated with its agonists or antagonists. The nature and possible role of histamine receptors were investigated in several microvascular beds, e.g., the lung (13, 412), peritoneum (21), human forearm (72), canine forelimb (155), kidney glomeruli (173), cheek pouch (8), stomach submucosa (157), nasal mucosa (167), skin (150), and capillary-rich fraction isolated from the brain (199). As identified physiologically and pharmacologically, histamine effects are mediated by two types of receptors: H_1 receptors, specifically inhibited by a classic antihistamine such as mepyramine, and H_2 receptors, blocked by antagonists such as cimetidine.

Recently the cellular localization of histamine receptors was detected with a biologically active histamine-ferritin conjugate. After its perfusion in situ this conjugate binds preferentially on restricted areas of luminal endothelial cell plasmalemma, especially in regions rich in filaments. Histamine-binding sites on vascular endothelium are more dense in venules and less dense in arterioles, muscular arteries, and veins; the binding has the lowest values in capillaries and aorta. Experiments employing specific antagonists (mepyramine and cimetidine) indicate that the venular endothelium contains mainly H_2 receptors (163). The effect of histamine on endothelium is Ca^{2+} dependent (218). Heparin can suppress the increased permeability induced by histamine, bradykinin, and prostaglandin E_1, probably by binding and occupying their receptors on the vascular endothelium (54). Diana et al. (108) report that histamine also can induce changes in the permeability properties of capillary endothelium.

Insulin. Insulin-binding sites have been identified by radioautography in the endothelium of liver sinusoids in situ (18) and in cultures of endothelial cells of human umbilical vein (12, 147).

The special affinity of lymphocytes for the high-endothelium venules of the lymphatic tissue is discussed in *Postcapillary venules of lymph nodes*, p. 73.

Enzyme activities. A growing body of information reveals a complex spectrum of enzymes associated with the luminal membrane of microvascular endothelium. Some enzymes also have been located histochemically within the plasmalemmal vesicles (239, 319, 426). Enzyme activities are more obvious in the pulmonary circulation probably because of the enormous endothelial surface area rather than because of some unique properties of pulmonary endothelium (144). However, because of the special position it occupies in the blood circulatory system, the lung monitors some circulating substances (e.g., by adjusting the concentration of vasoactive agents) before they reach the systemic circulation (315–317).

The rapid appearance of serotonin and norepinephrine metabolites in effluent from lungs perfused in vitro with these vasoactive hormones suggests that their inactivating enzymes, monoamine oxidase and catechol *O*-methyltransferase, occur at the level of the endothelial cell. These enzymes have not yet been convincingly detected histochemically.

The angiotensin I–converting enzyme (kinase II), however, is a dipeptidyl carboxypeptidase that Ryan et al. (319) localized by immunofluorescence and immunocytochemical techniques on the luminal membrane of endothelial cells. The enzyme was also demonstrated by immunofluorescence in the microvascular cells of kidney, liver, pancreas, spleen (52), and cultured endothelial cells (71). Bakhle and Vane (11) and Gillis (146) have shown that the converting enzyme and tissue-bound bradykininase (which inactivated bradykinin) are the same enzyme.

Lipoprotein lipase. The major hydrolase of circulating lipoprotein triglycerides is lipoprotein lipase (269, 390). Using Gomori's histochemical method for lipase, Blanchette-Mackie and Scow (27) and Brecher and Kuan (36) localized the lipoprotein lipase activity in capillary endothelia and in the subendothelial spaces (adipose tissue). It was also detected in the intima scraped off the bovine aorta. Circulating molecules of lipoprotein lipase could be captured through electrostatic interactions by the negatively charged sulfated glycosaminoglycans (possibly heparan sulfate) of the endothelial cell surface; very-low-density lipoprotein particles attached to the cell membrane induce the movement of lipoprotein lipase molecules toward their substrate by lateral diffusion of proteins carrying the oligosaccharide residues within the plane of the cell membrane. Heparin inhibits lipoprotein lipase binding to the endothelial cell surface (269), whereas apoprotein C-II promotes the hydrolysis of chylomicron triacylglycerols by endothelium-bound lipoprotein lipase (227).

α_2-Macroglobulin. The immunofluorescence technique shows that α_2-macroglobulin is associated with the endothelial cell surface (15). This protein may protect the vascular endothelium during various protease-generating reactions at the blood–vessel wall interface. Endothelial cells can synthesize and secrete factor VIII [antihemophilic factor (177)], thrombospondin (110), von Willebrand factor (178), prostacyclin (257, 258, 434), and elastase (288).

Other plasma proteins. Fibrinogen was not yet convincingly demonstrated to be adsorbed on the luminal endothelial membrane. However, heparin intravenously injected has a marked tendency to attach to the endothelial surface. Factor VIII antigen was localized by immunofluorescence microscopy in the endothelial cell (28, 176, 264). The measurement of factor VIII antigen has been proposed as a marker of endothelial injury: increase in its plasma levels may reflect the degree of vascular involvement in several diseases (33, 86).

GROWTH AND REGENERATION. Most of the information on endothelial growth and regeneration concerns the large vessels, especially in cultured conditions (217, 330); very little is known about these processes at the level of microvascular endothelium (405). The vascular endothelium generally represents a slowly renewing cell population that in normal conditions in vivo rarely divides. The turnover of endothelial cells depends on their location: e.g., the life span in areas around aortic branches is 60–120 days as compared with 100–180 days in the rest of the aorta (280). In the aorta of 3-mo-old rats, 0.3%–1.5% of the total number of endothelial cells examined enter deoxyribonucleic acid (DNA) synthesis each day (330). The same approach gives a figure of 0.01% for capillaries of mouse retina and ~0.15% for myocardial capillaries (113). Disparate data reveal some of the factors that can influence endothelial regeneration in microvessels. Endothelial proliferation was reported during the hair-growth cycle in the rat skin (342), after thermal injury (341), and during the delayed hypersensitivity reaction in the guinea pig (289). Widmann and Fahimi (440) observed multiplication of liver endothelial cells after estrogen administration. A tumor angiogenesis factor was identified and implicated as a major stimulus of the migration and proliferation of endothelial cells in the neovascularization of tumors (9, 128).

ENDOTHELIUM AS TISSUE: INTERCELLULAR JUNCTIONS. In the microvascular endothelium the cells are linked to one another by intercellular junctions that consist of two basic types: occluding (tight) junctions and communicating (gap) junctions (349–352). The term *communicating junction* (macula communicans, maculae communicantes) evokes the geometry of this structure and its main function as so far established (344, 345, 350, 351). The alternative term *gap junction*, in spite of its much broader use, is particularly confusing for endothelium because junctions open to a gap of 6 nm have been described as occurring (instead of occluding zonulae) in microvascular endothelium (196–198, 371). As in other epithelia, the occluding junctions are considered the physical link between two adjoining cells and the sealing of the intercellular space, which controls the passage of molecules along this pathway. Communicating junctions presumably represent the structural substrate of the direct two-way communication between cells. These junctions are considered instrumental in the electrotonic coupling and intercellular exchange of ions and small metabolites. Recent evidence has shown, however, that even in endothelia known to lack morphologically distinct communicating junctions such as capillaries and pericytic venules, an interendothelial transfer of dye (Lucifer yellow) can occur. This transfer may take place either via very small gap junctions (one or a few particles as seen in freeze-fracture preparations) that are commonly missed during investigation or via the tight junctions provided by cell-to-cell channels (339).

Information about the organization of endothelial junctions was obtained either from thin sections of fixed and embedded specimens or from replicas of freeze-cleaved preparations (83, 453). The latter method has the advantage of exposing large membrane areas; its emerging images should, however, be interpreted bearing in mind that the features observed on the cleavage plane show the interior situation of the cell membrane. These images do not indicate the organization of the cell contact at the true cell surface. These static morphological data should always be tested with electron-opaque tracers of known molecular size, shape, and charge. The three combined approaches were applied on well-identified sequential segments of a given microvascular field [e.g., rat omentum and mesentery (349–352) or rat diaphragm (371–372)]. The results indicate that each microvascular segment has characteristically organized endothelial junctions (Figs. 17 and 18) that reflect various degrees of tightness and intercellular coupling. The endothelium in arterioles has continuous and elaborate occluding junctions with interpolated large communicating junctions (Figs. 17*A* and 18*A*). The capillary endothelium has occluding junctions made up of either branching or staggered strands; morphologically detectable communicating junctions are absent in these vessels (Figs. 17*B* and 18*B*). Pericytic venules show loosely organized endothelial junctions with discontinuous low-profile ridges and grooves devoid of particles; no communicating junctions were found at this level. The endothelium of muscular venules has the same type of junctions as those observed in the pericytic venules but also displays isolated communicating junctions of smaller size and lower frequency than those in arterioles [Fig. 17*C*; (349–352, 371)]. As seen in freeze-cleaved preparations, the transition from the capillary to the venular type of junctions seems to occur abruptly (371). In thin-sectioned specimens the appearance of endothelial junctions generally parallels that observed in freeze-cleaved replicas (75, 78, 433). These endothelial junctions are characterized by membranes in close contact or displaying points of membrane fusion (occluding junctions) or by the pentalaminar pattern typical for communicating junctions (Fig. 18*A*). About 25%–30% of the junctions in venular endothelium appear to be open to a gap up to 6 nm wide [Fig. 18*C*; (371–373)], but this may not reflect exactly the dimensions existing in vivo. The conclusion that the number of strands in a junction reflects the tightness (74) is apparently an oversimplification (241). Based on previous studies (350), endothelial junctions were identified as belonging to a given microvascular segment in freeze-fracture replicas of the lung (326, 327), microvessels of rat choroid plexus (107, 417), small vessels of the brain (40, 41, 83, 404, 453), and alveolar capillaries (174). The patency of endothelial junctions to permeant molecules is discussed in *Search for pores: electron microscopy and tracer experiments*, p. 84.

DIFFERENTIATIONS OF MICROVASCULAR ENDOTHELIUM. Analysis reveals that each organ and tissue and each segment of their microvascular beds has its own characteristic endothelium. Interspecies variations in ultrastructure appear as quantitative and qualitative differentiations on a common theme. The differentiations are primarily represented by cell constituents, e.g., plasmalemmal vesicles, channels, fenestrae, diaphragms, coated vesicles, intercellular junctions, and basal lamina. The existence of intermediary appearances suggests that the key structures of this common theme are the vesicles. They appear as highly modulating features functioning as either discrete units or fused as channels, the ultimate expression of which could be considered the fenestra (a channel reduced to its minimal length). On this common theme, schematically, four degrees of differentiation can be recognized in the fine structural organization of the microvascular endothelium (362).

First degree: general differentiation. Based on variations in the continuity of the endothelium and its basal lamina and on the existence or absence of fenestrae, three main categories of endothelium have been described: *1*) continuous, occurring in large vessels, arterioles, most venules, and capillaries of somatic tissues, nervous system, and lung; *2*) fenestrated, characteristic for visceral capillaries and also found in some pericytic venules (in kidney glomeruli the fenestrae are devoid of diaphragms); *3*) discontinuous (sinusoid), occurring in liver, spleen, and bone marrow. For details see the excellent reviews by Majno and Joris (231, 233).

Second degree: tissue or organ differentiation. In each of the capillary types described, structural modulations may involve the vesicle frequency (e.g., in the continuous endothelium ~1,000 vesicles/μm^3 of endothelium in myocardium vs. ~130 vesicles/μm^3 in the lung, and many fewer in brain capillaries) or may involve fenestrae density of endothelium (e.g., ~54/μm^2 in capillaries of adrenal cortex vs. ~15/μm^2 in pancreas) (348, 372).

FIG. 17. Characteristic organization of endothelial junctions in sequential segments of microvasculature (rat omentum). *A*: arteriole. Elaborate occluding junction (*oj*) with intercalated large communicating (gap) junction (*cj*). × 140,000. *B*: capillary. Only occluding junctions are present, as branching or staggered strands. × 120,000. *C*: muscular venule. Discontinuous low-profile ridges (*r*) and grooves (*g*) usually devoid of particles are seen on the protoplasmic (*P*) face and external (*E*) face, respectively. *cj*, Small, isolated communicating (gap) junction; *v*, vesicle opening. × 100,000. [From Simionescu, Simionescu, and Palade (350, 371).]

Third degree: segmental differentiation. Comparative examination of well-identified sequential microvascular segments (arterioles, capillaries, venules) collected from rat omentum (350) and mouse diaphragm (371) revealed that vesicle numerical density is highest in the endothelium of true capillaries with a maximum

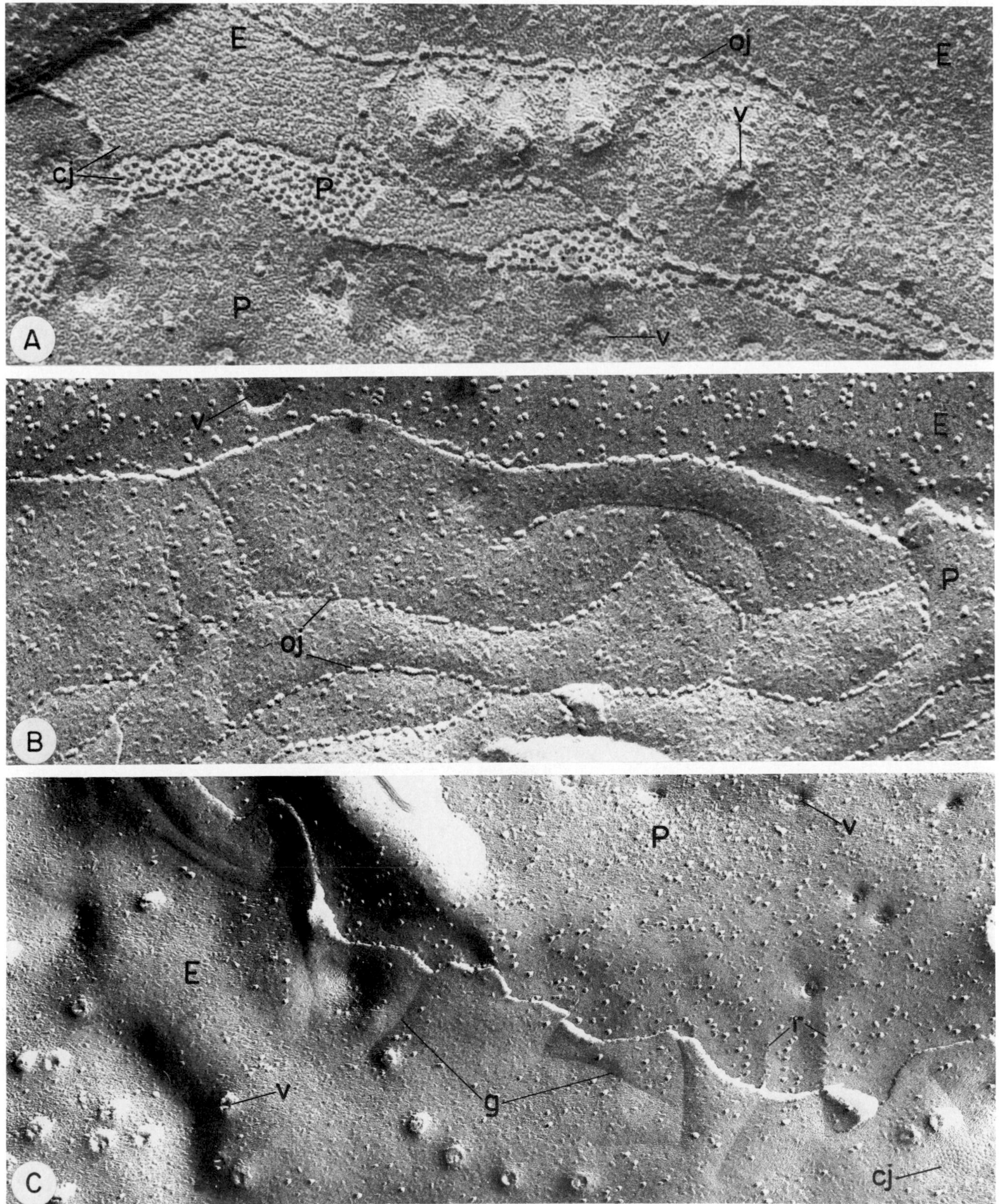

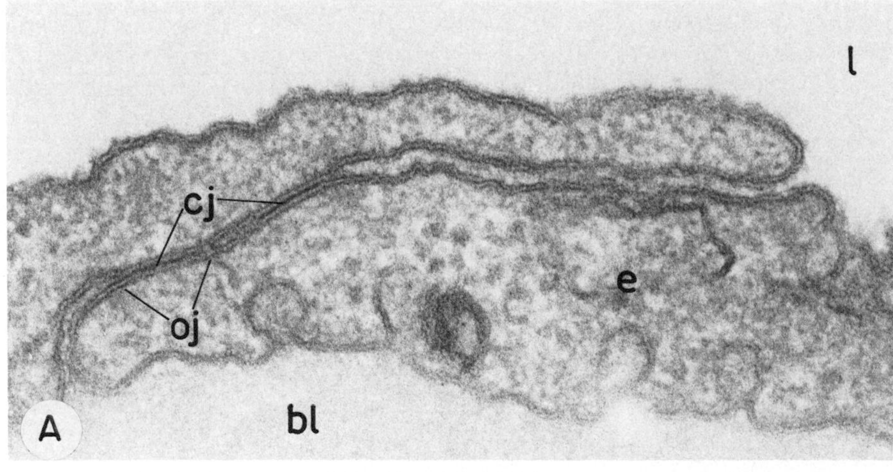

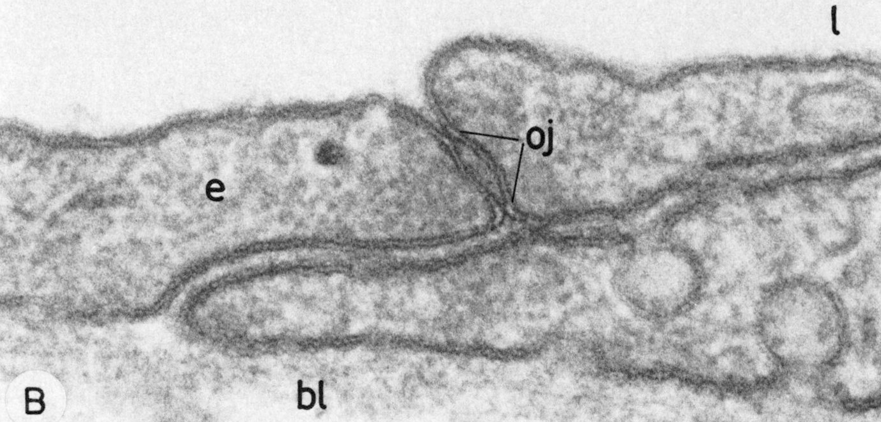

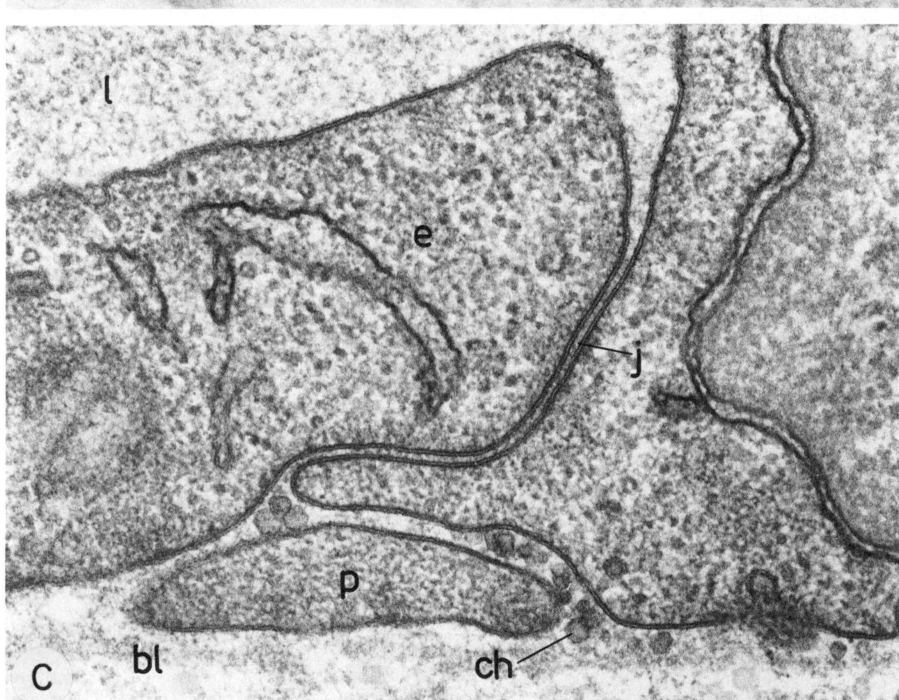

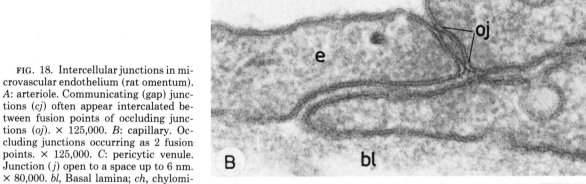

FIG. 18. Intercellular junctions in microvascular endothelium (rat omentum). *A*: arteriole. Communicating (gap) junctions (*cj*) often appear intercalated between fusion points of occluding junctions (*oj*). × 125,000. *B*: capillary. Occluding junctions occurring as 2 fusion points. × 125,000. *C*: pericytic venule. Junction (*j*) open to a space up to 6 nm. × 80,000. *bl*, Basal lamina; *ch*, chylomicrons; *e*, endothelium; *l*, lumen; *p*, pericyte.

numerical density in their venular end (Table 2). The latter also contains a particularly high number of single vesicle transendothelial channels (371, 372). Endothelial junctions are represented in arterioles by an elaborate combination of occluding junctions intercalated with communicating junctions. Capillary endothelium has occluding junctions only, whereas in venules the junctions have characteristically a very loose organization and ~30% of them appear to be open to a space up to 6 nm (371) (see ENDOTHELIUM AS TISSUE: INTERCELLULAR JUNCTIONS, p. 59).

Fourth degree: locally differentiated microdomains. The surface of endothelial cell (fenestrated capillaries) contains biochemically distinct microdomains generated by the preferential distribution of some glycosaminoglycans and glycoproteins (see CELL SURFACE BIOCHEMISTRY: DIFFERENTIATED DOMAINS, p. 52).

The various levels of endothelial differentiations appear more sophisticated if the metabolic activities are also taken into account.

Basal Lamina, Subendothelial Matrix, and Pericytes

As in the rest of the circulatory system, the endothelium of microvessels rests on the basal lamina (basement membrane), a feltwork (~40–80 nm thick) of collagens, glycoproteins, laminin, and probably fibronectin produced by the endothelial cells themselves (170, 179, 180, 201, 228, 229). The abluminal front of the endothelial cell is linked to the basal lamina via fine anchoring fibers (388, 389), the chemical nature of which is still unknown. In capillaries and pericytic venules the basal lamina also surrounds the pericytes.

Basal lamina is continuous in the case of continuous and fenestrated endothelium and discontinuous in sinusoids. Basal lamina can be thought of as part of a more complex subendothelial extracellular matrix.

By using affinity-purified collagen type-specific antibodies, Biempica et al. (23) have shown that types IV and V (AB_2) collagens are the major constituents of the basal lamina and the subendothelium in endocardium, heart, glomerular capillaries, and pulmonary capillaries (170, 201, 230). It has been claimed that collagen type V is also associated with the luminal endothelial cell surface. Because neither types IV and/or V cause platelet aggregation, they both may function as an antithrombotic barrier. Once this barrier is breached and interstitial collagens (types I and III, which promote platelet aggregation) and other thrombogenic molecules are exposed, a thrombus can be initiated. Indirect immunofluorescence has demonstrated that in the normal rat pancreas, type IV collagen and laminin closely surround the blood vessels. Fibronectin was detected in the rat glomerulus mainly at the interface between endothelial and mesangial cells; type IV collagen is present in the lamina densa, whereas laminin is concentrated in the laminae rarae of the basement membrane. These distinct patterns suggest that these three components could constitute different sets of fibrils within the glomerular matrix (89–91). The existence in the glomerular basement membrane of a quasi-regular network of anionic sites in the laminae rarae has been demonstrated with cationic probes (63, 192); these anionic sites consist mostly of sulfated glycosaminoglycans rich in heparan sulfate (80, 193, 194). As clearly demonstrated in the glomerulus, the basal lamina behaves as a primary size and charge barrier (117–119).

Interstitial injection of cationized ferritin or alcian blue demonstrated the distribution of anionic sites on the basal lamina in the fenestrated endothelium (pancreas capillaries). The basal lamina network contains two parallel, polyanionic interfaces (toward the endothelium and stroma, respectively) formed by clusters of anionic sites, almost regularly spaced at ~80–100 nm (Fig. 12). The negative charge is generally greater on endothelial cells and basal lamina than on neighboring connective tissue cells that bind the cationized ferritin to a lesser extent (M. Simionescu, unpublished observations).

In arterioles and occasionally in muscular venules, the basal lamina is penetrated by endothelial cell processes that establish contact with the subjacent smooth muscle cell (myoendothelial junction).

Because of its high content of collagen the microvascular basal lamina can be digested by collagenase (232), allowing isolation of microvessels of various origins (106, 347, 424, 426–428). Reportedly, basal lamina can be detached by using ethylenediaminetetraacetic acid (76) or vinblastine (413).

The thickening of endothelial basal lamina occurring in diabetes is presumed to be the result of alteration in collagen glycosylation.

The extracellular matrix is important in the maintenance of vessel shape, cell configuration, flow of solutes across the vessel wall, local reactions in inflammation, involution, and metastasis. The subendothelium consists of fibrils, embedded in an amorphous ground substance through which the interstitial fluid percolates, and acts as a vehicle for molecules exchanged between the three adjoining compartments: the plasma, the intracellular fluid, and the lymph (82, 165, 215).

The matrix extends also into the intercellular space (67), away from the occluding junction proper. Fibrils are represented by collagens, both striated and nonstriated: the prevalence of types I and III, known to promote platelet adhesion and aggregation, renders the subendothelium highly thrombogenic. Bundles of collagen fibers are particularly developed in the arteriolar and venular adventitia. Microfibrils and elastic fibrils also are occasionally encountered in these two locations. The elastic fibrils form a characteristic internal lamina in arterioles (see *Arterioles*, p. 67). Fibronectin, so far detected only in a few microvascular walls, seems to be a major component of their matrix. Fibronectin, primarily by its interaction with collagens and glycosaminoglycans, appears to be involved in attachment (26, 313) and polarity of endothelial cells (429). Fibronectin may also be involved in directing endothelial cell migration during neovascularization (35, 247). A loss of fibronectin occurs at sites of early inflammation, where polymorphonuclear neutrophils are present and release their granule content (neutral proteases) into the surrounding matrix (248, 323). Fibronectin apparently increases at inflammation sites at later stages, concomitantly with fibroblast accumulation (395).

The microvascular wall contains a continuous but heterogeneous gel of proteoglycans with domains of different composition and hydration. Some capillaries are surrounded by a thin layer of ground substance; others are embedded in much matrix, which may contribute to their patency and apparent rigidity (132, 137, 263, 422, 423).

The closest cells to the microvascular endothelium are the pericytes, ~150–200 μm long and 10–25 μm wide, which form a discontinuous layer extending from the terminal arteriole to the muscular venule (130, 141, 407, 408, 430). Transitional forms between smooth muscle cells and pericytes exist at both arteriolar and venular ends of the microvascular unit (262, 304) and around capillaries and immediate postcapillary venules (pericytic venules) (363). Pericytes are completely wrapped by an endothelial cell basal lamina: the latter is absent in some discrete areas of direct contact between endothelial cells and the neighboring pericyte. In several tissues (e.g., skeletal muscle capillaries) endothelial evaginations protrude deeply into pericytes (407, 408), a feature reminiscent of myoendothelial junctions (304), but the exact nature of this endothelial-pericyte contact and of those contacts between pericytes themselves needs clarification. Sheridan (339) recently showed that injection of Lucifer yellow into pericytes led to extensive transfer to other pericytes and occasionally to endothelial cells. Several primary processes, which are oriented in the long axis of the vessel, emerge from the pericyte cell body; from these primary processes several short secondary processes of variable size and shape partially encircle the endothelium (Fig. 19).

With certain regional variations, pericytes are ubiquitous in the microvasculature of virtually all tissues. In the cerebral vessels the pericytes form an elaborate system that almost completely invests the endothelium (1). The phagocytosis of the pericytes suggests their possible role as microglial cells in the periendothelial compartment of the blood-brain barrier (245, 396, 415).

The salient features of these cells are the numerous cytoplasmic microfilaments with occasional dense bodies. The number of plasmalemmal vesicles is characteristically smaller than that of the adjoining endothelial cell (Fig. 19). Weibel-Palade bodies were reported also in pericytes (455), but this observation is unconfirmed.

Tilton et al. (408) have proposed that pericyte function may vary in different tissues despite their ultrastructural similarities: e.g., vasoactive substances that induce a contractile response in pericytes of skeletal muscle capillaries were without effect on heart capillary pericytes. Until there is convincing evidence to the contrary, the roles most frequently attributed to pericytes are *1*) mechanical support for endothelial cells, *2*) contraction, *3*) potential phagocytic activity (210), and *4*) source of undifferentiated mesenchymal cells in repair and inflammation (92).

Smooth Muscle Cells

The contractile elements of the microvascular wall can be conceived of as an integrated cell system represented successively by the smooth muscle cells of the arteriole, the pericytes of capillaries and pericytic venules, and the smooth muscle cells of the muscular venules. Cells with intermediate features are found at the transitions between these segments, particularly between pericytic venules and muscular venules. Unlike pericytes, which are located within the endothelial basal lamina, the microvascular smooth muscle cells have their own basement membrane. Both smooth muscle cells and pericytes have discrete areas of close contact with endothelium. Neither the myoendothelial junctions nor the pericytic-endothelial junctions have been clearly characterized, but Rhodin (305) suggests that these close contacts may be instrumental in the transfer of information (e.g., effects of vasoactive substance) recorded by endothelium and transmitted to the adjoining smooth muscle. In arterioles and muscular venules, each muscle cell (usually 25–50 μm long) is surrounded by the basal lamina it secretes and by various amounts of collagen fibers. These collagen fibers may anchor the muscle cell to neighboring elastic fibers and occasionally (e.g., metarterioles) to the endothelium and its basal lamina. Smooth muscle cells are coupled by communicating junctions, generally more numerous in arterioles. The large population of sarcolemmal vesicles is distributed in characteristic longitudinal rows with vesicle-free areas in between. The latter may correspond to areas of myofilament attachment to dense bodies (363, 384). By their topological position the microvascular smooth muscle cells are immediately exposed to the locally produced substances that modulate the myogenic activity of these vessels. At this level the vasodilator effect of histamine, serotonin, prostacyclin, and acetylcholine can be counterbalanced by angiotensins, catecholamines, and sex steroids (2). It is very likely that in the microvascular wall, as demonstrated in arteries, the smooth muscle cells are largely responsible for the biosynthesis and secretion of most components of the extracellular matrix (e.g., glycosaminoglycans, collagens, glycoproteins, and elastin) and are thus directly involved in local repair processes after inflammation, injuries, and ischemia, for example.

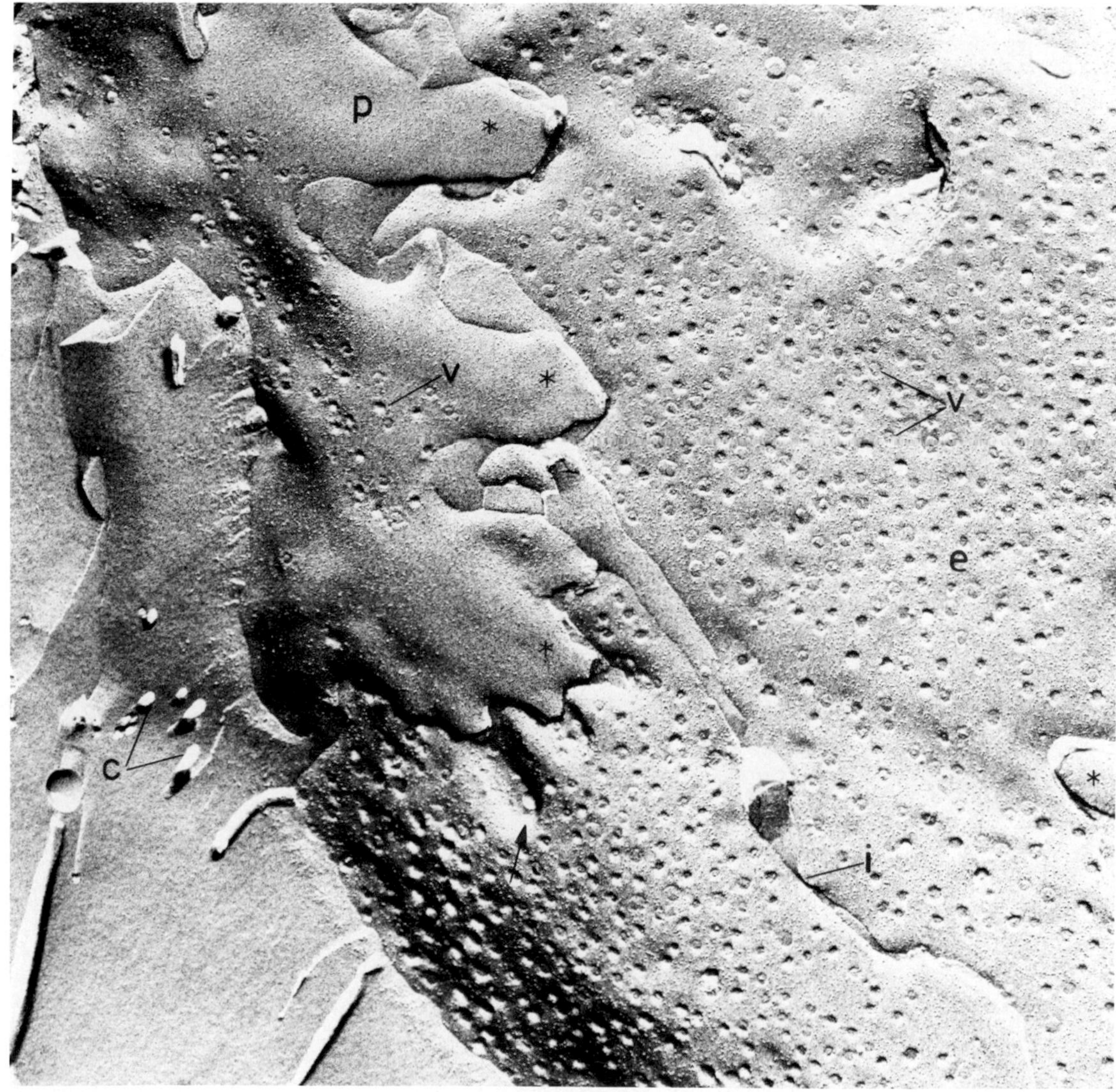

FIG. 19. Freeze-fracture preparation of a blood capillary (rat diaphragm). Endothelial cells (*e*) are partially covered by a pericyte (*p*), the processes (*) of which were in some places removed by fracture, exposing complementary depressions (*arrow*). Low density of vesicular openings (*v*) on pericyte as compared with endothelial cell. *c*, Collagen; *i*, intercellular line. × 35,000.

Connective Tissue

In addition to the subendothelial components (e.g., fibronectin, collagens, glycosaminoglycans), most of which occur throughout the entire microvascular wall, in some locations the adventitia also contains elastic fibers, connective tissue cells, and nerves.

ELASTIC FIBERS. Research suggests that although the collagen fibers impart the tensile strength that supports and binds together coherent groups of other structural elements, the elastic fibers secure the resilient rebound of the stretched vessel wall (363). Elastic fibers occur either isolated (e.g., in the terminal arteriole and occasionally in some muscular venules), in sheets several micrometers thick (e.g., internal elastic lamina of the arteriole), or as scattered elastic bundles (in the adventitia of some muscular venules) (see MICROVESSELS, p. 67). Two constituents have been identified in an elastic fiber: *1*) the amorphous-appearing elastin, which imparts the elastometric properties to the fiber, and *2*) the cylindrical microfibrils, of unknown significance. Elastic fibers are oriented so that mechanical forces are complexly promoted and/or balanced.

CONNECTIVE TISSUE CELLS. As components of the partition between the internal medium and the surrounding tissues, the connective tissue cells of the microvascular wall represent a pluripotential and multifunctional system. The adventitia of the small vessels is actually continuous with the stroma of the host tissue, the boundary between the two compartments being arbitrary. This complex cell population, depending on its location, is involved in several functions.

1. The synthesis, storage, and secretion of some vasoactive mediators (e.g., histamine and serotonin) are carried out primarily by mast cells preferentially located along the microvasculature. The action of these mediators seems to be particularly prominent on venules and on some arterioles.

2. Phagocytosis, in which to a certain extent endothelium and pericytes are involved, is on a larger scale performed by professional macrophages located along microvessels.

3. Local immunological reactions may involve the plasma cells and eosinophils of the vessel wall.

4. Secretion of some extracellular components of the vessel wall is also contributed by fibrocytes (fibroblasts), which constitute a pluripotential pool for cell renewal and local repair.

Within the entire microvascular wall the interstitial fluid circulates through preferential pathways in the matrix, carrying some substances toward the cells of host tissue, draining some through the walls of initial

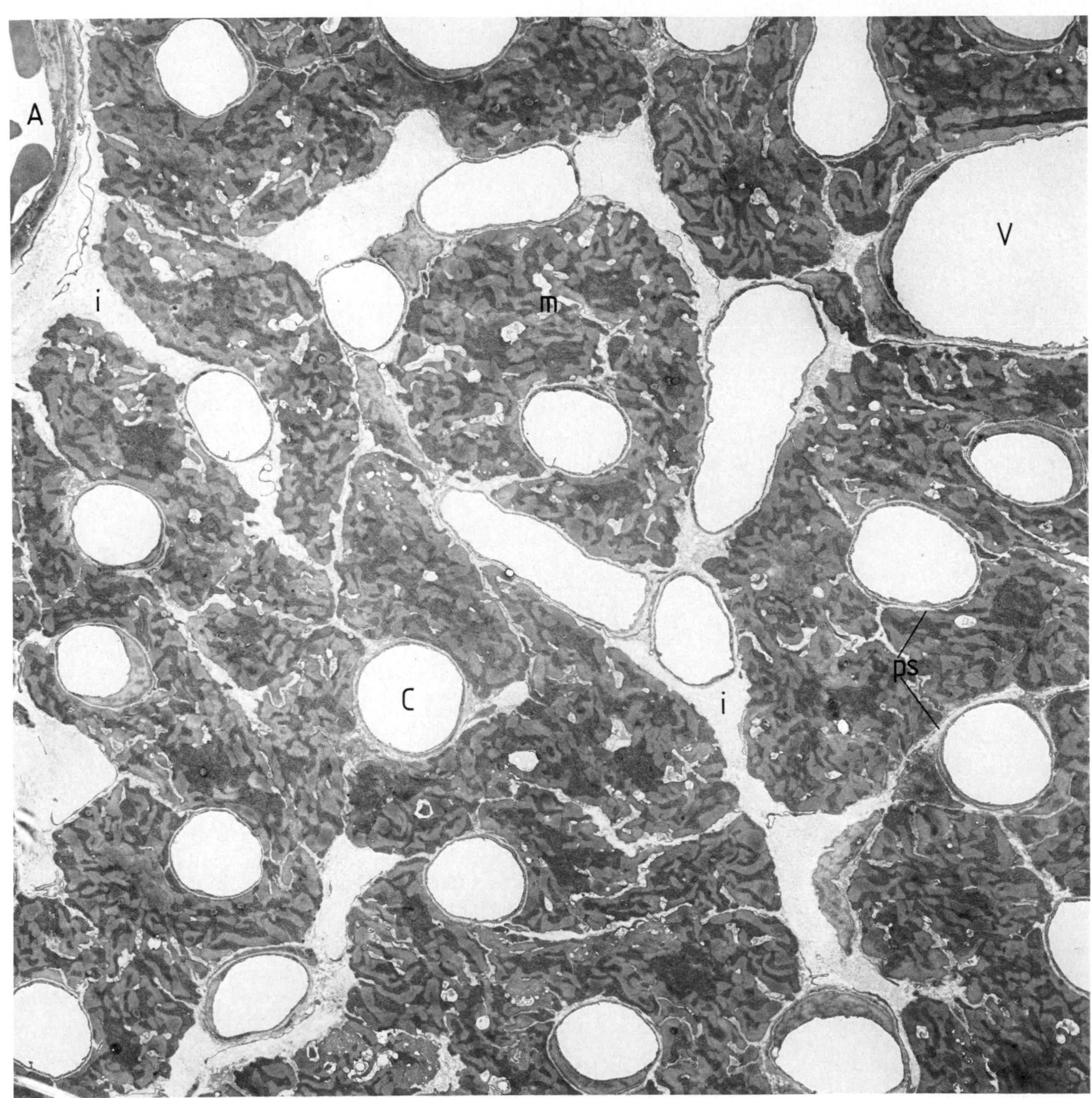

FIG. 20. Rabbit myocardium. Low magnification electron micrograph showing in cross section the density and diameter of microvessels. *A*, arteriole; *C*, capillary; *i*, interstitia; *m*, muscle cell; *ps*, pericapillary space; *V*, venule (pericytic). × 4,000.

lymphatics, and transporting fewer by backdiffusion to the lumina of capillaries and venules.

NERVES. This subject is discussed in the chapter by Renkin in this *Handbook* and in the second volume of the *Handbook* section on the cardiovascular system.

MICROVESSELS

Small arteries entering tissues branch into tiny ramifications, the arterioles, which resolve into a fine network of capillaries that are drained by venules (Fig. 20). In some locations the blood from arterioles can be shunted directly to venules via arteriovenous anastomoses.

The ultrastructural organization of each microvascular segment varies according to the nature and activity of the surrounding tissue to which the microvessels functionally belong.

Arterioles

The smallest arterial ramifications, which decrease in diameter progressively from ~300 μm to ~30 μm, are named arterioles. The terminal part may have a muscular sphincterlike structure [precapillary sphincter (304)]; the arteriolar lumen may be reduced to ~5 μm. This area is often called the metarteriole or precapillary sphincter area. In arterioles the wall thickness may be as much as half the inner diameter.

The *intima* consists of endothelium, basal lamina, subendothelium, and internal elastica. Endothelial cells in the intima are usually thicker (0.3–0.6 μm) than in capillaries and venules and are attached to each other by an elaborate junctional system of multiple-strand occluding junctions with relatively large intercalated communicating junctions. Concomitantly, from the basal part of the cell, small processes penetrate through fenestrae of the internal elastic lamina to form myoendothelial junctions with the subjacent smooth muscle cell (Fig. 7*B*). Arteriolar endothelium is relatively rich in filaments, especially near the abluminal part of the cells. Basal lamina, relatively thin and less distinct in arterioles larger than 50 μm, appears more conspicuous in metarterioles. The subendothelium is commonly thin and contains relatively few collagen and scattered elastic fibers. The internal elastica (Figs. 21 and 22) is fenestrated and thin and disappears at the level of terminal arterioles (Fig. 23), except in the kidney, where it occurs even in the terminal arterioles.

The *media* includes one or two layers of relatively small smooth muscle cells helically arranged. In metarterioles, especially at the level of the precapillary sphincter, the muscular layer appears thicker when compared with the narrow lumen (Fig. 24). Muscle

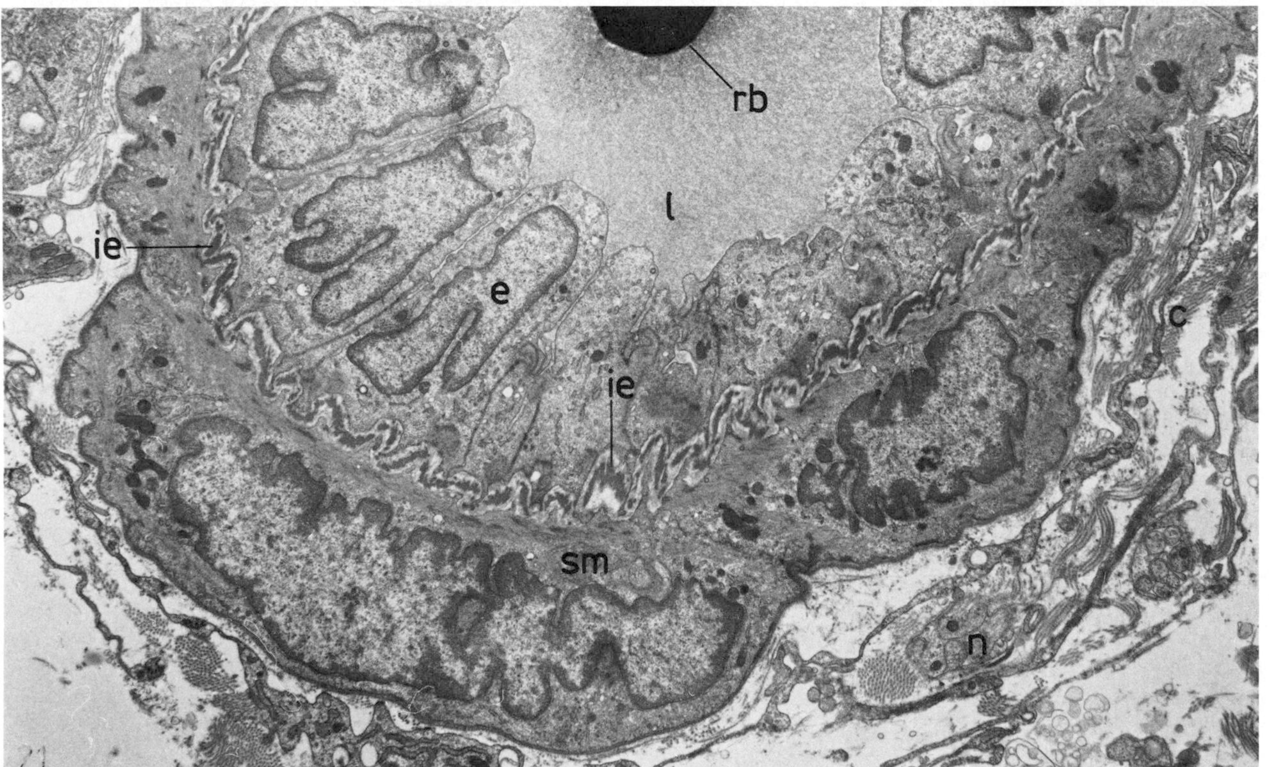

FIG. 21. Arteriole (contracted state) cross section characterized by scalloped appearance of internal elastica (*ie*) interposed between endothelial cells (*e*) and smooth muscle cells (*sm*). *c*, Collagen; *l*, lumen; *n*, nerve; *rb*, red blood cell. × 28,000.

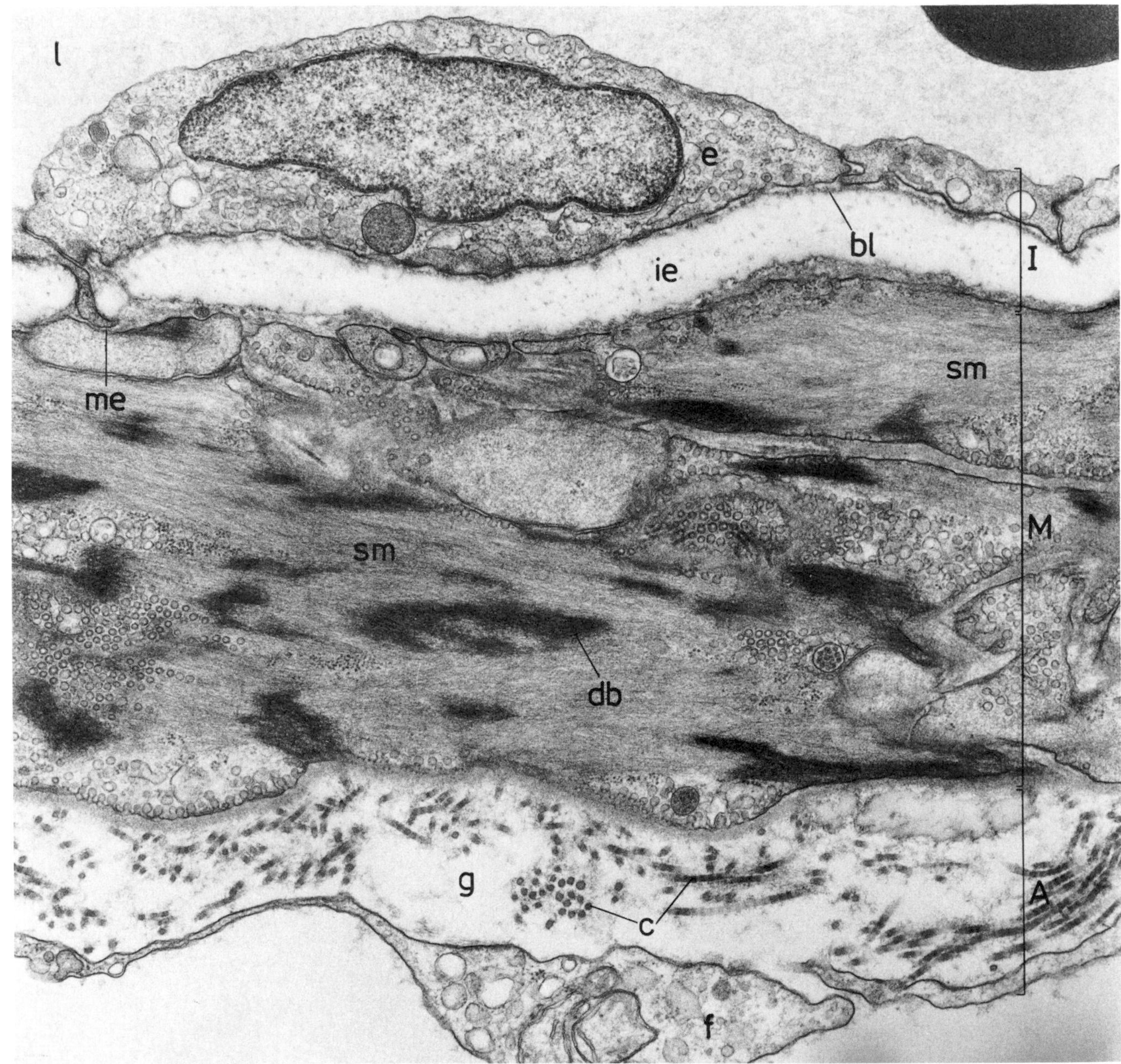

FIG. 22. Arteriole cross section displaying the intima (*I*) composed of endothelium (*e*), basal lamina (*bl*), and internal elastica (*ie*). Media (*M*) consists of 2 layers of smooth muscle cells (*sm*). Adventitia (*A*) contains collagen (*c*), fibroblasts (*f*), and ground substance (*g*). *db*, Dense body; *l*, lumen; *me*, myoendothelial junction. × 38,000.

cells are surrounded by their own basal laminae and collagen fibers. Occasionally, communicating junctions between smooth muscle cells are encountered. The existence of well-developed interendothelial, myoendothelial, and intermuscular junctions suggests that these cells have an extensive synchronized metabolic coupling.

The arterioles represent the major site of resistance to and regulator of the local blood flow because of their structure and their dual control (nervous and hormonal). The contraction of arteriolar smooth muscle cells produces intermittent opening and closing of arteriolar-capillary communication. (See the second volume of the *Handbook* section on the cardiovascular system.) Arteriolar resistance is increased by sympathetic stimulation.

The *adventitia*, made up of fibrils, macrophages, mast cells, fibroblasts, and unmyelinated nerve fibers, is thin (Figs. 22–24). Cervos-Navarro and Matakas (66) report a high frequency of nerve endings in arte-

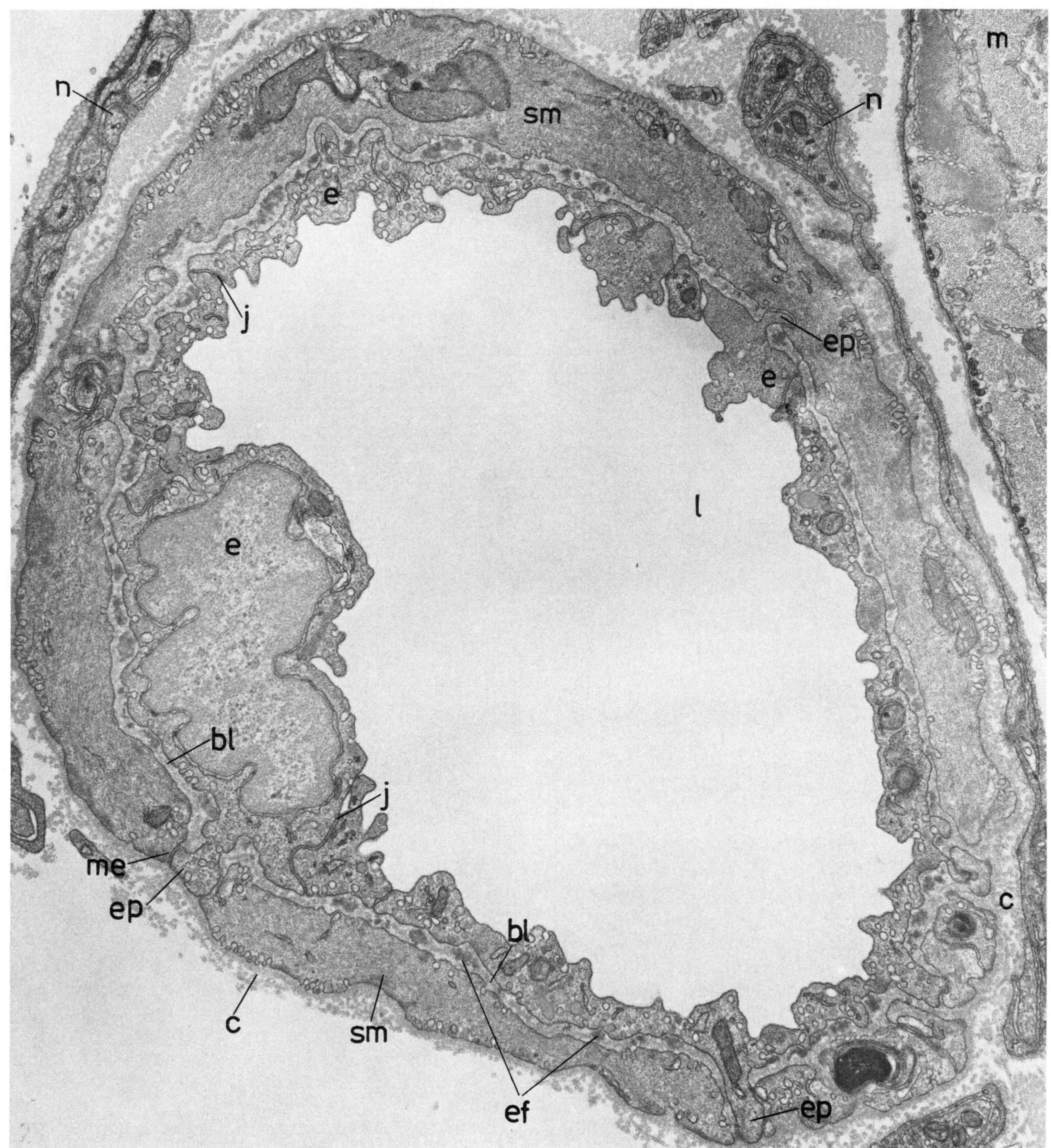

FIG. 23. Terminal arteriole (distended state). Basal lamina (*bl*) and scattered bundles of elastic fibers (*ef*) interposed between endothelium (*e*) and a single layer of smooth muscle cells (*sm*). *c*, Collagen; *ep*, endothelial processes establishing myoendothelial junctions (*me*); *j*, junction; *l*, lumen; *m*, skeletal muscle; *n*, nerves. × 22,000.

rioles. (See the chapter by Renkin in this *Handbook*.) Pharmacological evidence indicates that at least in some vascular beds the arterioles contain specific α- and β-adrenergic receptors (2).

Capillaries

The smallest ramifications are the blood capillaries, with an inner diameter of 5–10 μm and a wall reduced

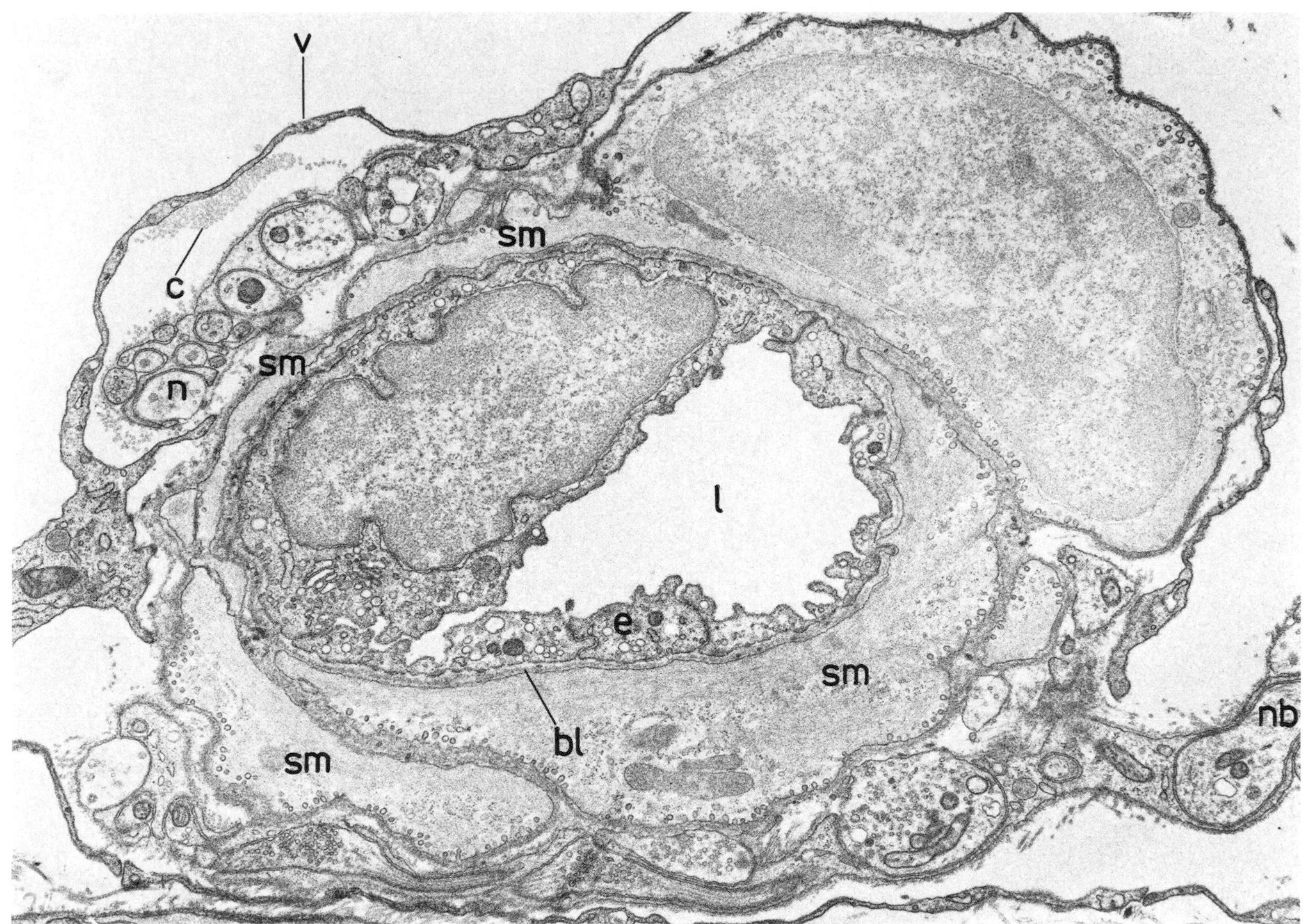

FIG. 24. Pericapillary sphincter (mouse intestinal submucosa) characterized by a circular layer of smooth muscle cells (*sm*) surrounding endothelium (*e*) and a narrow lumen (*l*) ~3–4 μm diam. The structure is ensheathed by a veil cell (*v*) and collagen (*c*). *bl*, Basal lamina; *n*, nerve; *nb*, nerve bundle. × 16,000.

to endothelium, basal lamina, and a few pericytes (121, 191). Although the boundary between arteriole and capillary is marked by the disappearance of the muscle cells, the transition from capillary to venule is morphologically less defined and occurs gradually, except for capillaries that open abruptly into venules at almost right angles (e.g., diaphragm) (371–373). Capillary density in various tissues is related to the magnitude of metabolic rates, especially the oxygen uptake. The magnitude of transcapillary exchanges largely depends on the extent of the endothelial surface available, which is a function of the general geometry of the microvascular bed.

Capillary *intima* consists of endothelium, basal lamina, and pericytes; *media* is virtually absent; *adventitia* is represented by a thin layer of connective tissue continuous with that of the host tissue. In addition to ground substance and fibers, the capillary adventitia may contain a few fibrocytes, macrophages, and mast cells. The composition of the adventitial connective tissue may influence the capillary patency and the dynamics of fluid exchanges. During experimental or pathological interstitial edema, basal lamina usually remains attached to endothelium. The detailed structure of the capillary wall varies characteristically from one microvascular bed to another, reflecting local differences in the magnitude and nature of plasma–interstitial fluid exchanges. Based primarily on modulations in the fine structure and continuity of the endothelium and its basal lamina, three main types of blood capillaries are encountered: continuous, fenestrated, and discontinuous (sinusoids).

CONTINUOUS CAPILLARIES. The most common type of capillaries encountered in somatic tissues [Fig. 25; (42)], nervous system (41), lung (324, 345), and vasa vasorum are continuous capillaries (17, 21, 159, 261, 274). The endothelium is of continuous type (devoid of fenestrations), ~0.2–0.3 μm thick, and contains plasmalemmal vesicles and transendothelial channels, which vary in frequency from one tissue to another (see *Plasmalemmal vesicles*, p. 44 and *Transendothelial channels*, p. 45). In the lung capillaries the endothelium has a very thin area (~0.03 μm) that does not

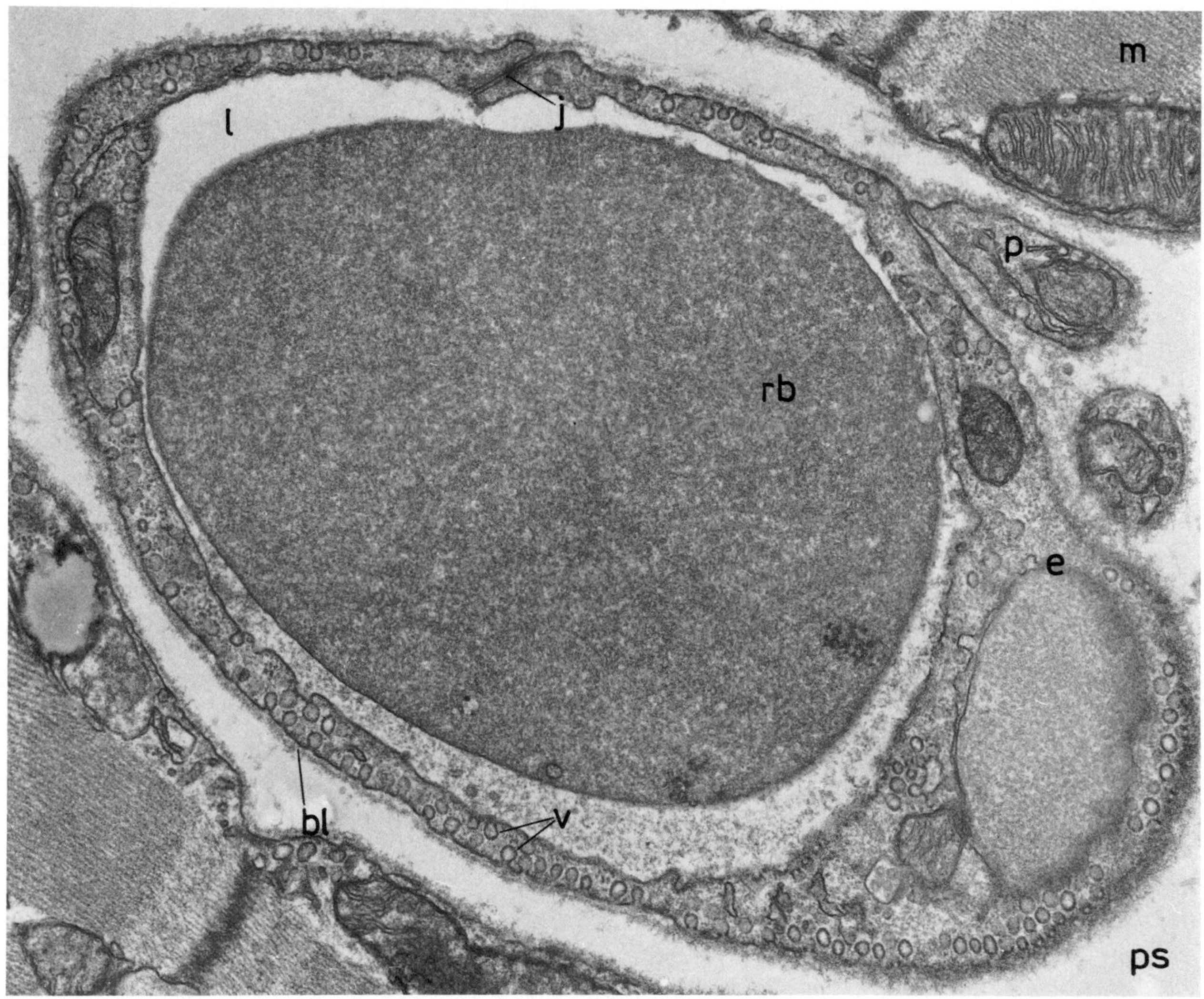

FIG. 25. Rat myocardium. Blood capillary made up of a single endothelial cell (*e*) conjoined to itself. *bl*, Basal lamina; *j*, endothelial junction; *l*, lumen; *m*, muscle; *p*, pericyte; *ps*, pericapillary space; *rb*, red blood cell; *v*, plasmalemmal vesicles. × 34,000.

contain vesicles. This avesicular endothelial zone faces the flattened epithelial type I cell; the basal laminae of these two extremely attenuated cells are fused and reduced in thickness.

The intercellular spaces are interrupted by one or more lines of occluding junctions, which appear in thin sections to vary from close fusion to the elimination of the outer leaflets of the opposing membranes.

Basal lamina is continuous and splits to enclose the pericytes. Using immunocytochemistry, Courtoy and Boyles (89) detected that fibronectin seems to be concentrated in the endothelium-pericyte interstitium in capillaries of skeletal muscle. The basal lamina is less conspicuous in bone and lymphoid tissues.

A wide spectrum of modulations, involving vesicle frequency and junctional tightness for example, characterizes the continuous capillaries in special locations. At the two extremes of vesicle numerical density are the brain capillaries (the lowest) and myocardial capillaries (the highest). For particular cases, see the pertinent chapters in this *Handbook*.

FENESTRATED CAPILLARIES. The endothelium is attenuated (~0.05–0.1 μm) and displays fenestrae (see *Fenestrae*, p. 47) distributed either randomly or in patches (Fig. 6). Fenestrae usually occur in the capillary wall facing the epithelium (Fig. 26). The fenestrae are commonly closed by diaphragms; occasionally these are not detectable (75, 81). In glomerular capillaries the fenestrae are devoid of diaphragms. Examples of variations in fenestrae frequency in some visceral capillaries are given in Table 2. Fenestrae are not static features; several reports show that fenestrae are labile and dynamic features that can form and disappear under a variety of circumstances (53, 233).

Formation of fenestrations may involve both genetic and humoral factors. In rat endonasal microvessels,

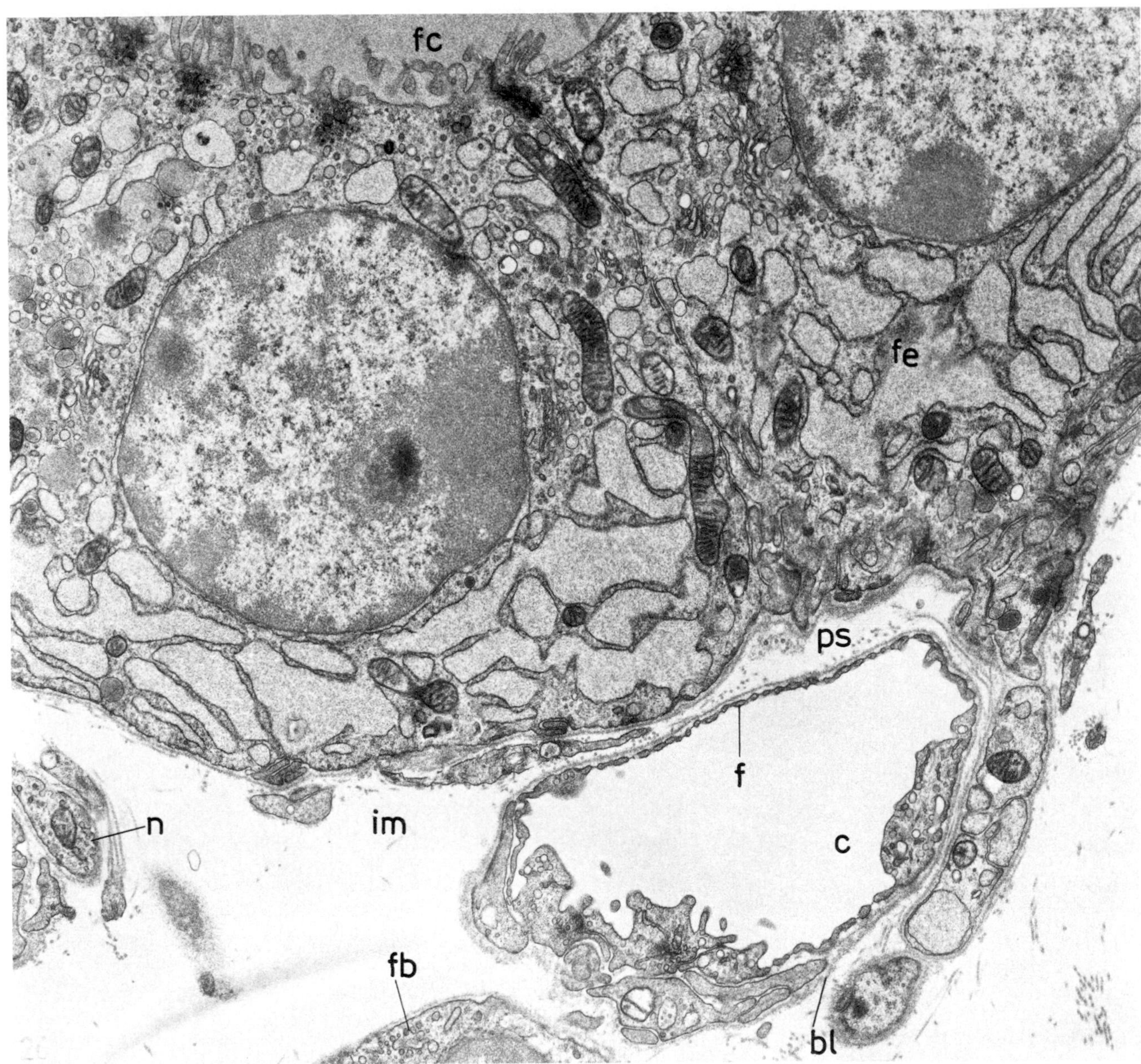

FIG. 26. Rat thyroid. Blood capillary (*c*) facing with the fenestrated regions of endothelium (*f*) the base of follicular epithelium (*fe*). *bl*, Basal lamina; *fb*, fibroblast; *fc*, follicular colloid; *im*, interstitial matrix; *n*, nerve; *ps*, pericapillary space. × 18,000.

fenestrations appear prenatally and increase in number toward full term and during postnatal life (419). In the continuous capillaries of the vagina, endothelial fenestrae can be induced by administration of estrone; this phenomenon can be reversed by treating the animals with progesterone and testosterone (449–451). The number of fenestrae can be augmented in hypertension [rat choriocapillaries; (454)], encephalomyelitis [nervous system; (382)], and inflammation, when some fenestrae can be greatly enlarged and the diaphragms dissolved (363). Endothelial cells of adrenal cortex maintained in cultured conditions lose their fenestration (106, 129). Basal lamina is continuous. Fenestrated capillaries are encountered in the endocrine glands, mucosa of the gastrointestinal tract, pancreas (164), choroid plexus, ciliary body, glomerulus, peritubular capillaries, and area postrema. Occasionally they have been detected in skeletal muscle (209, 251) or in lung capillaries after experimental pulmonary fibrosis (399).

DISCONTINUOUS CAPILLARIES (SINUSOIDS). These thin-walled vessels with irregular outline and caliber are usually molded on the neighboring epithelial cells, e.g., those of the liver, spleen, and bone marrow (101, 446). Endothelium exhibits large gaps and some scat-

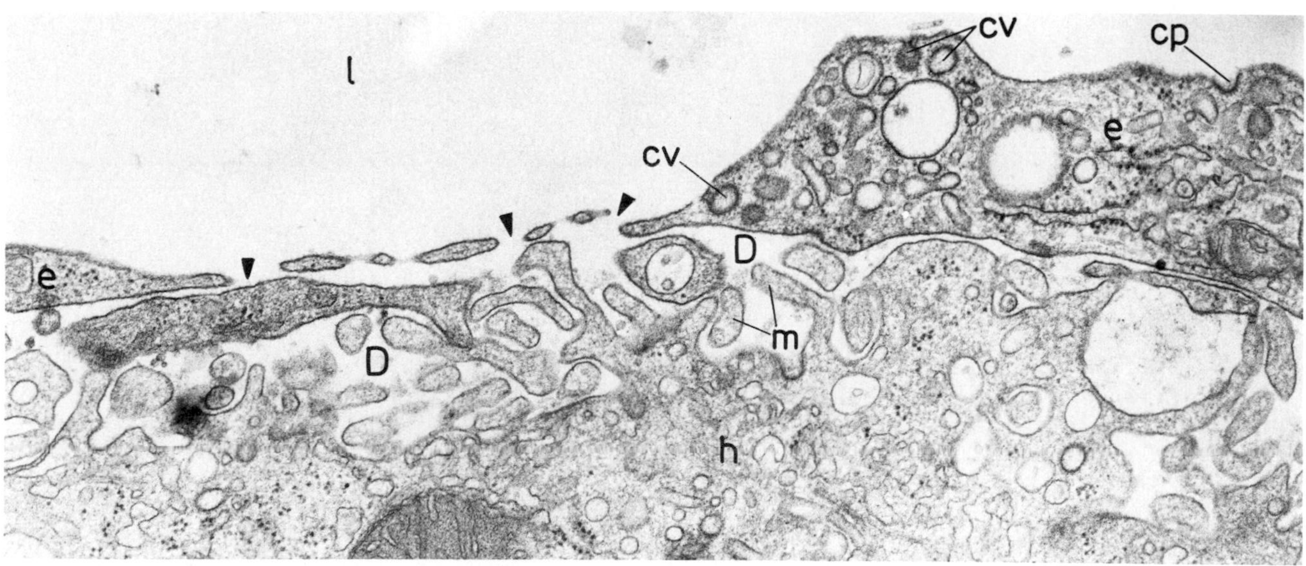

FIG. 27. Sinusoid capillary (rat liver). Endothelium (*e*) displays several large diaphragm-free openings (*arrowheads*) through which capillary lumen (*l*) communicates freely with space of Disse (*D*). High frequency of endothelial coated pits (*cp*) and coated vesicles (*cv*). *h*, Hepatocyte; *m*, microvilli. × 32,000.

tered fenestrae up to hundreds of nanometers in diameter. Basal lamina is either discontinuous or absent [Fig. 27; (265)]. Endothelial cells have a relatively small population of plasmalemmal vesicles but a large number of coated pits, coated vesicles, and lysosomes. Unlike Kupffer cells, the sinusoidal endothelial cells exhibit endogenous peroxidase activities (116, 439). The phagocytic activity is particularly prominent in liver sinusoids and much less so in spleen. The discontinuous endothelium is more subject to complex modulations than are other types of endothelia because of continual interactions generated by several cellular and local humoral factors (e.g., cell passage through intercellular clefts).

Venules

The gradual transition from capillaries to venules and the variation in the absolute size of the venules very often render tracing a boundary between these two microvascular segments difficult. The immediate postcapillary venules, ranging in length from ~50 to ~700 μm and in diameter from 10 to 50 μm, have pericytes (pericytic venules) in their intima. They are continued by venules with increasing inner diameter (from ~50 to ~200 μm), which contain in their media one or two layers of thin smooth muscle cells (muscular venules) (Fig. 28).

PERICYTIC (POSTCAPILLARY) VENULES. The *intima* consists of endothelium that is relatively thin (0.2–0.3/μm) and of the continuous type; however, in some locations it may exhibit a few clusters of fenestrations (e.g., mesentery). Lysosomes, multivesicular bodies, Weibel-Palade bodies, and microfilaments (especially in the parajunctional cytoplasm) are often encountered. The loosely organized intercellular junctions (see ENDOTHELIUM AS TISSUE: INTERCELLULAR JUNCTIONS, p. 59) represent the weakest endothelial contacts encountered along the entire vascular system. The particular sensitivity to prostaglandins, histamine (Figs. 29–31), serotonin, and bradykinin (which induce the opening of their junctions) renders the venules a very special vascular segment (311, 314, 403), the preferential site for extensive plasma extravasation and diapedesis (Fig. 30*B*), as happens in inflammation (123, 140, 171, 234–237, 314, 357, 371–373, 401, 402) or under toxic effects (268, 284).

The thin basal lamina envelops the numerous pericytes, which in some venules are extensively branched and make an almost continuous layer, establishing more endotheliopericytic contacts than in capillaries. Toward the distal end of these venules the pericytes are particularly rich in intermediate filaments (10 nm), microfilaments (6–8 nm), and dense bodies reminiscent of smooth muscle cells to which these cells appear to be related (Fig. 28*A*). Myosinlike filaments have not been found in pericytes.

Media is virtually lacking; the thin *adventitia* contains connective tissue elements, among which the mast cells are frequently prominent; nerve endings are practically absent. However, Forbes et al. (130, 131) claim that the venular pericytes may be innervated by both adrenergic and cholinergic axons.

Postcapillary venules of lymph nodes. Lymphocytes from the blood enter the lymph node parenchyma through the wall of postcapillary venules (3, 4, 73, 120, 149, 240, 266, 329, 333, 386, 387). Lymphocyte recirculation is a complex process involving a series of

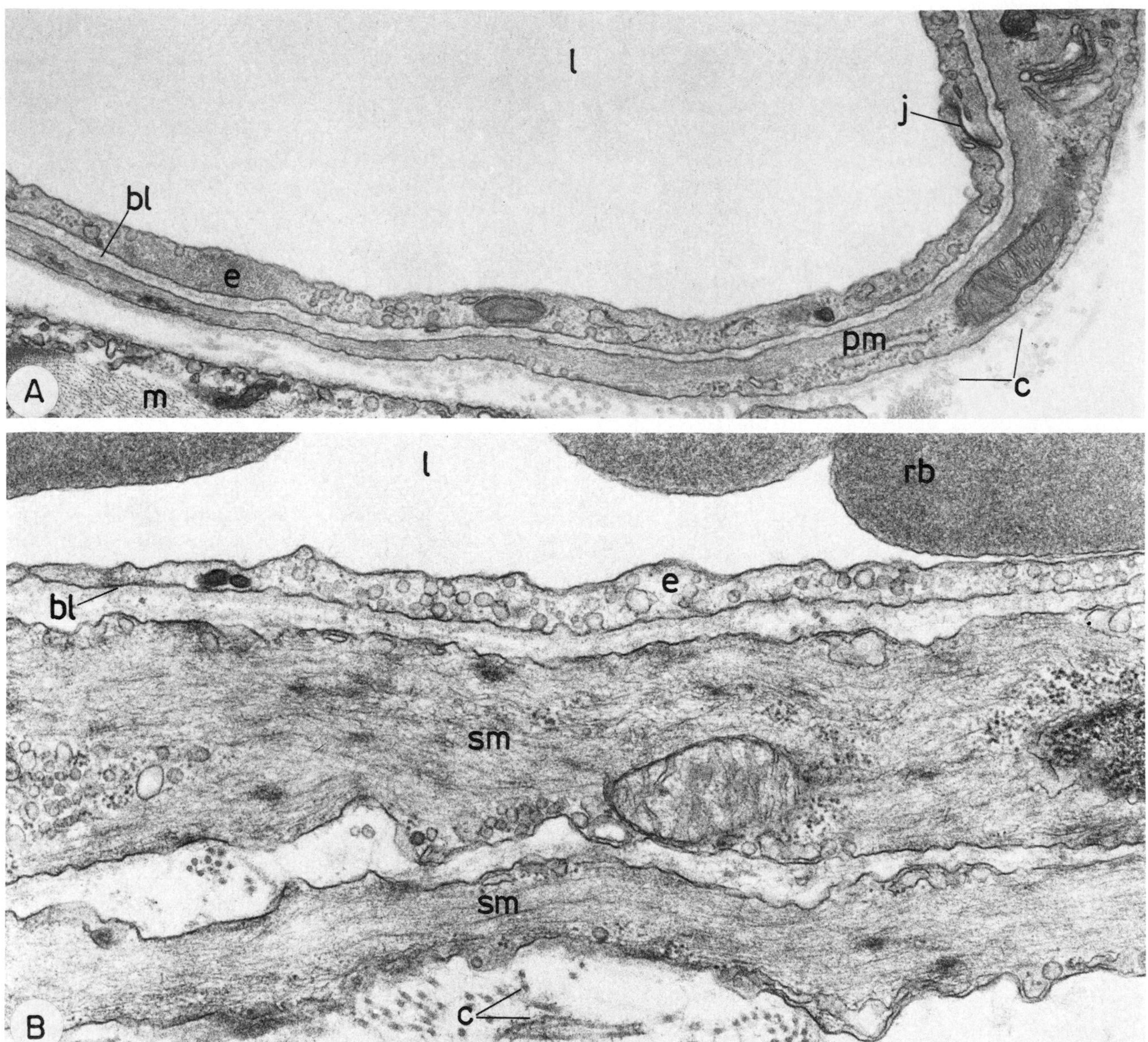

FIG. 28. *A*: cross section through a venule (rat diaphragm) at the transition between pericytic and muscular venule, as revealed by structural appearance of the cell marked *pm* (this shares characteristics of both pericyte and smooth muscle cell). × 27,000. *B*: cross section through a muscular venule (rat diaphragm). Media consists of 2 layers of smooth muscle cells (*sm*). × 32,000. *bl*, Basal lamina; *c*, collagen; *e*, endothelium; *j*, intercellular junction; *l*, lumen; *m*, skeletal muscle fiber; *rb*, red blood cell.

compartments and multiple-point controls; the high endothelium of postcapillary venules of the lymph nodes represents a unique, selective, transvascular passage of lymphocytes. Butcher et al. (51) and Gowans and Knight (149) assume that lymphocyte recirculation facilitates the immune process by allowing lymphocytes to meet antigen, interact with other lymphocyte subsets, and—if needed—be recruited to inflammation sites. Postcapillary venules are also present in Peyer's patches and tonsils (414) in several mammalian species, including humans. These venules have polygonal, high endothelial cells linked together by discontinuous junctions (435). Woodruff and Rasmussen (452) also demonstrated a specific attachment of lymphocytes on these venules in vitro on tissue sections. This binding is sensitive to inhibition by cytochalasin B, which suggests that formation of a stable complex between high-endothelial venule binding sites and lymphocyte receptors also depends on contractile forces generated by lymphocyte microfilaments (452). The molecular basis of this process is unknown, but it must involve a highly specific mechanism of recognition. The results from morphological studies of the lymphocyte pathway across this endo-

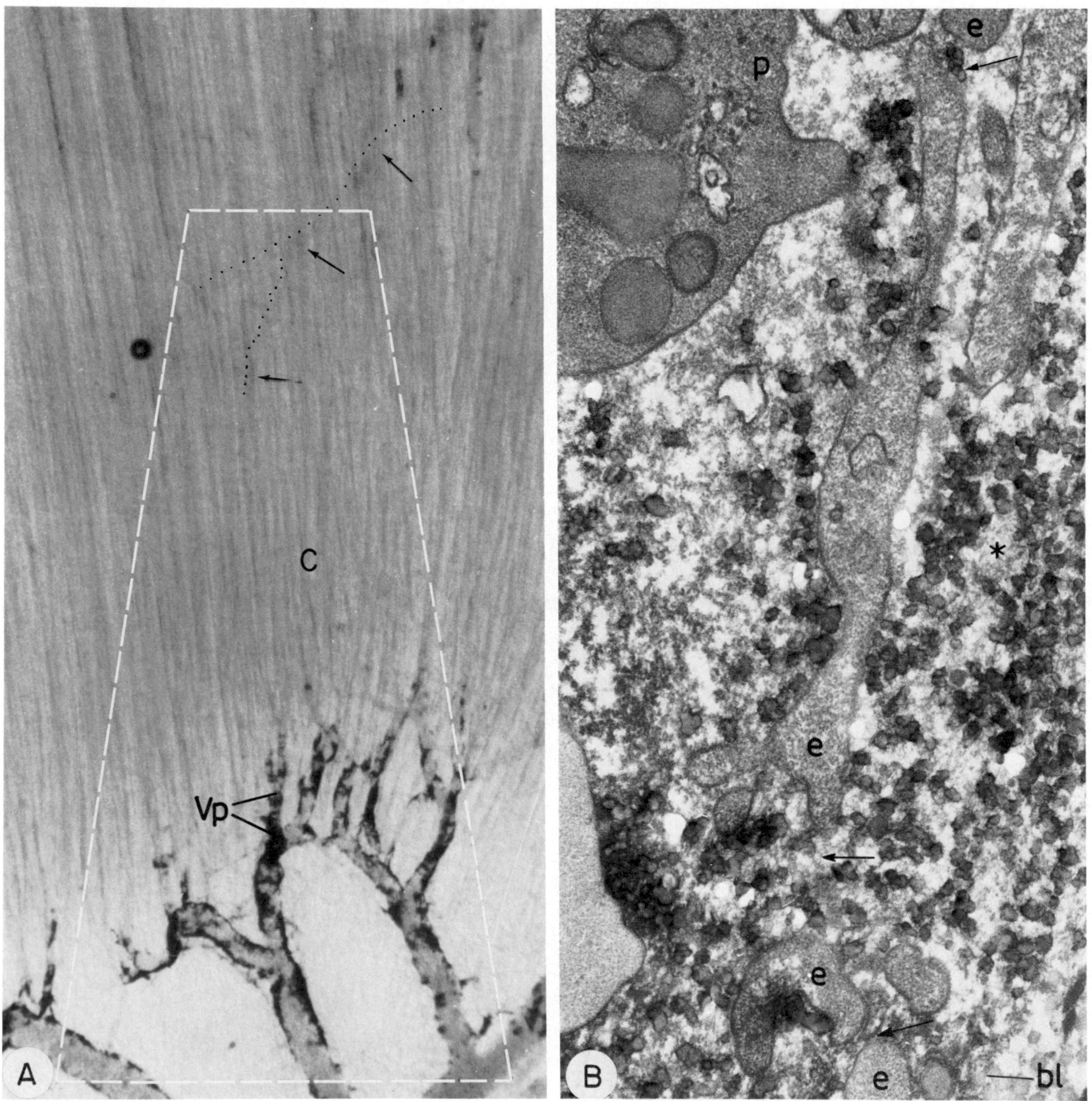

FIG. 29. *A*: mouse diaphragm 30 min after iv injection of carbon black and topical application of histamine. Bipolar microvascular field in which arteriole can be detected with some difficulty in upper part of the field (*arrows*). Capillaries (*C*) are hardly visible in this type of preparation, whereas postcapillary venules (*Vp*) are clearly seen because of intramural deposits of carbon black. × 600. *B*: mouse diaphragm 45 min after iv injection of carbon black followed by histamine. Intercellular junctions in this field appear open at 3 sites (*arrows*). Intramural deposits of carbon particles (*) are sequestrated between endothelium (*e*) and its basal lamina (*bl*). *p*, Platelet. × 65,000. [From Simionescu, Simionescu, and Palade (371).]

thelium are still conflicting; De Bruyn et al. (103) believe that lymphocyte passage is first transcellular, then intercellular.

The endothelial cells of these specialized venules are higher and contain more Golgi elements in the female than the male, a difference augmented by administration of estrogens (202, 203).

MUSCULAR VENULES. Because of their thin wall and collapsed lumen, muscular venules can be relatively easily distinguished from the accompanying arterioles in tissue sections.

Intima consists of a continuous endothelium slightly thicker in muscular venules than in pericytic venules and particularly rich in microfilaments (Fig. 28*B*).

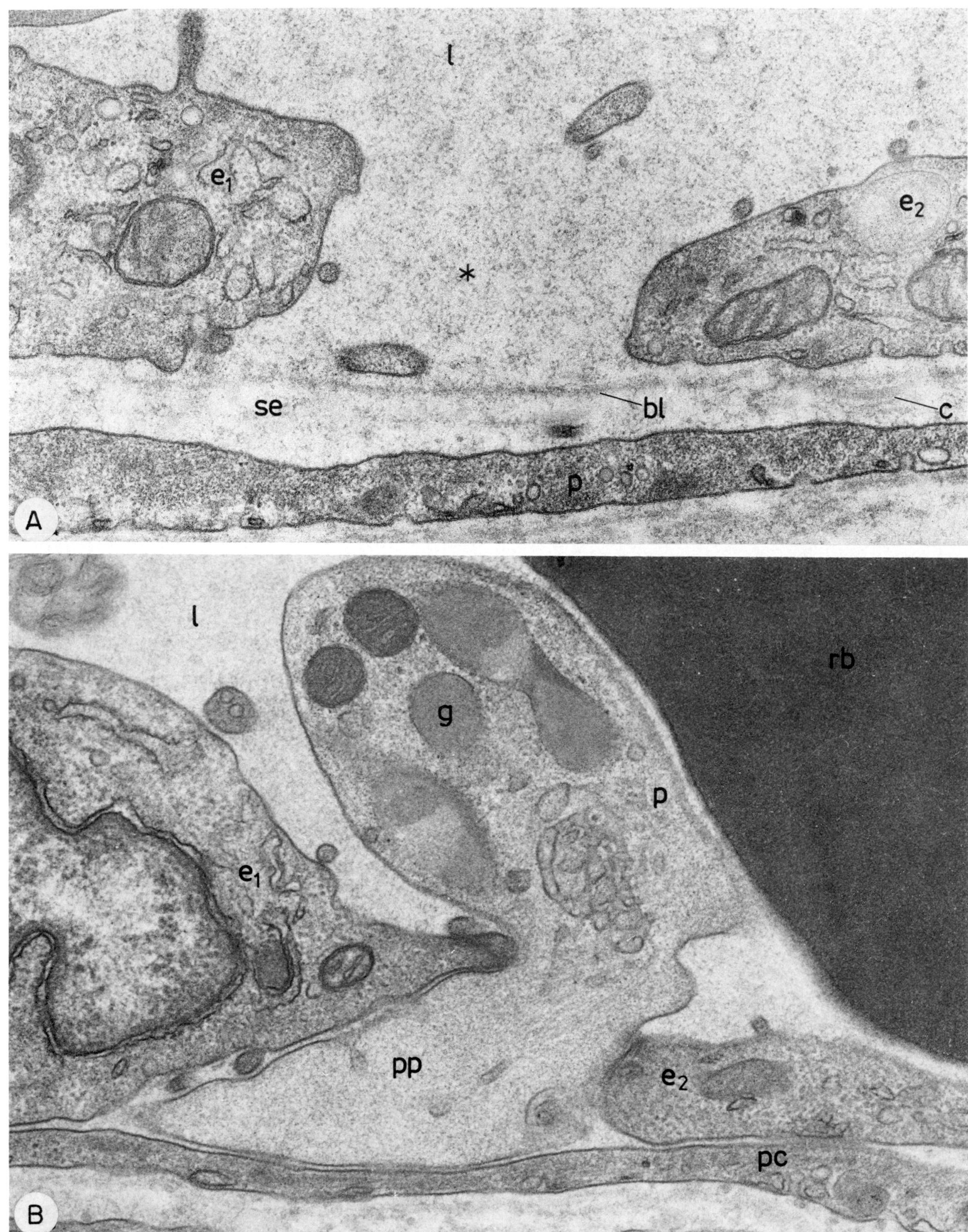
l
e1
e2
*
se
bl
c
p
A
l
rb
g
p
e1
pp
e2
pc
B

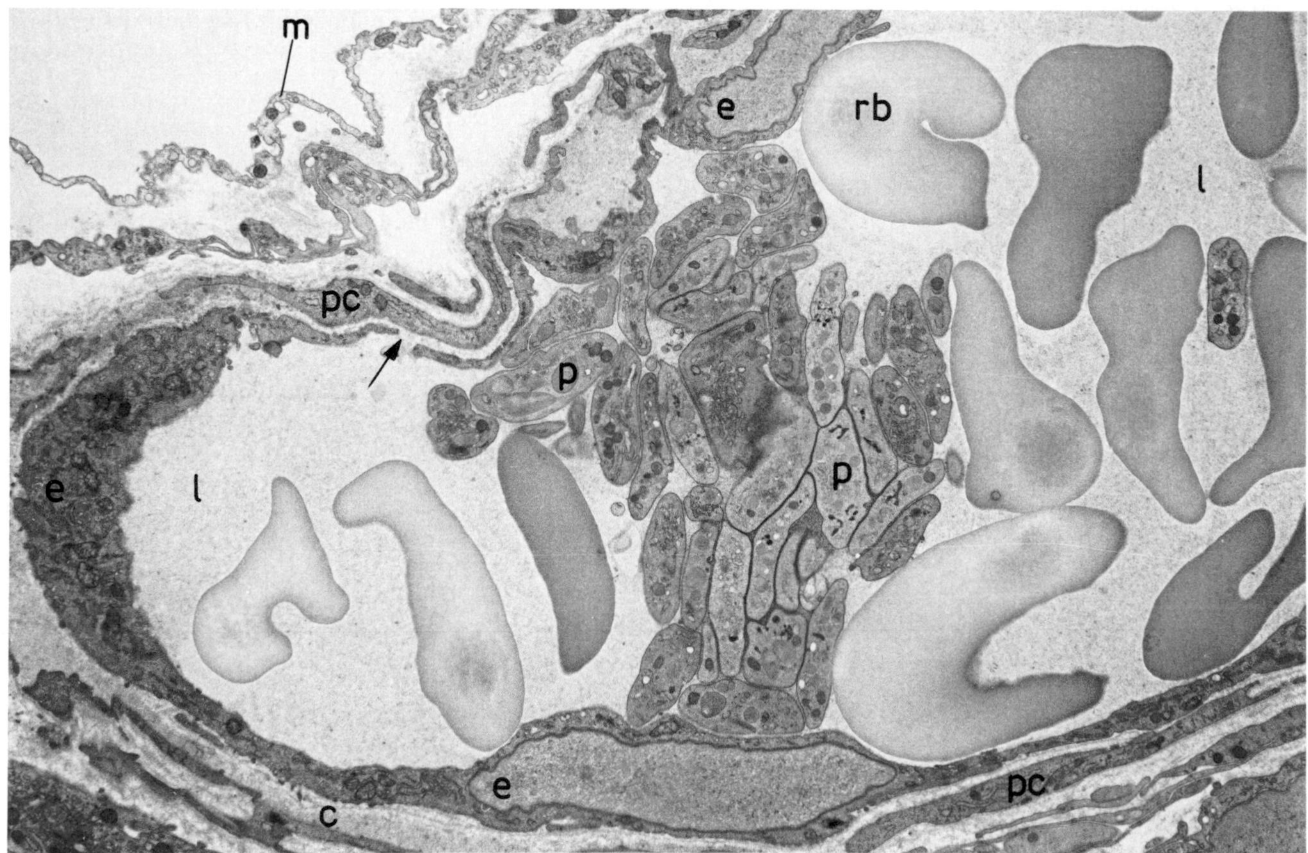

FIG. 31. Postcapillary (pericytic) venule (rat omentum) exposed to histamine; in addition to the opening of the endothelial junction (*arrow*), platelet (*p*) adheres to cell surface of endothelium (*e*) to form a plug. *c*, Collagen; *l*, lumen; *m*, mesothelium; *pc*, pericyte; *rb*, red blood cell. × 8,500.

The set of organelles is identical to that found in pericytic venules. The intercellular junctions between endothelial cells, like those of the pericytic venules, consist of loosely organized cell contacts of occluding type. Rare, small, and isolated communicating junctions are also encountered in muscular venules. Their endothelium is provided with high-affinity histamine receptors, as is the endothelium of the pericytic venules (see *Receptors*, p. 57). Specific α-adrenergic receptors and β-adrenergic receptors have been inferred to promote contraction and relaxation of the venular smooth muscle, indicating that the muscular venules may play a rather active role in controlling the blood flow. Muscular venules of various vascular beds appear to be heterogeneous not only with respect to ultrastructure but also with respect to their responsiveness to vasoactive agents (2).

The thin basal lamina is perforated at the level of the relatively rare myoendothelial junctions.

Media contains one or two layers of smooth muscle cells, thinner than in arterioles. These cells often make an incomplete layer, a common feature in venules of kidney and spleen.

Adventitia is thicker in muscular venules than in pericytic venules. Among other connective tissue elements long, thin, and flattened fibrocytes called *veil cells* are present. Unlike pericytes, veil cells are not surrounded by basal lamina (130, 305). Unmyelinated

---

FIG. 30. *A*: histamine-induced opening (∗) of an endothelial junction in postcapillary venule (rat omentum). *bl*, Basal lamina; *c*, collagen; *se*, subendothelial space. × 62,000. *B*: as a subsequent event, an open junction (similar to that in Fig. 30*A*) is plugged by a platelet (*p*) that implants filament-rich pseudopodia (*pp*) into the gap, adhering to subendothelial components. *bl*, Basal lamina; e_1 and e_2, separated endothelial cells; *g*, granules; *l*, lumen; *pc*, pericyte; *rb*, red blood cell. × 64,000. [From Simionescu (357). In: *Advances in Inflammation Research*, © 1979, Raven Press, New York.]

nerve fibers occasionally occur, but in most microvascular beds, unlike the arterioles, the muscular venules have little or no sympathetic innervation.

Arteriovenous Anastomoses

In regions where the blood flow varies largely over time, arterioles may be directly connected to venules by short bypasses (~30–100 nm long) called arteriovenous anastomoses (110, 361), which may have a relatively thick wall surrounding a lumen 12–15 μm in diameter. Such vessels are often found in the microvascular beds of the fingertips, toes, skin, nailbeds, lips, intestinal mucosa, thyroid, erectile tissue, and in the aortic, carotid, and coccygeal bodies. In some locations (e.g., skin) these shunts form convolutions embedded in connective tissue that can extend partially around the arteriole (glomus). In these vessels the endothelium rests upon a sphincterlike muscular media composed of polygonal cells that resemble a stratified cuboidal epithelium. Both myelinated and nonmyelinated nerve fibers are present in the adventitia.

STRUCTURAL CORRELATIONS IN BASIC PROCESSES OF MICROVASCULAR ENDOTHELIUM

Synthetic and Metabolic Activities

Most of the information on the biosynthetic and metabolic capabilities of the endothelial cells was obtained from cultures of endothelium isolated from large vessels. Very little is known of the metabolic function and structural correlations in microvascular endothelium of various vascular beds; in these cases data have been collected primarily from cultured cells. Some functions have been discussed in *Receptors*, p. 57.

Endocytosis and Transcytosis: Traffic of Membranes

Microvascular endothelium is highly differentiated to mediate and monitor the bidirectional exchange of substances between two adjoining fluid compartments: plasma and interstitial fluid. The endothelial cell has the complete set of components that are usually involved in endocytosis and exocytosis; to accomplish an extensive and rapid transport the cell has developed the ability to couple these two phenomena in a special process, transcytosis (357, 359). *Cytopempsis* (261) and *diacytosis* (175) were names previously proposed for this vesicular transport (*dissipative transcytosis* in the present nomenclature). Transcytosis, a major function of the endothelium, secures the vital plasma-tissue exchanges of substances. True endocytosis, by which endothelium takes up material for its own metabolic needs, is a relatively minor event by comparison.

ENDOCYTOSIS. Three endocytic processes occur in the endothelium: phagocytosis, pinocytosis, and receptor-mediated endocytosis.

Phagocytosis. In physiological conditions phagocytosis is only occasionally detected. Experimentally it was demonstrated in heart microvessels exposed to repeated injections of colloidal carbon (88, 162).

Pinocytosis. In the vascular endothelium, pinocytosis is the process by which plasmalemmal (uncoated) vesicles carry material to the lysosomal compartment. A minor event in most endothelia, pinocytosis is particularly developed in the high endothelium of postcapillary venules in lymph nodes (416, 418). In most cases pinocytosis occurs as a fluid-phase endocytosis. Adsorptive pinocytosis can also take place: e.g., the route taken by intravascularly injected polycationic ligands such as cationized ferritin, cationized horseradish peroxidase, and cytochrome *c*. Shortly after intravenous administration, cationized ferritin strongly binds to coated pits, which are subsequently internalized and within 5–10 min reach multivesicular bodies. In such experiments no plasmalemma domains, other than coated pits and coated vesicles, are internalized (359).

Lectin-peroxidase conjugates perfused in situ have been shown to bind avidly to the endothelial cell surface but do not induce significant capping or stimulation of endocytosis (354, 357–359).

The uptake and transendothelial passage of macromolecules are often thought to be governed solely by differences in physical forces acting on both sides of the endothelium, namely the hydrostatic pressure, osmotic pressure, and concentration gradients. In this process the endothelium would have only the passive role of a porous membrane. To find out whether the endothelial cell isolated from its normal environment is able to take up macromolecules in the absence of physical forces operating in vivo, microvascular endothelial cells isolated from rabbit myocardium were incubated with various molecules. The results indicate that incubation in protein-free medium is accompanied by a massive internalization of plasmalemmal vesicles, without a significant change in their numerical density (Fig. 32*A*). Vesicle reappearance on the cell surface and uptake of molecules occurs after the addition of proteins, especially anionic species, to the incubation medium at 37°C (Fig. 32*B*). When isolated endothelial cells incubated with ^{125}I-labeled ferritin were transferred into a diluted medium, they released part of the internalized tracer.

These findings showed that *1*) plasmalemmal vesicles appear to be a relatively stable population of cell components; *2*) endothelial cells have an intrinsic ability to take up and discharge macromolecules; *3*) vesicular uptake discriminates in favor of anionic proteins (true with most plasma proteins); *4*) the process is temperature dependent and influenced by the molecular composition of the medium (346, 357, 359, 362). Endocytic abilities also have been demonstrated for microvascular endothelial cells obtained from epididymal fat (424–426, 428, 442–444), myocardium (338), and bovine retinal and brain microvessels (168).

Vesicular transport across endothelial cells, here named transcytosis, has been inadequately referred to as pinocytosis or micropinocytosis.

Receptor-mediated endocytosis. Vasile, Simionescu, Simionescu, et al. (420, 420a) followed the path taken by the intravascularly injected low-density lipoproteins in mouse aorta and demonstrated the existence of receptor-mediated endocytosis (148). The low-density lipoprotein particles were rendered visible with the electron microscope either by directly enhancing their contrast or by coupling with ferritin or their peroxidase-conjugated antibodies. In their passage across aortic endothelium and the endothelium of vasa vasorum, low-density lipoproteins take a dual pathway: after binding to their receptors, these particles are taken up by coated pits and brought up to lysosomes; more particles are transcytosed across endothelium and discharged into the subendothelial space by fluid-phase endocytosis via plasmalemmal vesicles (420). Stein and Stein (393) suggest that some low-density lipoprotein particles also pass through transendothelial channels.

TRANSCYTOSIS: DISSIPATIVE/CONVECTIVE. Experiments with macromolecular tracers with molecular diameters ranging from ~30 nm [glycogens and dextrans; (360, 364)] to ~2 nm [hemepeptides; Table 3; (366, 371, 373)] demonstrated that molecules of this size pass through the continuous endothelium mainly via vesicles and channels. The kinetics of vesicle labeling suggests that in sequential events that involve the fusion-fission of vesicles and plasmalemma most probe molecules are taken up in a fluid phase by vesicles open on the luminal front; these probe molecules are then internalized and eventually discharge their contents into the subendothelial space (182–185, 275–279, 343, 359, 365–373). Very likely, not all loaded vesicles follow this process entirely; some of them probably return to the cell front of origin (154, 334–336). A fraction of molecules passes through transendothelial channels. During all these phases the lysosomes are bypassed and remain unmarked by the tracers. Thus transcytosis, which directly and efficiently couples endocytosis to exocytosis (357, 359), can transport molecules both in quanta via discrete plasmalemmal vesicles [dissipative transcytosis; (Fig. 33)] and via channels and fenestrae [convective transcytosis; (Fig. 34)]. The two processes are bidirectional (182–185, 363, 369) and may be interconvertible, thus imparting to the endothelial transport a large adaptability required by the continuously changing local conditions. Although transcytosis is the principal activity of the endothelia of all the capillaries and postcapillary venules, endocytosis is well developed especially in sinusoids and high-endothelial venules. Transport of molecules by vesicles (the uncoated variety especially) that cross the cell without reaching and fusing with the lysosomes has been revealed also in other epithelial cells [e.g., intestinal and mammary; (211, 309)]. Transcytosis is particularly well developed in microvascular endothelium (357, 359).

Despite the existence of many biosynthetic and secretory activities in endothelial cells, true exocytosis involving membranous organelles has not yet been identified.

Membrane traffic. The fate of the inbound traffic of membranes in microvascular endothelium was traced by using—in various combinations—three types of markers applied in vivo on the luminal or abluminal

TABLE 3. *Tracers Used in Studies of Capillary Permeability*

	Molecular Weight	Effective Molecular Radius, nm	Isoelectric Point	Optimum pH*	Ref.
Particulate tracers					
Glycogens		~12–15			360, 364
Dextrans	15,000–300,000	~7–10			62, 360, 364
Ferritin					
Native	440,000	5.5	4.5		75, 207, 346, 359, 371
Anionic		5.5	3.8		302
Cationized		5.5	8.4		302, 346, 353–355, 359
Enzymatic tracers					
Hemeoctapeptide	1,550	1.0	5.4	12.0	366
Hemenonapeptide	1,630	1.0	4.95	12.5	287, 356
Hemeundecapeptide	1,880	1.0	4.85	13.5	122, 346, 359, 366, 371, 373, 448
Cytochrome *c*	12,800	1.5	10.0	2.5	196, 198
Myoglobin	17,800	1.7	7.0	5.0	365
Horseradish peroxidase					
Native	40,000	2.98	7.4	4.3	75, 151, 195, 303, 371, 441
Anionic		3.18	4.0	4.3	303
Cationized		3.0	8.4–9.2	4.3	303
Hemoglobin	68,000	2.8			285, 371
Lactoperoxidase	82,000	3.6	8.0		356
Myeloperoxidase	160,000	4.4	10.0		356
Catalase	240,000	5.2	5.7		356

* Diaminobenzidine (DAB) as H_2 donor.

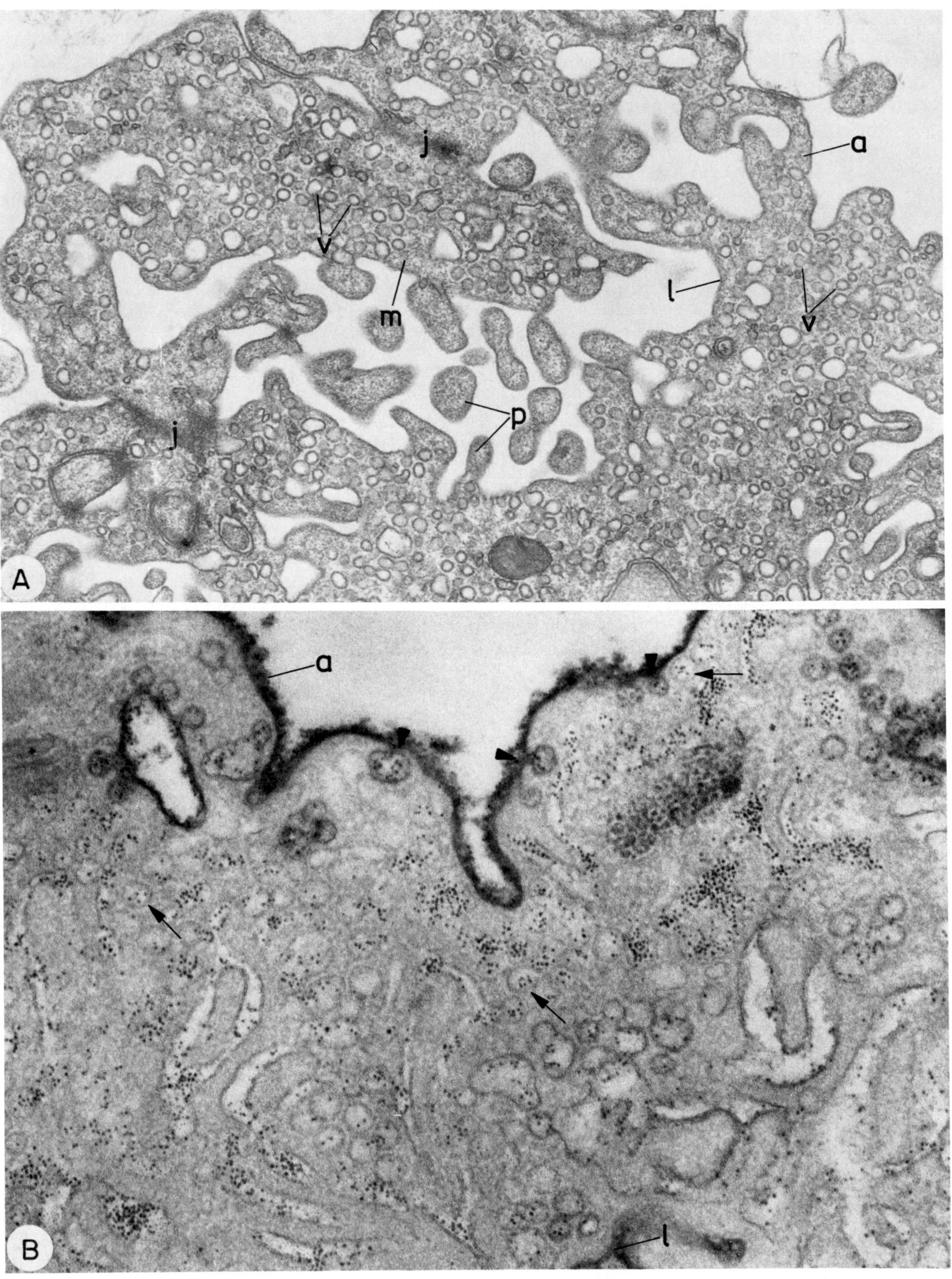
j
a
v
m
l
v
p
j
A
a
B
l

surface of endothelial cells: *1)* membrane markers (e.g., cationized ferritin or cationized horseradish peroxidase); *2)* fluid-phase markers (e.g., glycogens, dextrans, native ferritin, horseradish peroxidase, myoglobin, hemepeptides); *3)* markers that can be taken up by both mechanisms (e.g., conjugates of low-density lipoproteins and ferritin) (357, 359). The results indicate that in the microvascular endothelial cells membrane traffic can take two distinctly compartmented routes: *1)* the endocytic route, involving coated pits, coated vesicles, and possibly some uncoated vesicles, which reach the lysosomal apparatus; *2)* the transcytotic route, involving the plasmalemmal vesicles, which shuttle across the endothelial cell carrying substances between plasma and interstitial fluid.

The endocytic route can supply the endothelial cell with a variety of materials bound to carriers, e.g., iron (in iron-binding proteins), vitamin B_{12} (in transcobalamins), cholesterol (in lipoproteins), and hormones. Traffic of internalized vesicles through the Golgi complex does not appear to be a salient process in the endothelial cell. The adsorptive endocytosis presumably recycles the temporarily coated regions of cell membrane; multivesicular bodies appear to play a major role in the inbound route and reutilization of some membrane domains.

The transcytotic route involves plasmalemmal vesicles. Double-tracer experiments in which endothelial cell membrane was labeled in vivo with cationized ferritin, and hemeundecapeptide was injected as a fluid-phase marker, indicate that although the hemepeptide was transported across the endothelium by vesicles and channels, none of these features were labeled by cationized ferritin; no domains of plasmalemma labeled with cationized ferritin were internalized (Figs. 35 and 36). These and similar experiments suggest that during transcytosis most plasmalemmal vesicles are not formed by invagination of cell membrane but probably represent a separate population of membranes that undergo fusion-fission with plasmalemma without membrane translocation between the opposite cell fronts [Fig. 37; (357, 359)]. This endows endothelium with a dynamic transport system of modulating geometry that requires little energy and is easily and readily adapted to the local metabolic requirements and conditions. In endothelial cells, in general, membrane turnover and recycling appear to occur primarily through endocytosis (especially the adsorptive type) and much less by transcytosis.

Regulation. Information on factors that modulate and control transcytosis and endocytosis in microvascular endothelial cells is very scarce, emerging more from studies on cultured cells than from in vivo investigations. In addition to the physical properties of permeant molecules, hemorheological conditions, and some structural and chemical properties of the endothelial cell, endocytosis and transcytosis can be influenced by several factors: temperature (79, 346, 357, 359, 425), molecular charge (346), serotonin, prolactin, divalent cations (442–444), glucose concentration, and hypertension (400, 438), etc.

Permeability

LIPIDS AND LIPID-SOLUBLE MOLECULES. The endothelial cell membrane, like that in other systems, can be penetrated by free diffusion of lipid-soluble molecules, including gases.

There is reliable biochemical evidence of passage of plasma lipoproteins into the wall of large vessels. Experimental data on lipid transport across the microvascular endothelium are scanty. Because human high-density lipoproteins and low-density lipoproteins are ~10–20 nm in size, Stein and Stein (393) presume that they can be transported by plasmalemmal vesicles. That appears to be true at least for low-density lipoprotein particles, which have been found to cross the endothelium of aorta and vasa vasorum by transcytosis (420) (see *Receptor-mediated endocytosis*, p. 79). Human and rat very-low-density lipoproteins (~30-nm diam) perfused in rat lung were selectively taken up and metabolized (283). Because of their large size (50–500 nm) chylomicrons do not have direct access to vesicles. At least in capillaries of adipose tissue it is thought that chylomicrons are trapped at the endothelial surface where they are hydrolyzed by lipoprotein lipase. The resulting fat-soluble products (fatty acids, mono-, di-, triglycerides) dissolve into the cell membrane and by lateral diffusion within the outer leaflet of cell membrane (along channels or clefts or by vesicle transport) can reach other cells at membrane contact points (27, 331).

WATER AND WATER-SOLUBLE MOLECULES. *Pore theory.* The unusually extensive and rapid transcapillary

FIG. 32. *A*: microvascular endothelial cell isolated from rabbit myocardium and incubated for 30 min at 37°C with phosphate-buffered saline (PBS). More than 90% of plasmalemmal vesicles (*v*) are internalized; accumulation of microfilaments (*m*) beneath plasma membrane. *j*, Intercellular junction; *p*, pseudopodia. × 48,000. *B*: microvascular endothelial cell isolated from rabbit myocardium and incubated with PBS and native ferritin for 30 min at 37°C. After 5 min fixation with 2% buffered glutaraldehyde, cells were exposed for 20 min to horseradish peroxidase and subsequently processed for peroxidatic reaction: ferritin particles labeled ~95% of vesicles (*arrows*). Reaction product marks those vesicles actually open on the cell surface (*arrowheads*) at time of fixation. *l*, Luminal contour; *a*, abluminal contour. × 80,000. [From Simionescu (359).]

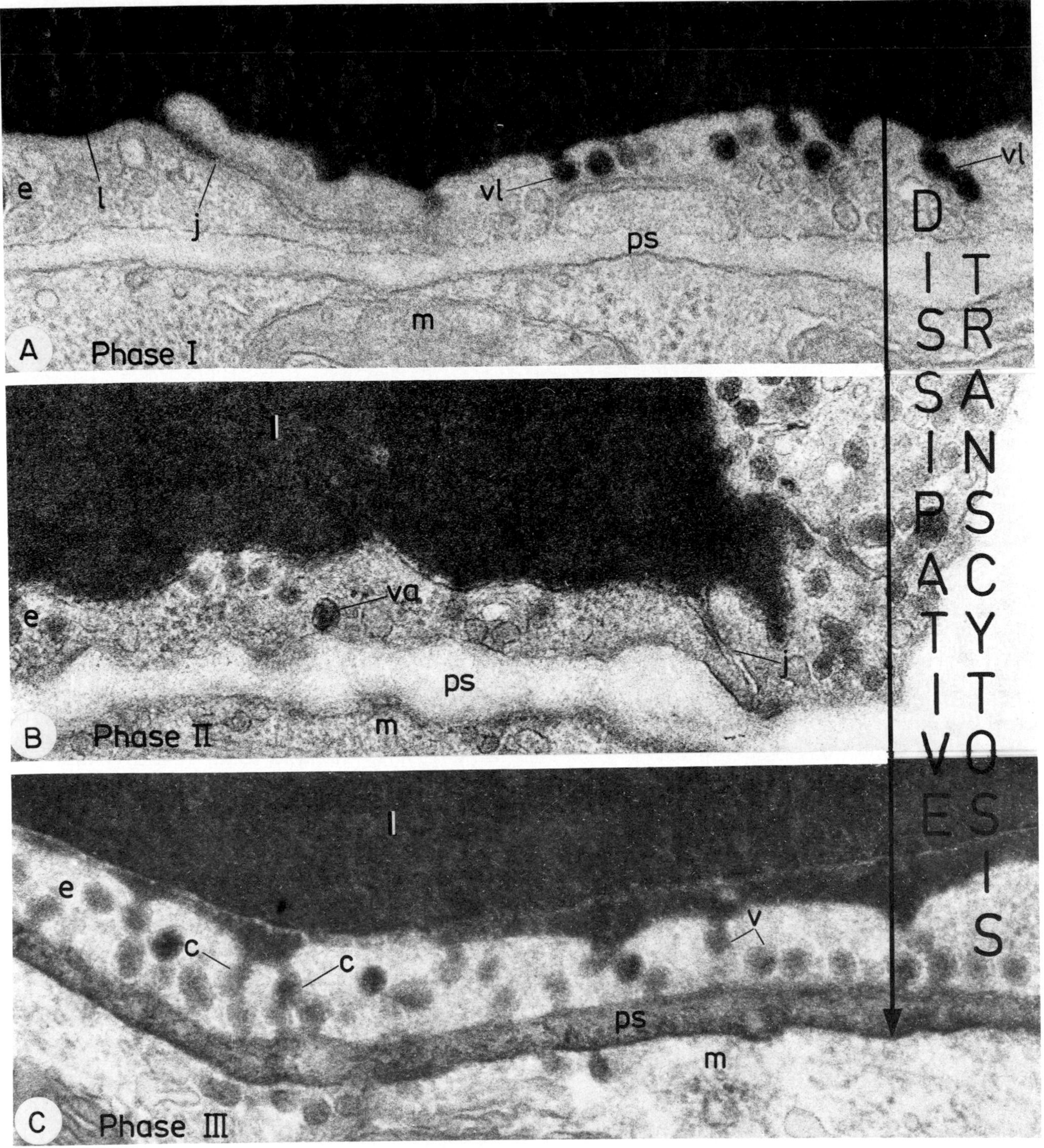

FIG. 33. Rat diaphragm. Blood capillaries at different time intervals after iv injection of microperoxidase as tracer showing sequential events during dissipative transcytosis. *A*: after 30 s (*phase I*) the reaction product present in the lumen (*l*) marks vesicles open on the luminal front (*vl*), whereas the junction (*j*) and intercellular space are free of detectable amounts of reaction product. *B*: after ~40–45 s (*phase II*) the first labeled vesicles reach the abluminal front of endothelium (*va*), whereas the junction still remains unmarked. *C*: at ~60 s (*phase III*) vesicles in all locations are marked. Note 2 transendothelial channels (*c*) connecting directly 2 endothelial fronts. *e*, Endothelium; *m*, muscle; *ps*, pericapillary space; *v*, vesicles. × 50,000. [From Simionescu, Simionescu, and Palade (365, 366).]

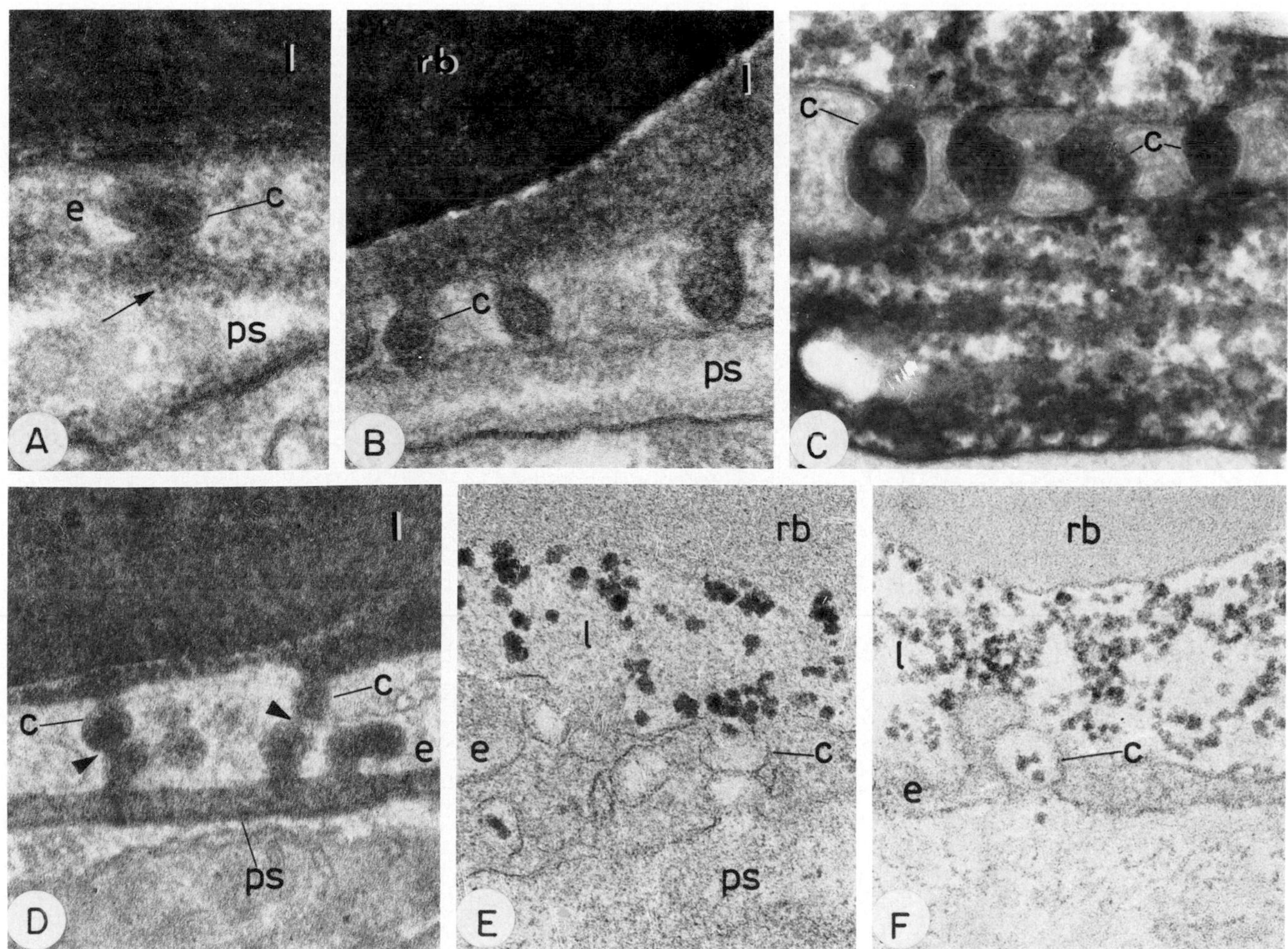

FIG. 34. Gallery of transendothelial channels permeated by probe molecules for both small pores (hemepeptides) (*A–D*) and large pores (shellfish glycogen) (*E* and *F*). Channels (*c*) in *A*, *B*, probably some of those in *C*, and that in *F* are made up of single vesicles, whereas channels in *D*, *E*, and probably some of those in *C* consist of 2 fused vesicles. *Arrow* in *A* points to a transitory concentration gradient facing the channel, whereas *arrowheads* in *D* indicate a stricture connecting fused vesicles. *e*, Endothelium; *l*, lumen; *ps*, pericapillary space; *rb*, red blood cell. *A*: × 120,000; *B*: × 86,000; *C*: × 130,000; *D*: × 60,000; *E*: × 90,000; *F*: × 80,000. [From Simionescu, Simionescu, and Palade (366, 373) and Simionescu (343).]

passage of water and water-soluble molecules implies the existence of some fluid-filled or hydrophilic paths directly connecting the vascular lumen with the tissue interstitia.

According to the main paradigm in capillary permeability, the pore theory, by analogy with the inert artificial membranes, the capillary endothelium has two sets of pores of relatively stable and rigid geometry, size, and density (156, 212). The small pores would have a diameter of ~9 nm, a frequency of 15–20 units/μm^2, and an aggregate area of ~0.1%. Large pores with a diameter of 50–70 nm would be fewer: 1/20 μm^2. These parameters have been repeatedly revised because of studies of various capillary beds and the use of different methods for estimating the equivalent pore radius (93–95, 295–300). According to recent estimates, the small pores should be either cylindrical channels with a diameter of ~12 nm or slits ~8 nm wide, with a frequency as high as 10–15 units/μm^2 (94) or as low as 1–2 pores/μm capillary length (272). In the last two decades, attempts have been made with ultrastructural studies and tracer experiments to identify the endothelial structures that could represent the morphological substrate(s) of the two pore systems.

The transendothelial transport in various capillaries can no longer be analyzed and explained with the simplicity of the initial formulation of the pore theory. Moreover, recent information on the cell and molecular biology of capillary endothelium indicates that the endothelium is structurally and biochemically

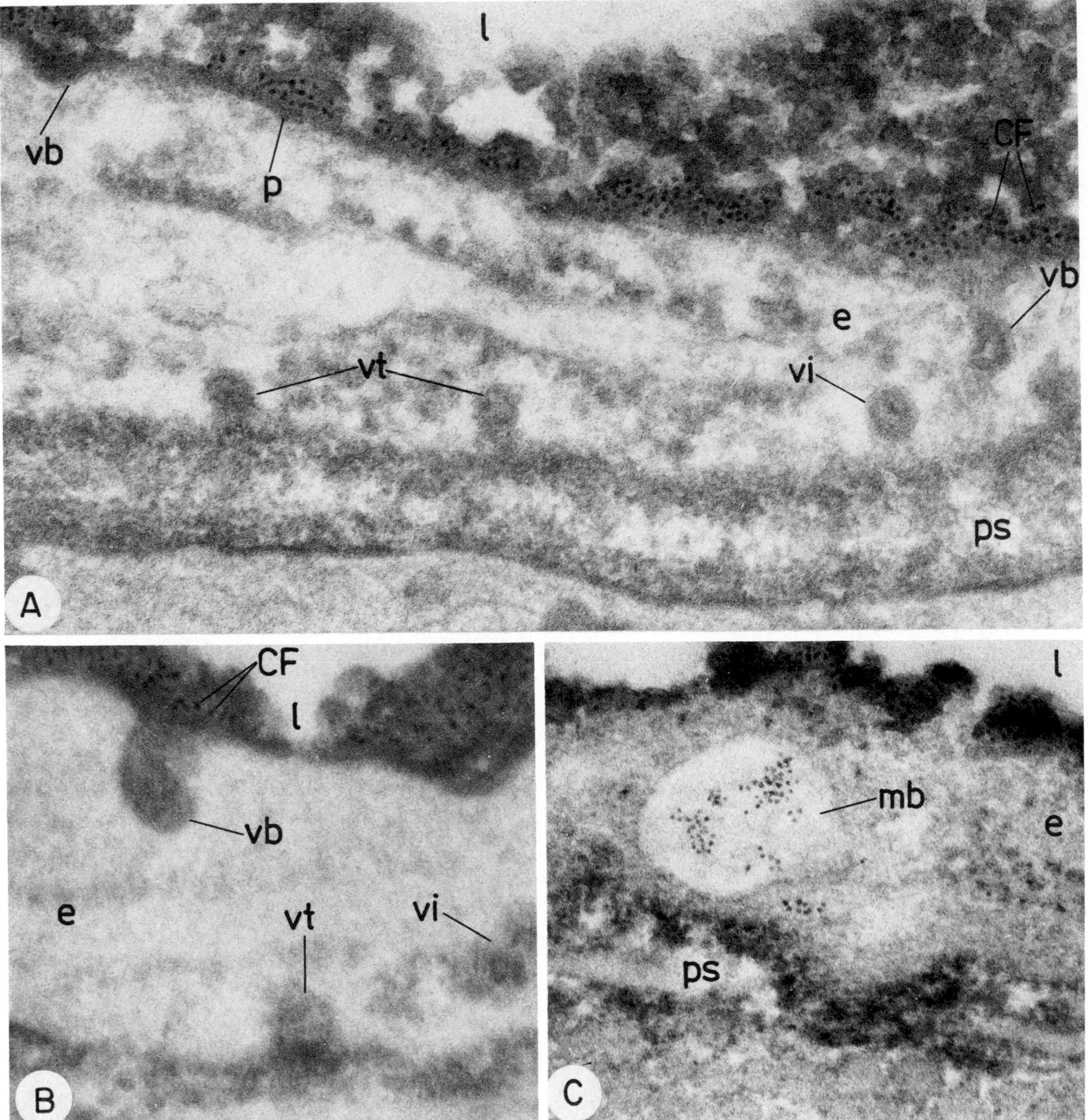

FIG. 35. Diaphragm capillary (mouse) injected first with cationized ferritin (*CF*) to label plasma membrane (*p*) and after 2 min with hemeundecapeptide. *A*: after 3 min the tissue was fixed in situ and subsequently processed for peroxidatic reaction. Although CF remained confined to plasma membrane and no domains of the latter were internalized, hemeundecapeptide reaction product marked plasmalemmal vesicles on the blood front (*vb*), inside the cytoplasm (*vi*), and open on the tissue front (*vt*), suggesting that dissipative transcytosis took place without vesiculation of plasmalemma. *e*, Endothelium; *l*, lumen; *ps*, pericapillary space. × 92,000. *B*: same as *A*, but 5 min after hemeundecapeptide injection. Vesicles labeled by reaction product; no areas of CF-labeled plasmalemma were internalized. × 120,000. *C*: same as *B*. Multivesicular body (*mb*) containing ferritin particles (presumably carried by coated vesicles or some pinocytic vesicles that selectively internalized the adsorptive marker). × 58,000. [From Simionescu (359).]

highly differentiated, rendering its participation in transport a more active, dynamic, and refined process than that ascribed to it by the pore theory (362).

Search for pores: electron microscopy and tracer experiments. Electron microscopy has revealed that capillary endothelium has features (diaphragms of vesicles, channels, and fenestrae) devoid of a lipid bilayer that are penetrated by water-soluble probe molecules ≥1.7 nm. However, none of these features have the exact size, geometry, and frequency of the postulated pores.

Until recently, ultrastructural observations on microvascular endothelium relied on randomly collected micrographs of vascular profiles without pertinent

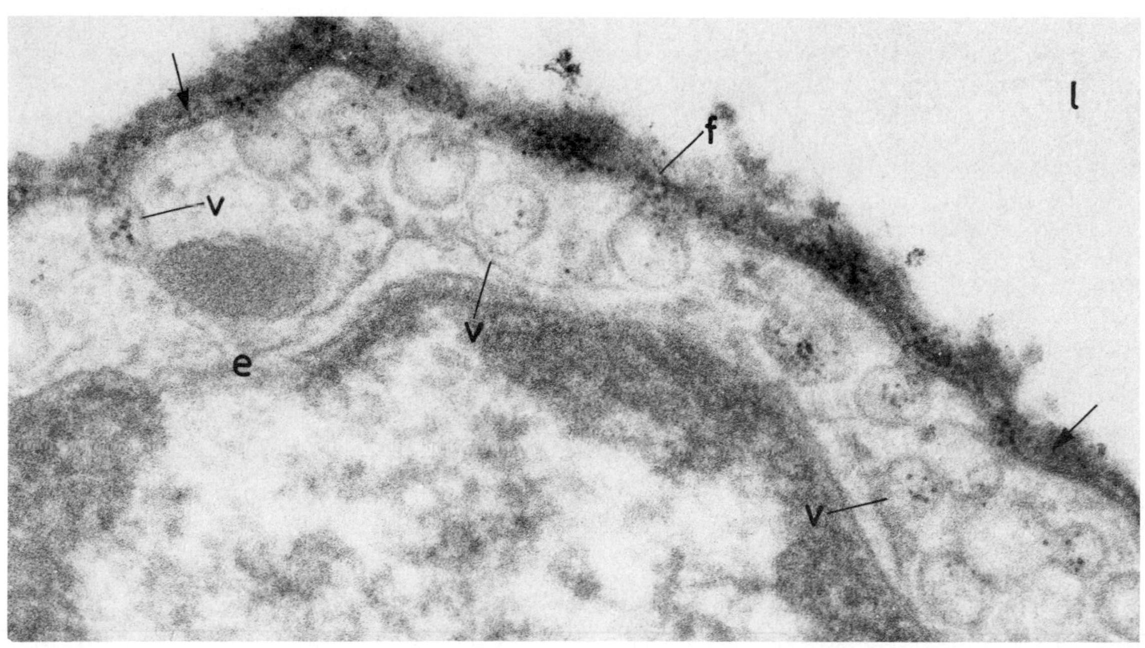

FIG. 36. Diaphragm capillary (mouse) injected first with native ferritin (*f*) (as fluid-phase marker) and after 3 min with 0.5% alcian blue (as adsorptive marker). Ferritin taken up by vesicles (*v*); some vesicles internalized. Alcian blue marked plasma membrane (*arrows*), but not transporting vesicles. *e*, Endothelium; *l*, lumen. × 164,000. [From Simionescu (359).]

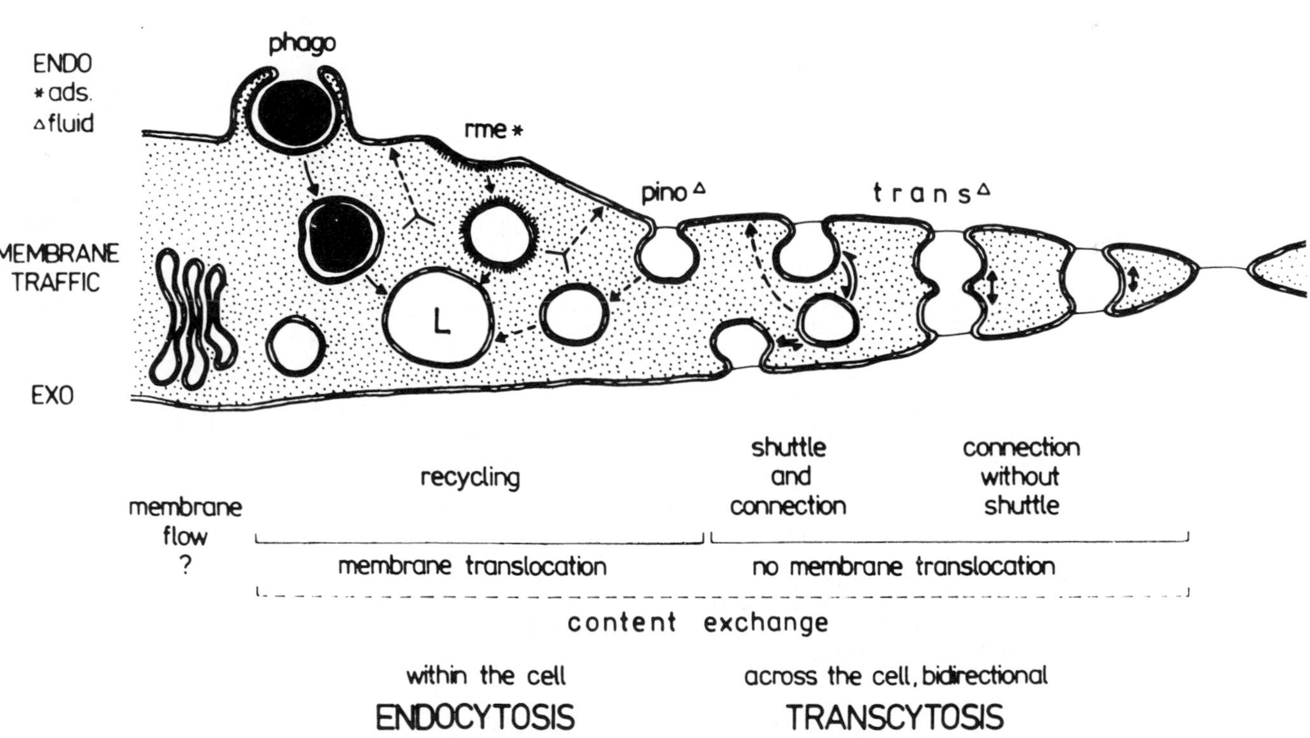

FIG. 37. Endocytosis and transcytosis in a fenestrated endothelial cell and possible routes taken by membranes involved in these processes. ads, Adsorptive endocytosis; ENDO, endocytosis; EXO, exocytosis; fluid, fluid-phase endocytosis; L, lysosomes (includes multivesicular bodies and dense bodies); phago, phagocytosis; pino, pinocytosis; rme, receptor-mediated endocytosis; trans, transcytosis. [From Simionescu (359).]

information regarding their location within the microvascular bed. Tracer experiments also used the same type of approach. This produced some controversial results that still persist. Moreover some physiological data referred to *capillary* as an operational term for any small exchange vessel and not as a term for a well-defined and characterized microvascular segment. Electron-microscopic examination of well-identified segments of the microvasculature, e.g., in omentum, mesentery (350, 354), or skeletal muscle (370–373), has revealed that the endothelium of each microvascular segment has its own junctional organization and significantly differs in thickness, vesicle density, occurrence of channels, and other characteristics (see GENERAL STRUCTURE, p. 42). Thus the search for the structural basis of permeability should be specifically related to a given microvessel of a certain circulatory bed (32, 126, 200, 255, 272, 327, 445).

Recently ultrastructural and cytochemical studies have shown that the microvascular wall, particularly the capillary wall, is made up of continuous series-coupled components, e.g., the endothelial glycocalyx (of heterogeneous and differentiated chemical composition), endothelium (containing highly modulating features with different electrical charges), basal lamina, and subendothelium (complex chemistry). During its transcapillary passage each permeant molecule has to interact (to a different extent) with these successive constituents. These layered components make a structural and functional unit that should be thought of as part of the surrounding tissue.

Tracer experiments, initially intended to identify indirectly the two postulated sets of pores, have been used lately to detect the actual pathways taken by water-soluble probe molecules of known size, shape, and charge, with less emphasis on the possible pore equivalents.

The adsorbed layer of plasma proteins may influence the accessibility of tracers or plasma macromolecules to the endothelium (77, 97, 223, 224, 243, 254).

Permeability studies have used two types of tracers: *1*) particulate tracers that can be directly detected by electron microscopy because of their native electron opacity [e.g., ferritin (75, 119, 207), colloidal gold] or can be rendered opaque by adequate staining [e.g., glycogens, dextrans (360)]; *2*) enzymatic tracers that can be localized indirectly via a histochemical reaction based on their peroxidatic activity [Table 3; (122, 151, 195–198, 285, 287, 356, 365, 366)].

Time-course experiments have concentrated on continuous capillaries and to a lesser extent on fenestrated capillaries. The data so far apply to probe molecules ranging from ~30 nm [glycogens and dextrans (364)] to ~2.0 nm [hemepeptides (356, 366)]. Direct evidence regarding the passage of molecules with a diameter smaller than 2.0 nm is still lacking. Results have shown that the transendothelial pathways of such molecules may vary significantly from one microvascular segment to another. The contribution of arterioles to the transport of these molecules in various vascular beds (373, 437) appears small, as expected from the reduced number of such vessels, the low frequency of vesicles and channels in their endothelium, and the strong organization of their occluding junctions.

The kinetics of vesicle labeling indicate that in the continuous capillary endothelium, probe molecules ≥2.0 nm are transported primarily via plasmalemmal vesicles (6, 182–184, 275–279, 365–373, 441) and vesicle-derived transendothelial channels (182–184, 343, 357, 359, 366–373). The process takes place in succes-

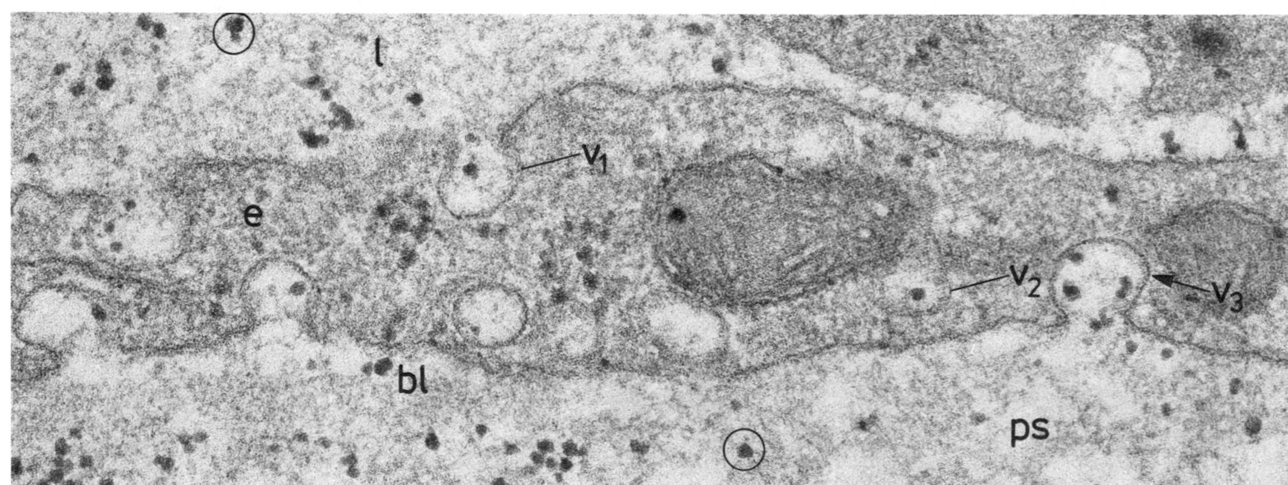

FIG. 38. Mouse diaphragm 10 min after iv injection of tracer solution of shellfish glycogen. Tracer particles are present in lumen (*l*), in pericapillary space (encircled), and in vesicles open on blood front (v_1) or tissue front (v_3) or free in the cytoplasm (v_2). *bl*, Basal lamina; *e*, endothelium; *ps*, pericapillary space. × 110,000. [From Simionescu and Simionescu (363), reprinted by permission of Elsevier Science Publishing Co., copyright 1983.]

sive resolvable phases: *1*) the tracer first labels the vesicles open on the luminal front, *2*) marked vesicles appear free in the cytoplasm, and *3*) the vesicles eventually reach the abluminal front and discharge their contents into the subendothelial compartment (Fig. 38; Table 4). Such molecules also concomitantly label transendothelial channels. Depending on their size-limiting structures (stomatal diaphragms, necks, strictures), channels can behave as either small (366) or large pores (136, 343, 357, 359). Intercellular junctions in the same capillary endothelia are not marked by detectable amounts of tracer used in the experiments (Fig. 39). In some capillaries, water and some water-soluble molecules with a diameter <1.7 nm may pass along the intercellular pathways (385). However, some investigators working on randomly collected microvessels claim that at least some endothelial junctions are permeated by horseradish peroxidase (195–197), cytochrome *c* (196, 198), or microperoxidase (448). Interstitial injection of myoglobin, ferritin (184, 369), hemeundecapeptide (369), and horseradish peroxidase (182) demonstrated that the backdiffusion of such molecules also occurs through vesicles and channels (Fig. 40).

TABLE 4. *Time Sequence of Vesicular Labeling in Capillary Endothelium (Rat Diaphragm)*

Labeled Vesicles, %	Phase I, 0–30 s	Phase II, 30–40 s	Phase III, 40–60 s
Total	38 ± 8	58 ± 10	93 ± 6
Blood front	80 ± 14	91 ± 6	95 ± 4
Inside	35 ± 11	68 ± 15	89 ± 7
Tissue front	0	15 ± 8	94 ± 6

Hemeundecapeptide experiments. For each phase, 520–610 vesicles counted. Data refer only to peripheral zone of endothelial cell. [Adapted from Simionescu, Simionescu, and Palade (366).]

The intercellular passage of water-soluble molecules ≥1.7 nm seems to be restricted to a fraction of endothelial junctions of pericytic venules. They appear to be permeable to hemeundecapeptide (~1.7 nm) and to a lesser extent to horseradish peroxidase (~5.5 nm) but exclude hemoglobin (~7.0 nm) and ferritin (~11 nm) [Fig. 41; (371)]. The open junctions of venular endothelium would not likely correspond to the large-pore system because they are not permeable to molecules of ~11 nm, such as ferritin. They also could not correspond to the small-pore system because of their dimensions (narrower than those postulated for the small pores), the limited diffusion through them, and their restricted distribution (371). They may constitute an additional route for molecules with a diameter ≤6 nm; physiological experiments did not detect this pathway as a distinct set of pores, possibly because it falls within the range of the small-pore system. The passage through this pathway may become exacerbated during inflammatory reactions.

Peculiarities in the transport of probe molecules across special endothelia (e.g., brain, liver, and lung) are described in the respective chapters in this *Handbook*.

In fenestrated capillaries, large probes [e.g., ferritin (75), dextrans, glycogens (364)] exit only through a small fraction of the fenestral population (Fig. 42), whereas tracers such as horseradish peroxidase (75)

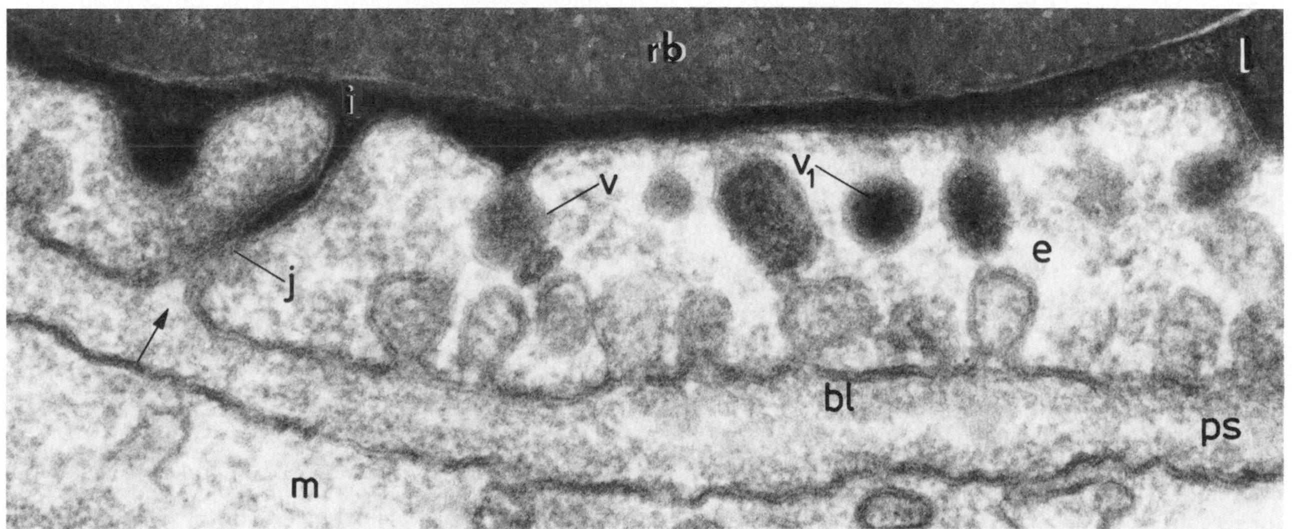

FIG. 39. Mouse diaphragm 25 s after tracer injection of hemeundecapeptide. Middle segment of a capillary showing labeling of plasmalemmal vesicles open on the blood front (*v*) or apparently free in the cytoplasm (v_1). The hemeundecapeptide reaction product fills the infundibulum (*i*) leading to the junction (*j*) but stops at the level of the latter. In *v*, note the concentration gradient from lumen to vesicle. No detectable reaction product in the abluminal part of the intercellular space (*arrow*). *bl*, Basal lamina; *e*, endothelium; *l*, capillary lumen; *m*, muscle fiber; *ps*, pericapillary space; *rb*, red blood cell. × 120,000. [From Simionescu, Simionescu, and Palade (373).]

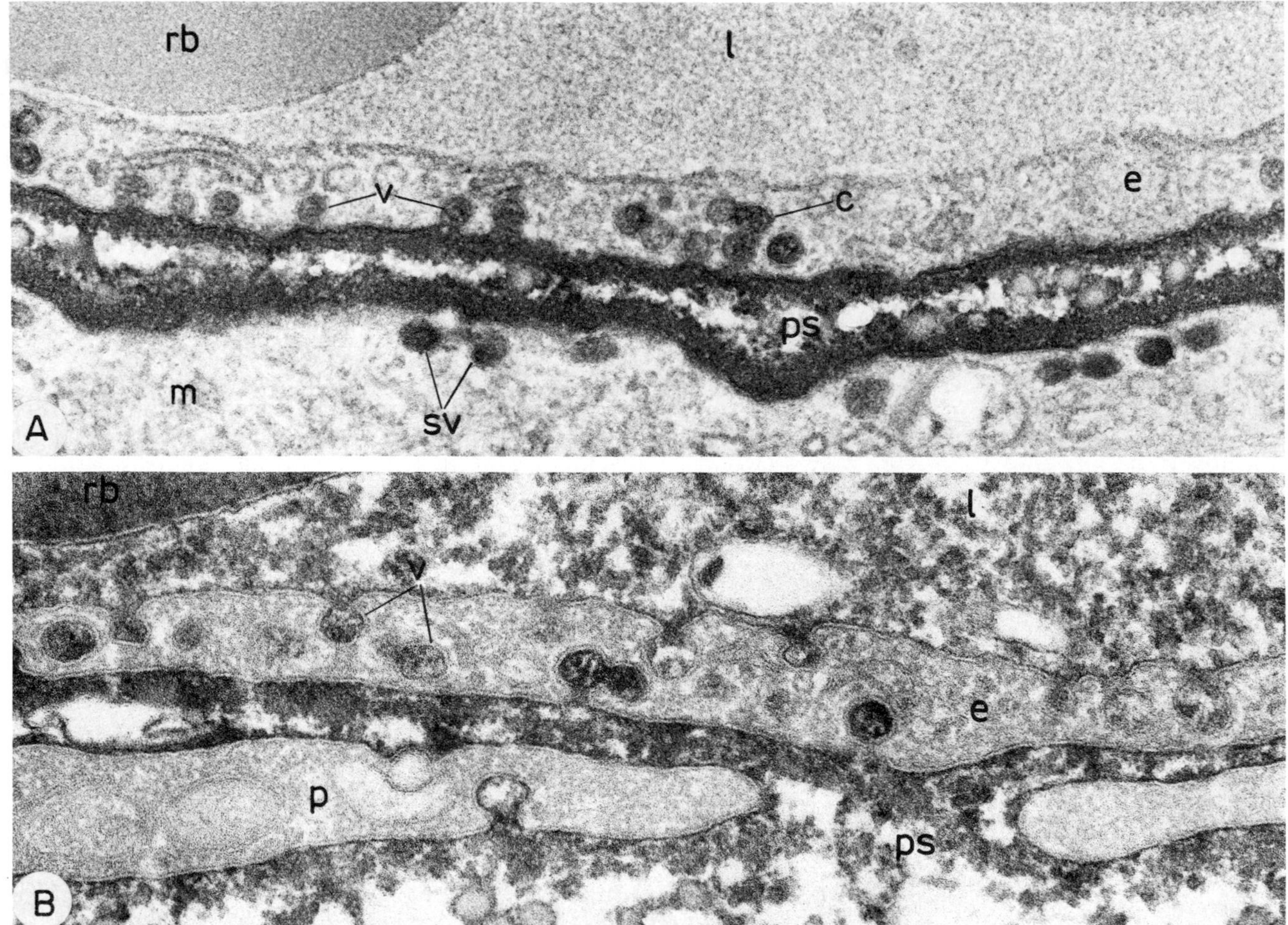

FIG. 40. Muscle capillaries (rat cremaster). Hemeundecapeptide tracer solution interstitially injected. *A*: 30 s after injection the reaction product marks pericapillary space (*ps*), sarcolemmal vesicles (*sv*) of muscle cells (*m*), and endothelial vesicles open on tissue front (*v*). *c*, Chain of fused vesicles. × 80,000. *B*: 5 min after injection the reaction product labels the pericapillary space, endothelial vesicles in all positions, and capillary lumen (*l*). *e*, Endothelium; *p*, pericyte; *rb*, red blood cell. × 90,000.

have access to all plasmalemmal vesicles and permeate all channels and fenestrae (172). Despite the proven permeability of fenestrae, they do not appear to impart to visceral capillaries a higher permeability to water-soluble macromolecules than continuous capillaries, but rather less (94, 152, 153, 208, 296–298). Although the permeability of fenestrated capillaries for albumin is lower, the permeability for glucose is four- to fivefold greater. The filtration coefficient is ~20 times higher in fenestrated capillaries than in continuous capillaries (94). These data indicate that the endothelial fenestrations are especially associated with augmentation of permeability to water and small solutes rather than with that of macromolecules (296–298, 362).

Because of the highly negative charge of fenestral diaphragms, experiments were designed to check the possible role in permeability of the dense anionic sites of fenestral diaphragms. Preliminary observations show that removal of these anionic sites (contributed primarily by heparan sulfate–proteoglycans) with heparinase enhances fenestrae permeability to native and anionic ferritin. With the use of probe molecules of the same dimensions but with different electrical charge (e.g., anionic, neutral, and cationic ferritin, or anionic, neutral, and cationic horseradish peroxidase), it appears that although vesicles are thought to favor the transcytosis of anionic proteins, these proteins are largely repelled from fenestrae (N. Ghinea and N. Simionescu, unpublished observations). The size limit of these charge restrictions needs to be determined. In glomerular capillaries with a highly fenestrated endothelium, the size (62) and charge barrier have been localized to the basement membrane, which can discriminate against anionic macromolecules past a certain molecular size (37, 68, 69, 302, 303).

In view of these findings, the local differentiations of microvascular endothelium that can account for its special permeability properties should be conceived as

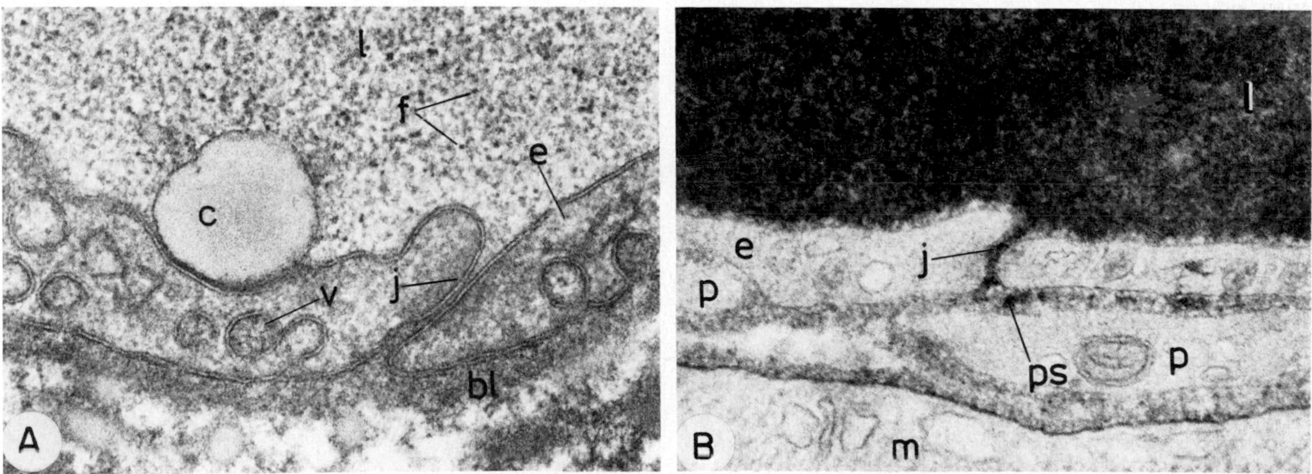

FIG. 41. *A*: pericytic venule in mouse diaphragm 3 min after iv injection of ferritin. Intercellular junction (*j*) is open to a measurable gap of 3–6 nm between dense outer leaflets of opposed membranes. Intercellular space is free of tracer on both adluminal and abluminal side of the junction. × 78,000. *B*: mouse diaphragm 25 s after hemeundecapeptide injection, illustrating a patent intercellular space [or open endothelial junction (*j*)] in a pericytic venule. Entire length of intercellular space is evenly marked by hemeundecapeptide reaction product, and a concentration gradient appears facing its abluminal end in adjoining periendothelial space (*ps*). *bl*, Basal lamina; *c*, chylomicron; *e*, endothelium; *f*, ferritin particles; *l*, lumen; *m*, muscle fiber; *p*, pericyte, *v*, vesicle. × 64,000. [From Simionescu, Simionescu, and Palade (371, 373).]

special structurally and chemically integrated devices that are able to discriminate among permeant macromolecules according to their size, shape, charge, and chemical nature.

Dynamic hydrophilic system of microvascular endothelium. The passage of water and water-soluble molecules across microvascular endothelium can take two hydrophilic (fluid-filled) pathways: transmembranous and extramembranous (362). Terms such as *transcellular* versus *paracellular* (or *extracellular*), commonly applied to other epithelia, are less suitable in the special case of capillary endothelium because channels and fenestrae can be equally considered transcellular and extracellular, although these routes cross neither the cell membrane nor the cytoplasm (359).

The transmembranous route crosses sequentially the plasma membrane of one cell front, the cytoplasm, and the opposite plasma membrane (Fig. 43). The cell membrane, permeated by pores with a radius of ~0.7 nm, is assumed to be the principal barrier to transport (383). By extrapolation from other systems, the cell membrane of the capillary endothelium is presumed to behave as a passive transport pathway for water, small nonpolar solutes, and lipid-soluble molecules. Information regarding the permeability characteristics of the endothelial cell plasmalemma is needed. The transmembranous route becomes very short in regions of close contact between two vesicles concomitantly open on opposite cell fronts, or in special zones of endothelium, e.g., the avesicular part of the lung capillary. As extrapolated from physiological data, the contribution of endothelial plasma membrane to the hydraulic conductivity shows a certain constancy and does not exceed 10% (94, 296). Because the particular biochemical organization of the endothelial cell membrane is not yet known, the only factors that can now be inferred from its permeability for water are the large surface area exposed and the endothelium thinness.

Extramembranous routes are transcellular (via vesicles, channels, fenestrae, and diaphragms) and intercellular (via endothelial junctions). The endothelial junctions, as in other epithelia, are assumed to be permeable to water and small solutes. The extracellular pathways account for ~90% of volume flow (94, 296). The fractional contribution of each route may vary largely from one microvascular bed to another and according to the physical properties of permeant molecules. The magnitude and mechanisms of the active transport of ions, e.g., carrier-mediated transport, need investigation. All features involved in the extramembranous pathways (vesicles, channels, fenestrae, diaphragms, junctions) are not just simple fluid-filled pores but dynamic, highly organized, and chemically sophisticated features. Although such diversified equipment of hydrophilic transcellular pathways exists in the endothelium, the term *leakiness*—if defined as in other epithelia as the ratio between cellular and extracellular conductance—may be misleading. The features involved in these pathways constitute a dynamic hydrophilic system: dynamic, as proved by its variable geometry, modulation, and segmental differentiations; hydrophilic, because they are fluid-filled routes of complex molecular and electro-

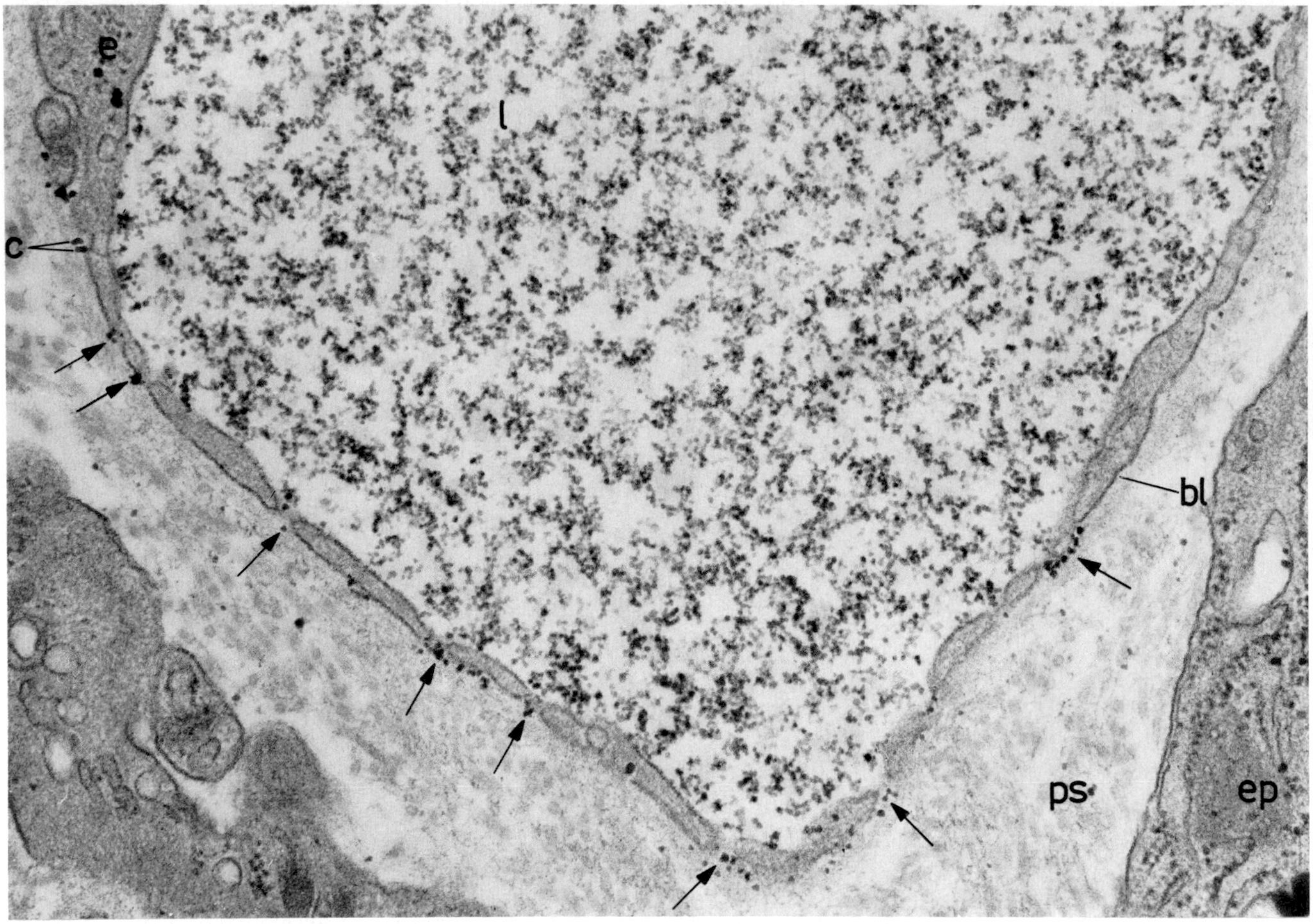

FIG. 42. Blood capillary of jejunal submucosa (rat) 4 min after iv injection of shellfish glycogen. Tracer particles are evenly distributed in lumen (*l*) and some particles have penetrated fenestrae (*arrows*) with transitory accumulation against basal lamina (*bl*), whereas some have reached pericapillary space (*ps*). *c*, Glycogen particles at level of transendothelial channel; *e*, endothelium; *ep*, epithelium. × 52,000.

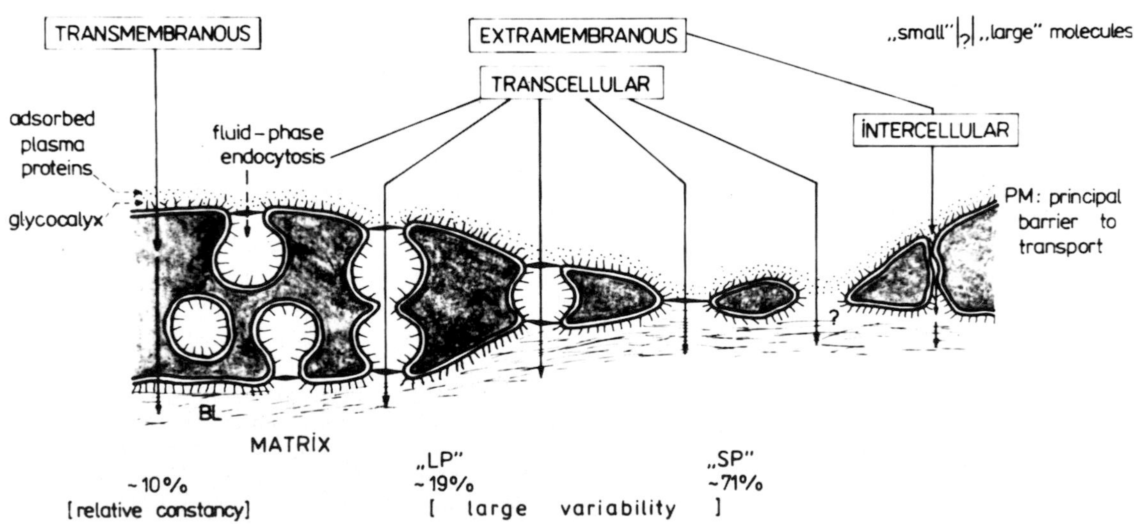

FIG. 43. Dynamic, transient hydrophilic pathways assumed to be involved in endothelial transport of water and water-soluble molecules. Hydraulic conductivity occurs with and without diffusion and carrier-mediated transport. Same feature can concomitantly be the site for filtration and diffusion (coupling of volume flux to protein flux). Interconversion between features (large pores ⇌ small pores: e.g., channels). Interconversion between mechanisms (dissipative ⇌ convective: e.g., vesicles ⇌ channels). Characteristic variations of structures generate a spectrum of tightness/leakiness. Fractional contribution of each pathway varies in different endothelia. BL, basal lamina; LP, large pores, PM, plasma membrane; SP, small pores. [Adapted from Simionescu and Simionescu (362).]

chemical organization; system, because they appear to be morphogenetically related. Filtration and diffusion may occur concomitantly in the same feature (e.g., channel, fenestrae), thus coupling volume flow to protein flux. Channel formation by vesicle fusion may represent interconversion between features (large pores ⇌ small pores) and between transport mechanisms (dissipative ⇌ convective) [Fig. 43; (362)].

This review is based partly on work carried out in collaboration with George E. Palade. Guy Ionescu's excellent photographic reproductions and Corina Stancu's graphic work are gratefully acknowledged.

REFERENCES

1. ALLSOPP, G., AND H. J. GAMBLE. An electron microscopic study of the pericytes of the developing capillaries in human fetal brain and muscle. *J. Anat.* 128: 155–168, 1978.
2. ALTURA, B. M., AND B. T. ALTURA. Interactions of locally produced humoral substances in regulation of the microcirculation. In: *Mechanisms of Vasodilatation*, edited by P. M. Vanhoutte and I. Leusen. Basel: Karger, 1978, p. 98–106.
3. ANDERSON, A. O., AND N. D. ANDERSON. Lymphocyte emigration from high endothelial venules in rat lymph nodes. *Immunology* 31: 731–748, 1976.
4. ANDERSON, N. D., A. O. ANDERSON, AND R. G. WYLLIE. Specialized structure and metabolic activities of high endothelial venules in rat lymphatic tissues. *Immunology* 31: 455–473, 1976.
5. ANDERSON, R. G., M. S. BROWN, AND J. L. GOLDSTEIN. Role of the coated endocytic vesicle in the uptake of receptor-bound low density lipoprotein in human fibroblasts. *Cell* 10: 351–364, 1977.
6. ANVERSA, P., F. GIACOMELLI, AND J. WIENER. Regional variation in capillary permeability of ventricular myocardium. *Microvasc. Res.* 6: 273–285, 1973.
7. APPERLEY, E., W. FENIUK, P. P. A. HUMPHREY, AND G. P. LEVY. Evidence for two types of excitatory receptor for 5-hydroxytryptamine in dog isolated vasculature. *Br. J. Pharmacol.* 68: 215–224, 1980.
8. ARFORS, K. E., G. RUTILI, AND E. SVENSJÖ. Microvascular transport of macromolecules in normal and inflammatory conditions. *Acta Physiol. Scand.* 463: 93–103, 1979.
9. AUSPRUNK, D. H., AND J. FOLKMAN. Migration and proliferation of endothelial cells in preformed and newly formed blood vessels during tumor angiogenesis. *Microvasc. Res.* 14: 53–65, 1977.
10. BAENZIGER, N. L., P. R. BECHERER, AND P. W. MAJERUS. Characterization of prostacyclin synthesis in cultured human arterial smooth muscle cells, venous endothelial cells and skin fibroblasts. *Cell* 16: 967–974, 1979.
11. BAKHLE, Y. S., AND J. R. VANE. Pharmacokinetic function of the pulmonary circulation. *Physiol. Rev.* 54: 1007–1045, 1974.
12. BAR, R. S., J. C. HOAK, AND M. L. PEACOCK. Insulin receptors in human endothelial cells: identification and characterization. *J. Clin. Endocrinol. Metab.* 47: 699–702, 1978.
13. BARER, G. R., C. J. EMERY, F. H. MOHAMMED, AND I. P. MUNGALL. H_1 and H_2 histamine actions on lung vessels: their relevance to hypotoxic vasoconstriction. *Q. J. Exp. Physiol.* 63: 157–169, 1978.
14. BECKER, C. G. Contractile and relaxing proteins of smooth muscle and platelets: their presence in the endothelium. *Ann. NY Acad. Sci.* 275: 78–86, 1976.
15. BECKER, C. G., AND P. C. HARPEL. Alpha 2-macroglobulin on human vascular endothelium. *J. Exp. Med.* 144: 1–9, 1976.
16. BECKER, C. G., AND R. L. NACHMAN. Contractile proteins of endothelial cells, platelets and smooth muscle. *Am. J. Pathol.* 71: 1–20, 1973.
17. BENNETT, H. S., J. H. LUFT, AND J. C. HAMPTON. Morphological classifications of vertebrate blood capillaries. *Am. J. Physiol.* 196: 381–390, 1959.
18. BERGERON, J. J. M., R. SIKSTROM, A. R. HAND, AND B. I. POSNER. Binding and uptake of ^{125}I-insulin into rat liver hepatocytes and endothelium. An in vivo radioautographic study. *J. Cell Biol.* 80: 427–443, 1979.
19. BERTINI, F., AND R. SANTOLAYA. A novel type of granules observed in toad endothelial cells and their relationship with blood pressure active factors. *Experientia* 26: 522–523, 1970.
20. BEVAN, J. A., AND S. P. DUCKLES. Evidence for alpha-adrenergic receptors on intimal endothelium. *Blood Vessels* 12: 307–310, 1975.
21. BHARGAVA, K. P., R. NATH, AND G. PALIT. Nature of histamine receptors concerned in capillary permeability. *Br. J. Pharmacol.* 59: 349–351, 1977.
22. BHAWAN, J., L. EDELSTEIN, AND J. B. JACOBS. Endothelial fenestrations in cellular blue naevus and halo naevus. *Lancet* 1: 1350–1351, 1975.
23. BIEMPICA, L., R. MORECKI, C. H. WU, M. A. GIMBRONE, JR., AND M. ROJKIND. Immunocytochemical localization of type B collagen. A component of basement membrane in human liver. *Am. J. Pathol.* 98: 591–596, 1980.
24. BIGNON, J., P. CHANINIAN, G. FELDMANN, AND C. SPAIN. Ultrastructural immunoperoxidase demonstration of autologous albumin in the alveolar capillary membrane and in the alveolar lining material in normal rats. *J. Cell Biol.* 64: 503–509, 1975.
25. BIGNON, J., F. JAUBERT, AND M. C. JAURAND. Plasma protein immunocytochemistry and polysaccharide cytochemistry at the surface of alveolar and endothelial cells in the rat lung. *J. Histochem. Cytochem.* 24: 1076–1084, 1976.
26. BIRDWELL, C. R., D. GOSPODAROVICZ, AND G. NICOLSON. Identification, localization and role of fibronectin in cultured bovine endothelial cells. *Proc. Natl. Acad. Sci. USA* 75: 3273–3277, 1978.
27. BLANCHETTE-MACKIE, E. J., AND R. O. SCOW. Sites of lipoprotein lipase activity in adipose tissue perfused with chylomicrons: electron microscope cytochemical study. *J. Cell Biol.* 51: 1–25, 1971.
28. BLOOM, A. L., S. C. GIDDINGS, AND C. J. WILKS. Factor VIII on vascular intima: possible importance in haemostasis and thrombosis. *Nature London New Biol.* 241: 217–219, 1973.
29. BLOSE, S. H. Ten-nanometer filaments and mitosis: maintenance of structural continuity in dividing endothelial cells. *Proc. Natl. Acad. Sci. USA* 76: 3372–3376, 1979.
30. BLOSE, S. H., AND S. CHACKO. Rings of intermediate (100 Å) filament bundles in the perinuclear region of vascular endothelial cells. Their mobilization by colcemid and mitosis. *J. Cell Biol.* 70: 459–466, 1976.
31. BLOSE, S. H., M. L. SHELANSKI, AND S. CHACKO. Localization of bovine brain filament antibody on intermediate (100 Å) filaments in guinea pig vascular endothelial cells and chick cardiac muscle cells. *Proc. Natl. Acad. Sci. USA* 74: 662–665, 1977.
32. BOHRER, M. P., H. D. HUMENS, C. BAYLIS, C. R. ROBERTSON, AND B. M. BRENNER. Facilitated transglomerular passage of circulating polycations (Abstract). *Clin. Res.* 25: 505A, 1977.
33. BONEU, B., M. ABBAL, J. PLANTE, AND R. BIERME. Factor-VIII complex and endothelial damage. *Lancet* 1: 1430, 1975.
34. BOWERS, W. D., JR., R. W. HUBBARD, R. C. DAUM, P. ASHBAUGH, AND E. NILSON. Ultrastructural studies of muscle cells and vascular endothelium immediately after freeze-thaw injury. *Cryobiology* 10: 9–21, 1973.
35. BOWERSOX, J. C., AND N. SORGENTE. Chemotactic response of vascular endothelial cells to fibronectin (Abstract). *J. Cell Biol.* 87: 64a, 1980.
36. BRECHER, P., AND H. T. KUAN. Lipoprotein lipase and acid lipase activity in rabbit brain microvessels. *J. Lipid Res.* 20:

77–129, 1979.

37. BRENNER, B. M., M. P. BOHRER, C. BAYLIS, AND W. M. DEEN. Determinants of glomerular permselectivity: insights derived from observations in vivo. *Kidney Int.* 12: 229–237, 1977.
38. BRETTON, R., AND J. BARIETY. Ultrastructural localization of concanavalin A in normal rat kidney-glomeruli and arterioles. *J. Ultrastruct. Res.* 48: 396–403, 1974.
39. BRIGHTMAN, M. W. Morphology of blood-brain interfaces. *Exp. Eye Res. Suppl.* 25: 1–25, 1977.
40. BRIGHTMAN, M. W., AND T. S. REESE. Junctions between intimately apposed cell membranes in the vertebrate brain. *J. Cell Biol.* 40: 648–677, 1969.
41. BRIGHTMAN, M. W., T. S. REESE, AND N. FEDER. Assessment with the electron microscope of the permeability to peroxidase of cerebral endothelium and epithelium in mice and sharks. In: *Capillary Permeability,* edited by C. Crone and N. A. Lassen. New York: Academic, 1970, p. 463. (Alfred Benzon Symp. 2.)
42. BRUNS, R. R., AND G. E. PALADE. Studies on blood capillaries. I. General organization of blood capillaries in muscle. *J. Cell Biol.* 37: 244–276, 1968.
43. BRUNS, R. R., AND G. E. PALADE. Studies on blood capillaries. II. Transport of ferritin molecules across the wall of muscle capillaries. *J. Cell Biol.* 37: 277–299, 1968.
44. BUNDGAARD, M. Transport pathways in capillaries—in search of pores. *Annu. Rev. Physiol.* 42: 325–336, 1980.
45. BUNDGAARD, M., C. CRONE, AND J. FRØKJAER-JENSEN. Extreme rarity of transendothelial channels in the frog mesenteric capillary (Abstract). *J. Physiol. London* 291: 38P, 1979.
46. BUNDGAARD, M., J. FRØKJAER-JENSEN, AND C. CRONE. Endothelial plasmalemmal vesicles as elements in a system of branching invaginations from the cell surface. *Proc. Natl. Acad. Sci. USA* 76: 6439–6442, 1979.
47. BUONASSISI, V. Sulfated mucopolysaccharide synthesis and secretion in endothelial cell cultures. *Exp. Cell Res.* 76: 363–368, 1973.
48. BUONASSISI, V., AND M. POOT. Enzymatic degradation of heparin-related mucopolysaccharides from the surface of endothelial cell cultures. *Biochim. Biophys. Acta* 385: 1–10, 1975.
49. BUONASSISI, V., AND J. C. VENTER. Hormone and neurotransmitter receptors in an established vascular endothelial cell line. *Proc. Natl. Acad. Sci. USA* 73: 1612–1616, 1976.
50. BURRI, P. H., AND E. R. WEIBEL. Beeinflussung einer spezifischen cytoplasmatischen Organelle von Endothelzellen durch Adrenalin. *Z. Zellforsch. Mikrosk. Anat.* 88: 426–440, 1968.
51. BUTCHER, E. C., R. G. SCOLLAY, AND I. L. WEISSMAN. Lymphocyte adherence to high endothelial venules: characterization of a modified in vitro assay, and examination of the binding of syngeneic and allogeneic lymphocyte populations. *J. Immunol.* 123: 1996–2003, 1979.
52. CALDWELL, P. R. B., B. C. SEEGAL, K. C. HSU, M. DAS, AND R. L. SOFFER. Angiotensin-converting enzyme: vascular endothelial localization. *Science* 191: 1050–1052, 1976.
53. CAMPBELL, G. R., AND Y. UEHARA. Formation of fenestrated capillaries in mammalian vas deferens and ureter transplants. *Z. Zellforsch. Mikrosk. Anat.* 134: 167–173, 1972.
54. CARR, J. The anti-inflammatory action of heparin: heparin as an antagonist to histamine, bradykinin and prostaglandin E_1. *Thromb. Res.* 16: 507–516, 1979.
55. CASLEY-SMITH, J. R. The functioning of endothelial fenestrae on the arterial and venous limbs of capillaries, as indicated by differing directions of passage of proteins. *Experientia* 26: 852–853, 1970.
56. CASLEY-SMITH, J. R. Endothelial fenestrae in intestinal villi: differences between the arterial and venous ends of the capillaries. *Microvasc. Res.* 3: 49–68, 1971.
57. CASLEY-SMITH, J. R. Freeze-substitution of capillary endothelium: the passage of ions and the artefactual nature of "thoroughfare channels" (Abstract). *Microvasc. Res.* 17: S8, 1979.
58. CASLEY-SMITH, J. R., AND D. B. CARTER. The passage of macromolecules across inflamed capillary endothelium via large vacuoles. *Microvasc. Res.* 18: 319–324, 1979.
59. CASLEY-SMITH, J. R., AND J. C. CHIN. The passage of cytoplasmic vesicles across endothelial and mesothelial cells. *J. Microsc. Oxford* 93: 167–189, 1971.
60. CASLEY-SMITH, J. R., AND H. I. CLARCK. The dimensions and numbers of small vesicles in blood capillary endothelium in the hind legs of dogs, and their relation to vascular permeability. *J. Microsc. Oxford* 96: 263–267, 1972.
61. CASLEY-SMITH, J. R., H. S. GREEN, AND H. J. L. WADEY. The quantitative morphology of skeletal muscle capillaries in relation to permeability. *Microvasc. Res.* 10: 43–64, 1975.
62. CAULFIELD, J. P., AND M. G. FARQUHAR. The permeability of glomerular capillaries to graded dextrans. Identification of the basement membrane as the primary filtration barrier. *J. Cell Biol.* 63: 883–903, 1974.
63. CAULFIELD, J. P., AND M. G. FARQUHAR. Distribution of anionic sites in glomerular basement membranes. Their possible role in filtration and attachment. *Proc. Natl. Acad. Sci. USA* 73: 1646–1650, 1976.
64. CAVALLO, T., R. SADE, J. FOLKMAN, AND R. S. COTRAN. Ultrastructural autoradiographic studies of the early vasoproliferative response in tumor angiogenesis. *Am. J. Pathol.* 70: 345–362, 1973.
65. CECIO, A. Ultrastructural features of cytofilaments within mammalian endothelial cells. *Z. Zellforsch. Mikrosk. Anat.* 83: 40–48, 1967.
66. CERVOS-NAVARRO, J., AND F. MATAKAS. Electron microscopic evidence for innervation of intracerebral arterioles in the cat. *Neurology* 24: 282–286, 1974.
67. CHAMBERS, R., AND B. W. ZWEIFACH. Intercellular cement and capillary permeability. *Physiol. Rev.* 27: 436–463, 1947.
68. CHANG, R. L. S., W. M. DEEN, C. R. ROBERTSON, AND B. M. BRENNER. Permselectivity of the glomerular capillary wall. III. Restricted transport of polyanions. *Kidney Int.* 8: 212–223, 1975.
69. CHANG, R. L. S., I. F. VEKI, J. L. TROY, W. M. DEEN, C. R. ROBERTSON, AND B. M. BRENNER. Permselectivity of the glomerular capillary wall to macromolecules. II. Experimental studies in rats using neutral dextrans. *Biophys. J.* 15: 887–906, 1975.
70. CHINARD, F. P. The alveolar-capillary barrier: some data and speculations. *Microvasc. Res.* 19: 1–17, 1980.
71. CHING, S. F., L. W. HAYES, AND L. L. SLAKEY. Angiotensin converting enzyme in cultured endothelial cells and growth medium. Relationships to enzyme from kidney and plasma. *Biochim. Biophys. Acta* 657: 222–231, 1981.
72. CHIPMAN, P., AND W. E. GLOVER. Histamine H_2-receptors in the human peripheral circulation. *Br. J. Pharmacol.* 56: 494–496, 1976.
73. CHO, Y., AND P. P. H. DE BRUYN. The endothelial structure of the postcapillary venules of the lymph node and the passage of lymphocytes across the venule wall. *J. Ultrastruct. Res.* 69: 13–21, 1979.
74. CLAUDE, P., AND D. A. GOODENOUGH. Fracture faces of zonulae occludentes from "tight" and "leaky" epithelia. *J. Cell Biol.* 58: 390–400, 1973.
75. CLEMENTI, F., AND G. E. PALADE. Intestinal capillaries. I. Permeability to peroxidase and ferritin. *J. Cell Biol.* 41: 33–58, 1969.
76. CLEMENTI, F., AND G. E. PALADE. Intestinal capillaries. II. Structural effects of EDTA and histamine. *J. Cell Biol.* 42: 706–714, 1969.
77. CLOUGH, G., AND C. C. MICHEL. The effect of albumin on the labelling of endothelial cell vesicles with ferritin in the frog (Abstract). *J. Physiol. London* 289: 72P–73P, 1978.
78. CLOUGH, G., AND C. C. MICHEL. The sequence of labelling of endothelial cell vesicles with ferritin in the frog (Abstract). *J. Physiol. London* 292: 61P–62P, 1979.
79. CLOUGH, G., AND C. C. MICHEL. The effects of temperature on the transport of ferritin through endothelial cell vesicles (Abstract). *Microvasc. Res.* 20: 255, 1980.

80. COHEN, M. P., AND C. J. CIBOROWSKI. Presence of glycosaminoglycans in retinal capillary basement membrane. *Biochim. Biophys. Acta* 674: 400–406, 1981.
81. COLLIN, H. B. Ultrastructure of fenestrated blood capillaries in extraocular muscles. *Exp. Eye Res.* 8: 16–20, 1979.
82. COMPER, W. D., AND T. C. LAURENT. Physiological function of connective tissue polysaccharides. *Physiol. Rev.* 58: 255–315, 1978.
83. CONNELL, C. J., AND L. MERCER. Freeze-fracture appearance of the capillary endothelium in the cerebral cortex of mouse brain. *Am. J. Anat.* 140: 595–599, 1974.
84. COOPER, M., AND J. H. WYLLIE. Some properties of 5-hydroxytryptamine receptors in the hindquarters of the rat. *Br. J. Pharmacol.* 67: 79–85, 1979.
85. COPLEY, A. L. Hemorheological aspect of the endothelium-plasma interface. *Microvasc. Res.* 8: 192–212, 1974.
86. CORDA, R., M. ALBERTI, L. CAOCCI, G. PUTZOLU, AND P. M. MANUNCCI. An increased factor VIII antigen as an indicator of endothelial damage in measles. *Thromb. Res.* 14: 805–810, 1979.
87. COSTABELLA, M. O. P., O. LINDQUIST, Y. KAPAUCI, AND T. SALDEEN. Increased vascular permeability in the delayed microembolism syndrome. Experimental and human findings. *Microvasc. Res.* 15: 275–286, 1978.
88. COTRAN, R. S. Endothelial phagocytosis: an electron-microscopic study. *Exp. Mol. Pathol.* 4: 217–231, 1965.
89. COURTOY, P. J., AND J. BOYLES. Fibronectin localization in rat capillaries (Abstract). *Eur. J. Cell Biol.* 22: 423, 1980.
90. COURTOY, P. J., Y. S. KANWAR, R. O. HYNES, AND M. G. FARQUHAR. Fibronectin localization in the rat glomerulus. *J. Cell Biol.* 87: 691–696, 1980.
91. COURTOY, P. J., Y. S. KANWAR, R. TIMPL, R. O. HYNES, AND M. G. FARQUHAR. Comparative distribution of fibronectin, type IV collagen and laminin in rat glomerulus (Abstract). *J. Cell Biol.* 87: 124a, 1980.
92. CROCKER, D. J., T. D. MURAD, AND J. C. GEER. Role of the pericyte in wound healing. An ultrastructural study. *Exp. Mol. Pathol.* 13: 51–65, 1970.
93. CRONE, C. Permeability of single capillaries compared with results from whole-organ studies. *Acta Physiol. Scand. Suppl.* 463: 75–80, 1979.
94. CRONE, C., AND O. CHRISTENSEN. Transcapillary transport of small solutes and water. In: *Cardiovascular Physiology III*, edited by A. C. Guyton and D. B. Young. Baltimore, MD: University Park, 1978, vol. 18, p. 149–213. (Int. Rev. Physiol. Ser.)
95. CRONE, C., J. FRØKJAER-JENSEN, J. J. FRIEDMAN, AND O. CHRISTENSEN. The permeability of single capillaries to potassium ions. *J. Gen. Physiol.* 71: 195–220, 1978.
96. CROSS, S. A. M., V. A. ALABASTER, Y. S. BAKHLE, AND J. R. VANE. Sites of uptake of ^{3}H-5-hydroxytryptamine in rat isolated lung. *Histochemistry* 39: 83–91, 1974.
97. DANIELLI, J. F. Capillary permeability and edema in the perfused frog. *J. Physiol. London* 98: 109–129, 1940.
98. DANON, D., AND E. SKUTELSKY. Endothelial surface charge and its possible relationship to thrombogenesis. *Ann. NY Acad. Sci.* 275: 47–63, 1976.
99. DE BRUYN, P. P. H., AND Y. CHO. Contractile structures in endothelial cells of splenic sinusoids. *J. Ultrastruct. Res.* 49: 24–33, 1974.
100. DE BRUYN, P. P. H., AND S. MICHELSON. Changes in the random distribution of sialic acid at the surface of the myeloid sinusoidal endothelium resulting from the presence of diaphragmated fenestrae. *J. Cell Biol.* 82: 708–714, 1979.
101. DE BRUYN, P. P. H., S. MICHELSON, AND R. P. BECKER. Endocytosis, transfer tubules, and lysosomal activity in myeloid sinusoidal endothelium. *J. Ultrastruct. Res.* 53: 133–151, 1975.
102. DE BRUYN, P. P. H., S. MICHELSON, AND R. P. BECKER. Nonrandom distribution of sialic acid over the cell surface of bristle-coated endocytic vesicles of the sinusoidal endothelium cells. *J. Cell Biol.* 78: 379–388, 1978.
103. DE BRUYN, P. P. H., S. MICHELSON, AND T. B. THOMAS. The migration of blood cells of the bone marrow through the sinusoidal wall. *J. Morphol.* 133: 417–438, 1971.
104. DE FOUW, D. O., AND P. B. BERENDSEN. A morphometric analysis of isolated perfused dog lungs after acute oncotic edema. *Microvasc. Res.* 17: 90–103, 1979.
105. DE KRUIJFF, B., W. J. GERRISTEN, A. OERLEMANS, R. A. DEMEL, AND L. L. M. VAN DEENEN. Polyene antibiotic-sterol interactions in membranes of *Acholeplasma laidlawii* cells and lecithin liposomes. I. Specificity of the membrane permeability changes induced by the polyene antibiotics. *Biochim. Biophys. Acta* 339: 30–43, 1974.
106. DEL VECCHIO, P., U. S. RYAN, AND J. W. RYAN. Isolation of capillary segments from rat adrenal gland (Abstract). *J. Cell Biol.* 75: 73a, 1977.
107. DERMIETZEL, R. Junctions in the central nervous system of the cat. IV. Interendothelial junctions of cerebral blood vessels from selected areas of the brain. *Cell Tissue Res.* 164: 45–62, 1975.
108. DIANA, J. N., S. C. LONG, AND H. YAO. Effect of histamine on equivalent pore radius in capillaries of isolated dog hindlimb. *Microvasc. Res.* 4: 413–437, 1972.
109. DOWNEY, H. F., F. A. BASHOUR, B. JISHI, AND P. E. PARKER. Arteriovenous shunts in dilated or reperfused canine coronary vasculature. *Microvasc. Res.* 17: 22–26, 1979.
110. DOYLE, M. J., D. F. MOSHER, AND E. A. JAFFE. Endothelial cells synthesize and secrete thrombospondin (Abstract). *J. Cell Biol.* 87: 306a, 1980.
111. ELIAS, P. M., D. S. FRIEND, AND J. GOERKE. Membrane sterol heterogeneity. Freeze-fracture detection with saponins and filipin. *J. Histochem. Cytochem.* 27: 1247–1260, 1979.
112. ELVIN, L. G. The ultrastructure of the capillary fenestrae in the adrenal medulla of the rat. *J. Ultrastruct. Res.* 12: 687–704, 1965.
113. ENGERMAN, R. L., D. PFAFFENBACH, AND M. D. DAVIS. Cell turnover of capillaries. *Lab. Invest.* 17: 738–743, 1967.
114. ERICSON, L. E., AND S. H. WOLLMAN. Increase in the rough endoplasmic reticulum in capillary endothelial cells and pericytes in hyperplastic rat thyroid glands. *Endocrinology* 107: 732–737, 1980.
115. EVENSEN, S. A., AND T. HENRIKSEN. Sterol synthesis in human endothelial cells (Abstract). *Thromb. Diath. Haemorrh.* 34: 330, 1975.
116. FAHIMI, H. D., B. A. GRAY, AND V. K. HERZOG. Cytochemical localization of catalase and peroxidase in sinusoidal cells of rat liver. *Lab. Invest.* 34: 192–201, 1976.
117. FARQUHAR, M. G. The primary filtration barrier: basement membrane or epithelial slits? *Kidney Int.* 8: 197–211, 1975.
118. FARQUHAR, M. G. Structure and function in glomerular capillaries. Role of the basement membrane in glomerular filtration. In: *Biology and Biochemistry of Basement Membranes*, edited by N. Kefalides. New York: Academic, 1978, p. 43–80.
119. FARQUHAR, M. G., AND G. E. PALADE. Glomerular permeability. II. Ferritin transfer across the glomerular capillary wall in nephrotic rats. *J. Exp. Med.* 114: 699–716, 1961.
120. FARR, A. G., AND P. P. H. DE BRUYN. The mode of lymphocyte migration through postcapillary venule endothelium in lymph node. *Am. J. Anat.* 143: 59–92, 1975.
121. FAWCETT, D. W. Comparative observations on the fine structure of blood capillaries. In: *The Peripheral Blood Vessels*, edited by J. L. Orbison and D. Smith. Baltimore, MD: Williams & Wilkins, 1963, p. 17–44.
122. FEDER, N. Microperoxidase. An ultrastructural tracer of low molecular weight. *J. Cell Biol.* 51: 339–343, 1971.
123. FIELD, J., J. V. HURLEY, AND N. E. W. MCCALLUM. The mechanism of escape of plasma protein from small blood vessels in the mucosa of the small intestine of the rat. *J. Pathol.* 121: 51–58, 1976.
124. FIELDING, P. E., I. VLODANSKY, D. GOSPODAROVICZ, AND C. J. FIELDING. Effect of contact inhibition on the regulation of cholesterol metabolism in cultured endothelial cells. *J. Biol. Chem.* 254: 749–755, 1979.

125. FISHMAN, A. P., AND G. G. PIETRA. Handling of bioactive materials by the lung. *N. Engl. J. Med.* 291, pt. 1: 884–890, 1974.
126. FISHMAN, A. P., AND G. G. PIETRA. Permeability of pulmonary vascular endothelium. In: *Lung Liquids*, edited by R. Porter and M. O'Connor. New York: Elsevier, 1976, p. 3–28. (Ciba Found. Symp. 38.)
127. FLUMERFELT, B. A., P. R. LEWIS, AND D. G. GWYN. Cholinesterase activity of capillaries in the rat brain. A light and electron microscopic study. *Histochem. J.* 5: 67–79, 1973.
128. FOLKMAN, J., AND C. HAUDENSCHILD. Angiogenesis in vitro. *Nature London* 288: 551–556, 1980.
129. FOLKMAN, J., C. C. HAUDENSCHILD, AND B. R. ZETTER. Long-term culture of capillary endothelial cells. *Proc. Natl. Acad. Sci. USA* 76: 5217–5221, 1979.
130. FORBES, M. S., M. L. RENNELS, AND E. NELSON. Ultrastructure of pericytes in mouse heart. *Am. J. Anat.* 149: 47–69, 1977.
131. FORBES, M. S., M. L. RENNELS, AND E. NELSON. Innervation of myocardial microcirculation: terminal autonomic axons associated with capillaries and postcapillary venules in mouse heart. *Am. J. Anat.* 149: 71–92, 1977.
132. FRANK, J. S., AND G. A. LANGER. The myocardial interstitium: its structure and its role in ionic exchange. *J. Cell Biol.* 60: 586–601, 1974.
133. FRANKE, W. W., E. SCHMID, M. OSBORN, AND K. WEBER. Intermediate-sized filaments of human endothelial cells. *J. Cell Biol.* 81: 570–580, 1979.
134. FRIEDERICI, H. H. R. The tridimensional ultrastructure of fenestrated capillaries. *J. Ultrastruct. Res.* 23: 444–460, 1968.
135. FRIEDERICI, H. H. R. On the diaphragm across fenestrae of capillary endothelium. *J. Ultrastruct. Res.* 27: 373–385, 1969.
136. FRØKJAER-JENSEN, J. Three-dimensional organization of plasmalemmal vesicles in endothelial cells. An analysis by serial sectioning of frog mesenteric capillaries. *J. Ultrastruct. Res.* 73: 9–20, 1980.
137. FUNG, Y. C., B. W. ZWEIFACH, AND M. INTAGLIETTA. Elastic environment of the capillary bed. *Circ. Res.* 19: 441–461, 1966.
138. GABBIANI, G., AND G. MAJNO. Fine structure of endothelium. In: *Microcirculation*, edited by G. Kaley and B. M. Altura. Baltimore, MD: University Park, 1976, vol. 1, p. 133–144.
139. GADDUM, J. H., C. O. HEBB, A. SILVER, AND A. A. B. SWAN. 5-Hydroxytryptamine. Pharmacological action and destruction in perfused lung. *Q. J. Exp. Physiol. Cogn. Med. Sci.* 38: 255–262, 1953.
140. GALEY, F., AND H. WAYLAND. Pathways of histamine-induced albumin leakage from venules. *Microvasc. Res.* 15: 263–264, 1978.
141. GAMBARELLI, D., J. F. PELLISSIER, AND J. HASSOUN. Structures tubuloréticulaires dans les cellules endothéliales et péricytaires, les lymphocytes et les cellules satellites du muscle dans un cas de sclérodermie. *C. R. Seances Soc. Biol. Paris* 168: 308–310, 1974.
142. GIACOMELLI, F., J. WIENER, AND D. SPIRO. Cross-striated arrays of filaments in endothelium. *J. Cell Biol.* 45: 188–192, 1970.
143. GIL, J., AND M. MAGNO. Fusion of pinocytotic vesicles in liquid filled lungs: a mechanism of cellular damage. *Exp. Lung Res.* 1: 43–56, 1980.
144. GIL, J., AND D. A. SILAGE. Morphometry of pinocytotic vesicles in the capillary endothelium of rabbit lungs using automated equipment. *Circ. Res.* 47: 384–391, 1980.
145. GIL, J., D. A. SILAGE, AND J. M. MCNIFF. Distribution of vesicles in cells of air-blood barrier in the rabbit. *J. Appl. Physiol.: Respirat. Environ. Exercise Physiol.* 50: 334–340, 1981.
146. GILLIS, C. N. Metabolism of vasoactive hormones by pulmonary vascular endothelium: possible functional significance. In: *Vascular Neuroeffector Mechanisms*, edited by J. A. Bevan et al. New York: Raven, 1980, p. 304–314.
147. GIMBRONE, M. A., JR., AND R. W. ALEXANDER. Insulin receptors in cultured human vascular endothelial cells (Abstract). *Circulation* 56: 809, 1977.
148. GOLDSTEIN, J. L., R. G. W. ANDERSON, AND M. S. BROWN. Coated pits, coated vesicles, and receptor-mediated endocytosis. *Nature London* 279: 679–685, 1979.
149. GOWANS, J. L., AND E. J. KNIGHT. The route of recirculation of lymphocytes in the rat. *Proc. R. Soc. London Ser. B* 159: 257–282, 1964.
150. GRAEVES, M. W., R. MARKS, AND I. ROBERTSON. Subclasses of histamine receptors on human skin blood vessels and their possible clinical significance (Abstract). *Br. J. Clin. Pharmacol.* 4: 657P, 1977.
151. GRAHAM, R. C., AND M. J. KARNOVSKY. The early stage of absorption of injected horseradish peroxidase in the proximal tubule of the mouse kidney. Ultrastructural cytochemistry by a new technique. *J. Histochem. Cytochem.* 14: 291–302, 1966.
152. GRANGER, D. N., J. C. PARKER, AND A. E. TAYLOR. Permeability of visceral exchange vessels to endogenous macromolecules (Abstract). *Microvasc. Res.* 17: S105, 1979.
153. GRANGER, H. J. Dynamics and control of the microcirculation. *Adv. Biomed. Eng.* 7: 1–63, 1979.
154. GREEN, H. S., AND J. R. CASLEY-SMITH. Calculations on the passage of small vesicles across endothelial cells by Brownian motion. *J. Theor. Biol.* 35: 103–111, 1972.
155. GREGA, G. J., J. J. MACIEJKO, R. M. RAYMOND, AND D. P. SAK. The interrelationship among histamine, various vasoactive substances, and macromolecular permeability in the canine forelimb. *Circ. Res.* 46: 264–275, 1980.
156. GROTTE, G. Passage of dextran molecules across the blood-lymph barrier. *Acta Chir. Scand. Suppl.* 211: 1–84, 1956.
157. GUTH, P. H., T. L. MOLER, AND E. SMITH. H_1 and H_2 histamine receptors in rat gastric submucosal arterioles. *Microvasc. Res.* 19: 320–328, 1980.
158. HAM, K. N., J. L. HURLEY, A. LOPATA, AND G. B. RYAN. A combined isotopic and electron microscopic study of the response of the rat uterus to exogenous estradiol. *J. Endocrinol.* 46: 71–82, 1970.
159. HAMMERSEN, F. Ultrastructure and functions of capillaries and lymphatics. *Pfluegers Arch. Suppl.*: 43–63, 1972.
160. HAMMERSEN, F. Endothelial contractility—an undecided problem in vascular research. *Beitr. Pathol.* 157: 327–348, 1976.
161. HASHIMOTO, P. Intercellular channels as a route for protein passage in the capillary endothelium of the shark brain. *Am. J. Anat.* 134: 41–58, 1972.
162. HAUSMANN, K., U. WULFHEKEL, J. DÜLLMANN, AND R. KUSE. Iron storage in macrophages and endothelial cells. Histochemistry, ultrastructure and clinical significance. *Blut* 32: 289–295, 1976.
163. HELTIANU, C., M. SIMIONESCU, AND N. SIMIONESCU. Histamine receptors of the microvascular endothelium revealed in situ with a histamine-ferritin conjugate: characteristic high affinity binding sites in venules. *J. Cell Biol.* 93: 357–364, 1982.
164. HENDERSON, J. R., AND M. C. MOSS. The ultrastructure of endocrine and exocrine capillaries in the pancreas (Abstract). *Microvasc. Res.* 20: 253, 1980.
165. HENQUELL, L., AND C. R. HONIG. Intercapillary distances and capillary reserve in right and left ventricles: significance for control of tissue P_{O_2}. *Microvasc. Res.* 12: 35–41, 1976.
166. HIEBERT, L. M., AND L. B. JAQUES. Heparin uptake on endothelium. *Artery* 2: 26–37, 1976.
167. HILEY, C. R., H. WILSON, AND M. S. YATES. Identification of β-adrenoceptors and histamine receptors in the cat nasal vasculature. *Acta Oto-Laryngol.* 85: 444–448, 1978.
168. HJELLE, T. J., J. BAIRD-LAMBERT, G. CARDINALE, S. SPECTOR, AND S. UDENFRIEND. Isolated microvessels: the blood-brain barrier in vitro. *Proc. Natl. Acad. Sci. USA* 75: 4544–4548, 1978.
169. HOWARD, B. V. Uptake of very low density lipoprotein triglyceride by bovine aortic endothelial cells in culture. *J. Lipid Res.* 18: 561–571, 1977.
170. HOWARD, B. V., E. J. MACARAK, D. GUNSON, AND N. A. KEFALIDES. Characterization of the collagen synthesized by endothelial cells in culture. *Proc. Natl. Acad. Sci. USA* 73:

2361–2364, 1976.

171. HULSTRÖM, D., AND E. SVENSJÖ. Simultaneous fluorescence and electron microscopical detection of bradykinin induced macromolecular leakage. In: *Recent Advances in Basic Microcirculatory Research: Proceedings, Part 1*, edited by G. Wolf-Heidegger and D. H. Lewis. Basel: Karger, 1977, p. 466–468.
172. HURLEY, J. V., AND N. E. W. MCCALLUM. The degree and functional significance of the escape of marker particles from small blood vessels with fenestrated endothelium. *J. Pathol.* 113: 183–196, 1974.
173. ICHIKAWA, I., AND B. M. BRENNER. Mechanisms of action of histamine and histamine antagonists on the glomerular microcirculation in the rat. *Circ. Res.* 45: 737–745, 1979.
174. INOUE, S., R. P. MICHEL, AND J. C. HOGG. Zonulae occludentes in alveolar epithelium and capillary endothelium in dog lungs studied with the freeze-fracture technique. *J. Ultrastruct. Res.* 56: 215–225, 1976.
175. JACQUES, P. J. Endocytosis. In: *Lysosomes in Biology and Pathology*, edited by J. T. Lucy and H. B. Fell. Amsterdam: North-Holland, 1969, vol. 2, chapt. 13, p. 395–420.
176. JAFFE, E. A. Endothelial cells and the biology of factor VIII. *N. Engl. J. Med.* 296: 377–383, 1977.
177. JAFFE, E. A., L. W. HOYER, AND R. L. NACHMAN. Synthesis of antihemophilic factor antigen by cultured human endothelial cells. *J. Clin. Invest.* 52: 2757–2764, 1973.
178. JAFFE, E. A., L. W. HOYER, AND R. L. NACHMAN. Synthesis of von Willebrand factor by cultured human endothelial cells. *Proc. Natl. Acad. Sci. USA* 71: 1906–1919, 1974.
179. JAFFE, E. A., C. R. MINIK, B. ADELMAN, C. G. BECKER, AND R. NACHMAN. Synthesis of basement membrane collagen by cultured human endothelial cells. *J. Exp. Med.* 144: 209–225, 1976.
180. JAFFE, E. A., AND D. F. MOSHER. Synthesis of fibronectin by cultured human endothelial cells. *J. Exp. Med.* 147: 1779–1791, 1978.
181. JENNINGS, M. A., V. T. MARCHESI, AND H. FLOREY. The transport of particles across the walls of small blood vessels (Abstract). *Proc. R. Soc. London Ser. B* 156: 14, 1962.
182. JOHANSSON, B. R. Permeability of muscle capillaries to interstitially microinjected horseradish peroxidase. *Microvasc. Res.* 16: 340–353, 1978.
183. JOHANSSON, B. R. Movement of interstitially microinjected ^{125}I-labelled albumin into blood capillaries of rat skeletal muscle demonstrated with electron microscopic autoradiography. *Microvasc. Res.* 16: 354–361, 1978.
184. JOHANSSON, B. R. Permeability of muscle capillaries to interstitially microinjected ferritin. *Microvasc. Res.* 16: 362–368, 1978.
185. JOHANSSON, B. R. Capillary permeability to interstitial microinjections of macromolecules and influence of capillary hydrostatic pressure on endothelial ultrastructure. *Acta Physiol. Scand.* 463: 45–50, 1979.
186. JOHANSSON, B. R. Size and distribution of endothelial plasmalemmal vesicles in consecutive segments of the microvasculature in cat skeletal muscle. *Microvasc. Res.* 17: 107–117, 1979.
187. JOHANSSON, B. R. Quantitative ultrastructural morphometry of blood capillary endothelium in skeletal muscle. Effect of venous pressure. *Microvasc. Res.* 17: 118–130, 1979.
188. JORIS, I., G. MAJNO, AND G. B. RYAN. Endothelial contraction in vivo: a study of the rat mesentery. *Virchows Arch. B* 12: 73–83, 1972.
189. JUNOD, A. F. Uptake, metabolism and efflux of ^{14}C-5-hydroxytryptamine in isolated perfused rat lungs. *J. Pharmacol. Exp. Ther.* 183: 341–355, 1972.
190. JUNOD, A. F. Metabolism of vasoactive agents in lung. *Am. Rev. Respir. Dis.* 115, pt. 2: 51–57, 1977.
191. KALEY, G., AND B. M. ALTURA (editors). *Microcirculation.* Baltimore, MD: University Park, 1977, vol. 1.
192. KANWAR, Y. S., AND M. G. FARQUHAR. Anionic sites in the glomerular basement membrane. In vivo and in vitro localization to the laminae rarae by cationic probes. *J. Cell Biol.* 81: 137–153, 1979.
193. KANWAR, Y. S., AND M. G. FARQUHAR. Presence of heparan sulfate in the glomerular basement membrane. *Proc. Natl. Acad. Sci. USA* 76: 1303–1307, 1979.
194. KANWAR, Y. S., AND M. G. FARQUHAR. Detachment of endothelium and epithelium from the glomerular basement membrane produced by kidney perfusion with neuraminidase. *Lab. Invest.* 42: 375–384, 1980.
195. KARNOVSKY, M. J. The ultrastructural basis of capillary permeability studied with peroxidase as a tracer. *J. Cell Biol.* 35: 213–236, 1967.
196. KARNOVSKY, M. J. Morphology of capillaries with special reference to muscle capillaries. In: *Capillary Permeability*, edited by C. Crone and N. A. Lassen. Copenhagen: Munksgaard, 1970, p. 341–350. (Alfred Benzon Symp. 2.)
197. KARNOVSKY, M. J., AND M. M. LEVENTHAL. Some aspects of the structural basis for permeability of small blood vessels. In: *Small Vessel Angiography*, edited by S. K. Hilal. St. Louis, MO: Mosby, 1973.
198. KARNOVSKY, M. J., AND D. F. RICE. Exogenous cytochrome c as an ultrastructural tracer. *J. Histochem. Cytochem.* 17: 751–753, 1969.
199. KARNUSHINA, J. L., J. M. PALACIOS, G. BARBIN, E. DUX, F. JOO, AND J. C. SCHWARTZ. Studies on a capillary-rich fraction isolated from brain: histaminic components and characterization of the histamine receptors linked to adenylate cyclase. *J. Neurochem.* 34: 1201–1208, 1980.
200. KAYE, G. I., AND G. D. PAPPAS. Studies of the cornea. I. The fine structure of the rabbit cornea and the transport of colloidal particles by the cornea in vivo. *J. Cell Biol.* 12: 457–479, 1962.
201. KEFALIDES, N. A., J. D. CAMERON, E. A. TOMICHEK, AND M. YANOFF. Biosynthesis of basement membrane collagen by rabbit corneal endothelium in vitro. *J. Biol. Chem.* 251: 730–733, 1976.
202. KITTAS, C., AND L. HENRY. An electron microscopic study of the changes induced by oestrogens on the lymph-node post-capillary venules. *J. Pathol.* 129: 21–29, 1979.
203. KITTAS, C., AND L. HENRY. Ultrastructural effects of sex hormones and infection on lymph node post-capillary venules. *J. Pathol.* 132: 121–131, 1980.
204. KLEINFELD, A. N., W. J. PJURA, R. L. HOOVER, R. D. KLAUSNER, AND M. J. KARNOVSKY. Lipid domains in membranes (Abstract). *Biophys. J.* 33: 192a, 1981.
205. KLYNSTRA, F. B. On the passage-restricting role of acid mucopolysaccharides in the endothelium of pig aortas. *Atherosclerosis* 19: 215–220, 1974.
206. KOBAYASHI, S. Occurrence of unique colloidal particles in snake blood and their transport across the capillary wall. A proposal of a new hypothesis on the permeability of the blood capillaries. *Arch. Histol. Jpn.* 31: 511–528, 1970.
207. KOBAYASHI, S. Ferritin labeling in the fixed muscle capillary. A doubt on the tracer experiments as the basis for the vesicular transport theory. *Arch. Histol. Jpn.* 32: 81–86, 1970.
208. KOO, A., L. H. SMAJE, K. A. DZIELGIELEWSKA, P. H. SPENCER, AND W. P. PENN. Low permeability to macromolecules of the fenestrated capillaries in the cat mandibular salivary gland (Abstract). *Microvasc. Res.* 20: 256, 1980.
209. KORNELIUSSEN, H. Fenestrated blood capillaries and lymphatic capillaries in rat skeletal muscle. *Cell Tissue Res.* 163: 169–174, 1975.
210. KRISTENSEN, K., AND Y. OLSSON. Accumulation of protein tracers in pericytes of the central nervous system following systemic injection in immature mice. *Acta. Neurol. Scand.* 49: 189–194, 1973.
211. KUHN, L. C., AND J. P. KRAEHENBUHL. Role of secretory component, a secreted glycoprotein, in the specific uptake of IgA dimer by epithelial cells. *J. Biol. Chem.* 254: 11072–11081, 1979.
212. LANDIS, E. M., AND J. R. PAPPENHEIMER. Exchange of substances through the capillary walls. In: *Handbook of Physiology. Circulation,* edited by W. F. Hamilton. Washington, DC:

Am. Physiol. Soc., 1963, sect. 2, vol. II, chapt. 29, p. 961–1034.

213. LATTA, H., AND W. H. JOHNSTON. The glycoprotein inner layer of glomerular capillary basement membrane as a filtration barrier. *J. Ultrastruct. Res.* 51: 65–67, 1976.

214. LATTA, H., W. H. JOHNSTON, AND T. M. STANLEY. Sialoglycoproteins and filtration barriers in the glomerular capillary walls. *J. Ultrastruct. Res.* 51: 354–376, 1975.

215. LAURENT, T. C. The structure and function of the intercellular polysaccharides in connective tissue. In: *Capillary Permeability*, edited by C. Crone and N. A. Lassen. Copenhagen: Munksgaard, 1970, p. 261. (Alfred Benzon Symp. 2.)

216. LE BEAU, Y. J., AND J. WILLEMOT. Actin-like filaments in the endothelial cells of adult rat brain capillaries. *Exp. Neurol.* 58: 446–454, 1978.

217. LEWIS, L. J., J. C. HOAK, R. D. MACA, AND G. L. FRY. Replication of human endothelial cells in culture. *Science* 181: 453–454, 1973.

218. LIDDEL, R. H. A., AND J. G. SIMPSON. The effect of EDTA on the endothelial changes induced in post-capillary venules by histamine (Abstract). *Microvasc. Res.* 20: 255, 1980.

219. LIN, S. Y., AND T. L. GOODFRIEND. Angiotensin receptors. *Am. J. Physiol.* 218: 1319–1328, 1970.

220. LOLLAR, P., J. C. HOAK, AND W. G. OWEN. Binding of thrombin to cultured human endothelial cells. Nonequilibrium aspects. *J. Biol. Chem.* 255: 10279–10283, 1980.

221. LOLLAR, P., AND W. G. OWEN. Evidence that the effects of thrombin on arachidonate metabolism in cultured human endothelial cells are not mediated by a high affinity receptor. *J. Biol. Chem.* 225: 8031–8034, 1980.

222. LOSSINSKY, A. S., J. H. GARCIA, L. IWANOVSKI, AND W. E. LIGHTFOOTE, JR. New ultrastructural evidence for a protein transport system in endothelial cells of gerbil brains. *Acta Neuropathol.* 47: 105–110, 1979.

223. LOUDON, M. F., C. C. MICHEL, AND I. F. WHITE. Proceedings: some observations upon the rate of labeling of endothelial vesicles by ferritin in frog mesenteric capillaries (Abstract). *J. Physiol. London* 252: 79P–80P, 1975.

224. LOUDON, M. F., C. C. MICHEL, AND I. F. WHITE. The labelling of vesicles in frog endothelial cells with ferritin. *J. Physiol. London* 296: 97–112, 1979.

225. LUFT, J. H. Fine structure of the diaphragm across capillary "pores" in mouse intestine (Abstract). *Anat. Rec.* 148: 307, 1964.

226. LUFT, J. H. Fine structure of capillary and endo-capillary layer as revealed by ruthenium red. *Federation Proc.* 25: 1773–1783, 1966.

227. LUKENS, T. W., AND J. BORENSZTAJN. Effects of C apoproteins on the activity of endothelium-bound lipoprotein lipase. *Biochem. J.* 175: 1143–1146, 1978.

228. MACARAK, E. J., B. V. HOWARD, AND N. A. KEFALIDES. Biosynthesis of collagen and metabolism of lipids by endothelial cells in culture. *Ann. NY Acad. Sci.* 275: 104–113, 1976.

229. MACARAK, E. J., E. KIRBY, T. KIRK, AND N. A. KEFALIDES. Synthesis of cold insoluble globulin by cultured calf endothelial cells. *Proc. Natl. Acad. Sci. USA* 75: 2621–2625, 1978.

230. MADRI, J. A., B. DREYER, F. A. PITLICK, AND H. FURTHMAYR. The collagenous components of the subendothelium. Correlation of structure and function. *Lab. Invest.* 43: 303–315, 1980.

231. MAJNO, G. Ultrastructure of the vascular membrane. In: *Handbook of Physiology. Circulation*, edited by W. F. Hamilton. Washington, DC: Am. Physiol. Soc., 1965, sect. 2, vol. III, chapt. 64, p. 2293–2375.

232. MAJNO, G. Two endothelial "novelties": endothelial contraction; collagenase digestion of the basement membrane. In: *Vascular Factors and Thrombosis*, edited by F. Koller et al. Stuttgart, West Germany: Schattauer, 1970, p. 23–30.

233. MAJNO, G., AND, I. JORIS. Endothelium 1977: a review. In: *The Thrombotic Process in Atherogenesis*, edited by A. B. Chandler, K. Eurenius, G. C. McMillan, C. B. Nelson, C. J. Schwartz, and S. Wessler. New York: Plenum, 1978, p. 169–227.

234. MAJNO, G., AND M. LEVENTHAL. Pathogenesis of "histamine-type" vascular leakage. *Lancet* 2: 99, 1967.

235. MAJNO, G., AND G. E. PALADE. Studies on inflammation. I. The effect of histamine and serotonin on vascular permeability: an electron microscopic study. *J. Biophys. Biochem. Cytol.* 11: 571–605, 1961.

236. MAJNO, G., G. E. PALADE., AND G. I. SCHOEFL. Studies on inflammation. II. The site of action of histamine and serotonin along the vascular tree: a topographical study. *J. Biophys. Biochem. Cytol.* 11: 607–626, 1961.

237. MAJNO, G., S. M. SHEA, AND M. LEVENTHAL. Endothelial contraction induced by histamine-type mediators. An electron microscopic study. *J. Cell Biol.* 42: 647–672, 1969.

238. MARCHESI, V. T. The role of pinocytotic vesicles in the transport of material across the wall of small blood vessels (Abstract). *J. Invest. Ophthalmol.* 4: 1111, 1965.

239. MARCHESI, V. T., AND R. J. BARRNETT. The demonstration of enzymatic activity in pinocytic vesicles of blood capillaries with the electron microscope. *J. Cell Biol.* 17: 547–556, 1963.

240. MARCHESI, V. T., AND J. L. GOWANS. The migration of lymphocytes through the endothelium of venules in lymph nodes: an electron microscope study. *Proc. R. Soc. London Ser. B* 159: 283–296, 1964.

241. MARTINEZ-PALOMO, A., AND D. ERLIJ. Structure of tight junctions in epithelia with different permeability. *Proc. Natl. Acad. Sci. USA* 72: 4487–4491, 1975.

242. MASON, J. C., F. E. CURRY, I. F. WHITE, AND C. C. MICHEL. The ultrastructure of frog mesenteric capillaries of known filtration coefficient. *Q. J. Exp. Physiol.* 64: 217–224, 1979.

243. MASON, J. C., C. C. MICHEL, AND J. E. TOOKE. The effect of plasma proteins and capillary pressure upon the filtration coefficient of frog mesenteric capillaries (Abstract). *J. Physiol. London* 229: 15P–16P, 1973.

244. MASON, R. G., D. SHARP, H. Y. K. CHUANG, AND S. F. MOHAMMAD. The endothelium. *Arch. Pathol. Lab. Med.* 101: 61–64, 1977.

245. MATSUSAKA, T. Tridimensional views of the relationship of pericytes to endothelial cells of capillaries in the human choroid and retina. *J. Electron Microsc.* 24: 13–18, 1975.

246. MAUL, G. G. Structure and formation of pores in fenestrated capillaries. *J. Ultrastruct. Res.* 36: 768–782, 1971.

247. MCAUSLAN, B. R., G. N. HANNAU, W. REILLY, AND F. H. C. STEWART. Variant endothelial cells. Fibronectin as a transducer of signals for migration and neovascularization. *J. Cell Physiol.* 104: 177–186, 1980.

248. MCDONALD, J. A., B. J. BAUM, D. M. ROSENBERG, J. A. KELMAN, S. C. BRIN, AND R. G. CRYSTAL. Destruction of a major extracellular adhesive glycoprotein (fibronectin) of human fibroblasts by neutral proteases from polymorphonuclear leukocyte granules. *Lab. Invest.* 40: 350–357, 1979.

249. MCGRATH, J. M., AND G. J. STEWART. The effects of endotoxin on vascular endothelium. *J. Exp. Med.* 129: 833–848, 1969.

250. MCGRATH, M. A., AND J. T. SHEPHERD. Histamine and 5-hydroxytryptamine inhibition of transmitter release mediated by H_2- and 5-hydroxytryptamine receptors. *Federation Proc.* 37: 195–198, 1978.

251. MCKINNEY, R. V., JR., B. BALDEV SINGH, AND P. D. BREWER. Fenestrations in regenerating skeletal muscle capillaries. *Am. J. Anat.* 150: 213–218, 1977.

252. MCNAMEE, J. E., AND N. C. STAUB. Pore models of sheep lung microvascular barrier using new data on protein tracers. *Microvasc. Res.* 18: 229–244, 1979.

253. MICHEL, C. C. The investigation of capillary permeability in single vessels. *Acta Physiol. Scand. Suppl.* 463: 67–74, 1979.

254. MICHEL, C. C. The flow of water through the capillary wall. In: *Water Transport Across Epithelia. Barriers, Gradients, and Mechanisms,* edited by H. H. Ussing, N. B. Bindslev, N. A. Lassen, and O. Sten-Knudsen. Copenhagen: Munksgaard, 1981, p. 268–282. (Alfred Benzon Symp. 15.)

255. MICHEL, C. C., AND J. R. LEVICK. Variations in permeability

along individually perfused capillaries of the frog mesentery. *Q. J. Exp. Physiol.* 62: 1–10, 1977.
256. MOHAMED, A. H., J. P. WATERHOUSE, AND H. H. R. FRIEDERICI. The fine structure of gingival terminal vascular bed. *Microvasc. Res.* 6: 137–152, 1973.
257. MONCADA, S., H. G. HERMAN, E. A. HIGGS, AND J. R. VANE. Differential formation of prostacyclin by layers of the arterial wall. An explanation for the antithrombotic properties of vascular endothelium. *Thromb. Res.* 11: 323–344, 1977.
258. MONCADA, S., E. A. HIGGS, AND J. R. VANE. Human arterial and venous tissues generate prostacyclin, a potent inhibitor of platelet aggregation. *Lancet* 1: 18–20, 1977.
259. MONTESANO, R., A. PERRELET, P. VASSALI, AND L. ORCI. Absence of filipin-sterol complexes from large coated pits on the surface of culture cells. *Proc. Natl. Acad. Sci. USA* 76: 6391–6395, 1979.
260. MOORE, A., E. A. JAFFE, C. G. BECKER, AND R. L. NACHMAN. Myosin in cultured human endothelial cells. *Br. J. Haematol.* 35: 71–79, 1977.
261. MOORE, D. H., AND H. RUSKA. The fine structure of capillaries and small arteries. *J. Biophys. Biochem. Cytol.* 3: 457–479, 1957.
262. MOVAT, H. Z., AND N. V. P. FERNANDO. The fine structure of the terminal vascular bed. IV. The venules and their perivascular cells (pericytes, adventitial cells). *Exp. Mol. Pathol.* 3: 98–114, 1964.
263. MURPHY, E. M., AND P. C. JOHNSON. Possible contribution of basement membrane to the structural rigidity of blood capillaries. *Microvasc. Res.* 9: 243–245, 1975.
264. NACHMAN, R. L., E. A. JAFFE, AND B. FERRIS. Multiple molecular forms of endothelial cell factor VIII related antigen. *Biochim. Biophys. Acta* 667: 361–369, 1981.
265. NAITO, M., AND E. WISSE. Filtration effect of endothelial fenestrations on chylomicron transport in neonatal rat liver sinusoids. *Cell Tissue Res.* 190: 371–382, 1978.
266. NORBERG, B., AND L. RYDGREN. Lymphocyte migration through the walls of the post-capillary venules. *Lymphology* 11: 211–215, 1978.
267. NORMAN, A. W., A. M. SPIELVOGEL, AND R. G. WONG. Polyene antibiotic-sterol interaction. *Adv. Lipid Res.* 14: 127–170, 1976.
268. OHSAKA, A., K. SUZUKI, AND M. OHASHI. The spurting of erythrocytes through junctions of the vascular endothelium treated with snake venom. *Microvasc. Res.* 10: 208–213, 1975.
269. OLIVECRONA, T., G. BENGTSSON, S. MARKLUND, U. LINDAHL, AND M. HOOK. Heparin-lipoprotein lipase interactions. *Federation Proc.* 36: 60–65, 1977.
270. OWMAN, C., L. EDVINSSON, AND J. E. HARDEBO. Amine mechanisms and contractile properties of the cerebral microvascular endothelium. In: *Vascular Neuroeffector Mechanisms*, edited by J. A. Bevan et al. New York: Raven, 1980, p. 277–290.
271. OWMAN, C., L. EDVINSSON, J. E. HARDEBO, U. GROSCHEL-STEWART, K. UNSICKER, AND B. WALLES. Immunohistochemical demonstration of actin and myosin in brain capillaries. *Acta Neurol. Scand. Suppl.* 64: 384–385, 1977.
272. PAASKE, W. P. Capillary permeability in skeletal muscle. *Acta Physiol. Scand.* 101: 1–14, 1977.
273. PAASKE, W. P., AND P. SEJRSEN. Transcapillary exchange of ^{14}C-inulin by free diffusion in channels of fused vesicles. *Acta Physiol. Scand.* 100: 437–445, 1977.
274. PALADE, G. E. Fine structure of blood capillaries (Abstract). *J. Appl. Phys.* 24: 1424, 1953.
275. PALADE, G. E. Transport in quanta across the endothelium of blood capillaries (Abstract). *Anat. Rec.* 136: 254, 1960.
276. PALADE, G. E. Blood capillaries of the heart and other organs. *Circulation* 24: 368–384, 1961.
277. PALADE, G. E., AND R. R. BRUNS. Structural modulations of plasmalemmal vesicles. *J. Cell Biol.* 37: 633–649, 1968.
278. PALADE, G. E., M. SIMIONESCU, AND N. SIMIONESCU. Transport of solutes across the vascular endothelium. In: *Transport of Macromolecules in Cellular Systems*, edited by S. Silverstein. Berlin: Dahlem Konferenzen, 1978, 145–166.
279. PALADE, G. E., M. SIMIONESCU, AND N. SIMIONESCU. Structural aspects of the permeability of the microvascular endothelium. *Acta Physiol. Scand. Suppl.* 463: 11–32, 1979.
280. PAYLING-WRIGHT, H. Endothelial turnover. In: *Vascular Factors and Thrombosis*, edited by F. Koller et al. Stuttgart, West Germany: Schattauer, 1970, p. 79–84.
281. PEARSE, B. M. F. Clathrin: a unique protein associated with intracellular transfer of membrane by coated vesicles. *Proc. Natl. Acad. Sci. USA* 73: 1255–1259, 1976.
282. PELIKAN, P., M. A. GIMBRONE, JR., AND R. S. COTRAN. Distribution and movement of anionic cell surface sites in cultured human vascular endothelial cells. *Atherosclerosis* 32: 69–80, 1979.
283. PIETRA, G. G., L. C. SPAGNOLI, D. M. CAPUZZI, C. E. SPARKS, A. P. FISHMAN, AND J. B. MARSH. Metabolism of ^{125}I-labeled lipoprotein by the isolated rat lung. *J. Cell Biol.* 70: 33–46, 1976.
284. PIETRA, G. G., J. P. SZIDON, H. A. CARPENTER, AND A. P. FISHMAN. Bronchial venular leakage during endotoxin shock. *Am. J. Pathol.* 77: 387–406, 1974.
285. PIETRA, G. G., J. P. SZIDON, M. M. LEVENTHAL, AND A. P. FISHMAN. Hemoglobin as a tracer in hemodynamic pulmonary edema. *Science* 166: 1643–1645, 1969.
286. PJURA, W. J., A. M. KLEINFELD, R. L. HOOVER, R. D. KLAUSNER, AND M. J. KARNOVSKY. Free fatty acid associated plasma membrane perturbation (Abstract). *Biophys. J.* 33: 177a, 1981.
287. PLATTNER, H., E. WACHTER, AND P. GROBNER. A heme-nonapeptide tracer for electron microscopy. Preparation, characterization and comparison with other heme-tracers. *Histochemistry* 53: 223–242, 1977.
288. PODOR, T. J., AND N. SORGENTE. Elastase activity in the media of cultured endothelial cells (Abstract). *J. Cell Biol.* 87: 64a, 1980.
289. POLIVERNI, P. J., R. S. COTRAN, AND M. M. SHOLLEY. Endothelial proliferation in the delayed hypersensitivity reaction: an autographic study. *J. Immunol.* 118: 529–532, 1977.
290. RABB, J. M., M. L. RENAUD, P. A. BRANDT, AND C. W. WITT. Effect of freezing and thawing on the microcirculation and capillary endothelium of the hamster cheek pouch. *Cryobiology* 11: 508–518, 1974.
291. RACKER, D. K. Negative staining of whole cells: transmission electron microscopy of peripheral organelles in rat venous endothelial cells. *J. Histochem. Cytochem.* 26: 417–421, 1978.
292. RASTOGI, B. K., AND A. NORDOY. Lipid composition of cultured human endothelial cells. *Thromb. Res.* 18: 629–641, 1980.
293. RECKLESS, J. P. D., T. B. WEINSTEIN, AND D. STEINBERG. Lipoprotein and cholesterol metabolism in rabbit arterial endothelial cells in culture. *Biochim. Biophys. Acta* 529: 475–487, 1978.
294. REESE, T. C., AND M. J. KARNOVSKY. Fine structural localization of a blood-brain barrier to exogenous peroxidase. *J. Cell Biol.* 34: 207–217, 1976.
295. RENKIN, E. M. Transport of large molecules across capillary walls. *Physiologist* 7: 13–28, 1964.
296. RENKIN, E. M. Multiple pathways of capillary permeability. *Circ. Res.* 41: 735–743, 1977.
297. RENKIN, E. M. Transport pathways through capillary endothelium. *Microvasc. Res.* 15: 123–136, 1978.
298. RENKIN, E. M. Relation of capillary morphology to transport of fluid and large molecules: a review. *Acta Physiol. Scand. Suppl.* 463: 81–91, 1979.
299. RENKIN, E. M., AND F. E. CURRY. Transport of water and solutes across capillary endothelium. In: *Transport Organs*, edited by G. Giebisch, D. C. Tosteson, and H. H. Ussing. Berlin: Springer-Verlag, 1978, vol. 4, pts. A and B, p. 1–45. (Membrane Transport in Biology Ser.)
300. RENKIN, E. M., W. L. JOYNER, C. H. SLOOP, AND P. D. WATSON. Influence of venous pressure on plasma-lymph transport in the dog's paw: convective and dissipative mecha-

nisms. *Microvasc. Res.* 14: 191–204, 1977.

301. RENNELS, M. L., AND E. NELSON. Capillary innervation in the mammalian central nervous system: an electron microscopic demonstration. *Am. J. Anat.* 144: 233–241, 1975.
302. RENNKE, H. G., R. S. COTRAN, AND M. A. VENKATACHALAM. Role of molecular charge in glomerular permeability. Tracer studies with cationized ferritins. *J. Cell Biol.* 67: 638–646, 1975.
303. RENNKE, H. G., Y. PATEL, AND M. A. VENKATACHALAM. Glomerular filtration of proteins: clearance of anionic, neutral and cationic horseradish peroxidase in the rat. *Kidney Int.* 13: 278–288, 1978.
304. RHODIN, J. A. G. The ultrastructure of mammalian arterioles and pericapillary sphincters. *J. Ultrastruct. Res.* 18: 181–223, 1967.
305. RHODIN, J. A. G. Ultrastructure of mammalian venous capillaries, venules, and small collecting veins. *J. Ultrastruct. Res.* 25: 452–500, 1968.
306. RICHARDSON, J. B., AND A. BEAULNES. The cellular site of action of angiotensin. *J. Cell Biol.* 51: 419–432, 1971.
307. RIPPE, B., A. KAMIYA, AND B. FOLKOW. Transcapillary passage of albumin, effects of tissue cooling and of increases in filtration and plasma colloid osmotic pressure. *Acta Physiol. Scand.* 105: 171–187, 1979.
308. ROBINSON, J. M., AND M. J. KARNOWSKY. Evaluation of the polyene antibiotic filipin as a cytochemical probe for membrane cholesterol. *J. Histochem. Cytochem.* 28: 27–42, 1980.
309. RODEWALD, R. Distribution of immunoglobulin G receptors in the small intestine of the young rat. *J. Cell Biol.* 85: 18–32, 1980.
310. ROHLICH, P., AND I. OLAH. Cross-striated fibrils in the endothelium of the rat myometrial arterioles. *J. Ultrastruct. Res.* 18: 667–676, 1967.
311. ROUS, P., AND F. SMITH. The gradient of vascular permeability. III. The gradient along the capillaries and venules of frog skin. *J. Exp. Med.* 53: 219–224, 1931.
312. RUBIN, B. T. A theoretical model of the pinocytic vesicular transport process in endothelial cells. *J. Theor. Biol.* 64: 619–647, 1977.
313. RUOSLAHTI, E., AND E. ENGVALL. Complexing of fibronectin glycosaminoglycans and collagen. *Biochim. Biophys. Acta* 631: 350–358, 1980.
314. RYAN, G. B., AND G. MAJNO. Acute inflammation. A review. *Am. J. Pathol.* 86: 183–276, 1977.
315. RYAN, J. W., AND U. S. RYAN. Pulmonary endothelial cells. *Federation Proc.* 36: 2683–2691, 1977.
316. RYAN, J. W., AND V. SMITH. The metabolism of angiotensin I by endothelial cells. In: *Protides of the Biological Fluids*, edited by H. Peeters. Oxford, UK: Pergamon, 1973, vol. 20, p. 379–384.
317. RYAN, U. S., AND J. W. RYAN. Correlations between the fine structure of the alveolar-capillary unit and its metabolic activities. In: *Lung Biology in Health and Disease. Metabolic Functions of the Lung*, edited by Y. S. Bakhle and J. R. Vane. New York: Dekker, 1977, vol. 4, p. 197–232.
318. RYAN, U. S., J. W. RYAN, D. S. SMITH, AND H. WINKLER. Fenestrated endothelium of the adrenal gland: freeze-fracture studies. *Tissue Cell* 7: 181–190, 1975.
319. RYAN, U. S., J. W. RYAN, C. WHITAKER, AND A. CHIN. Localization of angiotensin converting enzyme (kininase II). II. Immunocytochemistry and immunofluorescence. *Tissue Cell* 8: 125–145, 1976.
320. SANTOLAYA, R. C., AND F. BERTINI. Fine structure of endothelial cells of vertebrates. Distribution of dense granules. *Z. Anat. Entwicklungsgesch.* 131: 148–155, 1970.
321. SAWYER, P. N., AND S. SRINIVASAN. The role of electrochemical surface properties in thrombosis at vascular interface: cumulative experience of studies in animals and man. *Bull. NY Acad. Med.* 48: 235–249, 1972.
322. SAWYER, P. N., B. STANCZEWSKI, N. RAMASAY, W. S. RAMSEY, JR., AND S. SRINIVASAN. Electrochemical interactions at the endothelial surface. *J. Supramol. Struct.* 1: 417–436, 1973.
323. SCHLEEF, R., AND C. BIRDWELL. Proteases and endothelial cell migraton in vitro (Abstract). *J. Cell Biol.* 87: 319a, 1981.
324. SCHNEEBERGER, E. E. Ultrastructural basis for alveolar-capillary permeability to protein. In: *Lung Liquids*, edited by R. Porter and M. O'Connor. Amsterdam: Excerpta Med. Found., 1976, p. 3–28. (Ciba Found. Symp. 38.)
325. SCHNEEBERGER, E. E., AND M. J. KARNOVSKY. The influence of intravascular fluid volume on the permeability of newborn and adult mouse lungs to ultrastructural protein tracers. *J. Cell Biol.* 49: 319–334, 1971.
326. SCHNEEBERGER, E. E., AND M. J. KARNOVSKY. Substructure of intercellular junctions in freeze-fractured alveolar-capillary membranes of mouse lung. *Circ. Res.* 38: 404–411, 1976.
327. SCHNEEBERGER-KELLEY, E. E., AND M. J. KARNOVSKY. The ultrastructural basis of alveolar-capillary membrane permeability to peroxidase used as a tracer. *J. Cell Biol.* 37: 781–793, 1968.
328. SCHOEFL, G. J. Studies on inflammation. III. Growing capillaries: their structure and permeability. *Virchows Arch. A* 377: 97–121, 1963.
329. SCHOEFL, G. J. The migration of lymphocytes across the vascular endothelium in lymphoid tissue. *J. Exp. Med.* 136: 568–588, 1972.
330. SCHWARTZ, S. M., AND E. P. BENDITT. Cell replication in the aortic endothelium: a new method for study of the problem. *Lab. Invest.* 28: 699–707, 1973.
331. SCOW, R. O., E. J. BLANCHETTE-MACKIE, AND L. C. SMITH. Role of capillary endothelium in the clearance of chylomicrons. A model for lipid transport from blood by lateral diffusion in cell membranes. *Circ. Res.* 39: 149–162, 1976.
332. SCOW, R.O., C. R. MENDELSON, O. ZINDER, M. HAMOSH, AND E. J. BLANCHETTE-MACKIE. Role of lipoprotein lipase in the delivery of dietary fatty acids to lactating mammary tissue. In: *Dietary Lipids and Postnatal Development,* edited by C. Galli, G. Jacini, and A. Pecile. New York: Raven, 1973, p. 91–114.
333. SEDGLEY, M., AND W. L. FORD. The migration of lymphocytes across specialized vascular endothelium. I. The entry of lymphocytes into the isolated mesenteric lymph-node of the rat. *Cell Tissue Kinet.* 9: 231–243, 1976.
334. SHEA, S. M., AND W. H. BOSSERT. Vesicular transport across endothelium: a generalized diffusion model. *Microvasc. Res.* 6: 305–315, 1973.
335. SHEA, S. M., AND M. J. KARNOVSKY. Brownian motion: a theoretical explanation for the movement of vesicles across the endothelium. *Nature London* 212: 353–355, 1966.
336. SHEA, S. M., AND M. J. KARNOVSKY. Vesicular transport across endothelium; simulation of a diffusion model. *J. Theor. Biol.* 24: 30–42, 1969.
337. SHEPRO, D., J. C. BARBOUTA, L. S. ROBBLEE, M. P. CARSON, AND F. A. BELAMARICH. Serotonin transport by cultured bovine aortic endothelium. *Circ. Res.* 36: 799–806, 1975.
338. SHEPRO, D., A. ROBINSON, AND H. B. HECHTMAN. Serotonin transport and plasminogen activator activity by isolated microvessels (Abstract). *J. Cell Biol.* 83: 244a, 1979.
339. SHERIDAN, J. D. Dye transfer in small vessels from the rat omentum: homologus and heterologus junctions (Abstract). *J. Cell Biol.* 87: 61a, 1980.
340. SHIRAHAMA, T., AND A. S. COHEN. The role of mucopolysaccharides in vesicle architecture and endothelial transport. An electron microscopic study of myocardial blood vessels. *J. Cell Biol.* 52: 198–206, 1972.
341. SHOLLEY, M. M., T. CAVALLO, AND R. S. COTRAN. Endothelial proliferation in inflammation. I. Autoradiographic studies following thermal injury to the skin of normal rats. *Am. J. Pathol.* 89: 277–296, 1977.
342. SHOLLEY, M. M., AND R. S. COTRAN. Endothelial DNA synthesis in the microvasculature of rat skin during the hair growth cycle. *Am. J. Anat.* 147: 243–254, 1976.
343. SIMIONESCU, M. Transendothelial movement of large molecules in the microvasculature. In: *Pulmonary Edema*, edited by A. P. Fishman and E. M. Renkin. Bethesda, MD: Am. Physiol. Soc., 1979, p. 39–52.

344. SIMIONESCU, M. The cell membrane of vascular endothelium as revealed by the freeze-fracture technique. In: *Atherogenesis*, edited by W. Auerswald, H. Sinzinger, and K. Widhalm. Munich, West Germany: Mandrich, 1980, vol. 4, suppl. III, p. 152. (Int. Austrian Atherosclerosis Conf. 2nd.)
345. SIMIONESCU, M. Ultrastructural organization of the alveolar-capillary unit. In: *Metabolic Activities of the Lung*. Amsterdam: Excerpta Med. Found., 1980, p. 11–36.
346. SIMIONESCU, M., AND N. SIMIONESCU. Constitutive endocytosis of the endothelial cell (Abstract). *J. Cell Biol.* 79: 381a, 1978.
347. SIMIONESCU, M., AND N. SIMIONESCU. Isolation and characterization of endothelial cells from the heart microvasculature. *Microvasc. Res.* 16: 426–452, 1978.
348. SIMIONESCU, M., N. SIMIONESCU, AND G. E. PALADE. Morphometric data on the endothelium of blood capillaries. *J. Cell Biol.* 60: 128–152, 1974.
349. SIMIONESCU, M., N. SIMIONESCU, AND G. E. PALADE. Characteristic endothelial junctions in sequential segments of the microvasculature (Abstract). *J. Cell Biol.* 63: 316a, 1974.
350. SIMIONESCU, M., N. SIMIONESCU, AND G. E. PALADE. Segmental differentiations of cell junctions in the vascular endothelium. The microvasculature. *J. Cell Biol.* 67: 863–885, 1975.
351. SIMIONESCU, M., N. SIMIONESCU, AND G. E. PALADE. Characteristic endothelial junctions in different segments of the vascular system. *Thromb. Res.* 8, Suppl. II: 247–256, 1976.
352. SIMIONESCU, M., N. SIMIONESCU, AND G. E. PALADE. Segmental differentiations of cell junctions in the vascular endothelium. Arteries and veins. *J. Cell Biol.* 68: 705–723, 1976.
353. SIMIONESCU, M., N. SIMIONESCU, AND G. E. PALADE. Differentiated microdomains on the luminal surface of the capillary endothelium. I. Partial characterization of their anionic sites. *J. Cell Biol.* 90: 614–621, 1981.
354. SIMIONESCU, M., N. SIMIONESCU, AND G. E. PALADE. Differentiated microdomains on the luminal surface of the capillary endothelium. Distribution of lectin receptors. *J. Cell Biol.* 94: 406–413, 1982.
355. SIMIONESCU, M., N. SIMIONESCU, AND G. E. PALADE. Asymmetrical distribution of anionic sites on the abluminal front of capillary endothelium, basal lamina and pericytes. *J. Cell Biol.* 95: 425–434, 1982.
356. SIMIONESCU, N. Enzymatic tracers in the study of vascular permeability. *J. Histochem. Cytochem.* 27: 1120–1130, 1979.
357. SIMIONESCU, N. The microvascular endothelium: segmental differentiations, transcytosis, selective distribution of anionic sites. In: *Advances in Inflammation Research*, edited by G. Weissman, B. Samuelson, and R. Paoletti. New York: Raven, 1979, p. 61–70.
358. SIMIONESCU, N. Studies on the biochemistry of the cell surface of capillary endothelium. In: *Atherogenesis*, edited by W. Auerswald, H. Sinzinger, and K. Widhalm. Munich, West Germany: Mandrich, 1980, vol. 4, suppl. III, p. 153. (Int. Austrian Atherosclerosis Conf. 2nd.)
359. SIMIONESCU, N. Transcytosis and traffic of membranes in the endothelial cell. In: *International Cell Biology 1980–1981*, edited by H. G. Schweiger. Berlin: Springer-Verlag, 1981, p. 657–672.
359a. SIMIONESCU, N., F. LUPU, AND M. SIMIONESCU. Annuli of membrane sterols surround the opening of vesicles and fenestrae, in capillary endothelium (Abstract). *Biol. Cell* 45: 236, 1982.
360. SIMIONESCU, N., AND G. E. PALADE. Dextrans and glycogens as particulate tracers for studying capillary permeability. *J. Cell Biol.* 50: 616–624, 1971.
361. SIMIONESCU, N., AND M. SIMIONESCU. Differential distribution of anionic sites on the capillary endothelium (Abstract). *J. Cell Biol.* 79: 59a, 1978.
362. SIMIONESCU, N., AND M. SIMIONESCU. The hydrophilic pathways of capillary endothelium, a dynamic system. In: *Water Transport Across Epithelia. Barriers, Gradients, and Mechanisms*, edited by H. H. Ussing, N. B. Bindslev, N. A. Lassen, and O. Sten-Knudsen. Copenhagen: Munksgaard, 1981, p. 228–247. (Alfred Benzon Symp. 15.)
363. SIMIONESCU, N., AND M. SIMIONESCU. The cardiovascular system. In: *Histology* (5th ed.), edited by L. Weiss. New York: Elsevier, 1983, p. 371–433.
364. SIMIONESCU, N., M. SIMIONESCU, AND G. E. PALADE. Permeability of intestinal capillaries. Pathway followed by dextrans and glycogens. *J. Cell Biol.* 53: 365–392, 1972.
365. SIMIONESCU, N., M. SIMIONESCU, AND G. E. PALADE. Permeability of muscle capillaries to exogenous myoglobin. *J. Cell Biol.* 57: 424–452, 1973.
366. SIMIONESCU, N., M. SIMIONESCU, AND G. E. PALADE. Permeability of muscle capillaries to small heme-peptides. Evidence for the existence of patent transendothelial channels. *J. Cell Biol.* 64: 586–607, 1975.
367. SIMIONESCU, N., M. SIMIONESCU, AND G. E. PALADE. Recent studies on vascular endothelium. *Ann. NY Acad. Sci.* 275: 64–75, 1976.
368. SIMIONESCU, N., M. SIMIONESCU, AND G. E. PALADE. Structural basis of permeability in sequential segments of the microvasculature (Abstract). *J. Cell Biol.* 70: 186a, 1976.
369. SIMIONESCU, N., M. SIMIONESCU, AND G. E. PALADE. Structural-functional correlates in the transendothelial exchange of water-soluble macromolecules. *Thromb. Res.* 8, Suppl. II: 257–269, 1976.
370. SIMIONESCU, N., M. SIMIONESCU, AND G. E. PALADE. Pathways followed by microperoxidase across the endothelium in sequential segments of the microvasculature (Abstract). *Anat. Rec.* 187: 713, 1977.
371. SIMIONESCU, N., M. SIMIONESCU, AND G. E. PALADE. Open junctions in the endothelium of the postcapillary venules of the diaphragm. *J. Cell Biol.* 79: 27–46, 1978.
372. SIMIONESCU, N., M. SIMIONESCU, AND G. E. PALADE. Structural basis of permeability in sequential segments of the microvasculature. I. Bipolar microvascular fields in the diaphragm. *Microvasc. Res.* 15: 1–16, 1978.
373. SIMIONESCU, N., M. SIMIONESCU, AND G. E. PALADE. Structural basis of permeability in sequential segments of the microvasculature. II. Pathways followed by microperoxidase across the endothelium. *Microvasc. Res.* 15: 17–33, 1978.
374. SIMIONESCU, N., M. SIMIONESCU, AND G. E. PALADE. Sulfated glycosaminoglycans are major components of the anionic sites of fenestral diaphragms in capillary endothelium (Abstract). *J. Cell Biol.* 83, pt. 2: 78a, 1979.
375. SIMIONESCU, N., M. SIMIONESCU, AND G. E. PALADE. Differentiated microdomains on the luminal surface of capillary endothelium. I. Preferential distribution of anionic sites. *J. Cell Biol.* 90: 605–613, 1981.
377. SKUTELSKY, E., AND D. DANON. Redistribution of surface anionic sites on the luminal front of blood vessel endothelium after interaction with polycationic ligand. *J. Cell Biol.* 71: 232–241, 1976.
378. SKUTELSKY, E., Z. RUDICH, AND D. DANON. Surface charge properties of the luminal front of blood vessel walls. An electron microscopical analysis. *Thromb. Res.* 7: 623–634, 1975.
379. SLATER, D. N. The synthesis of lipids from (1-^{14}C) acetate by human venous endothelium in tissue culture. *Atherosclerosis* 25: 237–244, 1976.
380. SMITH, U., AND J. W. RYAN. Substructural features of pulmonary endothelial caveolae. *Tissue Cell* 4: 49–54, 1972.
381. SMITH, U., J. W. RYAN, AND D. S. SMITH. Freeze-etch studies of the plasma membrane of pulmonary endothelial cell. *J. Cell Biol.* 56: 492–499, 1973.
382. SNYDER, D. H., A. HIRANO, AND C. S. RAINE. Fenestrated CNS blood vessels in chronic experimental allergic encephalomyelitis. *Brain Res.* 100: 645–648, 1975.
383. SOLOMON, A. K. Characterization of biological membranes by equivalent pores. *J. Gen. Physiol.* 51: 355S–364S, 1968.
384. SOMLYO, A. P., AND A. V. SOMLYO. Vascular smooth muscle. I. Normal structure, physiology, biochemistry and biophysics. *Pharmacol. Rev.* 22: 249–353, 1970.
385. SØRENSEN, S. C. The permeability to small ions of tight

junctions between cerebral endothelial cells. *Brain Res.* 70: 174–178, 1974.

386. STAMPER, H. B., JR., AND J. J. WOODRUFF. Lymphocyte homing into lymph nodes: in vitro demonstration of the selective affinity of recirculating lymphocytes for high-endothelial venules. *J. Exp. Med.* 144: 828–833, 1976.
387. STAMPER, H. B., JR., AND J. J. WOODRUFF. An in vitro model of lymphocyte homing. I. Characterization of the interaction between thoracic duct lymphocytes and specialized high-endothelial venules of lymph nodes. *J. Immunol.* 119: 772–780, 1977.
388. STEHBENS, W. E. The basal attachment of endothelial cells. *J. Ultrastruct. Res.* 15: 389–399, 1966.
389. STEHBENS, W. E. Subendothelial edema. Haemodynamic production of lipid deposition, intimal tears, mural dissection and thrombosis in the blood vessel wall. *Proc. R. Soc. London Ser. B* 185: 357–373, 1974.
390. STEIN, O., T. CHAJEK, AND Y. STEIN. Transport of lipoprotein lipase in the endothelium of rat heart (Abstract). *Paroi Arterielle* 3: 136, 1976.
391. STEIN, O., T. CHAJEK, AND Y. STEIN. Ultrastructural localization of concanavalin A in the perfused rat heart. *Lab. Invest.* 35: 103–110, 1976.
392. STEIN, O., AND Y. STEIN. High density lipoproteins reduce the uptake of low density lipoproteins by human endothelial cells in culture. *Biochim. Biophys. Acta* 431: 363–368, 1976.
393. STEIN, Y., AND O. STEIN. Interaction between serum lipoproteins and cellular components of the arterial wall. In: *The Biochemistry of Arteriosclerosis*, edited by A. M. Scanu, R. W. Wissler, and G. S. Getz. New York: Dekker, 1979, p. 313–344.
394. STEINSIEPE, K. F., AND E. R. WEIBEL. Elektronenmikroskopische Untersuchungen an spezifischen Organellen von Endothelzellen des Frosches (Rana temporaria). *Z. Zellforsch. Mikrosk. Anat.* 108: 105–126, 1970.
395. STENMAN, S., AND A. VAHERI. Distribution of a major connective tissue protein fibronectin, in normal human tissues. *J. Exp. Med.* 147: 1054–1066, 1978.
396. STENSAS, L. J. Pericytes and perivascular microglial cells in the basal forebrain of the neonatal rabbit. *Cell Tissue Res.* 158: 517–541, 1975.
397. STONE, F. J., H. A. COHEN, AND D. FRISCH. The ultrastructural localization of fibrinogen at the erythrocyte surface and in the capillary endothelium. *Cell Tissue Res.* 153: 253–260, 1974.
398. STRUM, J. M., AND A. F. JUNOD. Radioautographic demonstration of 5-hydroxytryptamine-^{3}H uptake by pulmonary endothelial cells. *J. Cell Biol.* 54: 456–467, 1972.
399. SUZUKI, Y. Fenestration of alveolar capillary endothelium in experimental pulmonary fibrosis. *Lab. Invest.* 21: 304–308, 1969.
400. SUZUKI, Y., S. OOKAWARA, AND G. OONEDA. Increased permeability of the arteries in hypertensive rats: an electron-microscopic study. *Exp. Mol. Pathol.* 15: 198–208, 1971.
401. SVENSJÖ, E., AND K. E. ARFORS. Bradykinin-induced macromolecular permeability: repeated application and potentiation by PGE_1, PGE_2, and $PGE_{2\alpha}$ (Abstract). *Microvasc. Res.* 10: 235, 1975.
402. SVENSJÖ, E., C. G. A. PERSSON, AND K. E. ARFORS. Effects of bradykinin and terbutalin on macromolecular leakage and its relation to other microvascular effects (Abstract). *Microvasc. Res.* 11: 425, 1976.
403. TAKADA, M., AND K. MORI. Spontaneous separation of the endothelial cell junctions of the venules in the large salivary glands in the intact mouse. *Microvasc. Res.* 3: 204–206, 1971.
404. TANI, E., S. YAMAGATA, AND Y. ITO. Freeze-fracture of capillary endothelium in rat brain. *Cell Tissue Res.* 176: 157–165, 1977.
405. TANNOCK, I. F., AND S. HAYASHI. The proliferation of capillary endothelial cells. *Cancer Res.* 32: 77–83, 1972.
406. THOMAS, D. P., AND J. R. VANE. 5-Hydroxytryptamine in the circulation of the dog. *Nature London* 216: 335–338, 1967.
407. TILTON, R. G., C. KILO, AND J. R. WILLIAMSON. Pericyte-endothelial relationships in cardiac and skeletal muscle capillaries. *Microvasc. Res.* 18: 325–335, 1979.
408. TILTON, R. G., C. KILO, J. R. WILLIAMSON, AND D. W. MURCH. Differences in pericyte contractile function in rat cardiac and skeletal muscle microvasculatures. *Microvasc. Res.* 18: 336–352, 1979.
409. TOMLLIN, S. G. Vesicular transport across endothelial cells. *Biochim. Biophys. Acta* 13: 559–564, 1969.
410. TRILLO, A. A., AND R. W. PRICHARD. Early endothelial changes in experimental primate atherosclerosis. *Lab. Invest.* 41: 294–302, 1979.
411. TULENCO, T. N. Drug receptor activity in the small blood vessels of the human placenta and their possible significance. In: *Fetal and Newborn Cardiovascular Physiology*, edited by L. Longo. New York: Garland, 1978, p. 17–32.
412. TURKER, R. K. Presence of histamine H_2-receptors in the guinea-pig pulmonary vascular bed. *Pharmacology* 9: 306–311, 1973.
413. TYSON, G. E., AND R. E. BULGAR. Endothelial detachment sites in glomerular capillaries of vinblastine-treated rats. *Anat. Rec.* 172: 669–674, 1972.
414. UMETANI, Y. Postcapillary venule in rabbit tonsil and entry of lymphocytes into its endothelium: a scanning and transmission electron microscope study. *Arch. Histol. Jpn.* 40: 77–94, 1977.
415. VAN DEURS, B. Observations on the blood-brain barrier in hypertensive rats, with particular reference to phagocytic pericytes. *J. Ultrastruct. Res.* 56: 65–77, 1976.
416. VAN DEURS, B. Endocytosis in high-endothelial venules. Evidence for transport of exogenous material to lysosomes by uncoated "endothelial" vesicles. *Microvasc. Res.* 16: 280–293, 1978.
417. VAN DEURS, B. Cell junctions in the endothelia and connective tissue of the rat choroid plexus. *Anat. Rec.* 195: 73–94, 1979.
418. VAN DEURS, B., C. ROPKE, AND E. WESTERGAARD. Permeability properties of the postcapillary high-endothelial venules in lymph nodes of the mouse. *Lab. Invest.* 32: 201–208, 1975.
419. VAN DIEST, P., AND M. W. KANAN. An ultrastructural study of the endonasal microcirculation in the Wistar rat during fetal and early postnatal life. *J. Anat.* 128: 293–300, 1979.
420. VASILE, E., A. NISTOR, S. NEDELCU, M. SIMIONESCU, AND N. SIMIONESCU. Dual pathway of low density lipoprotein transport through aortic endothelium and vasa vasorum in situ (Abstract). *Eur. J. Cell Biol.* 22: 181, 1980. (Int. Congr. Cell Biol. 2nd.)

420a. VASILE, E., M. SIMIONESCU, AND N. SIMIONESCU. Visualization of the binding, endocytosis and transcytosis of low density lipoprotein in the arterial endothelium in situ. *J. Cell Biol.* 96: 1677–1689, 1983.

421. VLODAVSKY, I., P. E. FIELDING, C. J. FIELDING, AND D. GOSPODAROWICZ. Role of contact inhibition in the regulation of receptor-mediated uptake of low density lipoprotein in cultured vascular endothelial cells. *Proc. Natl. Acad. Sci. USA* 75: 356–360, 1978.
422. VRACKO, R. Basal lamina scaffold-anatomy and significance for maintenance of orderly tissue structure. *Am. J. Pathol.* 77: 314–346, 1974.
423. VRACKO, R., AND E. P. BENDITT. Capillary basal lamina thickening. Its relationship to endothelial cell death and replacement. *J. Cell Biol.* 47: 281–285, 1970.
424. WAGNER, R. C., S. B. ANDREWS, AND M. A. MATTHEWS. A fluorescence assay for micropinocytosis in isolated capillary endothelium. *Microvasc. Res.* 14: 67–80, 1977.
425. WAGNER, R. C., AND J. R. CASLEY-SMITH. Endothelial vesicles. *Microvasc. Res.* 21: 267–298, 1981.
426. WAGNER, R. C., P. KREINER, R. J. BARRNETT, AND M. W. BITENSKY. Biochemical characterization and cytochemical localization of a catecholamine-sensitive adenylate cyclase in isolated capillary endothelium. *Proc. Natl. Acad. Sci. USA* 69: 3175–3179, 1972.
427. WAGNER, R. C., AND M. A. MATTHEWS. The isolation and culture of capillary endothelium from epididymal fat. *Micro-*

vasc. Res. 10: 286–297, 1975.

428. WAGNER, R. C., S. K. WILLIAMS, M. A. MATTHEWS, AND S. B. ANDREWS. Exclusion of albumin from vesicular ingestion by isolated microvessels. *Microvasc. Res.* 19: 127–130, 1980.
429. WAXLER, B., B. SCHUMACHER, AND R. EISENSTEIN. Cell-stroma interactions in aortic endothelial cell cultures. *Lab. Invest.* 41: 128–134, 1979.
430. WEIBEL, E. R. On pericytes, particularly their existence on lung capillaries. *Microvasc. Res.* 8: 218–235, 1974.
431. WEIBEL, E. R., AND G. E. PALADE. New cytoplasmic components in arterial endothelia. *J. Cell Biol.* 23: 101–112, 1964.
432. WEIHE, E., AND P. KALMBACH. Ultrastructure of capillaries in the conducting system of the heart in various mammals. *Cell Tissue Res.* 192: 77–87, 1978.
433. WEINSTEIN, R. S., AND N. S. MCNUTT. Electron microscopy of freeze-cleaved and etched capillaries. In: *Microcirculation, Perfusion, and Transplantation of Organs*, edited by T. J. Malinin, B. S. Linn, A. B. Callahan, and W. D. Warren. New York: Academic, 1970, p. 23.
434. WEKSLER, B. B., A. J. MARCUS, AND E. A. JAFFE. Synthesis of PGI_2 by cultured human and bovine endothelial cells. *Proc. Natl. Acad. Sci. USA* 74: 3922–3926, 1977.
435. WENK, E. J., D. ORLIC, E. J. REITH, AND J. A. G. RHODIN. The ultrastructure of mouse lymph node venules and the passage of lymphocytes across their walls. *J. Ultrastruct. Res.* 47: 214–241, 1974.
436. WESTERGAARD, E. Enhanced vesicular transport of exogenous peroxidase across cerebral vessels, induced by serotonin. *Acta Neuropathol.* 32: 27–42, 1975.
437. WESTERGAARD, E., AND M. W. BRIGHTMAN. Transport of proteins across normal cerebral arterioles. *J. Comp Neurol.* 152: 17–44, 1973.
438. WESTERGAARD, E., B. VAN DEURS, AND H. E. BRØNDSTED. Increased vesicular transfer of horseradish peroxidase across cerebral endothelium, evoked by acute hypertension. *Acta Neuropathol.* 37: 141–152, 1977.
439. WIDMANN, J. J., R. S. COTRAN, AND H. D. FAHIMI. Mononuclear phagocytes (Kupffer cells) and endothelial cells. Identification of two functional cell types in rat liver sinusoids by endogenous peroxidase activity. *J. Cell Biol.* 52: 159–170, 1972.
440. WIDMANN, J. J., AND H. D. FAHIMI. Proliferation of endothelial cells in oestrogen-stimulated rat liver. A light and electron microscopic cytochemical study. *Lab. Invest.* 34: 141–149, 1976.
441. WILLIAMS, M. C., AND S. L. WISSIG. The permeability of muscle capillaries to horseradish peroxidase. *J. Cell Biol.* 66: 531–555, 1975.
442. WILLIAMS, S. K., J. J. DEVENNY, AND M. W. BITTENSKY. Micropinocytosis in isolated microvessels: carbohydrate-selective ingestion of protein labelled with different sugars (Abstract). *Microvasc. Res.* 21: 263, 1981.
443. WILLIAMS, S. K., M. A. MATTHEWS, R. C. WAGNER, AND S. B. ANDREWS. Capillary endothelial metabolism and micropinocytotic ingestion (Abstract). *J. Cell Biol.* 75: 364a, 1977.
444. WILLIAMS, S. K., AND R. C. WAGNER. Regulation of micropinocytosis by divalent cations in isolated capillary endothelium (Abstract). *J. Cell Biol.* 79: 382a, 1978.
445. WILLIAMSON, J. R., D. GIBSON, AND D. MURCH. Selective microvesicular transport of macromolecules by endothelium (Abstract). *Microvasc. Res.* 21: 263, 1981.
446. WISSE, E. An electron microscopic study of the fenestrated endothelial lining of rat liver sinusoids. *J. Ultrastruct. Res.* 31: 125–150, 1970.
447. WISSIG, S. L. Identification of the small pore in muscle capillaries. *Acta Physiol. Scand.* 463: 33–44, 1979.
448. WISSIG, S. L., AND M. C. WILLIAMS. Permeability of muscle capillaries to microperoxidase. *J. Cell Biol.* 76: 341–359, 1978.
449. WOLFF, J. On the meaning of vesiculation in capillary endothelium. *Angiologica* 4: 64–68, 1967.
450. WOLFF, J. Ultrastructure of the terminal vascular bed as related to function. In: *Microcirculation*, edited by G. Kaley and B. M. Altura. Baltimore, MD: University Park, 1977, vol. 2, p. 95–130.
451. WOLFF, J. R. Elektronenmikroskopische Untersuchungen über die Vesikulation in Kapillarendothel. Lokalisation, Variation und Fusion der Vesikel. *Z. Zellforsch. Mikrosk. Anat.* 73: 143–164, 1966.
452. WOODRUFF, J., AND R. A. RASMUSSEN. In vitro adherence of lymphocytes to unfixed high endothelial cells of lymph nodes. *J. Immunol.* 123: 2369–2372, 1979.
453. YAMAMOTO, K., S. FUJIMOTO, AND Y. TAKESHIGE. The fine structure of endothelial cells in freeze-fracture preparations. *J. Ultrastruct. Res.* 54: 22–28, 1976.
454. YOSHIMOTO, H., M. MURATA, AND K. TSUSHIMA. Morphometrical studies on choriocapillary in spontaneously hypertensive rats utilizing freeze-fractured preparations. *Jpn. Heart J.* 19: 650–651, 1978.
455. ZELICKSON, A. S. A tubular structure in the endothelial cells and pericytes of human endothelium. *J. Invest. Dermatol.* 46: 167–172, 1966.
456. ZWEIFACH, B. W. Microcirculatory aspects of tissue injury. *Ann. NY Acad. Sci.* 116: 831–838, 1964.

Physiology and biochemistry of the vascular wall endothelium

DAVID SHEPRO | *Department of Biology and Surgery, Boston University, Boston, Massachusetts*

PATRICIA A. D'AMORE | *Department of Pathology and Surgical Research, Children's Hospital Medical Center, Harvard Medical School, Boston, Massachusetts*

CHAPTER CONTENTS

In Vitro Endothelial Cell Technology
- History and state of the art
- Criteria for identification
  - Morphological
  - Immunological
  - Physiological

Growth Control
- Endothelial cell culture studies
  - Shape
  - Extracellular matrix
  - Cell surface protein
  - Variant endothelial cells
  - Growth factors
- Angiogenic studies
  - In vitro assays
  - In vivo assays
  - Angiogenic factors
- Endothelial cell regeneration

Synthesis
- Subendothelium
  - Basement membrane
  - Extracellular matrix
- Releasable products
  - Collagenase
  - Elastase
  - Factor VIII
  - Fibronectin
  - Plasminogen activator
  - Prostaglandins
  - Colony-stimulating factor

Motility
- Intracellular constituents
- Evidence supporting contraction
- Evidence negating contraction
- Pericyte regulation
- Endothelial contractile pathophysiology
- Regulation of postcapillary venule junctions: theoretical model

Membrane-Associated Activities
- Receptor mediation
  - Vasoactive substances
  - Nonvasoactive substances
- Cell surface molecules
  - Enzymes
  - Molecules related to thrombosis
  - Antigenic determinants
  - Other molecules

Metabolism
- Circulating vasoactive agents
  - Adenosine and adenine nucleotides
  - Amines
  - Angiotensin-converting enzyme
  - Prostaglandins
  - Substance P
- Other metabolic activities
  - Microvessels
  - Endothelial cells in tissue culture

THE TERM *endothelium* [from the Greek *endon* (within) and *thelio* (nipple)] was coined by Wilhelm His, Sr., in 1865 (474) to describe cells that line surfaces within the body. The word was created as a convenient name to parallel the already accepted term *epithelium*, established earlier by Frederick Ruysch to designate the cellular layer covering the papillae of the tongue (474). There were no words to describe papillae, and Ruysch apparently selected *thelium* (nipple) to solve the problem.

Endotheliology, especially at the microvascular level, appears to have suffered from its misnomer; approximately 100 years elapsed before endothelial cells (EC) were regarded as more than a passive barrier lining. Intimal and microvascular EC are currently understood to be an active metabolic tissue, which responds to changes in the milieu to maintain not only its own homeostasis but also systemic homeostasis. This view and the knowledge that EC are anatomically heterogeneous, even within a given microcirculatory bed, are probably two of the most important recent contributions to vascular physiology. The strategic location of endothelium and the capaciousness of the microvasculature also suggest that EC dysfunction may be the root of certain systemic diseases, apart from thrombosis and vascular diseases.

Writing about a nascent discipline has inherent problems. Because so little information is available, new experimental data tend to be accepted as fact, e.g., the use of Weibel-Palade bodies (WPB) as a definitive marker to demonstrate that EC in culture are truly EC (Fig. 1). Named for the investigators who first described them in EC (675), WPB were once believed unique for intimal endothelium. However, Hammersen (253) observed WPB in human cutaneous microvessel endothelium, and Kumar et al. (350) suggested that WPB may also be markers for proliferating capillaries. Explanations of WPB absence, presence, or function are still needed; this organelle's significance or inclusion as an exclusive criterion to identify normal EC should be viewed cautiously.

However, most problems with writing about microvascular metabolism and physiology occur because most of the experiments cited used large-vessel EC in culture, obtained principally from bovine aortas (BA) and human umbilical veins (HUV). The culturing of endothelium has provided a great impetus, apart from that provided by electron microscopy, for learning about its functions. Capillary and intimal EC in suspension or in culture show many anatomic features and metabolic and physiological properties ascribed to microvessel endothelium in situ (210, 390, 568). The functional profile of an EC in a lung capillary is different from the profile of an EC in a skeletal muscle capillary. However, presenting data obtained primarily from intimal endothelium as an aid to understanding microvascular endothelial function is justified. No better experimental system exists; the information provides a base line for comparisons between cultured intimal cells and capillary endothelium as these cells become available; similar functions will then become part of the taxonomic literature that characterizes endothelium as a tissue.

This chapter identifies for the reader documented data, e.g., the presence of converting enzyme or factor VIII antigen on the EC plasma membrane, that distinguish EC from other cells. Preliminary results, e.g., a newly isolated mitogen or growth factor or an absence of a plasminogen-activator inhibitor in capillary endothelium, are also provided but accompanied with a note to alert the reader that the conclusions are still in the speculative stage. Some redundancy in this chapter is unavoidable; e.g., fibronectin citations appear under IN VITRO ENDOTHELIAL CELL TECHNOLOGY, p. 105 and BASEMENT MEMBRANE, p. 119.

Although many relevant publications are included, some important publications obviously are missed; we ask to be excused for any omission. For other omissions, we request the understanding and sympathy of the reader in light of the certainty that at times we all know more that we can tell.

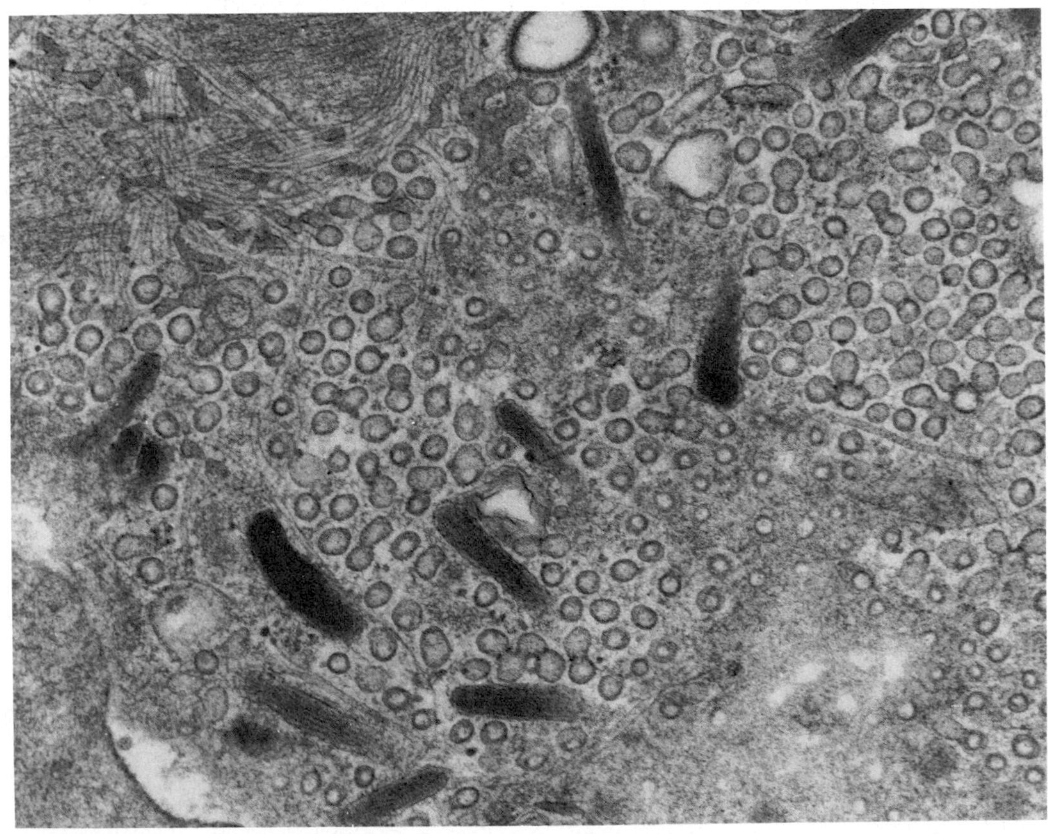

FIG. 1. Transmission electron micrograph of cytoplasm of cultured human umbilical vein endothelial cell cut parallel to culture surface through basal aspect of cell. Numerous pinocytotic vesicles and endothelial-specific (rod-shaped) Weibel-Palade bodies. × ~35,000. (Micrograph courtesy of M. A. Gimbrone, Jr.)

IN VITRO ENDOTHELIAL CELL TECHNOLOGY

History and State of the Art

Lewis (369) first reported vascular endothelium in tissue culture in 1922 when he described the explantation of chick embryo livers, consisting of liver parenchymal cells and "loose reticular outgrowths." Because the liver contains principally two cell types, liver cells proper and endothelia of the sinusoids, the loose reticular outgrowths were, by the process of elimination, endothelium. For the next 50 years, endothelial culture was accomplished by explanting a variety of tissues: the pia mater (405), chick embryo heart (447), rabbit aorta (577), chicken bone marrow (682), and visceral arterioles (165). These systems, however, yielded heterogeneous cell populations and very limited numbers of cells.

The technological advance that allowed investigators to obtain large numbers of cells from the intimal layer for culturing or suspensions involved the enzymatic dissociation of the endothelial layer. Maruyama (401) first implemented this technique with the use of trypsin to remove the endothelial layer from an HUV. Two years later Murata et al. (439) trypsinized the endothelium from veins of 3-wk-old chicks. He maintained these cells in culture through 18 generations, documenting growth and division by monitoring [^{3}H] thymidine and [^{3}H]uridine incorporation. The following year Fryer et al. (197) obtained cultures of both EC and fibroblasts from HUV and demonstrated that EC in culture could be distinguished morphologically from fibroblasts. Jaffe et al. (309) and Gimbrone et al. (215) used crude bacterial collagenase to remove cells from the HUV. The efficiency of obtaining homogeneous cultures with collagenase is probably due to the selective digestion of the basement membrane (BM) that underlies the intima, thus freeing aggregates of EC (210). In contrast, trypsin attacks not only the subendothelium but also the luminal surface of the endothelium.

Scraping the luminal surface of the blood vessel also provides sufficient EC to seed a culture (368). Ryan et al. (526) developed a procedure to eliminate the use of enzymes in subculturing large-vessel EC. Light scraping of the luminal surface of the pulmonary artery removes the cells that are then seeded onto microcarrier beads in roller bottles. Subculture is accomplished by mixing fresh beads and media with the confluent beads. The cells from the established beads colonize the new beads. This technique establishes pure cultures of EC without exposure to proteolytic enzymes (Fig. 2).

During the 17 years since Maruyama (401) first used enzymatic treatments to obtain endothelium from large blood vessels, scores of laboratories [Table 1; (210)] have utilized enzymes, primarily trypsin and collagenase, to obtain endothelium from a variety of blood vessel sources. Human umbilical vein has proved a useful source of EC for tissue culture (197, 215, 309, 341, 368, 401). The umbilical cord is easily obtained aseptically and is technically convenient to incubate with enzymes because there are no branching vessels as in other large blood vessels. The two major disadvantages of an umbilical vein as a source of venous EC are the relatively slow growth rate of the cells [doubling times from 40 to 92 h (309, 368)] and the

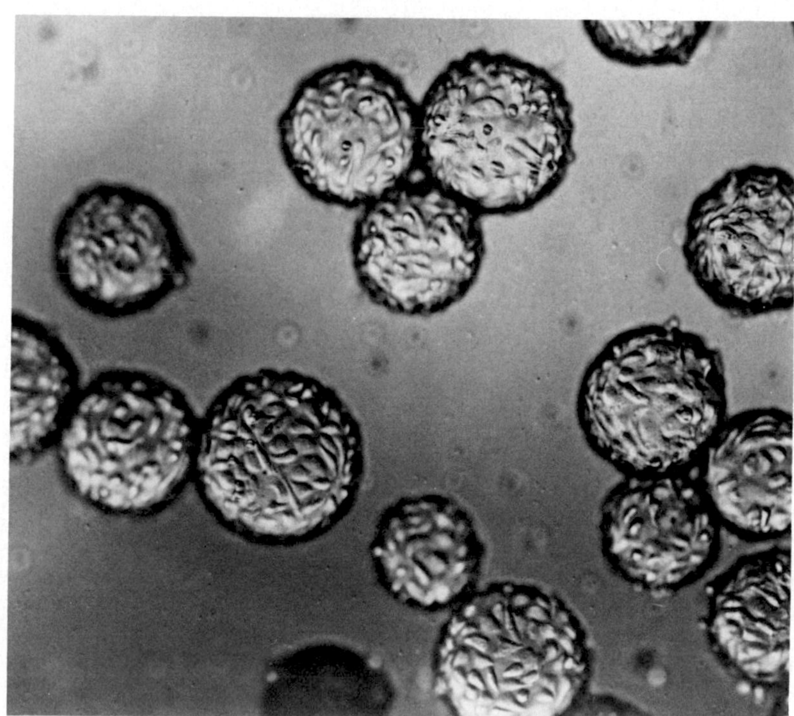

FIG. 2. Bovine aortic endothelial cells cultured on Cytodex 3 microcarriers (Pharmacia Fine Chemicals, Uppsala, Sweden) for 3 wk. Cells were initially seeded at 3×10^5 cells/ml (3 mg Cytodex/ml) and maintained in RPMI 1640 growth medium supplemented with 17% calf serum. $\times$ 100. (Micrograph courtesy of D. Bottaro and D. Shepro.)

TABLE 1. *Harvesting Endothelium by Enzymatic Dissociation*

	Dissociation Method	Identification/ Morphology	Ref.
Human			
Umbilical cord vein	Trypsin	Silver nitrate	401
	Trypsin		197
	Scraping*	WPB, caveolae	368
	Collagenase	WPB; immunology, ABH antigens	307
	Collagenase	WPB	215
	Chymotrypsin, dispase, elastase	WPB	623
Ovarian and pulmonary artery and vein	Collagenase	Immunology, factor VIII, physiology, ACE	312
Bovine			
Aorta	Balanced salt solution	WPB; silver nitrate	417, 572
	Collagenase	WPB; silver nitrate	574
	Collagenase	WPB; immunology, factor VIII and thrombosthenin	557
	Collagenase	Immunology, factor VIII	378
	Collagenase	WPB	162
Fetal aorta	Collagenase	WPB	169
	Collagenase	Silver nitrate, contact inhibition; immunology, factor VIII	436
Vena cava	EDTA	Silver nitrate	673
Saphenous vein	Collagenase	WPB	162
Pulmonary artery	Collagenase	Immunology, factor VIII and α_2-macroglobulin; physiology, ACE	525
	Scraping*; microcarrier beads	Biochemical studies	526
Pig			
Aorta	Collagenase, EDTA, trypsin		422, 589
Vena cava	Collagenase, EDTA, trypsin	WPB	589
Rabbit			
Aorta	Trypsin		486
Marginal ear vein	Trypsin		332
Guinea pig			
Thoracic and portal veins	Collagenase and trypsin		57
Rat			
Lung	Collagenase and trypsin	WPB; physiology, ACE	466

WPB, Weibel-Palade bodies; ACE, angiotensin-converting enzyme; EDTA, ethylenediaminetetraacetic acid. * No enzymes.

inability of the cells to be passaged repeatedly. Many factors may account for the difficulty encountered in maintaining human umbilical vein endothelial cells (HUVEC) in long-term culture. The cells may have a preprogrammed shorter life span because the tissue is functionally terminal. Gospodarowicz et al. (232) have related the problem to the observation that human but not bovine EC require thrombin to respond to added growth factors in vitro.

Another popular source for obtaining EC is the BA. Shepro et al. (567) first described the isolation and culture of EC from neonatal BA (Table 1). The doubling times for EC derived from BA are shorter than for venous EC in culture [from 18 to 65 h; (238, 378)], and the cells can be readily passaged. Mueller et al. (436) determined that the average maximal cumulative population-doubling level for fetal bovine aorta endothelial cells (BAEC) is 80. Gospodarowicz et al. (238), however, reported more than 100 population doublings from human EC growth with fibroblast growth factor (FGF) and thrombin and 390 population doublings from fetal EC cloned in FGF.

Rosen et al. (514), studying clonal strains of fetal BAEC, reported in vitro life spans of 53–125 population doublings compared with 60–143 for bovine fetal lung and 85–147 for vascular smooth muscle cells. Increases in cell area, cell volume, and protein content characterized senescent EC with factor VIII antigen retained throughout the life spans.

In a study of the proliferation of BAEC, Duthu and Smith (154) determined that FGF influenced EC proliferation only when the cell inocula were $<1 \times 10^4$ cells/cm^2; at higher densities there were no effects. Furthermore a 50% increase in replicative life-span occurred in cultures grown in 10% fetal bovine serum (FBS) with FGF (50 ng/ml) over cultures grown in 10% FBS alone. Although the presence of FGF could extend the life-span of the cultures, the cultures "eventually ceased to divide." Duthu and Smith concluded that cell seeding density, growth medium, serum supplement, and concentration of FGF all influence the population-doubling time.

The methodologies of enzymatic dissociation employed various other large blood vessels as sources for EC cultures (Table 1), but HUV and BA remain the most widely used tissues.

Difficulty in separating capillary endothelium from the pericytes that are an integral part of the microvasculature has hampered efforts to culture capillary endothelium (Fig. 3). Early attempts at culturing endothelium involved explanting blood vessels from skin (370), bone marrow (682), human synovial membranes (22), and visceral arterioles (165). Although these early investigations reported maintenance of healthy patent capillaries and formation of new vessels, these methods still had disadvantages: cell populations were heterogeneous and the yield was small.

Many investigators developed methodologies for obtaining microvessel preparations from various tissues (Table 2). Each technique involves a purification step that isolates the capillaries after an enzymatic or mechanical dispersement of the tissue. The most successful protocols for tissue culture purposes to date

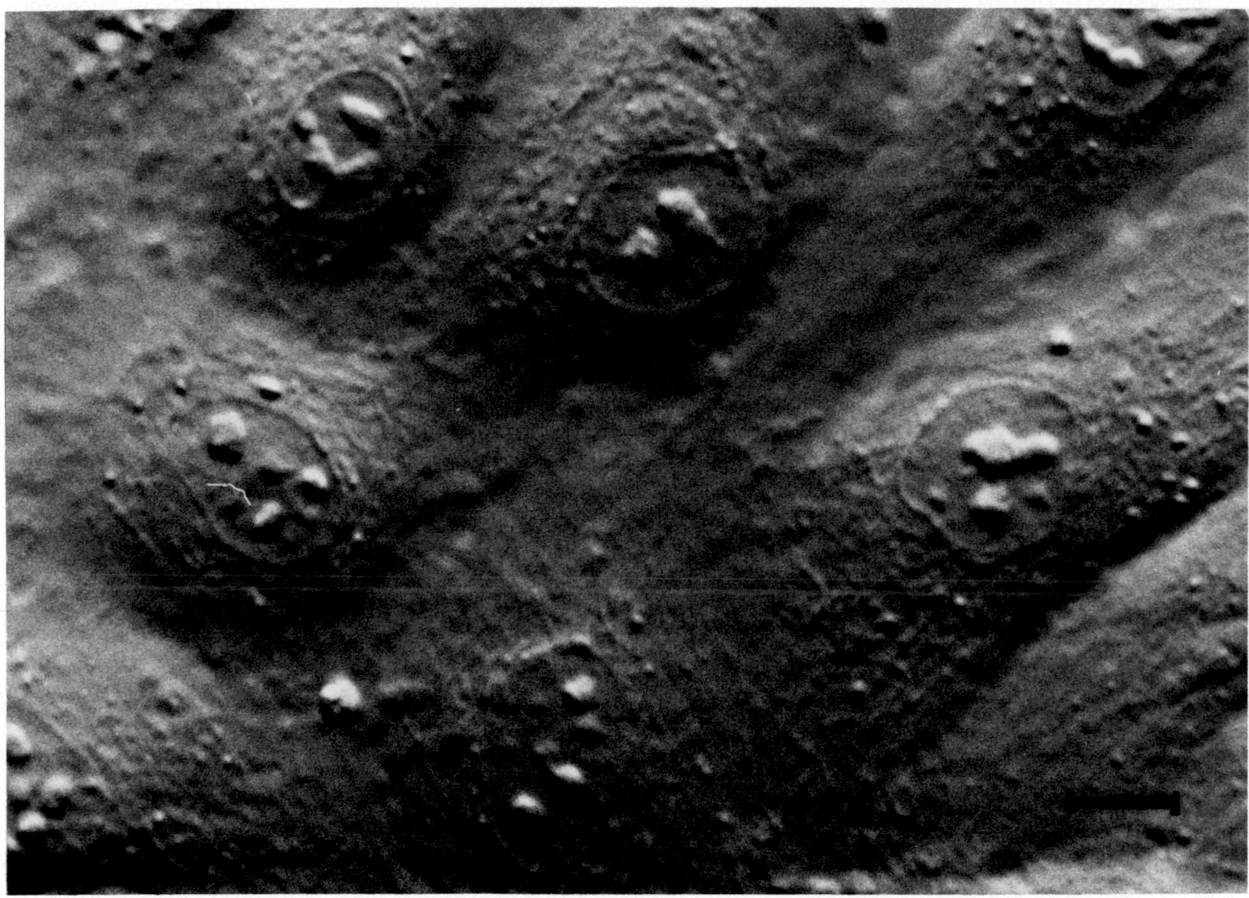

FIG. 3. Bovine aortic endothelial cells; primary cultures 3 days postconfluency (10 days). Cobblestone appearance typical of monolayer of endothelial cells. Differential interference-contrast microscopy. *Bar*, 10 μm.

involved filtration through screens of various meshes to separate capillary fragments after collagenase digestion of the tissue. Other means of tissue dispersion, including mechanical dispersion (homogenization) or trypsinization, have proved too harsh, resulting in low viability of the isolated capillary fragments. Folkman et al. (186) combined collagenase digestion and filtration with cloning techniques designed to enrich the endothelial elements and eliminate contaminating cell types. They report that bovine capillary EC differ from BAEC in that they require a gelatin-coated substratum and conditioned medium, which they obtained from mouse sarcoma cells. The doubling time in the presence of the regular media is 67 h; in tumor-conditioned media it is 28 h. Under these conditions the cells have been maintained by serial passage for more than 8 mo.

More recently Gitlin and D'Amore (219a) and Bowman et al. (62) have succeeded in culturing EC from bovine retina. These investigators have taken advantage of the fact that, although other mammalian cells require serum, vascular EC can grow in media supplemented with platelet-poor plasma. By culturing the isolated capillary fragments in plasma the growth of the pericytes, which appear to require a serum component(s), is kept to a minimum. In addition, Gitlin and D'Amore (219a) supplement the culture media of the EC with a partially purified extract of retina-derived growth factor, which they have shown to be a mitogen for EC but not for pericytes.

Criteria for Identification

Investigators who have attempted to culture vascular endothelium have been plagued by a question best stated by Shibuya (577) in 1971: "How can it be reasoned that my culture was the pure culture of the endothelial cells?" Maruyama (401) first endeavored to obtain pure cultures by checking selected segments of each HUV used for culture. When a defect was noted in the vessel's subendothelium, the culture established from that vessel was considered contaminated with fibroblasts. At one time the only criteria available for EC identification were morphological—the epithelial growth pattern of the cells and the ability of the intercellular cement to stain with silver

TABLE 2. *Microvessel Isolation Methods*

	Procedure	Use	Ref.
Brain			
Rat	Homogenization, filtration, differential density gradient centrifugation	H	321
	Mincing, filtration	MS	62, 228
Rat, bovine	Trypsin digestion	TC	477, 549
	Homogenization, filtration	MS, TC	64, 134
Bovine	Homogenization, density gradient centrifugation	H	560
	Homogenization, differential density gradient centrifugation, foam concentration, glass beads	MS	581
Rabbit	Homogenization, density gradient centrifugation	H, MS	435
Retina			
Rabbit	Explant	TC	640
Rat	Mincing, collagenase, filtration	MS	690
Bovine	Mincing, collagenase, filtration	MS, TC	62a, 219a
Kitten, calf	Homogenization, filtration	TC	80, 190a, 190b
Skin			
Human	Mincing, collagenase, filtration, trypsin	TC	132, 575
Adrenal gland			
Rat	Collagenase digestion	TC	142
Rat, bovine, human	Collagenase digestion, filtration	TC	186
Heart			
Rabbit	Collagenase digestion, homogenization, rate sedimentation	M	584
Epididymal fat			
Rat	Collagenase digestion	TC	665

H, histochemistry; MS, metabolic studies; TC, tissue culture; M, microscopy.

nitrate (179). However, even the silver nitrate stain is not unique to endothelium, as it is a feature of all epithelial cells (6). Today identifying features for EC in culture may be divided into three categories: morphological, immunological, and physiological.

MORPHOLOGICAL. A standard criterion for a culture of large-vessel EC is the appearance of a monolayer in culture; the cells are said to form characteristic mosaics of nonoverlapping, polygonal cells. In contrast, fibroblasts or smooth muscle cells (the two most likely contaminants) are more spindle shaped or polar and can overgrow in culture to form multiple layers (213). Ultrastructurally the WPB is a certain feature of EC. First described in 1964 by Weibel and Palade (675), WPB are rod-shaped cytoplasmic components that consist of a bundle of tubules surrounded by a unit membrane. Researchers have described WPB in the arterial and venous endothelium of many species (198, 465, 542, 675), including fish, reptiles, birds, rodents, cats, and humans. Until recently WPB were not thought to occur in capillary endothelium (280, 389). The single published report of the organelles in capillary endothelium had only one micrograph displaying a capillary section with WPB (275). More recently Hammersen (253) and Kumar et al. (350) have published electron micrographs demonstrating WPB in cutaneous capillaries and brain tissues, respectively. Although Kumar et al. do not posit a function for the organelles in the dividing cells, they suggest that the presence of a large number of these organelles may be a marker for actively proliferating capillaries.

Although not yet elucidated, several possible functions for WPB have been suggested. Bertini and Santolaya (41) suggest a role for these organelles in blood pressure regulation, based on a study in which a partially purified preparation of the organelles from toad aorta, when administered to a rat, increased blood pressure. Burri and Weibel (75) suggest a procoagulative function for the granules, based on a coincident decrease in the number of WPB in a rabbit aorta associated with the onset of procoagulative activity. Recently Fujimoto et al. (199) showed that WPB contain histamine. A storage and/or secretory function for WPB would be logical because the inclusions are believed to be assembled and possibly synthesized in the Golgi (559).

Many other ultrastructural features, in addition to the presence of WPB, help distinguish EC from contaminating cell types. Haudenschild et al. (262) studied these features in HUV endothelium through 19 passages. Weibel-Palade bodies were present in all 19 passages of cells. They also concluded that the distribution of intermediate-sized filaments, number and location of pinocytotic vesicles and multivesicular bodies, and the types of junctions could be utilized to distinguish EC from smooth muscle cells or fibroblasts.

Franke et al. (191) biochemically characterized intermediate-sized filaments (7–11 nm). They demonstrated with fluorescently labeled antibodies that these filaments are distinct from the intermediate filaments found in epithelial cells (prekeratin) and smooth muscle cells (desmin). The EC filaments consist of a molecule, vimentin, with a molecular weight of 57,000, that is the major protein of intermediate filaments in mesenchymally derived cells. Blose and co-workers (56–58) described these filaments that occur in bundles and have sometimes been found in large aggregates such as the perinuclear ring. Smith and Ryan (593) studied the characteristic pinocytotic vesicles of EC and showed that lung capillary EC contain these vesicles, which are the sites of phosphatase activity.

IMMUNOLOGICAL. The most widely used criteria for the positive identification of EC in culture is the immunofluorescent staining of factor VIII antigen. Bloom et al. (54), Hoyer et al. (296), and Jaffe et al. (304) first used fluorescent anti–factor VIII antibodies to demonstrate the presence of factor VIII antigen on endothelium. Platelets and megakaryocytes also contain factor VIII (480), but smooth muscle cells and fibroblasts do not contain the protein. Factor VIII is also localized ultrastructurally with ferritin-labeled factor VIII antibody in EC that line bone marrow sinusoids (409).

Another antigen believed to be associated with EC is tissue factor, or thromboplastin. Zeldis et al. (701) first used peroxidase-conjugated antibodies to localize this antigen. The highest concentrations are in the intima of blood vessels, particularly in the plasma membranes of EC. However, many cell types possess the tissue-factor antigen, including kidney cells, hepatocytes, alveolar cells, and the sarcolemma of myofibrils. Additionally, Maynard et al. (408) showed tissue-factor activity associated with the surface of a variety of cultured cells, including smooth muscle cells, HUVEC, and fibroblasts. In contrast, Stemerman et al. (603), using antibody to tissue-factor apoprotein coupled to horseradish peroxidase, report that this anti–tissue-factor antibody bound selectively with EC. The parenchymal cells of other organs tested (brain, heart, lung, liver, spleen, kidney, bone marrow, mesothelial gut lining, erythrocytes, leukocytes, platelets) were negative for the stain. The cause of the discrepancy is not apparent. Stemerman et al. (603) suggest that it may be related to special conditions of tissue culture that Maynard et al. (408) may have employed. In any case, positive staining of a culture with antiserum to factor VIII antigen is a widely used criterion for endothelium in culture.

PHYSIOLOGICAL. Of the many enzyme activities demonstrated in EC, plasminogen-activator (PA) activity and angiotensin-converting enzyme (ACE) are most often used as identifying characteristics. Using the fibrin-plate technique, Todd (632) first localized PA activity to the endothelium of large blood vessels; Warren and Khan (669) corroborated this with an ultrastructural study. However, Bernik and Kwaan (39, 40) assayed tissue culture cells other than EC (kidney, ureter, bladder, lung, heart) and found that these cells also synthesize and secrete both PA and PA inhibitor. Thus PA secretion is not unique to endothelium and is not a valid marker for EC identification in culture. Another enzyme believed to reside in vascular EC is ACE. Using fluorescein-labeled antibody to rabbit pulmonary ACE, Caldwell et al. (81) localized the enzyme in the vascular endothelium of lung, liver, adrenal gland, cortex, pancreas, kidney, and spleen. [The only parenchymal cells that stain positively for ACE are the epithelial cells of the renal proximal tubules (668).] Because the validity of ACE as a marker for an EC culture is limited by the nature of possible contaminants and neither smooth muscle cells nor fibroblasts contain ACE, ACE constitutes a valid criterion for identifying EC isolated from large blood vessels.

In summary, investigators should apply multiple criteria, including morphological features, e.g., presence of WPB (where appropriate) and factor VIII staining, to confirm the identity of EC cultures. Furthermore, where cell lines are established and/or maintained through multiple passages, EC should be monitored for these identifying features to assure that cultures have not become overgrown with contaminating cell types or been altered phenotypically.

GROWTH CONTROL

Endothelial Cell Culture Studies

One of the most widely investigated areas of EC biology concerns the control of their growth. Knowledge of the factors and conditions that influence EC proliferation is necessary to understand the pathologies that involve EC injury, regeneration, and proliferation in vivo and to understand ontogenetic angiogenesis (261). The most obvious indication that endothelium is subject to stringent growth-control mechanisms is the morphological appearance of an intima in vitro (Fig. 4*A*, *B*). Here the endothelium forms a flat monolayer of closely apposed nonoverlapping cells with a very low mitotic index (160). Haudenschild et al. (264), who first suggested that the endothelium in culture is subject to the same kind of control as in vivo, demonstrated that, unlike density-inhibited 3T3 cells (289), a confluent layer of EC could not be stimulated into another round of division. Sholley et al. (579) showed that a confluent monolayer of EC in culture could only be stimulated to proliferate if a scrape or wound was made in the monolayer.

Taggart and Stout (616) have shown that EC in tissue culture grow as well in platelet-poor plasma as in serum or platelet-rich plasma. This contrasts with smooth muscle cells, which will not grow in platelet-poor plasma and require serum for normal growth. The difference in growth requirements between EC and other cell types that allows EC to grow in plasma although other cells require serum needs to be defined.

What causes the endothelium to maintain such a tightly controlled state of contact inhibition? The observation by Haudenschild et al. (264) that postconfluent EC would not respond to serum factors and the injury-repair data cited suggest that EC first have to be released from their contact-inhibited configuration in order to divide.

SHAPE. Folkman and Moscona (188) tested the effect of cell shape on proliferation in an elegant series of experiments. Poly(2-hydroxyethyl methacrylate) was used to alter the adhesiveness of the substrate, thus controlling the degree of cell spreading. With this system, [^{3}H]thymidine incorporation was inversely proportional to the cell height, and DNA synthesis decreased as the cells became more spherical (Fig. 5). The behavior of the cells in vivo corroborated these observations. At a confluent density, when cells are

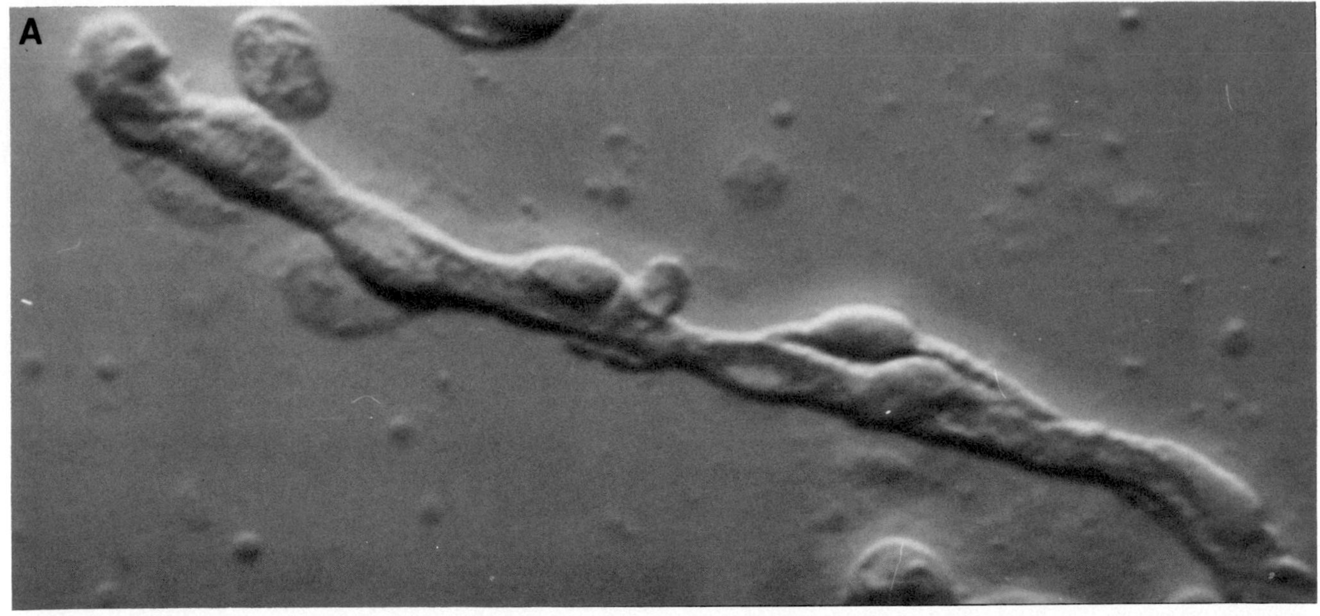

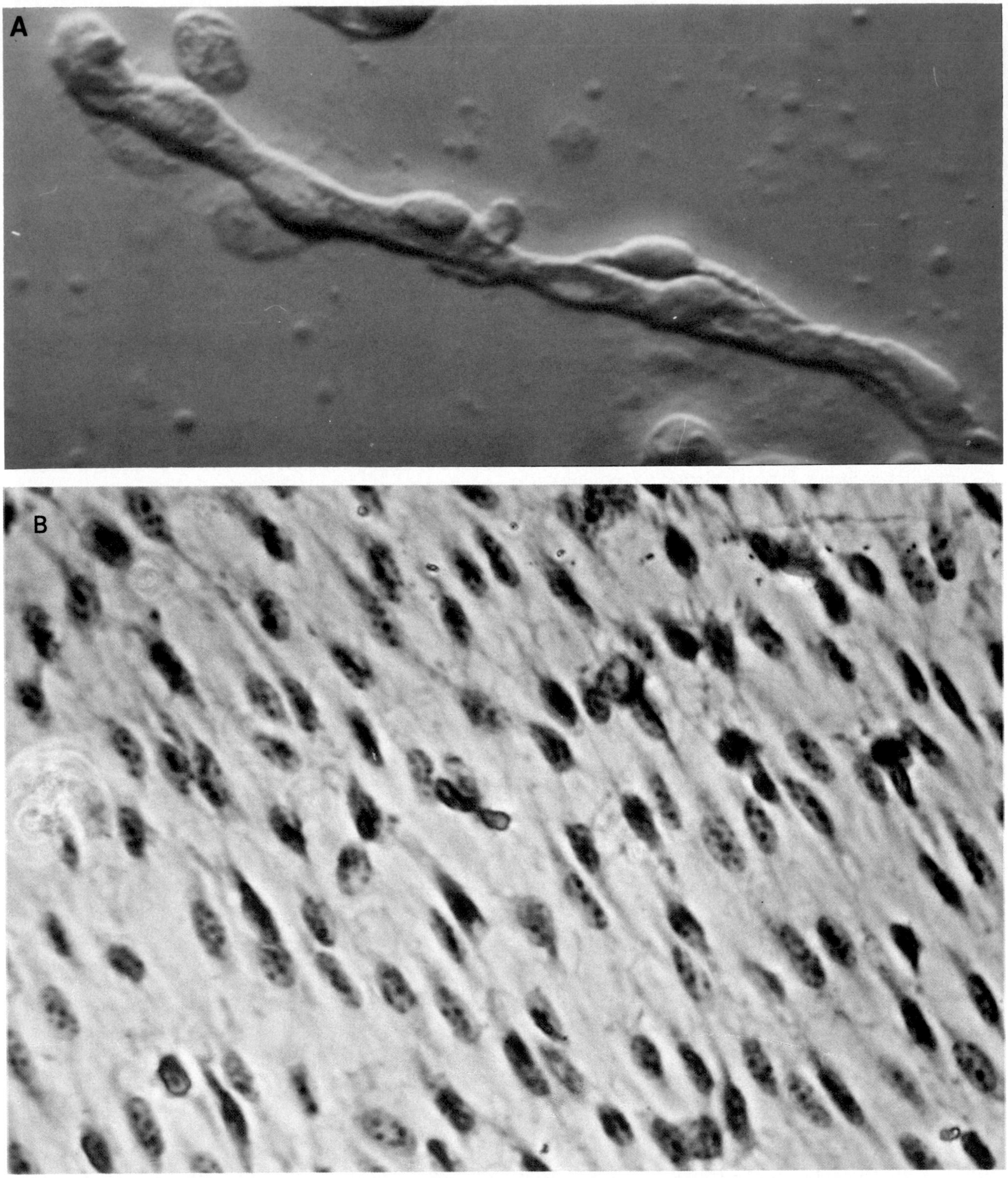

FIG. 4. *A*: segment of microvessel isolated from rat cardiac muscle. *B*: contiguous layer of bovine aortic endothelium obtained by stripping with cellulose acetate. Stained by Feulgen reaction.

crowded by their neighbors, they are most spherical and do not divide. When a gap is created, e.g., by a wound, the cells at the wound edge flatten within 1 h and DNA synthesis may commence. In transformed cells (SV3T3) growth is rapid regardless of the substrate and varied shape. Folkman and Moscona (188) conclude that shape is "tightly coupled" to DNA synthesis in normal cells.

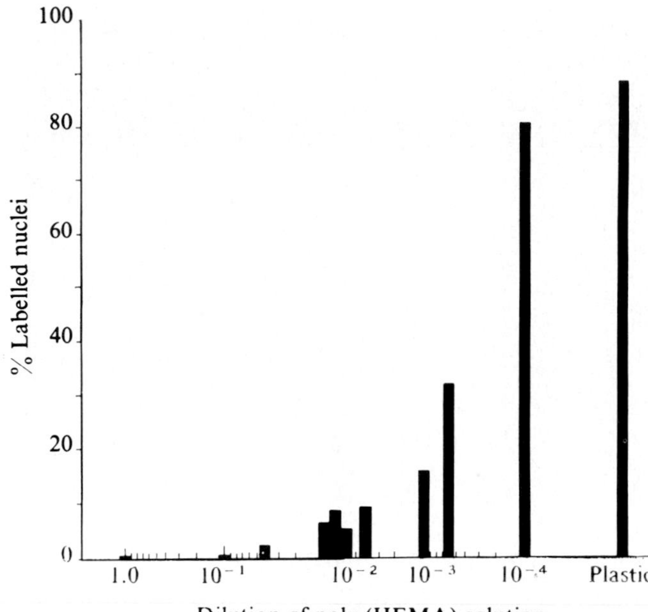

FIG. 5. Variation of DNA synthesis with endothelial cell shapes. Endothelial cells were plated on poly(2-hydroxyethyl methacrylate) [poly(HEMA)] substrates and plastic. Four wells were used for each dilution. Cell height was measured in 1st well. Cells in 2nd well were counted at end of experiment (48 h). Cells in 3rd and 4th wells were exposed to [^{3}H]thymidine (1 μCi/ml) for 42 h; counts/min per 1,000 cells were determined on precipitated DNA. Similar results were obtained with Wistar Institute cells (WI-38) and A-31 cells. Wide standard deviations in wells of 10^{-2} to 10^{-3} partly due to microscopic ripples at periphery of each well, mostly related to rapid drying of polymer film. [From Folkman and Moscona (188). Reprinted by permission from *Nature*, Copyright 1978, Macmillan Journals Limited.]

EXTRACELLULAR MATRIX. A series of studies by Gospodarowicz et al. (240) indicates that the extracellular matrix (ECM) of the EC functions in its growth control. This type of investigation stems from the observation that corneal epithelial cells in culture do not respond to epidermal growth factor (EGF), although they do respond in organ culture (236). The major difference between the two systems is the presence of an ECM in organ culture and its absence in vitro. The restored ability to respond to EGF when cells were plated on collagen confirmed this hypothesis. Gospodarowicz et al. (240) further suggest that vascular endothelium can be maintained in culture as long as FGF, a mitogen for vascular endothelium (231, 232), is included. When cultures reach confluency the EC exhibit a structure characteristic of their in vivo epithelial appearance, which the investigators suggest is a function of the formation of a BM similar to that found in vivo. They further suggest that the presence of the ECM is essential for the formation of an irreversibly contact-inhibited monolayer. The ECM causes this morphological and physiological state by allowing the cells to adopt a configuration that will determine the sensitivity or insensitivity of a cell to a mitogen. Another observation, which points to an important role for the ECM, came from Waxler et al. (672), who reported that in a confluent culture of BAEC a ruthenium red staining material is localized below the cells. As the cultures age a second population of EC undergrows the first monolayer. The orientation of these cells differs from the others: the apex is facing the plastic, and the base is oriented to the extracellular materials laid down by the first layer. Waxler et al. suggest that it is the ECM that determines the polarity of the cells both in vivo and in vitro.

Gospodarowicz et al. (240) and Harris et al. (260) have indicated that FGF is essential for the maintenance of EC cultures with true phenotypic expression. In their system FGF is necessary for the differentiation of the EC that involves the production of an ECM. In the presence of FGF, BAEC have a normal structure and make type III collagen and BM collagen at a ratio of 3:1 (233, 234, 240). The cells lose their normal structure and become overgrown when cultured without FGF. They also make type I collagen, lose their polarity with respect to ECM production, and become capable of binding platelets.

Vascular EC are able to secrete an ECM. A layer of ECM is left behind when EC are grown to confluence and the culture is detergent treated to remove the cells (240). Gospodarowciz and Ill (234) state that if vascular EC are plated onto such an ECM, FGF is no longer required. The growth rate of EC grown on ECM is a function of the concentration of serum or plasma added, indicating that the ECM has a permissive effect rather than a mitogenic effect. If confluent EC cultures, maintained in the absence of FGF, are exposed to medium conditioned by cells grown in the presence of FGF, then the altered cells revert to the normal phenotype within 4–8 days (244). Greenburg et al. (244) suggest that "vascular endothelial cells secrete a soluble factor(s) which can restore the normal morphology and function lost following removal of FGF from the medium."

CELL SURFACE PROTEIN. How does the presence of an ECM control cell shape, which can in turn control cell growth? Fibronectin (FN) seemed a likely regulator because of its presence in the ECM and its role in adhesion. However, the experimental data of Vlodavsky et al. (659) suggest that FN does not play this role: *1*) large amounts of FN are secreted in cultures that have lost the ability to form a monolayer; *2*) if the confluent monolayer is trypsinized, thereby removing surface FN, and then reseeded at a high density, a confluent monolayer forms within 12 h. Vlodavsky et al. (659) also demonstrated in confluent monolayers the presence of a cell surface protein susceptible to iodination by lactoperoxidase. The cell surface protein with a molecular weight of 60,000 (CSP-60) is not present in growing or subconfluent cultures, smooth muscle cells, or EC that have been maintained in the absence of FGF and have lost the ability to form a monolayer. Vlodavsky et al. (659) theorize that CSP-60 may control cell shape by influ-

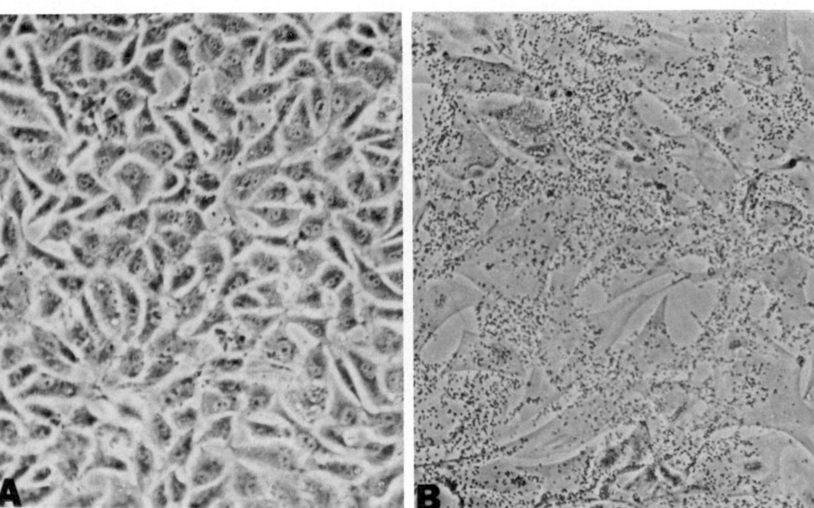

FIG. 6. Adherence of platelets to normal and variant endothelial cells; 2×10^8 platelets in 1 ml culture medium containing 0.25% bovine serum albumin were incubated with normal (*A*) and variant 2-chloroacetaldehyde ABAE (CA_1) (*B*) cells for 30 min at 37°C, washed 10 times, and observed under phase-contrast microscopy. × 150. [From Zetter et al. (705).]

encing the distribution of the microfibrillar system, which in turn determines cell shape. Using stereomicroscopic methods, transmission electron microscopy and scanning electron microscopy, Ausprunk and Berman (15) described a four-stage reorganization of cytoplasmic structures during EC spreading: *1*) spreading of the plasma membrane and unstructured cytoplasm; *2*) spreading of the fiber systems (microtubules, microfilaments, and microtrabecular system); *3*) alignment of microfilament bundles and formation of microtubule tracts; and *4*) movement of organelles along the tracts. Thus intracellular changes associated with EC spreading in culture may be related to the process(es) by which cell growth is regulated in vivo.

VARIANT ENDOTHELIAL CELLS. Normally EC at confluence form a nonoverlapping monolayer of polygonal cells. Gospodarowicz and Mecher (235) and Schwartz (550) observed a second growth pattern by a population of elongated cells and termed this phenomenon *sprouting* (235). Recently several lines of sprouting or variant EC have been established and described. Two arose spontaneously (115, 414); one developed after injection with wild-type SV40 (217); another was formed using the mutagen, 2-chloroacetaldehyde (705); the fifth was induced by FGF withdrawal (660). In all cases the cells are morphologically atypical; they undergrow or overgrow the cultures at confluence (Fig. 6). Other characteristics differ from cell line to cell line. Not all features were studied by each investigator (Table 3). Clear-cut differences exist between the variants established through use of the mutagen and those that arose spontaneously. The cell line established with a mutagen lacked factor VIII antigen and acquired the ability to bind platelets; the spontaneously derived lines retained factor VIII antigen and remained nonthrombogenic.

The physiological significance of these altered cell types is unknown. McAuslan et al. (412) suggest a specific function for these cells in vivo. They have shown that the variant cells, like normal cells, synthesize FN, but that 3 times more FN is distributed on their surface than on the surface of normal cells. The variant cells leave a trace of FN when stimulated to migrate by copper ions. McAuslan et al. (412) hypothesize that during neovascularization the variant cells migrate first and act as pathfinder cells by laying down an FN spoor on which trailing endothelium can become established.

TABLE 3. *Variant Endothelial Cell Lines*

Source	Platelet Binding	FN Synthesis Distribution	Altered Protein Synthesis and Other Change	Factor VIII Staining	Ref.
SV40-transformed	ND	ND	Occasional ACE, no WPB	−	217
Mutagenesis, SV40	ND	ND	No WPB	+	505
Mutagenesis*	+	+	↑ 400,000† 285,000† ↓ 220,000† 177,000† 150,000† 26,000†	−	705
Spontaneous‡	−	+	↑ Concanavalin A binding	+	414
	ND	−	Type I collagen		115
FGF withdrawal	+	+	No CSP-60	ND	660

Morphology altered in all cell lines examined. FN, fibronectin; ND, not done; ACE, angiotensin-converting enzyme; WPB, Weibel-Palade bodies; FGF, fibroblast growth factor; CSP-60, cell surface protein, M_r = 60,000. * Binding of concanavalin A in cap formation. † Values are mol wt. ‡ Increased binding of concanavalin A.

The variant EC lines established by Zetter et al. (705) and Vlodavsky et al. (660) are unique in that the cells lose their nonthrombogenic surface characteristics. Further characterization of these cell lines, therefore, may help elucidate the physiological and biochemical features of EC nonthrombogenicity. The other variant cell lines, all of which lack the growth characteristics of the endothelium, are potentially useful as model systems in investigations of the growth-control mechanisms of EC and in studies of oncogenesis and differentiation control. To this end Vlodavsky et al. (660) investigated the alterations that occur in variant EC that had been induced by FGF withdrawal from the culture medium. The most obvious changes were the loss of contact inhibition and the appearance of large overlapping cells. These EC showed a greatly increased production of FN, the disappearance of CSP-60, and the loss of their nonthrombogenic surface properties. Vlodavsky et al. interpret this to mean that EC in vitro depend on FGF for maintenance of their in vivo differentiated properties. Other investigators do not agree that FGF is essential for the maintenance of characteristic EC structure and function (383, 416, 552). One concern is that the primary cultures of these EC are in a medium containing FGF, and a population of FGF-dependent cells has been selected.

Finally, a class of EC termed *giant* EC (300–600 μm diam vs. 40–60 μm diam for normal cells) has been observed in vitro and in vivo. In vitro the large, multinucleate cells appear during long-term culture (557) and after a scrape injury to a confluent culture (215). In vivo they have been reported in the atherosclerotic aorta (116, 583) and during repair and regeneration (488). Tulloss and Booyse (645) reported that the addition of a number of agents (e.g., epinephrine, nicotine sulfate, 7-ketocholesterol, and estradiol) can increase the frequency of these cells in culture. Within 2 days after the treated cultures reach confluence the giant cells undergo necrosis and slough off, leaving holes in the monolayer. Platelets added to the culture do not bind the normal or giant EC but can interact with the matrix left behind by a lifted giant cell. Addition of serotonin (10^{-6} M) can suppress the formation of these giant cells. Tulloss and Booyse (645) note that this formation of giant cells in vitro in response to chemical or physical injury is similar to the morphological changes that occur with injury or disease in vivo.

GROWTH FACTORS. Although this *Handbook* deals primarily with the microvasculature, more studies of the growth control of EC in culture are needed. Information from the investigation of large-vessel EC in culture is important for at least two reasons. *1*) The technology for long-term culture of microvessel endothelium was only recently developed. Thus it is not yet known how EC from large vessels compare structurally and functionally with cells derived from microvessels. Only if both cell types are studied in culture is it valid to extrapolate information about large-vessel EC to cells derived from the microvasculature. *2*) In vivo assays for studying the growth control of the microvasculature are tedious, time-consuming, expensive, and difficult to quantify. Comparison of the results from tissue culture studies with those from in vivo studies determines the validity of in vitro assays as a reflection of in vivo events.

Various substances able to alter EC growth in vitro have been described recently. These substances have been identified in a medium conditioned by other cell types in long- and short-term culture, by homogenates or extracts of cells and tissues, and by the addition of known purified substances (Table 4). Some growth stimulatory factors have been purified to homogeneity and characterized, and many others are currently being purified. It is difficult now to comment on the possible relationship of the different growth factors to one another.

It should be interesting to see if each of these growth factors fits into a class of EC stimulants; current information is that EC growth factors vary widely (see Table 4). For instance, known EC growth factors vary in molecular weight from ~500 for the tumor-derived material (170, 413, 676) to 120,000 for the growth activity derived from 3T3 cells (411). Whether these factors have physiological significance remains to be demonstrated. Various investigators suggest in vivo functions for the growth factors. Klagsbrun et al. (344) identified an EC growth factor in cartilage and suggest that the polypeptide may be the growth stimulus for chondrocytes and blood vessels in vivo in a developmental sequence. Similarly, mitogenic factors identified from macrophages (243), retina (127, 220), differentiated 3T3 adipocytes (89), and a variety of tumors (see Table 4) are thought to function in the stimulation of neovascular growth in vivo (see next section). In contrast, although growth factors such as FGF (231, 232, 235) and the hypothalamus-derived activity (383) are functional in vitro, no function has been suggested for these materials in vivo. Lack of a physiological role does not render the growth factors in question less valid. The use of the substances in vitro provides important information on the regulation of growth and differentiation and the stimulation mechanisms.

Angiogenic Studies

Blood vessel proliferation (angiogenesis) is a component of a number of biological processes, both normal and pathological, including vascularization of tissues in embryogenesis, regeneration of blood vessels in wound healing, formation of the corpus luteum, inflammation, tumor vascularization, rheumatoid arthritis, and the proliferative retinopathies. Early investigations of blood vessel growth involved continuous observation of the embryonic development of vascular endothelium in a living organism. The amphibian larva, whose transparent tail region afforded a clear view of the growing vasculature, was a popular animal for these experiments (99). Initially chlorobutunol anesthesia and a specially designed observation chamber were used to observe blood vessel growth in the amphibian larvae over several weeks. Insertion of a transparent chamber into a rabbit ear also allowed microscopic observation of capillary formation (541). Many studies using these systems led in 1935 to the important conclusion of Clark and Clark (99):

> It appears that although the blood vascular system differentiates, acquires the power of growth by sprouting and forms a primitive system of arteries, veins and capillaries as the result of hereditary factors, it very early

Brouty-Boyé and Zetter (66) reported that interferon derived from human leukocytes and human and mouse fibroblasts inhibited tumor-induced phagokinesis of capillary EC. Interferon could also block the spontaneous migration of aortic EC and human diploid skin fibroblasts. This inhibitory activity is eliminated by interferon antibodies, indicating the specificity of the stimulation. Brouty-Boyé and Zetter speculate that if interferon functions in vivo to inhibit the migration of capillary EC then tumor vascularization could be prevented. Furthermore metastases could be eliminated because the invasive tumor cells would not enter the general circulation.

Azizkhan et al. (19) used this assay to demonstrate that mast cells contain a factor that stimulates migration of capillary EC. Investigation of the secretory products of mast cells found that only heparin induces migration. The heparin antagonists, heparin lyase and protamine, blocked both the heparin-induced migration and the migration induced by mast cell CM. Lastly, the migration-stimulating activity derived from the mast cell was resistant to treatment with heat, protease, and trypsin, characteristics that are also true of commercially available heparin. Thus both tumor cell CM and mast cell CM are able to stimulate migration. The activities differ, however, in that the tumor cell CM can also stimulate proliferation of the capillary EC in vitro, whereas the mast cell CM does not. Although these data indicate that proliferation and migration are not always coupled in vitro, it is not known if these events are also regulated separately in vivo.

McAuslan and Reilly (415) also employed the phagokinetic assay to study the response of BAEC to metal ions and demonstrated that salts of copper, nickel, selenium, and indium induce EC motility in vitro, although zinc, cobalt, manganese, chromium, iron, aluminum, antimony, and molybdenum do not. On the basis of this work and other studies on the angiogenic capacity of copper, McAuslan and Reilly (410, 415) proposed that "the primary event in angiogenesis induced by bovine derived fractions, and perhaps fractions from other sources, is the mobilization of EC *in vivo* by copper ions" (415).

Another assay system developed to quantitate EC migration in vitro is a modification of the Boyden chamber, an apparatus initially used to measure leukocyte chemotaxis (63). Glaser et al. (221) and Bowersox and Sorgente (61) adapted this system to measure EC chemotaxis. Employing this blind-well chamber, Glaser et al. (221) identified chemoattractants for EC in extracts of many adult tissues, e.g., retina, liver, kidney, heart, and skeletal muscle. The action of these extracts, observed with different gradients of the extracts across the membrane, is chemotactic (as opposed to chemokinetic). In all cases the EC in vitro migrate preferentially from the lower to higher concentration of extract. Bowersox and Sorgente (61) also used the Boyden chemotaxis chamber to test the ability of FN to elicit a chemotactic response from vascular EC. Fibronectin induced chemotaxis in a time- and dose-dependent manner with maximal stimulation of a sevenfold increase at 250 μg/ml. Furthermore EC growth supplement did not increase EC migration above the control levels (61), which again indicates that the migratory and proliferative responses of EC (at least in vitro) may be regulated independently.

Lastly, a factor's ability to stimulate the proliferation of EC can reflect angiogenic activity (Table 4). Proliferation can be measured by increases in [^{3}H]-thymidine incorporation (421) or by increases in actual cell number determined by hemocytometer or Coulter counter.

TABLE 6. *Sources of Angiogenic Activity*

Tissue/Cell Line	Assay	Ref.
Choriocarcinoma	Hamster cheek pouch	158
Melanoma and mammary adenocarcinoma*	Hamster cheek pouch	242, 670
Wilms' tumor, neuroblastoma, and hemangioma†	Rat dorsal air sac	478
Walker 256 carcinoma	Rat dorsal air sac	187
	CAM, corneal pocket	183
	CAM, rat dorsal air sac	478
	CAM	676
	Mouse kidney hypertrophy	413
	CAM, corneal pocket	170
Epidermis	Hamster cheek pouch	449, 692
Neutrophils	Intracorneal injections	194
BALB C3T3	CAM	343
Parotid gland‡ and salivary gland§	Mouse kidney hypertrophy	287
Lymph node and spleen cells§	CAM	13
	Hamster cheek pouch	448
Activated macrophages	Guinea pig cornea	102, 485
Corpus luteum	Corneal pocket	239
Endothelial cells and smooth muscle cells	Cells on Sephadex beads on CAM	260
Cells transformed by adenovirus type 3‡	CAM	642
Synovial fluid	CAM	67
Vitreous	CAM	97
	Cornea pocket	97
Retina	CAM	127, 220

CAM, chick chorioallantoic membrane. * Rat. † Human. ‡ Bovine. § Mouse.

IN VIVO ASSAYS. Most laboratories isolating angiogenic factors have used EC proliferation or migration in tissue culture as an assay (Table 6). However, because angiogenesis involves the stimulation of new capillary growth, the researcher must demonstrate the action of the purified materials in an in vivo assay. Five in vivo assay systems are commonly used to test the angiogenic capacity of a material: the hamster cheek pouch technique, rat dorsal air sac technique, rabbit and rat corneal pocket technique, rabbit ear chamber technique, and chick chorioallantoic membrane (CAM) assay.

Hamster cheek pouch technique. This assay was one of the first used to monitor tumor-induced vascularization (242, 670). The cheek pouch preparation is attractive because the tissue is immunologically "privileged" (454). Acrylic chambers containing the material to be tested are implanted in the cheek pouch of an anesthetized hamster. Vascular responses to the implant are monitored during the following days.

Rat dorsal air sac technique. In this technique an air sac is produced on the back of a rat by aseptically injecting a subcutaneous bulbus of air (187). Material is then incorporated into the appropriate vehicle and implanted in the air sac. The response to the material is determined 48 h later by incising the area over the implant and observing with a stereoscope. Folkman et al. (187) commented that the system is "cumbersome but very reliable." In 900 rat assays performed in 2 yr they seldom observed a false positive.

Corneal pocket technique. The cornea is a transparent, avascular structure. Because of this unique combination of features it has been utilized by many workers to investigate the phenomenon of neovascularization (10, 83, 356, 699). Gimbrone et al. (216) more recently rediscovered it as an experimental system to test mediators of neovascularization. In this assay an incision is made in the corneal stroma of the rabbit (216) or rat eye (190), creating a pocket; the material in question is implanted 1–2 mm from the limbus. A slit-lamp microscope can be used to monitor the response of the limbal blood vessels to the angiogenic stimulus. However, the presence of new corneal vessels cannot be accepted as proof without other appropriate criteria. The possibility that the neovascularization is part of an inflammatory response must be eliminated. The absence of gross corneal edema and pyrogenic infiltration also needs documentation.

Chick chorioallantoic membrane. In this assay fertilized chicken eggs are used to determine angiogenic activity of a test substance (183, 343). Between days 6 and 7, candling of fertilized eggs determines the location of the air sac, and a small hole is made in the shell above the air sac. A 1.0-cm-square window is then made in the egg shell, the shell and the egg shell membrane are gently removed, and the CAM and yolk sac separate from the shell. On day 8 the implant is made onto the CAM. The material to be tested is often incorporated into Elvax, an ethylene-vinyl acetate copolymer that allows continuous release of the material over the course of the experiment (355). The response is monitored over the following days and graded according to the investigators' criteria. In one system the number of complete capillary loops are counted and the egg is given a value from 0 to +5. Although the grading systems may appear arbitrary, a double-masked format with large sample numbers and appropriate controls allows statistical analysis and increases the validity of the assay system.

Rabbit ear chamber. In 1924 Sandison (540, 541) first introduced the transparent ear chamber, which has been used to observe new blood vessel growth (103, 157). The most recent modification of the technique (700) includes punching four holes in the ear of an anesthetized rabbit. The holes consist of three outer cuts (3.5 mm diam) used to position the chamber and a central 5.4-mm perforation for locating the transparent chamber. A plate is placed on the inside of the ear and aligned with the existing holes, and a thin 200-μm cover of mica glass is placed over the cartilage. Fastening the two plates together creates the chamber into which new tissue grows during wound healing. Researchers have used time-lapse cinemicroscopy (103), photomicroscopy, and stereology (700) to analyze the dynamics of neovascularization.

ANGIOGENIC FACTORS. Angiogenic factors, substances able to elicit new blood vessel growth, have been identified in a variety of tissues and cells (Table 6). Folkman et al. (187) first suggested the significance of the angiogenesis process when they identified a partially purified soluble factor from human and animal neoplasms that was able to induce new capillary formation. Folkman et al. (185) and Gimbrone et al. (212) also demonstrated that tumors that did not become vascularized would not grow beyond a particular diameter (3–4 mm). Other investigators had earlier hypothesized on the ability of tumor tissue to induce vascularization (5). Ehrmann and Knoth (158) and Greenblatt and Shubik (242) had also shown that the tumor-derived factor in question was diffusible because tumor cells grown in diffusion chambers in hamster cheek pouches were equally able to elicit blood vessel growth. Since this time a number of laboratories (Table 6) have become involved in the investigation of a tumor-derived factor, which is called tumor angiogenesis factor. Recent reports indicate that the material is a small molecule, with a molecular weight <500 (100, 413, 676). Although the approximate size of the active molecule is generally agreed on, the exact nature of the factor needs to be determined.

Angiogenic activity can be demonstrated in a number of cell lines and tissues (Table 6). However, as is the case with the EC growth factors, few of the substances have been purified to homogeneity. Thus it is impossible to draw conclusions about relationships between these molecules. For instance, the angiogenic activity that has been partially purified from bovine retinal extracts has one form with a molecular weight >50,000 (127) and a second form [separated by high-pressure liquid chromatography (HPLC)] with a molecular weight of 18,000–22,000 (127). Angiogenic activity isolated from macrophage CM has a molecular weight >80,000 (400). The EC growth factor that Klagsbrun et al. (344) have isolated from cartilage is a polypeptide with a molecular weight of 16,300. (This factor also induces capillary EC proliferation and migration.)

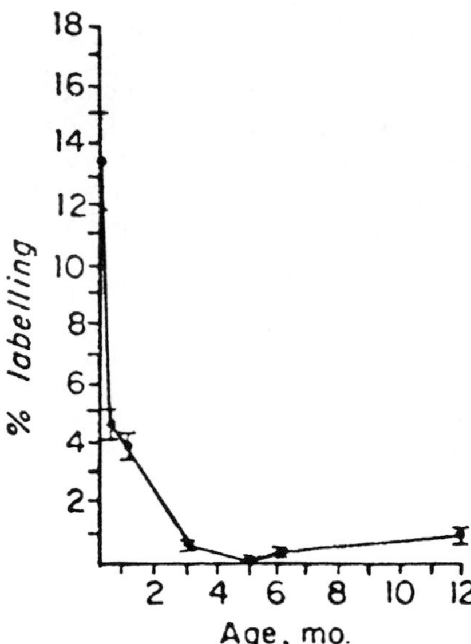

FIG. 8. Effect of age on endothelial cell replication. Values are means ± SD for female rats, between 24 h and 12 mo after birth. Numbers of rats: newborn, 5; 2 wk, 9; 3 mo, 6; 5 mo, 6; 5.5 mo, 4; 6 mo, 7; 1 yr, 6. [From Schwartz and Benditt (551), by permission of the American Heart Association, Inc.]

Endothelial Cell Regeneration

Injury to the vessel wall resulting in EC loss is theorized to be the initial event of the sequelae that lead to atherosclerosis (176, 487, 517). The exposed subendothelium provides a substrate to which platelets adhere and release their constituents. One constituent, a mitogen called platelet-derived growth factor (518), stimulates smooth muscle cell proliferation, a step considered central to atherosclerosis (516). Because loss of the endothelium is necessary to expose the subendothelium and trigger these events, there is much interest in the source of EC injury in vivo and how the endothelium repairs itself.

The turnover rate of EC in vivo is very slow (695). Schwartz and Benditt (551) studied the effect of age and hypertension on the replication rate in the rat aorta and found the rate maximal at birth (13%) and minimal at 6 mo (0.1%–0.3%), when the rate plateaus (Fig. 8). In the same study, the replication rate in animals made renal hypertensive rose 10-fold to 1.6%. Although the exact nature of the increase was not clear, Schwartz and Benditt suggested that increased EC replication could be caused by injury. Wright (695) tested the hypothesis that modifications in blood flow pattern can cause EC damage. Clamping certain areas of the guinea pig aorta, she altered blood pressure and created flow perturbations above the clips. In these areas the average percent of labeled cells was higher than in controls, indicating that pulsatile flow may, in fact, injure the endothelium. Furthermore these areas of increased EC turnover coincide with sites in the vascular system that appear most highly disposed to develop atherosclerosis (85, 195, 695). Hyperlipidemia also has been implicated as a cause of atherosclerosis (198, 494). However, subsequent studies in animals with injured aortas indicate that hypercholesterolemia is not responsible for smooth muscle cell proliferation because equivalent intimal thickening is noted in both control and cholesterol-fed animals (108). Comparison of the lesions in control and cholesterol-fed animals after 6 mo and 1 yr suggests that a hypercholesterolemic state does not result in chronic EC injury or the development of fibrous plaques on established smooth muscle cell lesions (107). Hardin et al. (258), who studied the effect of high cholesterol in EC regeneration where injury was induced by immunological means, agree with these results.

Various in vivo model systems have been designed to examine how the endothelium in vivo repairs itself when cells are lost. Injury is induced by cauterization (544), allergic reaction to injections of horse serum (258), local freezing (69), infusion of an air stream along an arterial segment (176), mechanical injury (235), and balloon catheterization (28, 104, 553). Schwartz and co-workers (263, 502, 553) conducted a series of studies on EC regeneration of a wound in a rat aorta. The balloon-catheter technique was used to damage a portion of the EC lining. Regeneration, including proliferation and migration, was measured by autoradiography and light and scanning electron microscopy. The proliferative response of the cells was not confined to the border of the injury. Schwartz and Benditt (551) found that up to 100 cells behind the line of injury, cells enter the *S* phase of DNA synthesis and change shape, developing a perinuclear elevation oriented parallel to the blood flow. The number of new EC produced in this zone exceeds the original number, and the final cell density in the regeneration zone can be up to 3 times that in an uninjured area. In 8–16 h after injury, cell migration commences and takes place preferentially along the vessel axis.

One interesting observation from these studies is the difference between EC regeneration in vivo and the response seen in vitro. Whereas the regeneration zone in vivo encompasses an area of up to 100 cells behind the line of injury, wounding experiments in vitro indicate that only the cells located around the periphery of the wound are involved in the response (476). One explanation for this phenomenon is termed the *diffusion barrier hypothesis.* According to this theory an unknown factor regulates the final density of a density-inhibited monolayer in competition with nutrients and growth factors (606). However, as Schwartz et al. (552) noted, the diffusion barrier hypothesis cannot account for the hyperplasia seen in vivo:

> First, unlike tissue culture, medium blood plasma is continuously replaced at high exchange rates and all nutrients are available in finite supply. Second, the effects of the injury extend well back from the line of injury, affecting cells in the apparently continuous, uninjured portion of the cell sheet. Third, unlike the tissue culture models, these cells overrespond, rapidly producing cell densities in excess of the normal "saturation density."

In another study this group found that endothelialization of a balloon-catheter injury in the aorta results from EC migration from intercostal vessels. The EC proliferate as a continuous sheet, which extends circumferentially at a rate of 0.01 mm/day and about 6 times faster in the axial direction.

Endothelial cell regeneration has also been investigated in vitro. Selden and Schwartz (558) used cytochalasin B to inhibit the migration and proliferation of cultured EC at the wound edge (a lateral cut with a stainless steel razor blade). Because the background replication levels are unaffected by cytochalasin B, the investigators concluded that some form of movement may be required for the initiation of proliferation in this system. Wall et al. (666) assessed the relative contributions of migration and proliferation to the endothelial repair process with an assay for EC migration that measured the ability of a circular monolayer of irradiated and nonirradiated cells to cover a particular surface area under agarose gel. The nonirradiated cells migrated outward for the first 24 h, reducing the cell density in the original monolayer, which then underwent active proliferation. The EC at the advancing edge did not divide. The irradiated cells, on the other hand, covered the same surface area as the control cells during the first 3 days of the experiment. The addition of a nondialyzed, heat-stable factor derived from platelets doubled the migration rate. Fibroblast growth factor, macrophage CM, and human serum (zymosan treated) did not alter the EC migration rate.

Similar studies by Thorgeirsson et al. (627) show that EC do not require platelet factors for migration nor is the migration rate in the presence of platelet-rich plasma altered in comparison to the rate in the presence of platelet-poor plasma. Furthermore the addition of cytochalasin B, dibutyryl cyclic adenosine 5′-monophosphate (cAMP), and theophylline inhibits EC migration (and the migration of smooth muscle cells). Thorgeirsson and Robertson (625, 626) observed migratory responses of EC to platelet-poor plasma and platelet-rich plasma that are similar to responses they observed in proliferation studies. In these studies platelet factors are shown to be essential for vascular smooth muscle cell proliferation but unnecessary for EC growth. The incorporation of [^{3}H]thymidine into EC is linearly related to serum concentrations, but there is no difference between serum derived from platelet-poor plasma and that derived from platelet-rich plasma, leading to the conclusion that EC proliferation in vitro is independent of platelet factors. Finally, Thorgeirsson and Robertson (626) point out that the comparison of the migratory properties of EC and smooth muscle cells show two distinct types of behavior: EC move as part of a continuous sheet, which is apparently refractile to platelet factors; smooth muscle cells move individually and are very responsive to platelet factors. That smooth muscle migration and proliferation can be stimulated by platelet-released factors may be significant in the initial stages of atherosclerosis.

SYNTHESIS

Subendothelium

Endothelial cells in vivo are polar cells, i.e., they exhibit sidedness. Only the EC apical surface faces the lumen, the dorsal surface faces an array of connective tissue, collectively termed the *subendothelium.* The subendothelium may be arbitrarily divided into the BM and extracellular matrix (ECM). The BM is a complex of connective tissue that separates EC from the connective tissue of the ECM (662).

BASEMENT MEMBRANE. The term *basement membrane* describes the continuous, sheetlike layer of periodic acid–Schiff (PAS)–staining material seen at the base of epithelial cells by light microscopy (87). After the development of the electron microscope, analyses indicated that the BM was not membranous, as the name suggested, but a sheet of filamentous, electron-dense material (168). Thus the BM is the electron-dense layer that isolates parenchymal cells from the ECM. [Carlson et al. (87) found exceptions to this arrangement in the kidney glomerulus, the lung, and the central nervous system, where only the BM is found between the EC and the parenchymal tissues.] Three types of investigation have been used to study BM synthesis and nature: synthesis by microvessel EC in vivo and in vitro and by EC in culture.

Isolated rat glomeruli are the tissue of choice for many of the studies, and for this reason this discussion will be confined to this model system. There is no ECM connective tissue separating EC from epithelial cells in the glomeruli, and the isolation procedure is straightforward. Also important, glomerular BM may play a role in the ultrafiltration process of urine formation. Finally, the morphological alterations that develop in the glomerular BM as a complication in diabetes mellitus and nephrosis make understanding its composition and synthesis essential (35, 587).

The synthesis and secretion of BM have been mostly investigated in isolated glomeruli; only recently have the biosynthesis and turnover of the renal glomerular BM been studied in vivo (110) by prelabeling the renal BM of rats with tracer amounts of radiolabeled glycine and proline. A time course of incorporation is conducted, after which glomeruli are isolated by osmotic lysis and extraction with detergents. Biochemical analysis of the BM preparations indicates maximal incorporation of [^{3}H]glycine at 24 h postadministration; the peak for [^{3}H]proline is 48 h. The turnover rates for the proline-labeled BM vary somewhat from the glycine-labeled BM but are comparable to that seen for fibrillar collagen. Cohen and Surma (110) point out that this method of in vivo study of BM biochemistry may be more valid than the isolated glomeruli procedures because it "allows pertinent systemic influences to prevail during the period of study." Most in vitro studies using isolated glomeruli involve an analysis of the secreted connective tissue products after incubation with a radiolabeled amino acid. A number of workers report the production of BM collagen by isolated renal glomeruli (111, 241, 340). Cells prelabeled with [^{14}C]lysine and hydroxy[^{14}C]lysine are studied for the appearance of the label in the medium, the plasma membrane, and in intracellular proteins as a function of time (111). The peak for incorporation of radioactivity into the various compartments occurs within 2 h. Sixty percent of the protein secreted into the medium is acetic acid soluble; 75% of the newly synthesized BM has this characteristic, indicating that a majority of the total collagen made by these preparations is BM collagen. Glomerular BM collagen is synthesized as a large molecule (M_r 140,000), which is later converted to a collagen polypeptide that migrates with tendon proα-chains (M_r 120,000) (241). This study also demonstrates that over a 6-h time course the synthesis of collagen, determined by 4-hydroxy[^{14}C]proline incorporation, represents <5% of the protein synthesized. In vivo procedures are generally not feasible because of the large quantity of label that is required for this type of testing.

The ability of the glomerular BM to stain with ruthenium red and the absence of this staining after heparitin sulfate lyase treatment suggest the presence of glycosaminoglycans (GAGs) (229, 230). In vivo digestion of glomerular BM with a variety of GAG-degrading enzymes indicates that removal of heparan sulfate, but no other GAG, dramatically increases BM permeability (331). Isolated rat glomeruli incorporate radiolabeled sulfate, and the carbazole:orcinol ratio quantitated suggests that the secretory product is like heparan sulfate (109). Previous biochemical analyses of glomerular BM failed to detect uronic acid or sulfate, GAG markers. However, Cohen (109) suggests that sonic disruption, the method of isolation, may have removed the anionic molecules. The potential disruptive nature of sonication as a method for isolation of renal glomeruli led others to devise a new method for the isolation and purification of BM. Triton X-100 and deoxycholate solubilization of the membranes and intracellular and plasma proteins (87) produced purified BM that was "ultrastructurally intact, non-fragmented and which retained its histoarchitectural relationships" (Fig. 9). Courtoy et al. (118) have localized FN in the rat glomerulus. Fluorescently labeled antibodies demonstrated FN in frozen sections of kidney. Fibronectin was also localized at the ultrastructural level in fixed glomeruli with peroxidase and ferritin-labeled antibodies and in isolated glomeruli with ferritin-labeled antibodies. Courtoy et al. (118) suggest that FN may be involved in cell-cell and cell-substrate attachment.

The third category of BM studies utilizes EC in culture. Howard et al. (295) used BAEC and Jaffe et al. (306) used HUVEC to provide evidence that the secretory material is morphologically, immunologically, and biochemically similar to BM collagen (type IV collagen). The collagen in these cases is characterized by *1*) the amount of 3-hydroxy[^{14}C]proline found in the collagen, *2*) the molecular weight of the pepsin-resistant collagen fraction, *3*) the percent of glycosylation of hydroxy[^{14}C]lysine, and *4*) the proportion of hydroxy[^{14}C]lysine-linked glycoside, glucosylgalactose. The procollagen molecule that EC synthesize is pepsin digested to a molecular weight of 115,000. This differs from smooth muscle cell procollagen, which on pepsin digestion yields a molecule with a molecular weight of 95,000 (379). Guinea pig aortic EC make a collagenous molecule that contains two CNBr peptides, CP45A and CP45B, that are also found in smooth muscle cells (409). These peptides are pepsin-resistant components of the BM of EC and smooth muscle cells. Bovine aorta EC secrete a noncollagenous glycoprotein, which in its reduced state has a molecular weight of 135,000 (532). The lack of cross-reactivity with antisera to FN or α_2-macroglobulin distinguishes this product from the latter two products of EC synthesis. Timpl et al. (631) isolated a large noncollagenous protein, which they termed *laminin*, from a mouse tumor cell BM. Laminin has a molecular weight of ~850,000 and consists of four polypeptide chains (M_r 220,000) (510). The glycoprotein differs from FN in immunological reactivity and in amino acid composition. Timpl et al. (631) used purified antibody against laminin to demonstrate the presence of laminin in the BM of normal tissues, including kidney, placenta, and skin.

EXTRACELLULAR MATRIX. Whereas the BM is com-

FIG. 9. *A*: basement membrane (*BM*) in isolated rat encapsulated renal glomerulus. Fenestrated capillary endothelium (*E*) lines capillary space (*C*). Interdigitating foot processes (*fp*) of podocytes (*pod*) form boundary of Bowman's space. Frequently cytoplasmic processes of a podocyte abut on *BM* of more than 1 glomerular capillary. × 41,000. *B*: isolated rat renal glomerular *BM* in mesangial region of glomerulus. Unstructured *BM* material on inner (mesangial) surface of *BM*. Smooth and crisply demarcated outer (epithelial) surface of lamina. × 41,000. *C*: high-power electron micrograph of glomerular *BM* interposed between capillary endothelium and foot processes of podocytes. *Arrows*, slit membranes between adjacent foot processes. *BM* ~2,000 Å thick with a finely granular texture. × 135,000. *D*: electron micrograph of glomerular *BM* isolated by Triton X-100 and deoxycholate. *BM* ~2,200 Å thick and morphologically identical to in vivo control. × 135,000. [From Carlson et al. (87).]

posed principally of collagen and GAGs, the ECM is composed of collagen fibrils, microfibrils, elastic fibers, and GAGs. Most investigations of the biosynthesis of these materials have used EC in a tissue culture system.

Collagen. Both pig (26) EC and BAEC (532) synthesize type III procollagen. Sage et al. (532) identified the material as type III by direct comparison with type III collagen from bovine skin. Barnes et al. (26) report that the major species of collagen synthesized

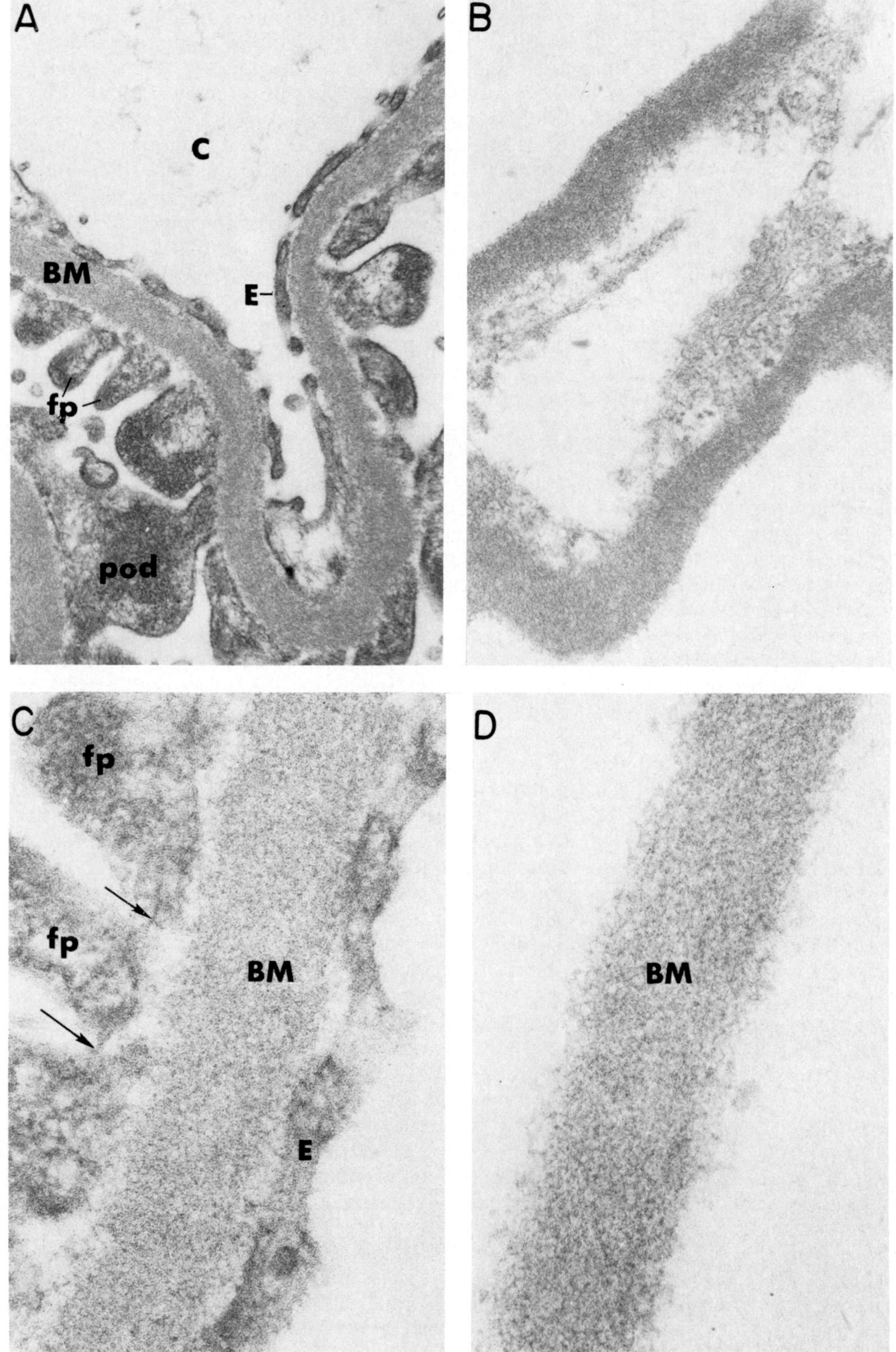

by pig EC is type I and conclude that "much (if not all) of the collagen synthesized by the cells in culture is interstitial in character." Sage et al. (532) suggest that the type IV collagen secreted into the medium (306) could be derived from type III procollagen and that the only cultures found to synthesize type I collagen are highly prone to sprouting (lacking growth control). Thus synthesis of type I procollagen is not truly indicative of EC biosynthesis. More recently, Sage et al. (534) have isolated two types of collagen, $\alpha1$(III) and $\alpha1$(V), from cultured BAEC and the associated ECM. Although type III collagen was found in both the culture medium and the cell layer, type V was restricted to the cell layer; both were identified in the ECM. Furthermore Sage et al. (533) have isolated a unique pepsin-sensitive collagen from the culture medium of adult BAEC. This collagen can be digested within 10 min to fragments with a molecular weight <60,000, under conditions that do not significantly affect other collagens. In addition, the primary structure differs from that of the other identified collagen types.

Elastin. Jaffe et al. (306) reported that human EC in culture synthesize a material that is morphologically similar to elastic fibers. Carnes et al. (88) demonstrated that rabbit aortic EC in culture synthesize and secrete into the medium protein with a molecular weight of 75,000, which has a number of properties (i.e., its solubility in propanol-butanol and its hydroxyproline and dipeptide valylproline content) that identify it as elastin. Comparison of the amount of labeled elastin extracted by sodium dodecyl sulfate (SDS) in the cell extract to that in the culture medium indicates that the protein accumulates in the cells. Furthermore the low level of label in the medium and the presence of three labeled fragments of lower molecular weight suggest that the elastin may undergo degradation after its secretion. Carnes et al. (88) also comment that the "lack of significant amounts of labeled insoluble elastin in the culture suggests a deficiency in the steps leading to crosslinkage." In contrast, Cantor et al. (84) identified cross-linked elastin production by an established clone of rat lung EC. Two techniques demonstrate that the secreted material is elastin: *1*) the isolation and identification of the elastin-specific cross-linking amino acids desmosine and isodesmosine by thin-layer electrophoresis after prelabeling the cells with [^{14}C]lysine; *2*) staining the EC in culture with fluorescently labeled guinea pig antirat elastin antiserum.

Mucopolysaccharides/glycosaminoglycans. Staining rat aorta EC with the mucopolysaccharide stain, alcian blue–PAS, Buonassisi (70) found that the perinuclear area of the cells is stained, which led to an investigation of the possibility that EC are able to synthesize these molecules. By labeling the EC with [^{35}S]sulfuric acid, he determined that the cells could synthesize and secrete various species of sulfated mucopolysaccharides. The mucopolysaccharide that occurs in largest proportion is resistant to chondroitinase ABC, a feature associated with heparin-related molecules. Additionally, more than half of the ^{35}S label in the chondroitinase-resistant material is labile to mild acid hydrolysis (0.04 N HCl, 90 min, 100°C), another characteristic associated with heparin. This material constitutes only a small amount of the GAG that is secreted into the medium. In autoradiographic studies, most of the sulfated mucopolysaccharides are transported from the perinuclear site of synthesis to the periphery where they presumably become membrane components. Buonassisi and Root (71) confirmed these indications in a study that prelabeled EC with $H_2{}^{35}SO_4$ and then exposed EC to purified heparitin sulfate lyase and heparin lyase (*Flavobacterium heparinum*). The fragments of the material released from the cell by this treatment migrate as glucosamine, a heparin-breakdown product. Comparison of the ^{35}S-labeled material that remains in the enzyme-treated EC with that in untreated control EC and their media indicates that the enzyme acts on the EC itself, confirming previous suggestions that the heparitin sulfate chains are at the EC surface.

Bihari-Varga et al. (48), who studied the GAG profile of pig aortic EC in culture as a function of time course of culture, found that the concentration of hyaluronic acid and chondroitin sulfate increased with time while heparan sulfate decreased. Furthermore the addition of chondroitin sulfate or hyaluronic acid to the culture medium increased hexuronic acid until 7 days in culture, after which time the levels decreased. These results support the idea that extracellular GAGs influence GAG synthesis in culture with the internalization of chondroitin sulfate or hyaluronic acid, resulting in a suppression of GAG synthesis within the cells.

In a comparative study of GAG synthesis in rat and pig aortic EC, Merrilees and Scott (422) showed that the rat cells produced large amounts of GAG, 80% hyaluronic acid, whereas the pig cells produced moderate amounts, most of which were sulfated. Merrilees and Scott suggest that differential production of GAGs may result in a difference in strength of attachment to the blood vessel wall in vivo and thus determine susceptibility to atherosclerosis. The rat, an animal not predisposed to atherosclerosis, has EC that are resistant to collagenase; the pig, which is susceptible to atherosclerosis, has EC that the enzyme treatment can remove.

Fibronectin. Fibronectin or cold-insoluble globulin is a glycoprotein that is composed of two polypeptide subunits (M_r 220,000). These adhesive proteins on the surfaces of cells are localized in the connective tissue matrix and in serum and may be functional in cell attachment, growth regulation, and embryonic differentiation (696). Endothelial cells in culture synthesize FN, secrete it into their medium, and incorporate it into the ECM (307, 380). When the cultured EC are prelabeled with a labeled amino acid they secrete a radioactive polypeptide with a molecular weight of 200,000 into the medium. This contrasts with the subunit size of fibroblast FN, which has a molecular weight of 220,000 (696). Jaffe and Mosher (307) suggest that the endothelium may be the site of plasma FN synthesis because the plasma FN molecule also has a subunit with a molecular weight of 200,000 (431). Birdwell et al. (50) have compared plasma and EC (both cellular and secreted) FNs by SDS–polyacrylamide gel electrophoresis (PAGE) and by two-dimensional peptide mapping. Under reducing conditions the FNs of the EC migrated as single bands, each with a molecular weight of 220,000; the plasma molecule migrated as two bands with molecular weights of 220,000 and 210,000. However, all three FN molecules had identical peptide maps. Some difference between the plasma and FNs of the EC is indicated by their different susceptibilities to plasmin but not *Staphylococcus aureus* proteinase (351). Birdwell et al. (50) suggest that differences in glycosylation may be responsible for the differential migration of the FNs on SDS gels. About 15% of the protein secreted by the EC in culture is FN, as opposed to ~5.5% factor VIII antigen (304). Using indirect immunofluorescent techniques, Birdwell et al. (52) observed that when EC are sparse, FN is distributed only on the dorsal surface at areas of cell contact. At confluence, however, FN is redistributed and is detectable only underneath the cell in the ECM. The physiological function of FN is not clear. The localization of FN to the ECM of confluent cultures may imply a role for FN in cell-substrate adhesion and the maintenance of contact inhibition.

Releasable Products

COLLAGENASE. Teleologically it would make good sense if EC had the means to break down the collagen in their extracellular environment. Such proteolytic activity associated with angiogenesis and paralleling the growth of tumors has been reported. Ausprunk and Folkman (16) observed migrating EC with pseudopods devoid of a basal lamina or fragments of the BM after tumor-induced capillary proliferation. Busuttil et al. (79) also suggest that endogenous aortic collagenase activity is significant in aneurysm formation and rupture. Reddi and Huggins (500) associate angiogenesis of cartilaginous tissue with chondrolysis, which suggests that collagenase synthesis is an obligatory function of invasive capillary EC.

Moscatelli et al. (432) demonstrated EC secretion of collagenase with cultured HUV intimal cells. The HUV endothelium in culture does not secrete detectable levels of collagenase into the medium, but in cultures treated with trypsin or plasmin, low levels of the enzyme are detectable. In addition, when tumor-promoting substances (e.g., 12-*o*-tetradecanoyl phorbol-13-acetate) are added to these cultures, there is a 5- to 30-fold increase of collagenase, secreted in a latent form. After activation this collagenase cleaves collagen into two fragments, and ethylenediaminetetraacetic acid (EDTA) and serum inhibit the action. An angiogenic factor obtained from synovial fluid degraded BM collagen (type IV) in the presence of latent synovial collagenase. A new band (M_r 26,000) was identified by gel electrophoresis of the degraded collagen (J. Weiss, unpublished observations).

ELASTASE. Although the biosynthesis of soluble elastin by cultured large-vessel endothelium has been shown (see EXTRACELLULAR MATRIX, p. 120), little evidence exists for EC synthesis of the enzyme elastase. Podor and Sorgente (483) reported the identification of elastase activity in the media of cultured EC.

FACTOR VIII. The localization of factor VIII antigen on EC (54, 306, 309, 644) has increased our understanding of coagulation and provided an important technique for distinguishing EC in culture from anatomically similar non-EC. Using radiolabeled precursor amino acids and radioimmunoassay, Jaffe and coworkers (305, 306) demonstrated that HUVEC in culture synthesize and release factor VIII antigen and von Willebrand factor, but not the factor VIII antihemophilic factor. This group also reported that a single subunit with a molecular weight of ~225,000 obtained from the procoagulant glycoprotein secreted in culture was similar to a fragment derived from the circulating antigen in blood. Because factor VIII antigen is not detected in the cultured cells and media or in vascular smooth muscle or fibroblasts, EC are now accepted as the primary sites for synthesis of factor VIII antigen. In a study of the synthesis and release of factor VIII, Tuddenham et al. (643) concluded that factor VIII–related antigen is a "constitutive gene product" of HUVEC, although factor VIII coagulant antigen is not made. Furthermore the addition of a number of agents, including epinephrine, serotonin, 2,3-diphosphoglycerate (2,3-DPG), cAMP, thyroxine, hydrocortisone, and human growth hormone, did not affect the synthesis of factor VIII antigen.

Nachman et al. (442) have isolated heterogeneous factor VIII–related antigen from EC postculture medium. On SDS-PAGE the factor VIII synthesized by EC moved as two discrete bands of different molecular weights; the plasma molecules moved as a single protein band. The two forms had identical peptide maps. The molecular heterogeneity of factor VIII–related antigen may reflect polymeric associations of identical subunits and in vivo conditions may change the "ratio of the polymer subsets."

Booyse et al. (59) showed that HUVEC obtained from a female infant with von Willebrand's disease could not be maintained in culture and subcultured without the use of FN-coated surfaces and the addition of EC growth factor. Staining for the antigen was less intense and more diffuse in these abnormal EC than in normal HUV endothelium in culture. Platelet adhesion to the subendothelial layer of EC from patients with von Willebrand's disease was also slightly decreased with less platelet spreading (<5%). Booyse et al. (59) reported similar data with cultured aortic EC from pigs with von Willebrand's disease. These investigators proposed that the molecular defect is partly caused by an increase in plasminogen-dependent protease activity as seen in the porcine aortic EC culture assay.

FIBRONECTIN. Biochemical analyses have established that FN is a major constituent of the BM. This glycoprotein has been shown to be immunologically identical to cold-insoluble globulin, which is presumably the plasma form of FN. [The polypeptide is also immunologically similar to large external transformation-sensitive (LETS) protein found on the surface of fibroblasts.] Several groups have shown that EC in culture contain FN and secrete the glycoprotein into the culture medium. Macarak et al. (380) reported that when radiolabeled amino acids are incubated with cultures of BAEC, ~36% of the radioactivity is precipitated specifically with an antibody prepared against bovine plasma cold-insoluble globulin as measured by double-antibody immunoprecipitation. Analysis of the immunoprecipitate by gel filtration and PAGE shows a single protein species with a molecular weight similar to that of plasma-derived cold-insoluble globulin. The EC also stained specifically with the antiglobulin antibody by indirect immunofluorescence microscopy. Using a clonal line of adult BAEC, Birdwell et al. (52) showed that these cells form FN, which is the principal constituent of the subendothelial cell matrix. Jaffe and Mosher (307), using HUVEC, reported that cultured endothelium secretes large amounts of FN. Upon assay of the culture medium, 15% of the total protein yield was FN in contrast to factor VIII, which accounted for only ~5%. Because FN is found in EC and the ECM, the structural protein is thought to be involved in EC attachment to the substrate, possibly by FN cross-linking with other FN molecules or binding with collagen.

In a study designed to correlate surface proteins with structural organization of a tissue, Vlodavsky et al. (659) identified a cell surface protein with a molecular weight of 60,000 (CSP-60; see *Endothelial Cell Culture Studies*, p. 109). This high-molecular-weight component, found in cultured EC only at a confluent state, could be iodinated by lactoperoxidase. The investigators claim the CSP-60, unlike FN, is essential for the formation of a contact-inhibited monolayer. They further theorize that FN is a key for substrate adhesion, but unlike CSP-60, FN does not contribute to the two-dimensional organization of EC.

PLASMINOGEN ACTIVATOR. Most of the principal components of the fibrinolytic system have been identified. It is well known that PA converts the zymogen plasminogen to the active form plasmin, which in turn acts principally on the polymerized fibrin (11). Immediately after Todd (633) localized PA by histochemical methods in blood vessels (303, 304), contradictory observations were reported about the principal site for PA activity (464, 508, 535, 543). The most recent consensus is that PA synthesis and secretion is probably a characteristic of all EC, intimal and microvascular.

Buonassisi and Venter (72) first reported the presence of PA in BAEC cultures. Shortly thereafter Loskutoff and Edgington (372) showed PA to be membrane bound in EC of the rabbit vena cava and identified a PA inhibitor in the cytosol. Dosne et al. (147) and Laüg et al. (358) substantiated the presence of PA in cultured EC as well as the presence of an acid-labile inhibitor. Laüg et al. (358) also suggested that anchorage-independent growth may stimulate PA production. Shepro et al. (573) demonstrated that EC in their logarithmic phase of growth (simulating a condition similar to angiogenesis or to vessel damage) also secreted PA and an acid-labile inhibitor. The PA activity in this system could be inhibited by steroids, dibutyryl cAMP, theophylline, colchicine, and cycloheximide in dose-dependent concentrations. However, circulating agents generally associated with inflammation or vascular trauma, e.g., thrombin, serotonin, catecholamines, histamines, and endotoxins, did not significantly alter PA activity in this system.

Junod and Ody (327) have shown that the addition of fresh serum suppresses synthesis of PA activity by confluent aortic EC 70%–80%. The decrease is dose dependent with the addition of 0.1% serum resulting in a 50% depression and 1% serum yielding the maximal decrease. This suppressing activity of serum is also found in platelet-poor plasma and has been shown to be nondialyzable and heat labile. It is not inactivated by isofluorphate or hirudin, indicating that neither thrombin nor other serine proteases are responsible for the decrease in PA. Levin and Loskutoff (367) suggest that the production of PA by the endothelium in vivo may be regulated by suppressor molecules in the blood.

Shepro et al. (570) demonstrated that capillary and other microvessel EC possess PA activity. Using isolated cardiac muscle microvessel EC in suspension, they reported that the elaboration of PA activity was a function of time and that a substantial reduction of activity occurred at pH values <4.0. Thus cardiac microvessel EC do not appear to secrete an acid-labile inhibitor similar to that reported for aortic EC and HUVEC.

The factors that regulate the synthesis and secretion of PA and the role of fibrinolysis in the microvasculature are not yet known. Is PA activity (possibly without a PA inhibitor) obligatory for capillaries to maintain a fibrin-free interface (609) or "lubricant zone" (633), to prevent clotting in response to ischemia (357, 512), for angiogenesis (205, 358, 617), for wound healing (553), or for tumorigenesis (187)? Whatever the function of PA activity, if all capillary EC synthesize and secrete PA, fibrinolysis appears to be one of the broadest homeostatic processes of life (11).

PROSTAGLANDINS. *Prostaglandin* (PG) is a general term for a large number of acidic lipids with a wide spectrum of biological functions, e.g., vasomotor agents, mediators of inflammation, enhancers or repressors of platelet aggregation. Prostaglandins were first discovered indirectly by Kurzrok and Lieb (352), who observed that fresh human semen stimulated human myometrial muscle, and by Goldblatt (226) and von Euler (661), who independently observed that genital glands secrete a vasoactive substance. Simply stated, with the proper stimulus PG synthesis occurs when inaccessible polyunsaturated fatty acids are made available to the cyclooxygenase system. In the presence of molecular oxygen these phospholipids are converted to arachidonic acid and then to different PG products dependent on specific enzymes. Two important metabolites of the arachidonic cascade are prostacyclin (PGI_2) and thromboxane (TXA_2). Prostacyclin, a PG with a half-life of ~2.5 min, acts as a potent vasodilator and antiaggregator of platelets. Thromboxane, a prostanoid but not a PG, has a half-life of ~30 s and acts as a potent vasoconstrictor and proaggregator of platelets. Early studies of PG synthesis indicated competition between platelets and EC for exogenous endoperoxides as a substrate, the so-called yin-yang theory (PGI_2 vs. TXA_2). However, it now appears that no exchange of endoperoxides between the EC and platelet occurs and that in most cell systems studied, both in vivo and in vitro, EC are able to synthesize PGs and TXA_2 from endogenous precursors (688, 689).

Many cells are able to produce PGs at some time in their life span, but high yields of certain PGs, e.g., PGI_2 and PGE_2, appear characteristic of only certain cells, e.g., EC and vascular smooth muscle fibers, respectively. Gryglewski et al. (247), Moncada et al. (424, 425), and Szulman (615) first suggested that the vessel wall was a primary source of PG. Utilizing substrates such as arterial rings or vessel wall microsomes, the researchers found that the incubating medium contains a substance that inhibits platelet aggregation. Subsequently many laboratories showed that cultured EC from bovine and porcine aortas and HUV are major sources of PGI_2. Because PGI_2 has such a short half-life, most systems test for its stable metabolite, 6-keto-$PGF_{2\alpha}$ (211, 384, 398, 681). Using pig aortic EC in culture, Pearson et al. (468) presented evidence (measured at 24 h) that these cells secreted more PGI_2 than PGE_2, although the relative amounts of both substances secreted depended on time and culture. Compared with primary cultures, subcultures had a depressed synthesis of PGI_2. The synthesis of PGE_2 was less affected by subculturing after the first passage. Thromboxane, measured as the stable metabolite TXB_2, was always <1% of the total PG quantitated. In many studies, glucocorticoids, which inhibit the release of inaccessible membrane phospholipids, and a wide variety of cyclooxygenase inhibitors (nonsteroidal agents, e.g., aspirin, ibuprofen, indomethacin) inhibit PG and TXA_2 synthesis by cultured EC. Thromboxane synthesis is also inhibited by imidazole and imidazole derivatives, which antagonize the enzyme TXA_2 synthetase.

Regulation of prostaglandin synthesis and secretion. The investigation of the regulation of PG synthesis and secretion by physiological and pharmacological biogenic substances is relatively new. Because the endothelium is the primary site for PGI_2 synthesis and because this PG is important in thrombosis, the data on endothelial PG regulation are centered on PGI_2. Still unclear is whether PGI_2 is synthesized only on demand or if some sequestered PGI_2 escapes quantitation by assay techniques now in use and is present within EC. Likewise no evidence presently exists that indicates a precursor pool that awaits an appropriate stimulus. However, both in vivo and in vitro studies show that the appearance of PGI_2 in response to a stimulus is very rapid.

The most potent agonists for PGI_2 synthesis and secretion, as measured in HUV and aortic EC in culture, appear to be thrombin and angiotensin. These cells synthesize PGI_2 from arachidonic acid or from exogenous endoperoxides in 2–3 min poststimulation (125, 680, 681). Even metabolized thrombin has some stimulating effect, and thrombocytin, a proteolytic enzyme extracted from snake venom (*Bothrops marajoensis*), is also an effective stimulus for PGI_2 secretion (125). Only MacIntyre et al. (384) reported that porcine aortic EC in culture do not synthesize PGI_2 when exposed to thrombin; this lack of response may be caused by differences in procedure, species, and cell number. Both PGE_2 and PGI_2 secretion by HUVEC in culture respond to angiotensin stimulation (153, 211). As expected, angiotensin II is a more potent agonist than angiotensin I, with more PGI_2 secreted than PGE_2 (153). Bradykinin is another vasoactive substance that appears to stimulate EC to secrete PG (621). Both PGE and PGF were found in the incubating medium of arterial and venous sections in amounts greater than in controls. Production of PGI_2 by BAEC and adrenal capillary EC in culture was stimulated as much as 100-fold by platelet-derived growth factor (117). Coughlin et al. (117) suggest that because the levels required for maximal stimulation are in the physiological range, platelet-derived growth factor may function in vivo as part of a feedback mechanism for controlling platelet aggregation. Weksler et al. (680) provide preliminary evidence, principally for HUV endothelium, that trypsin and the fungal ionophore A23187 stimulate PGI_2 release. Fetal calf serum stimulates HUV arterial and venous EC to secrete PGI_2. Quantitated over a 4-h incubation period, the effect of fetal calf serum is greater for PGF activity than PGE activity, and venous EC are more sensitive to the fetal calf serum than arterial EC (324).

β-Thromboglobulin appears to suppress PGI_2 synthesis when added to BAEC (293), and linoleic acid (598) and estrogens suppress PGI_2 synthesis in HUVEC (451). Controversy exists about an inhibitory effect of PGE on PGI_2 synthesis; PGE_2 inhibited PGI_2 synthesis in a hepatic cell fraction, which Tomasi et al. (636) claim is rich in sinusoidal EC. In a similar experiment with porcine aortic EC as a substrate, Gordon et al. (229) observed no effect of PGE_2 on PGI_2 synthesis. Adenosine diphosphate (ADP) and epinephrine are two other substances tested on EC in vitro that have shown an appreciable effect on PG synthesis (680). Our laboratory has found both enhancement and inhibition in vitro of PGI_2 and TXA_2 secretion in the presence of serotonin, which depends on the source of the EC (D. Shepro, unpublished observations). Rat myocardial microvessel EC in suspension synthesize PGI_2 in the presence of serotonin, whereas the monoamine added to the medium of cultured BAEC inhibits synthesis.

The vast literature relating to substances that interfere with PG and TXA_2 synthesis, e.g., the cyclooxygenase inhibitors or specific inhibitors of a single pathway, is not specified here; we remind the reader of the excellent review articles on PG cited previously in *Endothelial Cell Culture Studies*, p. 109.

Metabolism. Endothelial cells also appear to be involved in the uptake and degradation of circulating PGs, although the type of endothelium, its location, and even the species appear to be important variables. A number of reports make some generalizations possible. Most microvascular beds, except for the pulmonary microvasculature, clear and metabolize (to some degree) PGs indiscriminately. The pulmonary microvasculature appears to be refractory to PGI_2, even at pharmacological levels. In contrast, the pulmonary vessels transport and metabolize almost all circulating PGE and PGF. However, it is still unclear which pulmonary cells are involved in the selective metabolism of PG. For example, using a preparation of pig lung slices, Ody et al. (454) found that PGA_1 and $PGF_{2\alpha}$ formed 15-keto metabolites. However, this investigation did not demonstrate that pulmonary and aortic EC, freshly isolated or in culture, were able to metabolize PG. On the other hand, with spiral strips from different arteries as a bioassay, PGI_2 was partially inactivated in passage through the hindquarters and livers of anesthetized dogs (152, 651). In contrast, PGI_2 was apparently untouched as it perfused across the lungs (9, 151, 651).

Prostaglandins in homeostasis. New observations suggest additional actions of EC-derived PGs. For example, PGI_2 and to a lesser degree PGE_1 and PGE_2 increase nutritive flow to the many microvascular beds, dampen sympathetic drive, stabilize lysosomal membranes, and inhibit or lessen the action of a circulating negative inotropic factor (268, 364–366, 650, 652). Although the action of PG in discrete processes of inflammation is still unclear, it appears that most fatty acid derivatives mediate, in some fashion, the classic signs of inflammation: redness, edema, increased temperature, pain, and loss of function (678). By suppressing TXA_2 formation by the polymorphonuclear leukocytes, PGI_2 inhibits lipopolysaccharide-induced and complement-induced adherence of neutrophils to EC. This mechanism is similar to that described for platelets in that it is believed to be cAMP mediated (419). Lethal endotoxemia in dogs is prevented by infusion of PGs above physiological levels (348). The PGI_2 and PGE_1 reverse serotonin-induced bronchoconstriction, and the target sites for the PG appear to extend to the small peripheral airways and the central resistant airways (597). The possibility that PGB_x, a PG derived from PGB (484), may be a natural ionophore for neutrophil secretion (679) has been proposed, although no evidence exists for a PGB_x function in EC.

Davison and Karasek (132) have shown that cyclic nucleotide metabolism in HUVEC is regulated by PGs. The most potent agonist of cAMP synthesis was PGI_2, with PGE_α next. There are two potential effects of PGI_2 synthesis by EC. First, the PGI_2 can elevate cAMP in platelets; second, the EC levels of cAMP can be raised, attenuating further PGI_2 production.

Pulmonary prostaglandins. Various stimuli to the lungs cause the elaboration of PGI_2 and/or TXA_2 by pulmonary EC. Typically the secretion of one or the other of these subtances is emphasized; this secretory function is assumed to be a function of these EC because of the extensiveness of the pulmonary microvasculature. However, the stimulatory mechanisms are unknown. Major surgery, for example, leads to a predominance of PGI_2 (266), whereas end-expiratory pressure in awake human subjects causes the selective release of TXA_2 (267). In animal studies the combination of pressure breathing and anesthesia leads to the release of PGI_2 and TXA_2 and a decrease in cardiac contractility (150). The results suggest that PGI_2 and TXA_2 are involved in the negative inotropic effect, but the mode of action is still unclear. Pressure breathing also leads to the release of PGI_2, which in turn appears to affect PA secretion (268). This heightened fibrinolytic activity can be blocked with indomethacin or increased with a PGI_2 infusion. Other metabolic events stimulated by PGI_2 or TXA_2 are poorly understood, e.g., the PGI_2-induced fall in plasma serotonin levels and simultaneous rise in platelet serotonin.

COLONY-STIMULATING FACTOR. Quesenberry and Gimbrone (494) have reported the production of colony-stimulating factor, a substance that regulates the differentiation of stem cells to form granulocytes and macrophages, in cultured human EC. When exposed to endotoxin and granulocytes, human EC in culture produced elevated levels of the colony-stimulating factor and more of the factor than blood monocytes under similar conditions. Quesenberry and Gimbrone suggest that vascular endothelium may function in the regulation of granulopoiesis.

MOTILITY

> In the variations in calibre, the walls of the capillary play a passive part; the material of the epithelioid plates is extensible, and the pressure of the blood within the capillary distends the walls, and the material being also elastic, the walls shrink and collapse when the pressure is removed, being assisted in this by the pressure of the lymph in the spaces outside the capillary. But besides this, in a young animal, at all events, the capillary wall is to a certain extent contractile; the epithelioid cells, which then appear to contain a large amount of undifferentiated protoplasm, seem able, under the influence of stimuli, to change their form, passing from a longer and narrower shape to a shorter and broader one, and thus influencing the calibre of the tube of which they form the walls. And there are reasons for thinking that such an active change of form may also take place in the capillaries of the adult body.
>
> M. Foster, 1877 (189a)

A long-standing dialogue has centered on whether EC contract. Much of this controversy stems from the third Silliman lecture, "The Independent Contractility of Capillaries," that Nobel laureate August Krogh presented at Yale University (349). Krogh theorized that blood distribution would be controlled more effectively if capillaries and the vessels that supplied and drained the microvasculature contracted. The Rouget cell, now termed the *pericyte*, which lies in close apposition to EC, was also thought to affect microvascular blood flow by contracting. Krogh's insight foreshadowed the current view that capillaries are more than a passive tube and that pericytes may play a role in capillary physiology. Although the EC contractile hypothesis posed by Krogh and others was appealing conceptually, it had little supportive data. The few investigations of EC contraction to explain the waxing and waning of the microcirculation, the transit of macromolecules, and diapedesis added little to recommend Krogh's supposition.

This theorized function for EC lost favor until the 1960s. At this time Majno and co-workers (391, 394), studying increased permeability associated with inflammation, showed that histamine-type receptors on venular EC were responsible for their contraction. This research was appealing because the results suggested a unifying mechanism for histamine stimulation of vascular smooth muscle with a concomitant increase in permeability. However, equally persuasive arguments from other investigators suggest that EC do not contract. Zweifach (706), who has studied the contractile mechanism since his graduate days with R. Chambers, states that evidence against EC contractility continues to mount. Hammersen (254) countered with other interpretations of the observations of Majno et al. (394) (see *Evidence Negating Contraction*, p. 129). However, these differences of opinion may be only dialectical. For example, if the word *motility* is substituted for *contractility*, many of the disagreements disappear. Endothelial cell movement may be possible without a contraction of the whole cell by an energy-dependent mechanism. Endothelial cells in situ could change shape by a recoil mechanism of a restricted area of the cell. Or, as Tilney (628) has shown for *Limulus* sperm, actin polymerization at a regional area of the plasma membrane may extend a local region of a cell.

Intracellular Constituents

Because all eucaryotic cells at some time exhibit motility (e.g., in mitosis and morphogenesis), it is not surprising that contractile proteins similar to those in skeletal muscle have been found in all nonmuscle cells studied (255, 443). Actin, myosin, troponin, tropomyosin, tubulin, and calcium-binding proteins have been isolated and characterized in many cells of different species. In addition, all eucaryotic cells have a cytoskeleton of cross-linked contractile proteins, which Porter (489) and others propose forms a three-dimensional lattice work supporting an array of filamentous structural proteins, e.g., decamin and desmin. Even the cytoskeletal matrix is thought to have motility, which may affect the tubular and filamentous structures supported by the network.

Becker and co-workers (29–33) first reported contractile and relaxing proteins in different blood vessel EC. Actomyosin was identified by indirect immunofluorescent techniques with antisera to human uterine and platelet actomyosin generated in rabbits. Jaffe and Mosher (307) also observed a similar positive reaction for HUV endothelium in culture. However, some EC actomyosin does not react or reacts minimally, including fenestrated glomerular and brain capillary endothelium, which do not cross-react with human uterine actomyosin antisera (345). Moore et al. (428) reported a direct identification of endothelial myosin for HUV tissue. Actomyosin from aortic intima has a different Ca^{2+} sensitivity than actomyosin from aortic media. The functional implication of this difference is not known (341).

Palade (460) first reported the presence of filaments (24 nm) in EC. Many reports have since described filaments of varying diameters in EC from different vessels and tissues (Table 7). The presence of cytoplasmic filaments in arterial, venous, and capillary EC is not questioned. An interrelationship between size, numbers, and orientation specific to EC functions, however, is still unclear, partly because of the inaccessibility of the tissue and the poor fixation of filamentous proteins. New techniques for preserving filaments, e.g., pretreatment with mild osmium tetroxide vapors and preservation with tannic acid, will undoubtedly dovetail these filaments with specific functions.

Mindful of technical limitations in the past, a conservative assessment is that EC contain both actin-containing microfilaments (~6 nm) and intermediate filaments (8–11 nm), which play a role in motility, maintenance of shape, attachment to substrate, and maintenance of junctions (Figs. 10–13). These junc-

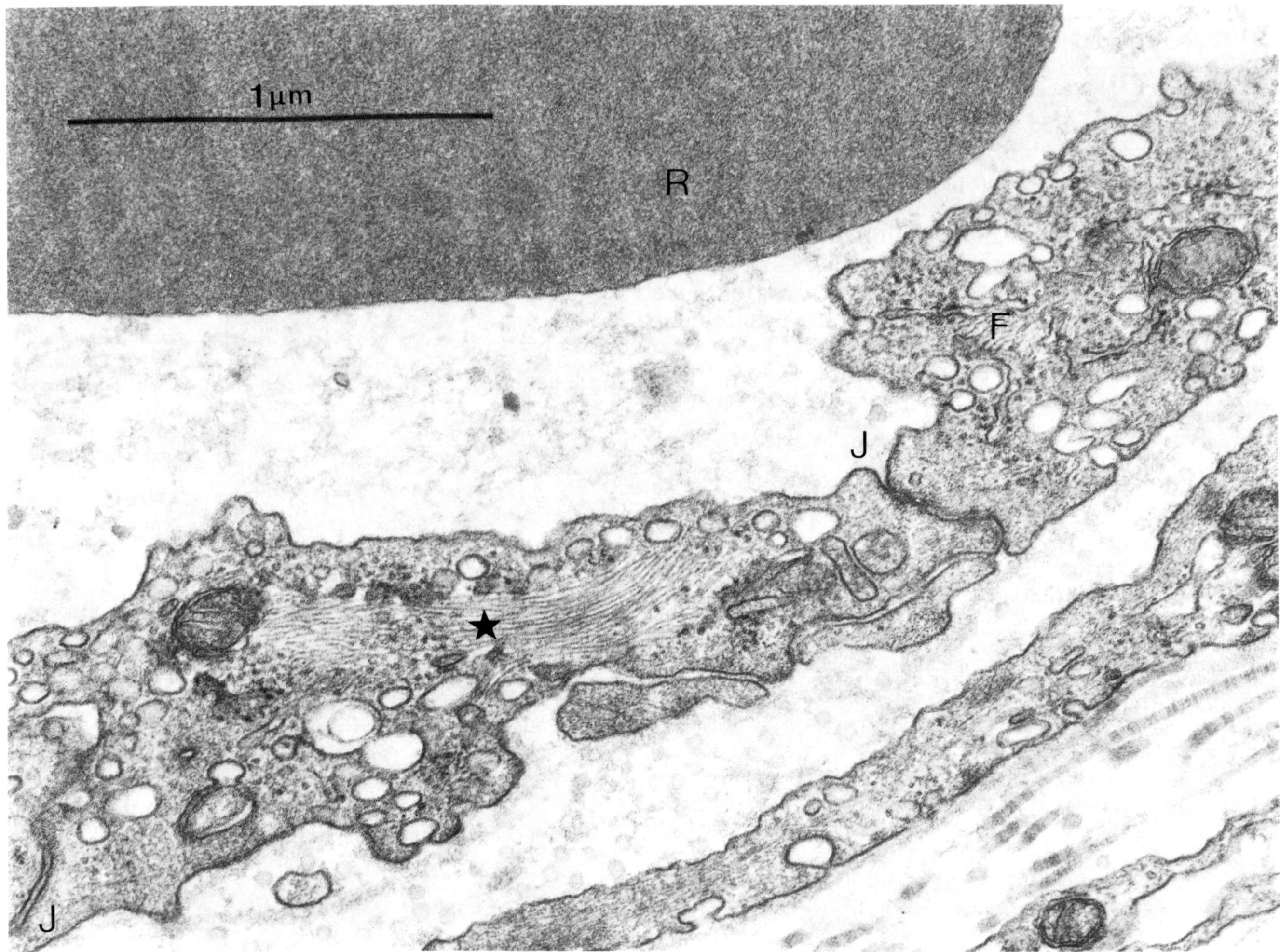

FIG. 11. Thick bundle (★) of parallel filaments (~5 nm diam) in endothelium of pericytic venule from rat subcutaneous tissue. *R*, red blood cell; *J*, interendothelial junction; *F*, filaments. × 58,000.

mentally induced thrombocytopenia in rabbits caused skeletal muscle capillaries to attenuate. They suggest this may account for the increased permeability. To reconcile these different explanations of permeability with structural data is difficult. Hammersen (254, 255) also pointed out that many of the relevant micrographs of Majno and colleagues (394) contain structural details at interendothelial gaps that might explain increased permeability in ways other than by cell contraction; e.g., plasma membrane projections into an interendothelial gap may be an early step in forming a patent channel (much as a zipper looks when unzipped). This interpretation is, of course, as speculative as the arguments favoring EC contractility.

Pericyte Regulation

A theory now enjoying a renaissance is that microvascular flow is regulated partly by the contraction of Rouget cells or pericytes. Krogh (349) described a relationship between pericyte and capillary contractility in cold-blooded vertebrates. These relationships, however, were not always evident (especially in mammals) (30, 98, 99); for this and other reasons the pericyte hypothesis remained dormant for many years. Primarily because of an elegant electron-microscopic study (Figs. 16–18), which clearly demonstrates a morphological orientation between the plasma membranes of pericytes and EC, the theory is once again being reviewed (189, 404, 628, 629, 667, 674). Tilton et al. (629) recently reported that skeletal muscle pericytes constricted skeletal capillaries after an injection of a vasoactive substance such as angiotensin. This constriction, however, was not observed in cardiac muscle capillaries. Pericyte contraction is marked by buckling of the EC at a site in apposition to the pericyte, as measured by electronic planimetry of the electron micrographs (628). Although the latter investigation does not rule out completely that EC contraction affects pericytes, the observation that EC plasmalemma is convoluted only at points of close association

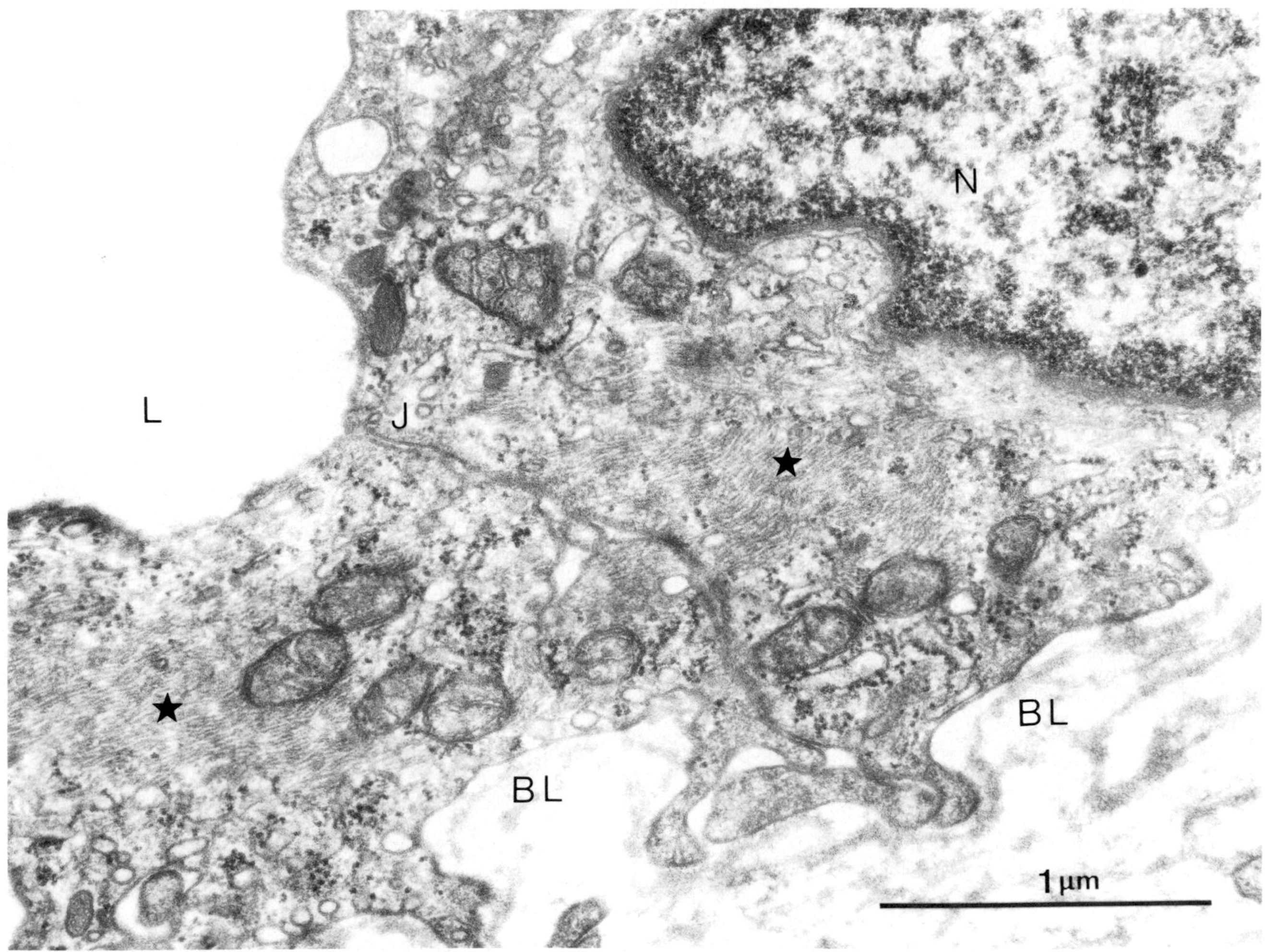

FIG. 12. Endothelial cell junction (*J*) from human cutaneous capillary with thick bundles (★) of parallel filaments (7 nm mean diam) converging on endothelial cell membranes. *N*, endothelial nucleus; *BL*, endothelial basal lamina; *L*, vascular lumen. × 46,000.

with the pericytes, and not randomly, suggests that pericyte contraction is the principal activity.

Endothelial Contractile Pathophysiology

Endothelial cell contractility has also been suggested to be important in the sequence of events leading to atherogenesis and thrombogenesis. Ultrastructural studies showing that aortic EC have banded fibrils that appear analogous to the Z bands of striated muscle provide most of the support for this view (138, 511, 697). Free access to the subendothelial tissue by circulating blood elements would obviously contribute to atherosclerosis, but the assumption that abnormal contractility of EC creates this access has little support. The same evaluation applies to those studies that demonstrate increased permeability, e.g., the appearance of injected carbon particles in interendothelial cell junctions and luminal surface wrinkles, as proof for the inducement of thrombosis (578). Another possible explanation of atherosclerosis is related to endocytosis; i.e., an abnormal vesicular transport would circumvent the rate-limiting barrier function of the EC membrane in the transport of large lipid molecules. Various aspects of micropinocytosis and phagocytosis are treated in depth in the chapters by Simionescu and Simionescu, Curry, Michel, and Crone and Levitt in this *Handbook.* We call attention to a possible relationship between contractile proteins and orientation of actin-containing filaments and endocytosis.

Regulation of Postcapillary Venule Junctions: Theoretical Model

Complex, specialized junctions such as desmosomes or tight junctions are rare in postcapillary venules; the cell junctions are usually of the interdigitating, abutting, or overlapping types. Microfilaments and intermediate filaments are found at the sites of attachment and junction, especially in cutaneous and mesenteric capillaries. Two explanations for this morphology are

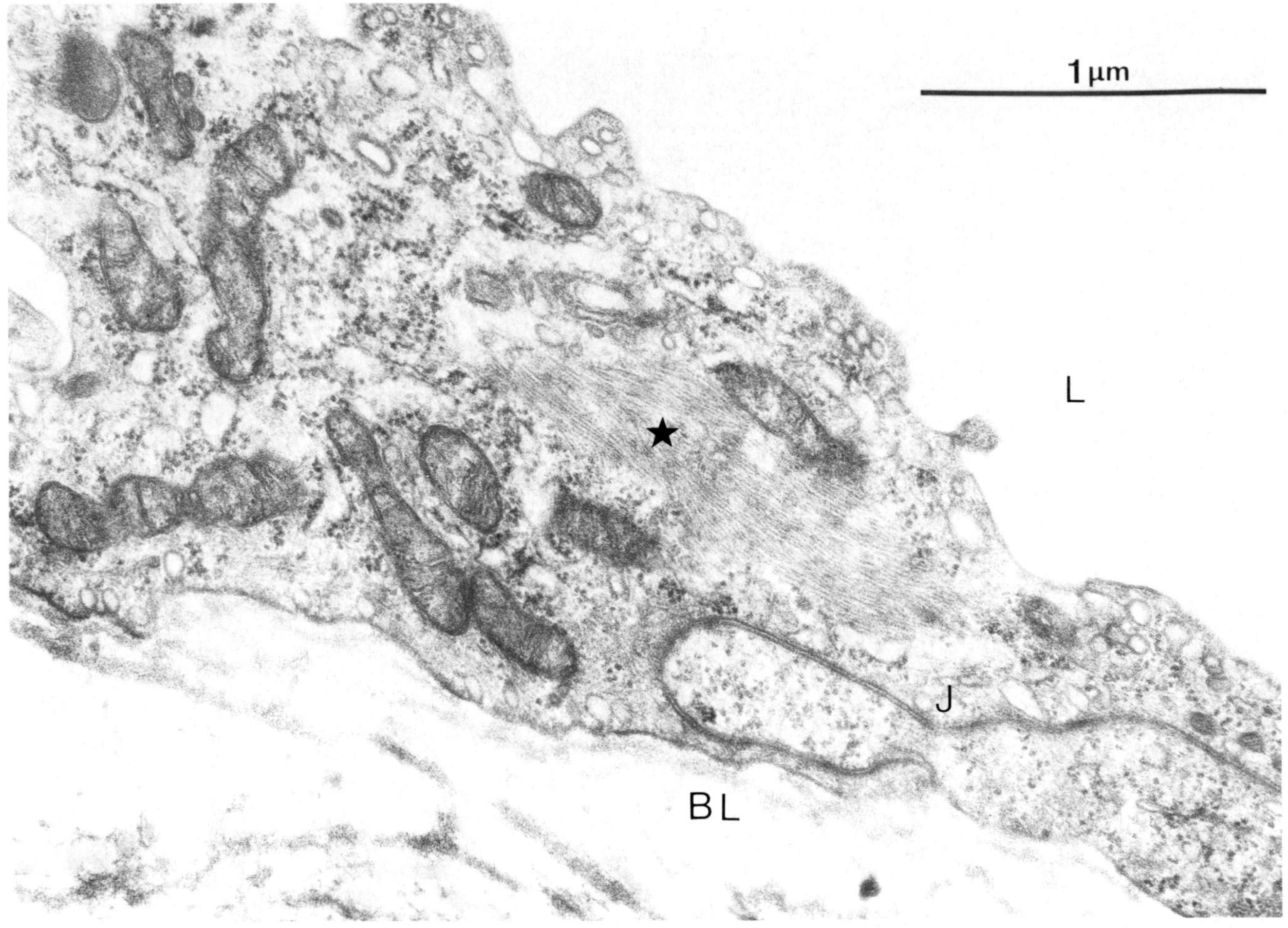

FIG. 13. Segment of microvessel isolated from rat cardiac muscle. *L*, vascular lumen; *J*, interendothelial junction; *BL*, endothelial basal lamina; ★, thick bundle of filaments (7 nm mean diam). × 46,000.

that *1*) these cytoskeletal elements play some role in closing the potential interendothelial gaps, and *2*) a circulating agonist maintains the polymerized state and orientation of these filaments to affect microvascular tone. Enhanced permeability is commonly observed in experimental and clinical thrombocytopenia (TCP). Evidence for this permeability includes increased disappearance rates of ^{125}I-labeled albumin (14), particulate tracers that usually remain within the lumen (126, 342, 653), and the appearance of red blood cells in lymph (146). Although the importance of platelets in maintaining microvascular integrity and preventing microhemorrhages is well supported, there is no acceptable explanation of how platelets function in maintaining structural integrity.

Djerassi et al. (146) first reported the effectiveness of exogenous serotonin in preventing petechial formation in TCP animals. More recently, Sweetman, Shepro, and Hechtman (611) provided evidence supporting this therapeutic function of serotonin; even in severe TCP animals, maintenance with intravenous or intraperitoneal injections of exogenous serotonin prevents petechial formation for as long as 6 h. This protective effect was blocked by pretreatment of the TCP animals with serotonin uptake antagonists, e.g., imipramine and fluoxetine. In addition, animals with normal levels of circulating platelets could be made petechial sensitive with a single injection of fluoxetine (610). Because almost all blood serotonin is stored in platelet-dense bodies (25,000:1, platelet:plasma) (131), these studies suggest that platelets are needed to deliver serotonin, in amounts above plasma levels, to the microvasculature.

Support for a platelet-serotonin function in EC

FIG. 14. Endothelial cells at different stages of spreading, treated with antitubulin serum to visualize microtubule distribution. Samples taken at 0.5 h (*A*), 1 h (*B*), 2 h (*C*), and 4 h (*D–F*) after plating. Cells are shown in stage I (*A*), stage II (*B* and *C*), stage III (*D*, *right*), and stage IV (*D* and *E*, *left* and *center*) of spreading. *Arrows* (*B* and *C*), microtubules extending from perinuclear regions to cell periphery at right angles to cell margin. [From Soni et al. (595).]

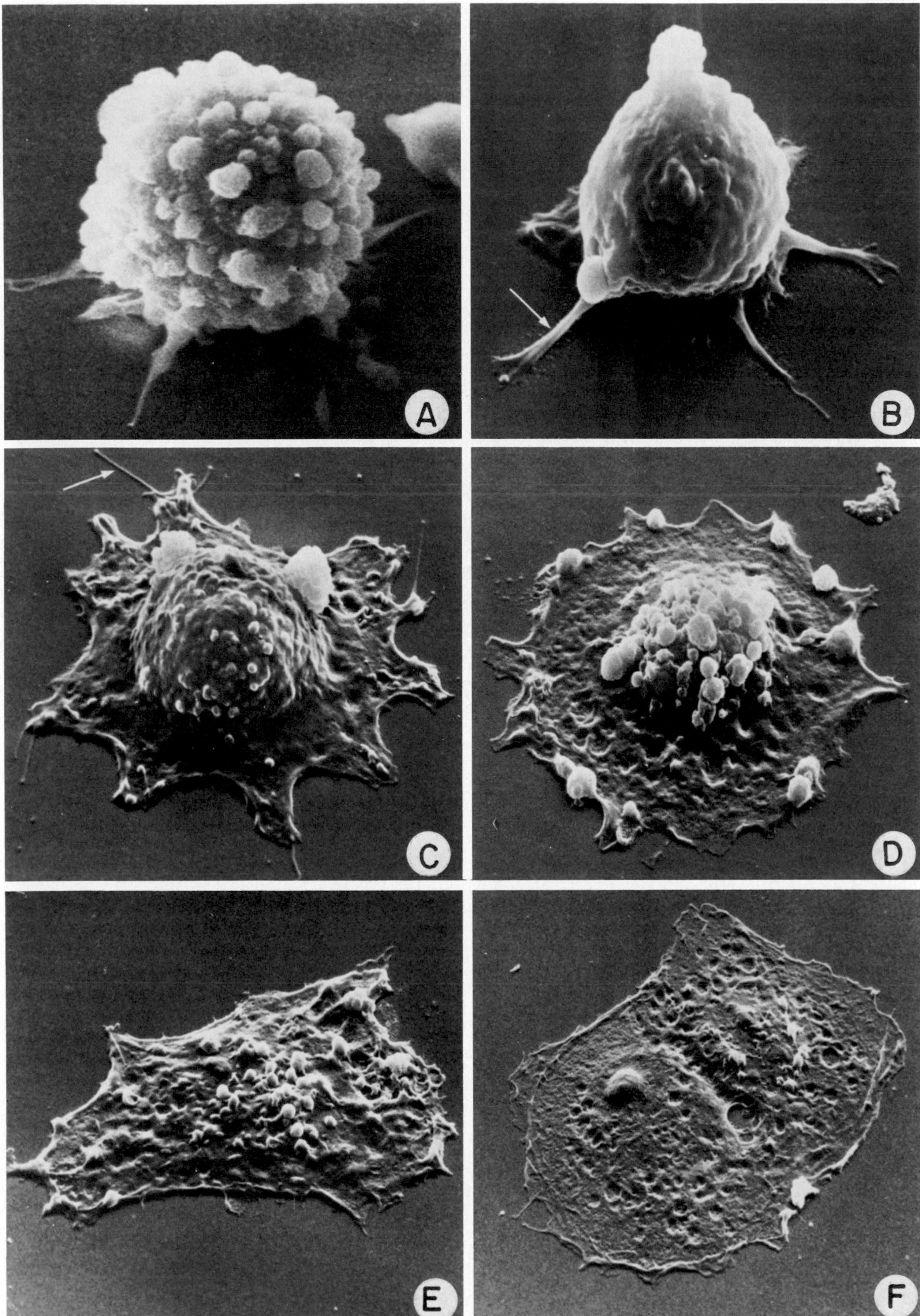
A
B
C
D
E
F

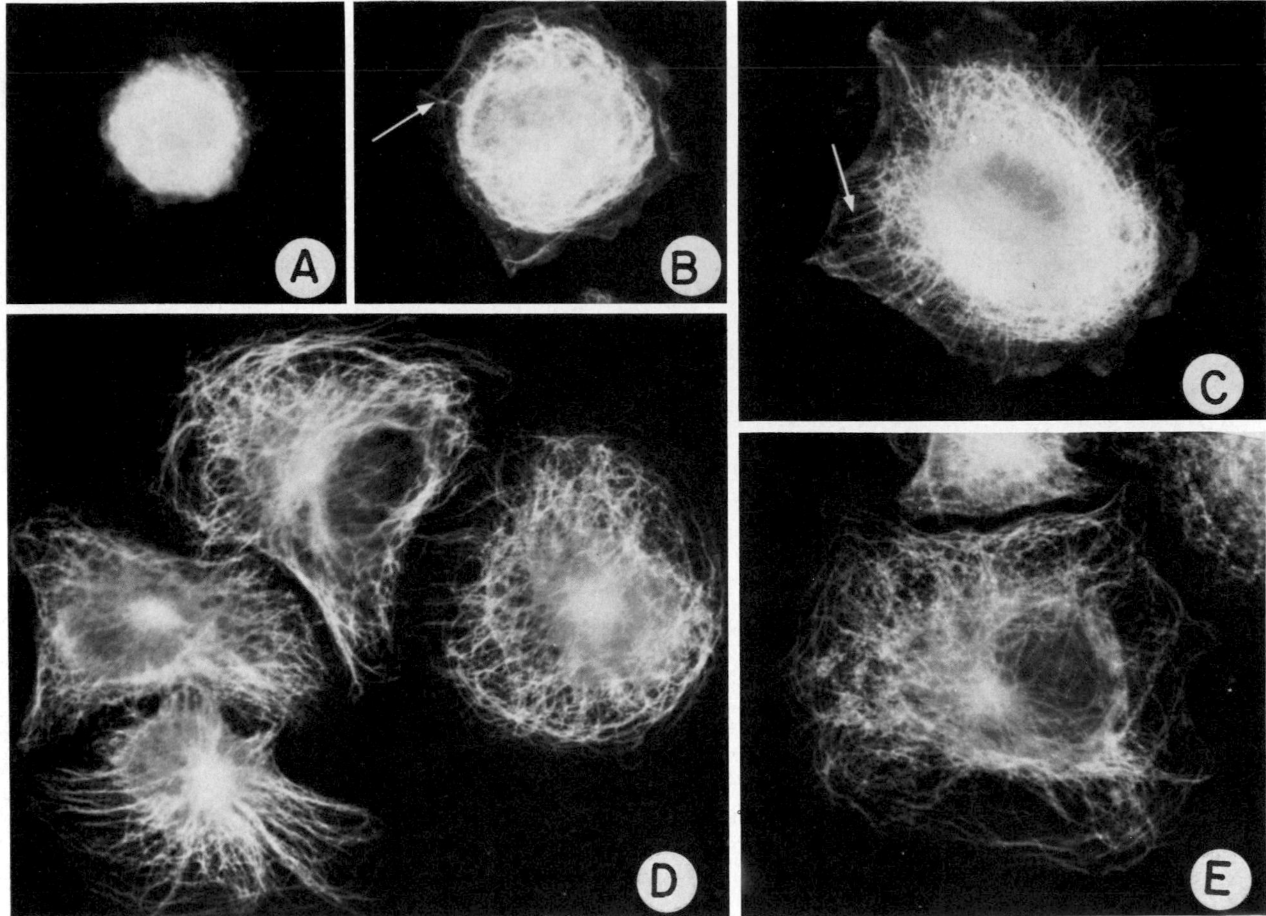

FIG. 15. Endothelial cells at different stages of spreading, stained with antitropomyosin antibodies to visualize microfilaments. Samples taken at 0.5 h (*A*), 1 h (*B*), 2.5 h (*C*), and 4 h (*D* and *E*) after plating. Cells in stage I (*A*), stage II (*B*), stage III (*C*), and stage IV (*E*) of spreading. *D*, polygonally shaped cell at stage intermediate between those in *C* and *E*. *Arrows* (*B* and *C*), prominently stained fibers running parallel and close to edge of stage II cell. [From Soni et al. (595).]

physiology comes from many sources. *1*) Kornstein, Robblee, and Shepro (346) and Reimers et al. (503) showed that platelets respond to low levels of thrombin with a partial release of serotonin. In addition, Okuda and Nemerson (455) described a pump-leak system for serotonin transport in platelets. D'Amore and Shepro (129, 130) theorize that platelets release or leak serotonin at concentrations that are physiologically significant within the microenvironment of the capillary. *2*) The effect of histamine and serotonin on intracellular junctions of the venular endothelium was studied in microvascular fields of the diaphragm. Simionescu et al. (585, 586) found that administration of the amines resulted in typical focal separation of junctions with intramural deposit of carbon particles exclusively in the pericytic venules. Although these effects are the opposite of those in cutaneous pericytic vessels, the difference may reflect the heterogeneity of microvascular beds. That serotonin appears to affect EC motility is significant. *3*) A regulatory function for serotonin in the arrangement and motility of blastomere cytoskeleton has been reported in studies of embryogenesis. Inhibitors of serotonin synthesis and uptake produce malformation and arrested development. In the latter studies the teratogenic serotonin antagonists were theorized to interfere with the serotonin promotion of activity of microfilaments (159, 250, 461).

In severe TCP with purpuric hemorrhages and inflammation, ultrastructural changes that would suggest EC contraction are not observed (126, 522, 653), with one exception (342). Despite an absence of dramatic change in ultrastructure, EC motility may function as a cellular basis for maintaining microvascular structural integrity. A change in microfilament or intermediate filament orientation, caused by a decrease in serotonin or some other regulating agent, could result in functional recoil (with no energy required), forming a patent interendothelial channel. Such a transient response would be difficult to preserve by present means of fixation, which would explain why junctional regions of microvessels generally appear normal, even in severe inflammation and TCP.

Recently we observed an action for platelet norepi-

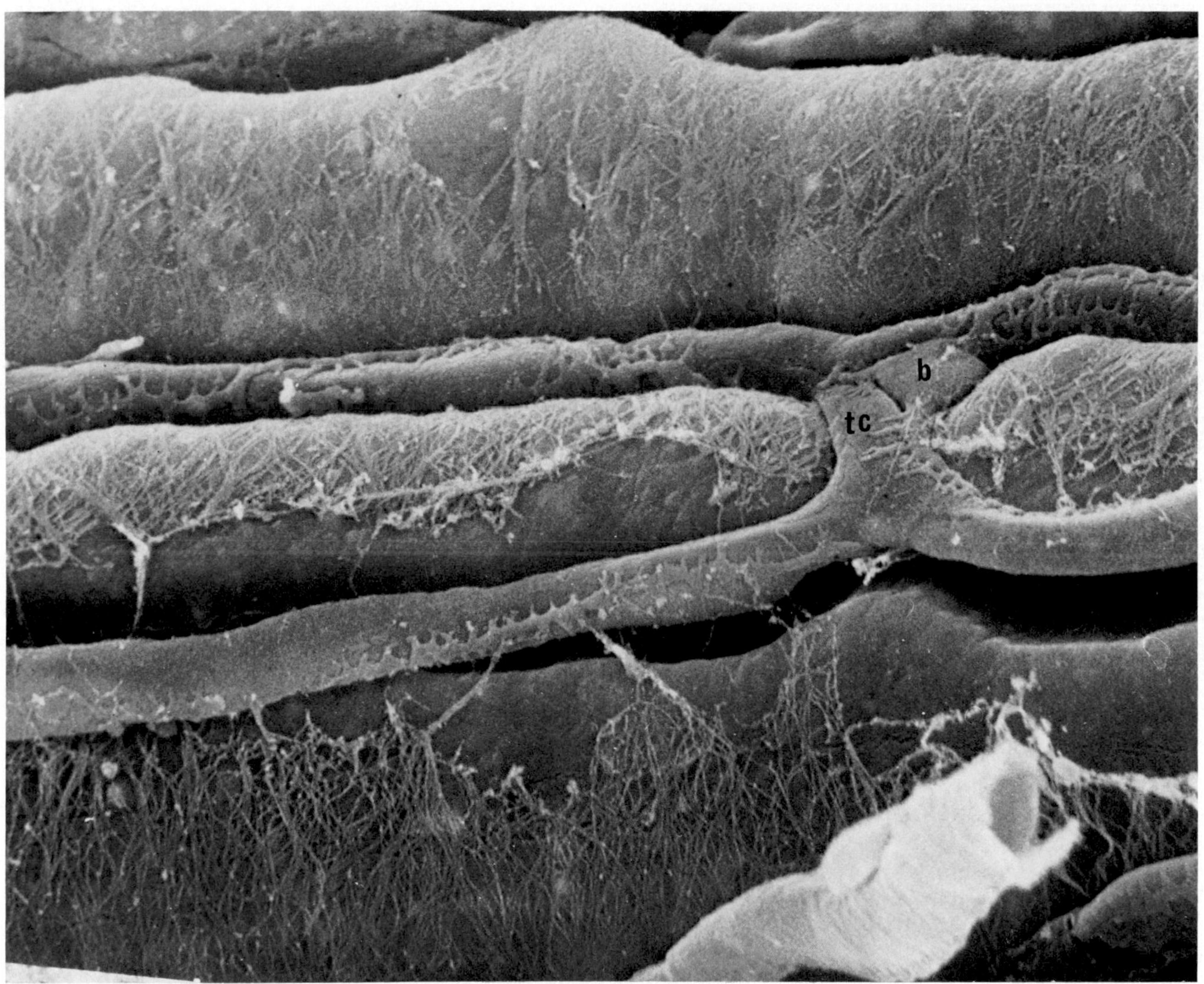

FIG. 16. Scanning electron micrograph of pericyte cell body (*b*) nestled in transverse capillary connection (*tc*). Long pericyte extensions along capillary perimeter cover most of capillary; processes run parallel to long axis of vessel. × 1,400. (Micrograph courtesy of R. Mazanet and C. Franzini-Armstrong.)

nephrine that matched the values reported for serotonin inhibition of petechial formation in TCP animals. Also, adrenergic blockers antagonized the agonistic action of norepinephrine to inhibit the extravasation of red blood cells. In normal animals the injection of adrenergic blockers produced a petechial sensitivity that mimicked the condition associated with severe TCP (D. Shepro, unpublished observations).

In conclusion, the controversy over EC contractility may be merely a problem in semantics. In the 1960s comparing any cell in which contractile proteins were identified with skeletal muscle contraction was reasonable. At that time more was known about skeletal muscle dynamics than probably any other somatic cell function, and the sliding-filament theory was the model. However, as Taylor (620) stated, "Cell motility used to be a quiet field." Investigations on nonmuscle cell motility have provided a rich lode of information that may apply to movement of and within an EC, and as often is true when an old ambiguity is tackled with new techniques, the problem and the solutions have become more complex. It is now known that EC in different microvascular beds differ in their structure, function, and response to similar signals. From the vast literature on eucaryotic cell motility, it is also known that in regional movements (e.g., the ruffled moving edge of cells moving in culture, phagocytosis, pseudopod formation, and substrate and junctional attachment) the presence and orientation of filaments appear to be critical factors. The identification of filamentous structures and other contractile proteins in EC suggests that EC motility may be similar to that described in detail for other nonmuscle cells. Whether EC motility can account for changes in microvascular flow is not known [notwithstanding some reports, e.g., that of endothelial regulation of hepatic

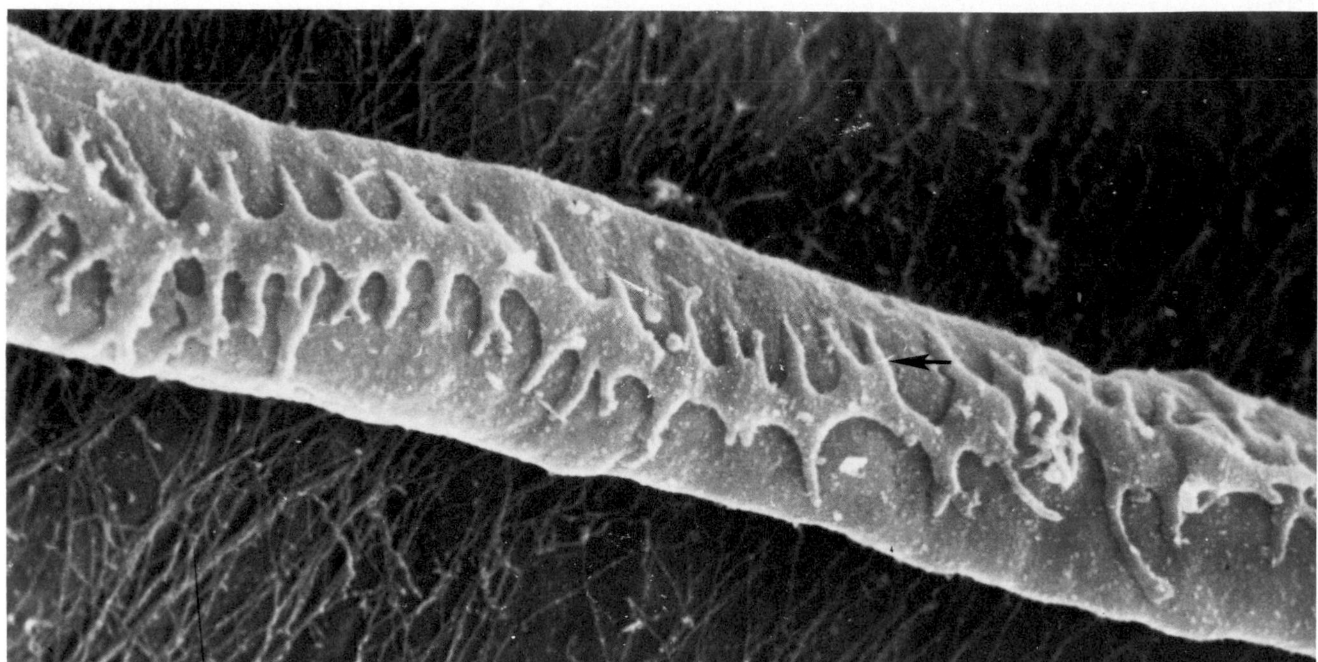

FIG. 17. Scanning electron micrograph of pericyte secondary branches (*arrow*) rising from major longitudinal process and running circumferentially. × 4,400. (Micrograph courtesy of R. Mazanet and C. Franzini-Armstrong.)

local blood flow (138)]. The phylogenetic dictate for the microvasculature is a mechanism able to affect transcapillary exchange. A large body of literature suggests that transport can occur by opening interendothelial cell junctions; the regulatory mechanism for this is unclear. An obligatory role for microvascular EC vis-à-vis pericyte function is also debatable. A role for EC in the pathophysiology of certain diseases must remain provisional until these questions on normal endothelial physiology are answered.

MEMBRANE-ASSOCIATED ACTIVITIES

Receptor Mediation

In vitro EC assays have been especially fruitful for identifying specific surface receptors and developing the present view of endothelium as an active metabolic tissue. A primary function of EC in maintaining homeostasis appears to be the monitoring of circulating levels of specific vasoactive substances that in turn regulate vessel diameter. Some of these substances also function in altering the permeability of capillaries at the microvascular level (see MOTILITY, p. 127) and act as primary messengers in mediating EC synthesis of materials required for maintaining blood fluidity and angiogenesis.

VASOACTIVE SUBSTANCES. *Acetylcholine.* Added to the medium of cultured rabbit aortic EC in the presence of neostigmine, acetylcholine increases both cAMP and cyclic guanosine 5′-monophosphate (cGMP) levels. Preincubation of the cultured EC with the acetylcholine-blocking agent atropine blocks the cyclic nucleotide–linked hormone receptors (72). Information on the acetylcholine metabolism by EC is still unavailable.

Adenosine. Pearson et al. (470) demonstrated that pig aortic EC in primary culture or subculture removed adenosine from the culture medium by two mechanisms: *1*) at millimolar substrate concentrations uptake is by nonmediated diffusion; *2*) at micromolar levels discrete receptor-mediated transport processes operate. Two apparent K_m values of 3 μM and 250 μM were obtained. Dipyridamole and nitrobenzylthioinosine selectively inhibited the high-affinity transport mechanism. In addition, 90% of the adenosine transported into the cell was converted rapidly and principally into adenosine 5′-triphosphate (ATP). Because adenosine is such a potent vasodilator, it is theorized that the signal is transduced via an adenylate cyclase system. Dieterle et al. (145) also observed that adenosine uptake occurred in porcine pulmonary EC and aortic EC in primary cultures by a saturable, temperature-dependent process. Both cell types have a high-affinity (K_m 3 μM) and low-affinity (K_m 0.3–1.1 mM) transport system. Although the end product for the adenosine is ATP, transport, not phosphorylation, was suggested as the rate-limiting step. In isolated capillaries and other microvessels from guinea pig cerebral cortex, adenosine enhances adenylate cyclase activity.

Angiotensin. The receptor-mediated dipeptidyl peptidase [angiotensin-converting enzyme (ACE)] located

FIG. 18. Pericyte and capillary in human quadriceps femoris muscle, biopsy tissue. (Micrograph courtesy of J. R. Williamson.)

on EC membranes apparently in all microvascular beds can convert angiotensin I to angiotensin II and degrade bradykinin. However, the principal site for ACE appears to be the pulmonary capillary EC, probably because of the extensiveness of the lung microcirculation. Using fluorescein-labeled antibodies to ACE, Ryan et al. (520) found activity localized along the luminal surface of capillary and venule EC. Endothelial cells in culture also convert angiotensin I to angiotensin II (568), and the angiotensin in this in vitro system also stimulates cyclic nucleotides (72).

Anaphylatoxins. Complement activation forms fragments, e.g., C3a anaphylatoxin, that can affect vessel diameter and increase vascular permeability. When incubated with C3a purified from human serum, HUVEC in culture can clear and inactivate this peptide (144). Although a mode of uptake has not been defined, data indicate that the mechanism is not pinocytosis. The uptake is probably dependent on an interaction with some anionic groups on the plasma membrane. Interestingly, bovine pulmonary EC in primary culture are refractory to C3b and to the Fc portion of immunoglobulin G molecule (206, 528). These results suggest that the absence of receptors for the Fc fragment in part contributes to EC maintenance of a nonthrombogenic surface.

Catecholamines. Buonassisi and Venter (72) reported indirect evidence for catecholamine receptors in EC for an established line of cultured rabbit aortic intimal tissue. When changes in cAMP and cGMP levels were used as an assay system, norepinephrine (NE) and other biogenic amines significantly increased both cyclic nucleotides. The receptor-linked activity can be inhibited with propranolol and phentolamine, both at the final concentration of 10^{-5} M. Norepinephrine attached to beads stimulates aortic smooth muscle contraction (47). These data indicate that the signal is transduced from specific receptors

little binding to the endothelium. However, when a 50-μg excess of unlabeled insulin was added to the perfusion mixture, labeling was seen over the entire cell, suggesting a low-affinity receptor.

Glucocorticoids. Duval et al. (155) have shown that rabbit aortic EC contain high-affinity cytosolic (1.3×10^{-8} mol) binding sites for dexamethasone. These investigators feel these sites represent physiological glucocorticoid receptors for three reasons. *1*) The binding is saturable, an essential characteristic of hormone receptors. *2*) The binding sites have a high affinity for dexamethasone, similar to that of glucocorticoid receptors in other target tissues. *3*) The [^{3}H]dexamethasone binding is displaced easily by unlabeled dexamethasone or corticosterone.

Multiplication-stimulatory activity. Bar et al. (24) localized receptors for multiplication-stimulatory activity (MSA) in primary cultures of HUV and human arterial EC. Using ^{125}I-labeled MSA and insulin, Bar and his co-workers demonstrated that neither of these proteins can block the binding of the other, indicating that human EC have "specific and distinct receptors" for both MSA and insulin.

Lipoproteins. Endothelial cells most likely contain both high-density lipoprotein (HDL) and low-density lipoprotein (LDL) receptors. Stein and Stein (600) reported that HUVEC exposed to both HDL and LDL preferentially bind LDL over HDL. Other data suggest that HDL affects the plasma membrane by decreasing LDL binding. Henriksen et al. (274), who showed earlier that lipoprotein removal stimulated sterol incorporation by HUVEC in primary cultures (273), reported that endothelial injury affected lipoprotein clearance and metabolism. The exposure of cultured HUVEC to high concentrations of LDL resulted in injury, as measured by the release of ^{51}Cr from prelabeled EC. Addition of HDL to the medium protected the EC against LDL-induced injury, but preincubation with HDL did not minimize the LDL effect. Albumin provided a weaker but similar protective effect to HDL. High concentrations of LDL at a cholesterol concentration of 160 μg/ml significantly reduced the number of HUVEC per culture dish (277). In contrast, HDL had no cytotoxic effect at any concentrations tested. Vlodavsky et al. (658) reported that actively growing vascular EC bind and metabolize LDL by way of a receptor-mediated mechanism. The organization of the EC monolayer appears to control the regulation and uptake of the LDL receptors, because confluency and contact inhibition affect LDL internalization but not binding. Using both sparse and confluent cultures of aortic EC, Vlodavsky and co-workers demonstrated a redistribution of LDL receptor sites that is related to changes in density and organization of the monolayers. Vascular smooth muscle cells in culture used as a control are unaffected by the culture density. Fielding et al. (173) conclude that LDL binding, at least in actively growing vascular EC, is associated with the lateral mobility of receptor sites, which at confluence is restricted because of the monolayer configuration.

Kothari et al. (347) studied cholesterol esterase, the enzyme responsible for the hydrolysis of cholesterol esters, in the dry acetone powder of normal rat and rabbit aortas. The enzymes from both species were similar in stability, solubility, and kinetic properties, which is interesting because the levels of hydrolytic and synthetic activity are lower in the rabbit aorta than in the rat aorta. The rat, which is usually resistant to cholesterol-induced atherosclerosis, has a hydrolysis:synthesis ratio of 1.5 compared with the rabbit, which has a ratio of 0.91. These authors suggest that an innate inability to hydrolyze the cholesterol ester may cause the rabbit's high susceptibility to cholesterol-induced atherosclerosis.

Preliminary evidence suggests specific receptors for a host of circulating substances, e.g., plasminogen, plasmin, fibrin, hormones, factor XIIa, and anti–thrombin III. We believe these preliminary observations will prove factual and that the endothelial surface is covered with receptor sites. Because of the preliminary nature of these studies, they are not included in this chapter. However, there is sufficient receptor data to support the concept that EC are primary transmitters in a servomechanism between blood and tissues. For example, the demonstration of catecholamine receptivity suggests an obligatory role for intimal endothelium in the regulation of vessel diameter. Vasoactive agonists appear to regulate synthesis of materials, e.g., PGs, that help maintain a nonthrombogenic surface and blood fluidity for capillary endothelium.

Cell Surface Molecules

Because of the varied roles EC perform and their continuous contact with the blood, EC must possess substances that enable the tissue to cope with a changing environment. Many of the newly identified molecules involved in homeostasis have been localized on the EC surface.

ENZYMES. At the interfaces between the blood and luminal wall or between interstitial fluid and the abluminal surface the EC is the first "to see" a variety of materials. Enzyme activities able to interact with such molecules have been localized on the EC blood surface. One of these activities, ACE (81, 520, 525), is discussed in ANGIOTENSIN-CONVERTING ENZYME, p. 143. The identification of the converting enzyme in the caveolae may be significant because of the increased surface area that caveolae afford. Ryan et al. (520) refer to the physiological significance of this localization: "The lungs appear to function as a solid phase reactor with immobilized enzyme being perfused continuously with its hormone substrate in liquid phase."

Another enzyme that resides on the EC surface is

lipoprotein lipase. Lipoprotein lipase is responsible for the hydrolysis of triglycerides to free fatty acids in a variety of tissues. Early studies on the lipoprotein lipase activity in adipose tissue suggest that the enzyme is localized mainly in fat cells (121). However, the demonstration that perfusion of this same tissue with heparin releases lipoprotein lipase implicates vascular tissue (285). An electron-microscopic study of the vasculature from the adipose tissue of animals fed high-lipid diets demonstrated chylomicrons only on the lumen or on the surface of EC but never beyond this point (688). Blanchette-Mackie and Scow (53) accomplished direct localization of the lipoprotein lipase activity to the plasma membrane of EC by perfusing rat adipose tissue in vivo with labeled chylomicron triglyceride so that it could react with the lipoprotein lipase. The distribution of the electron-opaque reaction products indicated that the hydrolysis occurred in capillary EC and in the subendothelial spaces between the EC and pericytes. Chajek et al. (95) documented the synthesis of lipoprotein lipase with a culture of mesenchymal cells "with features common to fibroblasts, smooth muscle cells or endothelial cells." Colchicine and vinblastine can block the transport of the lipase to its site of action on the EC surface (93, 94).

Bovine aortic EC in culture have both cell-surface and releasable proteolytic activities. Tökés and Sorgente (635) measured membrane-bound proteolytic activity in EC incubated with plastic beads to which ^{125}I-labeled casein was covalently linked. Released proteolytic activities are measured when there is no contact between the casein and the EC. The release rate of radiolabeled peptides is assumed to be a reflection of EC proteolytic activity. Proteolytic activity may have an invasive function during wound healing or neovascularization.

MOLECULES RELATED TO THROMBOSIS. Another important characteristic of the endothelium is its maintenance of a nonthrombogenic surface. What renders the surface nonthrombogenic is unknown. However, the finding by Buonassisi and Root (70, 71) that EC in culture are able to synthesize and incorporate a heparinlike molecule into their plasma membranes has led to the speculation that this membrane-bound heparin may contribute to maintaining the nonthrombogenic surface. Wasteson et al. (671) observed that platelets contain an endoglycosidase that is able to liberate and degrade EC surface-associated heparan sulfate and suggest that the released enzyme may act on the EC heparan sulfate, thereby altering the interactions between the endothelium and circulating blood cells. Busch et al. (76) tested this hypothesis by treating cultured EC with heparitinase, which removed 60%–70% of the cetylpyridinium chloride–precipitable ^{35}S-labeled material (GAGs). However, this treatment did not affect the adhesion of ^{51}Cr-labeled platelets to the EC. The use of heparin as a therapeutic agent is based on its association with EC. Heparin binds to both arterial and venous EC in vitro (279). Because repeated washing could not remove heparin, it was assumed that the heparin was bound, probably by specific receptors. Glimelius et al. (223), who found heparin binding to be time dependent, saturable, reversible, and trypsin sensitive, confirmed the presence of these receptors. Busch et al. (76) demonstrated that PF_4 can bind to EC with all of the characteristics of a receptor-mediated event. In addition, heparin, heparan sulfate, dermatan sulfate, chondroitin 6-sulfate, and chondroitin 4-sulfate all competed with PF_4 for binding to EC. Because of these findings, Busch and co-workers suggest that PF_4 may interfere with the heparin-mediated aspect of the EC nonthrombogenic surface.

Esmon and Owen (163) demonstrated that the surface of vascular endothelium provides a cofactor that increases the rate of protein C activation by thrombin. Perfusion of the myocardium with inactive protein C in the presence of thrombin resulted in an anticoagulant activity, which was identified as activated protein C. The activation rate of protein C during the perfusion was at least 20,000 times that of thrombin and protein C alone. The existence of a cofactor for protein C activation immobilized to the EC surface makes protein C a viable candidate for a negative regulator of the clotting process.

Tissue-factor activity is also localized to the plasma membrane of EC (408, 603, 701). Tissue factor is a lipoprotein that is central to the extrinsic pathway of coagulation. Both Zeldis et al. (701) and Maynard et al. (408) demonstrated that tissue factor is present in a dormant state. However, minimal trauma to the vascular EC makes the lipoprotein available to initiate coagulation. Maynard et al. (408) have warned that the degree of EC damage needed to initiate coagulation "may be significantly less than previously thought."

ANTIGENIC DETERMINANTS. Among the many molecules localized on the EC surface are the histocompatibility or transplantation antigens. Characterization of these antigens is important because the vasculature of organ transplants is a key site for immunological injury, which is thought to be a response to antigenic determinants on the donor blood vessel EC. When sera from patients who had rejected kidneys were screened for alloantibodies to EC antigens, half of the samples contained antibodies that were cytotoxic to EC (429). The alloantibody theory was also tested by determining the effect of various sera on pig aortic EC in vitro (135); xeno- and alloantisera in the presence of complement were toxic to the endothelium. However, other additions, e.g., pooled human serum or specific antibody without complement, did not harm the EC. Hirschberg et al. (284) similarly demonstrated that HUVEC in culture could be damaged by nonimmune peripheral lymphocytes in the presence of anti–human lymphocyte antigen (HLA) antibodies and that lymphocytes and EC compete for the same effector mechanism, the HLA. Hirschberg et al. (283) believe HLA-DRW are responsible for this cytotoxic effect. These antigens are primarily limited to B lymphocytes, monocytes, and epidermal Langerhans' cells. Both canine and human EC induce allogenic lymphocytes in vitro to undergo blastogenesis and synthesize DNA (282, 657), which again demonstrates the capacity of EC to initiate an immunoproliferative response.

Gibofsky et al. (208) have also identified these histocompatibility antigens on fresh and cultured EC using a microcytotoxicity method. Additionally, EC lose some HLA after prolonged time in culture. Ninety percent of those antigens deleted after 2 wk of culture are from the second HLA locus. Gibofsky et al. suggest this loss may be caused by culture conditions, i.e., the appropriate antigen precursors are not available. However, the observation of this phenomenon may prove worthwhile because selective antigen loss may be desirable when histocompatibility antigens on the donor EC do not match the recipient. Burger and Ford (73) reported activation of human T cells by an antigen presented by HLA-DR compatible HUVEC. If this preliminary observation is true, the mechanism may be significant in diapedesis and immunology—adding another quantum of importance to EC.

Blood group antigens (ABO) are also localized on the EC surface (225, 288, 613, 615). In a study of the distribution of blood group A antigens among human tissues, Holborow et al. (288) used both fluorescent antibodies and mixed agglutination techniques to demonstrate the presence of A antigen on EC. Both large blood vessel and capillary EC in fetal tissue, spleen, and adrenal sinusoids gave positive staining. Szulman (613), who used immunofluorescent antibodies to both the A and B antigens to map out their EC localization, confirmed these results. Szulman (614) later determined that another blood group antigen, the H antigen, is also present throughout the entire vascular system. Jaffe et al. (309) used the mixed agglutination reaction to show that HUVEC in culture contain ABH antigens appropriate to the donor's blood type; smooth muscle cells and fibroblasts are negative for this reaction.

OTHER MOLECULES. Endothelial cell surfaces possess α_2-macroglobulin (31), which is able to modify the activities of various proteases, including those that affect coagulation, fibrinolysis, and the kallikrein system (259). Using immunofluorescent techniques, Becker and Harpel (31) found α_2-macroglobulin localized on the luminal EC surface in veins, arteries, and lymphatics. This localization indicates that the molecule may perform a significant protective function by intervening in any one of numerous reactions that occur near the EC.

The CSP-60 protein is also an EC surface-associated molecule (659). Found only in confluent monolayers, CSP-60 is absent in subconfluent and rapidly growing cultures or in cell lines that form multiple layers at confluence, e.g., fibroblasts or smooth muscle cells. Vlodavsky et al. (659) suggest that CSP-60 may be one of the determinants of differentiation because it is found only on vascular or corneal EC that have adopted a monolayer configuration. The role of this protein in relation to growth is discussed in CELL SURFACE PROTEIN, p. 111.

Staining the EC surface with plant lectins conjugated to horseradish peroxidase demonstrates the presence of glycoproteins. Glycoproteins that contain mannose, glucose, and *N*-acetylgalactosamine are identified with concanavalin A and phytohemagglutinin. An average of 5,000 concanavalin A molecules are bound per square micrometer (599).

Pelikan et al. (473) investigated the distribution and movement of anionic cell surface sites in cultured EC and noted that cell surface properties, e.g., localization and movement of anionic sites, may be relevant to the normal function of the vascular wall. Ferritin binding to the surface of fixed cells was uniform in both the primary and transformed EC line when cationized ferritin was used to compare the distribution of anionic surface sites in primary and SV40-transformed EC in culture. This suggests an even distribution of anionic molecules over the EC surface. In unfixed cells the bound ferritin aggregated into patches and was internalized via endocytosis. Ferritin binding may induce a redistribution of transmembrane proteins, which in turn affects the membrane and endocytosis. De Bruyn et al. (139) used the highly endocytic endothelium of the bone marrow vasculature to demonstrate that the sialic acid groups (polycationic ferritin binds sialic acid at pH 1.8) on the luminal surface of EC are absent or markedly reduced at endocytic sites. An anionic material with a pK higher than sialic acid (pK 2.6) is, however, on the free surface of the EC and at endocytic sites. Furthermore, Pelikan et al. (473) point out that anionic sites may be functional in determining permeability characteristics, a mechanism recently demonstrated by Rennke and Venkatachalam (504) for glomeruli.

METABOLISM

Circulating Vasoactive Agents

The phylogenetic development of humoral substances that regulate blood vessel diameter paralleled the "need" for mechanisms to maintain normal circulating levels of these agonists. Because of its location endothelial tissue could be the prime site for maintaining normal titers of vasoactive substances. All EC have the ability to clear, sequester, and metabolize certain vasomotor agonists. What the EC metabolize is a reflection of their location. For instance, pulmonary EC are able to break down serotonin and NE but ignore circulating epinephrine or dopamine.

ADENOSINE AND ADENINE NUCLEOTIDES. Early studies on whole organs suggested that EC may be involved in the synthesis and degradation of adenine nucleotides. Binet and Burnstein (49) observed a disappearance of ATP from the blood during transpulmonary passage. Ryan and Ryan (523) and Ryan and Smith (524) reported a similar disappearance with an isolated perfused rat lung system in which ATP and 5′-AMP were hydrolyzed to adenosine. Several laboratories have obtained more direct information relating to EC metabolism of adenosine and adenine nucleotides. Pearson et al. (469, 470) measured labeled adenosine metabolites in the incubating medium of cultured pig aortic EC by thin-layer chromatography on silica gels and found that over 90% of the radioactivity was associated with adenine nucleotides at concentrations varying from 5 μM to 200 μM. The reaction apparently is not time dependent; a 5-min incubation gives the same qualitative metabolic pattern as a 20-min incubation. Pearson and Gordon (471) observed in a cognate study that EC in culture, when stimulated by thrombin (or other stimuli), released a high proportion of cellular ATP and ADP. The EC nucleotide metabolism accompanies this release (immediately before or after). In the same study EC catabolized added ATP, ADP, or AMP, with the half-lives of these materials $<$5 min, ~10 min, and $>$30 min, respectively. The EC release of adenine nucleotides, given the proper stimulus, suggests an interplay between EC and platelets, which are very responsive to ADP. Other supporting data from Pearson et al. (469) indicate that cultures of pig aortic EC rapidly catabolize adenine nucleotides by Mg^{2+} stimulation of ectonucleotidases (nucleoside triphosphatase, nucleosidediphosphatase, 5′-nucleotidase, and nucleosidediphosphate kinase). Dosne et al. (149) reported similar interactions with HUVEC. This comparative study shows that EC have a greater ability to degrade the adenyl nucleotides ATP and ADP than cultured fibroblasts; the latter, however, degrade AMP more efficiently. Adenosine deaminase activity of EC also results in a slight accumulation of adenosine in the medium. A follow-up study by Dosne et al. (148) confirms a role for EC in metabolizing circulating adenine nucleotides. In this system, EC uptake of ADP is slower than its hydrolysis rate. Aging also leads to a loss of ADP-degrading activity. This relationship between in vitro senescence and metabolism appears to be independent of cell density and morphology. Dieterle et al. (145) also report that porcine aortic and pulmonary EC in culture metabolize adenosine and ATP. In pulmonary EC, ATP is hydrolyzed and adenosine is phosphorylated efficiently and rapidly in the presence of adenosine kinase. The newly formed ATP is released slowly into the extracellular medium; this efflux is apparently independent of the precursor concentration.

AMINES. *Norepinephrine.* Studies on nonrespiratory functions of the lung first suggested that EC may clear and metabolize vasoactive amines (175). Vane (652) observed that NE is removed during a single circuit through the lung. Hughes et al. (298), however, first provided evidence that capillary EC may be the sites for such inactivation. Studying the perfused, isolated rat lung, these investigators found that both oxidative deamination and *O*-methylation were involved in NE breakdown. Junod and Ody (327) observed similar metabolism of NE by aortic and pulmonary EC (obtained either by collagenase treatment or by a Hautchen preparation).

Serotonin. Gaddum et al. (202) first suggested that serotonin may be metabolized by EC when they demonstrated the efficient removal of serotonin during its circulation through the lungs. Lung involvement in serotonin clearance and metabolism is confirmed with respiratory distress in experimental situations or with patients (209, 565, 651). Serotonin uptake is significantly impaired with a concomitant decrease in metabolites when compliance decreases or physiological shunt increases (684). Other pulmonary studies support the role of the lung in clearing and inactivating serotonin (2, 203, 326, 624). The study that directly implicates EC as the site of serotonin metabolism utilized [^{3}H]serotonin as a tracer and using radioautography found the endothelium to be the principal labeled cells. Data from a number of laboratories (210, 568) that used EC in culture obtained from different species and different large vessels support the view that EC in situ, in suspension, or in culture clear and metabolize serotonin. The principal breakdown product is 5-hydroxyindoleacetic acid, and the catabolic mechanism is mediated by monoamine oxidase (MAO). There is still some question which MAO, A or B, is the principal enzyme in intimal EC. Similar catabolic activity is seen with capillary EC in suspension, isolated from cardiac and epididymal fat-pad tissues of rats and hamsters, respectively. In these cells MAO-A appears to be the principal degrading enzyme (571).

ANGIOTENSIN-CONVERTING ENZYME. Angiotensin-converting enzyme, which converts angiotensin I to angiotensin II and degrades bradykinin at the EC surface, is discussed in several sections of this chapter (see IN VITRO ENDOTHELIAL CELL TECHNOLOGY, p. 105, and MEMBRANE-ASSOCIATED ACTIVITIES, p. 136); here we emphasize its metabolic role. Ryan and Ryan (523), who strongly suggest that ACE is associated with all vascular beds and not unique to pulmonary EC, state that because the lung receives the complete output of the heart, pulmonary EC are the principal determinants of the levels of angiotensin I and angiotensin II in the systemic arterial circulation. Other laboratories (81, 314) have demonstrated in vitro ACE activity in cultured HUVEC or aortic EC.

The conversion activity appears to be sensitive to

oxygen tension in vivo and to serum in vitro (265). Arterial EC show 3–5 times more ACE activity than venous EC (312). Angiotensinase A (aspartyl aminopeptidase) has a similar distribution, i.e., more activity in arterial EC than in venous EC. Microvessels of a cardiac allograph transplanted to the hamster cheek pouch also convert angiotensin I to angiotensin II in a manner similar to that quantitated for the coronary microcirculation in vivo (114). Rosen et al. (514), in a study of ACE activity as a function of long-term culture, report that the loss of ACE activity is a reflection of in vitro senescence. They were unable, however, to determine whether the loss of function was caused by faulty or blocked synthesis or breakdown of intracellular ACE (lysosomal enzymes in EC increased with age). The investigators pose an interesting question: if ACE activity is linked to cell division (aging), do EC exposed to high shear stress, which stimulates EC division, show decreased ACE activity compared with vascular tissue subjected to low shear stress? Finally, adrenal cortex capillary segments also contain the aminopeptidase A and show ACE activity (141). The ACE location in these capillary segments was not determined.

PROSTAGLANDINS. Endothelial cells synthesize a wide array of PGs via the arachidonic acid cascade and other fatty acid metabolic pathways (see SYNTHESIS, p. 119). Generally EC are able to break down arachidonic acid or endoperoxides to hydroperoxy and hydroxy acids by lipoxygenase and peroxidase activity, respectively, and by the cyclooxygenase pathway to prostacyclins or their stable metabolite 6-keto $PGF_{1\alpha}$. Less is known, however, about the selective metabolism of PGs by different vascular beds. For example, labeled $PGF_{1\alpha}$ is efficiently cleared in a single passage through the pulmonary circulation. About one-third of the radioactivity is retained in the lung in the form of a "metabolite less polar than $PGF_{1\alpha}$," and the product is distinguishable from most PGs (521). In culture, regardless of the source of intimal cells, some type of PG metabolism has been reported (308, 313, 452); sufficient pilot studies exist to indicate that there is selective degradation of PGs. For example, isolated and cultured EC harvested from pig pulmonary artery and aorta apparently do not significantly metabolize $PGF_{2\alpha}$ (454). Similar results are obtained when PGA_1 is added to the culture medium, even after 17 h of incubation. Ody et al. (454) conclude that the apparent absence of 15-OH-PG-dehydrogenase activity is not caused by a paucity of EC or altered viability, because control experiments on serotonin and adenosine metabolism are unaffected. The apparent inability of pulmonary EC to clear and metabolize PGI_2 is an example of this selectivity. After crossing the lungs, PGI_2 in varying concentrations shows no evidence of uptake or metabolism, in contrast to other organs where PGI_2 is readily degraded (9, 151, 651).

SUBSTANCE P. The vasoactive peptide substance P, which is believed to act directly on smooth muscle, is catabolized by HUVEC (313).

Other Metabolic Activities

MICROVESSELS. Many studies conducted to localize enzyme activities in EC focus on brain capillaries, where the EC function as a blood-brain barrier. Brain capillaries appear to have selective permeability for a variety of substances not observed in capillaries of other organs. The concentration of studies on brain microvessels thus stems partly from an interest in demonstrating a biochemical basis for these unique differences.

γ-Glutamyl transpeptidase. The histochemical demonstration of γ-glutamyl transpeptidase in brain capillary EC by Orlowski et al. (457) suggests a barrier function for brain microvessels. This enzyme catalyzes the transfer of the γ-glutamyl residue of glutathione to amino acids and may function in the selective transport of amino acids into the brain. Albert et al. (3) earlier studied the distribution of γ-glutamyl transpeptidase in the central nervous system of humans and different animal species and showed the enzyme to be present in the central nervous system of humans and all other mammals examined. The enzyme is demonstrable only in the cytoplasm of capillary EC; arterioles and venules do not show any activity. Stewart (605), however, reported that γ-glutamyl transpeptidase activity in chick brain capillaries was not present at sufficient levels to account for all amino acid transport across the blood-brain barrier.

Cyclases. Guanylate cyclase and adenylate cyclase are histochemically localized on the luminal membranes and BMs of rat brain capillaries (322, 337, 663). Although the role of the cyclases is not clearly understood in all cases, it has been suggested that guanylate cyclase may be involved in the regulation of transendothelial vesicular transport or in the maintenance of the integrity of the BM. Wagner et al. (663), who localized adenylate cyclase activity on the luminal capillary surface, feel this location is appropriate because the luminal capillary surface comes into contact with circulating hormones and adenylate cyclase activity is stimulated by NE, isoproterenol, glucagon, vasopressin, PGE_1, and PGE_2. Joó (319) similarly demonstrated the histochemical localization of adenylate cyclase in the walls of brain capillaries and showed that dibutyryl cAMP stimulated both pinocytotic activity and macromolecular transport.

Alkaline phosphatase. Alkaline phosphatase activity is localized histochemically in the myocardial capillaries, but large sinusoidal vessel EC have no detectable enzyme activity (375). One interpretation of the lack of alkaline phosphatase activity in sinusoidal vessels is that there is no selective transendothelial vesicular transport. After whole-brain perfusion, electron-microscopic examination shows that alkaline phosphatase is localized on both the luminal and abluminal plasma membranes of bovine brain capillaries (43). Sterry et al. (604), who studied the distribution of alkaline phosphatase activity in the capillary endothelium in both normal and psoriatic skin, found that in normal skin the enzyme is localized mainly on the arterial side of the capillary loop. Alkaline phosphatase activity increases in psoriatic skin and appears in the venous segment of the capillary loop.

Sodium-potassium–activated adenosine triphosphatase. Goldstein (227) used two lines of evidence to postulate a high-activity potassium transport system in brain EC. First, the potassium concentration on the interstitial surface of the brain capillary wall appears to be independent of the concentration on the luminal surface. Second, addition of excess potassium to the spinal fluid leads to a potassium efflux from the brain to the blood. Goldstein compared potassium transport of brain capillaries to transport by capillaries from the mammary gland to determine if brain capillary EC differ from the rest of the systemic microvessels. Ouabain-sensitive potassium uptake by brain capillaries was 10 times the uptake of mammary capillaries. Betz et al. (43) described a polarity in capillary membranes: Na^+-K^+-ATPase was located only in the abluminal capillary membrane. They suggest that the polarity conferred by this distribution produces active solute transport and may contribute to the existence of the blood-brain barrier.

Cholinesterase. Cholinesterase activity was demonstrated histochemically in blood vessels of the central nervous system in a number of species (65, 119, 180, 193, 251, 320, 333, 334, 344a, 565, 580). Koelle (344a) first described butyrylcholine esterase in capillary endothelium of the nervous system. Flumerfelt et al. (180) demonstrated by light microscopy that most microvessels in the rat brain stained intensely for butyrylcholine esterase. Blood vessels not anatomically involved with the blood-brain barrier lack cholinesterase activity. Electron-microscopic observation localized the reaction product in the intermembranous space of the EC nuclear envelope, occasionally in the endoplasmic reticulum, and within the BM matrix. The localization of the enzyme in the BM suggests a role for the basal lamina in transfer mechanisms. The enzyme is also thought to be associated with the regulation of vascular permeability. Greig and Holland (245) support this hypothesis with their report that various cholinesterase inhibitors increase the permeability of blood vessels to anesthetics.

Other enzymes. Various other enzymes have been localized in the wall of brain capillaries. For example, Samorajski and McCloud (536) report alkaline phosphomonoesterase in increased amounts where enhanced vascular permeability is evident. Adenosine triphosphatase (ATPase) appears to be concentrated in the BM of capillary EC of the blood-brain barrier (637). This localization is unique to the EC of the blood-brain barrier because brain capillaries outside of the blood-brain barrier and in other organs have an ATPase activity in the basal lamina. Inhibition of this ATPase activity by nickel chloride increases macromolecular transport (655) and alters the fine structure of the BM (316). Joó (317) postulates that ATPase in the BM maintains the molecular arrangement of the matrix components. Finally, Betler et al. (42) have demonstrated dopa decarboxylase in the wall of brain capillaries where the enzyme may gather monoamine precursor molecules.

ENDOTHELIAL CELLS IN TISSUE CULTURE. *γ-Glutamyl transpeptidase.* As discussed in MICROVESSELS, p. 144, EC derived from brain microvessels contain the enzyme γ-glutamyl transpeptidase. DeBault and Cancilla (133) reported that the enzyme is often absent from EC cultures derived from the rat brain. However, the enzyme can be induced in cultured EC if they are cocultured with glial cells. This is the first demonstration of the induction of a particular EC enzyme by another cell type. The inducement of a particular function in its neighboring capillary EC by a cell is one way capillary EC may be altered by their environment.

Histidine decarboxylase. Hollis and Rosen (290) studied the distribution of histidine decarboxylase activity in the bovine vascular wall. Comparison of the enzyme's activity in BAEC to that in intima-media homogenates indicated that the EC histidine decarboxylase system is 15-fold greater. Rosen et al. (515) later demonstrated that exposure of EC to various degrees of shear stress increases EC histidine decarboxylase activity significantly. This suggests that histamine synthesis responds rapidly to shear stress and that the enzyme may link rheological stresses and resultant changes in permeability.

DeForrest and Hollis (140) and Markle and Hollis (399) recently demonstrated a linear relationship between shear intensity and histamine formation by the aorta. Furthermore they note that the changes in vessel wall permeability by histamine coupled with alterations in hemodynamic states may be significant in the initiation of atherosclerosis.

Ornithine decarboxylase. D'Amore, Hechtman, and Shepro (128) demonstrated the stimulation of ornithine decarboxylase activity in cultured BAEC by serum, serotonin, and thrombin. The induction of ornithine decarboxylase is the rate-limiting step in the synthesis of the polyamines, a group of polycationic substances that function in a variety of cellular processes. The investigators suggest that stimulation of ornithine decarboxylase by these factors may be a mechanism by which platelet constituents contribute to the structural and metabolic integrity of EC in vivo. D'Amore and Shepro (130) later linked calcium influx into EC with the induction of ornithine decarboxylase activity. Preincubation of the EC with lanthanum chloride ($LaCl_3$) or the addition of ethylene glycol-bis(β-aminoethylether)-*N-N′*-tetraacetic acid (EGTA) to the medium inhibited serum induction of ornithine

88. CARNES, W. H., P. A. ABRAHAM, AND V. BUONASSISI. Biosynthesis of elastin by an endothelial cell culture. *Biochem. Biophys. Res. Commun.* 90: 1393–1399, 1979.
89. CASTELLOT, J. J., JR., M. J. KARNOVSKY, AND B. M. SPIEGELMAN. Potent stimulation of vascular endothelial cell growth by differentiated 3T3 adipocytes. *Proc. Natl. Acad. Sci. USA* 77: 6007–6011, 1980.
90. CATRAVAS, J. D., AND C. N. GILLIS. Pulmonary clearance of [^{14}C]-5-hydroxytryptamine and [^{3}H]norepinephrine in vivo: effects of pretreatment with imipramine or cocaine. *J. Pharmacol. Exp. Ther.* 213: 120–127, 1980.
91. CAVALLO, T. Ultrastructural autoradiographic studies of the early vasoproliferative response in tumor angiogenesis. *Am. J. Pathol.* 70: 345–362, 1973.
92. CECIO, A. Ultrastructural features of cytofilaments within mammalian endothelial cells. *Z. Zellforsch. Mikrosk. Anat.* 83: 40–48, 1967.
93. CHAJEK, T., O. STEIN, AND Y. STEIN. Colchicine-induced inhibition of plasma lipoprotein lipase release in the intact rat. *Biochim. Biophys. Acta* 380: 127–131, 1975.
94. CHAJEK, T., O. STEIN, AND Y. STEIN. Interference with the transport of heparin-releasable lipoprotein lipase in the perfused rat heart by colchicine and vinblastine. *Biochim. Biophys. Acta* 388: 260–267, 1975.
95. CHAJEK, T., O. STEIN, AND Y. STEIN. Lipoprotein lipase of cultured mesenchymal rat heart cells. I. Synthesis, secretion and releasability by heparin. *Biochim. Biophys. Acta* 528: 456–465, 1978.
96. CHALKLEY, H. W., G. H. ALGIVE, AND H. P. MORRIS. Effect of the level of dietary protein on vascular repair in wounds. *J. Natl. Cancer Inst.* 6: 363–372, 1946.
97. CHEN, C.-H., AND S. C. CHEN. Angiogenic activity of vitreous and retinal extract. *Invest. Ophthalmol. Vis. Sci.* 19: 596–602, 1980.
98. CLARK, E. R., AND E. L. CLARK. The relation of "Rouget" cells to capillary contractility. *Am. J. Anat.* 35: 265–282, 1925.
99. CLARK, E. R., AND E. L. CLARK. Observations on changes in blood vascular endothelium in the living animal. *Am. J. Anat.* 57: 385–438, 1935.
100. CLARK, E. R., AND E. L. CLARK. Microscopic observations on the extra-endothelial cells of living mammalian blood vessels. *Am. J. Anat.* 66: 1–49, 1940.
101. CLARK, E. R., H. T. KIRBY-SMITH, R. O. REX, AND R. G. WILLIAMS. Recent modifications in the method of studying living cells and tissues in transparent chambers inserted in the rabbit's ear. *Anat. Rec.* 47: 187–211, 1930.
102. CLARK, R. A., R. D. STONEY, D. Y. K. LEUNG, I. SILVER, D. C. HOHN, AND T. K. HUNT. Role of macrophages in wound healing. *Surg. Forum* 27: 16–19, 1976.
103. CLIFF, W. J. Kinetics of wound healing in rabbit ear chambers, a time lapse cinemicroscopic study. *Q. J. Exp. Physiol. Cogn. Med. Sci.* 50: 79–89, 1965.
104. CLOPATH, P., K. MÜLLER, W. STÄUBLI, AND R. R. BÜRK. *In vivo* and *in vitro* studies on endothelial regeneration. *Haemostasis* 8: 149–157, 1979.
105. CLOUGH, G., AND C. C. MICHEL. The effect of albumin on the labelling of endothelial cell vesicles with ferritin in the frog. *J. Physiol. London* 289: 724–738, 1979.
106. CLOUGH, G., AND C. C. MICHEL. The sequence of labelling of endothelial cell vesicles with ferritin in the frog. *J. Physiol. London* 292: 61–62, 1979.
107. CLOWES, A., J. L. BRESLOW, AND M. J. KARNOVSKY. Regression of myointimal thickening following carotid endothelial injury and development of aortic foam cell lesions in long term hypercholesterolemic rats. *Lab. Invest.* 36: 73–81, 1977.
108. CLOWES, A. W., G. B. RYAN, J. L. BRESLOW, AND M. J. KARNOVSKY. Absence of enhanced intimal thickening in the response of the carotid arterial wall to endothelial injury in hypercholesterolemic rats. *Lab. Invest.* 35: 6–17, 1976.
109. COHEN, M. P. Glycosaminoglycans are integral constituents of renal glomerular basement membrane. *Biochem. Biophys. Res. Commun.* 92: 343–348, 1980.
110. COHEN, M. P., AND M. SURMA. Renal glomerular basement membrane. In vivo biosynthesis and turnover in normal rats. *J. Biol. Chem.* 255: 1767–1770, 1980.
111. COHEN, M. P., AND C. A. VOGT. Collagen synthesis and secretion by isolated rat renal glomeruli. *Biochim. Biophys. Acta* 393: 78–87, 1975.
112. COLBURN, P., AND V. BUONASSISI. Estrogen-binding sites in endothelial cell cultures. *Science* 201: 817–819, 1978.
113. CORKEY, R. F., B. E. CORKEY, AND M. A. GIMBRONE, JR. Hexone transport in normal and SV-40 transformed human endothelial cells in culture. *J. Cell. Physiol.* 106: 425–434, 1981.
114. CORNISH, K. G., W. L. JOYNER, AND J. P. GILMORE. Evidence for the conversion of angiotensin I to angiotensin II by the coronary microcirculation. *Blood Vessels* 16: 241–246, 1979.
115. COTTA-PEREIRA, G., H. SAGE, P. BORNSTEIN, R. ROSS, AND S. SCHWARTZ. Studies of morphologically atypical ("sprouting") cultures of bovine aortic endothelial cells. Growth characteristics and connective tissue protein synthesis. *J. Cell. Physiol.* 102: 183–189, 1980.
116. COTTON, R., AND W. B. WARTMAN. Endothelial patterns in human arteries. *Arch. Pathol.* 71: 3–11, 1962.
117. COUGHLIN, S. R., M. A. MOSKOWITZ, B. R. ZETTER, A. N. ANTONIADES, AND L. LEVINE. Platelet-dependent stimulation of prostacyclin synthesis by platelet-derived growth factor. *Nature London* 288: 600–602, 1980.
118. COURTOY, P. J., Y. S. KANWAR, R. O. HYNES, AND M. G. FARQUHAR. Fibronectin localization in the rat glomerulus. *J. Cell Biol.* 87: 691–696, 1980.
119. CROOK, J. C. Acetylcholinesterase activity of capillary blood vessels in the central nervous system of the rabbit. *Nature London* 199: 41–43, 1963.
120. CSONKA, E., T. KERÉNYI, A. S. KOCH, AND H. JELLINEK. *In vitro* cultivation and identification of aortic endothelium from miniature pig. *Arterial Wall* 111: 31–37, 1975.
121. CUNNINGHAM, V. J., AND D. S. ROBINSON. Clearing factor lipase in adipose tissue. Distinction of different states of the enzyme and the possible role of the fat cell in the maintenance of tissue activity. *Biochem. J.* 112: 203–209, 1969.
122. CURWEN, K. D., M. A. GIMBRONE, JR., AND R. I. HANDIN. In vitro studies of thromboresistance: the role of prostacyclin (PGI_2) in platelet adhesion to cultured normal and virally transformed human vascular endothelial cells. *Lab. Invest.* 42: 366–374, 1980.
123. CZERVIONKE, R. L., J. C. HOAK, AND G. L. FRY. Effect of aspirin on thrombin-induced adherence of platelets to cultured cells from blood vessel wall. *J. Clin. Invest.* 62: 847–856, 1978.
124. CZERVIONKE, R. L., J. B. SMITH, G. L. FRY, J. C. HOAK, AND D. L. HAYCRAFT. Inhibition of prostacyclin by treatment of endothelium with aspirin. Correlation with platelet adherence. *J. Clin. Invest.* 63: 1089–1092, 1979.
125. CZERVIONKE, R. L., J. B. SMITH, J. C. HOAK, G. L. FRY, AND D. L. HAYCRAFT. Use of a radioimmunoassay to study thrombin-induced release of PGI_2 from cultured endothelium. *Thromb. Res.* 14: 781–786, 1979.
126. DALE, C., AND J. V. HURLEY. An electron microscope study of the mechanism of bleeding in experimental thrombocytopenia. *J. Pathol.* 121: 193–212, 1977.
127. D'AMORE, P. A. Purification of a retina-derived endothelial cell mitogen/angiogenic factor (Abstract). *J. Cell Biol.* 95: 201a, 1982.
127a. D'AMORE, P. A., B. M. GLASER, S. K. BRUNSON, AND A. H. FENSELAU. Angiogenic activity from bovine retina: partial purification and characterization. *Proc. Natl. Acad. Sci. USA* 78: 3068–3072, 1981.
128. D'AMORE, P. A., H. B. HECHTMAN, AND D. SHEPRO. Ornithine decarboxylase activity in cultured endothelial cells stimulated by serum, thrombin and serotonin. *Thromb. Haemost.* 39: 496–503, 1978.
129. D'AMORE, P. A., AND D. SHEPRO. Stimulation of growth and calcium influx in cultured bovine aortic endothelial cells by platelets and vasoactive substances. *J. Cell. Physiol.* 92: 117–184, 1977.

130. D'AMORE, P. A., AND D. SHEPRO. Calcium flux and ornithine decarboxylase activity in cultured endothelial cells. *Life Sci.* 22: 571–576, 1978.
131. DAPRADA, M., AND G. B. PICOLTI. Content and subcellular localization of catecholamines and 5-hydroxytryptamine in human and animal blood platelets: monoamine distribution between platelets and plasma. *Br. J. Pharmacol.* 65: 653–662, 1979.
132. DAVISON, P. M., AND M. A. KARASEK. Human dermal microvascular endothelial cells in vitro: effect of cyclic AMP on cellular morphology and proliferation rate. *J. Cell. Physiol.* 106: 253–258, 1981.
133. DEBAULT, L. E., AND P. A. CANCILLA. γ-Glutamyl transpeptidase in isolated brain endothelial cells: induction by glial cells in vitro. *Science* 207: 653–655, 1980.
134. DEBAULT, L. E., L. E. KAHAN, S. P. FROMMES, AND P. A. CANCILLA. Cerebral microvessels and derived cells in tissue culture: isolation and preliminary characterization. *In Vitro* 15: 473–487, 1979.
135. DE BONO, D. Effects of cytotoxic sera on endothelium *in vitro. Nature London* 252: 83–84, 1974.
136. DE BONO, D., AND D. J. WHITE. The classification of lymphocyte adherence to endothelium. *Bibl. Anat.* 16: 406–408, 1977.
137. DE BRUYN, P. P. The role of sialated glycoproteins in endocytosis, permeability and transmural passage in the myeloid endothelium. *J. Histochem. Cytochem.* 27: 1174–1176, 1979.
138. DE BRUYN, P. P., AND Y. CHO. Contractile structures in endothelial cells of splenic sinusoid. *J. Ultrastruct. Res.* 49: 24–33, 1974.
139. DE BRUYN, P. P., S. MICHELSON, AND R. P. BECKER. Nonrandom distribution of sialic acid over the cell surface of bristle-coated endocytic vesicles of the sinusoidal endothelium cells. *J. Cell Biol.* 78: 379–389, 1978.
140. DEFORREST, J. M., AND T. M. HOLLIS. Relationship between low intensity shear stress, aortic histamine formation, and aortic albumin uptake. *Exp. Mol. Pathol.* 32: 217–225, 1980.
141. DEL VECCHIO, P. J., J. W. RYAN, A. CHUNG, AND U. S. RYAN. Capillaries of the adrenal cortex possess aminopeptidase A and angiotensin-converting enzyme activities. *Biochem. J.* 186: 605–608, 1980.
142. DEL VECCHIO, P. J., U. S. RYAN, AND J. W. RYAN. Isolation of capillary segments from rat adrenal gland (Abstract). *J. Cell Biol.* 75: 73a, 1977.
143. DEMPSEY, G. P., S. BULLIVANT, AND W. B. WATKINS. Endothelial cell membranes: polarity of particles as seen by freeze-fracturing. *Science* 179: 190–192, 1973.
144. DENNY, J. B., AND A. R. JOHNSON. Uptake of ^{125}I-labelled C3a by cultured human endothelial cells. *Immunology* 36: 169–177, 1978.
145. DIETERLE, Y., C. ODY, A. EHRENSBERGER, H. STALDER, AND A. F. JUNOD. Metabolism and uptake of adenosine triphosphate and adenosine by porcine aortic and pulmonary endothelial cells and fibroblasts in culture. *Circ. Res.* 42: 869–876, 1978.
146. DJERASSI, I., E. KLEIN, S. FARBER, AND D. PALMER. Effects of 5-hydroxytryptamine on some aspects of hemorrhagic state in radiation induced thrombocytopenia. *Proc. Soc. Exp. Biol. Med.* 97: 552–554, 1958.
147. DOSNE, A. M., E. DUPUY, AND E. BODEVIN. Production of a fibrinolytic inhibitor by cultured endothelial cells derived from human umbilical vein. *Thromb. Res.* 12: 377–387, 1978.
148. DOSNE, A. M., B. ESCOUBET, E. BODEVIN, AND J. P. CAEN. Adenosine diphosphate metabolism by cultured human umbilical endothelial cells. *FEBS Lett.* 105: 286–290, 1979.
149. DOSNE, A. M., C. LEGRAND, B. BAUVOIS, E. BODEVIN, AND J. P. CAEN. Comparative degradation of adenylnucleotides by cultured endothelial cells and fibroblasts. *Biochem. Biophys. Res. Commun.* 85: 183–189, 1978.
150. DUNHAM, B. M., G. A. GRINDLINGER, T. UTSUNOMIYA, M. M. KRAUSZ, H. B. HECHTMAN, AND D. SHEPRO. Role of prostaglandins in positive end-expiratory pressure-induced negative inotropism. *Am. J. Physiol.* 241 (*Heart Circ. Physiol.* 10): H783–H788, 1981.
151. DUSTING, G. J., S. MONCADA, AND J. R. VANE. Recirculation of prostacyclin (PGI_2) in the dog. *Br. J. Pharmacol.* 64: 315–320, 1978.
152. DUSTING, G. J., AND E. M. MULLINS. Stimulation by angiotensin of prostacyclin biosynthesis in rats and dogs. *Clin. Exp. Pharmacol. Physiol.* 7: 545–550, 1980.
153. DUSTING, G. J., E. M. MULLINS, AND R. D. NOLAN. Stimulation of prostacyclin (PGI_2) release by angiotensins in isolated mesenteric vasculature of rats. In: *Progress in Microcirculation Research*, edited by D. Garlick. Sydney, Australia: Comm. Postgrad. Med. Ed., Univ. New South Wales, 1981, p. 512–522.
154. DUTHU, G. S., AND J. R. SMITH. In vitro proliferation and lifespan of bovine aorta endothelial cells: effect of culture conditions and fibroblast growth factor. *J. Cell. Physiol.* 103: 385–392, 1980.
155. DUVAL, D., J. W. FUNDER, M. A. DEVYNCK, AND H. MEYER. Arterial glucocorticoid receptors: the binding of tritiated dexamethasone in rabbit aorta. *Cardiovasc. Res.* 11: 529–535, 1977.
156. EAGLE, H. Buffer combinations for mammalian cell culture. *Science* 174: 500–503, 1971.
157. EBERT, R. H., H. W. FLOREY, AND D. PULLINGER. A modification of a Sandison-Clark chamber for observation of transplantation tissue in the rabbit's ear. *J. Pathol. Bacteriol.* 48: 79–94, 1939.
158. EHRMANN, R. L., AND M. KNOTH. Choriocarcinoma: transfilter stimulation of vasoproliferation in the hamster cheek pouch studied by light and electron microscopy. *J. Natl. Cancer Inst.* 41: 1329–1341, 1968.
159. EMANUELSSON, H. Serotonin in chick embryo cells during early morphogenesis (Abstract). *J. Cell Biol.* 70: 131a, 1976.
160. ENGERMAN, R. L., H. D. PFAFTENBACH, AND M. D. DAVIS. Cell turnover of capillaries. *Lab. Invest.* 17: 738–743, 1967.
161. ERDÖS, E. G., A. R. JOHNSON, AND N. T. BOYDEN. Hydrolysis of enkephalin by cultured human endothelial cells and by purified peptidyl dipeptidase. *Biochem. Pharmacol.* 27: 843–848, 1978.
162. ESKIN, S. G., H. D. SYBERS, L. TREVINO, J. T. LIE, AND J. E. CHIMOSKEY. Comparison of tissue-cultured bovine endothelial cells from aorta and saphenous vein. *In Vitro* 14: 903–910, 1978.
163. ESMON, C. T., AND W. G. OWEN. Identification of an endothelial cell cofactor for thrombin-catalyzed activation of protein C. *Proc. Natl. Acad. Sci. USA* 78: 2249–2252, 1981.
164. EVENSEN, S. A., AND D. SHEPRO. DNA synthesis in rat aortic endothelium: effect of bacterial endotoxin and trauma. *Microvasc. Res.* 8: 90–96, 1974.
165. FAED, M. J. W., A. B. MACGREGOR, AND D. L. GARDNER. Isolated visceral arterioles in culture. *J. Pathol.* 87: 131–136, 1964.
166. FALLON, J. T., AND W. E. STEHBENS. Venous endothelium of experimental arteriovenous fistules in rabbits. *Circ. Res.* 31: 546–550, 1972.
167. FAUCI, A. S., B. F. HAYNES, AND P. KATZ. The spectrum of vasculitis: clinical, pathologic, immunologic and therapeutic considerations. *Ann. Int. Med.* 89: 660–676, 1978.
168. FAWCETT, D. W. *An Atlas of Fine Structure. The Cell.* Philadelphia, PA: Saunders, 1969, p. 353–364.
169. FENSELAU, A., AND R. J. MELLO. Growth stimulation of cultured endothelial cells by tumor cell homogenates. *Cancer Res.* 36: 3269–3273, 1976.
170. FENSELAU, A., S. WATT, AND R. J. MELLO. Tumor angiogenic factor: purification from Walker 256 rat tumor. *J. Biol. Chem.* 256: 9605–9611, 1982.
171. FERRARI, E. The filtering structurings of the arterial wall, the endothelium in particular. *Panminerva Med.* 5: 162–167, 1963.
172. FERRERA, S. H., AND J. R. VANE. Prostaglandins: their disappearance from and release into the circulation. *Nature London* 216: 868–873, 1967.
173. FIELDING, P. E., I. VLODAVSKY, D. GOSPODAROWICZ, AND C. J. FIELDING. Effect of contact inhibition on the regulation of

cholesterol metabolism and cultured vascular endothelial cells. *J. Biol. Chem.* 254: 749–755, 1979.

174. FISHMAN, A. P. Nonrespiratory functions of the lungs. *Chest* 72: 84–89, 1977.
175. FISHMAN, A. P., AND G. G. PIETRA. Handling of bioactive materials by the lung. *N. Engl. J. Med.* 291: 884–889, 1974.
175a. FISHMAN, A. P., AND G. G. PIETRA. Handling of bioactive materials by the lung. *N. Engl. J. Med.* 291: 953–959, 1974.
176. FISHMAN, J. A., G. B. RYAN, AND M. J. KARNOVSKY. Endothelial regeneration in the rat carotid artery and the significance of endothelial denudation in the pathogenesis of myointimal thickening. *Lab. Invest.* 32: 339–351, 1975.
177. FISKUM, G., S. W. CRAIG, G. L. DECKER, AND A. H. LEHNINGER. Cytoskeleton network of digitonin-treated hepatocytes (Abstract). *J. Cell Biol.* 83: 309a, 1979.
178. FLORENTIN, R. A., B. H. CHOI, K. T. LEE, AND W. A. THOMAS. Stimulation of DNA synthesis and cell division *in vitro* by serum from cholesterol-fed swine. *J. Cell Biol.* 41: 641–645, 1969.
179. FLOREY, H. W., J. C. I. PODE, AND G. A. MEEK. Endothelial cells and "cement" lines. *J. Pathol. Bacteriol.* 77: 625–636, 1959.
180. FLUMERFELT, B. A., P. R. LEWIS, AND D. G. GWYN. Cholinesterase activity of capillaries in the rat brain. A light and electron microscopic study. *Histochem. J.* 5: 67–77, 1973.
181. FLYNN, J. T., G. A. BRIDENBAUGH, AND A. M. LEFER. Clearance of prostaglandin $F_{2\alpha}$ during circulatory shock. *Life Sci.* 17: 1699–1705, 1976.
182. FLYNN, S., AND D. A. A. OWEN. Histamine receptors in peripheral vascular beds in the cat. *Br. J. Pharmacol.* 55: 181–188, 1975.
183. FOLKMAN, J. Tumor angiogenesis factor. *Cancer Res.* 34: 2109–2113, 1974.
184. FOLKMAN, J., D. AUSPRUNK, AND R. LANGER. Connective tissue: small blood vessels and capillaries. In: *Textbook of Rheumatology*, edited by W. N. Kelley, E. D. Harris, Jr., S. Ruddy, and C. B. Sledge. Philadelphia, PA: Saunders, 1981, vol. I, p. 210–220.
185. FOLKMAN, J., P. COLE, AND S. ZIMMERMAN. Tumor behavior in isolated perfused organs. *Ann. Surg.* 164: 491–502, 1966.
186. FOLKMAN, J., C. C. HAUDENSCHILD, AND B. R. ZETTER. Long-term culture of capillary endothelial cells. *Proc. Natl. Acad. Sci. USA* 76: 5217–5221, 1979.
187. FOLKMAN, J., E. MERLER, C. ABERNATHY, AND G. WILLIAMS. Isolation of a tumor factor responsible for angiogenesis. *J. Exp. Med.* 133: 275–288, 1971.
188. FOLKMAN, J., AND A. MOSCONA. Role of cell shape in growth control. *Nature London* 273: 345–349, 1978.
189. FORBES, M. S., M. L. RENNELS, AND E. NELSON. Ultrastructure of pericytes in mouse hearts. *Am. J. Anat.* 149: 47–69, 1977.
189a. FOSTER, M. *Textbook of Physiology.* London: Macmillan, 1877.
190. FOURNIER, G. A., G. A. LUTTY, S. WATT, A. FENSELAU, AND A. PATZ. A corneal micropocket assay for angiogenesis in the rat eye. *Invest. Ophthalmol. Vis. Sci.* 21: 351–354, 1981.
190a. FRANK, R. N. Studies on retinal capillary cells in tissue culture. *Vision Res.* 21: 165–168, 1981.
190b. FRANK, R. N., V. E. KINSEY, K. P. MIKAS, AND A. RANDOLPH. Proliferation of endothelial cells from kitten retinal capillaries. *Invest. Ophthalmol Vis. Sci.* 18: 1195–1200, 1979.
191. FRANKE, W. W., E. SCHMID, M. OSBORN, AND K. WEBER. Intermediate-sized filaments of human endothelial cells. *J. Cell Biol.* 81: 570–580, 1979.
192. FRANKS, D., AND A. DAWSON. Variation in the expression of blood antigen A in clonal cultures of rabbit cells. *Exp. Cell Res.* 42: 543–561, 1966.
193. FRIEDE, R. L., AND L. M. FLEMING. A comparison of cholinesterase distribution in the cerebellum of several species. *J. Neurochem.* 11: 1–7, 1964.
194. FROMER, C. H., AND G. K. KLINTWORTH. An evaluation of the role of leukocytes in the pathogenesis of experimentally induced corneal vascularization. *Am. J. Pathol.* 82: 157–167, 1976.
195. FRY, D. L. Acute vascular endothelial changes associated with increased blood velocity gradients. *Circ. Res.* 22: 165–197, 1968.
196. FRY, G. L., R. L. CZERVIONKE, J. C. HOAK, J. B. SMITH, AND D. L. HAYCRAFT. Platelet adherence to cultured vascular cells: influence of prostacyclin (PGI_2). *Blood* 55: 271–275, 1980.
197. FRYER, D. G., G. BIRNBAUM, AND C. N. LUTTRELL. Human endothelium in cell culture. *J. Atheroscler. Res.* 6: 151–163, 1966.
198. FUCHS, A., AND E. R. WEIBEL. Morphometrische untersuchung der Verteilung einer spezifischen cytoplasmatischen Organelle in Endothelzellen der Ratte. *Z. Zellforsch. Mikrosk. Anat.* 73: 1–9, 1966.
199. FUJIMOTO, S., K. YAMAMOTO, AND Y. TAKESHIGE. Histochemical and autoradiographic findings on specific granules of the endothelial cells. In: *Int. Congr. Electron Microscopy, 9th, Toronto, 1978.* Toronto: Microsc. Soc. Can., 1978, vol. 2, p. 466–472.
200. GABBIANI, G., M. C. BADONNEL, AND G. RONA. Cytoplasmic contractile apparatus in aortic endothelial cells of hypertensive rats. *Lab. Invest.* 32: 227–234, 1975.
201. GABBIANI, G., AND D. MONTANDON. Reparative processes in mammalian wound-healing: the role of contractile phenomena. *Int. Rev. Cytol.* 48: 187–219, 1977.
202. GADDUM, J. H., C. O. HEBB, A. SILVER, AND A. A. B. SWAN. 5-Hydroxytryptamine: pharmacological action and destruction in perfused lungs. *Q. J. Exp. Physiol. Cogn. Med. Sci.* 38: 255–262, 1953.
203. GAJDUSEK, C., P. D. CORLETO, R. ROSS, AND S. M. SCHWARTZ. An endothelial cell derived growth factor. *J. Cell Biol.* 85: 467–472, 1980.
204. GALDAL, K. S., AND S. A. EVENSEN. Effects of divalent cations and various vasoactive and haemostatically active agents on the integrity of monolayers of cultured human endothelial cells. *Thromb. Res.* 21: 273–284, 1981.
205. GAYNOR, E. Increased mitotic activity in rabbit endothelium after endotoxin. An autoradiograph study. *Lab. Invest.* 24: 318–320, 1971.
206. GEILING, D., H. G. GEILING, K. J. HALBHUBER, R. FRÖBER, AND G. GEYER. Rat endo- and mesothelium lack FC receptors. *Exp. Pathol. Jena* 17: 171–175, 1979.
207. GIACOMELLI, F., K. B. JUECHTER, AND J. WIENER. The cellular pathology of experimental hypertension. VI. Alterations in retinal vasculature. *Am. J. Pathol.* 68: 81–96, 1972.
208. GIBOFSKY, A., E. A. JAFFE, M. FOTINO, AND C. G. BECKER. The identification of HL-A antigens on fresh and cultured human endothelial cells. *J. Immunol.* 115: 730–733, 1975.
209. GILLIS, C. N., L. H. CRONAN, N. M. GREEN, AND G. L. HAMMOND. Removal of 5-hydroxytryptamine and norepinephrine from the pulmonary vascular space of man: influence of cardiopulmonary bypass and pulmonary arterial pressure on these processes. *Surgery* 76: 608–616, 1974.
210. GIMBRONE, M. A., JR. Culture of vascular endothelium. *Prog. Hemostasis Thromb.* 3: 1–28, 1976.
211. GIMBRONE, M. A., JR., AND R. W. ALEXANDER. Prostaglandin production by vascular endothelial and smooth muscle cells in culture. In: *Prostaglandins in Hematology*, edited by M. J. Silver, J. M. Smith, and J. J. Kocsis. New York: Spectrum, 1977, p. 121–134.
212. GIMBRONE, M. A., JR., R. H. ASTER, R. S. COTRAN, J. CORKERY, J. H. JANDL, AND J. FOLKMAN. Preservation of vascular integrity in organs perfused *in vitro* with a platelet-rich medium. *Nature London* 222: 33–36, 1969.
213. GIMBRONE, M. A., JR., AND R. S. COTRAN. Human vascular smooth muscle in culture. *Lab. Invest.* 33: 16–27, 1975.
214. GIMBRONE, M. A., JR., R. S. COTRAN, AND J. FOLKMAN. Endothelial regeneration: studies with human endothelial cells in culture. *Ser. Haematol.* 6: 453–455, 1973.
215. GIMBRONE, M. A., JR., R. S. COTRAN, AND J. FOLKMAN. Human vascular endothelial cells in culture: growth and DNA

synthesis. *J. Cell Biol.* 60: 673–684, 1974.
216. GIMBRONE, M. A., JR., R. S. COTRAN, S. B. LEAPMAN, AND J. FOLKMAN. Tumor growth and neovascularization: an experimental model using the rabbit cornea. *J. Natl. Cancer Inst.* 52: 413–427, 1974.
217. GIMBRONE, M. A., JR., AND G. C. FAREED. Transformation of cultured human vascular endothelium by SV40 DNA. *Cell* 9: 685–693, 1976.
218. GINGRUH, R. D., AND J. C. HOAK. Platelet endothelial cell interactions. *Semin. Hematol.* 16: 208–220, 1979.
219. GINN, R., AND J. R. VANE. The disappearance of catecholamines from the circulation. *Nature London* 219: 740–742, 1968.
219a. GITLIN, J. D., AND P. A. D'AMORE. Retinal capillary endothelial cells: long-term culture using selective growth media. *Microvasc. Res.* 26: 74–80, 1983.
220. GLASER, B. M., P. A. D'AMORE, R. G. MICHELS, A. PATZ, AND A. FENSELAU. Demonstration of vasproliferative activity from mammalian retina. *J. Cell Biol.* 84: 298–304, 1980.
221. GLASER, B. M., P. A. D'AMORE, H. SEPPA, S. SEPPA, AND E. SCHIFFMAN. Adult tissues contain chemoattractants for vascular endothelial cells. *Nature London* 288: 483–484, 1980.
222. GLICKMAN, R. M., AND J. F. BOUHOURS. Characterization, distribution and biosynthesis of the major ganglioside of rat intestinal mucosa. *Biochim. Biophys. Acta* 424: 17–25, 1976.
223. GLIMELIUS, B., C. BUSCH, AND M. HÖÖK. Binding of heparin on the surface of cultured human endothelial cells. *Thromb. Res.* 12: 773–782, 1978.
224. GLOSMET, J., AND K. R. NORUM. The metabolic role of lecithin: cholesterol acyltransferase: perspectives from pathology. *Adv. Lipid Res.* 11: 1–65, 1973.
225. GLYNN, L. E., AND E. J. HOLBOROW. Distribution of blood group substances in human tissues. *Br. Med. Bull.* 15: 150–153, 1959.
226. GOLDBLATT, M. W. A depressor substance in seminal fluid (Abstract). *J. Soc. Chem. Ind. London* 52: 1056, 1933.
227. GOLDSTEIN, G. W. Metabolism of brain capillaries in relation to active ion transport. In: *Advances in Neurology*, edited by J. Cervos-Navarro, E. Betz, G. Ebhardt, R. Fersz, and R. Wüllenweber. New York: Raven, 1978, vol. 20, p. 11–16.
228. GOLDSTEIN, G. W., J. S. WOLINSKY, J. CSEJTEY, AND I. DIAMOND. Isolation of metabolically active capillaries from rat brain. *J. Neurochem.* 25: 715–717, 1975.
229. GORDON, J. L., J. D. PEARSON, AND D. E. MACINTYRE. Effect of prostaglandin E_2 on prostacyclin production by endothelial cells. *Nature London* 278: 480, 1979.
230. GOSPODAROWICZ, D. Purification of a fibroblast growth factor from bovine pituitary. *J. Biol. Chem.* 250: 2515–2520, 1975.
231. GOSPODAROWICZ, D., H. BIALECKI, AND G. GREENBURG. Purification of the fibroblast growth factor activity from bovine brain. *J. Biol. Chem.* 253: 3736–3743, 1978.
232. GOSPODAROWICZ, D., K. D. BROWN, C. R. BIRDWELL, AND B. R. ZETTER. Control of proliferation of human vascular endothelial cells. *J. Cell Biol.* 77: 774–788, 1978.
233. GOSPODAROWICZ, D., D. DELGADO, AND I. VLODAVSKY. Permissive effect of the extracellular matrix on cell proliferation in vitro. *Proc. Natl. Acad. Sci. USA* 77: 4094–4098, 1980.
234. GOSPODAROWICZ, D., AND D. ILL. Extracellular matrix and control of proliferation of vascular endothelial cells. *J. Clin. Invest.* 65: 1351–1364, 1980.
235. GOSPODAROWICZ, D., AND A. L. MESCHER. The control of cellular proliferation by the fibroblast and epidermal growth factors. *Natl. Cancer Inst. Monogr.* 48: 109–130, 1978.
236. GOSPODAROWICZ, D., A. C. MESCHER, K. BROWN, AND C. R. BIRDWELL. The role of fibroblastic growth factor and epidermal growth factor in the proliferative response of the cornea and lens epithelium. *Exp. Eye Res.* 25: 75–89, 1977.
237. GOSPODAROWICZ, D., J. S. MORAN, AND D. L. BRAUN. Control of proliferation of bovine vascular endothelial cells. *J. Cell. Physiol.* 91: 377–386, 1977.
238. GOSPODAROWICZ, D., J. MORAN, D. L. BRAUN, AND C. R. BIRDWELL. Clonal growth of bovine vascular endothelial cells in tissue culture: fibroblast growth factor as a survival agent. *Proc. Natl. Acad. Sci. USA* 73: 4120–4124, 1976.
239. GOSPODAROWICZ, D., AND K. K. THAKRAL. Production of a corpus luteum angiogenic factor responsible for proliferation of capillaries and neovascularization of the corpus luteum. *Proc. Natl. Acad. Sci. USA* 75: 847–851, 1978.
240. GOSPODAROWICZ, D., I. VLODAVSKY, G. GREENBURG, AND L. K. JOHNSON. Cellular shape is determined by the extracellular matrix and is responsible for the control of cellular growth and function. In: *Hormone and Cell Culture*, edited by G. Sato and R. Ross. New York: Cold Spring Harbor, 1979, vol. 6, p. 561–592. (Cold Spring Harbor Conf. Cell Proliferation.)
241. GRANT, M. E., R. HARWOOD, AND I. F. WILLIAMS. The biosynthesis of basement membrane collagen by isolated rat glomeruli. *Eur. J. Biochem.* 54: 531–540, 1975.
242. GREENBLATT, M., AND P. SHUBIK. Tumor angiogenesis: transfilter diffusion studies in the hamster by the transparent chamber technique. *J. Natl. Cancer Inst.* 41: 111–124, 1968.
243. GREENBURG, G. B., AND T. K. HUNT. The proliferative response *in vitro* of vascular endothelial and smooth muscle cells exposed to wound fluids and macrophages. *J. Cell. Physiol.* 97:353–360, 1978.
244. GREENBURG, G. B., I. VLODAVSKY, J. M. FOLDART, AND D. GOSPODAROWICZ. Conditioned medium from endothelial cell cultures can restore the normal phenotypic expression of vascular endothelium maintained *in vitro* in the absence of fibroblast growth factor. *J. Cell. Physiol.* 103: 333–347, 1980.
245. GRIEG, M. E., AND W. C. HOLLAND. Increased permeability of the hemo-encephalic barrier produced by physostigmine and acetylcholine. *Science* 110: 237–238, 1949.
246. GRYGLEWSKI, R. J. Prostacyclin as a circulatory hormone. *Biochem. Pharmacol.* 28: 2161–2166, 1979.
247. GRYGLEWSKI, R. J., S. BUNTING, S. MONCADA, R. J. FLOWER, AND J. R. VANE. Arterial walls are protected against deposition of platelet thrombi by a substance (prostaglandin X) which they make from prostaglandin endoperoxides. *Prostaglandins* 12: 685–713, 1976.
248. GRYGLEWSKI, R. J., R. KORBUT, AND A. OCETKIEWICZ. Generation of prostacyclin by lungs *in vivo* and its release into the arterial circulation. *Nature London* 273: 765–767, 1978.
249. GUILLAUMOND, M., AND P. LOUISOT. Glycoprotein biosynthesis in aortic wall. IV. Study of soluble nylosyl-transferase in intimal cells. *Int. J. Biochem.* 6: 491–496, 1975.
250. GUSTAFSON, T., AND M. TONEBY. On the role of serotonin and acetylcholine in sea urchin morphogenesis. *Exp. Cell Res.* 62: 102–117, 1970.
251. GWYN, D. G., AND J. H. WOLSTENCROFT. Cholinesterases in the area subpostrema, a region adjacent to the area postrema in the cat. *J. Comp. Neurol.* 133: 289–308, 1968.
252. HALL, M. *A Critical and Experimental Assay on the Circulation of the Blood; Especially as Observed in Minute and Capillary Vessels of the Batrachia and of Fissures.* London: Seeley & Burnside, 1831.
253. HAMMERSEN, F. Zur Ultrastruktur der kleinen Hautgefässe. *Arch. Klin. Exp. Dermatol.* 237: 356–367, 1970.
254. HAMMERSEN, F. Endothelial contractility—its pros and cons. *Bibl. Anat.* 16: 370–372, 1977.
255. HAMMERSEN, F. Endothelial contractility—does it exist? *Adv. Microcirc.* 9: 95–134, 1980.
256. HAN, Y. N., H. KATO, S. IWANAGA, AND T. SUZUKI. Primary structure of bovine plasma high-molecular-weight kininogen. The amino acid sequence of a glycopeptide portion (fragment 1) following the C-terminus of the bradykinin moiety. *J. Biochem. Tokyo* 79: 1201–1222, 1976.
257. HANSSON, G. K., G. BONDJERS, AND L. A. NILSSON. Plasma protein accumulation in injured endothelial cells. Immunofluorescent localization of IGg and fibrinogen in the rabbit aortic endothelium. *Exp. Mol. Pathol.* 30: 12–26, 1979.
258. HARDIN, N. J., C. R. MINICK, AND G. E. MURPHY. Experimental induction of atheroarteriosclerosis by the synergy of

allergic injury to arteries and lipid-rich diet. 3. The role of earlier acquired fibromuscular intimal thickening in the pathogenesis of later developing atherosclerosis. *Am. J. Pathol.* 73: 301–326, 1973.

259. Harpel, P. C., and R. D. Rosenberg. α_2-Macroglobulin and antithrombin-heparin cofactor: modulators of hemostatic and inflammatory reactions. *Prog. Hemostasis Thromb.* 3: 145–189, 1976.
260. Harris, S., C. Gajdusek, S. Schwartz, and T. Wight. Role of endothelial cell products in vascular growth responses and neovascularization (Abstract). *J. Cell Biol.* 83: 104a, 1979.
261. Haudenschild, C. C. Growth control of endothelial cells in atherogenesis and tumor angiogeneis. *Adv. Microcirc.* 9: 226–251, 1980.
262. Haudenschild, C. C., R. S. Cotran, M. A. Gimbrone, and J. Folkman. Fine structure of vascular endothelium in culture. *J. Ultrastruct. Res.* 50: 22–32, 1975.
263. Haudenschild, C. C., and S. M. Schwartz. Endothelial regeneration. II. Restitution of endothelial continuity. *Lab. Invest.* 41: 407–418, 1979.
264. Haudenschild, C. C., D. Zahniser, J. Folkman, and M. Klagsbrun. Human vascular endothelial cells in culture. Lack of response to serum growth factors. *Exp. Cell Res.* 98: 175–183, 1976.
265. Hayes, L. W., C. A. Gogven, S.-F. Ching, and L. L. Slakey. Angiotensin-converting enzyme: accumulation in medium from cultured endothelial cells. *Biochem. Biophys. Res. Commun.* 82: 1147–1153, 1978.
266. Hechtman, H. B., M. M. Krausz, T. Utsunomiya, L. Levine, and D. Shepro. Cardiovascular function following surgical stimulation of pulmonary prostacyclin synthesis (Abstract). *Thromb. Haemostasis* 46: 264A, 1981.
267. Hechtman, H. B., T. Utsunomiya, M. M. Krausz, B. Dunham, G. Feuerstein, and D. Shepro. Systemic effects of thromboxanes released by positive end-expiratory pressure (Abstract). *Thromb. Haemostasis* 46: 44A, 1981.
268. Hechtman, H. B., T. Utsunomiya, A. M. Vegas, G. A. Grindlinger, G. A. McLoughlin, M. M. Krausz, and D. Shepro. Prostaglandin mediation of pulmonary fibrinolytic activity. In: *Role of Chemical Mediators in the Pathophysiology of Acute Illness and Injury*, edited by R. McConn. New York: Raven, 1982, p. 243–251.
269. Heder, G., W. Jakob, W. Halle, B. Mauersberger, G. Kambach, K. D. Jentzsch, and P. Oehme. Influence of porcine corpus luteum extract on DNA synthesis and proliferation of cultivated fibroblasts and endothelial cells. *Exp. Pathol.* 17: 493–497, 1979.
270. Heinrich, D., J. Metz, E. Raviola, and W. G. Forssmann. Ultrastructure of perfusion-fixed fetal capillaries in the human placenta. *Cell Tissue Res.* 172: 157–170, 1976.
271. Heltianu, C., M. Simionescu, and N. Simionescu. Identification of histamine receptors by using histamine-ferritin conjugates: characteristic high affinity binding sites in venular endothelium (Abstract). *J. Cell Biol.* 87: 156a, 1980.
272. Hendry, W. F., N. W. Struthers, W. P. Duguid, and W. I. Hopkinson. Observations on kidneys stored by continuous hypothermic perfusion in hyperbaric oxygen. *Br. J. Surg.* 55: 431–436, 1968.
273. Henriksen, T., and S. A. Evensen. Human endothelial cells in primary culture. Incorporation of acetate and mevalonate into lipids. *Microvasc. Res.* 15: 339–347, 1978.
274. Henriksen, T., S. A. Evensen, and B. Carlander. Injury to cultured endothelial cells induced by low density lipoproteins: protection by high density lipoproteins. *Scand. J. Clin. Lab. Invest.* 39: 369–375, 1979.
275. Herrlinger, H., A. P. Anzil, K. Blinzinger, and D. Kronski. Endothelial microtubular bodies in human brain capillaries and venules. *J. Anat.* 118: 205–209, 1974.
276. Herzog, G., and W. Schopper. Ueber das Verhatten der Blutgefässe in der Kultur. *Arch. Exp. Zellforsch. Besonders Gewebezuecht.* 11: 202–218, 1931.
277. Hessler, J. R., A. L. Robertson, Jr., and G. M. Chisolm III. LDL-induced cytotoxicity and its inhibition by HDL in human vascular smooth muscle and endothelial cells in culture. *Atherosclerosis* 32: 213–229, 1978.
278. Hibbs, R. G., G. E. Burch, and J. H. Phillips. The fine structure of the small blood vessels of human dermis and subcutis. *Am. Heart J.* 56: 662–670, 1958.
279. Hiebert, L. M., and L. B. Jaques. Heparin uptake on endothelium. *Artery* 2: 26–37, 1976.
280. Hirano, A., N. R. Ghatak, N. H. Becker, and H. M. Zimmerman. A comparison of the fine structure of small blood vessels in intracranial and retroperitoneal malignant lymphomas. *Acta Neuropathol.* 27: 93–104, 1974.
281. Hirsch, E. Z., and A. L. Robertson, Jr. Selective acute arterial endothelial injury and repair. I. Methodology and surface characteristics. *Atherosclerosis* 28: 271–287, 1977.
282. Hirschberg, H., S. A. Evensen, and T. Henriksen. Stimulation of human lymphocytes by allogenic endothelial cells *in vitro*. *Tissue Antigens* 4: 257–261, 1974.
283. Hirschberg, H., T. Moen, and E. Thorsby. Specific destruction of human endothelial cell monolayers by anti-DRW antisera. *Transplantation* 28: 116–120, 1979.
284. Hirschberg, H., E. Thorsby, and B. Rolstad. Antibody-induced cell-mediated damage to human endothelial cells *in vitro*. *Nature London* 255: 62–64, 1975.
285. Ho, S. J., R. J. Ho, and H. C. Meng. Comparison of heparin-released and epinephrine-sensitive lipases in rat adipose tissue. *Am. J. Physiol.* 212: 284–290, 1967.
286. Hoak, J. C., R. L. Czervionke, and L. J. Lewis. Uptake and utilization of free fatty acids (FFA) by human endothelial cells. *Thromb. Res.* 4: 879–883, 1974.
287. Hoffman, H., B. McAuslan, D. Robertson, and E. Burnett. An endothelial growth-stimulating factor from salivary glands. *Exp. Cell Res.* 102: 269–275, 1976.
288. Holborow, E. J., P. C. Brown, L. E. Glynn, M. D. Hawes, G. A. Gresham, T. F. O'Brien, and R. R. A. Coombs. The distribution of the blood group A antigen in human tissues. *Br. J. Exp. Pathol.* 41: 430–437, 1960.
289. Holley, R. W., and J. A. Kierman. Control of the initiation of DNA synthesis in 3T3 cells: serum factors. *Proc. Natl. Acad. Sci. USA* 71: 2908–2911, 1974.
290. Hollis, T. M., and L. A. Rosen. Histidine decarboxylase activity of bovine aortic endothelium and intima-media. *Proc. Soc. Exp. Biol. Med.* 4163: 978–981, 1972.
291. Holm, M., J. E. Mansson, M. T. Vanier, and L. Svennerholm. Gangliosides of human, bovine, and rabbit retinas. *Biochim. Biophys. Acta* 280: 356–364, 1972.
292. Hoover, R. L., R. T. Briggs, and M. J. Karnovsky. The adhesive interaction between polymorphonuclear leukocytes and endothelial cells *in vitro*. *Cell* 14: 423–428, 1978.
293. Hope, W., T. J. Martin, C. N. Chesterman, and F. J. Morgan. Human β-thromboglobulin inhibits PGI_2 production and binds to a specific site in bovine aortic endothelial cells. *Nature London* 282: 210–212, 1979.
294. Hopkins, N. K., and R. R. Gorman. Regulation of endothelial cell cyclic nucleotide metabolism by prostacyclin. *J. Clin. Invest.* 67: 540–546, 1981.
295. Howard, B. V., E. J. Macarak, D. Gunson, and N. A. Kefalides. Characterization of the collagen synthesized by endothelial cells in culture. *Proc. Natl. Acad. Sci. USA* 73: 2361–2364, 1976.
296. Hoyer, L. W., R. P. De los Santos, and J. R. Hoyer. Antihemophilic factor antigen. Localization in endothelial cells by immunofluorescent microscopy. *J. Clin. Invest.* 52: 2737–2744, 1973.
297. Huand, M., and G. I. Drummond. Adenylate cyclase in cerebral microvessels: action of guanine nucleotides, adenosine, and other agonists. *Mol. Pharmacol.* 16: 462–472, 1979.
298. Hughes, J., C. N. Gillis, and F. E. Bloom. The uptake and disposition of dl-norepinephrine in perfused rat lung. *J. Pharmacol. Exp. Ther.* 169: 237–248, 1969.
299. Hurley, J. V., and N. E. McCallum. The degree and functional significance of the escape of marker particles from small

blood vessels with fenestrated endothelium. *J. Pathol.* 113: 183–196, 1974.

300. HWANG, S. M., S. WEISS, AND S. SEGAL. Uptake of L-[^{35}S] cystine by isolated rat brain capillaries. *J. Neurochem.* 35: 417–424, 1980.
301. ILLIG, L. Capillar contractilität, Capillar sphincter, und Zentralkanale. *Klin. Wochenschr.* 35: 7–22, 1957.
302. IWASAWA, Y., AND C. N. GILLIS. Pharmacological analysis of norepinephrine and 5-hydroxytryptamine removal from the pulmonary circulation: differentiation of uptake sites for each amine. *J. Pharmacol. Exp. Ther.* 188: 386–393, 1974.
303. IWASAWA, Y., C. N. GILLIS, AND G. AGHAJANIAN. Hypothermic inhibition of 5-hydroxytryptamine and norepinephrine uptake by lung: cellular location of amines after uptake. *J. Pharmacol. Exp. Ther.* 186: 498–507, 1973.
304. JAFFE, E. A., L. W. HOYER, AND R. L. NACHMAN. Synthesis of antihemophilic factor antigen by cultured human endothelial cells. *J. Clin. Invest.* 52: 2757–2764, 1973.
305. JAFFE, E. A., L. W. HOYER, AND R. L. NACHMAN. Synthesis of von Willebrand factor by cultured human endothelial cells. *Proc. Natl. Acad. Sci. USA* 71: 1906–1909, 1974.
306. JAFFE, E. A., C. R. MINICK, B. ADELMAN, C. G. BECKER, AND R. NACHMAN. Synthesis of basement membrane collagen by cultured human endothelial cells. *J. Exp. Med.* 144: 209–225, 1976.
307. JAFFE, E. A., AND D. F. MOSHER. Synthesis of fibronectin by cultured human endothelial cells. *J. Exp. Med.* 147: 1779–1791, 1978.
308. JAFFE, E. A., AND R. L. NACHMAN. Subunit structure of factor VIII antigen synthesized by cultured human endothelial cells. *J. Clin. Invest.* 56: 698–702, 1975.
309. JAFFE, E. A., R. L. NACHMAN, C. G. BECKER, AND C. R. MINICK. Culture of human endothelial cells derived from umbilical veins. *J. Clin. Invest.* 52: 2745–2756, 1973.
310. JAFFE, E. A., AND B. B. WEKSLER. Recovery of endothelial cell prostacyclin production after inhibition by low doses of aspirin. *J. Clin. Invest.* 63: 532–535, 1979.
311. JAKOB, W., K. D. JENTZSCH, B. MAUERSBERGER, AND P. OEHME. Demonstration of angiogenesis activity in the corpus luteum of cattle. *Exp. Pathol.* 13: 231–236, 1977.
312. JOHNSON, A. R. Human pulmonary endothelial cells in culture. Activities of cells from arteries and cells from veins. *J. Clin. Invest.* 65: 841–850, 1980.
313. JOHNSON, A. R., N. T. BOYDEN, AND C. M. WILSON. Growth promoting actions of extracts from mouse submaxillary glands on human endothelial cells in culture. *J. Cell. Physiol.* 101: 431–438, 1979.
314. JOHNSON, A. R., AND E. G. ERDÖS. Inactivation of substance P by cultured human endothelial cells. In: *Substance P*, edited by U. S. Von Euler and B. Pernow. New York: Rayburn, 1977, p. 253–260.
315. JOHNSON, A. R., AND E. G. ERDÖS. Metabolism of vasoactive peptides by human endothelial cells in culture. *J. Clin. Invest.* 59: 684–695, 1977.
316. JOÓ, F. The effect of the inhibition of adenosine triphosphatase activity on the fine structural organization of brain capillaries. *Nature London* 219: 1378–1379, 1968.
317. JOÓ, F. Changes in the molecular organization of the basement membrane after inhibition of adenosine triphosphatase activity in rat brain capillaries. *Cytobios* 3: 289–301, 1969.
318. JOÓ, F. The role of adenosine triphosphatase in the maintenance of molecular organization of the basal lamina in the brain capillaries. *Front. Matrix Biol.* 166–182, 1979.
319. JOÓ, F. Significance of adenylate cyclase in the regulation of the permeability of brain capillaries. In: *Pathophysiology of Cerebral Energy Metabolism*, edited by B. B. Mršulja, L. M. Rakić, I. Klatz, and M. Spatz. New York: Plenum, 1979, p. 211–237.
320. JOÓ, F., AND B. CSILLIK. Topographic correlation between the hematoencephalic barrier and the cholinesterase activity of brain capillaries. *Exp. Brain Res.* 1: 147–151, 1966.
321. JOÓ, F., AND I. KARNUSHINA. A procedure for the isolation of capillaries from rat brain. *Cytobios* 8: 41–48, 1973.
322. JOÓ, F., I. TÓTH, AND G. JANCSÓ. Brain adenylate cyclase: its common occurrence in the capillaries and astrocytes. *Naturwissenschaften* 8: 397, 1975.
323. JORIS, I., G. MAJNO, AND G. B. RYAN. Endothelial contraction *in vivo*: a study of the rat mesentery. *Virchows Arch. B* 12: 73–83, 1972.
324. JOYNER, W. L., AND J. C. STRAND. Differential release of prostaglandin E-like and F-like substances by endothelial cells cultured from human umbilical arteries and veins. *Microvasc. Res.* 16: 119–131, 1978.
325. JUNOD, A. F. Uptake, metabolism and efflux of ^{14}C-5-hydroxytryptamine in isolated perfused rat lungs. *J. Pharmacol. Exp. Ther.* 183: 341–355, 1972.
326. JUNOD, A. F. Metabolism, production and release of hormones and mediators in the lung. *Am. Rev. Respir. Dis.* 112: 93–108, 1975.
327. JUNOD, A. F., AND C. ODY. Amine uptake and metabolism by endothelium of pig pulmonary artery and aorta. *Am. J. Physiol.* 232 (*Cell Physiol.* 1): C88–C94, 1977.
328. KALNINS, V. I., L. SUBRAHMANYAN, AND A. I. GOTLIEB. The reorganization of cytoskeletal fibre systems in spreading porcine endothelial cells in culture. *Eur. J. Cell Biol.* 24:36–44, 1981.
329. KANWAR, Y. S., AND M. G. FARQUHAR. Partial characterization of anionic sites in the glomerular basement membrane (Abstract). *J. Cell Biol.* 79: 150a, 1978.
330. KANWAR, Y. S., AND M. G. FARQUHAR. Presence of heparan sulfate in the glomerular basement membrane. *Proc. Natl. Acad. Sci. USA* 76: 1303–1307, 1979.
331. KANWAR, Y. S., A. LINKER, AND M. G. FARQUHAR. Increased permeability of the glomerular basement membrane to ferritin after removal of glycosaminoglycans (heparan sulfate) by enzyme digestion. *J. Cell Biol.* 86: 688–693, 1980.
332. KARASEK, M., AND M. CHARLTON. Isolation and growth of skin endothelial cells in cell culture (Abstract). *J. Invest. Dermatol.* 62: 542, 1974.
333. KARCSÚ, S., G. JANCSÓ, AND L. TÓTH. Butyrylcholinesterase in fenestrated capillaries of the rat area postrema. *Brain Res.* 120: 146–150, 1977.
334. KARCSÚ, S., AND L. TÓTH. Fine structural localization of acetylcholinesterase in capillaries surrounding the area postrema. *Brain Res.* 95: 137–141, 1975.
335. KARIM, S. M. M. The identification of prostaglandins in human umbilical cord. *Br. J. Pharmacol. Chemother.* 29: 230–237, 1967.
336. KARNUSHINA, I. L., J. M. PALACIOS, G. BARBIN, E. DUX, F. JOÓ, AND J. C. SCHWARTZ. Studies on a capillary-rich fraction isolated from brain: histaminic components and characterization of the histamine receptors linked to adenylate cyclase. *J. Neurochem.* 34: 1201–1208, 1980.
337. KARNUSHINA, I. L., I. TÓTH, E. DUX, AND F. JOÓ. Presence of the guanylate cyclase in brain capillaries: histochemical and biochemical evidence. *Brain Res.* 189: 588–592, 1980.
338. KELLY, P. J., R. L. SUDDITH, H. T. HUTCHINSON, K. WERRBACH, AND B. HABER. Endothelial growth factor present in tissue culture of CNS tumors. *J. Neurosurg.* 44: 342–346, 1976.
339. KERÉNYI, C. E., A. S. KOCH, AND H. JELLINEK. *In vitro* cultivation and identification of aortic endothelium from miniature pig. *Arterial Wall* 111: 31–37, 1975.
340. KILLEN, P. D., J. L. QUADRACCI, AND G. E. STRIKER. Basal lumina synthesis *in vitro* by glomerular cells (Abstract). *Federation Proc.* 33: 617, 1974.
341. KIRA, Y., K. EBISAWA, T. COIZUMI, AND E. OGATA. Actomyosin extracted from bovine aortic intima. *Biochim. Biophys. Acta* 624: 329–331, 1980.
342. KITCHENS, C. S., AND L. WEISS. Ultrastructural changes of endothelium associated with thrombocytopenia. *Blood* 46: 567–578, 1975.
343. KLAGSBRUN, M., D. KNIGHTON, AND J. FOLKMAN. Tumor angiogenesis activity in cells grown in tissue culture. *Cancer Res.* 36: 110–114, 1976.

344. KLAGSBRUN, M., R. LANGER, C. J. SCHEINER, J. FOLKMAN, AND B. ZETTER. The isolation from cartilage of an inducer and an inhibitor of capillary endothelial cell growth and migration (Abstract). *J. Supramol. Struct.* 4: 198a, 1980.

344a. KOELLE, G. B. The histochemical localization of cholinesterases in the central nervous system of the rat. *J. Comp. Neurol.* 100: 211–228, 1954.

345. KOJIMAHARA, M. Filaments in rod-shaped tubulated bodies in the endothelia of anterior cerebral arteries in young rats. *Cell Tissue Res.* 182: 505–511, 1977.

346. KORNSTEIN, L. B., L. S. ROBBLEE, AND D. SHEPRO. Thrombin-platelet interactions investigated with the calcium electrode. *Thromb. Res.* 2: 471–483, 1977.

347. KOTHARI, H. V., B. F. MILLER, AND D. KRITCHEVSKY. Aortic cholesterol esterase: characteristics of normal rat and rabbit enzyme. *Biochim. Biophys. Acta* 296: 446–454, 1980.

348. KRAUSZ, M. M., T. UTSUNOMIYA, G. FEUERSTEIN, J. H. WOLFE, D. SHEPRO, AND H. B. HECHTMAN. Prostacyclin reversal of lethal endotoxemia in dogs. *J. Clin. Invest.* 67: 1118–1125, 1981.

349. KROGH, A. *The Anatomy and Physiology of Capillaries.* New Haven, CT: Yale Univ. Press, 1922.

350. KUMAR, P., S. KUMAR, H. B. MARSDEN, P. G. LYNCH, AND E. EARNSHAW. Weibel-Palade bodies in endothelial cells as a marker for angiogenesis in brain tumors. *Cancer Res.* 40: 2010–2019, 1980.

351. KURKINEN, M., T. VARTIO, AND A. VAHERI. Polypeptides of human plasma fibronectin are similar but not identical. *Biochim. Biophys. Acta* 624: 490–498, 1980.

352. KURZROK, R., AND C. C. LIEB. Biochemical studies of human semen. II. The action of semen on the human uterus. *Proc. Soc. Exp. Biol. Med.* 28: 268–272, 1930.

353. KUUSI, T., P. SAARINEN, AND E. A. NIKKILA. Evidence for the role of hepatic endothelial lipase in the metabolism of plasma high-density lipoprotein$_2$ in man. *Atherosclerosis* 36: 589–593, 1980.

354. LACKIE, J. M., AND D. DE BONO. Interactions of neutrophil granulocytes (PMNS) and endothelium *in vitro. Microvasc. Res.* 13: 107–112, 1977.

355. LANGER, R., AND J. FOLKMAN. Polymers for the sustained release of proteins and other macromolecules. *Nature London* 263: 797–800, 1976.

356. LANGHAM, M. Observations on the growth of blood vessels into the cornea. *Br. J. Ophthalmol.* 37: 210–222, 1953.

357. LARSSON, J., AND B. RISBERG. Fibrinolytic activity in human legs in tourniquet ischemia. *Thromb. Res.* 13: 817–825, 1977.

358. LAUG, W. E., Z. A. TÖKES, W. F. BENEDICT, AND N. SORGENTE. Anchorage-independent growth of plasminogen activator production by bovine endothelial cells. *J. Cell Biol.* 84: 281–293, 1980.

359. LAUWERYNS, J. M., J. BAERT, AND W. DE LOECKER. Fine filaments in lymphatic endothelial cells. *J. Cell Biol.* 68: 163–167, 1976.

360. LAUWERYNS, J. M., AND L. BOUSSAUW. Striated filamentous bundles associated with centrioles in pulmonary lymphatic endothelial cells. *J. Ultrastruct. Res.* 42: 25–28, 1973.

361. LAZZARINI, A. A. Studies of the Effect of Lipoid Emulsion on Arterial Intimal Cells in Tissue Culture in Relation to Atherosclerosis. Ithaca, NY: Cornell Univ., 1959. Thesis.

362. LEAK, L. V. Electron microscopic observations on lymphatic capillaries and the structural components of the connective tissue–lymph interface. *Microvasc. Res.* 2: 361–391, 1970.

363. LE BEUX, Y. J., AND J. WILLEMOT. Actin-like filaments in the endothelial cells of adult rat brain capillaries. *Exp. Neurol.* 58: 446–454, 1978.

364. LEFER, A. M., M. L. OLGLETREE, J. B. SMITH, M. J. SILVER, K. C. NICOLAOU, W. E. BARNETTE, AND G. P. GASIC. Prostacyclin: a potentially valuable agent for preserving myocardial tissue in acute myocardial ischemia. *Science* 200: 52–54, 1978.

365. LEFER, A. M., AND E. F. SMITH III. Protective action of prostacyclin in myocardial ischemia and trauma. In: *Prostacyclin*, edited by J. R. Vane and S. Bergström. New York: Raven, 1979, p. 339–348.

366. LEFER, A. M., S. L. SOLLOTT, AND M. J. GALVIN. Beneficial actions of prostacyclin in traumatic shock. *Prostaglandins* 17: 761–767, 1979.

367. LEVIN, E. G., AND D. J. LOSKUTOFF. Serum-mediated suppression of cell-associated plasminogen activator activity in cultured endothelial cells. *Cell* 22: 701–777, 1980.

368. LEWIS, L. J., J. C. HOAK, R. D. MACA, AND G. L. FRY. Replication of human endothelial cells in culture. *Science* 181: 453–454, 1973.

369. LEWIS, W. H. Endothelium in tissue cultures. *Am. J. Anat.* 30: 39–59, 1922.

370. LEWIS, W. H. The outgrowth of endothelium and capillaries in tissue culture. *Johns Hopkins Hosp. Bull.* 48: 242–253, 1931.

371. LOLLAR, P., AND W. G. OWEN. Clearance of thrombin from circulation in rabbits by high-affinity binding sites on endothelium. *J. Clin. Invest.* 66: 1222–1230, 1980.

372. LOSKUTOFF, D. S., AND T. S. EDGINGTON. Synthesis of a fibrinolytic activator and inhibitor by endothelial cells. *Proc. Natl. Acad. Sci. USA* 74: 3903–3907, 1977.

373. LOUDON, M. F., C. C. MICHEL, AND I. F. WHITE. Proceedings: some observations upon the rate of labelling of endothelial vesicles by ferritin in frog mesenteric capillaries (Abstract). *J. Physiol. London* 252: 79P–80P, 1975.

374. LOUDON, M. F., C. C. MICHEL, AND I. F. WHITE. The labelling of vesicles in frog endothelial cells with ferritin. *J. Physiol. London* 296: 97–112, 1979.

375. LUNKENHEIMER, P. P., AND H. J. MERKER. Distribution of alkaline phosphatase in the microcirculatory pathways of the coronary system. *Acta Histochem.* 57: 14–19, 1976.

376. LYNCH, R. S. The cultivation *in vitro* of liver cells from the chick embryo. *Am. J. Anat.* 29: 281–311, 1921.

377. MACA, R. D., G. L. FRY, J. C. HOAK, AND P. T. LOH. The effects of intact platelets on cultured human endothelial cells. *Thromb. Res.* 11: 715–727, 1977.

378. MACARAK, E. J., B. V. HOWARD, AND N. A. KEFALIDES. Properties of calf endothelial cells in culture. *Lab. Invest.* 36: 62–67, 1977.

379. MACARAK, E. J., B. V. HOWARD, E. KIRBY, AND N. A. KEFALIDES. Biosynthesis of membrane collagen by cultured endothelial cells. *Front. Matrix Biol.* 7: 27–36, 1979.

380. MACARAK, E. J., E. KIRBY, T. KIRK, AND N. A. KEFALIDES. Synthesis of cold-insoluble globulin by cultured calf endothelial cells. *Proc. Natl. Acad. Sci. USA* 75: 2621–2625, 1978.

381. MACGREGOR, R. R., H. M. FRIEDMAN, AND E. J. MACARAK. Virus infection of endothelial cells increase granulocyte adherence. *J. Clin. Invest.* 65: 1469–1477, 1980.

382. MACGREGOR, R. R., E. J. MACARAK, AND N. A. KEFALIDES. Comparative adherence of granulocytes to endothelial monolayers and nylon fiber. *J. Clin. Invest.* 61: 697–702, 1978.

383. MACIAG, T., J. CERUNDOLO, S. ILSLEY, P. R. KELLEY, AND R. FORAND. An endothelial cell growth factor from bovine hypothalamus: identification and partial purification. *Proc. Natl. Acad. Sci. USA* 76: 5674–5678, 1979.

384. MACINTYRE, D. E., J. D. PEARSON, AND J. L. GORDON. Localization and stimulation of prostacyclin production in vascular cells. *Nature London* 271: 549–551, 1978.

385. MAGARGAL, W. W., E. S. DICKINSON, AND L. L. SLAKEY. Distribution of membrane marker enzymes in cultured arterial endothelial and smooth muscle cells. *J. Biol. Chem.* 253: 8311–8318, 1978.

386. MAHIEU, P., AND R. J. WINAND. Chemical structure of tubular and glomerular basement membranes of human kidney. *Eur. J. Biochem.* 12: 410–418, 1970.

387. MAJNO, G. Ultrastructure of the vascular membrane. In: *Handbook of Physiology. Circulation*, edited by W. F. Hamilton. Washington, DC: Am. Physiol. Soc., 1965, sect. 2, vol. III, chapt. 64, p. 2293–2375.

388. MAJNO, G. Two endothelial "novelties": endothelial contraction; collagenase digestion of the basement membrane. *Thromb. Diath. Haemorrh. Suppl.* 40: 23–30, 1970.

389. MAJNO, G., AND I. JORIS. Endothelium 1977: a review. In:

Advances in Experimental Medicine and Biology. The Thrombotic Process in Atherogenesis, edited by A. B. Chandler, K. Eurenius, G. C. McMillan, C. B. Nelson, C. J. Schwartz, and S. Wessler. New York: Plenum, 1977, vol. 104, p. 169–225.

390. MAJNO, G., AND I. JORIS. Atherosclerosis and inflammation. In: *Advances in Experimental Medicine and Biology. The Thrombotic Process in Atherogenesis,* edited by A. B. Chandler, K. Eurenius, G. C. McMillan, C. B. Nelson, C. J. Schwartz, and S. Wessler. New York: Plenum, 1977, vol. 104, p. 227–233.

391. MAJNO, G., AND M. LAGATTUTA. Über die durch Chemische Mediatoren Induzierte Gefäss-durchlässigheit: Eine *in vivo*-Untersuchung mit "Russmarkierung". In: *Die Entzündung,* edited by R. Heister and H. F. Hofmann. Munich, West Germany: Burman & Schwarzenberg, 1966, p. 3–6.

392. MAJNO, G., AND M. LEVENTHAL. Pathogenesis of "histamine-type" vascular leakage. *Lancet* 2: 99–100, 1967.

393. MAJNO, G., AND G. E. PALADE. Studies on inflammation. 1. The effect of histamine and serotonin on vascular permeability: an electron microscopic study. *J. Biophys. Biochem. Cytol.* 11: 571–605, 1961.

394. MAJNO, G., S. M. SHEA, AND M. LEVENTHAL. Endothelial contraction induced by histamine-type mediators. An electron microscopic study. *J. Cell Biol.* 42: 647–672, 1969.

395. MANDLE, R., JR., AND A. P. KAPLAN. Hageman factor substrates. Human plasma prekallikrein: mechanism of activation by Hageman factor and participation of Hageman factor-dependent fibrinolysis. *J. Biol. Chem.* 252: 6097–6104, 1977.

396. MANGUM, C., AND D. TOWLE. Physiological adaptation to unstable environments. *Am. Sci.* 65: 67–75, 1977.

397. MANSFIELD, P. B., A. R. WECHEZAK, G. DIBENEDETTO, AND L. R. SAUVAGE. Antithrombogenic functions of the endothelium. In: *Vascular Grafts,* edited by P. N. Sawyer and M. J. Kaplitt. New York: Appleton-Century-Crofts, 1978.

398. MARCUS, A. J., D. B. WEKSLER, AND E. A. JAFFE. Enzymatic conversion of prostaglandin endoperoxide H_2 and arachidonic acid to prostacyclin by cultured human endothelial cells. *J. Biol. Chem.* 253: 7138–7141, 1978.

399. MARKLE, R. A., AND T. M. HOLLIS. Influence of locally altered in vivo shear stress on aortic histamine-forming capacity and aortic albumin uptake. *Blood Vessels* 18: 47–57, 1981.

400. MARTIN, B. M., W. M. BALDWIN, M. A. GIMBRONE, JR., E. R. UNANUE, AND R. S. COTRAN. Macrophage factor(s): stimulation of cell growth *in vitro* and new blood vessels *in vivo* (Abstract). *J. Cell Biol.* 83: 376a, 1979.

401. MARUYAMA, Y. The human endothelial cell in tissue culture. *Z. Zellforsch. Mikrosk. Anat.* 60: 69–79, 1963.

402. MASON, R. G., H. Y. CHUANG, S. F. MOHAMMAD, AND D. E. SHARP. Endothelium: newly discovered functions and methods of study. *J. Bioenerg.* 1: 3–10, 1976.

403. MASON, R. G., S. F. MOHAMMAD, H. I. SABA, H. Y. CHUANG, E. L. LEE, AND J. U. BALIS. Functions of endothelium. *Pathobiol. Annu.* 9: 1–48, 1979.

404. MATSUSAKA, T. Pericytes and endothelial cells of capillaries in the human choroid and retina. *J. Electron Microsc.* 24: 13–18, 1975.

405. MAXIMOW, A. A. Behavior of endothelium of blood vessels in tissue culture (Abstract). *Anat. Rec.* 29: 369a, 1925.

406. MAXIMOW, A. A. Ueber die Entwicklungsfähigkeiten der Blutleukocyten und des Blutgefässendothels bei Entzündung und in Gewebskulturen. *Klin Wochenschr.* 4: 1486–1488, 1925.

407. MAYNARD, J. R., D. E. BURKHOLDER, AND D. J. PIZZUTI. Comparative pharmacologic effects on tissue factor activity in normal cells and an established cell line. *Lab. Invest.* 38: 14–20, 1978.

408. MAYNARD, J. R., C. A. HECKMAN, F. A. PITLICK, AND Y. NEMERSON. Association of tissue factor activity with the surface of cultured cells. *J. Clin. Invest.* 55: 814–824, 1975.

409. MAYNE, R., AND P. M. MAYNE. Characterization of the collagenous components synthesized by cultured endothelial cells derived from guinea pig thoracic aorta (Abstract). *J. Cell Biol.* 79: 147a, 1978.

410. MCAUSLAN, B. R. A new theory of neovascularization based on identification of an angiogenic factor and its effect on cultured endothelial cells. In: *Control Mechanisms in Animal Cells. Specific Growth Factors,* edited by L. J. de Asua, E. Shields, R. Levi-Montalcini, and S. Lacobelli. New York: Raven, 1980, p. 285–292.

411. MCAUSLAN, B. R., G. N. HANNAN, AND W. REILLY. Characterization of an endothelial cell proliferation factor from cultured 3T3 cells. *Exp. Cell Res.* 128: 95 101, 1980.

412. MCAUSLAN, B. R., G. N. HANNAN, W. REILLY, AND F. H. C. STEWART. Variant endothelial cells. Fibronectin as a transducer of signals for migration and neovascularization. *J. Cell. Physiol.* 104: 177–186, 1980.

413. MCAUSLAN, B. R., AND H. HOFFMAN. Endothelium stimulating factor from Walker carcinoma cells. *Exp. Cell Res.* 119: 181–190, 1979.

414. MCAUSLAN, B. R., AND W. REILLY. A variant vascular endothelial cell line with altered growth characteristics. *J. Cell. Physiol.* 101: 419–430, 1979.

415. MCAUSLAN, B. R., AND W. REILLY. Endothelial cell phagokinesis in response to specific metal ions. *Exp. Cell Res.* 130: 147–158, 1980.

416. MCAUSLAN, B. R., W. REILLY, AND G. N. HANNAN. Stimulation of endothelial cell proliferation by precursors of thymidylate. *J. Cell. Physiol.* 100: 87–94, 1979.

417. MCDONALD, R. I., D. SHEPRO, M. ROSENTHAL, AND F. M. BOOYSE. Properties of cultured endothelial cells. *Ser. Haematol.* 6: 469–478, 1973.

418. MCGIFF, J. C., N. A. TERRAGNO, J. C. STRAND, J. B. LEE, A. J. LONIGRO, AND K. K. F. NG. Selective passage of prostaglandins across the lung. *Nature London* 223: 742–744, 1969.

419. MCGILLEN, J., R. PATTERSON, AND J. PHAIR. Adherence of polymorphonuclear leukocytes to nylon: modulation by prostacyclin, corticosteroids and complement activation. *J. Infect. Dis.* 141: 382–388, 1980.

420. MEEZAN, E., K. BRENDEL, AND E. C. CARLSON. Isolation of a purified preparation of metabolically active retinal blood vessels. *Nature London* 251: 65–67, 1974.

421. MELLO, R. Vascular Endothelial Cell Culture: Use in Studies of an Endothelial Cell Mitogen Derived From the Walker 256 Rat Carcinoma. Baltimore, MD: Johns Hopkins Univ. Sch. Med., 1977. Dissertation.

422. MERRILEES, M. J., AND L. SCOTT. Culture of pig and rat aortic endothelial cells. *Atherosclerosis* 38: 19–26, 1981.

423. MILSTONE, L. M., AND J. MCGUIRE. Different polypeptides form the intermediate filaments in bovine hoof and esophageal epithelium and in aortic endothelium. *J. Cell Biol.* 88: 312–316, 1981.

424. MONCADA, S., R. GRYGLEWSKI, S. BUNTING, AND J. R. VANE. An enzyme isolated from arteries transforms PG endoperoxides to an unstable substance that inhibits platelet aggregation. *Nature London* 263: 663–665, 1976.

425. MONCADA, S., A. G. HERMAN, E. A. HIGGS, AND J. R. VANE. Differential formation of prostacyclin (PGX or PGI_2) by layers of the arterial wall. An explanation for the anti-thrombotic properties of vascular endothelium. *Thromb. Res.* 11: 323–344, 1977.

426. MONCADA, S., R. KORBUT, S. BUNTING, AND J. R. VANE. Prostacyclin is a circulating hormone. *Nature London* 273: 767–768, 1978.

427. MONCADA, S., AND J. R. VANE. Pharmacology and endogenous roles of prostaglandin endoperoxides, thromboxane A_2, and prostacyclin. *J. Pharmacol. Exp. Ther.* 30: 293–331, 1979.

428. MOORE, A., E. A. JAFFE, C. G. BECKER, AND R. L. NACHMAN. Myosin in cultured human endothelial cells. *Br. J. Haematol.* 35: 71–79, 1977.

429. MORAES, J. R., AND P. STASTNY. Allo-antibodies to endothelial cell antigens. In: *Histocompatibility Testing.* Copenhagen: Munksgaard, 1975, p. 391–397.

430. MORRISON, A. D., L. BERWICK, L. ORCI, AND A. I. WINEGRAD. Morphology and metabolism of an aortic intima media preparation in which an intact endothelium is preserved. *J. Clin. Invest.* 57: 650–660, 1976.

431. MORRISON, P. R., J. T. EDSALL, AND S. G. MILLER. Preparation and properties of serum and plasma proteins. XVIII. The separation of purified fibrinogen from fraction 1 of human plasma. *J. Am. Chem. Soc.* 70: 3103–3108, 1948.
432. MOSCATELLI, D., E. JAFFE, AND D. B. RIFKIN. Tetradecanoyl phorbol acetate stimulates latent collagenase production by cultured human endothelial cells. *Cell* 20: 343–351, 1980.
433. MOSESSON, M. W., AND R. A. UMFLEET. The cold-insoluble globulin of human plasma. I. Purification, primary characterization, and relationship to fibrinogen and other cold-insoluble fraction components. *J. Biol. Chem.* 245: 5728–5736, 1970.
434. MOSHER, D. F., O. SAKSELA, AND A. VAHERI. Synthesis and secretion of alpha-2-macroglobulin by cultured adherent lung cells: comparison with cell strains derived from other tissues. *J. Clin. Invest.* 60: 1036–1045, 1977.
435. MRŠULJA, B. B., B. J. MRŠULJA, T. FUJIMOTO, I. KLATZO, AND M. SPATZ. Isolation of brain capillaries: a simplified technique. *Brain Res.* 110: 361–365, 1976.
436. MUELLER, S. N., E. M. ROSEN, AND E. M. LEVINE. Cellular senescence in a cloned strain of bovine fetal aortic endothelial cells. *Science* 207: 889–891, 1980.
437. MULLER, J. *Elements of Physiology.* London: Taylor & Walton, 1838.
438. MURATA, K., K. NAKAZAWA, AND A. HAMAI. Distribution of acidic glycosaminoglycans in the intima, media and adventitia of bovine aorta and their anticoagulant properties. *Atherosclerosis* 21: 93–103, 1975.
439. MURATA, K., J. J. QUILLIGAN, AND L. M. MORRISON. Growth of chick aortic endothelial cells: incorporation of tritiated uridine and thymidine. *Experientia* 21: 637–638, 1965.
440. MURPHY, M. E., AND P. C. JOHNSON. Possible contribution of basement membrane to the structural rigidity of blood capillaries. *Microvasc. Res.* 9: 242–245, 1975.
441. MURRAY, M. R., AND A. P. STOUT. Cultural characteristics of a hemangio endothelioma. *Am. J. Pathol.* 20: 277–283, 1944.
442. NACHMAN, R. L., E. A. JAFFE, AND B. FERRIS. Multiple molecular forms of endothelial cell factor VIII related antigen. *Biochim. Biophys. Acta* 667: 361–369, 1981.
443. NACHMAN, R. L., A. J. MARCUS, AND L. B. SAFIER. Platelet thrombosthenin: subcellular localization and function. *J. Clin. Invest.* 46: 1380–1389, 1967.
444. NAM, S. C., W. M. LEE, J. JARMOLYCH, AND W. A. THOMAS. Rapid production of advanced atherosclerosis in swine by a combination of endothelial injury and cholesterol feeding. *Exp. Mol. Pathol.* 18: 369–379, 1973.
445. NEMECEK, G. M. Properties of adenylate cyclase and cyclic nucleotide phosphodiesterase in hamster isolated capillary preparations. *Biochim. Biophys. Acta* 628: 125–135, 1980.
446. NEWKIRK, J. D., AND M. WAITE. Phospholipid hydrolysis by phospholipases A_1 and A_2 in plasma membranes and microsomes of rat liver. *Biochim. Biophys. Acta* 298: 562–576, 1973.
447. NISHIBE, M. Growth of endocardial cells from the chick embryo heart *in vitro*. *Arch. Exp. Zellforsch. Besonders Gewebezuecht.* 7: 333–343, 1928–1929.
448. NISHIOKA, K., AND I. KATAYAMA. Angiogenic activity in culture supernatant of antigen-stimulated lymph node cells. *J. Pathol.* 126: 63–69, 1978.
449. NISHIOKA, K., AND T. J. RYAN. The influence of the epidermis and other tissues on blood vessel growth in the hamster cheek pouch. *J. Invest. Dermatol.* 58: 33–45, 1972.
450. NORDØY, A. Albumin-bound fatty acids, platelets and endothelial cells in thrombogenesis. *Haemostasis* 8: 193–202, 1979.
451. NORDØY, A., B. SVENSSON, D. HAYCRAFT, J. C. HOAK, AND D. WIEBE. The influence of age, sex, and the use of oral contraceptives on the inhibitory effects of endothelial cells and PGI_2 on platelet function. *Scand. J. Haematol.* 21: 177–187, 1978.
452. NORDØY, A., B. SVENSSON, AND J. C. HOAK. The effects of albumin bound fatty acids on the platelet inhibitory function of human endothelial cells. *Eur. J. Clin. Invest.* 9: 5–10, 1979.
453. ODLAND, G. F. The fine structure of cutaneous capillaries. In: *Advances in Biology of Skin*, edited by W. Montagna and R. A. Ellis. New York: Pergamon, 1961, vol. II, p. 57–69.
454. ODY, C., Y. DIETERLE, I. WAND, H. STALDER, AND A. F. JUNOD. PGA_1 and $PGF_{2\alpha}$ metabolism by pig pulmonary endothelium, smooth muscle, and fibroblasts. *J. Appl. Physiol.: Respirat. Environ. Exercise Physiol.* 46: 211–216, 1979.
455. OKUDA, M., AND Y. NEMERSON. Transport of serotonin by blood platelets: a pump-leak system. *Am. J. Physiol.* 220: 283–288, 1971.
456. OLANDER, J., J. MARASA, AND J. FEDER. Stimulation of several types of bovine endothelial cells by growth factor(s) derived from human tumor cells (Abstract). *In Vitro* 16: 209a, 1980.
457. ORLOWSKI, M., G. SESSA, AND J. P. GREEN. γ-Glutamyl transpeptidase in brain capillaries: possible site of a blood-brain barrier for amino acids. *Science* 184: 66–68, 1974.
458. OSTERUD, B. The role of endothelial cells and subendothelial components in the initiation of blood coagulation. *Haemostasis* 8: 324–331, 1979.
459. OWMAN, C., L. EDVINSSON, J. E. HARDEBO, U. GRÖSCHEL-STEWART, K. UNSICKER, AND B. WALLES. Immunohistochemical demonstration of actin and myosin in brain capillaries. *Acta Neurol. Scand. Suppl.* 64: 384–385, 1977.
460. PALADE, G. E. Fine structure of blood capillaries (Abstract). *J. Appl. Phys.* 24: 1424, 1953.
461. PALEN, K., L. THORNEBY, AND H. EMANUELSSON. Effects of serotonin and serotonin antagonists on chick embryogenesis. *Wilhelm Roux Arch.* 187: 89–103, 1979.
462. PALMER, G. C. Beta adrenergic receptors mediate adenylate cyclase responses in rat cerebral capillaries. *Neuropharmacology* 19: 17–23, 1979.
463. PALMER, G. C., AND S. J. PALMER. 5-Guanylylimidodiphosphate actions on adenylate cyclase in homogenates of rat cerebral cortex plus neuronal and capillary fractions. *Life Sci.* 23: 207–216, 1978.
464. PANDOLFI, M. Persistence of fibrinolytic activity in fragments of human veins cultured *in vitro*. *Thromb. Diath. Haemorrh.* 24: 43–49, 1970.
465. PARRY, E. W., AND D. R. ABRAMOVICH. The ultrastructure of human umbilical vessel endothelium from early pregnancy to full term. *J. Anat.* 111: 29–42, 1972.
466. PARSHLEY, M. S., J. M. CERRETA, I. MANDEL, J. A. FIERER, AND G. M. TURRINO. Characteristics of a clone of endothelial cells derived from a line of normal adult rat lung cells. *In Vitro* 15: 709–722, 1979.
467. PAYLING-WRIGHT, H. Endothelial turnover. *Thromb. Haemost.* 40: 79–87, 1971.
468. PEARSON, J. D., E. A. AGER, M. A. TREVETHICK, AND J. L. GORDON. Prostaglandin production by cultured vascular cells. In: *Arachidonic Acid Metabolism in Inflammation and Thrombosis: Proc. European Workshop on Inflammation, 1st, Basel*, edited by K. Brune and M. Baggiolini. Basel: Springer-Verlag, 1979, p. 120–124.
469. PEARSON, J. D., J. S. CARLETON, AND J. L. GORDON. Metabolism of adenine nucleotides by ectoenzymes of vascular endothelial and smooth-muscle cells in culture. *Biochem. J.* 190: 421–429, 1980.
470. PEARSON, J. D., J. S. CARLETON, A. HUTCHINGS, AND J. L. GORDON. Uptake and metabolism of adenosine by pig aortic endothelial and smooth-muscle cells in culture. *Biochem. J.* 170: 265–271, 1978.
471. PEARSON, J. D., AND J. L. GORDON. Vascular endothelial and smooth muscle cells in culture selectively release adenine nucleotides. *Nature London* 281: 384–386, 1979.
472. PEARSON, J. D., H. J. OLVERMAN, AND J. L. GORDON. Transport of 5-hydroxytryptamine by endothelial cells. *Biochem. Soc. Trans.* 5: 1181–1183, 1977.
473. PELIKAN, P., M. A. GIMBRONE, JR., AND R. S. COTRAN. Distribution and movement of anionic cell surface sites in cultured human vascular endothelial cells. *Atherosclerosis* 32: 69–80, 1979.
474. PEPPER, O. H. P. *Medical Etymology.* Philadelphia, PA: Saunders, 1949.
475. PERLMAN, M., J. L. BAUM, AND G. I. KAYE. Fine structure

and collagen synthesis activity of monolayer cultures of rabbit corneal endothelium. *J. Cell Biol.* 63: 306–311, 1974.
476. PFISTER, R. R. The healing of corneal epithelial abrasions in the rabbit: a scanning electron microscopic study. *Invest. Ophthalmol. Vis. Sci.* 14: 648–661, 1975.
477. PHILLIPS, P., P. KUMAR, S. KUMAR, AND M. WAGHE. Isolation and characterization of endothelial cells from the rat and cow brain white matter. *J. Anat.* 129: 261–272, 1979.
478. PHILLIPS, P., J. K. STEWARD, AND S. KUMAR. Tumour angiogenesis factor (TAF) in human and animal tumours. *Int. J. Cancer* 17: 549–558, 1976.
479. PIOMELLI, S., M. STEFANINI, AND R. MELE. Antigenicity of human vascular endothelium: lack of relationship to the pathogenesis of vasculitis. *J. Lab. Clin. Med.* 48: 241–256, 1959.
480. PIOVELLA, F., E. ASCARI, G. M. SITAR, G. D. MALAMANI, G. YATTANEO, E. MAGIULO, AND E. STORTI. Immunofluorescent detection of factor VIII-related antigen in human platelets and megakarocytes. *Haemostasis* 3: 288–299, 1974.
481. PIOVELLA, F., G. NALLI, G. D. MALAMANI, I. MAJOLINO, F. FRASSONI, G. M. SITAR, A. RUGGERI, C. DELL'ORBO, AND E. ASCARI. The ultrastructural localization of factor VIII-antigen in human platelets, megakarocytes and endothelial cells utilizing a ferritin-labelled antibody. *Br. J. Haematol.* 39: 209–213, 1978.
482. PIOVELLA, F., M. M. RICETTI, P. ALMASIO, C. CASTAGNOLA, R. DESENTI, M. CAMPUGHONI, P. GALLOTTI, F. R. FEOLI, AND E. ASCARI. Characterization and synthesis of some factor VIII related properties in cultured human endothelial cells. *Haematologia* 64: 714–725, 1979.
483. PODOR, T. J., AND N. SORGENTE. Elastase activity in the media of cultured endothleial cells (Abstract). *J. Cell Biol.* 87: 64A, 1890.
484. POLLIS, D., E. POLLIS, AND S. KWANG. Protection and reaction of oxidative phosphorylation in mitochondria by a stable free radical prostaglandin polymer (PGB_x). *Proc. Natl. Acad. Sci. USA* 76: 1598–1602, 1979.
485. POLVERINI, P. J., R. S. COTRAN, M. A. GIMBRONE, AND E. R. UNANUE. Activated macrophages induced vascular proliferation. *Nature London* 269: 804–806, 1977.
486. POMERAT, C. M., AND W. C. SLICK. Isolation and growth of endothelial cells in tissue culture. *Nature London* 198: 859–861, 1963.
487. POOLE, J. C. F., S. B. CROMWELL, AND E. P. BENDITT. Behavior of smooth muscle cells and formation of extracellular structures in the reaction of arterial wall cells to injury. *Am. J. Pathol.* 62: 391–414, 1970.
488. POOLE, J. C. F., A. G. SAUNDERS, AND H. W. FLOREY. Regeneration of aortic endothelium. *J. Pathol. Bacteriol.* 75: 133–143, 1958.
489. PORTER, K. R. Motility in cells. In: *Cell Motility*, edited by R. Goldman, T. Pollard, and J. Rosenbaum. New York: Cold Spring Harbor, 1976, vol. 3, p. 1–28. (Cold Spring Harbor Conf. Cell Proliferation.)
490. PORTER, K. R., H. R. BYERS, AND M. H. ELLISMAN. The cytoskeleton. *Neurosci. Res. Program Bull.* 4: 703–722, 1979.
491. PORTMAN, O. W., AND D. R. ILLINGWORTH. Factors determining the concentrations of lysolecithin in plasma and tissues. *Scand. J. Clin. Lab. Invest. Suppl.* 137: 49–55, 1974.
492. PUGATCH, E. M. J., AND A. M. SANDERS. A new technique for making Hautchen preparations of unfixed aortic endothelium. *J. Atheroscler. Res.* 8: 735–738, 1968.
493. PURDY, R. E., D. E. HURLBUT, AND L. A. RAINS. Receptors for 5-hydroxytryptamine in rabbit isolated ear artery and aorta. *Blood Vessels* 18: 16–27, 1981.
494. QUESENBERRY, P. J., AND M. A. GIMBRONE. Vascular endothelium as a regulator of granulopoiesis: production of colony-stimulating activity by cultured human endothelial cells. *Blood* 56: 1060–1067, 1980.
495. RAHI, A., AND N. ASHTON. Contractile proteins in retinal endothelium and other non-muscle tissues of the eye. *Br. J. Ophthalmol.* 62: 627–643, 1978.
496. RAPAPORT, S. I., K. AAS, AND P. A. OWREN. The effect of glass upon the various clotting factors. *J. Clin. Invest.* 34: 9–19, 1955.
497. RATHOFF, O. D., E. W. DAVIE, AND D. L. MALLET. Studies on the action of Hageman factor: evidence that activated Hageman factor in turn activates plasma thromboplastin antecedent. *J. Clin. Invest.* 40: 803–819, 1961.
498. RAVID, M., R. SILMAN-SOCHER, Y. B. SHAUL, AND E. SOHAR. Quantitative electron microscopic study of capillaries in diabetes mellitus. *Beitr. Pathol.* 159: 280–291, 1976.
499. RECKLESS, J. P., D. B. WEINSTEIN, AND D. STEINBERG. Lipoprotein and cholesterol metabolism in rabbit arterial endothelial cells in culture. *Biochim. Biophys. Acta* 529: 475–487, 1978.
500. REDDI, A. H., AND C. B. HUGGINS. Biochemical sequences in the transformation of normal fibroblasts in adolescent rats. *Proc. Natl. Acad. Sci. USA* 69: 1601–1605, 1972.
501. REGHAULT, F., N. ROMQUIN, J. BURE, AND J. DUHAULT. Platelet aggregation inhibition by an endothelial cell factor. *Bibl. Anat.* 16: 226–230, 1977.
502. REIDY, M. A., AND S. M. SCHWARTZ. Endothelial regeneration. III. Time course of intimal changes after small defined injury to rat aortic endothelium. *Lab. Invest.* 44: 301–308, 1981.
503. REIMERS, H. J., M. A. PACKHAM, R. L. KINLOUGH-RATHBONE, AND J. F. MUSTARD. Effect of repeated treatment of rabbit platelets with low concentrations of thrombin on their function, metabolism and survival. *Br. J. Haematol.* 25: 675–681, 1973.
504. RENNKE, H. G., AND M. A. VENKATACHALAM. Structural determinants of glomerular permselectivity. *Federation Proc.* 36: 2619–2626, 1977.
505. REZNIKOFF, C. A., AND R. DE MARS. *In vitro* chemical mutagenesis and viral transformation of a human endothelial cell strain. *Cancer Res.* 41: 1114–1126, 1981.
506. RHODIN, J. A. G. The ultrastructure of mammalian arterioles and precapillary sphincters. *J. Ultrastruct. Res.* 18: 181–223, 1967.
507. RIENHOFF, W. F., JR. Development and growth of the metanephros or permanent kidney in chick embryos (8–10 days' incubation). *Johns Hopkins Hosp. Bull.* 33: 392–406, 1922.
508. ROBERTS, J. T. Localization of plasminogen activator in neonatal lung in the presence of hyaline membrane disease. *J. Clin. Pathol.* 18: 586–593, 1965.
509. ROBINSON-WHITE, A., S. PETERSON, H. B. HECHTMAN, AND D. SHEPRO. Serotonin uptake by isolated adipose capillary endothelium. *J. Pharmacol. Exp. Ther.* 216: 125–128, 1980.
510. ROHDE, H., G. WICK, AND R. TIMPL. Immunochemical characterization of the basement membrane glycoprotein laminin. *Eur. J. Biochem.* 102: 195–201, 1979.
511. RÖHLICH, P., AND I. OLAH. Cross-striated fibrils in the endothelium of the rat myometrial arterioles. *J. Ultrastruct. Res.* 18: 667–676, 1967.
512. ROMANUS, M., AND B. RISBERG. Fibrinolysis in the ischemic hamster cheek pouch. *Thromb. Res.* 12: 421–429, 1978.
513. ROSEN, E. M., S. N. MUELLER, J. P. NOVERAL, AND E. M. LEVINE. Aging of endothelium in culture: decrease in angiotensin stimulating converting enzyme activity. *Cell Biol. Int. Rep.* 6: 379–384, 1981.
514. ROSEN, E. M., S. N. MUELLER, J. P. NOVERAL, AND E. M. LEVINE. Proliferative characteristics of clonal endothelial cell strains. *J. Cell. Physiol.* 107: 123–137, 1981.
515. ROSEN, L. A., T. M. HOLLIS, AND M. G. SHARMA. Alterations in bovine endothelial histidine decarboxylase activity following exposure to shearing stress. *Exp. Mol. Pathol.* 20: 329–343, 1974.
516. ROSS, R., AND J. A. GLOMSET. The pathogenesis of atherosclerosis. *N. Engl. J. Med.* 295: 369–376, 1976.
517. ROSS, R., AND L. HARKER. Hyperlipidemia and atherosclerosis. *Science* 193: 1044–1049, 1976.
518. ROSS, R., AND A. VOGEL. The platelet-derived growth factor. *Cell* 14: 203–210, 1978.
519. RUBIN, B. T. A theoretical model of the pinocytotic vesicular transport process in endothelial cells. *J. Theor. Biol.* 64: 619–

647, 1977.

520. RYAN, J. W., A. R. DAY, D. R. SCHULTZ, U. S. RYAN, A. CHUNG, D. I. MARLBOROUGH, AND F. E. DORER. Localization of angiotensin converting enzyme (kininase II). I. Preparation of antibody-hemeoctapeptide conjugates. *Tissue Cell* 8: 111–124, 1976.
521. RYAN, J. W., R. S. NIEMEYER, AND U. S. RYAN. Metabolism of prostaglandin $F_{1\alpha}$ in the pulmonary circulation. *Prostaglandins* 10: 101–108, 1975.
522. RYAN, J. W., J. ROBLERO, AND J. M. STEWART. Inactivation of bradykinin in the pulmonary circulation. *Biochem. J.* 110: 795–797, 1968.
523. RYAN, J. W, AND U. S. RYAN. Pulmonary endothelial cells. *Federation Proc.* 36: 2683–2691, 1977.
524. RYAN, J. W., AND U. SMITH. Metabolism of adenosine 5-monophosphate during circulation through the lungs. *Trans. Assoc. Am. Physicians* 84: 297–306, 1971.
525. RYAN, U. S., E. CLEMENTS, D. HABLISTON, AND J. W. RYAN. Isolation and culture of pulmonary artery endothelial cells. *Tissue Cell* 10: 535–554, 1978.
526. RYAN, U. S., M. MORTARA, AND C. WHITAKER. Methods for microcarrier culture of bovine pulmonary artery endothelial cells avoiding the use of enzymes. *Tissue Cell* 12: 619–635, 1981.
527. RYAN, U. S., J. W. RYAN, C. WHITAKER, AND A. CHIU. Localization of angiotensin converting enzyme (kininase II). II. Immunocytochemistry and immunofluorescence. *Tissue Cell* 8: 125–145, 1976.
528. RYAN, U. S., D. R. SCHULTZ, P. J. DEL VECCHIO, AND J. W. RYAN. Endothelial cells of bovine pulmonary artery lack receptors for C3a and for the Fc portion of immunoglobulin G. *Science* 208: 748–750, 1980.
529. SABA, S. R., AND R. G. MASON. Effects of platelets and certain platelet components on growth of cultured human endothelial cells. *Thromb. Res.* 7: 807–812, 1975.
530. SACKS, T., C. F. MOLDOW, AND P. R. CRADDOCK. Oxygen radicals mediate endothelial cell damage by complement/stimulated granulocytes. *J. Clin. Invest.* 61: 1161–1167, 1978.
531. SACKS, T., C. F. MOLDOW, P. R. CRADDOCK, T. K. BOWERS, AND H. S. JACOB. Endothelial damage provoked by toxic oxygen radicals released from complement-triggered granulocytes. *Prog. Clin. Biol. Res.* 21: 719–726, 1978.
532. SAGE, H., E. CROUCH, AND P. BORNSTEIN. Collagen synthesis by bovine aortic endothelial cells in culture. *Biochemistry* 18: 5433–5442, 1979.
533. SAGE, H., P. PRITZL, AND P. BORNSTEIN. A unique, pepsin-sensitive collagen synthesized by aortic endothelial cells in culture. *Biochemistry* 19: 5747–5755, 1980.
534. SAGE, H., P. PRITZL, AND P. BORNSTEIN. Characterization of cell matrix associated collagens synthesized by aortic endothelial cells in culture. *Biochemistry* 20: 436–442, 1981.
535. SALDEEN, T. The disappearance of fibrin from the pulmonary vessels in experimental fat embolism. *Thromb. Diath. Haemorrh.* 22: 360–366, 1969.
536. SAMORAJSKI, T., AND J. MCCLOUD. Alkaline phosphomonoesterase and blood-brain permeability. *Lab. Invest.* 10: 492–501, 1961.
537. SAMPSON, P., M. S. PARSHLEY, I. MANDL, AND G. M. TURINO. Glycosaminoglycans produced in tissue culture by rat lung cells. *Connect. Tissue Res.* 4: 41–49, 1975.
538. SAMUELSSON, B., AND R. PAOLETTI (editors). *Advances in Prostaglandin and Thromboxane Research.* New York: Raven, 1980, vol. 6–8.
539. SANDERS, A. G. Microcirculation in grafts of normal and malignant tissue (Abstract). *J. Anat.* 97: 631a, 1963.
540. SANDISON, J. C. A new method for the microscopic study of living growing tissues by the introduction of a transparent chamber in the rabbit's ear. *Anat. Rec.* 28: 281–287, 1924.
541. SANDISON, J. C. Observation on growth of blood vessels as seen in transparent chamber introduced into rabbit's ear. *Am. J. Anat.* 41: 475–496, 1928.
542. SANTOLAYA, R. C., AND F. BERTINI. Fine structure of endothelial cells of vertebrates. Distribution of dense granules. *Z. Anat. Entwicklungsgesch.* 131: 148–155, 1970.
543. SATO, G., L. ZAROFT, AND S. L. MILLS. Tissue culture populations and their relation to the tissue of origin. *Proc. Natl. Acad. Sci. USA* 46: 963–972, 1960.
544. SCHLECTER, J. G., L. N. KATZ, AND J. MEYER. The occurrence of atheromarous lesions after cauterization of the aorta followed by cholesterol administration. *Am. J. Med. Sci.* 218: 603–609, 1949.
545. SCHMID-SCHOENBEIN, G. W., Y. C. FUNG, AND B. W. ZWEIFACH. Vascular endothelium-leukocyte interaction: sticking shear force in venules. *Circ. Res.* 36: 173–184, 1975.
546. SCHOEFL, G. I. Studies on inflammation. III. Growing capillaries: their structure and permeability. *Virchows Arch. Pathol. Anat.* 337: 97–141, 1963.
547. SCHOPPER, W. Netzexplanation. *Verh. Dtsch. Ges. Pathol.* 24: 25–28, 1929.
548. SCHOR, A. M., S. KUMAR, AND P. J. PHILLIPS. Quantitation of extracts containing tumour angiogenesis factor (TAF) by radioimmunometric and radioimmunoassays. *Int. J. Cancer* 25: 773–779, 1980.
548a. SCHOR, A. M., S. L. SCHOR, AND S. KUMAR. Importance of a collagen substratum for stimulation of capillary endothelial cell proliferation by tumor angiogenesis factor. *Int. J. Cancer* 24: 225–234, 1979.
549. SCHOR, A. M., S. L. SCHOR, J. B. WEISS, R. A. BROWN, S. KUMAR, AND P. PHILLIPS. Stimulation by a low-molecular-weight angiogenic factor of capillary endothelial cells in culture. *Br. J. Cancer* 41: 790–799, 1980.
550. SCHWARTZ, S. Selection and characterization of bovine aortic endothelial cells. *In Vitro* 14: 966–980, 1978.
551. SCHWARTZ, S. M., AND E. P. BENDITT. Aortic endothelial cell replication. I. Effects of age and hypertension in the rat. *Circ. Res.* 41: 248–255, 1977.
552. SCHWARTZ, S. M., C. M. GAGDUSEK, M. A. REIDY, S. C. SELDEN, AND C. C. HAUDENSCHILD. Maintenance of integrity in aortic endothelium. *Federation Proc.* 39: 2618–2625, 1980.
553. SCHWARTZ, S. M., C. C. HAUDENSCHILD, AND E. M. EDDY. Endothelial regeneration. I. Quantitative analysis of initial stages of endothelial regeneration in rat aortic intima. *Lab. Invest.* 38: 568–580, 1978.
554. SCOW, R. O., E. J. BLANCHETTE-MACKIE, AND L. C. SMITH. Role of lipoprotein lipase and capillary endothelium in the clearance of chylomicrons from blood: a model for lipid transport by lateral diffusion in cell membranes. *Expos. Annu. Biochim. Med.* 33: 143–164, 1977.
555. SCRIBA, K. Explantationsstudien über das Gefässwachstum bei 9 Tage alten Hühnerembryonen. *Arch. Exp. Zellforsch. Besonders Gewebezuecht.* 17: 68–77, 1935.
556. SEALEY, J. E., M. SILVERBERG, M. LARAUGH, S. A. ATLAS, AND A. P. KAPLAN. Activation of plasma prorenin by enzymes of the coagulation and fibrinolytic systems (Abstract). *Federation Proc.* 38: 677, 1979.
557. SEDLAK, B. J., F. M. BOOYSE, S. BELL, AND M. E. RAFELSON. Comparison of two types of endothelial cells in long term culture. *Thromb. Haemost.* 35: 167–177, 1976.
558. SELDEN, S. C., AND S. M. SCHWARTZ. Cytochalasin B inhibition of endothelial proliferation at wound edges *in vitro*. *J. Cell Biol.* 81: 348–354, 1979.
559. SENGEL, A., AND P. STOEBNER. Golgi origin of tubular inclusions in endothelial cells. *J. Cell Biol.* 44: 223–226, 1970.
560. SESSA, G., M. ORLOWSKI, AND J. P. GREEN. Isolation from bovine brain of a fraction containing capillaries and a fraction containing membrane fragments of the choroid plexus. *J. Neurobiol.* 7: 51–61, 1976.
561. SHAKLAI, M., AND M. TAVASSOLI. Endothelial cell membrane: differences in the density of intramembranous particles between tissue and blood fronts revealed by freeze-fracture. *Am. J. Anat.* 151: 139–158, 1978.
562. SHEBUSKI, R. J., AND J. W. AIKEN. Angiotensin II–induced renal prostacyclin release suppresses platelet aggregation in the anesthetized dog. In: *Advances in Prostaglandin and*

Thromboxane Research. New York: Raven, 1980, vol. 7, p. 1149–1152.
563. SHEN, S. C., P. GREENFIELD, AND E. J. BOELL. The distribution of cholinesterase in the frog brain. *J. Comp. Neurol.* 102: 717–743, 1955.
564. SHEPRO, D. Endothelial cells are more than a barrier. *Bibl. Anat.* 16: 384–386, 1977.
565. SHEPRO, D. Non-respiratory, metabolic functions of pulmonary endothelial cells. In: *Acute Respiratory Failure. Etiology and Treatment*, edited by H. B. Hechtman. Boca Raton, FL: CRC, 1979, p. 34–74.
566. SHEPRO, D. The microvascular system. In: *Handbook of Inflammation*, edited by G. Weissmann. New York: Elsevier, 1980, p. 27–52.
567. SHEPRO, D., J. C. BATBOUTA, L. S. ROBBLEE, M. P. CARSON, AND F. A. BELAMARICH. Serotonin transport by cultured bovine aortic endothelium. *Circ. Res.* 36: 799–806, 1975.
568. SHEPRO, D., M. P. CARSON, AND H. B. HECHTMAN. Modes of serotonin transport by intimal and capillary endothelial cells (Abstract). *Microvasc. Res.* 21: 254, 1981.
569. SHEPRO, D., AND P. A. D'AMORE. Endothelial cell metabolism. *Adv. Microcirc.* 9: 161–195, 1980.
570. SHEPRO, D., S. LI, AND H. B. HECHTMAN. Plasminogen activator activity of isolated cardiac muscle microvessel endothelial cells. *Thromb. Res.* 18: 600–616, 1980.
571. SHEPRO, D., A. ROBINSON, AND H. B. HECHTMAN. Serotonin clearance by capillaries isolated from epididymal fat. *Bibl. Anat.* 18: 108–110, 1979.
572. SHEPRO, D., M. ROSENTHAL, J. BATBOUTA, L. S. ROBBLEE, AND F. A. BELAMARICH. The cultivation of aorta endothelium (Abstract). *Anat. Rec.* 178: 523, 1973.
573. SHEPRO, D., R. SCHLEEF, AND H. B. HECHTMAN. Plasminogen activator activity by cultured bovine aortic endothelial cells. *Life. Sci.* 26: 415–422, 1980.
574. SHEPRO, D., H. E. SWEETMAN, AND H. B. HECHTMAN. Experimental thrombocytopenia and capillary ultrastructure. *Blood* 56: 937–940, 1980.
575. SHERER, G. K., T. P. FITZHARRIS, W. P. FAULK, AND E. C. LEROY. Cultivation of microvascular endothelial cells from human preputial skin. *In Vitro* 16: 675–684, 1980.
576. SHIBATA, N., H. AKAGAMI, K. TANAKA, Y. OKAMURA, AND M. OIYAMA. A consideration of a mechanism of augmentation of peripheral vascular resistance in hypertension. Presence of F-actin filament in renal arterioles and electrolytes contents in arterial wall in hypertensive rat (Goldblatt type). *Jpn. Circ. J.* 37: 1285–1291, 1973.
577. SHIBUYA, T. On the pure cultivation of endothelial cells from aorta and their differentiation. *Kitasato Arch. Exp. Med.* 8: 68–88, 1971.
578. SHIMAMOTO, T. Contracting and swallowing activity of arterial endothelial cells induced by cholesterol or epinephrine or angiotensin II or bradykinin. An electron microscopic study. *J. Jpn. Atheroscl. Soc.* 1: 29–44, 1973.
579. SHOLLEY, M. M., M. A. GIMBRONE, JR., AND R. S. COTRAN. Cellular migration and replication in endothelial regeneration: a study using irradiated endothelial cultures. *Lab. Invest.* 36: 18–25, 1977.
580. SHUTE, C. C. D., AND P. R. LEWIS. Cholinesterase-containing systems of the brain of the rat. *Nature London* 199: 1160–1164, 1963.
581. SIAKOTOS, A. N., G. ROUSER, AND S. FLEISCHER. Isolation of highly purified human and bovine brain endothelial cells and nuclei and their phospholipid composition. *Lipids* 4: 234–239, 1969.
582. SILBERBERG, M. Endothel in der Gewebskultur. *Arch. Exp. Zellforsch. Besonders Gewebzuecht.* 9: 36–53, 1929.
583. SILKWORTH, J. B., B. MCLEAN, AND W. E. STEBBENS. The effect of hypercholesterolemia on aortic endothelium studied en face. *Atherosclerosis* 22: 335–348, 1975.
584. SIMIONESCU, M., AND N. SIMIONESCU. Isolation and characterization of endothelial cells from the heart microvasculature. *Microvasc. Res.* 16: 426–452, 1978.
585. SIMIONESCU, M., N. SIMIONESCU, AND G. E. PALADE. Segmental differentiations of cell junctions in the vascular endothelium. Arteries and veins. *J. Cell Biol.* 68: 705–723, 1976.
586. SIMIONESCU, N., M. SIMIONESCU, AND G. E. PALADE. Structural basis of permeability in sequential segments of the microvasculature. I. Bipolar microvascular fields in the diaphragm. *Microvasc. Res.* 15: 1–16, 1978.
587. SIPERSTEIN, M. D., A. R. COLWELL, AND K. MEYER (editors). *Small Blood Vessel Involvement in Diabetes Mellitus*. Washington, DC: Am. Inst. Biol. Sci., 1964, 308 p.
588. SKEGGS, L. T., J. R. KAHN, AND N. P. SHUMWAY. The preparation and function of the hypertensin-converting enzyme. *J. Exp. Med.* 103: 295–299, 1956.
589. SLATER, D. N., AND J. M. SLOAN. The porcine endothelial cell in culture. *Atherosclerosis* 21: 259–272, 1975.
590. SMALL, R., E. MACARAK, AND A. B. FISHER. Production of 5-hydroxyindolacetic acid from serotonin by cultured endothelial cells. *J. Cell. Physiol.* 90: 225–232, 1976.
591. SMITH, U., AND J. W. RYAN. An electron microscopic study of the vascular endothelium as a site for bradykinin and adenosine-5-triphosphate inactivation in rat lung. *Adv. Exp. Med. Biol.* 8: 249–261, 1970.
592. SMITH, U., AND J. W. RYAN. Pulmonary endothelial cells and the metabolism of adenine nucleotides. *Adv. Exp. Med. Biol.* 21: 267–276, 1972.
593. SMITH, U., AND J. W. RYAN. Substructural features of pulmonary endothelial caveolae. *Tissue Cell* 4: 49–54, 1972.
594. SMITH, U., AND J. W. RYAN. Electron microscopy of endothelial and epithelial components of the lungs: correlations of structure and function. *Federation Proc.* 32: 1957–1966, 1973.
595. SONI, S. L., A. I. GOTLIEB, AND V. I. KALNINS. In vitro spreading of porcine aortic endothelial and smooth muscle cells. In: *Scanning Electron Microscopy*. Chicago, IL: SEM, 1980, vol. III, p. 263–270.
596. SPAGNUOLO, P. J., J. J. ELLNER, A. HASSID, AND M. J. DUNN. Thromboxane A_2 mediates augmented polymorphonuclear leukocyte adhesiveness. *J. Clin. Invest.* 66: 406–414, 1980.
597. SPANNHAKE, E. W., J. L. LEVIN, B. T. MELLION, C. A. GRUETTER, A. L. HYMAN, AND P. J. KADOWITZ. Reversal of 5HT-induced bronchoconstriction by PGI_2: distribution of central and peripheral actions. *J. Appl. Physiol.: Respirat. Environ. Exercise Physiol.* 49: 521–527, 1980.
598. SPECTOR, A. A., J. C. HOAK, G. L. FRY, G. M. DENNING, L. L. STOLL, AND J. B. SMITH. Effect of fatty acid modification on prostacyclin production by cultured human endothelial cells. *J. Clin. Invest.* 65: 1003–1012, 1980.
599. STEIN, O., T. CHAJEK, AND Y. STEIN. Ultrastructural localization of concanavalin A in the perfused rat heart. *Lab. Invest.* 35: 103–110, 1976.
600. STEIN, Y., AND O. STEIN. Interactions of serum lipoproteins with human endothelial cells in culture. *Expo. Annu. Biochim. Med.* 33: 131–135, 1977.
601. STEMERMAN, M. B. Platelets and the vessel wall. In: *Platelets, Drugs, and Thrombosis*, edited by J. Hirsh. Basel: Karger, 1975, p. 54–69.
602. STEMERMAN, M. B. Vascular intimal components: precursors of thrombosis. In: *Progress in Hemostasis and Thrombosis*, edited by T. H. Spaet. New York: Grune & Stratton, 1975, vol. 2, p. 1047.
603. STEMERMAN, M. B., F. A. PITLICK, AND H. M. DEMBITZER. Electron microscopic immunohistochemical identification of endothelial cells in the rabbit. *Circ. Res.* 38: 146–156, 1976.
604. STERRY, W., G. K. STEIGLEDER, AND G. NEUMANN. Characterization of activity of alkaline phosphatase (AAP) in capillary endothelium of normal and psoriatic skin. *Arch. Dermatol. Res.* 267: 131–139, 1980.
605. STEWART, P. A. Histochemical absence of γ-glutamyl transpeptidase in chick brain capillary endothelium. *Exp. Neurol.* 67: 442–446, 1980.
606. STOKER, M., AND D. PIGGOT. Shaking 3T3 cells: further studies on diffusion boundary effects. *Cell* 3: 207–215, 1974.
607. STRUM, J. M., AND A. JUNOD. Radioautographic demonstration of 5-hydroxytryptamine-^{3}H uptake by pulmonary endo-

thelial cells. *J. Cell Biol.* 54: 456–467, 1972.

608. SUDDITH, R. L., P. J. KELLY, H. T. HUTCHINSON, E. A. MURRAY, AND B. HABER. *In vitro* demonstration of an endothelial proliferative factor produced by neural cell lines. *Science* 190: 682–684, 1975.
609. SUN, N. C. J., D. L. CONN, A. L. SCHROETER, AND F. J. KAZMIER. Skin fibrinolytic activity in cutaneous and systemic vasculitis (Abstract). *Mayo Clin. Proc.* 51: 216, 1976.
610. SUZUKI, K., S. OOKAWARA, AND G. OONEDA. Increased permeability of the arteries in hypertensive rats: an electron microscopic study. *Exp. Mol. Pathol.* 15: 198–208, 1971.
611. SWEETMAN, H. E., D. SHEPRO, AND H. B. HECHTMAN. Inhibition of thrombocytopenic petechiae by exogenous serotonin administration. *Haemostasis* 10: 65–78, 1981.
612. SZCZEKLIK, A., R. J. GRYGLEWSKI, E. NIZANKOWSKA, R. NIZANKOWSKI, AND J. MUSIAL. Pulmonary and anti-platelet effects of intravenous and inhaled prostacyclin in man. *Prostaglandins* 16: 651–660, 1978.
613. SZULMAN, A. E. The histological distribution of blood group substances A and B in man. *J. Exp. Med.* 111: 785–801, 1960.
614. SZULMAN, A. E. The histological distribution of blood group substances in man as disclosed by immunofluorescence. II. The H antigen and its relation to A and B antigens. *J. Exp. Med.* 115: 977–997, 1962.
615. SZULMAN, A. E. The histological distribution of the blood group substances in man as disclosed by immunofluorescence. III. A, B, and H antigens in embryos and fetuses from 18 mm in length. *J. Exp. Med.* 119: 503–507, 1964.
616. TAGGART, H., AND R. W. STOUT. Control of DNA synthesis in cultured vascular endothelial cells and smooth muscle cells—response to serum, platelet-deficient serum, lipid-free serum, insulin and oestrogens. *Atherosclerosis* 37: 549–577, 1980.
617. TANNOCK, I. F., AND S. HAYASHI. The proliferation of capillary endothelial cells. *Cancer Res.* 32: 77–82, 1972.
618. TATESON, J., S. MONCADA, AND J. R. VANE. Effects of prostaglandin (PGX) on cAMP in human platelets. *Prostaglandins* 13: 389–399, 1977.
619. TAUBER, J. P., J. CHENG, AND D. GOSPODAROWICZ. Effect of high and low density lipoproteins on proliferation of cultured bovine vascular endothelial cells. *J. Clin. Invest.* 66: 696–708, 1980.
620. TAYLOR, E. W. The cell motility conference: a summary. In: *Cell Motility*, edited by R. Goldman, T. Pollard, and J. Rosenbaum. New York: Cold Spring Harbor, 1976, vol. 3, p. 1367–1373. (Cold Spring Harbor Conf. Cell Proliferation.)
621. TERRAGNO, D. A., K. CROWSHAW, N. A. TERRAGNO, AND J. C. MCGIFF. Prostaglandin synthesis by bovine mesenteric arteries and veins. *Circ. Res.* 36, Suppl. 1: 176–180, 1975.
622. TERZAKIS, J. A. The ultrastructure of the normal human first trimester placenta. *J. Ultrastruct. Res.* 9: 268–284, 1963.
623. THILO, D. G. S., S. MÜLLER-KÜSEL, D. HEINRICH, I. KÄUFER, AND E. WEISS. Isolation of human venous endothelial cells by different proteases. *Artery* 8: 259–266, 1980.
624. THOMAS, D. P., AND J. R. VANE. 5-Hydroxytryptamine in the circulation of the dog. *Nature London* 215: 335–338, 1967.
625. THORGEIRSSON, G., AND A. L. ROBERTSON, JR. Platelet factors and the human vascular wall: variations in growth response between endothelial and medial smooth muscle cells. *Atherosclerosis* 30: 67–78, 1978.
626. THORGEIRSSON, G., AND A. L. ROBERTSON, JR. Platelet factors and the human vascular wall. Part 2. Such factors are not required for endothelial cell proliferation and migration. *Atherosclerosis* 31: 231–238, 1978.
627. THORGEIRSSON, G., A. L. ROBERTSON, AND D. H. COWAN. Migration of human vascular endothelial and smooth muscle cells. *Lab. Invest.* 41: 51–62, 1979.
628. TILNEY, L. G. Actin filament in the acrosomal reaction of Limulus sperm. Motion generated by alteration in the packing of the filaments. *J. Cell Biol.* 64: 289–310, 1975.
629. TILTON, R. G., C. KILO, AND J. R. WILLIAMSON. Pericyte-endothelial relationships in cardiac and skeletal muscle capillaries. *Microvasc. Res.* 18: 325–335, 1979.
630. TILTON, R. G., C. KILO, J. R. WILLIAMSON, AND D. MURCH. Differences in pericyte contractile function in rat cardiac and skeletal muscle. *Microvasc. Res.* 18: 336–352, 1979.
631. TIMPL, R., H. ROHDE, P. G. ROBEY, S. I. RENNARD, J.-M. FOIDART, AND G. R. MARTIN. Laminin—a glycoprotein from basement membranes. *J. Biol. Chem.* 254: 9933–9937, 1979.
632. TODD, A. S. The histological localization of fibrinolysin activator. *J. Pathol.* 78: 281–283, 1959.
633. TODD, A. S. Endothelium and fibrinolysis. *Bibl. Anat.* 12: 98–105, 1973.
634. TOFF, B., AND R. V. WILSON. Blood vessel tumor genesis by 1,2-dimethyl-hydrazine dihydrachloride: gross, light and electron microscopic descriptions. *Am. J. Pathol.* 64: 585–600, 1971.
635. TÖKÉS, Z. A., AND N. SORGENTE. Cell surface associated and released proteolytic activities of bovine aorta endothelial cells. *Biochim. Biophys. Res. Commun.* 73: 965–971, 1976.
636. TOMASI, V., C. MERINGOLO, G. BARTOLINI, AND M. ORLANDI. Biosynthesis of prostacyclin in rat liver endothelial cells and its control by prostaglandin E_2. *Nature London* 273: 670–671, 1978.
637. TORACK, R. M., AND P. BARRNETT. The fine structural localization of nucleotide phosphatase activity in the blood-brain barrier. *J. Neuropathol. Exp. Neurol.* 23: 46–59, 1964.
638. TÖRÖ, E. Untersuchen über die Potenz der Endothelzellen bei der Gefässbildung in der Gewebekultur. *Arch. Exp. Zellforsch. Besonders Gewebezuecht.* 20: 156–171, 1937.
639. TREVETHICK, M. A., J. D. PEARSON, H. J. OLVERMAN, AND J. L. GORDON. Metabolism of phenethylamine and 5-hydroxytryptamine by cultured vascular cells. *Biochem. Soc. Trans.* 7: 170–171, 1979.
640. TRIPATHI, B. Tissue culture of retinal endothelium. *Biorheology* 10: 493–494, 1973.
641. TSENG, S. C. G., N. SAVION, R. STERN, AND D. GOSPODAROWICZ. Fibroblast growth factor modulates synthesis of collagen in cultured vascular endothelial cells. *Eur. J. Biochem.* 112: 355–360, 1982.
642. TSUKAMOTO, K., AND Y. SUGINO. Tumor angiogenesis in clonal cells transformed by bovine adenovirus type 3. *Cancer Res.* 39: 1305–1309, 1979.
643. TUDDENHAM, E. G. D., J. LAZARCHICK, AND L. W. HOYER. Synthesis and release of factor VIII by cultured human endothelial cells. *Br. J. Haematol.* 47: 617–626, 1981.
644. TUDDENHAM, E. G., A. M. SHEARN, I. R. PEAKE, J. C. GIDDINGS, AND A. L. BLOOM. Tissue localization and synthesis of factor-VIII-related antigen in the human foetus. *Br. J. Haematol.* 26: 669–677, 1974.
645. TULLOSS, J. H., AND F. M. BOOYSE. Effect of various agents and physical damage on giant cell formation in bovine aortic endothelial cell cultures. *Microvasc. Res.* 16: 51–58, 1978.
646. TURITTO, V. T., AND H. R. BAUMGARTNER. Platelet interaction with subendothelium in flowing rabbit blood: effect of blood shear rate. *Microvasc. Res.* 17: 38–54, 1979.
647. TUVEMO, T., K. STRANDBERG, M. HAMBERG, AND B. SAMUELSSON. Formation and action of prostaglandin endoperoxides in the isolated human umbilical artery. *Acta Physiol. Scand.* 96: 145–156, 1976.
648. TUVEMO, T., AND L. WIDE. Prostaglandin release from the human umbilical artery *in vitro*. *Prostaglandins* 4: 689–694, 1973.
649. UEHARA, Y., G. R. CAMPBELL, AND G. BURNSTOCK. Cytoplasmic filaments in developing and adult vertebrate smooth muscle. *J. Cell Biol.* 50: 484–497, 1971.
650. UTSUNOMIYA, T., M. M. KRAUSZ, C. R. VALERI, L. LEVINE, D. SHEPRO, AND H. B. HECHTMAN. Treatment of pulmonary embolism with positive end-expiratory pressure and prostaglandin E_1. *Surg. Gyn. Obstet.* 153: 161–168, 1981.
651. UTSUNOMIYA, T., M. M. KRAUSZ, C. R. VALERI, D. SHEPRO, AND H. B. HECHTMAN. Treatment of pulmonary embolism with prostacyclin. *Surgery* 88: 25–30, 1980.
652. VANE, J. R. The release and assay of hormones in the circu-

lation. In: *Scientific Basis of Medicine*. London: Athlone, 1968, p. 336–358.

653. Van Horn, D. L., and S. A. Johnson. The escape of carbon from intact capillaries in experimental thrombocytopenia. *J. Lab. Clin. Med.* 71: 301–311, 1968.
654. Van Houten, M., and B. I. Posner. Insulin binds to brain blood vessels *in vivo*. *Nature London* 282: 623–625, 1979.
655. Várkinyi, T., and F. Joó. The effect of nickel chloride on the permeability of the blood-brain barrier. *Experientia* 24: 452–453, 1968.
656. Venter, J. C., J. E. Dixon, P. R. Maroko, and N. O. Kaplan. Biologically active catecholamines covalently bound to glass beads. *Proc. Natl. Acad. Sci. USA* 69: 1141–1145, 1972.
657. Vetto, R. M., and D. R. Burger. Endothelial cell stimulation of allogenic lymphocytes. *Transplantation* 14: 652–654, 1972.
658. Vlodavsky, I., P. E. Fielding, L. K. Johnson, and D. Gospodarowicz. Inhibition of low density lipoprotein uptake in confluent endothelial cell monolayers correlates with a restricted surface receptor redistribution. *J. Cell. Physiol.* 100: 481–496, 1979.
659. Vlodavsky, I., L. K. Johnson, and D. Gospodarowicz. Appearance in confluent vascular endothelial cell monolayers of a specific cell surface protein (CSP-60) not detected in actively growing endothelial cells or in cell types growing in multiple layers. *Proc. Natl. Acad. Sci. USA* 76: 2306–2310, 1979.
660. Vlodavsky, I., L. K. Johnson, G. Greenburg, and D. Gospodarowicz. Vascular endothelial cells maintained in the absence of fibroblast growing factor undergo structural and functional alterations that are incompatible with their *in vivo* differentiated properties. *J. Cell Biol.* 83: 468–486, 1979.
661. Von Euler, U. S. Über die spezifische blutdrucksenkende Substanz des meschlichen Prostata-und Samenblazensekretes. *Klin. Wochenschr.* 14: 1182–1185, 1935.
662. Vracko, R. Basal lamina scaffold—anatomy and significance for maintenance of orderly tissue structure. *Am. J. Pathol.* 77: 314–346, 1974.
663. Wagner, R. C., P. Kreiner, R. J. Barrnett, and M. W. Bitensky. Biochemical characterization and cytochemical localization of a catecholamine-sensitive adenylate cyclase in isolated capillary endothelium. *Proc. Natl. Acad. Sci. USA* 69: 3175–3179, 1972.
664. Wagner, R. C., and M. A. Matthews. Capillary endothelium *in vitro* (Abstract). *J. Cell Biol.* 63: 361a, 1974.
665. Wagner, R. C., and M. L. Matthews. The isolation and culture of capillary endothelium from epididymal fat. *Microvasc. Res.* 10: 286–297, 1975.
666. Wall, R. T., L. A. Harker, and G. E. Striker. Human endothelial cell migration stimulation by a released platelet factor. *Lab. Invest.* 39: 523–529, 1978.
667. Wallow, I. H., and B. Burnside. Actin filaments in retinal pericytes and endothelial cells. *Invest. Ophthalmol. Vis. Sci.* 19: 1433–1441, 1980.
668. Ward, P. E., C. D. Gedney, R. M. Dowben, and E. G. Erdös. Isolation of membrane-bound renal kallikrein and kininase. *Biochem. J.* 151: 755–758, 1975.
669. Warren, B. A., and S. Khan. The ultrastructure of the lysis of fibrin by endothelium *in vitro*. *Br. J. Exp. Pathol.* 55: 138–148, 1974.
670. Warren, B. A., and P. Shubik. The growth of the blood supply to melanoma transplants in the hamster cheek pouch. *Lab. Invest.* 15: 464–478, 1966.
671. Wasteson, A., B. Glimelius, C. Busch, B. Westermark, C.-H. Heldin, and B. Norling. Effect of a platelet endoglycosidase on cell surface associated heparin sulfate of human cultured endothelial and glial cells. *Thromb. Res.* 11: 309–321, 1977.
672. Waxler, B., B. Schumacher, and R. Eisenstein. Cell stroma interactions in aortic endothelial cell cultures. *Lab. Invest.* 41: 128–134, 1979.
673. Wechezak, A. R., and P. B. Mansfield. Isolation and growth characteristics of cell lines from bovine venous endothelium. *In Vitro* 9: 39–45, 1973.
674. Weibel, E. R. On pericytes, particularly their existence on lung capillaries. *Microvasc. Res.* 8: 218–235, 1974.
675. Weibel, E. R., and G. E. Palade. New cytoplasmic components in arterial endothelia. *J. Cell Biol.* 23: 101–112, 1964.
676. Weiss, J. B., R. A. Brown, S. Kumar, and P. Phillips. Tumour angiogenesis factor: a potent low molecular weight compound. *Br. J. Cancer* 40: 493–496, 1979.
677. Weiss, L. The structure of fine splenic arterial vessels in relation to hemoconcentration and red cell destruction. *Am. J. Anat.* 111: 131–179, 1962.
678. Weissman, G. Prostaglandins in acute inflammation. In: *Current Concepts*. Kalamazoo, MI: Upjohn, 1980, p. 1–32.
679. Weissmann, G., P. Anderson, C. Serhan, E. Samuelsson, and E. Goodman. A general method, employing arsenazo III in liposomes, for study of calcium ionophores: results with A23187 and prostaglandins. *Proc. Natl. Acad. Sci. USA* 77: 1506–1510, 1980.
680. Weksler, B. B., C. W. Ley, and E. A. Jaffe. Stimulation of endothelial cell prostacyclin production by thrombin, trypsin and the ionophore A23187. *J. Clin. Invest.* 923–930, 1978.
681. Weksler, B. B., A. J. Marcus, and E. A. Jaffe. Synthesis of prostaglandin I_2 (prostacyclin) by cultured human and bovine endothelial cells. *Proc. Natl. Acad. Sci. USA* 74: 3922–3926, 1977.
682. White, J. F., and M. S. Parshley. Growth *in vitro* of blood vessels from bone marrow of adult chickens. *Am. J. Anat.* 89: 321–345, 1951.
683. White, J. G., and C. C. Clawson. Blood cells and blood vessels. In: *Ultrastructure of Normal and Abnormal Skin*, edited by A. S. Zelickson. Philadelphia, PA: Lea & Febiger, 1967.
684. White, M. K., H. B. Hechtman, and D. Shepro. Canine lung uptake of plasma and platelet serotonin. *Microvasc. Res.* 9: 131–143, 1975.
685. White, M. K., D. Shepro, and H. B. Hechtman. Pulmonary function and platelet-lung interaction. *J. Appl. Physiol.* 34: 697–703, 1973.
686. White, R., E. C. Carlson, K. Brendel, and E. Meezan. Basement membrane biosynthesis by isolated bovine retinal vessels: incorporation of precursors into extracellular matrix. *Microvasc. Res.* 18: 185–208, 1979.
687. Wiggins, R. C., D. L. Loskutoff, C. G. Cochrane, J. H. Griffin, and T. S. Edgington. Activation of rabbit Hageman factor by homogenates of cultured rabbit endothelial cells. *J. Clin. Invest.* 65: 197–206, 1980.
688. Willems, C., and W. G. van Aken. Production of prostacyclin by vascular endothelial cells. *Haemostasis* 8: 266–273, 1979.
689. Willems, C., W. G. van Aken, E. M. Peuscher-Prakke, J. A. Van Mourik, C. Dutilh, and F. Ten Hoor. Prostaglandin I_2 (prostacyclin) production by cultured human vascular endothelial cells in the absence of platelets. *J. Mol. Med.* 3: 195–201, 1978.
690. Williams, S. K., J. F. Gillis, M. A. Matthews, R. C. Wagner, and M. W. Bitensky. Isolation and characterization of brain endothelial cells: morphology and enzyme activity. *J. Neurochem.* 35: 374–381, 1980.
691. Williamson, J. R. Adipose tissue, morphological changes associated with lipid mobilization. *J. Cell Biol.* 20: 57–74, 1964.
692. Wolf, J. E., Jr., and R. F. Harrison. Demonstration and characterization of an epidermal angiogenic factor. *J. Invest. Dermatol.* 61: 130–141, 1973.
693. Wolff, J. Beiträge zur Ultrastruktur der Kapillaren in der normalen Grosshirnrinde. *Z. Zellforsch. Mikrosk. Anat.* 60: 409–431, 1963.
694. Woodward, W. C., and C. M. Pomerat. The development of patent blood vessels from adult human rib marrow in tissue culture. *Anat. Rec.* 117: 663–683, 1953.
695. Wright, H. P. Endothelial turnover. *Thromb. Diath. Haemorrh. Suppl.* 40: 79–87, 1971.
696. Yamada, K. M., and K. Olden. Fibronectins—adhesive glycoproteins of cell surface and blood. *Nature London* 275: 179–

184, 1978.

697. Yohro, T., and G. Burnstock. Filament bundles and contractility of endothelial cells in coronary arteries. *Z. Zellforsch. Mikrosk. Anat.* 138: 85–96, 1973.

698. Yong, M. S., and J. B. Richardson. Stability and biological activity of catecholamines and 5-hydroxytryptamine immobilized to sepharose and glass beads. *Can. J. Physiol. Pharmacol.* 53: 616–628, 1975.

699. Zauberman, H., I. C. Michaelson, and F. Bergmann. Stimulation of neovascularization of the cornea by biogenic amines. *Exp. Eye Res.* 8: 77–83, 1969.

700. Zawicki, D. F., R. K. Jain, G. W. Schmid-Schoenbein, and S. Chien. Dynamics of neovascularization in normal tissue. *Microvasc. Res.* 21: 27–47, 1981.

701. Zeldis, S. M., Y. Nemerson, F. A. Pitlick, and T. C. Lentz. Tissue factor (thromboplastin): localization to plasma membranes by peroxidase conjugated antibodies. *Science* 175: 766–767, 1972.

702. Zetter, B. R. Migration of capillary endothelial cells is stimulated by tumour-derived factors. *Nature London* 285: 41–43, 1980.

703. Zetter, B. R., and H. N. Antoniades. Stimulation of human vascular endothelial cell growth by a platelet-derived growth factor and thrombin. *J. Supramol. Struct.* 11: 361–370, 1979.

704. Zetter, B. R., and D. Gospodarowicz. The effect of thrombin endothelial cell proliferation. In: *Chemistry and Biology of Thrombin*, edited by R. L. Lundblad, J. W. Fenton, and K. G. Mann. Ann Arbor, MI: Ann Arbor Press, 1977, p. 551–560.

705. Zetter, B. R., L. K. Johnson, M. A. Shuman, and D. Gospodarowicz. The isolation of vascular endothelial cell lines with altered cell surface and platelet-binding properties. *Cell* 14: 501–509, 1978.

706. Zweifach, B. W. E. M. Landis Award acceptance speech. *Microvasc. Res.* 3: 345–353, 1971.

References in Addendum

1A. Clemmons, D. R., W. L. Isley, and M. T. Brown. Dialyzable factor in human serum of platelet origin stimulates endothelial cell replicaton and growth. *Proc. Natl. Acad. Sci. USA* 80: 1641–1645, 1983.

2A. Cohen, R. A., J. T. Shepard, and P. M. Vanhoutte. Inhibitory role of the endothelium in the response of isolated coronary arteries to platelets. *Science* 221: 273–274, 1983.

3A. DeMey, J. G., and P. M. Vanhoutte. Role of the intima in cholinergic and purinergic relaxation of isolated canine femoral arteries. *J. Physiol. London* 316: 347–354, 1981.

4A. DiCorletto, P. E., and D. F. Bowen-Pope. Cultured endothelial cells produce a platelet-derived growth factor-like protein. *Proc. Natl. Acad. Sci. USA* 80: 1919–1923, 1983.

5A. Furchgott, R., and J. Zawadzki. The obligatory role of endothelial cells in the relaxation of arterial smooth muscle by acetylcholine. *Nature London* 288: 373–374, 1980.

6A. Gajdusek, C. M., and S. M. Schwartz. Ability of endothelial cells to condition culture medium. *J. Cell. Physiol.* 110: 35–42, 1982.

7A. Herman, I. M., T. D. Pollard, and A. J. Wong. Contractile proteins in endothelial cells. *Ann. NY Acad. Sci.* 401: 50–60, 1983.

8A. Maciag, T., G. A. Hoover, M. B. Stemerman, and R. Weinstein. Serial propagation of human endothelial cells in vitro. *J. Cell Biol.* 91: 420–426, 1981.

9A. Madri, J. A., and S. K. Williams. Capillary endothelial cell cultures: phenotypic modulation by matrix components. *J. Cell Biol.* 97: 153–155, 1983.

10A. Pober, J. S., and M. A. Gimbrone. Expression of Ia-like antigens by human vacular endothelial cells is inducible in vitro: demonstration by monoclonal antibody binding and immunoprecipitation. *Proc. Natl. Acad. Sci. USA* 79: 6641–6645, 1982.

11A. Pober, J. S., M. A. Gimbrone, R. S. Cotran, C. S. Reiss, S. J. Burakoff, W. Fiers, and K. A. Ault. Ia expression by vascular endothelium is inducible by activated T cells and by human γ-interferon. *J. Exp. Med.* 157: 1339–1353, 1983.

12A. Rohrbach, D. H., and G. R. Martin. Structure of basement membrane in normal and diabetic tissue. *Ann. NY Acad. Sci.* 401: 203–209, 1983.

13A. Shing, Y., J. Folkman, J. Murray, and M. Klagsburn. Purification by affinity chromatography on heparin-Sepharose of a growth factor that stimulates capillary endothelial cell proliferation (Abstract). *J. Cell Biol.* 97: 395a, 1983.

14A. Van de Voorde, J., and I. Leusen. Role of the endothelium in the vasodilator response of rat thoracic aorta to histamine. *Eur. J. Pharmacol.* 87: 113–120, 1983.

15A. Vanhoutte, P. M., and T. J. Rimele. Role of the endothelium in the control of vascular smooth muscle function. *J. Physiol. Paris* 78: 681–686, 1983.

16A. Wagner, D. D., J. B. Olmsted, and V. J. Marder. Immunolocalization of von Willebrand protein in Weibel-Palade bodies of human endothelial cells. *J. Cell Biol.* 95: 355–360, 1982.

CHAPTER 5

Development of microcirculation: capillary growth and adaptation

O. HUDLICKÁ | *Department of Physiology, University of Birmingham Medical School, Birmingham, United Kingdom*

CHAPTER CONTENTS

Comparison of Capillary Density in Different Tissues
Techniques Used in Evaluation of Capillary Growth
  Light microscopy
  Electron microscopy
  Studies with incorporation of [^{3}H]thymidine
  Tissue cultures
  Tissue chambers and avascular regions
    Rabbit ear chambers
    Diffusion chambers
    Rabbit cornea
    Chick chorioallantoic membrane
Growth of Vessels During Prenatal and Postnatal Development
  Heart
  Central nervous system
  Skeletal muscles
  Skin
  Retina
  Changes in vascular growth with aging
Comparison of Differentiation and Growth of Microcirculation
Capillary Growth in Normal Adult Tissues
  Capillary growth in skeletal muscles during training
  Capillary growth in skeletal muscles during long-term electrical stimulation
  Capillary growth in cardiac muscle during exercise
  Capillary growth in the heart during long-term bradycardial pacing
  Capillary growth during exposure to high altitude
Growth of Microcirculation Under Pathological Conditions
  Hypertrophy and atrophy
  Wound healing and regeneration
    Observations on vessel growth in implanted rabbit ear chamber
    Muscle wound healing and regeneration
    Healing of skin wounds and grafts
    Healing in cornea
    Regeneration and growth of endothelium in large blood vessels
  Vascular growth in diabetes mellitus
  Vascular growth in psoriasis
  Retrolental fibroplasia
  Capillary growth in tumors
Factors in Capillary Growth and Its Inhibition
  Chemical factors in capillary growth
    Substances released from leukocytes
    Other factors contained in blood
    Mast cells and histamine
    Tumor angiogenic factor
    Fibroblast growth factor, epidermal growth factor, polypeptides, amino acids, and prostaglandins
    Hormones
    Hypoxia
  Mechanical factors in capillary growth
  Factors in inhibition of capillary growth

CAPILLARY GROWTH has been widely studied during development, inflammation, and regeneration and in different tumors. Initial investigations of capillary sprouts in tadpoles were made by Platner (313). Travers (406) and Meyer (267) found sprouts in healing wounds. Billroth (42) observed capillary growth in chick embryos and different tumors, and Arnold (16, 17) described growth during inflammation and regeneration. There are numerous accounts of capillary growth in developing organisms or under pathological conditions, but very little is known about capillary growth in normal adult tissues. This is not surprising, since the endothelial cells—not only in capillaries but also in larger arteries—represent an extremely stable population with a very low mitotic activity (421).

One of the few organs in adult organisms where capillaries are known to proliferate at regular intervals is the ovary. Bassett (36) described capillary sprouts invading the follicles 2–3 h after ovulation, with the capillary network beginning to transform into arteries and veins within 38 h and vascularization being completed within 62 h. Thus there is very fast growth of the whole vascular bed. Capillary growth also appears in the endometrium and around hair follicles (128), in the teeth (444a), and in skeletal muscle, heart, and brain in animals exposed to hypoxia (38). Recently capillary growth was demonstrated in adult skeletal and cardiac muscle during exercise (8, 212, 248), in skeletal muscle during long-term electrical stimulation (282), and in chronically bradycardially paced hearts (439).

Apart from direct observations of capillary sprouts and increased labeling of endothelial cells with radioactive thymidine, most data indicative of capillary growth are based on the number of capillaries. This is given in terms of either the number of capillaries per area, i.e., capillary density (CD), or the ratio of capillaries to fibers (C/F), or as the capillary length per volume of tissue (mm/mm^3).

The obvious question about capillary growth concerns the factors responsible for the great variety of arrangement and density of vascular networks in different organs. Hall (178) made the following observation:

> The number and distribution of minute vessels is accurately proportioned and adapted to the object of circulation. When the structure of the part is simple, and the object of circulation is its nutrition mainly, the vessels are few in number; when the part is more complicated, or other objects beside its nutrition are to be fulfilled, the number, character, and mode of distribution of the vessels are appropriately modified.

Ebner (113) specified this statement for different organs and demonstrated a very dense network in organs with either great metabolic or transport activity (liver, thyroid gland, lungs, kidneys, and intestinal mucosa). Ogawa (288) gave a good description of capillary networks in many different organs, classifying them into groups according to their complexity of function: *1*) simple networks used for nutrition only (skeletal muscle, serous membranes of visceral organs, mucous membranes in esophagus, rectum, ureter, and fallopian tubes); *2*) dense meshes in organs involved in absorption (intestine, colon, lungs, and thyroid gland); *3*) networks with numerous anastomoses involved in temperature regulation (skin, mucous membranes of tongue, mouth, pharynx, and trachea); *4*) glomeruli (kidneys, Langerhans' islets, and sweat glands); *5*) sinusoids (liver, spleen, and bone marrow); and *6*) portal circulation in the anterior hypophysis. A similar even if less elaborate classification is that of Sobin and Tremer (382), who divided networks into nutritional (skeletal, cardiac, and smooth muscle; central nervous system; bladder and gut wall) and operant (skin, trachea, lungs, liver, kidney, and endocrine and exocrine glands). Different arrangements of microvascular beds in different organs were described by many, e.g., Wiedeman, whose work is included in this *Handbook*. However, quantitative comparison of capillary supply to individual cells in different tissues, which may help elucidate some factors regulating capillary growth, is sadly lacking. Krogh's (233) plea for the study of quantitative anatomy is to a great extent still unanswered.

COMPARISON OF CAPILLARY DENSITY IN DIFFERENT TISSUES

There are some quantitative data comparing CD in organs injected by India ink or other dyes (225) showing that the lowest CD ($274/mm^2$) is in fat-rich adipose tissue of the rat and the highest is in mouse renal medulla ($7{,}400/mm^2$). Many quantitative data are also available on CD in the heart (320) and skeletal muscle (201), most of which were obtained from dye-injected specimens. Such data can perhaps be used for calculating diffusion distances, but they are not adequate for evaluating capillary growth. Capillary growth can only be determined if one is sure that all the capillaries present in the tissue (and expressed either as capillary length in mm/mm^3 or capillary density in cap/mm^2) are visualized. This can be achieved either by special histochemical staining of the capillary endothelium [with alkaline phosphatase, adenosine triphosphatase (ATPase), or by periodic acid–Schiff] or by counting capillaries in semithin sections or electron micrographs. Other methods, such as capillary counts based on either India ink or any other dye injections, or on staining for erythrocytes, may give an indication of capillary filling but not of capillary growth. Furthermore they are subject to too many uncertainties: whether there is maximal vasodilatation at the time of death, what the perfusion pressure is when perfusion with dyes is used, and whether the organ is preperfused with saline or other similar solution before the perfusion with India ink. (It is known that India ink forms clusters with plasma proteins and consequently could lead to incomplete and irregular filling.)

Thus it is not surprising that the variability in CD values in the heart (320) or in skeletal muscles (201, 202) is enormous. The most striking discrepancies are in comparison of values in the rat brain cortex, where India ink injection reveals $9{,}000/mm^2$ (101) but staining for capillary endothelium shows about $400/mm^2$ (244). The considerably higher counts reported in injected preparations could be explained partly by shrinkage and partly by the fact that counting was performed in rather thick sections in which one capillary may have been counted several times. Yet another complication is the state of tissue taken for processing, even if shrinkage is minimal in frozen sections. Gray and Renkin (170) pointed out differences in CD in skeletal muscles fixed at their resting length with those allowed to contract after removal from the animal. Similar discrepancies have been found in the heart, with higher CD reported in hearts arrested in systole than those arrested in diastole (438). Therefore comparisons of CD in different organs are made in this chapter with data based on the actual visualization of capillary endothelium whenever possible. In addition an attempt is made to relate CD to some of the characteristics of cells in different organs.

The high CD (or rather great length of capillaries—about $15{,}000\ mm/mm^3$) found by Olivetti et al. (294) in rat renal glomeruli is obviously related to the large volumes of filtered fluid passing through and may thus be induced by mechanical factors connected either with high blood flow (397) or high filtration (77). Rowinski et al. (344) studied CD in guinea pig colon and found the highest number of capillaries in the vicinity of DNA-synthesizing cells. Pictet and Rutter (312) described a close association between capillaries and secretory granules in the rat embryonic Langerhans' islets, the growth of the granules preceding the growth of capillaries. Capillary growth may thus be induced by factors connected with a high synthesis of DNA or proteins in the tissue.

A similar suggestion was made by Balashova (31), who compared capillary supply of different brain nuclei located either very close to (in young kittens) or further away from (in adult cats) the brain ventricles. Capillary supply of the cells in the motor nucleus of the cat trigeminal nerve or in the vestibular nucleus was very dense in adult cats, each cell encircled by one complete capillary loop. In kittens, where the vestibular nucleus lies close to the floor of the fourth ventricle and thus obtains nourishment from cerebrospinal fluid or the choroid plexus, CD is much lower and several cells are supplied by one capillary (Fig. 1). Dunning and Wolff (111) studied the same species and came to the conclusion that there is no correlation between the number of capillaries and the number of cell bodies (513 cap/mm^2 and 452 cells in the trigeminal nucleus, 689 cap/mm^2 and 1,826 cells in the parietal cortex). Thus they assumed that CD is related to the number of synapses on cell bodies.

Dyson et al. (112) demonstrated a correlation be-

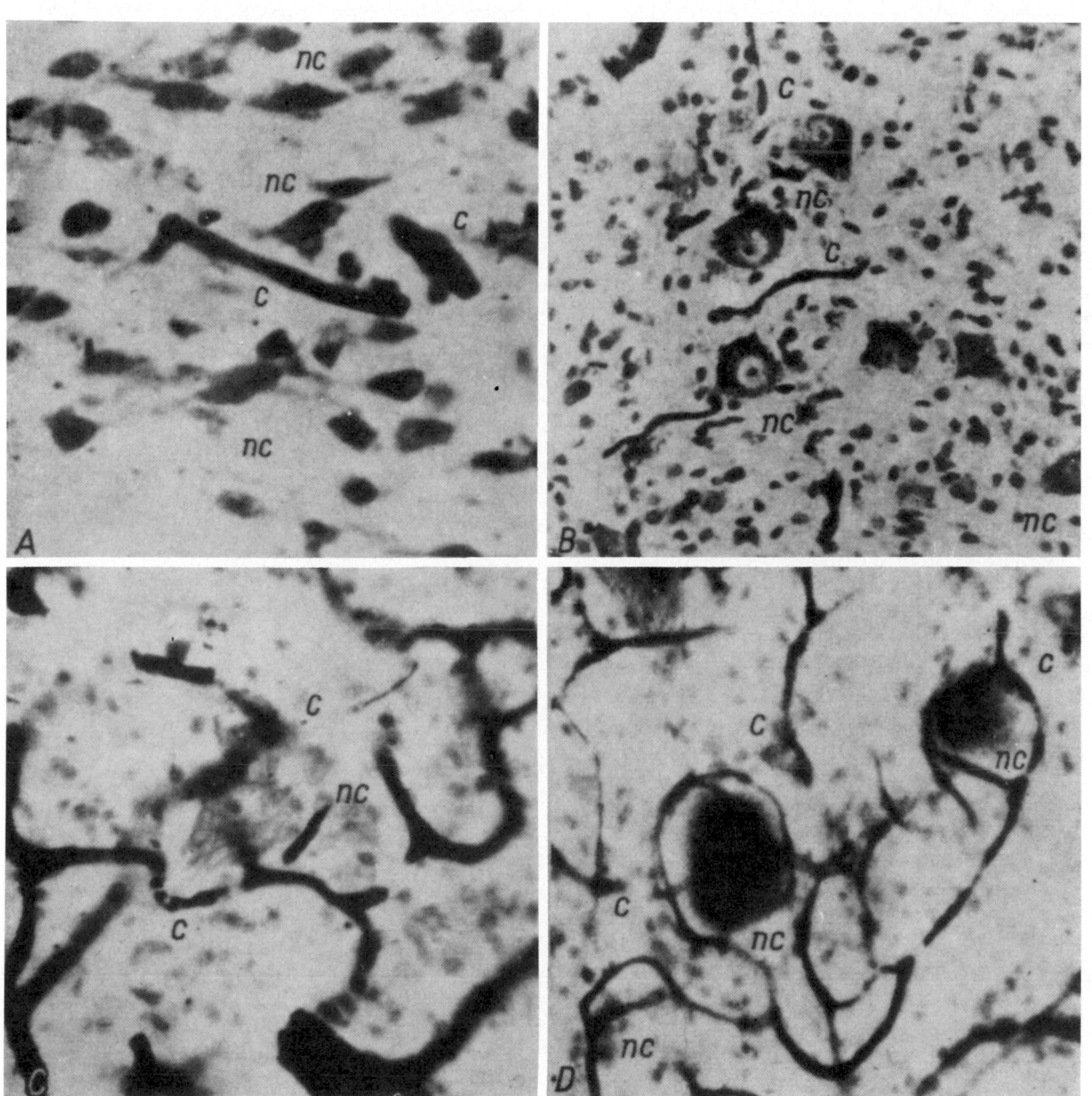

FIG. 1. *A–C*: capillaries (*c*) encircling nerve cells (*nc*) in kitten vestibular lateral nucleus during embryonal development. *D*: same region in adult cat. [From Balashova (31).]

tween CD, increased electrical activity, and transition toward oxidative metabolism during postnatal development of the cerebral cortex. Campbell (65) observed a correlation between CD and oxidative capacity in different parts of cat brain, with the highest values (1,350 cap/mm^2) in the dorsal part of the lateral geniculate body and the lowest in the globus pallidus (490 cap/mm^2). Similar conclusions, obtained through use of more reliable methods, were drawn by Kramer and Lierse (231) in the developing mouse brain between birth and the 20th day after birth. Here the increase in CD in different parts of the brain is closely related to the increase in succinate dehydrogenase (SDH) activity. However, Schüler and Lierse (372) found no such relationship in the developing brains of guinea pigs and chickens. An increase in CD during development was also observed in the white matter in cats (where CD is considerably lower than in the gray matter) and was attributed to the developing myelination (190). No difference in CD was found in the precentral gyrus of human adult brains 19–94 yr old (209), but regional differences in human brains vary from 120/mm^2 in the anterior pyramids to 850/mm^2 in the cerebellar stratum granulosum (244). All the data on CD in the brain seem to suggest that it is related either to protein synthesis in the brain cells or to the number of synapses, both of which would require higher oxygen consumption and better blood supply. However, Lierse's (244) extensive comparative study on CD in different parts of brain in the lizard, chicken, rat, cat, and human shows that the highest CD (1,610/mm^2) is in chicken paleostriatum, whereas values in different parts of the rat and cat brains are around 400/mm^2. The very high CD in the chick basal ganglia is attributed to the fact that they are particularly well developed, having highly differentiated cells with a high metabolic intensity (244). It is also worthwhile to note that endothelial cells in brain capillaries themselves have a high metabolism (152) and considerably more mitochondria than capillary endothelial cells in skeletal muscles (291). This indicates a greater role in active transcapillary transport and, of course, higher oxygen consumption. A stimulus for growth may be initiated by the capillary wall itself rather than by the surrounding cells.

Capillary density in the brain undoubtedly increases during development, indicating that capillaries grow faster than brain cells. The situation is different in skeletal and cardiac muscle: with a relatively fast growth of muscle fibers in relation to capillary growth the capillaries are spread further apart. Consequently CD decreases during development, while C/F increases as the number of fibers per unit area becomes smaller than the number of capillaries. This has been reported for rabbit and rat skeletal muscle as well as for rat heart (Table 1). Thus both in the heart and in skeletal muscle CD is related to fiber size. Such a relationship was shown in the heart by Shipley et al. (375) by using India ink injection and by Hakkila (177) by staining capillary endothelium (Fig. 2).

Capillary density in the heart is much higher than in skeletal muscle and more homogeneously distributed (Table 2). The ratio C/F is similar in the right and left ventricles in humans (185) and dogs (359) as well as in a variety of domestic and wild birds (269), but CD is somewhat higher in the right ventricle because the fibers are smaller (185). Despite some data showing higher CD in the subendocardial than in the subepicardial region (52), the transmural distribution of capillaries is homogeneous (37, 322, 438) or even higher in the middle or subepicardial than in subendocardial layers (144, 144a, 185, 390a). Capillary density within one species is related to heart size (439) and in mammals ranges from about 140/mm^2 in humans (185) to 3,800/mm^2 in wild rats (420). Hearts of

TABLE 1. *Capillary Density in Relation to Fibers in Skeletal and Cardiac Muscle During Development*

	Fiber Area, μm^2	Fiber Density, F/mm^2	Capillary Density, cap/mm^2	C/F
Rabbit				
EDL, 4 wk	1,660	600 ± 26	585 ± 25	0.97
EDL, adult	5,200	195 ± 5	256 ± 6	1.25 ± 0.02
Rat				
EDL, adult	3,020	330	380	1.15
Heart, 4 wk	185	5,400	3,600	0.67
Heart, adult	370	2,700	2,700	1.00

C/F, ratio of capillaries to fibers. EDL, extensor digitorum longus. Data for EDL from Cotter (96) and data for heart from Poupa et al. (318).

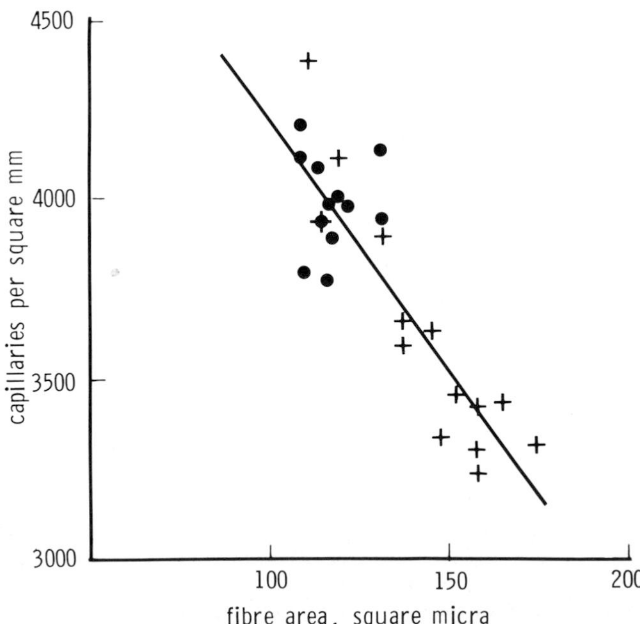

FIG. 2. Relationship between fiber area and capillary density (CD) in control guinea pigs (●) and guinea pigs trained by treadmill running (+). [From Hakkila (177).]

TABLE 2. *Capillary Density in Relation to Fibers in Various Regions of the Heart*

	Fiber Area, μm^2	Capillary Density, cap/mm²	C/F	Ref.
Humans				
LV				
Subendocardium	344	1,318	0.99	185
Middle	264	1,407	1.07	185
RV				
Subendocardium	334	1,963	0.99	185
Middle	230	1,843	0.81	185
LV, adult	607*	3,342	1.34	333
LV, 3 mo–16 yr	250*	3,744	3.23	333
Dog				
LV			1.1	359
RV			1.0	359
LV		2,500		37
Cat				
LV				
Subendocardium		2,812		52
Middle		2,361		52
Subepicardium		2,440		52
Rabbit				
LV	1,133*	3,420	1.14	375
RV	908*	3,310	0.99	375
LV				
Subepicardium		1,898† (1,424–2,780)		438
Subendocardium		1,960† (1,251–2,853)		438
Hare				
LV	267	3,456		419
Guinea pig				
LV		4,000		177
LV		2,080		143
Wild rat				
LV	300	3,803		420
Lab rat				
LV	375	2,908		420
LV		2,180		143
LV				
Subendocardium	278	3,468		322
Middle	304	3,597		322
LV				
Subendocardium	364	2,816		144
Subepicardium	224	3,885		144
LV, subendocardium		2,815		188
RV		2,530		188
Mouse				
LV	387	2,739		418
Bat				
LV	300	3,717		418
Pigeon‡				
LV		4,528		323

LV, left ventricle; RV, right ventricle; C/F, ratio of capillaries to fibers. * Calculated from fiber diameters. † Mean values; range in parentheses. ‡ Uniform distribution of capillaries and fibers observed in LV, RV, and septum of various types of domestic and wild birds (269).

more active animals of similar species have a higher CD. For example, CD in hares is greater than in rabbits, as is that of wild rats compared with laboratory rats or bats compared with mice (418–420). Birds have a higher CD than mammals (269, 323). The high CD of the heart thus seems to be connected with both higher general activity and a higher activity of oxidative enzymes as shown in Figure 3.

The relationship between fiber size and CD in skeletal muscle has been pointed out in different species by Plyley and Groom (314), Loats et al. (250), and Maxwell et al. (260); it was also studied in one species by Sillau and Banchero (379), and in one muscle by Ripoll et al. (332) and Aquin et al. (12). However, as seen from Table 3 and Figure 4 the relationship between fiber size and CD is only one factor to be considered, and a good exponential relationship does not apply to very small fibers. Skeletal muscle is much more complicated than the heart, since most muscles are composed not only of fibers of different sizes but

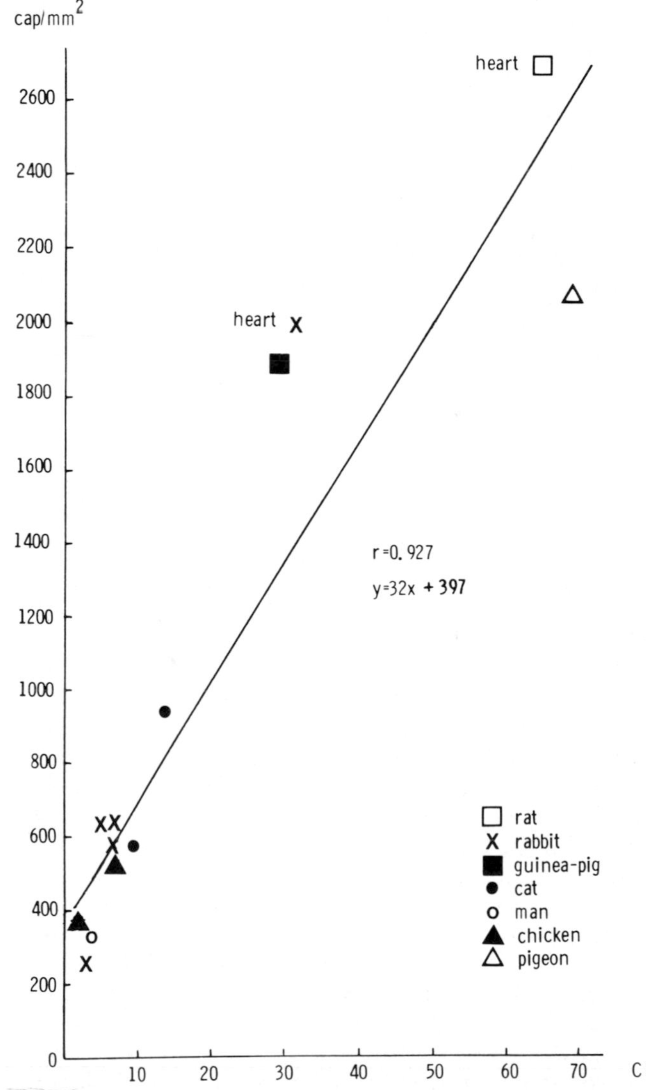

FIG. 3. Relationship between citrate synthase (CS) in international units per gram weight and CD in different muscles. [Data for CS in hearts and muscles of rabbits, chickens, and pigeons from Bass et al. (35a); other CS data from Staudte and Pette (385a). Data for CD in muscles of rats, rabbits, and chickens from Cotter (96), for cats from Myrhage (280), for humans from Andersen and Henriksson (8), and for pigeons from Rakušan (323).]

TABLE 3. *Capillary Density in Relation to Fibers in Various Skeletal Muscles*

	Fiber Area, μm^2	Fiber Density, F/mm^2	Capillary Density, cap/mm^2	C/F	Ref.
Human					
Male					
VL	*4,464*	224	277	*1.24*	*301*
			±99		
VL*	*5,405*	185	314	*1.69*	301
VL	*4,167*	240	329	1.36	8
			±11	±0.07	
	3,953	253	348	1.39	212
		±32	±29	±0.06	
	1,795	557	600†	1.08	189
		±30	±23		
	2,994	*334*	585†	1.75	55
			±40		
SOL	*7,752*	*129*	288	2.23	9
			±29	±0.19	
GL	*4,202*	*238*	365	1.53	9
			±28	±0.09	
Female					
VL	*2,029*	493	559†	1.11	213
		±27	±19	±0.07	
Rhesus monkey					
Male					
MA	*3,289*	*304*	656	2.16	
			±90	±0.26	
MP	*3,717*	*269*	546	2.03	
			±95	±0.10	
TEMA	*4,098*	*244*	523	2.14	
			±94	±0.15	
TEMA	*4,630*	*216*	395	1.83	
			±64	±0.33	
Female					259
MA	*2,667*	*375*	863	1.30	
			±68	±0.21	
MP	*2,475*	*404*	566	1.40	
			±82	±0.17	
TEMA	*3,003*	*333*	830	2.49	
			±198	±0.57	
TEMA	*2,544*	*393*	638	1.62	
			±78	±0.28	
Wildebeest					
D	1,654	*604*	1,194	*1.98*	
VL	1,960	*510*	440	*0.86*	
G	1,908	*524*	564	*1.08*	
SAR	1,093	*914*	1,024	*1.12*	
Dik-dik					198
D	1,453	*688*	1,788	*2.60*	
VL	1,804	*554*	804	*1.45*	
G	1,649	*606*	916	*1.51*	
SAR	1,295	*772*	931	*1.21*	
Dog					
G	*2,004*	499	706	1.45	
M	*1,443*	693	820	1.20	314
T	*1,013*	987	1,008	1.02	
M	*2,653*	*377*	830	2.20	369
Cat					
GM	*1,626*	*615*	695	1.13	280
			±49	±0.02	
G	*4,525*	221	369	1.62	314
GL	*1,984*	*504*	570	1.13	280
			±34	±0.02	
SOL	*4,049*	247	435	1.76	314
SOL	*2,024*	*494*	948	1.92	280
			±47	±0.01	
M	*1,811*	552	621	1.13	
M	*1,184*	*844*	760	0.90	314
T	*962*	1,039	1,440	1.39	369
TEN	*1,447*	*691*	657	0.95	314
			±54	±0.02	280

	Fiber Area, μm^2	Fiber Density, F/mm^2	Capillary Density, cap/mm^2	C/F	Ref.
Cat					
BF	*1,264*	797	617	0.78	280
			±66	±0.09	
Rabbit					
G	*1,930*	518	661	1.28	417
		±21	±19.6		
G	*4,785*	209	341	1.67	314
GM	*4,367*	*229*	381	1.11	170
			±35	±0.09	
GL	*3,717*	*269*	349	1.18	170
			±53	±0.11	
SOL	*2,146*	466	743	1.59	417
		±8	±38		
SOL	*4,082*	245	371	1.67	314
SOL	*3,571*	*280*	643	2.14	170
			±43	±0.16	
TA	*2,445*	*409*	628	1.61	170
			±50	±0.10	
EDL			271‡	1.25	
			±7	±0.02	56
Hare					
G	*1,183*	845	1,682	1.99	417
		±30	±92		
SOL	*1,342*	754	1,509	2.00	417
		±69	±132		
Guinea pig					
G	*2,008*	498	677	1.41	
SOL	*1,733*	577	725	1.27	
TA	*1,142*	876	1,210	1.38	314
GR	*1,715*	583	853	1 46	
M	*1,584*	631	1,704	2.70	369
Rat					
Laboratory					
G	*1,075*	930	1,780	1.91	417
		±47	±99		
G	*3,891*	257	487	1.87	314
SOL	*1,613*	620	1,265	1.88	417
		±38	±65		
SOL	*5,128*	195	396	2.05	314
EHP	*891*	*1,122*	1,043	0.93	281
			±64	±0.02	
F	*2,128*	*470*	460	0.98	2
			±64	±0.08	
Wild					
G	*759*	1,317	1,577	1.20	417
		±264	±283		
SOL	*633*	1,579	1,984	1.31	417
		±341	±320		
Japanese waltzer					
TA	*609*	1,642	1,948	1.24	10
		±474	±736	±0.15	
G	*845*	1,183	1,304	1.16	10
		±328	±315	±0.14	
Pigeon					
B	*608*	1,646	2,075	1.26	323
		±91	±106		
Chicken					
ALD				1.77	96
				±0.02	
ALD	1,967	529	699	1.24	169
	±60	±15	±20	±0.03	
PLD				1.11	96
				±0.02	
PLD	2,003	529	561	*1.08*	169
	±93	±20	±26	*±0.04*	
ALD	*2,000*	*500*	450	0.9	194
P	*750*	*1,333*	800	0.6	194

VL, vastus lateralis; SOL, soleus; GL, gastrocnemius lateralis; MA, masseter anterior; MP, masseter posterior; TEMA, temporalis anterior; D, diaphragma; G, gastrocnemius; SAR, sartorius; M, masseter; T, tongue; GM, gastrocnemius medialis; TEN, tenuissimus; BF, biceps femoris; TA, tibialis anterior; EDL, extensor digitorum longus; GR, gracilis; EHP, extensor hallucis proprius; F, forelimb; B, breast; ALD, anterior latissimus dorsi; PLD, posterior latissimus dorsi; P, patagialis. Data in italics calculated from values given by individual authors and consequently only approximate; all other data are means, some with SE. * Subject was older than others tested. † Uncorrected for shrinkage. ‡ From O. Hudlická, M. A. Cotter, and K. R. Tyler, unpublished observations.

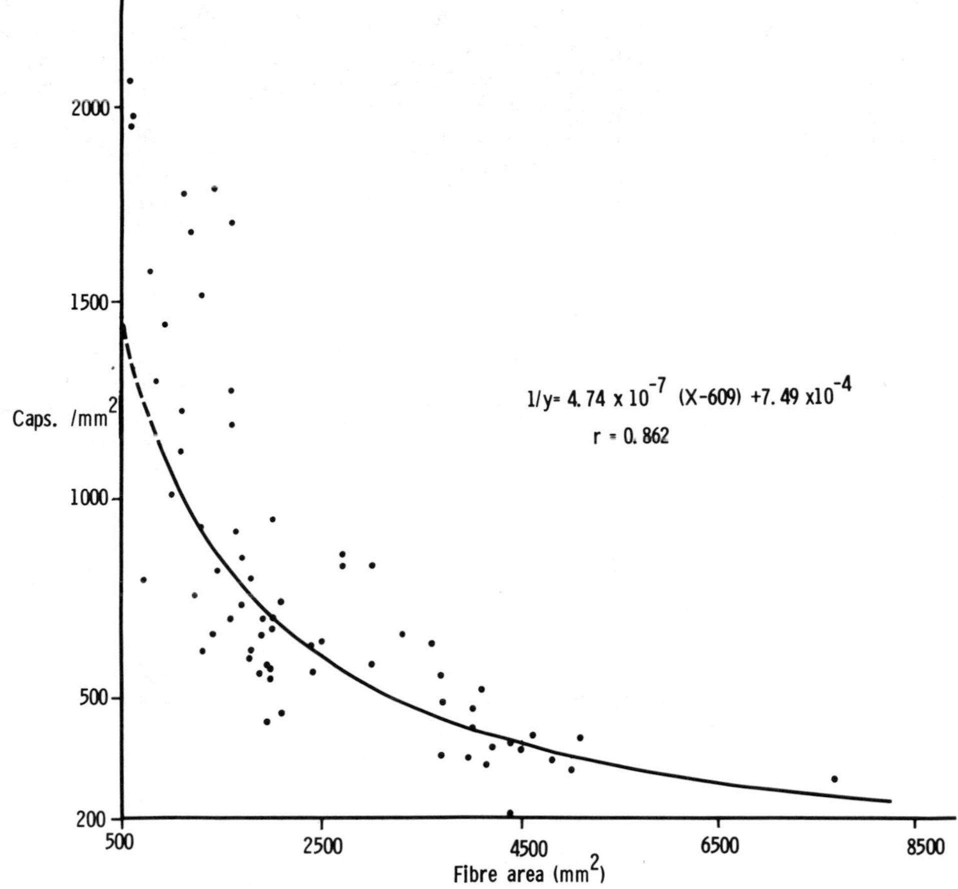

FIG. 4. Relationship between fiber area and CD in different skeletal muscles of various animals. Individual data given in Table 3.

also of fibers with differing content of oxidative and glycolytic enzymes. It has been known for a long time (201, 202, 326) that highly oxidative (red) muscles have a higher CD and more tortuous capillaries than white muscles, which have high glycolytic activity. Romanul (335) first showed that even in mixed muscles (most animal muscles and all human muscles are mixed), fibers with a high oxidative capacity are surrounded by a greater number of capillaries than those with a high content of glycolytic enzymes. Gray and Renkin (170) used the combined data of fiber sizes, CD, and histochemical classification of fibers by staining for SDH and myosin ATPase to evaluate CD and C/F quantitatively with respect to different fiber types: fast glycolytic, fast oxidative, and slow oxidative. They showed that CD (in cap/mm^2) with respect to highly oxidative fibers, whether fast or slow, is twice as high as that with respect to fast glycolytic fibers. Because the latter are usually (but not necessarily always) larger than the former, C/F shows much smaller differences than CD.

Maxwell et al. (260) found only a very poor correlation between CD and chemically estimated SDH in a variety of muscles and animals. Figure 3 shows, on the other hand, a rather good correlation between citrate synthase and CD both in different skeletal muscles and in the heart. Hoppeler et al. (199) found a very good correlation between the volume density of mitochondria and CD in a variety of muscles and animals and demonstrated a close relationship between capillaries and subsarcolemmal mitochondria (198). Romanul and Pollock (337) reported that CD increased in skeletal muscles with the increase in activity of oxidative enzymes, whether this was achieved by administration of thyroxine or by cross innervation of fast-contracting muscles by a nerve originally supplying a slow-contracting one. Innervation of slow-contracting, highly oxidative muscles by nerves originally supplying fast muscles resulted in a change toward low oxidative activity and lower CD. These changes indicate that capillary supply in skeletal muscle can be adjusted both to the activity of oxidative and glycolytic enzymes: it increases with the increase of the former and decreases with the increase of the latter. This relationship was also observed during development of fast and slow muscles in chickens and kittens. Slow-contracting muscles in chickens have a higher CD and higher C/F than fast-contracting muscles [Table 3; (96, 169)], and they also have a higher activity of oxidative and lower activity of glycolytic enzymes. The concentration of these enzymes is similar at hatching, but within a few days the activity of glycolytic enzymes sharply rises in fast-contracting muscles although it does not appreciably change in slow-contracting ones. The activity of oxidative enzymes decreases in both muscles together with decreasing motor activity [Fig. 5; (204)], the decrease being greater in fast-contracting ones. At the same time the capillary network, which is very dense in both muscles at 7 days (97), becomes much sparser in fast muscles compared with slow muscles (200). Similar differentiation takes place in kittens (204), where lower CD in gastrocnemius than in soleus muscle develops gradually as the activity of glycolytic enzymes increases considerably more in the former than in the latter (Fig. 5).

The meager knowledge about capillary supply to different organs seems to indicate that CD may be related to several factors: the amount of blood flow or filtration (in the kidney) and the activity of proteosynthesis or oxidative metabolism or both. There is also some indication that high activity of glycolytic metabolism can suppress the development of capillary supply. The role of both the mechanical and metabolic factors in capillary growth is discussed in this chapter.

TECHNIQUES USED IN EVALUATION OF CAPILLARY GROWTH

Light Microscopy

Platner (313) described growing capillaries in tadpoles and young *Tritons* as a cord of tissue forming sprouts (Fig. 6) ending as blind sacs whose diameters gradually increase, eventually connecting to another capillary. The newly formed connections were first too narrow to allow passage of erythrocytes, but gradually their diameter increased and blood cells passed through them. Cells between capillaries never took part in capillary formation. This basic description of capillary growth was extended to observations in inflammation and wound healing by Travers (406) and later by Meyer (267) and to chick embryos, granulation tissue, and tumors by Billroth (42). Clark (77) described capillary growth very extensively in tadpole tails, and Sandison (363, 364), Clark et al. (85), and Clark and Clark (80, 83, 84) observed capillaries in chambers implanted in rabbit ears. The growth in all cases was followed over a period of many weeks and even months in the same region.

In tadpole tails sprouting occurred before the differentiation of the endothelium was completed. It started from a thickening of the endothelial cell usually at a right angle to a parent capillary, with a lumen at the beginning and a solid process at the end. The lumen gradually widened and extended until it reached another capillary where it made connection. Growth of capillaries was associated with mitosis and migration of the new endothelial nuclei toward the end of the sprout (83), and longitudinal growth was supposedly caused by mechanical pulling of the growing tissues. Newly formed capillaries were wide, tortuous, and very fragile, with a low flow rate that increased later. Such development was observed more often near the venous end of capillaries, and it proceeded at a very fast rate (0.2–0.6 mm/day), particularly in rabbit ears (Fig. 7). The rate was slower when rabbits were kept at a lower environmental temperature. Capillaries with higher flow differentiated into arterioles and venules by gradual apposition of adventitial cells and fibroblasts; the latter eventually changed into smooth muscle cells [Fig. 8; (84)]. First contractions of new arterioles were observed as early as 8–9 days after the occurrence of new capillaries but sometimes did not appear until many weeks later (78). Capillaries poorly supplied with blood eventually disappeared (Fig. 7). All newly formed small vessels and even larger veins underwent frequent changes, arteries being more stable than veins. Formation of arteriovenous anastomoses took place in rabbit ear chamber when the increase in flow was extensive (84). This classic description of capillary growth was also confirmed in regenerating muscles (88, 370), damaged cornea (370), healing wounds (208), tumors (128), and recently in normal adult rabbit and rat muscles subjected to long-term indirect stimulation for several days (282). Eriksson and Zarem (121) and Wagner (421) give an excellent summary of microcirculatory growth and also review the findings on the ultrastructure of growing endothelial cells.

Electron Microscopy

Ultrastructure of normal capillaries is extensively dealt with in the chapter by M. and N. Simionescu in this *Handbook*. The developmental changes occurring in growing capillaries were described in rat embryonal brain (109), myocardium (255), and skeletal muscle (427), and in rat spinal cord (179) and skeletal muscle (368) during early postnatal development. Schoefl (370) found similar characteristics in growing cells in the endothelium of new capillaries in regenerating muscle, as did Warren (424) in capillaries of tissues surrounding tumor transplants and Parry and Abramovich (303) in human umbilical veins.

In summary, growing capillaries are characterized by an incomplete basement lamina, a highly irregular luminal surface with numerous microvilli, loose junctions and gaps between endothelial cells or intracellular clefts, scanty pinocytotic vesicles, and features of undifferentiated and highly active cells. Numerous free ribosomes are present together with a richly developed rough endoplasmic reticulum (involved in the synthesis of proteins), a prominent Golgi apparatus (that functions as an intermediate in secretory processes), and numerous large mitochondria with a great capacity for respiration (necessary for secretion and repeated cell division) (Figs. 8 and 9). Weibel-Palade bodies, characteristic of endothelium in larger vessels, are rarely present in capillary endothelium but can sometimes be identified in growing endothelial cells in tissue cultures. Growing capillaries have numerous

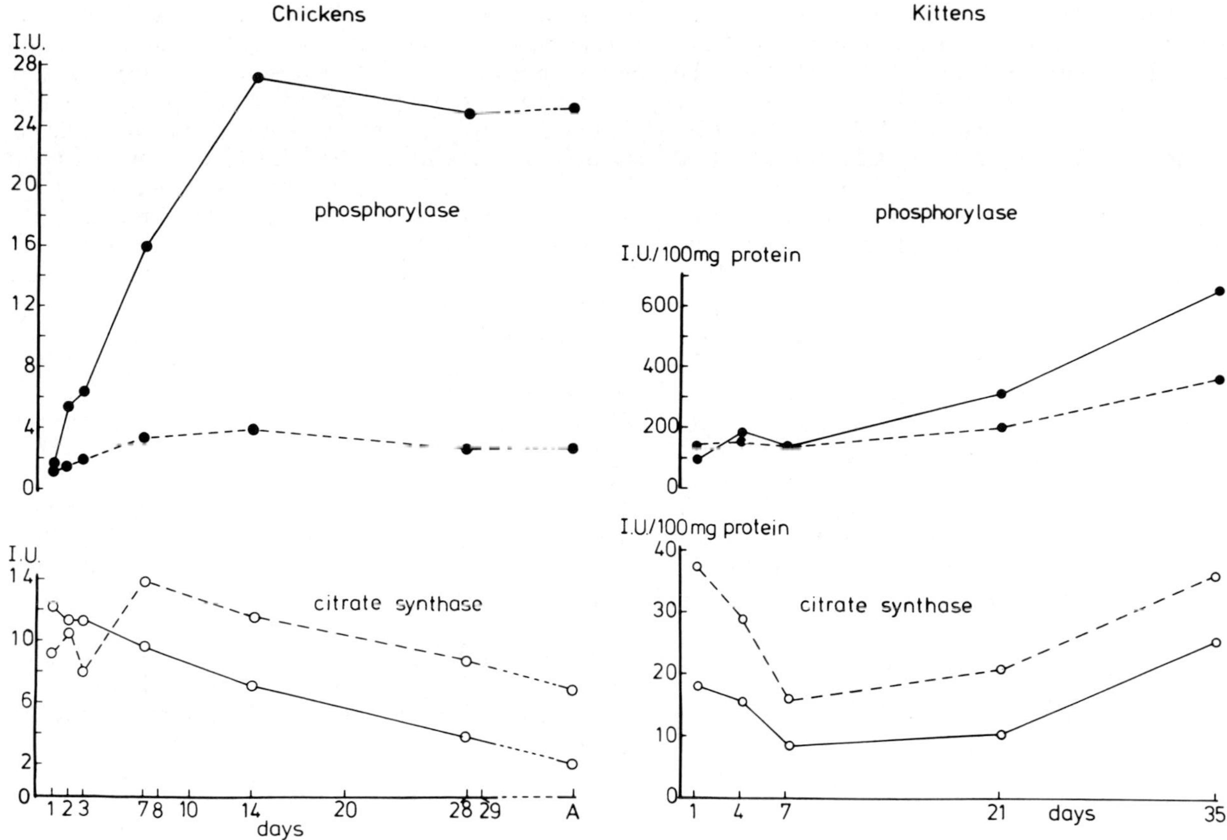

FIG. 5. Changes in the activities of oxidative enzyme citrate synthase, *open circles*, and glycolytic enzyme phosphorylase, *closed circles*, during postnatal development in chickens and kittens. Days on abscissa; A = adult. *Solid lines*, values in fast muscles; *broken lines*, values in slow muscles. [Adapted from Hudlická et al. (204).]

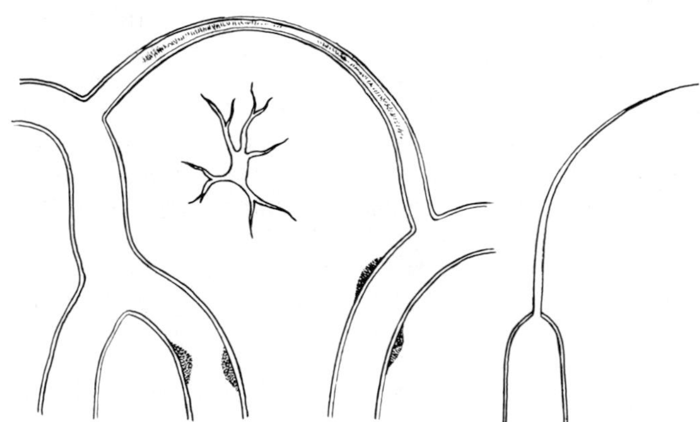

FIG. 6. Tadpole tail: capillary sprout (*right*) and arch connecting two capillaries at a later stage of development (*left*). [From Platner (313).]

mitotic figures that are, however, rarely seen in standard electron-microscope material. Mitotic division occurs more frequently at the beginning of the sprouts, which grow further by elongation—like "seamless" endothelium—before the tip of the sprout joins the capillary toward which it is growing (174, 421).

Electron-microscope findings also helped clarify the question of how the lumina of the sprouts are created. Billroth (42) originally suggested that it is by the formation of spaces between adjacent plasma membranes of endothelia in solid cords, and this was observed in developing capillaries in chick embryo by Thoma (397) and in wounds by Minervini (273). Another possibility is that the lumina form as a result of intracellular vacuolization (356). Aloisi and Schiaffino (5) found extensive vacuolization of the central parts of endothelial cords in capillary sprouts. Because mitosis was so rarely seen, Altschul (6) suggested that capillaries can divide amitotically. However, Wagner (421) pointed out the difficulty in observing mitosis because the mitotic phase is very short. Labeling tissues with [^{3}H]thymidine can provide an index of the number of cells in which mitosis is imminent and thus give a very good indication about capillary proliferation.

Studies With Incorporation of [^{3}H]Thymidine

Labeling with [^{3}H]thymidine has been used primarily as an index of endothelial growth in tissue cultures and in large vessels. The percentage of labeled cells, expressed per number of all cells counted (either in

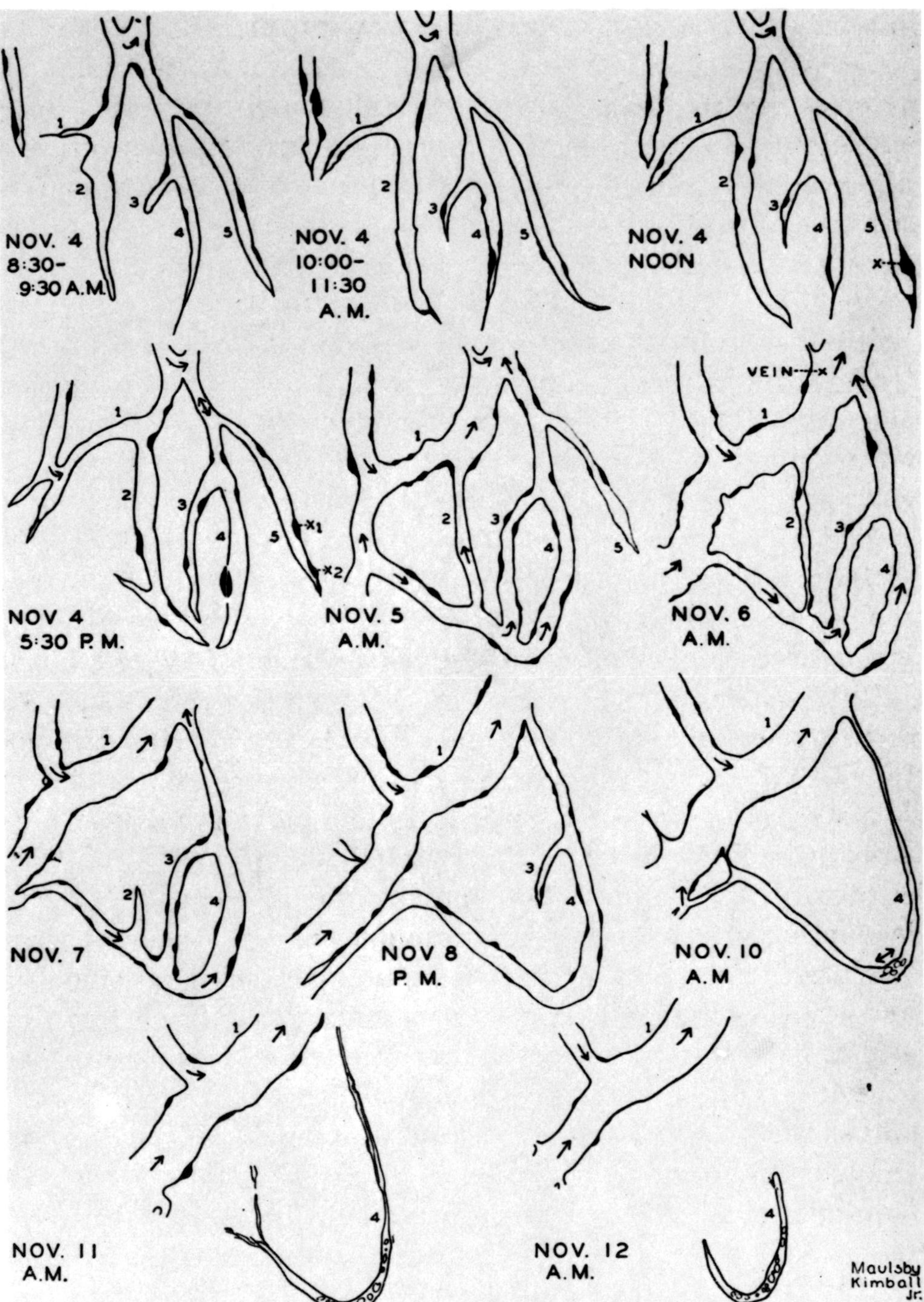

FIG. 7. Series of the same group of new capillaries in rabbit ear chamber, followed for 9 days. Capillary sprouts 1 and 3 gradually anastomose to form a small plexus. Capillary 1 receives greatest blood flow and enlarges to form a venule. Capillaries receiving less flow subsequently retract. Observations with Leitz drawing eyepiece. [From Clark and Clark (83).]

vitro per dish or in vivo in a visual field), is never very high. The highest value, 11.3%, was found in mesenteric arteries of immature rats; this decreased to 3.4% in adult animals (102). In rabbits Spaet and Lejnieks (384) found a higher labeling index in the endothelium of small arteries compared with aorta and a very low index (0.6%) in muscle capillaries. Other studies describe a higher labeling index in the upper than in the lower parts of the aorta, with a range of 0.01%–0.1% in adult rats (358) and 0.37%–1.76% in guinea pigs (441). Labeling was highest around arterial branching points (66, 140, 234) and in young animals

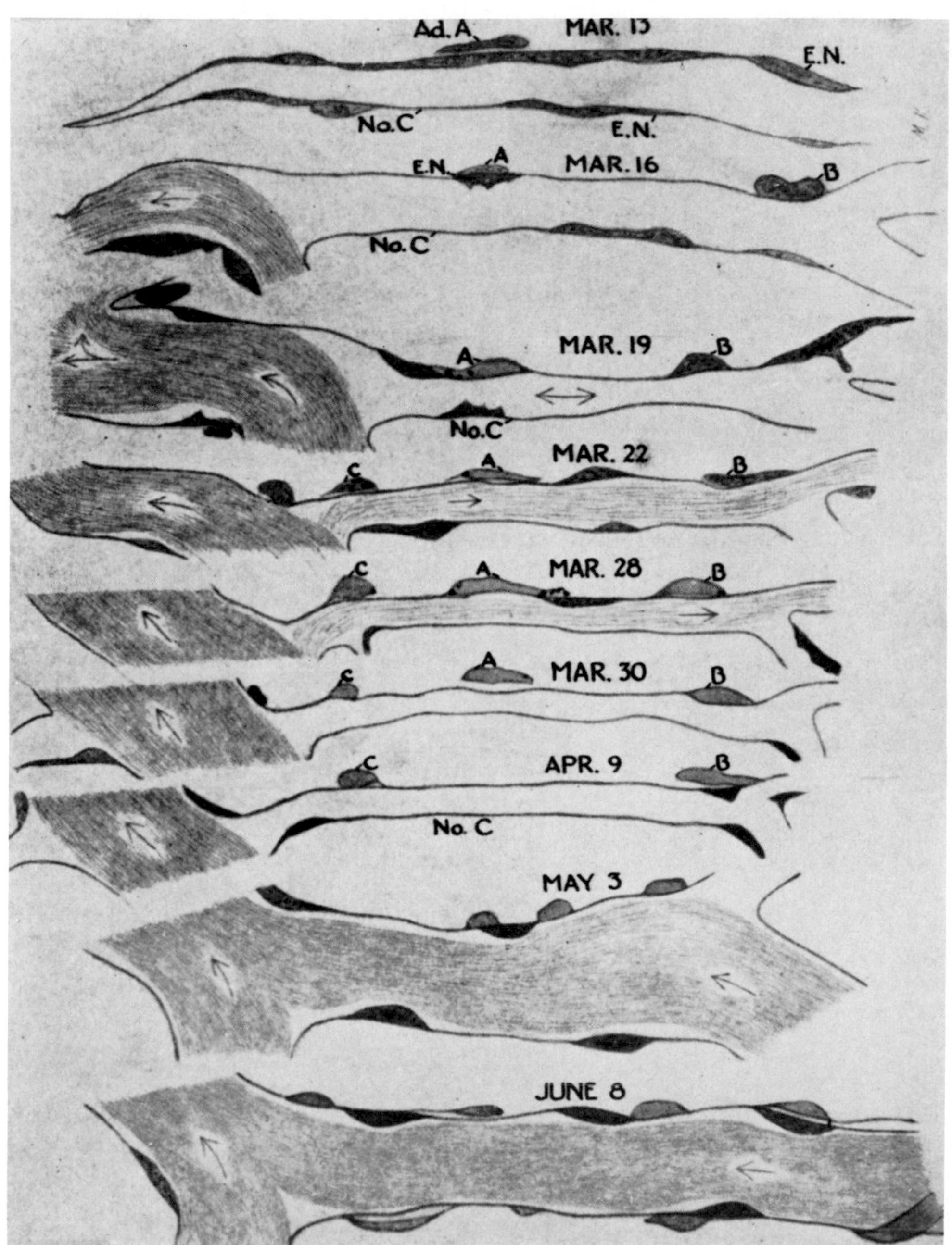

FIG. 8. Blood vessel growth observed in same vessel in rabbit ear chamber over 3 mo. Vessel starts as a capillary sprout with 1 adventitial cell (Ad) and remains as a capillary for almost 2 mo. As flow increases the capillary enlarges and becomes a venule with new adventitial cells. EN, endothelial nuclei. A, B, and C mark position of adventitial cells; *arrows*, direction of flow. Observations with Leitz drawing eyepiece. [From Clark and Clark (84).]

(234, 358). It increased considerably in endothelium damaged by vessel constriction (442) and either mechanical or chemical injury (345, 384). Adult capillaries incorporate label at very low rates with the exception of bone marrow sinusoids, whose value is 2.4% (394). The labeling index in the capillaries of the subendocardial layers of the heart was higher than in subepicardial [1.9% compared with 0.7% (115)] and both values were higher than those found by Engerman et al. (120) in the heart (0.14%) and in the retinal capillaries (0.01%). In the retina the label was clearly confined to the endothelial cells only (Fig. 10), but it was difficult to eliminate labeling of other cells in the heart. By using autoradiography and electron microscopy Mandache et al. (256) found that most of the [^{3}H]thymidine in the hearts of trained rats was local-

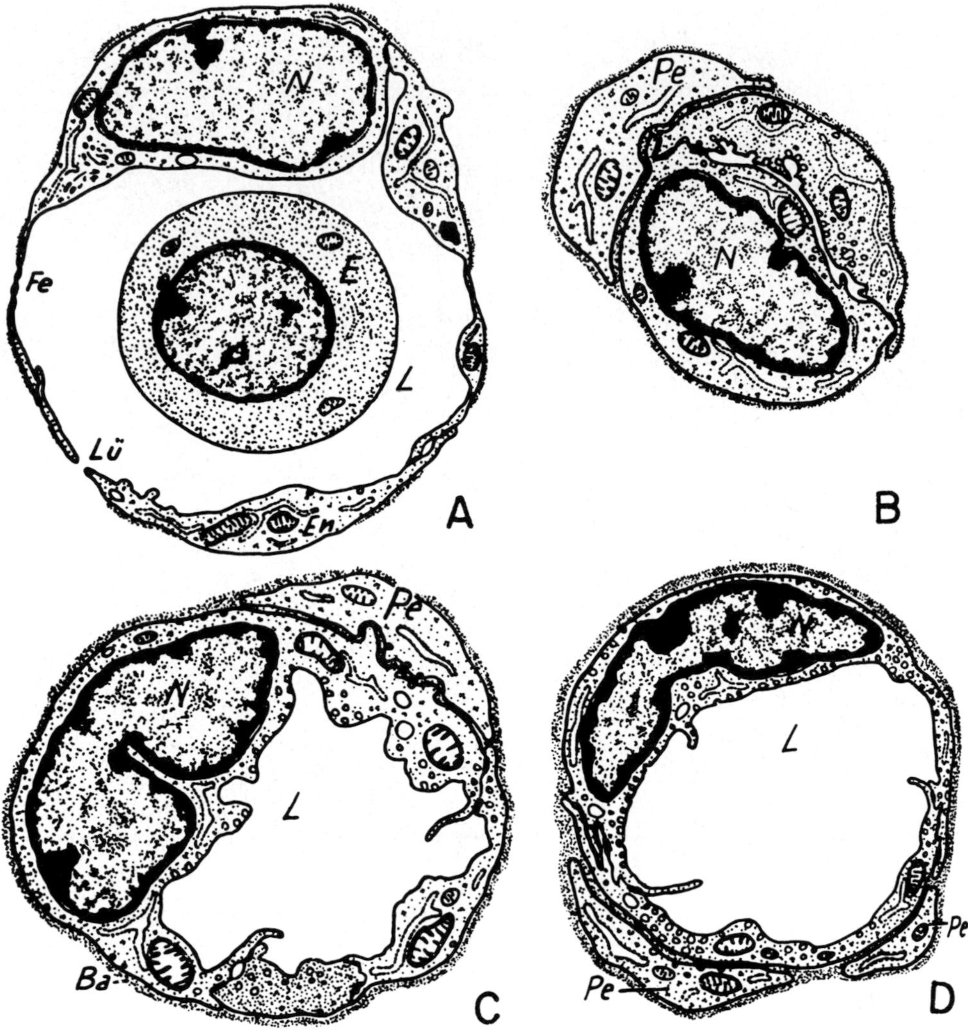

FIG. 9. Stages in capillary growth during embryonic development of the rat. *A*: embryonic capillary with wide lumen (L) and very thin endothelium (En) with pores (Lü) and fenestrations (Fe). Inside the capillary is a fetal erythroblast. N, endothelial nucleus; E, endothelial cells. *B*: capillary sprout with narrow lumen, thicker basement membrane, and adjacent pericyte (Pe). *C*: embryonal capillary with endothelium of irregular thickness, few vesicles, and thin basement lamina (Ba). *D*: capillary from early postnatal stage with more regular endothelium, more extensive vesiculation, and a thicker basement lamina. [From Welt et al. (427).]

ized in the endothelial nuclei, although some of the label was visible elsewhere (Fig. 11). The estimated turnover time of capillary endothelium in adult organisms is ~ 1,000 days (120), and with the few exceptions mentioned here, capillary endothelium represents a very stable population of cells. This is probably one of the reasons why factors affecting endothelial growth were studied in tissue cultures.

Tissue Cultures

Factors affecting endothelial growth in vitro are described in detail in the chapter by Shepro in this *Handbook*; therefore only a few comments are made here. Endothelial cells used most frequently in tissue cultures are those isolated from human umbilical veins or aortas of different animals (261). Both grow in monolayers, which is one of the characteristics of vascular endothelium in tissue cultures (145, 214). Both have a high mitotic activity until they reach the state of confluence within 7 days (145) and also have an ultrastructure similar to endothelial cells of the same origin in vivo (145, 183, 239, 261). Endothelial cells isolated from coronary arteries grow more slowly, reaching confluence within 2–4 wk, and can be maintained for at least 4 mo (283). On the other hand, tissue cultures from retinal vessels could not be maintained for more than 3 mo (61) even if endothelium was obtained from retinal vessels of kittens 3–4 wk old (134).

Cultures of vascular endothelium from chicken embryos showed formation of capillaries similar to those in vivo described by Clark and Clark (83, 84): small projections of endothelial cells spread toward the periphery and formed solid endothelial sprouts that at a later stage had a lumen without blood cells [Fig. 12; (240)]. Capillary plexuses began to form between 1 and 5 days after the cultures had been started and persisted for about 2 wk. There was no evidence that mesenchymal cells present in the cultures took part in capillary formation. Woodard and Pomerat (437) described formation of capillary sprouts in tissue cultures from human bone marrow that could be identified on the 3rd day and that began to degenerate between 10 and 12 days. Recently Wagner and Mat-

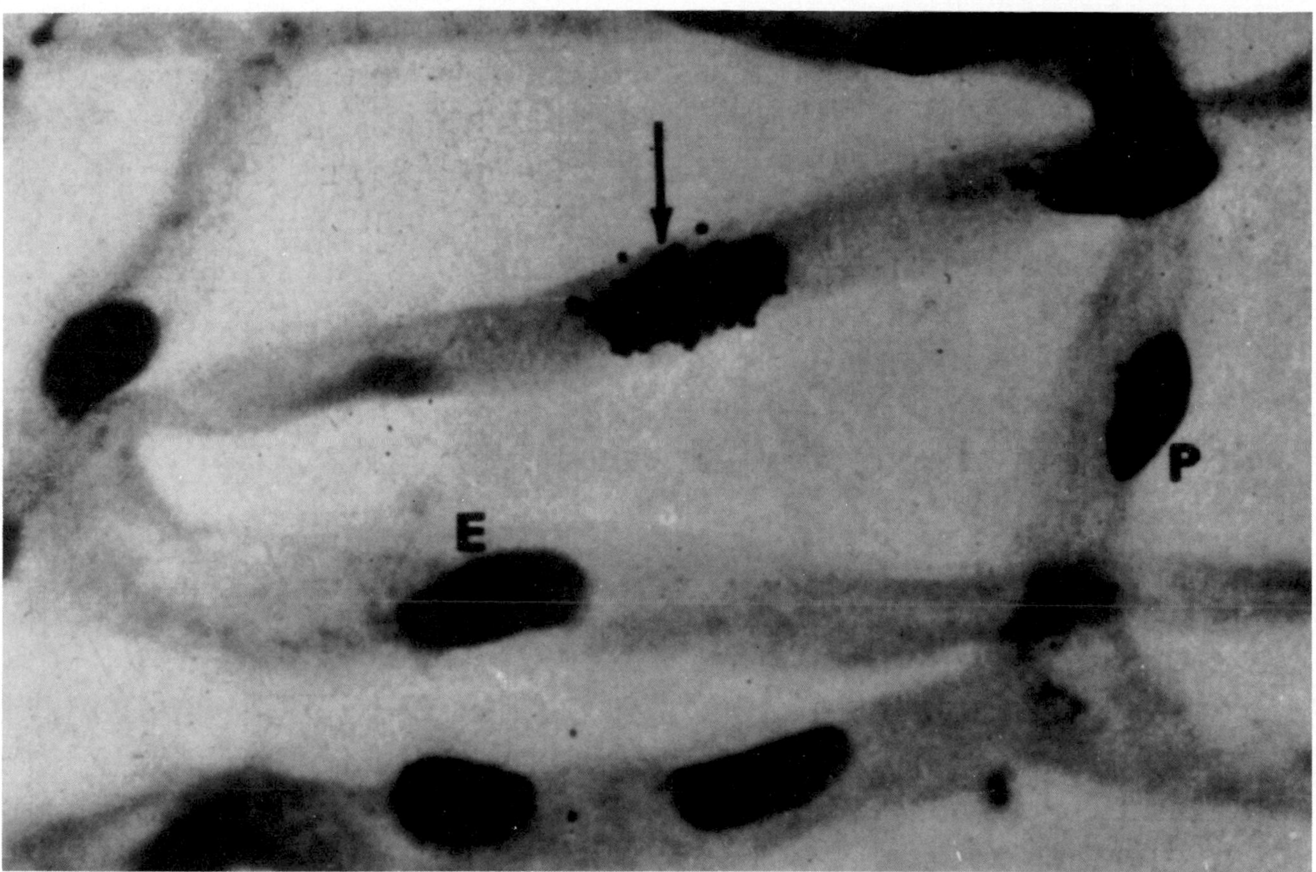

FIG. 10. Autoradiograph of retinal capillaries of a 22-mo-old mouse showing an endothelial cell labeled by [^{3}H]thymidine (*arrow*) and unlabeled endothelial cells (*E*) and pericytes (*P*). Stained with hematoxylin and periodic acid–Schiff. [From Engerman et al. (120).]

thews (422) reported growth of capillaries isolated from rat epididymal fat without admixture of other cells in vitro, and Folkman et al. (131) succeeded in maintaining cultures from human capillary endothelium isolated from adrenal glands for up to 8 mo. Growth of capillary endothelium was about half as fast as the growth of endothelial cells from the bovine aorta but could be accelerated to a similar rate by addition of tumor angiogenic factor. Folkman and Haudenschild (130) described formation of capillary tubes in cultures of capillary endothelium from human foreskin between 20 and 40 days after the cells had been plated (Fig. 13). The cells had all the characteristics of capillary endothelium (131) and grew in the absence of other cells (mast cells or fibroblasts) that at one stage of this research were considered necessary for capillary growth. Addition of tumor angiogenic factor was necessary for capillary growth in these cultures. However, endothelial cells derived from cerebral microvessels (310a, 499) or retinal capillaries (61, 134) appear to grow quite well in a medium supplemented with only 10%–20% calf serum.

Tissue cultures, particularly those where capillaries can be formed, are an excellent model for studying the factors involved in capillary growth. Alternative methods that have been applied much more extensively are observations in tissue chambers, in the chick chorioallantoic membrane, and in the rabbit cornea. These methods are described in the chapter by Shepro in this *Handbook*, and only some findings are mentioned here.

Tissue Chambers and Avascular Regions

Transparent chambers of different types have been used for observation of growing vessels since the first description of this method by Sandison (362, 363). Williams (432) and more recently Nims and Irwin (285) have described in detail the different types of chambers used. The great advantage of this method is the possibility of observing vessels in unanesthetized animals for a long period of time in the same area. A limitation is the fact that implantation of any chamber—however carefully performed—represents trauma, and consequently the growth of vessels is connected with wound healing. This method allowed for great progress in the knowledge of capillary growth, but because wound healing is accompanied by formation of connective tissue some confusion was caused over the origin of the newly growing capillaries. Thus

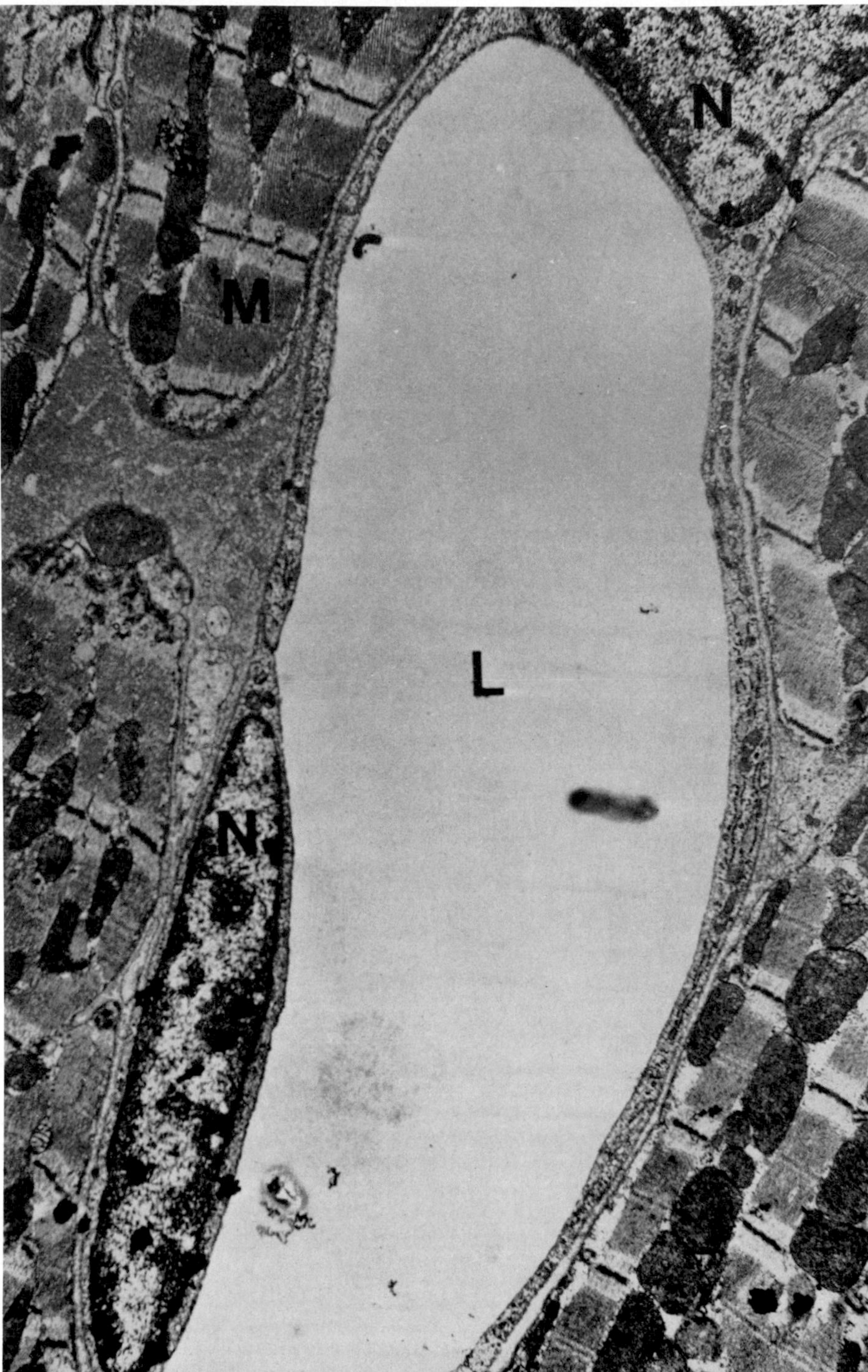

FIG. 11. Electron-microscope autoradiograph showing proliferative activity of capillary in rat heart in experimental cardiac hypertrophy induced by swimming. Endothelial nuclei (*N*) show labeling with [^{3}H]thymidine. *M*, myocardial cells; *L*, capillary lumen. [From Mandache et al. (257).]

it was asserted at one stage that growth of endothelial cells can be induced or can proceed from other cells such as fibroblasts (5). Careful studies by Clark and Clark (80, 83, 84) and other investigators showed, however, that new endothelium could develop from endothelial cells only.

RABBIT EAR CHAMBERS. Rabbit ear chambers were introduced by Sandison (362–364) and used extensively by Clark and Clark (80, 81, 83, 84). The basic pattern of growth was previously described. Growth was much faster in infected areas and was stopped when vessels came into contact with epidermis or

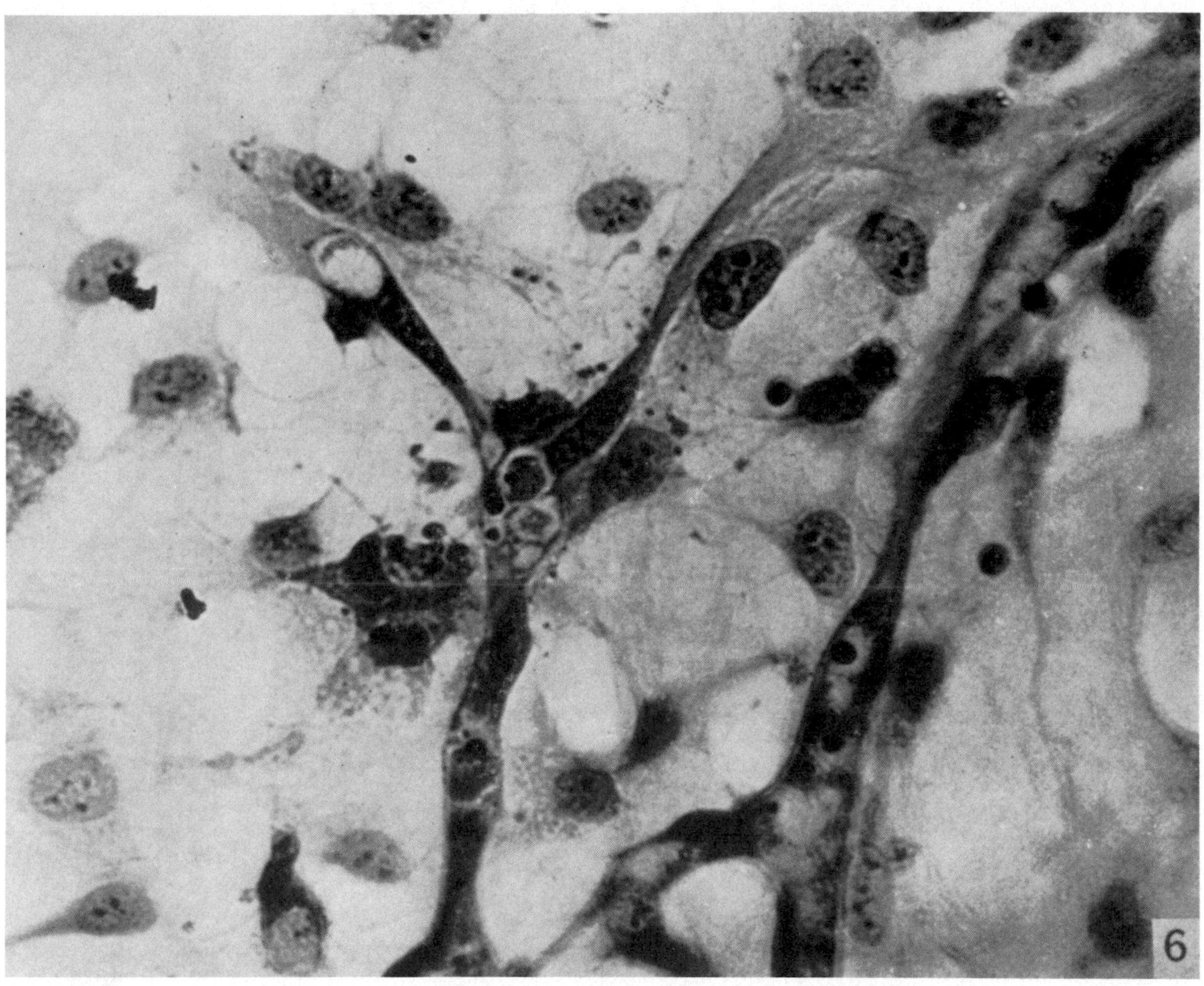

FIG. 12. Strands of capillary endothelium from a 6-day-old skin tissue culture of a 7-day-old chick embryo, with formation of small lumina with or without blood cells. [From Lewis (240).]

cartilage (83). Brånemark (51) modified this method for use in human subcutaneous tissue and was able to make extensive observations not only of capillary growth but also of capillary flow over a period of many months.

DIFFUSION CHAMBERS. In a dorsal skin flap in mice, Algire et al. (3) and Merwin and Algire (266) implanted transparent chambers formed by two Millipore filters with a graft of tissue between them. The chambers allowed observation of vessel growth in the implant as well as in the host. When the implant was normal tissue, such as thyroid gland (266) or heart (172), the vessels grew toward the host tissue and the vessels in the host were dilated but showed no sprouts. When, on the other hand, the implant consisted of pieces of tumors, a rich network of vessels was observed growing from the host toward the implant (266). Fulton et al. (141) used hamster cheek pouch for studies of vessels in vivo, and Warren and Shubik (425) described proliferation of vessels in this tissue after implantation of pieces of melanoma. In later studies Greenblatt and Shubik (173) and Greenblatt et al. (171) implanted diffusion chambers in hamster cheek pouch [similar to those described by Algire et al. (3)] to determine how vessel growth in the host is affected by foreign tissue such as tumors (173) and leukocytes (307) that are not in direct contact with the host tissue.

RABBIT CORNEA. This normally avascular tissue was first used by Arnold (17) for observation of vessel growth induced by injection of vermilion. Rabbit corneas were also used by Langham (237) to test the angiogenic effect of alloxan and by Zauberman et al. (445) to test different vasoactive substances (e.g., acetylcholine, bradykinin, serotonin). Recently both rabbit cornea and its anterior chamber were used to study vessel growth or its inhibition after implantation of different tumors or administration of factors that stimulate or inhibit vessel growth (26, 87, 147, 149, 157).

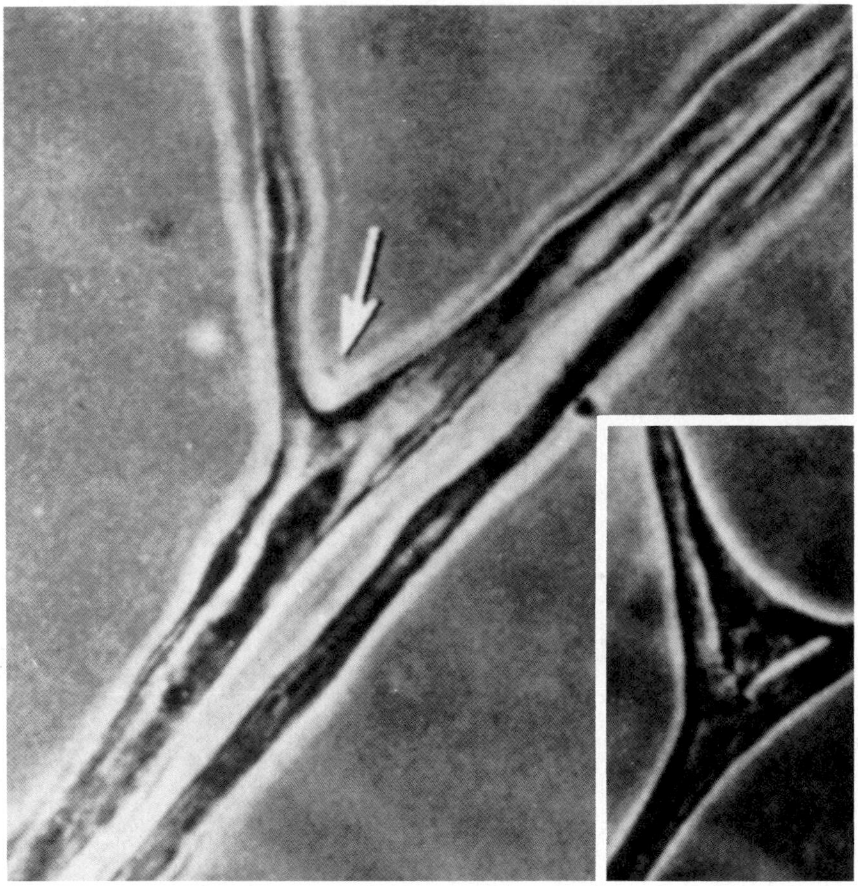

FIG. 13. Branches formed in vitro by capillary endothelial cells derived from human foreskin. *Arrow*, position of an endothelial cell that lies at the intersection of two limbs. *Inset*, another branch bridged by the endothelial cell from which the branch was formed. [From Folkman and Haudenschild (130). Reprinted by permission from *Nature*, copyright 1980 Macmillan Journals Limited.]

CHICK CHORIOALLANTOIC MEMBRANE. Folkman and Cotran (128) provide a helpful overview of different methods of observation of vessel growth, particularly in connection with tumor angiogenic factor. Their work also involved the use of chick chorioallantoic membrane. Ausprunk et al. (29) showed that implants of adult tissues on the chick chorioallantoic membrane were not vascularized and disintegrated within 9 days nor did they induce vascular growth in the membrane. Implants of embryonic tissue became vascularized but did not cause vessel growth outside the implant, whereas tumors produced vessel growth in the membrane [Fig. 14; (128)]. No detectable angiogenesis was created by human fibroblasts (228), but most foreign bodies produced inflammation connected with capillary growth (215). Recently Stockley (389) showed that implantation of glass rings containing a pool of fluid does not induce angiogenesis on its own, and this allows for study of the angiogenic effects of different agents added to the fluid without the complication of inflammatory reaction.

GROWTH OF VESSELS DURING PRENATAL AND POSTNATAL DEVELOPMENT

Arey (14), Frist and Stemerman (136), and Wagner (421) gave a good description of the development of the vascular bed in vertebrate embryos. In human embryos blood circulation begins at 4 wk gestation when simple diffusion of nutrients and waste products to and from the yolk sac is no longer adequate. The vessels in the embryo start to grow independently rather than by migration of cells from the extraembryonal endothelium of the yolk sac as originally suggested by His (191). Reagan (328) has shown that capillary development can occur even when the communication between extraembryonic and intraembryonic tissue has been destroyed.

According to Roux (343) the formation of the vascular system occurs in three stages: *1*) primary differentiation (predetermined genetically), *2*) a transitional state where hereditary factors are gradually overruled by functional adaptation, and *3*) final formation of vessels entirely by mechanical forces in the circulation. Hereditary factors are important in the development of the aorta and large veins, but even in these cases the differentiation starts from an endothelial network (122). This network develops from mesenchymal cells (271) that differentiate into angioblasts and further differentiate into blood cells and endothelial cells as described by Sabin (356):

primitive mesoderm → mesenchymal cells

→ angioblasts ↗ blood islands–erythroblasts
↘ endothelium

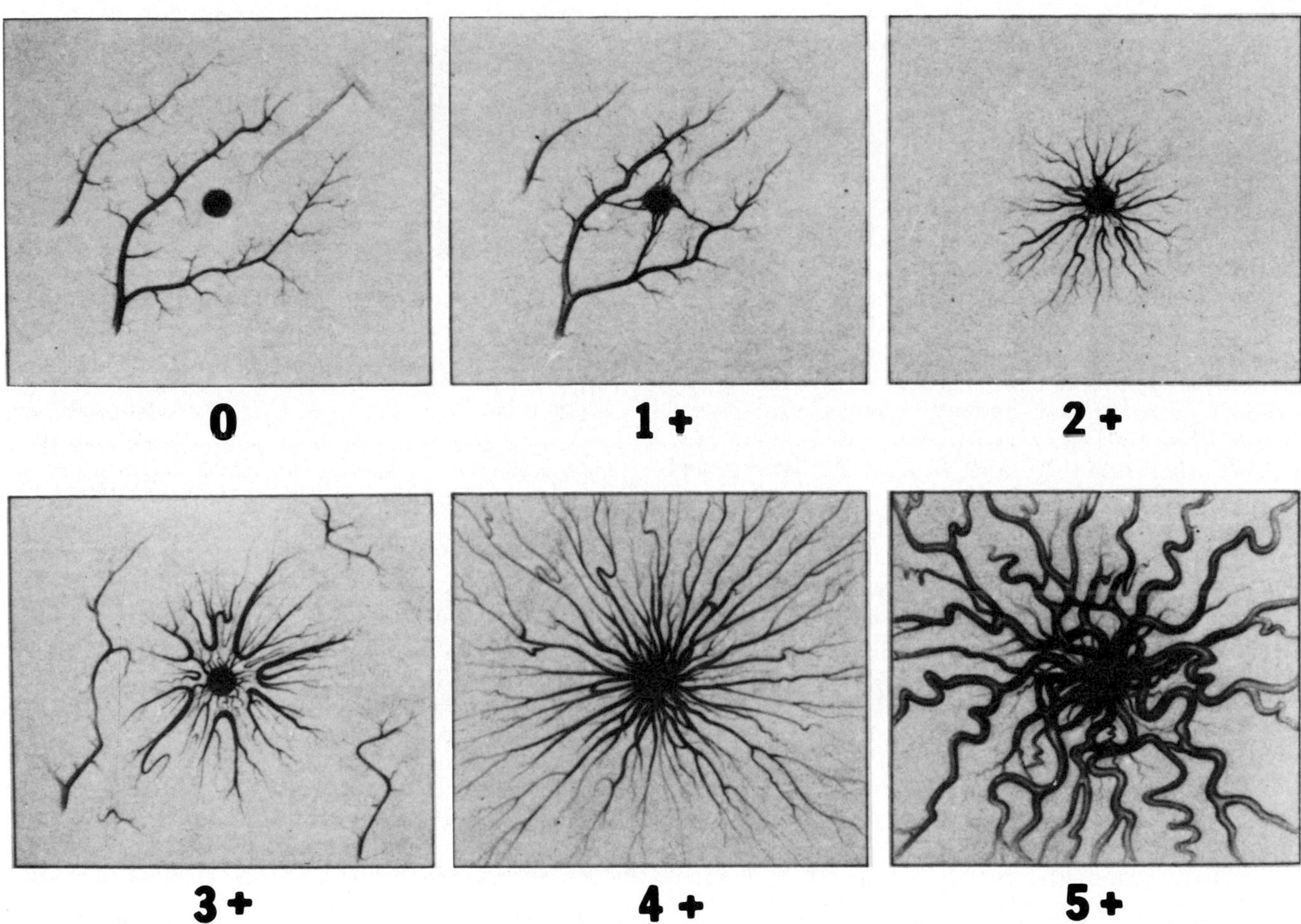

FIG. 14. Chick chorioallantoic membrane with implanted 1-mm Millipore filter disk soaked in tumor angiogenic factor placed over a tiny needle hole in the membrane. New vascular loops consisting of capillaries and venules converge on the filter within 48–72 h. The density of these new vessels is assigned a grade from 0 to 5+. [From Folkman and Cotran (128).]

The endothelial cells then divide and grow by sprouting, although it has recently been suggested by Ausprunk et al. (28) that lengthening of capillaries is more important in vessel growth than sprouting is. Both result in producing plexuses from which individual vessels can differentiate. The behavior and character of the capillaries is influenced from the beginning by the tissue in which they grow, possibly as a result of some metabolites specific to the tissues. In older embryos and in adult animals the endothelium is always derived from endothelial cells (123), except in bone marrow where it can grow from histiocytes (357). Remodeling of the vascular bed depends on mechanical factors related to the circulation of blood, but other factors are also involved. Loeb (251) and Stockland (388) found that the development of circulation in fish embryos proceeded even after the heartbeat had been stopped by addition of KCl or alcohol to the water in which they were kept. Knower (229) observed normal vessel growth up to 5 days after the heart had been removed from frog embryos, and Chapman (72) described similar results in chick embryos. From these experiments it was concluded that hypoxia and/or accumulation of waste products can create an impetus for angiogenesis (136).

Development of larger vessels from the capillary network proceeds by the apposition of pericytes and/or fibroblasts that then differentiate into vascular smooth muscle cells; these in turn produce elastic and collagen fibers (14, 221). The amount of collagen in the rat thoracic aorta trebled within the first 5 days after birth and again between 5 and 11 days, with a corresponding increase in the volume of the elastic lamina [3.7 and 2.3 times, respectively (239)]. The amount of actomyosin, protein, and DNA increased up to 5 wk postnatally (374) at a time when the endothelial growth rapidly decreased. Schwartz and Benditt (373) found 10%–20% labeling in the nuclei of the aortic endothelium of the newborn and 0.3%–1.5% in 3-mo-old rats. Smooth muscle cells also changed during postnatal development from predominantly secretory to predominantly contractile at 3 mo, and at the same time their orientation changed from predominantly circular to predominantly oblique

(90). Development of the coronary vessels is similar to that of the aorta (44), but different organs have different specific features.

Heart

The embryonic heart in birds and mammals receives its nutrition first from sinusoids located between the spongy musculature. Coronary vessels start to develop in the course of embryonic growth, the first signs of the veins appearing earlier than the arteries (168, 241, 297). Capillaries start to grow from the coronary vessels, but they are also formed from the sinusoids. With the growth of muscle fibers the intertrabecular spaces become narrower and gradually change into the venous ends of the capillaries; arteriolar ends are formed by sprouting from the branches of the coronary arteries (351). The transformation from sinusoidal to capillary supply takes about 30–48 h (105), and capillary growth proceeds from the subepicardial layer toward the sinuses (Fig. 15). Such development is similar in embryonic hearts of chickens (155, 350), rabbits (168), pigs (39), rats (105, 296, 298, 414), and humans (242), with the final arrangement of three capillary layers (subendocardial, middle, and subepicardial) occurring at different postnatal periods. The subepicardial layer in rat hearts is fully developed on the 2nd day after birth; the subendocardial is fully developed on the 5th postnatal day in the right ventricle and the 9th day in the left ventricle (296).

Primitive capillaries have no basement lamina, which in rats appears as a continuous fully developed layer only at birth (298). Capillary length and surface area increase postnatally 2–3 times more rapidly than myocardial mass during the first 11 days after birth (292), and there is faster growth of capillaries than muscle cells up to 45 days (321). From then on muscle fibers grow faster and CD gradually decreases [Table 1; (321, 325).] The ultrastructure of all developing capillaries is as described in *Electron Microscopy*, p. 172.

Central Nervous System

The first vessels to appear in rat cerebral cortex show a similar sinusoidal arrangement to that in the heart (35). Immature capillaries develop by sprouting from preexisting vessels in the embryo at about the 15th day. Further development is associated with the diminution of the extracellular space (35), and gradual maturation of capillaries takes place after birth, a well-defined basement lamina having developed by 14 days (109). Very few capillaries are patent at birth; there are numerous endothelial cells enclosing a slitlike lumen [Fig. 16; (179)]. The number of sprouts in the superficial third of the cortex decreases rapidly after birth from 65/mm^2 at 1 day to 5/mm^2 at 5 days, but then increases again to 35/mm^2 at 10–11 days. The sprouts were absent at 21 days. The second peak

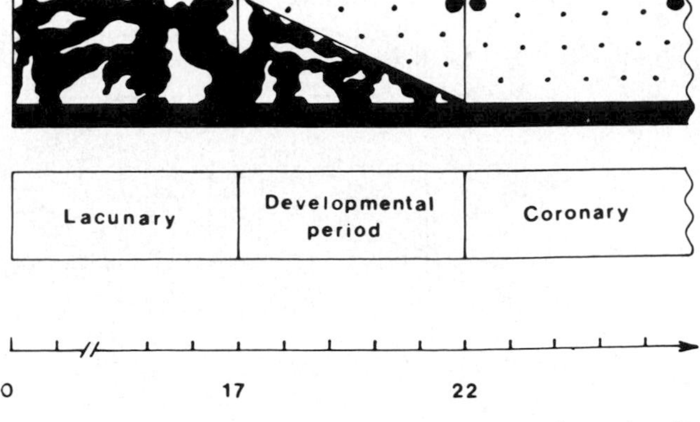

FIG. 15. Development of the terminal vascular bed in rat heart in prenatal and postnatal periods, showing the sinusoidal and cardiac capillary nutritive system. [From Oštádal et al. (299).]

in the angiogenic activity coincides with the beginning of intracortical myelination (343a). Increase in the volume density of blood vessels in connection with myelination was also described in the developing mouse spinal cord (391a). The gaps between endothelial cells in the telencephalon are very wide and decrease gradually, with tight junctions appearing in chickens as late as 30 days after hatching (106). Millen and Hess (270) have shown that the blood-brain barrier in rats is developed at birth. Capillary volume increases from 0.81% of the tissue (corpus callosum) at birth to 2.9% in 6-wk-old kittens. From this time on, gradual decrease appears (190) similar to that in CD in the heart. Pessacq and Reissenweber (306a) described saccular sprouts in the cortex of newborn babies (dying from asphyxia) that were found together with fibroblastlike angioblastic cells differentiated from glia, but no other data from human material are available.

Skeletal Muscles

The terminal vascular bed in rat skeletal muscle at birth consists mainly of capillaries, with arterioles and venules developing later (387). By postnatal day 11 there are quite a number of capillary sprouts representing up to 50% of the capillary network; these gradually disappear by 21 days postpartum (426). The ultrastructure of the endothelial cells is typical of growing endothelium (427). The number of mitochondria, ribosomes, and other organelles per capillary cross section decreases up to 1 mo while the number of pinocytotic vesicles gradually increases. Tight junctions appear first in 14-day-old rats. The fast growth of capillaries coincides with the differentiation of fiber types and increased motor activity (368). As is evident from Table 1 capillary growth gradually slows although fiber growth continues, and CD decreases while C/F increases—the latter being linearly related

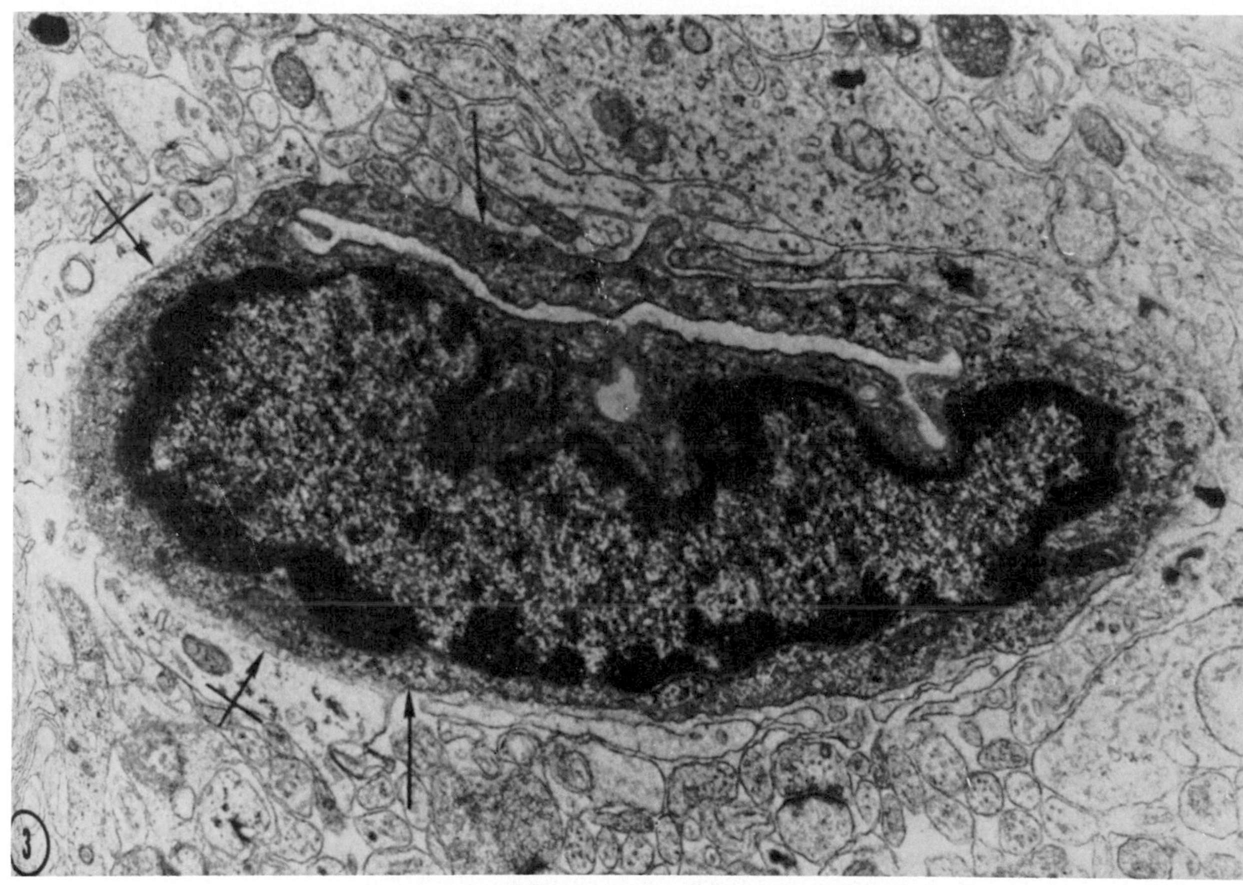

FIG. 16. Nonpatent blood capillary with a slitlike lumen from neonatal rat spinal cord. *Arrows*, areas whose astrocytic end feet are absent and where the basement lamina is composed of thin flocculent material. *Crossed arrows*, where astrocytic end feet enclose the vessel wall and the basement lamina is thicker. [From Hannah and Nathaniel (179).]

to fiber size in different muscles in guinea pigs (379) and rats (332).

Skin

Skin capillaries in a newborn infant form a network that is gradually organized into a subpapillary plexus at 3 mo by the formation of capillary loops and arteriovenous anastomosis (306). Regions that undergo a greater degree of stretch, such as elbows or knees, have more elongated and coiled capillaries sometimes with signs of sprouting even in adults (347).

Retina

The development of vessels in the retina is of particular interest because it could help to elucidate the regulation of capillary growth under pathological conditions such as retrolental fibroplasia or diabetic microangiopathy. Retinal vessels start to develop in human fetuses at about 4 mo, progressing from the optic nerve but not spreading over the whole retina until birth (93). Growth stops when mural cells (a form of pericytes) are apposed to the capillaries (235). The greatest part of the capillary growth starts on the venous side at a rate of 0.1 mm/day and spreads toward the neighboring artery. It stops before reaching the artery, which accounts for a capillary-free zone around retinal arteries in human embryos. In kittens almost the whole retina becomes vascularized by the 8th day after birth, and the vascular network is completed by 22 days (268). Since blood-retina exchange occurs through a layer of glia cells, the capacity of glia to synthesize and store glycogen is inversely proportional to the vascularity of the retina (93). These findings suggest that hypoxia as well as glycolytic metabolism plays a role in the normal development of retinal vascular growth.

Changes in Vascular Growth With Aging

Most changes occurring during postnatal development and increasing age were described in large vessels (91) and are beyond the scope of this chapter. There are, however, some findings in microcirculation worth mentioning. The capillary basement lamina becomes thicker and contains increasingly more mucopolysaccharides (32). Capillaries and venules show sacculations (151), and arterioles and capillaries in human cerebral cortex become wider (209). Rakušan and Poupa (324) suggested that capillaries in rat heart disappear with increasing age. In skeletal muscle, on the other hand, CD increases partly because the fiber diameter becomes smaller (301) and partly because the muscles become slower and have a higher content of oxidative enzymes (98), probably because of degeneration of fast motor units.

COMPARISON OF DIFFERENTIATION AND GROWTH OF MICROCIRCULATION

Growth of vessels during development was first observed in amphibians (154, 313, 342). Billroth (42) described similar patterns of growth in chick embryos, and Bobritzky (47) extended these observations to the embryos of dogs, rabbits, pigs, and sheep. The basic pattern of growth is similar everywhere (see *Light Microscopy*, p. 172), with lymphatic vessels developing independently of blood vessels (76).

The development of microcirculation in the heart varies, however, in different species. Poupa et al. (318) and Oštádal et al. (297, 299) recently described in detail the differentiation of the terminal vascular bed of the heart in relation to phylogeny (Fig. 17). Amphibians have almost completely spongy musculature that receives the supply of nutrients by direct diffusion. Fish and reptiles have a part of the subepicardial layer (10%–25%) supplied by a capillary network that in reptiles also supplies some trabeculae of the spongy musculature. Birds and mammals have no sinuses except during early embryonic development (Fig. 15).

The change from sinusoidal to capillary arrangement of the vascular bed varies in different species and is linked to the growth of the coronary arteries and veins. The first signs of coronary veins appear in chicken embryos on the 6th day of incubation and in the rat on about the 16th day gestation. Coronary arteries start to grow after 7–8 days incubation in chickens (350), around the 17th day gestation in rats (105), and between 6 and 7 wk gestation in human embryos (241, 243). Actual transformation of sinusoidal to capillary supply begins on the 12th day incubation in chickens and spreads to the outer two-thirds of the ventricular muscle by the 14th day (351). Primitive endothelial cells capable of secreting components for the formation of the basement lamina appear in chick embryos as early as 60–72 h after the start of incubation (278), but a continuous basement lamina is not present until after hatching (218). In rats the gradual change from sinusoids to capillaries begins on the 17th day gestation and is not completed until after birth.

Capillaries in human embryonic hearts start to develop between the 6th and 7th wk gestation (241, 242), at about the same time that the bases of coronary arteries appear as solid buds. In humans the transition from sinusoidal to capillary supply takes place much earlier in terms of the period of gestation than in rats or even chickens. The percentage of compact layers supplied by capillaries rapidly increases to almost 90% in embryos 10–11 wk old (243).

CAPILLARY GROWTH IN NORMAL ADULT TISSUES

Capillary growth is rarely observed in normal adult tissues except in tissues that show cyclical growth such as the corpus luteum in the ovary (86), the endometrium (128), hair follicles (377), and deer antlers (24). It can, however, occur in the heart, brain,

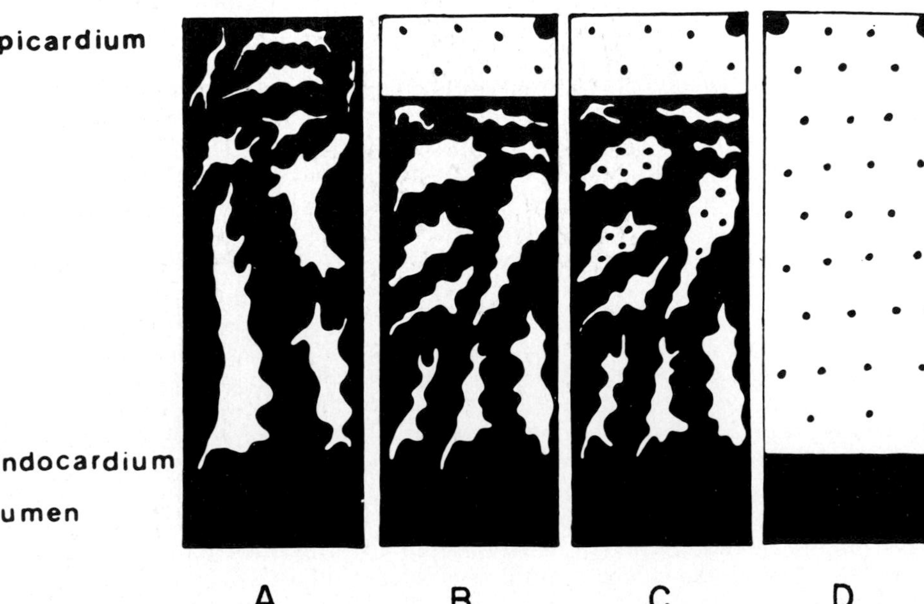

FIG. 17. Different types of myocardial blood supply in phylogenesis. *A*: spongiose musculature supplied from the ventricular lumen of amphibians. *B*: in fish the inner spongiose layer is covered by an outer compact musculature with vascular supply. *C*: in reptiles there is a similar arrangement as in fish, but capillaries are also present in some trabeculae of the spongy musculature. *D*: compact musculature supplied from coronary vessels in birds and mammals. [From Oštádal et al. (299).]

and skeletal muscles during exposure to hypoxia, and in the heart and skeletal muscles during some types of exercise. It was also described in fast skeletal muscles indirectly stimulated for more than 4–7 days, in long-term bradycardially paced hearts, and in muscles and hearts of animals after long-term administration of vasodilating drugs.

Capillary Growth in Skeletal Muscles During Training

Krogh (232) found that CD in contracting muscles is 10 times higher than in resting muscles. This initiated a great number of investigations aimed at finding out whether CD increases with training (202). However, for reasons mentioned in the beginning of this chapter, most of these studies showing an increase in functional CD in muscles in trained compared with untrained animals were not really indicative of capillary growth. Only recently has reliable evidence been presented demonstrating capillary growth during training.

Andersen and Henriksson (8) found a significant increase in both cytochrome *c* oxidase and SDH as well as increased CD in biopsies from human vastus lateralis muscle after 8 wk of endurance training. The C/F increased earlier—after only 5 wk—when the number of fibers per area had decreased but the number of capillaries was unchanged. This was a result of muscle fiber hypertrophy. A higher CD was also found in endurance-trained than in untrained muscles by Brodal et al. (55), although in a similar study with fewer subjects and muscle samples Saltin et al. (361) and Hermansen and Wachtlová (189) found no increase in CD. (There was, however, an increase in C/F also caused by fiber hypertrophy.) Brodal et al. (55) and Ingjer and Brodal (213) found higher CD in endurance-trained than untrained men and women with very little increase in fiber diameters, thus indicating real capillary growth.

In another study in humans (212) with biopsies taken before and after 24 wk of endurance training, C/F increased by 28% and the number of capillaries surrounding slow oxidative fibers increased more than those surrounding fast glycolytic fibers. There was a considerably greater increase in the number of subsarcolemmal mitochondria in slow oxidative than in fast glycolytic fibers, and it appears that the increase in CD was related more closely to the mitochondrial content than to fiber types. This finding in humans agrees with the experiments by Mai et al. (254) in guinea pigs and by Ogawa (289) in rats trained on a treadmill, in which the number of capillaries surrounding oxidative fibers increased more than those surrounding fast glycolytic fibers. A greater increase in CD was also found in the central red than in the peripheral white part of the biceps brachia in rats trained by tonic exercise on ladders (447). These findings could be explained by the fact that submaximal work performed during endurance training activates predominantly slow oxidative fibers, whereas fast glycolytic fibers are only active during maximal or supramaximal contraction of a very short duration (153, 274, 399). The study of Michel et al. (269a) further supports this suggestion: they found a significant increase in C/F in different mixed muscles of swine trained 3 days/wk for 6 mo but not in almost purely glycolytic muscle (psoas). Pařízková et al. (302) and Müller (277) found hardly any change in C/F in trained rat soleus (84% slow oxidative) in which the area of subsarcolemmal mitochondria had increased. This suggests that the amount of activity superimposed on normally very active soleus was not great enough to produce an increase in CD, although it was sufficient to produce an increase in aerobic capacity. Unfortunately the experiments were not carried out for a sufficiently long period to show whether any capillary growth would have been found later. Increased CD was also described in young but not in adult rats trained by swimming (2). The same group (248) did not find any changes in the incorporation of [^{3}H]thymidine into capillary endothelium in skeletal muscles of adult rats under similar conditions even though they did observe capillary proliferation in the heart.

Exercise thus seems to produce an increase in CD that can be explained by capillary growth in young animals or, if performed for a sufficiently long time (minimum 8 wk), in adults. This growth appears in the vicinity of permanently active slow oxidative fibers and may perhaps be preceded by an increase in the oxidative capacity.

Capillary Growth in Skeletal Muscles During Long-Term Electrical Stimulation

More-active animals have a higher number of mitochondria in muscle fibers and higher CD than less-active ones. This applies to fish (275, 276), wild and laboratory rats, hare and rabbits (417), and Japanese waltzers, rapidly moving mice with a disturbance of the vestibular apparatus (10). It has also been known since the time of Ranvier (326) that slowly contracting postural muscles with a high oxidative capacity have a high CD, whereas physiological flexors involved in short-lasting movements have a high glycolytic capacity and low CD.

Buller et al. (58) were able to change the contractile properties of slow postural muscles as well as fast muscles by cross innervation. Romanul and Pollock (337) showed that fast muscles innervated by a nerve originally supplying a slow muscle had not only a prolonged speed of contraction but also a high activity of oxidative enzymes and high CD. Converse changes were observed in slow muscles reinnervated by a nerve originally supplying fast muscles. Romanul (336) suggested that this change, which obviously induces capillary growth, may be a result of different rates of axon discharge and different amounts of released acetylcholine. Salmons and Vrbová (360) have utilized the fact that slow muscles have a different pattern of activity (continuous low frequency at 5–10 Hz) than fast muscles (whose fibers are activated intermittently giving bursts of short-lasting tetanic contractions). They were able to change the contractile properties of fast-contracting (fast-twitch) muscles in rabbits by chronic stimulation of their nerves at slow nerve frequency (by using low voltage and short stimulus duration to avoid stimulation of autonomic nerve fibers). The same frequency of stimulation applied for 8 h/day increased the activity of oxidative enzymes and decreased that of glycolytic enzymes (309), and it produced an increase in CD (56, 100). The muscles did not hypertrophy as they do during exercise. The average fiber diameter in extensor digitorum longus (EDL) stimulated for 28 days decreased from 72 ± 1.25 μm to 65 ± 1.0 μm, accompanied by disappearance of large fast glycolytic fibers. Consequently C/F increased to the value normally found in slow soleus muscle (56); a small increase in both CD and C/F appeared after only 4 days of such stimulation (Fig. 18). This preceded the increase in the activity of oxidative enzymes estimated chemically in muscle homogenates (309). The doubling of CD after 28 days of stimulation could only be explained by capillary growth, and this was confirmed by identification of sprouts in rat extensor hallucis proprius and rabbit tenuissimus stimulated for 7–12 days [Fig. 19; (282)]. Both saclike and tapering sprouts, similar in appearance to sprouts described by Clark and Clark (83), Cliff (88), and Schoefl (370), were found in muscles stimulated for 7 days. Their incidence increased to 4 sprouts per 10 capillaries (percentage similar to that found for CD) after 12–14 days of stimulation. The sprouts were more numerous on the venular side of the capillaries (Fig. 20), which were wider and more tortuous (Fig. 21). In these studies the growth of sprouts invariably started from a point at which the preexisting capillary was bent. Sprouts made connection to other capillaries whose lumens were too narrow for erythrocytes to pass through initially (Fig. 22) but which eventually widen and resemble normal capillar-

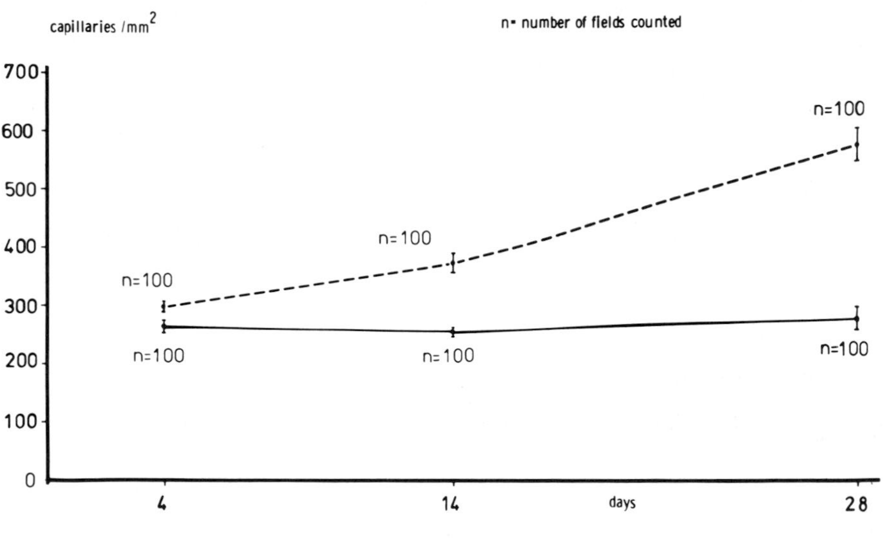

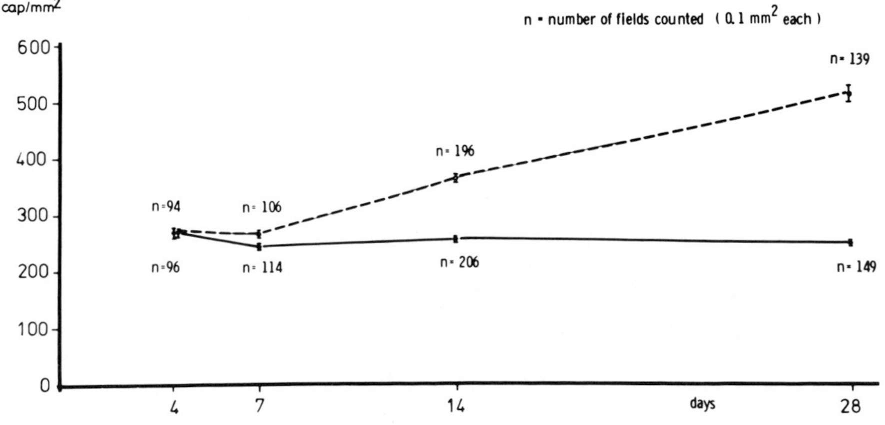

FIG. 18. *Broken lines*, CD in rabbit fast muscle, extensor digitorum longus (EDL). *Top*, stimulated continuously at 10 Hz or *bottom*, with equal numbers of stimuli in brief trains of 40 Hz. *Solid lines*, control muscles from contralateral side. Abscissa, days of stimulation. Means ± SE from several muscles at each period.

ies. No increase in CD and no sprouts were found in control or sham-operated muscles. The increase in CD in rat EDL again preceded the increase in the activity of oxidative enzymes (95).

Long-term stimulation of rabbit fast muscles at a pattern of frequency more similar to that occurring naturally in the muscles' supplying nerves (intermittent bursts of unfused tetani) did not change CD or C/F even after 28 days when electrically elicited contractions of 40 Hz were applied for 5 s every 100 s for 8 h/day (56). When the total number of impulses was increased to give the same number of stimuli per hour as the stimulation at 10 Hz (contractions at 40 Hz for 5 s, 3 times/min), no change in CD or C/F was found after 4 days (56). Prolonged stimulation for 14 and 28 days had a similar effect as stimulation at 10 Hz [Fig. 18; (206)]. At the same time the muscles changed from a mixed population of glycolytic and oxidative fibers to an apparently uniform population of highly oxidative fibers (Fig. 23). The qualitative increase in oxidative capacity preceded the increase in CD (99, 206). However, detailed quantitative examination of SDH activity in individual muscle fibers showed a 50% increase in fast glycolytic fibers stimulated for 4 days at 10 Hz and only a 20% increase in muscles stimulated at 40 Hz. The increase proceeded more rapidly in muscles stimulated at 10 Hz than 40 Hz, reaching 120% of the control values after 7 days in the former and 33% in the latter type of stimulation. There was no difference between the different types of stimulation after 14 or more days. Very little effect was found in fast oxidative fibers (310). Capillary growth in EDL muscle stimulated at 10 Hz for 4 days was found in the vicinity of the fast glycolytic fibers (108, 202a);

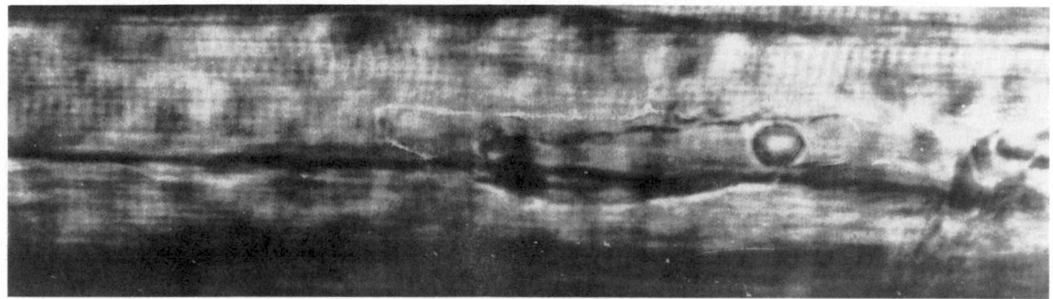

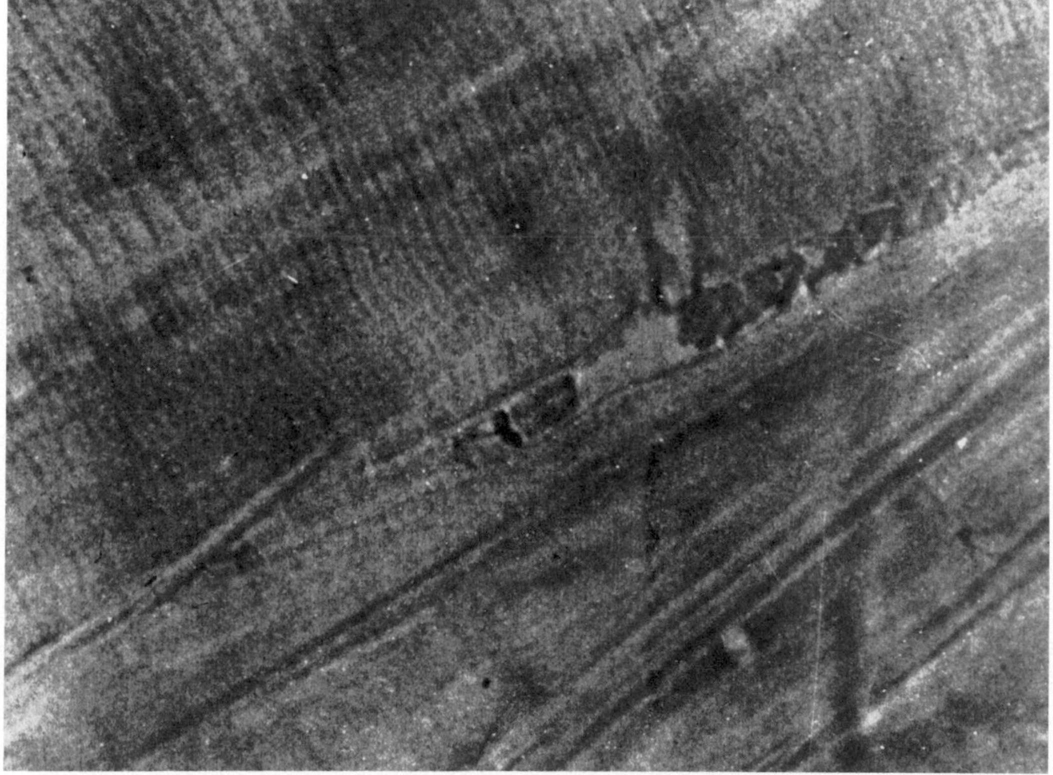

FIG. 19. Saclike sprout (*top*) and tapering sprout (*bottom*) in rat extensor hallucis proprius stimulated indirectly at 10 Hz for 12 days. [Adapted from Myrhage and Hudlická (281).]

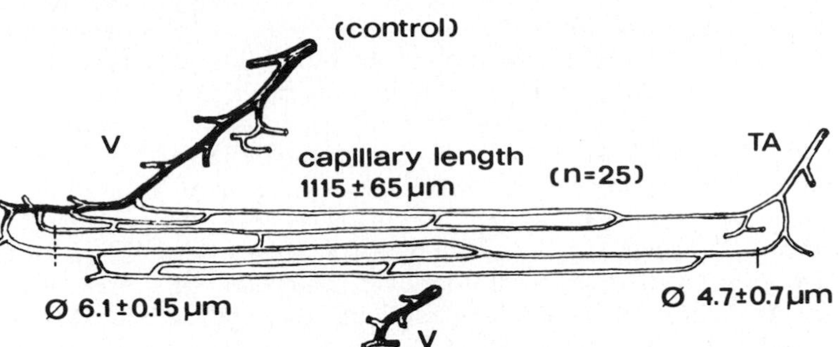

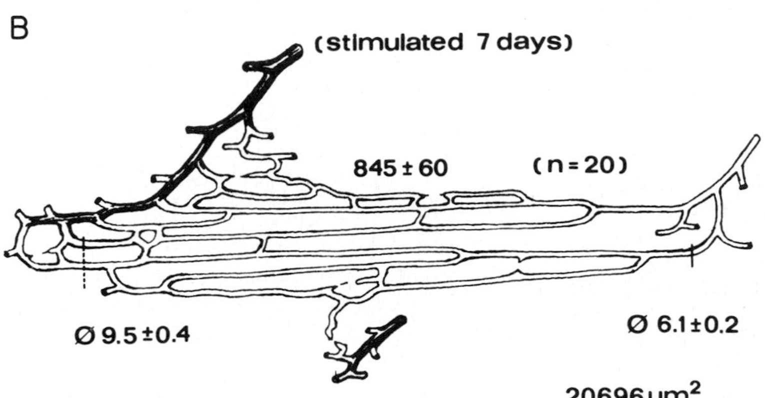

FIG. 20. *A*: schematic representation of capillary network illustrating branching pattern and capillary dimensions in rabbit tenuissimus muscle based on in vivo observations in a control muscle. *B*: after 7 days of stimulation. TA, terminal arteriole; V, two collecting venules. Note circle close to collecting venule and sprouts that occur after stimulation. At bottom of *B* a tortuous sprouting capillary is about to be connected to a new collecting venule. [From Myrhage and Hudlická (281).]

the increase in C/F in EDL muscle stimulated at 40 Hz for 7 days also showed preferential distribution of capillaries with respect to glycolytic fiber types.

All these results indicate that indirect muscle stimulation produces an increase in the activity of oxidative enzymes and in CD, affecting the fast glycolytic fibers first. Both types of stimulation increased CD much more than exercise. This may be because electrical stimulation activates all motor units (207), and its duration is much longer than in any type of exercise. Fast glycolytic fibers are activated equally with fast or slow oxidative fibers. Because their oxidative enzyme activity and CD are low and their glycogen stores are depleted, they may suffer from lack of nutrients and oxygen—a suspected stimulus for capillary growth.

Capillary Growth in Cardiac Muscle During Exercise

So-called athletic mammals have a higher CD in cardiac muscle than nonathletic ones of similar body weight (418–420), and flying birds have a higher CD than either of the previous groups (269, 323). It might thus be expected that training would considerably increase CD in the heart by stimulating capillary growth. This, however, does not appear to be so. Rakušan et al. (323) found only a small, insignificant increase in CD in flying pigeons compared with inactive ones, Hakkila (177) described a decrease in CD with no change in C/F in guinea pig hearts trained by treadmill running, and Pařízková et al. (302) found a small CD decrease in the hearts of trained adult laboratory rats. Tomanek (402) and Bloor and Leon (45) did not see any increase in CD in adult rats trained by treadmill running or swimming, although the latter authors found an increase in C/F. Increased CD (402) and capillary proliferation (410) were described in young rats. Since their hearts hypertrophied during exercise, increased CD must mean active capillary growth.

Ljungqvist and Unge (246–248) demonstrated a denser vascular bed and an increased incorporation of [^{3}H]thymidine into heart capillaries of rats trained by swimming, whereas Mandache et al. (257) showed, under the same conditions, the presence of mitosis in endothelial nuclei and an ultrastructure of capillary wall characteristic of growing capillaries (Fig. 24). Capillary proliferation was very obvious in young and growing rats but not in adults (410). Ogawa (287) found a lower CD in the subendocardial and a higher density in the middle layer of the ventricle in adult rats exercised by swimming. Rebel and Stegmann (329) described a considerable increase in chemically estimated alkaline phosphatase by swimming. The amount of this enzyme can serve as an index of

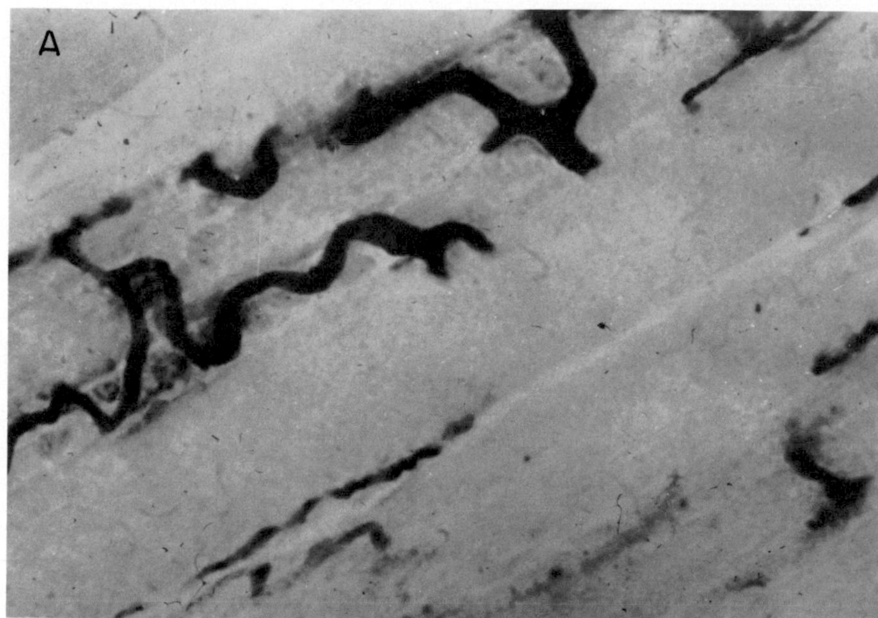

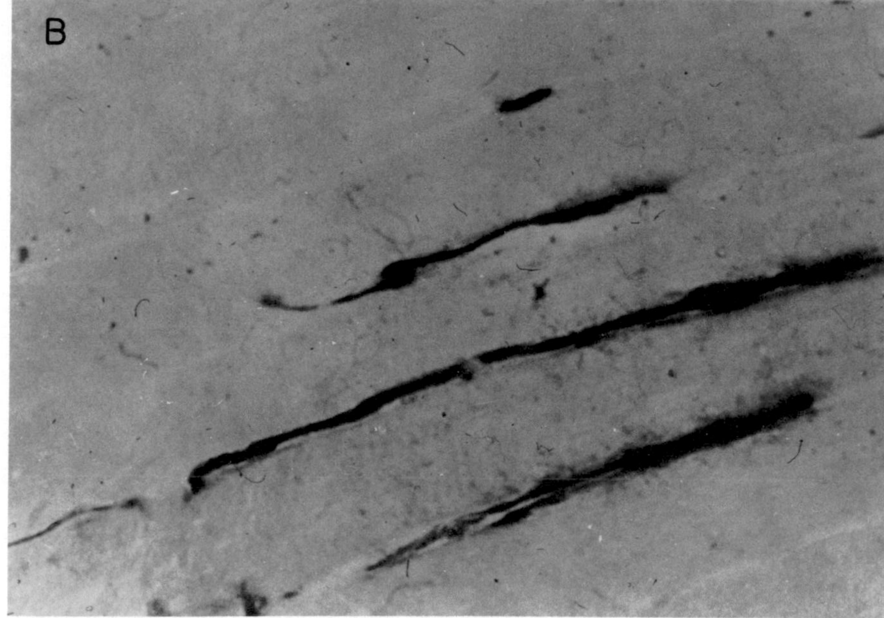

FIG. 21. *A*: longitudinal section of rat fast muscle, extensor hallucis proprius, stimulated at 10 Hz for 7 days. *B*: control muscle. Capillaries stained for alkaline phosphatase. [From Hudlická (202).]

vascular proliferation because it is mainly localized in capillary endothelium. Alkaline phosphatase was higher in young than in adult animals, and swimming slowed down its gradual decrease with age.

On the whole, capillary growth in the heart during training was convincingly demonstrated in young animals only. It may be possible, however, that the amount of training (usually swimming or treadmill running up to 1 h/day) was insufficient to produce it. It was shown previously that capillary growth in skeletal muscle was only achieved by very strenuous endurance training, and that athletic animals have a higher CD in their hearts than nonathletic ones also points to the fact that a constant load for a longer period may be necessary before any capillary growth occurs in adult hearts. Such an increased constant load is usually connected with resting bradycardia. Tomanek (402) found this condition in rats, together with increased CD, and it is known to be present in the hare but not in the rabbit. The former has a higher CD than the latter (419). It is also widely known that well-trained athletes have resting bradycardia, but there are no data on CD in such hearts.

Capillary Growth in the Heart During Long-Term Bradycardial Pacing

Wright and Hudlická (439) found up to 70% higher CD in rabbits whose heart rates were maintained at about half their original values by chronic electrical

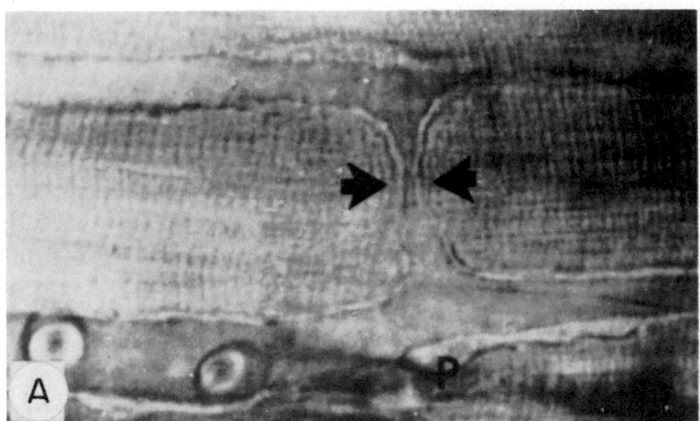

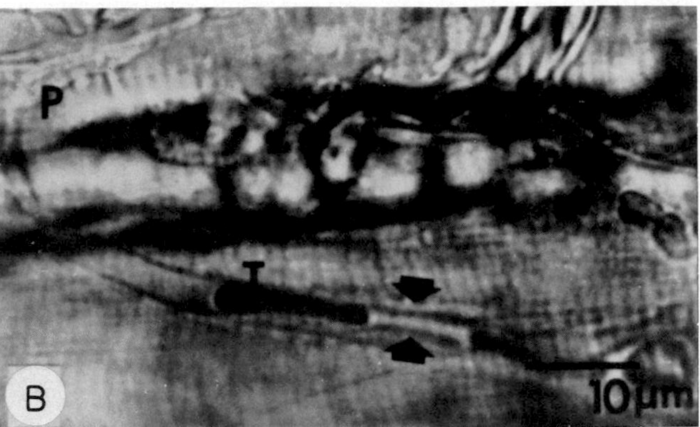

FIG. 22. Capillary sprouts in extensor hallucis proprius stimulated for 7 days. *Arrows*, recently fused sprouts form a capillary with a very narrow lumen. *Right*, capillary has a trapped and extremely deformed erythrocyte (*T*) in it. *P*, pericytes. [From Myrhage and Hudlická (281).]

bradycardial pacing (which eliminated every second heartbeat) for longer than 3 wk (Figs. 25 and 26). The paced hearts did not hypertrophy, so the increase in CD represented a real capillary growth of an extent not achieved by any other means. No increase in CD was found in sham-operated animals. The mechanism of this growth is unclear, except that increased flow during prolonged diastole may be involved.

Capillary Growth During Exposure to High Altitude

Exposure to high-altitude hypoxia leads to an increase in SDH activity in the diaphragm and red part of the rectus femoris muscle in guinea pigs (395) as well as to an increase in mitochondrial size and number in the red part of the vastus lateralis (412). Increased CD indicative of capillary growth was found in muscles of animals either born and bred at high altitude or chronically exposed to it. Valdivia (411) described a 26%–36% increase in CD in the red parts of different muscles of guinea pigs native to Peruvian mountains, and Eby and Banchero (114) found a considerably higher CD in dogs from a similar region compared with dogs bred at a much lower altitude. Exposure to high altitude was also associated with an increase in CD (33, 34, 69, 272), even if some of this effect may have been caused by a higher capillary tortuosity—one capillary may be counted twice if sectioned at a certain angle (11)—or to the lower temperatures usually present under high-altitude hypoxia (378). Wickler (429a) found a higher C/F in soleus of white-footed mice in winter than in summer, and Johnston (218a) described a C/F twice as high in carps acclimatized for 2 wk to 2°C than in those kept at 28°C.

Sillau et al. (378) did not find any increase in CD in guinea pigs exposed to hypoxia—in contrast to the findings of Valdivia (411)—and attributed the difference to the fact that other authors did not relate CD to fiber size. This seems to be an important factor in evaluating CD both in skeletal muscle and in the heart, larger hearts within the same species having a lower density (320, 438). Consequently all types of hypertrophy would be expected to have a lower CD, and increased CD in connection with heart hypertrophy is strongly indicative of capillary growth. Hypoxia produces hypertrophy of the right but not of the left ventricle and at the same time produces a higher CD in the right ventricle only (75, 167, 386, 407). Because CD in the left ventricle is usually unaffected (325a, 407), Turek et al. (409) suggested that low partial O_2 pressure (Po_2) per se could not be the stimulus for capillary growth. Rather, growth is more related to the increased work performed by the right ventricle necessary to overcome the increased pulmonary resistance found at high altitude and the subsequent increased blood flow in the right ventricle.

An increase in CD with exposure to high altitude was also found in the brain (295). Increased numbers of capillaries per tissue area were described in the brain, heart, and skeletal muscle (38, 272). Increased density of the vascular network in these organs was also induced by repeated transfusions of blood, which produced polycythemia similar to that found during high-altitude exposure (272). This finding suggests that hypoxia per se is probably not the stimulus responsible for capillary growth.

GROWTH OF MICROCIRCULATION UNDER PATHOLOGICAL CONDITIONS

Hypertrophy and Atrophy

Most of the studies on capillary growth—or rather its absence—in hypertrophy (other than that connected with exercise) were done on the heart. Few studies have been done on skeletal muscles and kidneys.

When evaluating CD in heart hypertrophy, one must bear in mind that it is related to either fiber

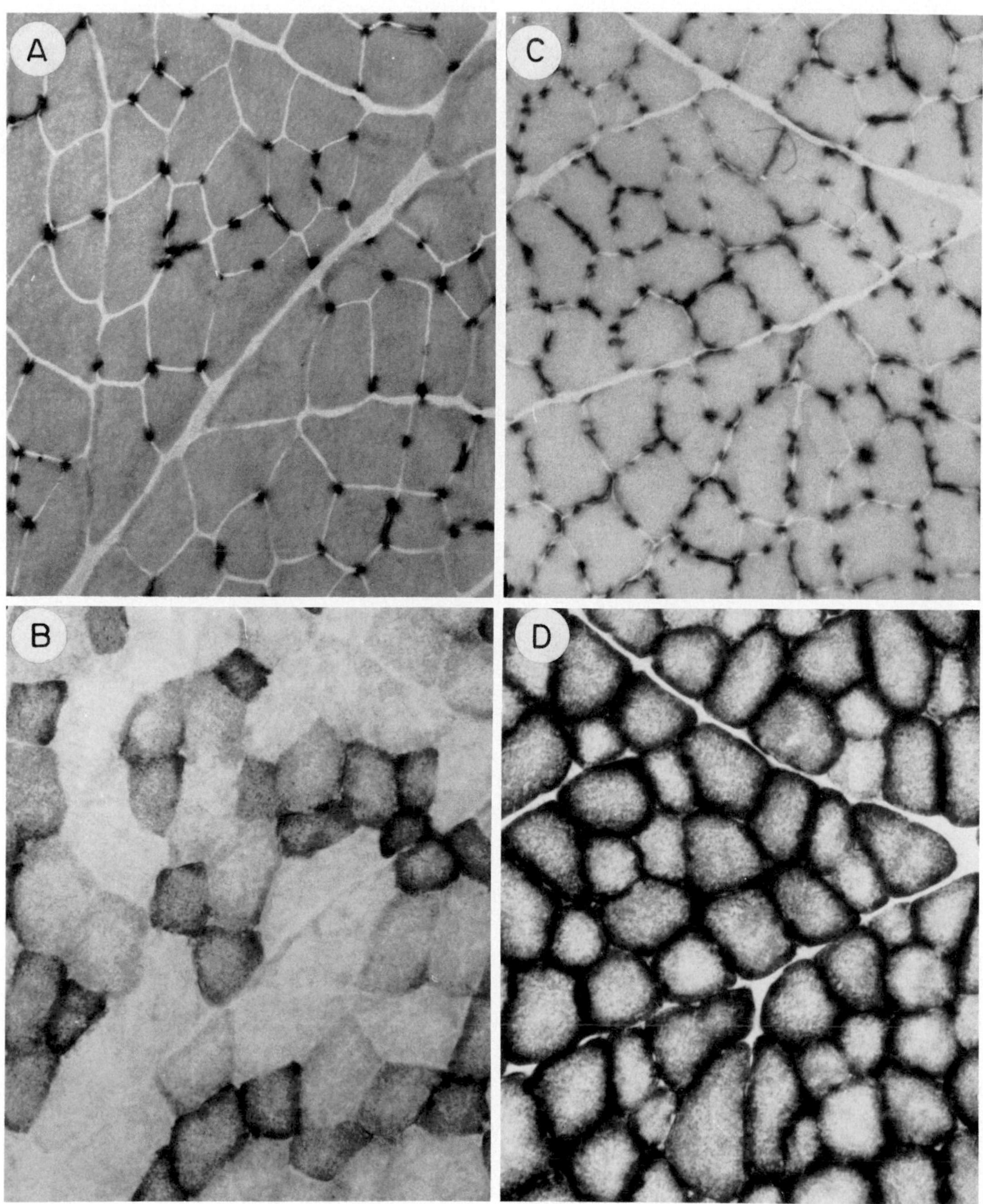

FIG. 23. Electrical stimulation induces the change from a mixed population of glycolytic and oxidative fibers to a homogeneous group of highly oxidative fibers. *A* and *B*: cross section from control rabbit extensor digitorum longus (*EDL*). *C* and *D*: *EDL* stimulated indirectly at 40 Hz for 28 days. Staining for alkaline phosphatase depicting capillary endothelium in *A* and *C*; staining for succinate dehydrogenase in *B* and *D*. (Courtesy of Dr. K. R. Tyler.)

diameters and/or heart weight. Figure 2 shows the relationship between fiber diameter and CD in normal and hypertrophic hearts. Wright (438) and Wright and Hudlická (439) showed a linear negative correlation between CD and heart weight in rabbit hearts up to 8 g. Heavier hearts had a more or less similar CD irrespective of weight (Fig. 26). It could thus be expected that all types of cardiac hypertrophy would have a lower CD, and most of the studies on pathologic heart hypertrophy confirm this assumption.

Turek et al. (408) described right ventricular hypertrophy in rats with ligated left coronary artery; CD was 1,639/mm^2 compared with 2,424/mm^2 in control hearts. Ljungqvist and his collaborators, as well as other investigators, found no signs of capillary proliferation with [^{3}H]thymidine, electron-microscope, or

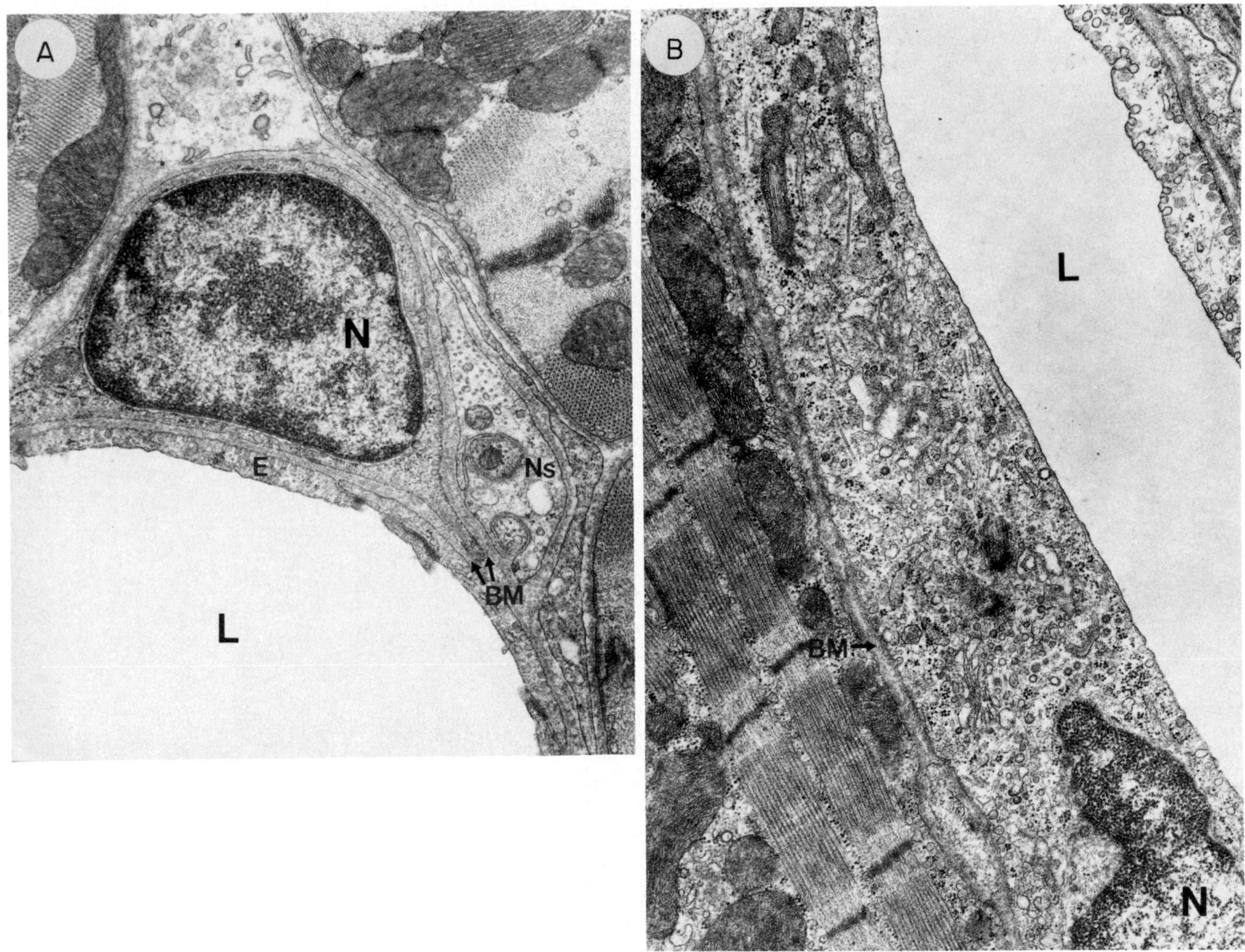

FIG. 24. *A*: part of myocardial blood capillary in normal rat. Endothelium (*E*) is thin; pericyte is enclosed between leaflets (*arrows*) of basement membrane (*BM*). *L*, lumen; *N*, nucleus; *Ns*, perivascular nervous structures. *B*: part of myocardial blood capillary in rat after 2 wk exercise by swimming showing thickened endothelium with increased numbers of cytoplasmic organelles. *N*, endothelium nucleus. [From Mandache et al. (257).]

injection methods in rat hearts made hypertrophic by aortic constriction or renal hypertension, although they did report capillary growth in hypertrophic hearts in rats trained by swimming (68, 246–248, 256, 257). Rakušan (320) gives a good review of CD in various types of heart hypertrophy induced by different experimental procedures (aortic constriction, hyperthyroidism, or cold acclimatization). In every case CD was lower in hypertrophic than in control hearts. The only type of cardiomegaly with increased CD was observed in rats made anemic by iron deficiency from the time of weaning. The increase in heart size in this case was caused by the increased number of fibers rather than by fiber hypertrophy, and capillaries grew together with the new fibers (317). However, the experiments were started on young animals in which capillary growth had not been completed, and it was impossible to say whether anemia presented a stimulus that only maintained capillary growth rather than initiating it.

Lund and Tomanek (252) found decreased CD in rats with heart hypertrophy induced by aortic constriction as well as in spontaneously hypertensive rats. The latter group had, however, higher CD for the same degree of hypertrophy than the former, indicating that some capillary growth may have occurred. They did not find any difference between CD in subendocardial and subepicardial regions. These results were not in agreement with those of Dowell (110), who measured a greater decrease in the activity of alkaline phosphatase (indicative of CD) in the subendocardial than in the subepicardial region in heart hypertrophy in rats with aortic constriction. Similar observations were reported by Gerdes et al. (144) on heart hypertrophy

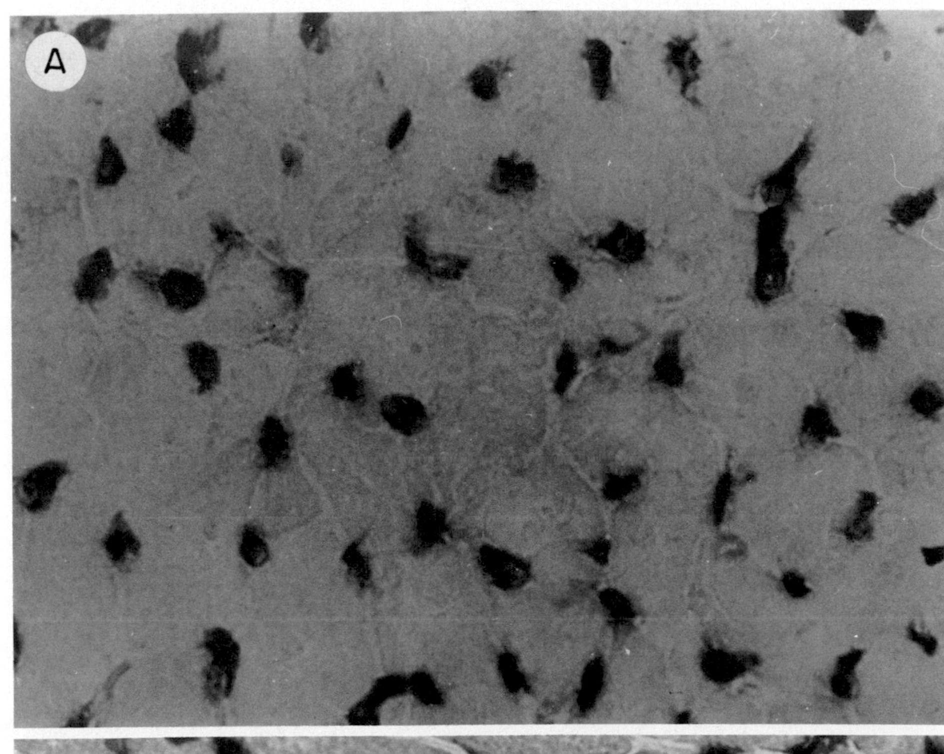

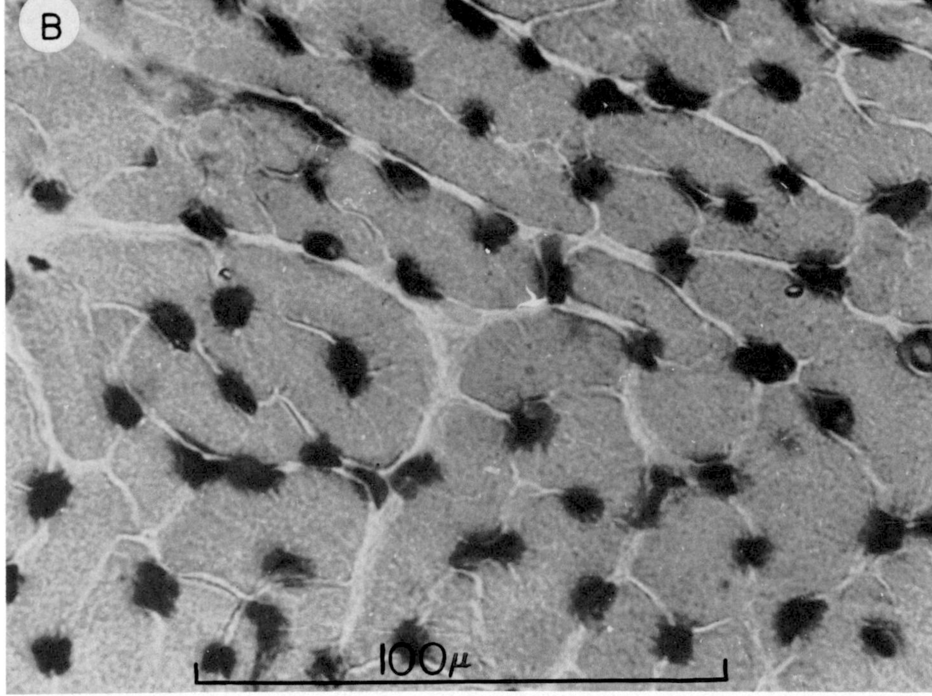

FIG. 25. Heart sections stained for alkaline phosphatase. *A*: control. *B*: chronically paced (52 days). The two hearts were very similar in weight. [From Wright and Hudlická (439).]

in hyperthyroid rats, by Wiener et al. (430) in rats with renal hypertension, and by Rakušan et al. (322) in rats with hypertrophy induced by aortocaval fistula.

On the whole, hypertrophic hearts show a lower CD under pathological compared with control situations, particularly in the subendocardial region. This region thus suffers more from hypoxia when intraventricular pressure increases during systole. It is also obvious from the experiments by Henquell et al. (188) that even if CD were similar, all capillaries are perfused at rest in hypertrophic hearts, leaving no reserve for recruitment in emergency. This and the lack of capillary growth produces hypoxia and eventually leads to decreased protein synthesis (57) and heart failure.

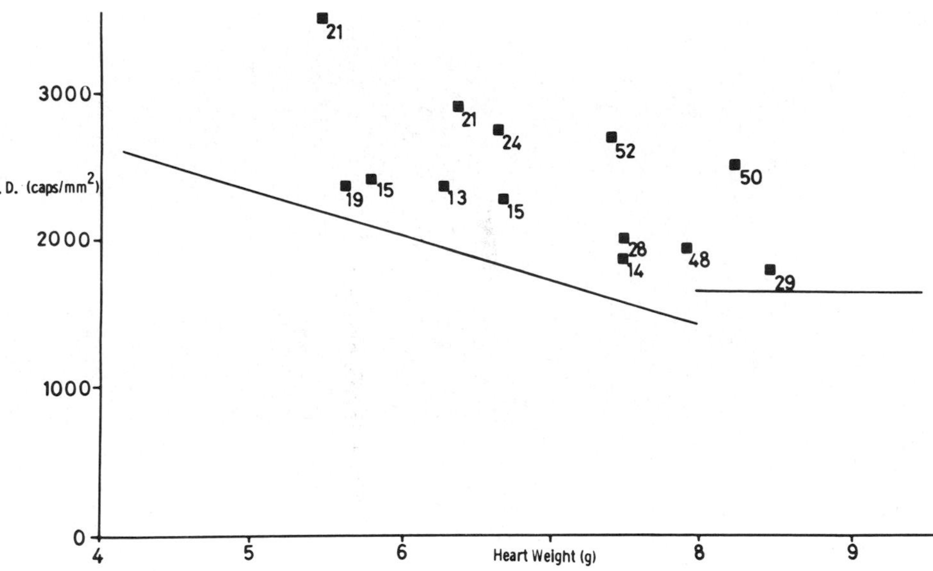

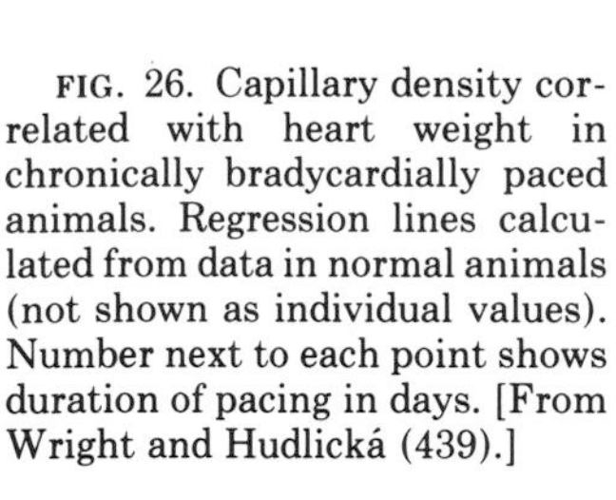
FIG. 26. Capillary density correlated with heart weight in chronically bradycardially paced animals. Regression lines calculated from data in normal animals (not shown as individual values). Number next to each point shows duration of pacing in days. [From Wright and Hudlická (439).]

A lower CD was also found in hearts made hypertrophic by aortic valve insufficiency in rabbits (375), by chronic pressure overload in cats (52), and in different types of hypertrophy in human hearts (333). However, Schaper et al. (366) described an increase in the labeling index and growth of endothelial, smooth muscle, and adventitial cells after the constriction of the coronary artery in dogs. Highest proliferation was in the smallest vessels, so perhaps there may be ways to stimulate capillary growth even in heart hypertrophy and to prevent heart failure. Wright and Hudlicka (439a) used chronic bradycardial pacing in hearts made hypertrophic by aortic valve lesions. A 60% increase in CD was achieved, with a greater increase in subendocardial than in subepicardial layers. The increases were accompanied by improved heart performance.

Very little is known about capillary growth in other organs undergoing hypertrophy. Reitsma's (330) experiments on the formation of new capillaries in soleus muscle made hypertrophic by a combination of extirpation of its agonists and training are not very convincing. Holly et al. (194) found slight increases in CD of chicken fast muscles but decreased CD in their slow muscles made hypertrophic by stretching. Olivetti et al. (294) found longer capillaries and increased volume of renal glomeruli in kidney hypertrophy caused by contralateral nephrectomy but only a slightly higher capillary surface area and no difference in CD. They concluded that the glomerular filtration rate was maintained by increased capillary pressure rather than by a larger surface area from the proliferation of capillaries.

Likewise, not much is known about changes in CD in muscle atrophy. A slight increase was found after denervation (176), and there was a considerable decrease in muscle autografts (259). Capillary filling and perfusion seem to be preserved for a long time in muscles undergoing atrophy from other causes such as denervation, tenotomy, or immobilization, probably because the degeneration of muscle fibers proceeds much faster than the changes in the vascular bed (201). Capillary growth obviously appears during regeneration after atrophy—whether it is in muscle, skin, or other damaged tissues.

Wound Healing and Regeneration

A detailed description of microcirculation during inflammation and injury is given in the chapter by Movat in this *Handbook*. Thus this chapter deals with capillary growth in injury only to a limited extent.

Travers (406) first described the principles of capillary growth in wound healing, and the topic was later studied extensively by Sandison (363), Clark and Clark (80, 81, 83, 84), Cliff (88), Schoefl (370), and others. Travers' observations clearly showed that new blood vessels grow only from preexisting vessels forming forks and arches that are later filled by red blood cells. These blood cells show only oscillatory movements for many hours, although normal circulation is established later. The number of different papers dealing with vessel growth during wound healing, regeneration, inflammation, and grafting is far too great to be reviewed here, and thus only a few important findings are mentioned.

OBSERVATIONS ON VESSEL GROWTH IN IMPLANTED RABBIT EAR CHAMBER. Sandison (363) extensively described the events occurring after chamber implantation: *1*) the formation of a fibrin network, *2*) the migration of fibroblasts and other cells (macrophages), and *3*) the growth of the connective tissue, sheets of capillaries forming afterward. Capillary growth proceeded with very fragile bulbous endings that showed some extravasation during the first 24 h after the implantation of the chamber. Clark et al. (85) and

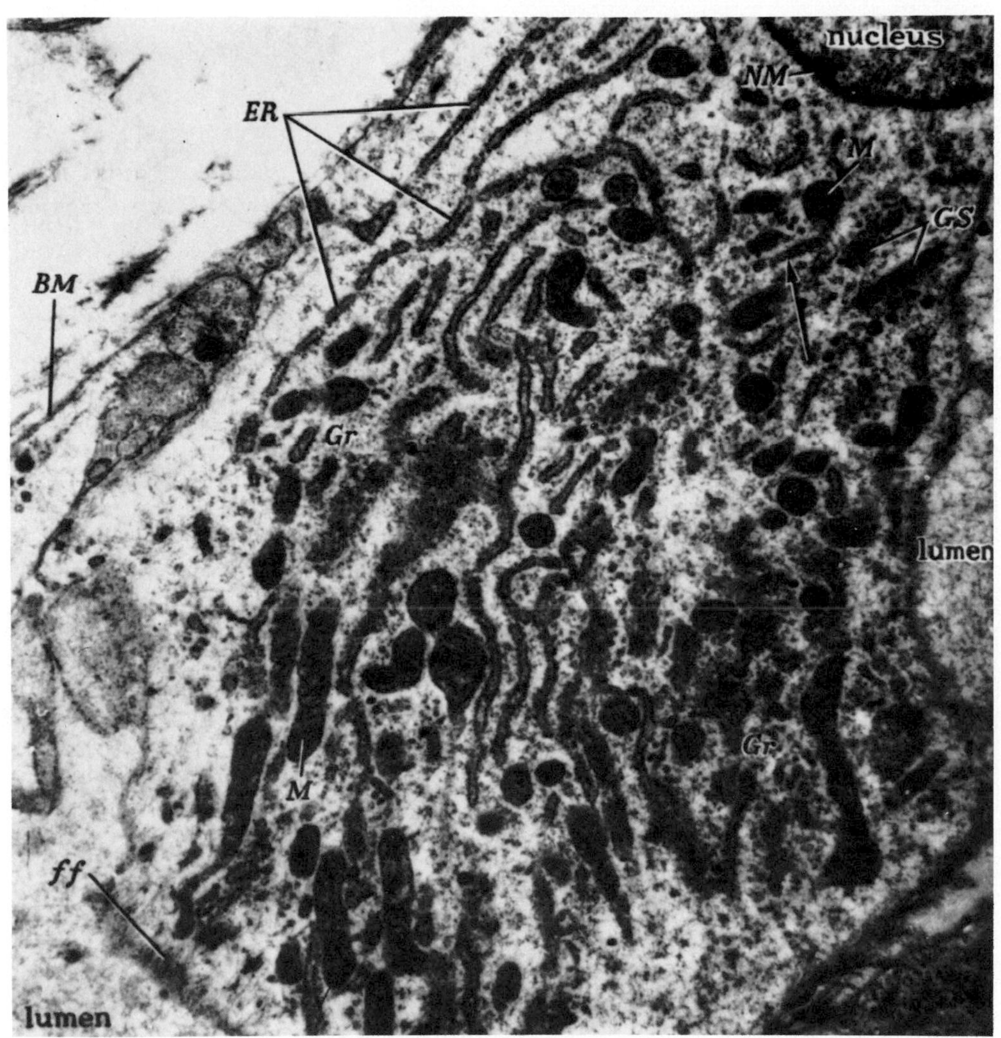

FIG. 27. Electron micrograph of endothelium from recently formed vessel. Note numerous elements of endoplasmic reticulum (*ER*) between paired membranes of moderately electron-dense material, numerous dense ribosomes (*arrow*), and numerous elongated mitochondria (*M*) with plentiful transverse cristae. The hyaloplasm contains much finely fibrous (*ff*) and granular (*Gr*) material. *BM*, basement membrane; *NM*, nuclear membrane; *GS*, Golgi substance. [From Cliff (88).]

Clark and Clark (80, 81, 83, 84) extended these studies. With careful operation and by avoiding local hemorrhage they achieved a complete healing within 4–6 days, although infection produced a prolonged capillary growth. The numerous granulocytes disappeared as healing progressed.

Cliff (88, 89) used a combination of light and electron microscopy to demonstrate that the newly formed endothelium has all the characteristics of rapidly growing cells (Fig. 27), with mitotic division taking place close to the growing tip of a sprout (Fig. 28). Saccular sprouts occurred more frequently than tapering ones and always had a well-developed basement lamina indicating a later stage of development; tapering sprouts sometimes had incomplete basement laminae. Vessel growth was also achieved by flattening of the endothelial cells and sliding of the cell substance forward from the site of formation (88). Newly formed endothelial cells could then migrate distally from their origin toward the tip of the sprouts, and from there the growth proceeded very quickly. One endothelial cell bulging into the lumen divided into two 36 s later, and both cells were quite apart after another 40 min (89). The newly formed sprouts had a high permeability that gradually decreased with maturation.

MUSCLE WOUND HEALING AND REGENERATION. In rat cremaster muscle, Schoefl (370) and Schoefl and Majno (371) observed very similar pictures to those described by Cliff in rabbit ear chamber. Tortuous capillaries appeared before sprouting occurred, and capillary growth observed both by light and electron microscopy had all the features described in the previous subsection. Remnants of sarcolemma or fibrin

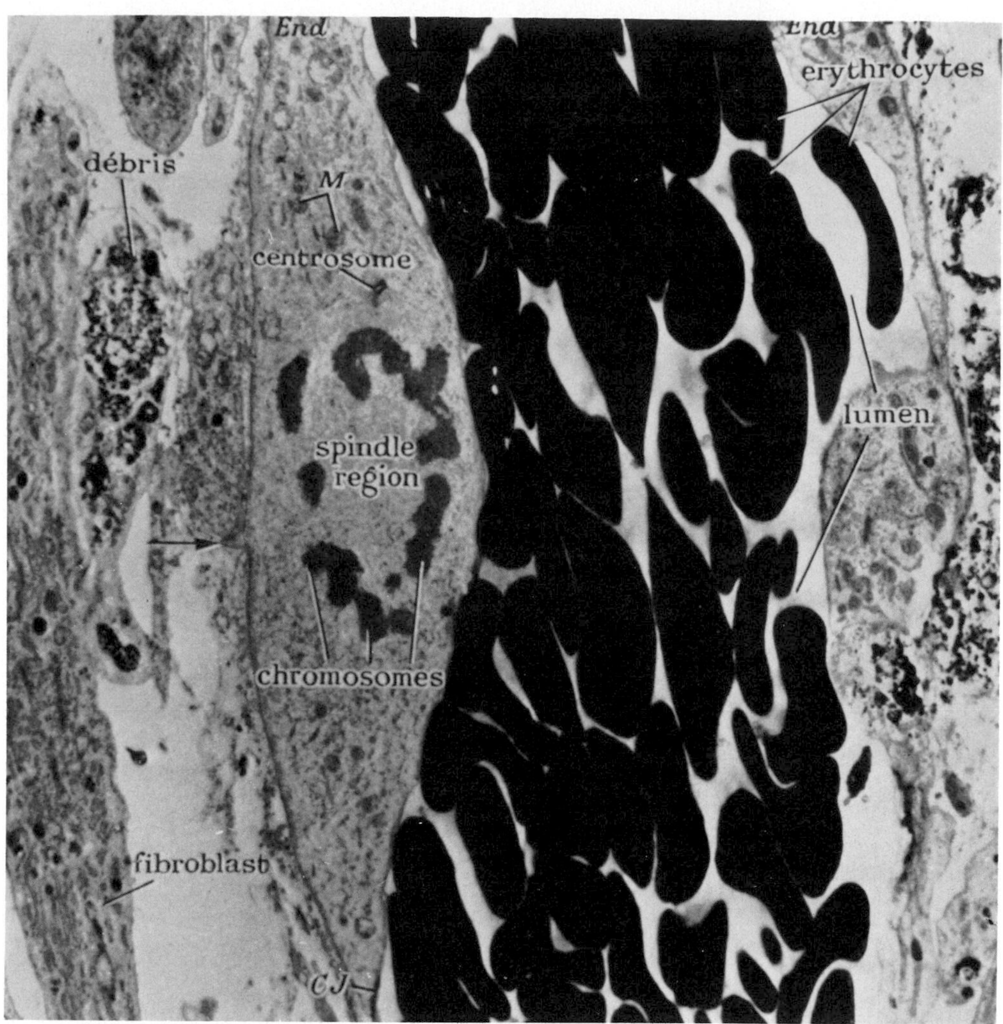

FIG. 28. Mitosis of endothelial cell situated just proximal to tip of young vessel. *Arrow*, projection from basement surface of cell. *CJ*, cell junction; *End*, endothelium; *M*, mitochondria. [From Cliff (88).]

may have acted as contact guidance for sprout growth. Young endothelial cells could travel by amoeboid movements at the rate of ~ 0.1–0.15 mm/day. McKinney et al. (263, 264) found similar pictures in healing wounds of guinea pig cremaster; permeability to macromolecules was 3–4 times higher than in normal muscles, and capillaries were fenestrated—changing gradually to the normal continuous type with maturation. Growth of new vessels was delayed in animals suffering from lack of vitamin C (262). Larger vessels appeared 5 days after muscle injury (216). Vracko and Benditt (416) described capillary growth in different kinds of muscle injury or regeneration. It begins later than the regeneration of muscle fibers and develops along the old capillary basement lamina that is sometimes preserved for several weeks after injury.

Capillary growth in muscle regeneration other than during wound healing has been studied mainly in the regenerating limbs of amphibians—minced muscle grafts and whole muscle grafts. Here the basic process of vascular growth is similar to that described already, i.e., with sprouts in regenerating tadpole tails needing about 2–4 h to form and another 4–6 h to open (16), invading the regenerating limb from the proximal part. Peadon and Singer (305) made the interesting observation that much faster growth occurs in poorly vascularized rather than well-vascularized tissues. They suggested that the Krebs cycle, in the early formative stage before vascularization appears, operates through the pentose shunt and that local hypoxia may have been an important factor in vascular growth. They also observed that the exposure of the regenerate to high oxygen prevented the development of vessels. Smith and Wolpert (380) slowed down vascular growth in regenerating limbs by denervation, which, however, had to be performed before vascularization had begun. Once the vessels started to grow, denervation was without effect. These observations suggested some formative role of nerves in vascular growth. Gospodarowicz et al. (161) supposed that a fibroblast growing factor isolated from the bovine pituitary gland and brain and known to stimulate endothelial growth in vitro could be such a neurotrophic factor.

Carlson (67) described vascularization in regenerating minced muscles prepared according to Studitsky (391). When rat triceps surae muscle was taken out, minced, and replaced with all nerves and vessels severed, vascular growth started 2–3 days after implantation from the regions around the Achilles tendon. By 4 days most of the regenerate was vascularized and by 9 days vascularization was completed, with myoblasts occurring in all regions slightly ahead of the capillaries. Revascularization of freely grafted whole muscles (rat EDL) started on the 2nd day; some larger vessels grew from the preexisting ones, and smaller vessels and capillaries were newly formed in between the connective tissue. Vascularization was completed by the end of the 1st wk (181). Revascularization in autotransplanted cat muscles was much slower; it started 5 days after transplantation and was completed after 40–44 wk (259). Capillary growth was faster in the reinnervated parts; growth never started from preexisting vessels that had degenerated while some of the larger vessels had survived (176). However, normal CD was not restored even after 400 days (124). When the grafted muscles were connected to the supplying nerves and vessels, complete functional recovery occurred within 6–9 mo and CD returned to normal (319).

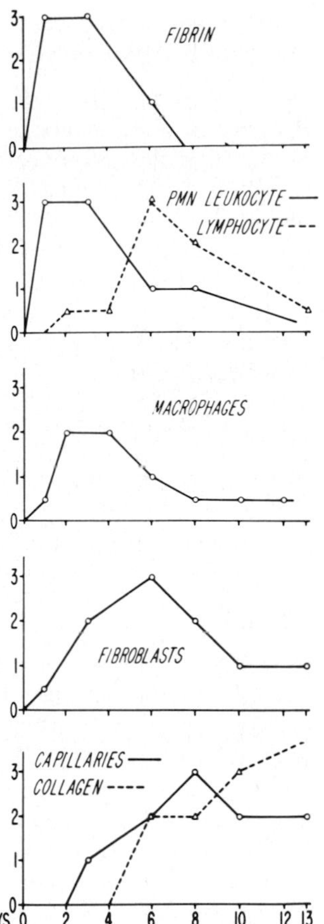

FIG. 29. Appearance of different elements in the healing skin wound in guinea pigs. Abscissa, days after wound was induced. Ordinate, number of cells per high-power field in light microscope: 1 = 2–4 cells, 2 = 4–10 cells, 3 = more than 10 cells. PMN, polymorphonuclear. [From Ross and Benditt (338).]

HEALING OF SKIN WOUNDS AND GRAFTS. Skin autografts were found to be invaded by growing blood vessels by the 4th day. These vessels are "engorged capillaries" with a very thin endothelium that often bursts, the majority of the vessels disappearing by the 9th day (94, 265). Homografts have a dense vascularization with the original vascular network completely disrupted (265). The intensively growing vessels from the host become thrombotic and do not grow into the graft, which therefore becomes necrotic and eventually is rejected (94).

Growth of new vessels in normal surgical wounds begins 4–5 days after surgery and is completed by 6–7 days. In burns it starts after 10 days, with a complete vascularization by 12–16 days (208). The pattern of growth is the same as described in *Light Microscopy*, p. 172. The final arrangement of vessels in healing skin wounds usually resembles that originally present in the area (348). The temporal sequence of growth of different components was described by Ross and Benditt [Fig. 29; (338)]. The wound is first filled with fibrin and with polymorphonuclear cells; macrophages and fibroblasts are formed next and capillaries appear later. These and similar observations initiated speculations concerning the role of granulocytes and fibroblasts in capillary growth (50, 245). It is quite clear, however, that whatever the sequence of appearance of different components in wounds, capillaries can only grow from preexisting endothelial cells; the fibroblasts are later apposed to them and differentiate into vascular smooth muscle cells. Pericytes, by contrast, are supposed to attenuate capillary proliferation by contact inhibition when incorporated into capillary basement lamina (103).

Inhibition or acceleration of capillary growth can also be affected by different systemic levels of oxygen. Vascularization of wounds was improved when animals were kept in a hyperbaric chamber for 1 h/day (224) or allowed to breathe pure oxygen (284). Wound healing was impaired when animals breathed a gas mixture with $P_{O_2} < 20$ mmHg (227), but this was probably a result of decreased collagen synthesis in hypoxia and not because of a direct effect on vascular growth. On the other hand, low local P_{O_2} values found in the center of the wounds (331) could stimulate endothelial proliferation. Vascular growth was also improved by the high-protein diet given to the animals before the wounds were produced (71). Vascular growth occurs not only in wound healing but also during inflammation (428) and may in this case be caused by substances released from lymphocytes (166) or macrophages (315).

HEALING IN CORNEA. This represents a special case, since the normally avascular cornea becomes vascularized by capillary ingrowth when damaged (17, 371) and capillary growth is preceded by a swelling of the corneal stroma. It is assumed that the reduction of the compactness of the tissue near the lesion is a necessary condition for vascular growth (92). Collagen fibers with fibrin filaments formed between them are loosened and can serve as scaffolding for the growth of new vessels. Any substance that produces edema in the cornea may stimulate capillary growth (371).

REGENERATION AND GROWTH OF ENDOTHELIUM IN LARGE BLOOD VESSELS. Sabin (355) studied regeneration of large vessels in end-to-end intestinal anastomosis. She found that the endothelium of large vessels first changed into original angioblast cells with a great multiplication of nuclei. Sprouting and formation of capillaries occurred from the 2nd day, and new vessels were formed from capillary plexuses in a way similar to that in embryonal development. Endothelial cells in large vessels start to divide very quickly when injured and show a high labeling index, but it may take a long time for the regeneration to be completed, especially if the damaged area is too large (316). Murray et al. (279) showed migration of smooth muscle cells into the injured zone in the femoral artery. Vessels in most organs regenerate after trauma, even if the vascular network is different from the original one. However, regeneration of vessels in the brain, at least in some species (367, 433), seems to be far from complete.

Vascular Growth in Diabetes Mellitus

Changes occurring in the microcirculation in diabetes were recently reviewed by Rossini and Chick (340a). One of the main changes both in humans and animals with experimentally induced diabetes is the thickening of the basement lamina (7, 415, 443, 444), which is probably related to the duration of the disease (300). It is explained by higher collagen synthesis resulting from higher incorporation and metabolism of glucose (327) and is related to the accelerated cell turnover in diabetes (415). However, the thickness of the basement lamina increases with age, and there is some speculation that age on its own may be equally (226) if not more (219) important than the duration of diabetes.

It is not at all clear how the thickening of the basement lamina—described mainly in capillaries of skeletal muscles—is connected with diabetic angiopathy, which appears in the kidney and in the retina. There is, of course, a possibility that a thick basement lamina may create some barrier for diffusion of nutrients, particularly of oxygen, and that the resulting hypoxia may be responsible for the disorder (107). However, there is no direct or even indirect evidence for this suggestion. On the contrary, Leinonen et al. (238a) found a greater diffusion capacity in skeletal muscles of diabetics. Because CD values for diabetics were not different from those in control subjects, the difference in diffusion capacity was explained by a higher capillary permeability in diabetics. Arquilla et al. (18) and Bohlen and Niggl (48) suggested that capillary proliferation in diabetes is decreased and thought that this was the cause of the well-known impairment of wound healing in diabetics. Nevertheless there is some indication of capillary proliferation in the retina of diabetics. New vessels were found growing not only on the surface of the retina but also protruding into the vitreous body (258). Cogan et al. (93) showed that retinal vascularization during development was poor when glycogen levels were high. It is thus possible that lack of glycogen synthesis and storage in the retina in diabetes may be connected with increased vascularization. Another factor is the disappearance of the mural cells, which are selectively damaged in diabetics (60) and which normally inhibit capillary proliferation in the retina. Capillaries devoid of mural cells form microaneurysms from which proliferation of capillaries can start (64, 93).

Vascular Growth in Psoriasis

The terminal vascular bed in psoriasis is characterized by numerous glomerulus-like capillary convolutions (210) that appear preferentially in the regions where the skin is stretched (elbows and knee joints) and the venous plexuses in the middle of the dermis are compressed. According to Ryan (346, 347) this leads to increased capillary permeability and sprouting. A contributory factor may be the hypoxia induced partly by the stagnation of blood and partly by high O_2 consumption by psoriatic plaques (347). Alternatively, psoriatic plaques may produce some angiogenic factor similar to tumor angiogenic factor (150), since implantation of psoriatic epidermis into hamster cheek pouch chamber induced a much greater angiogenesis than implantation of normal epidermis (434).

Retrolental Fibroplasia

Retrolental fibroplasia is an excessive proliferation of vasoformative tissue that spreads along the surface of the retina beneath the hyaloid membrane and into the vitreous body, eventually leading to retinal detachment. The basis of this disorder is an aberrant overgrowth of the developing retinal vessels as a reaction to exposure to high oxygen tension, usually in prematurely born babies (19). Ashton and Pedler (21) and Ashton et al. (22) found obliteration of retinal vessels in kittens exposed to 70%–80% oxygen for 6 h (Fig. 30). Ischemia resulted, and afterward there was capillary proliferation that developed frequently in the

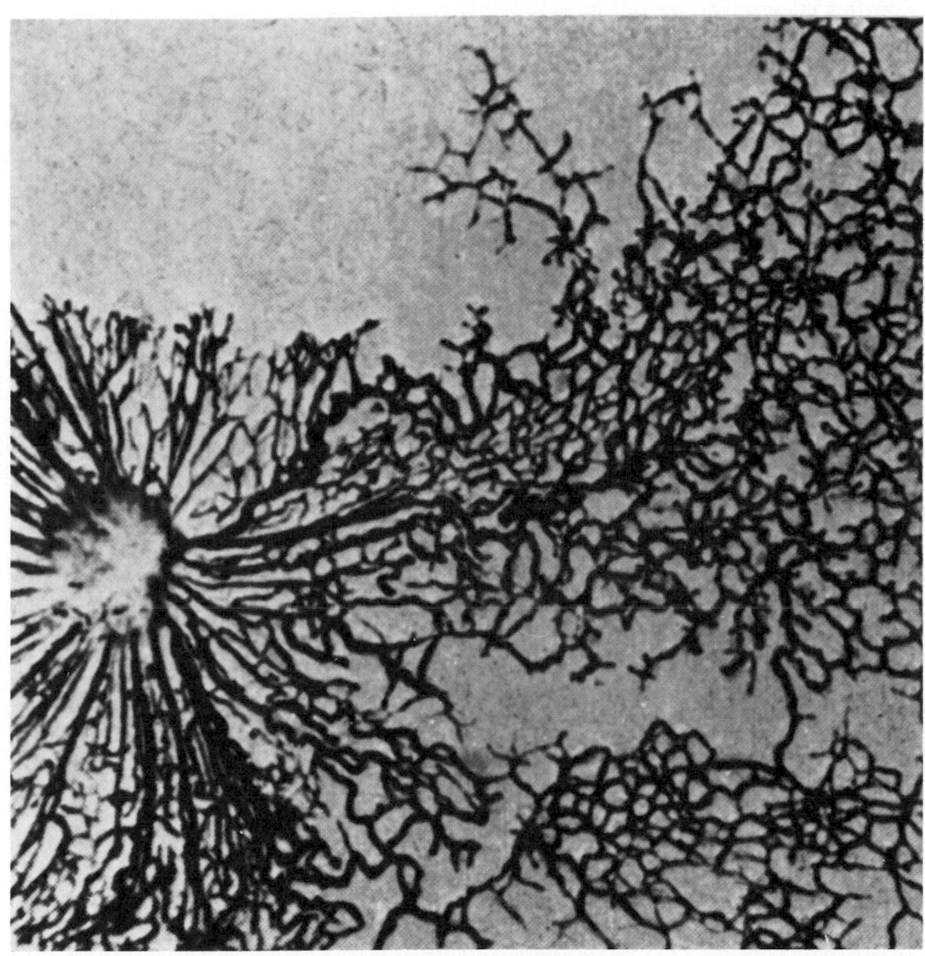

FIG. 30. Vascular network in kitten retina exposed for 4 days to 70%–80% O_2 followed by 3 days in air. Preexisting vascular complexes have partially reopened, but the capillary network is a grossly abnormal architecture, cobweb in type and without definition into arteries and veins. Vascularization of retina is recommencing from disk region. [From Ashton et al. (22).]

vicinity of closed vessels (304). It is supposed that hypoxic retina can produce some metabolic factors that stimulate neovascularization (235a). However, angiogenic factors were even found in extracts from normal retinas (149a, 226a, 226b).

Capillary Growth in Tumors

Growth of vessels in tumors was recently well reviewed by Folkman and Cotran (128), and the different factors involved in endothelial growth in tumors were reviewed by Haudenschild (182). Capillaries in growing tumors have all the characteristics of developing capillaries described elsewhere (Fig. 31). The [^{3}H]thymidine labeling index of 11.4% is very high (393), and the turnover time of endothelial cells is between 50 and 60 h (70). Tumors grow without vessel proliferation up to a diameter of 1–2 mm (or 10^5 cells). Thereafter further growth is impossible without angiogenesis (126, 127), probably because the oxygen consumption of the tumor cells is too high; this may contribute to the production of tumor angiogenic factor (46). As much as 40% of the tissue in a solid tumor may consist of vascular endothelial cells. The ingrowth of vessels is always from the surrounding tissue (126). Vascular growth in rabbit cornea stimulated by tumor implants is delayed if the implant is far away rather than close to the limbus, the point at which the vessel growth begins (147). Implantation of tumors inactivated by heat did not stimulate capillary growth (27). All these and other observations (128) indicate the presence of a specific factor involved in tumor angiogenesis that today is one of the best-described factors involved in capillary growth.

FACTORS IN CAPILLARY GROWTH AND ITS INHIBITION

Two basic groups of factors have been considered responsible for capillary growth since the first descriptions of capillary sprouts were made in the last century. *1*) Mechanical factors, connected with the bulk of flow or blood pressure in the terminal vascular bed, were primarily considered in normal developmental growth. *2*) Chemical factors, except hypoxia and the resultant release of metabolites, seem to be involved in the growth of microcirculation under pathological conditions. The second group was studied more thoroughly, and quite a few factors involved in angiogenesis and growth of endothelial cells were identified under different pathological conditions. It is impossi-

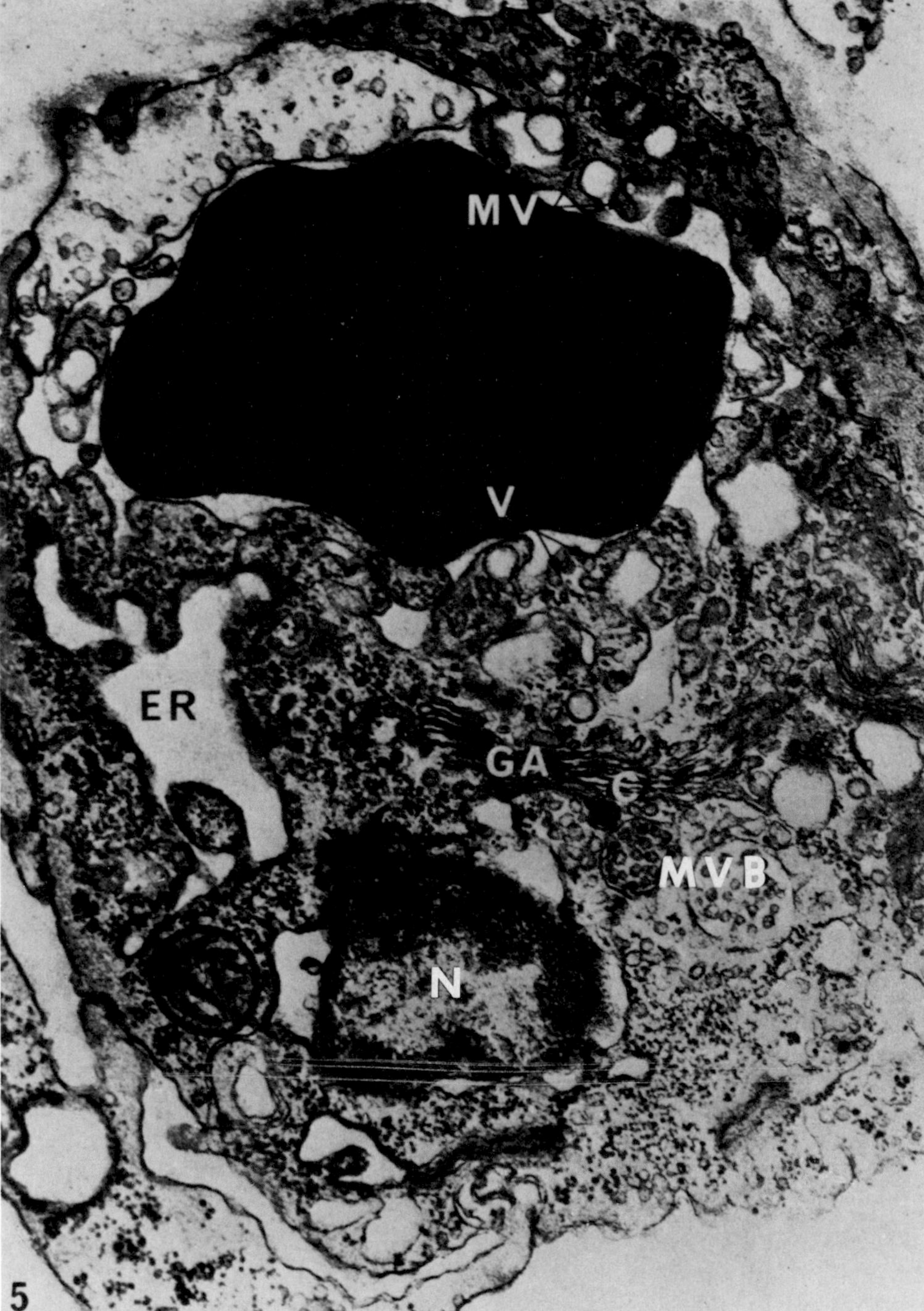

FIG. 31. Cross section of a capillary sprout 3 days after transplantation of a melanoma fragment. Red cell almost occludes the lumen. Endothelial cell shows a number of microvilli (*MV*) on their luminal surfaces, widely dilated endoplasmic reticulum (*ER*), a great many vesicles (*V*), and ribosomes. Golgi apparatus (*GA*) is represented by a series of vesicles and parallel, paired membranes. Near the nucleus (*N*) are a centriole (*C*) and two multivesicular bodies (*MVB*). [From Warren (424).]

ble to discuss all these factors, and this review is far from complete. I would much rather try to explain physiological capillary growth both during development and in adult organisms. Unfortunately this means greater reliance on hypotheses than on hard facts.

Chemical Factors in Capillary Growth

Clark and Clark (81) tried to alter the rate of capillary growth in tadpole tails and rabbit ear chambers by administration of different foreign substances (e.g., paraffin or olive oil, carbon granules, glass capillaries, powdered egg whites) without success. Only the injection of croton oil, which produced a strong inflammatory reaction, induced capillary growth. Extracts from different organs (muscles, heart, liver, or spleen) were tested for their angiogenic activity on the chicken chorioallantoic membrane (149a) or hamster cheek pouch (286), with negative results. Mammalian retina was the only adult tissue in which extracts caused vascular proliferation (149a, 226a, 226b). Vascular growth in hamster cheek pouch was also induced by extract from kidneys with collateral circulation (developed in response to stenosis of renal artery), whereas extract from normal kidneys was without effect (103a). It is well known that growth of endothelial cells in tissue cultures can be promoted by different blood components, which are also thought to be involved in capillary growth in different tissues under various circumstances.

SUBSTANCES RELEASED FROM LEUKOCYTES. Since capillary growth occurs during inflammation and formation of granulation tissue with a considerably increased accumulation of leukocytes, several authors suggested that it may be initiated by some substances released from these cells. Brånemark (50) observed disruption of granulocytes just before new capillaries started to grow into a rabbit ear chamber. Fromer and Klintworth (138) made similar observations in rabbit cornea injured by administration of different substances. They were able to suppress corneal neovascularization as well as leukocyte infiltration by administering methylprednisolone (137) and claimed that different proteolytic enzymes released from leukocytes may have acted as angiogenic factors (139). However, this enzymatic action may also produce liquefaction of the corneal proteins and loosening of the corneal compactness, as well as create mechanical conditions favorable for capillary growth (see HEALING IN CORNEA, p. 198). Polverini et al. (315) and Saba et al. (353) supposed that macrophages released some macromolecules that could initiate capillary growth, whereas Auerbach and Sidky (25) believed that lymphocytes contain some mediators of vascular growth. When the number of lymphocytes was reduced by whole-body irradiation, the labeling index of endothelial cells in the skin, previously increased as a result of thermal injury, dropped to values observed in control animals (376).

OTHER FACTORS CONTAINED IN BLOOD. Clark and Clark (82) noticed that adding fibrin promoted vascular growth in rabbit ear chamber, and Edwards et al. (116) saw extensive capillary proliferation in sponges containing tissue extracts with fibrin implanted into rabbit dorsal muscles. The stimulating effect of serum on the growth of different cells is well known from tissue culture studies, but the factors responsible for this effect have not yet been identified. Some data show increased proliferation of fibroblasts (401), smooth muscle cells, and endothelial cells after addition of fresh serum to tissue cultures that had reached the confluent state (423). However, according to Haudenschild et al. (194) proliferation of endothelial cells was not affected. Growth of fibroblasts was stimulated by the addition of thrombin (73). Since thrombin is a protease, Zetter et al. (446) suggested that the stimulation of growth could be explained by the disturbance of the boundary layer between cells and disruption of the confluent state.

Factors released from platelets stimulate the growth of endothelial cells cultured from large vessels (354) and the growth of fibroblasts (230) and arterial smooth muscle cells (340). D'Amore and Shepro (104) pointed out that the presence of platelets is important for maintenance of the integrity of capillary endothelium and that the increased level of adenosine diphosphate (ADP) released from platelets causes an increase in Ca^{2+} influx that may be necessary to induce endothelial growth; Ca^{2+} is supposed to be a prominent factor in cell division (40).

Fibrin, serum, and platelets may be important to endothelial growth in wound healing and vessel injury, but they are unlikely to be involved in the regulation of vessel growth in normal tissues (340). Gajdusek et al. (142) made the interesting observation of increased growth of fibroblasts and vascular smooth muscle cells—but not endothelial cells—cultured in medium conditioned by endothelium. They supposed that endothelial cells probably store and release a platelet-derived growth factor (a polypeptide of 10,000–30,000 daltons) that stimulates growth of those components of the vascular wall appearing in angiogenesis later than endothelial cells themselves.

MAST CELLS AND HISTAMINE. Smith (381) and Schoefl (370) claimed that mast cells and histamine are involved in vascular growth during injury. If histamine is involved in capillary growth (there is no direct evidence for such a suggestion), it is much more likely to be because of mechanical rather than chemical factors. Histamine produces vasodilatation and increases permeability particularly on the venous side of capillaries where capillary growth usually starts. Mast cells did not produce angiogenesis on the chick chorioallantoic membrane (223a). Azizkhan et al. (30) showed, however, that heparin released from mast cells stimulates migration of capillary endothelial cells rather than their proliferation. Since migration of endothelial cells is an important factor in angiogenesis, mast cells may play an indirect role in the process, particularly in chronic inflammation.

TUMOR ANGIOGENIC FACTOR. Tumor angiogenic factor is probably the best known of all factors responsible for capillary growth. It was described by Folkman and his group in many papers (128) and studied by many other investigators, including Suddith et al. (392), Kelly et al. (223), Fenselau and Mello (125), Phillips et al. (311), and Birdwell et al. (43). It is a polypeptide originally isolated from Walker 256 ascites tumor (132) but later found more potent in neuroblastoma and meningioma (392). It was found in the nonhistone fraction of proteins (228) isolated from Walker 256 rat carcinoma but not from normal tissues. It contains 1% DNA, 3% RNA, and 32% carbohydrates. The histone fraction without DNA and RNA has no angiogenic activity. The activity of tumor angiogenic factor is not affected by exposure to trypsin but is lost when it is heated at 56°C for 1 h or digested with ribonuclease (132). It can diffuse over a distance of several millimeters, and implantation of tumors into rabbit cornea or different diffusion chambers induces increased incorporation of [^{3}H]thymidine into endothelial cells of the host and growth of new vessels remote from the tumor implant (148). Labeling appears as early as 6–8 h after exposure to the tumor, and new vessels are formed within 48 h (70). Tumor angiogenic factor also produces a vigorous growth of endothelial cells with capillary formation in vitro (130).

FIBROBLAST GROWTH FACTOR, EPIDERMAL GROWTH FACTOR, POLYPEPTIDES, AMINO ACIDS, AND PROSTAGLANDINS. Armelin (15) discovered that extract from pituitary glands promotes the growth of fibroblasts in vitro. Gospodarowicz and his collaborators (161, 163) isolated this factor as a polypeptide devoid of carbohydrate residues not only from mammalian pituitary glands but also from the brain. Fibroblast growth factor stimulates growth of endothelial cells and fibroblasts in vitro (160, 163), improves wound healing and regeneration (160), and induces angiogenesis in rabbit cornea (157). In contrast, epidermal growth factor—a polypeptide of 53 residues and molecular weight of 6,000 isolated from male mouse submaxillary gland (63, 365)—has no effect on the growth of endothelial cells in tissue cultures but does stimulate the growth of vascular smooth muscle cells (162). It also induces angiogenesis in rabbit cornea. However, the latter effect appeared only after it had produced hyperplasia of the corneal epithelium, and it was therefore probably a secondary effect caused by hypoxia (157). Wolf and Harrison (435) described proliferation of capillaries in hamster cheek pouch after the implantation of epidermis. They claimed that the vascular growth in this case may have been the result of deposition of fibrin in the epidermis, but because they also found infiltration with leukocytes, the growth of capillaries in this case was probably not produced by epidermal growth factor. On the other hand Nishioka and Ryan (286) induced vessel growth in the hamster cheek pouch by using a diffusion chamber with epidermis from neonate hamsters. Dermis, heart, liver, spleen, and muscles were without effect.

Polypeptides isolated from salivary glands induced vascular growth in the kidney and in the vicinity of hair follicles (192), and heart extracts applied daily intraperitoneally for 4 wk caused capillary growth in rat hearts (390). Unfortunately this last experiment was not described in detail and was not confirmed either by the author himself or by other investigators.

A possible role of different amino acids in angiogenesis was studied in chick embryos by Jeney and Törö (217); growth was improved by arginine, leucine, valine, lysine, and creatine and slowed down by cysteine, proline, and serine. Zauberman et al. (445) achieved vascularization of the cornea by long-term local application of acetylcholine, serotonin, and histamine—but not bradykinin—in about half of the animals studied. All substances produced edema of the cornea and congestion of the limbic vessels from which capillary growth starts, and thus when growth occurred it could have been at least partly a result of mechanical factors. Frazer et al. (135) induced angiogenesis in the chick chorioallantoic membrane by local administration of serotonin, heparin, and ADP; the last substance was most effective. They also found that ATP, lactate, and epinephrine had some small effect on vascular growth. Ziche et al. (446a) induced angiogenesis in rabbit cornea with prostaglandin E_1. Neovascularization did not occur in animals treated with indomethacin.

HORMONES. The effect of hormones on angiogenesis was studied together with their effect on wound healing. Growth hormone stimulated capillary growth not only in wounds (396) but also in the metaphysial zone of the bone (175). Cortisone and adrenocorticotropic hormone depressed vascular growth (121, 175), although hydrocortisone potentiated the effect of fibroblast growth factor in vitro (345). Estrogens had an inhibitory effect on the growth of wound granulation tissue (396), whereas progesterone accelerated vascularization in rabbit ear chamber (121) and factors released from corpus luteum induced vascularization in rabbit cornea (164). All these factors, except hormones and polypeptides, certainly play some role in vascular growth under different pathological conditions. It is, however, unlikely that they are involved in capillary growth in normal tissues during exercise, muscle stimulation, or high-altitude exposure. Hypoxia may be the only factor responsible for capillary growth both under pathological conditions and in normal tissues.

HYPOXIA. It was shown previously that exposure to high altitude leads to capillary growth (due mainly to hypoxia) in the heart, skeletal muscle, and brain. Hypoxia has been suggested as the factor eliciting capillary growth in the cornea under conditions of riboflavin deficiency and subsequent corneal keratinization (41). A similar explanation was suggested for corneal neovascularization induced by epidermal growth factor (157). Stasis of blood in newly formed sprouts in regeneration also leads to local hypoxia, and this in turn can stimulate further vascular proliferation (371). Increase in the rate and volume of flow (and presumably increased delivery of oxygen) in autografts depresses endothelial growth (431). Hypoxia is also supposed to be the cause of neovascularization in retrolental fibroplasia (19, 304), whereas high oxygen tension is probably responsible for cessation of capillary network growth in the vicinity of arteries in the developing retina (268). Byerly (62) elicited development of anomalous and more numerous blood vessels in chick embryos where oxygen availability had been reduced by the application of shellac and paraffin on the egg surface, and Rotter (341) suggested hypoxia as the main factor in the proliferation of endothelial cells in ligated and occluded arteries. Gospodarowicz and Thakral (164) concluded that the lack of oxygen and nutrients is the most important factor in the vascularization of corpus luteum.

It is possible, of course, that the lack of oxygen per se does not induce capillary growth but rather leads to the accumulation of different metabolites that then act as angiogenic factors. One of these could be ADP, which cannot be rephosphorylated into ATP during hypoxia. Indeed ADP was shown to produce growth of vessels in chick chorioallantoic membrane (135) and may be involved in the stimulation of endothelial cell growth in tissue cultures (104). Another such metabolite could be lactic acid; it has been shown to induce capillary growth in the retina (211), although it did not affect growth of endothelial cells in tissue cultures (23).

Changes in pH have also been considered, but the findings are rather controversial. Arey (13) supposed that low pH was beneficial for endothelial proliferation in wound healing, partly because it evoked vasodilatation that could then mechanically contribute to capillary growth. However, White (429) described earlier and faster growth of capillaries and fibroblasts in the explants of chicken bone marrow at an alkaline pH of 7.4–8.0.

Hypoxia may also be involved in capillary growth in skeletal and cardiac muscle during exercise and in skeletal muscle during long-term electrical stimulation. Long-lasting endurance training and particularly electrical stimulation that activates all muscle fibers irrespective of their aerobic capacity can lead to local hypoxia in the active muscles. There are no data on Po_2 measurements in trained muscles with an increased CD. However, lower Po_2 was found after contractions in muscles stimulated at 10 Hz for 2 days than in control muscles, indicating a relative hypoxia in the former at a stage preceding the rapid growth of capillaries (205). This hypoxia can be particularly serious in fast glycolytic fibers. Pette and Tyler (310) found a 50% increase in SDH activity in these fibers in muscles stimulated for 4 days at 10 Hz. Dodd et al. (108) and Hudlická et al. (202a) showed, under similar conditions, an increase in CD in the vicinity of fast glycolytic but not other fibers. In muscles stimulated at 40 Hz the increase in SDH was smaller and less rapid than in muscles stimulated at 10 Hz (310), although by 14 days the values were similar. Capillary growth in muscles stimulated at 40 Hz also started later (99, 206). Thus a more sensitive method than that used previously by Pette et al. (309) or Cotter and Hudlická (99) shows that in both types of electrical stimulation an increase in the activity of SDH precedes apparent capillary growth. The activity of oxidative enzymes increases in muscles with a decreased blood supply (195), but so far there are no data on CD in patients with this condition. Even if the reasons for the increase in the activity of SDH either in exercise, electrical stimulation, or high-altitude exposure are not known, it is possible that muscle fibers with a high SDH activity are able to extract more oxygen from the blood, thus producing local regions of hypoxia. This may stimulate proliferation of endothelial cells as Ashton (20) suggested: endothelial cells may in some way be directly sensitive to oxygen—multiplying at low O_2 levels, resting at normal levels, and dying at high O_2 levels.

Some authors found that hypoxia is less likely to be involved in capillary growth in the hearts of exercised animals. It is known that the increase in coronary blood flow with increasing heart rate during exercise goes preferentially to subepicardial layers, creating relative hypoxia in the subendocardium (193). This could explain the higher density found in subendocardial than in subepicardial regions in normal hearts (52). However, Lund and Tomanek (252), Rakušan et al. (322), and Wright and Hudlická (439) did not see any difference in the transmural distribution of CD, and Gerdes et al. (144) and Gerdes and Kasten (144a) found greater CD in subepicardial than subendocardial layers. If hypoxia plays a role in capillary proliferation in the heart during exercise, one would expect a higher proliferation with higher heart rate if the oxygen supply is not sufficiently met by the increase in blood flow. This does not occur; rather, increased CD was usually found in connection with bradycardia, and it is therefore more likely that mechanical factors connected with increased blood flow are more important in capillary growth in the heart.

Mechanical Factors in Capillary Growth

The role of blood flow and blood pressure in the growth of the vascular bed was suggested by Thoma (397) on the basis of his observations in chicken embryos and was later confirmed by Clark (77) in tadpole tails and rabbit ear chambers (83, 85). These authors saw that capillaries with higher flow have more sprouts and change gradually into arterioles and venules, but capillaries with low flow gradually narrow and disappear. Thoma (398) also observed that longitudinal growth depends on the growth of the surrounding tissue and on the tension to which the vessels are subjected. Greater growth occurs where preexisting vessels bend because of greater wall tension. Although he considered the velocity of flow, increased pressure, and increased wall tension as the main factors initiating capillary growth, Clark (77) supposed that the growth is induced by mechanical friction connected with the increased amount of filtered fluid. Brånemark (50) argued that pulsatory movements of erythrocytes during the first phases of vascularization are of primary importance for capillary growth. His assumption may help to explain the increase in CD in the hearts, brains, and skeletal muscles of rats made polycythemic by repeated transfusions (272).

Increased capillary flow, and particularly increased

capillary pressure, may also make endothelial cells more sensitive to mitogenic factors. Folkman and Greenspan (129) noticed that flat cells in tissue cultures are more sensitive to serum growth factor than spherical cells. Since capillary endothelial cells are maintained flat in vivo by adherence to the basement lamina, Folkman and Moscona (133) and Gospodarowicz et al. (159) suggested that the combination of cell geometry and some mitogenic factors may be responsible for capillary proliferation in vitro and perhaps also in vivo (159). A similar suggestion was made by Ryan and Stockley (349), who induced vascular growth in chick chorioallantoic membrane by applying glass rings to it, indicating that the mechanically distorted endothelium could release some angiogenic factors.

A combination of chemical and mechanical factors may also be responsible for faster capillary growth in rabbit ear chambers in animals exposed to high temperature (85) or undergoing hypoxia. Both situations lead to an increased blood flow that can then stimulate capillary growth. The role of hypoxia in increasing blood flow in skeletal muscle during exercise was recently reviewed by Honig (197). Kasalický et al. (222) reported a higher blood flow in skeletal muscles and hearts of animals exposed to high altitude. Hypoxia also increased the number of perfused capillaries in the heart (49, 187). In addition, exercise and long-term stimulation produce a long-lasting increase in blood flow (202, 207) connected with an increased proportion of perfused capillaries in skeletal muscles (99, 308). These conditions preceded capillary growth (202a). Since capillary sprouts in chronically stimulated muscles were always found at bends of preexisting capillaries [Fig. 19; (282)], it is quite possible that mechanical factors of even a different nature than those suggested by Thoma or Clark may be involved. For example, slight damage to endothelial cells exposed to more frequently moving erythrocytes could induce their proliferation. Fry (140) and Caplan and Schwartz (66) described this in the aorta as being induced by increased shear stress, and Gimbrone et al. (146) studied it in tissue cultures where DNA synthesis was increased in the areas with damaged cell surface.

If any of the factors that cause increased blood flow are involved in capillary growth in skeletal muscle, it should be possible to elicit an increase by chronically induced vasodilatation. This has indeed been done by Tornling et al. (403, 404) in rats treated with dipyridamole and by Wright et al. (440) in rats and rabbits treated with a methylxanthine derivative, which preferentially increases flow in terminal arterioles (203). Hudlická et al. (207a) found an increased C/F in skeletal muscles and increased CD in the heart after long-term administration of adenosine, and Tornling (402a) described a higher C/F in hearts of animals treated with dipyridamole.

Increased blood flow and factors connected with it can also explain capillary growth in the heart during hypoxia, exercise, and long-term bradycardial pacing. Kasalický et al. (222) and Turek et al. (409) found a greater increase in coronary flow in the right than in the left ventricle during chronic exposure to hypoxia, with an increase in CD only in the right ventricle (75, 167, 386, 407). Increased blood flow in the left ventricle during exercise, of course, could be a factor involved in capillary growth in the left ventricle. Mandache et al. (256, 257), Ljungqvist and Unge (248), and Unge et al. (410) found capillary proliferation in rat hearts trained by swimming. Similarly Tomanek (402) and Bloor and Leon (45) found proliferation in rats trained by treadmill running for up to 1 h/day. However, more strenuous exercise did not produce any increase in heart CD (177, 302). Moreover resting coronary blood flow is usually higher in cases of pathological left ventricular hypertrophy and increases proportionately with heart weight (54, 196, 290), although CD is lower (320). Breisch et al. (52) demonstrated a high coronary blood flow and low CD in feline hearts made hypertrophic by aortic constriction, a maneuver also connected with a lower CD in rats.

Robert et al. (334) demonstrated an increased formation of anastomoses that indicates that increased coronary blood flow may be involved in capillary proliferation in the heart. Tornling et al. (405) found a greater incorporation of [^{3}H]thymidine in heart capillaries of young rats treated for 3 wk with dipyridamole. There is, of course, a possibility that an increase in the total coronary flow during exercise may not necessarily represent increased flow in the terminal arterioles and capillaries. Tillmans et al. (400) showed that the peak velocity in arterioles is in diastole, whereas in capillaries and venules it is in systole. The diameter of all vessels was greater in diastole than in systole. There is also a shift of flow toward subepicardial layers during systole (193); thus intracardial distribution of flow may be a factor in capillary growth. One might expect, for instance, that where increased coronary blood flow is associated with tachycardia, the increase in flow in the terminal vascular bed and the distension of capillaries would not be of sufficient duration and CD would decrease. The experiments of Lund and Tomanek (252) supported this hypothesis; they found a lower CD in rat hearts with higher rates (either spontaneously hypertensive rats or animals with aortic constriction) than in control hearts. On the other hand bradycardia with prolonged diastole may favor the blood flow and distension of the capillaries, contributing to the increase in capillary growth and CD, as Tomanek (402) found in exercised rats. The latter assumption is also corroborated by the fact that athletic animals such as the hare, wild rat, and bat have hearts with CD considerably higher than animals of similar body weight but higher heart rate, such as a rabbit, laboratory rat, or mouse (418–420).

A great increase in CD was also found in hearts of long-term bradycardially paced rabbits (439).

Other mechanical factors that possibly influence capillary growth have yet to be considered. Clark (79) suggested that fibrin, which usually precedes the growth of capillaries, may form a scaffolding for growing sprouts in rabbit ear chambers, whereas Wagner (421) attributed a similar role to collagen. However, the findings of Ross and Benditt [Fig. 29; (338)] that capillary growth in healing wounds precedes collagen formation do not support Wagner's idea.

Finally, capillary growth can proceed in the cornea when its compactness has been diminished by edema. Even if this is not a stimulus for capillary growth per se, it may create conditions for faster angiogenesis (186, 237, 238). Edema and increased capillary permeability may also contribute to capillary growth under different pathological conditions, such as inflammation or wound healing. They may even be present in exercising skeletal muscles where accumulation of metabolites increases intramuscular osmolarity and leads to an increased water content (253).

Factors in Inhibition of Capillary Growth

Mechanical factors limiting capillary growth, such as decreased blood flow or blood pressure, have been discussed. There are some well-known chemical factors—or rather a complex effect of some tissues—that inhibit capillary growth.

Adult cartilage is completely avascular (180), and Clark and Clark (83) observed that vessel growth in rabbit ear chamber stopped whenever the vessels came into contact with either cartilage or epidermis. Cartilage fragments or extracts also inhibited growth of vessels in the chorioallantoic membrane induced either by extracts of lymphocytes (220) or different tumors (53, 128, 236, 383). In addition, Eisenstein et al. (118) found that cartilage extract inhibits growth of endothelial cells from bovine aorta in tissue cultures and later showed that the chondroitin sulfate present in the bovine aorta inhibits the growth of both endothelial and smooth muscle cells (119). The extract from bovine aorta, which is supposed to be a protease inhibitor, also enhanced the regression of newly formed vessels in the cornea (117). Analogous effects could be achieved with extract from the corpus vitreum (117, 304), which contains some factors that inhibit vessel growth. Gimbrone et al. (148) found that tumors implanted in the middle of the anterior eye chamber were not vascularized from the iris and supposed that the fluid contained some angiogenic inhibitory factors; Henkind (186) made a similar suggestion for the cornea. Crocker et al. (103) assumed that pericytes that gradually encircle newly formed capillary endothelium in wounds suppress its growth. Vlodavsky et al. (413) explained the inhibition of endothelial cell growth in tissue cultures once the cells reach confluence by the presence of a lipoprotein bound on the cell surface that was not found in cultures of rapidly growing cells. Neovascularization and tumor growth were blocked or reduced by locally applied medroxyprogesterone, dexamethasone, or cortisone, drugs that supposedly act by inhibiting collagenase, which facilitates vascularization in normal tissues (173a). Similar inhibition of tumor growth and vascularization was achieved by protamine, which also inhibited capillary growth induced by implantation of foreign particles in rabbit cornea (396a).

It is obvious that all factors suppressing mitotic activity depress vascular growth, but so far there is no further indication [beyond the concept of chalone (352)] of which metabolites are involved. Capillary growth has so far been studied predominantly during development or under pathological conditions. Perhaps it would be helpful to look at vascular growth from a different point of view in order to find out more about its accentuation and inhibition under more physiological conditions. In this connection the work of Bullough and Laurence (59) is important. They point out the role of epinephrine in the suppression of mitotic activity in epidermal cells during stress, whereas activity is high in sleeping animals. It is quite possible that epinephrine and other hormones may be involved—either directly or indirectly by affecting the blood flow—in the control of angiogenesis, and it may be worthwhile to give them greater consideration in future studies on vascular growth.

I would like to thank my colleagues J. H. Coote, E. J. Johns, and G. Vrbová, for their critical advice, and K. R. Tyler, Jude Dawson, Jane Parsons, and Karen Kosakowski for help with manuscript preparation.

REFERENCES

1. ABELL, R. G. The permeability of blood capillary sprouts and newly formed capillaries as compared to that of older blood capillaries. *Am. J. Physiol.* 147: 237–241, 1946.
2. ADOLFSSON, J., A. LJUNGQVIST, G. TORNLING, AND G. UNGE. Capillary increase in the skeletal muscle of trained young and adult rats. *J. Physiol. London* 310: 529–532, 1981.
3. ALGIRE, G. H., J. M. WEAVER, AND R. T. PREHN. Growth of cells in vivo in diffusion chambers. I. Survival of homografts in immunized mice. *J. Natl. Cancer Inst.* 15: 493–401, 1954.
4. ALOISI, M., C. GIACOMIN, AND R. TESSARI. Growth of elementary blood vessels in diffusion chambers. *Virchows Arch. B* 6: 350–364, 1970.
5. ALOISI, M., AND S. SCHIAFFINO. Growth of elementary blood vessels in diffusion chambers. II. Electron microscopy of capillary morphogenesis. *Virchows Arch. B* 8: 328–341, 1971.
6. ALTSCHUL, R. *Endothelium. Its Development, Morphology, Function and Pathology.* New York: Macmillan, 1954.
7. AMHERDT, M., J. P. SCHERRER, C. RUFENER, AND D. POMETTA. Early capillary changes in diabetes mellitus. *Acta Diabetol. Lat. Suppl.* 8: 249–262, 1971.

8. ANDERSEN, P., AND J. HENRIKSSON. Capillary supply of the quadriceps femoris muscle of man: adaptive response to exercise. *J. Physiol. London* 270: 677–690, 1977.
9. ANDERSEN, P., AND A. J. KROESE. Capillary supply in soleus and gastrocnemius muscles of man. *Pfluegers Arch.* 375: 245–249, 1978.
10. APPELL, H. J. Zur Faserzusammensetzung und Kapillarversorgung besonderes beanspruchter Musklen. Cologne, West Germany: Deutsche Sporthochschule, 1977. Dissertation.
11. APPELL, H. J. Capillary density and patterns in skeletal muscle. III. Changes of the capillary pattern after hypoxia. *Pfluegers Arch.* 377: R-53, 1978.
12. AQUIN, L., A. H. SILLAU, A. J. LECHNER, AND N. BANCHERO. Growth and skeletal muscle microvascularity in the guinea pigs. *Microvasc. Res.* 20: 41–50, 1980.
13. AREY, L. B. Wound healing. *Physiol. Rev.* 16: 327–406, 1936.
14. AREY, L. B. The development of peripheral vessels. In: *The Peripheral Blood Vessels*, edited by J. L. Orbison and D. E. Smith. Baltimore, MD: Williams & Wilkins, 1963, p. 1–16.
15. ARMELIN, H. A. Pituitary extracts and steroid hormones in the control of 3T3 cell growth. *Proc. Natl. Acad. Sci. USA* 70: 2702–2706, 1973.
16. ARNOLD, J. Experimentelle Untersuchungen ueber die Blutkapillaren. *Virchows Arch. Pathol. Anat. Physiol.* 53: 70–92, 1871.
17. ARNOLD, J. Experimentelle Untersuchungen ueber die Entwicklung der Blutkapillaren. *Virchows Arch. Pathol. Anat. Physiol.* 54: 1–30, 1872.
18. ARQUILLA, E. D., E. Y. WERINGER, AND M. NAKAYO. Wound healing: a model for the study of diabetic angiopathy. *Diabetes* 25: 811–819, 1976.
19. ASHTON, N. Pathological basis of retrolental fibroplasia. *Br. J. Ophthalmol.* 38: 385–396, 1954.
20. ASHTON, N. Neovascularization in occular disease. *Trans. Ophthalmol. Soc. UK* 81: 145–161, 1961.
21. ASHTON, N., AND C. PEDLER. Studies on developing retinal vessels. IX. Reaction of endothelial cells to oxygen. *Br. J. Ophthalmol.* 46: 257–276, 1962.
22. ASHTON, N., B. WARD, AND G. SERPELL. Effect of oxygen on developing retinal vessels with particular reference to the problem of retrolental fibroplasia. *Br. J. Ophthalmol.* 38: 397–432, 1954.
23. ATHERTON, A. Growth stimulation of endothelial cells by simultaneous culture with sarcoma 180 cells in diffusion chambers. *Cancer Res.* 37: 3619–3622, 1977.
24. AUERBACH, R., L. KUBAI, AND Y. SIDKY. Angiogenesis induction by tumors, embryonic tissue and lymphocytes. *Cancer Res.* 36: 3435–3540, 1976.
25. AUERBACH, R., AND Y. SIDKY. Nature of the stimulus leading to lymphocyte-induced angiogenesis. *J. Immunol.* 123: 751–754, 1979.
26. AUSPRUNK, D. H., K. FALTERMAN, AND J. FOLKMAN. The sequence of events in the regression of corneal capillaries. *Lab. Invest.* 38: 284–294, 1978.
27. AUSPRUNK, D. H., AND J. FOLKMAN. Migration and proliferation of endothelial cells in preformed and newly formed blood vessels during tumor angiogenesis. *Microvasc. Res.* 14: 53–66, 1977.
28. AUSPRUNK, D. H., D. R. KNIGHTON, AND J. FOLKMAN. Differentiation of vascular endothelium in the chick chorioallantois: a structural and autoradiographic study. *Dev. Biol.* 38: 237–347, 1974.
29. AUSPRUNK, D. H., D. R. KNIGHTON, AND J. FOLKMAN. Vascularization of normal and neoplastic tissues grafted to the chick chorioallantois. Role of host and preexisting graft blood vessels. *Am. J. Pathol.* 79: 597–628, 1975.
30. AZIZKHAN, R. G., J. C. AZIZKHAN, B. R. ZETTER, AND J. FOLKMAN. Mast cell heparin stimulates migration of capillary endothelial cells in vitro. *J. Exp. Med.* 152: 931–944, 1980.
31. BALASHOVA, E. G. The relation of nerve cells to capillaries. In: *The Development of the Brain and Its Disturbance by Harmful Factors*, edited by B. M. Klosovskii. Oxford, UK: Pergamon, 1963, p. 70–82.
32. BALLARD, K. W., S. BERNICK, AND S. S. SOBIN. Changes in the human microcirculation with age. *Microvasc. Res.* 17: S11, 1979.
33. BANCHERO, N. Capillary density of skeletal muscle in dogs exposed to simulated altitude. *Proc. Soc. Exp. Biol. Med.* 148: 435–439, 1975.
34. BANCHERO, N., M. GIMENEZ, A. ROSTAMI, AND S. H. EBY. Effects of simulated altitude on O_2 transport in dogs. *Respir. Physiol.* 27: 305–321, 1976.
35. BÄR, T., AND J. R. WOLFF. The formation of capillary basement membranes during internal vascularization of the rat's cerebral cortex. *Z. Zellforsch. Mikrosk. Anat.* 133: 231–248, 1972.
35a. BASS, A., D. BRDICZKA, P. EYER, S. HOLSER, AND D. PETTE. Metabolic differentiation of distinct muscle types at the level of enzymatic organization. *Eur. J. Biochem.* 10: 198–206, 1969.
36. BASSETT, D. L. The changes in the vascular pattern of the ovary of the albino rat during the estrous cycle. *Am. J. Anat.* 73: 251–292, 1943.
37. BASSINGTHWAIGHTE, J. B., T. YIPINTSOI, AND R. B. HARVEY. Microvasculature of the dog left ventricular myocardium. *Microvasc. Res.* 7: 229–249, 1974.
38. BECKER, E. L., R. G. COOPER, AND G. D. HATAWAY. Capillary vascularization in puppies born at a simulated altitude of 20,000 feet. *J. Appl. Physiol.* 8: 166–168, 1955.
39. BENNETT, H. S. The development of the blood supply to the heart in the embryo pig. *Am. J. Anat.* 60: 27–53, 1936.
40. BERRIDGE, M. Y. The interaction of cyclic nucleotides and calcium in the control of cellular activity. *Adv. Cyclic Nucleotide Res.* 6: 1–98, 1975.
41. BESSEY, D. A., AND S. B. WOLBACH. Vascularization of the cornea of the rat in riboflavin deficiency, with a note on corneal vascularization in vitamin A deficiency. *J. Exp. Med.* 69: 1–12, 1969.
42. BILLROTH, T. *Untersuchungen über die Entwicklung der Blutgefässe.* Berlin, 1856.
43. BIRDWELL, C. R., D. GOSPODAROWICZ, AND G. L. NICOLSON. Factors from 3T3 cells stimulate proliferation of cultured vascular endothelial cells. *Nature London* 268: 528–531, 1977.
44. BLATT, H. J. Ueber die Entwicklung der Coronararterien bei der Ratte. Licht und electromicroscopische Untersuchungen. *Z. Anat. Entwicklungsgesch.* 142: 53–64, 1973.
45. BLOOR, C. M., AND A. S. LEON. Interaction of age and exercise on the heart and its blood supply. *Lab. Invest.* 22: 160–165, 1970.
46. BLUMENSON, L. E., AND I. D. BROSS. A possible mechanism for enhancement of increased production of tumor angiogenic factor. *Growth* 40: 205–209, 1976.
47. BOBRITZKY, C. Entwicklung der Capillargefässe. *Zentralbl. Med. Wiss.* 23: 769–771, 1885.
48. BOHLEN, H. G., AND B. A. NIGGL. Early arteriolar disturbances following streptozotocin-induced diabetes mellitus in adult mice. *Microvasc. Res.* 20: 19–29, 1980.
49. BOURDEAU-MARTINI, J., C. L. ODOROFF, AND C. R. HONIG. Dual effect of oxygen on magnitude and uniformity of coronary intercapillary distance. *Am. J. Physiol.* 226: 800–810, 1974.
49a. BOWMAN, P. D., AND A. L. BETZ. Characteristics of cultured brain capillaries (Abstract). *J. Cell Biol.* 83: 95a, 1979.
50. BRÅNEMARK, P.-I. Capillary form and function. *Bibl. Anat.* 7: 9–28, 1965.
51. BRÅNEMARK, P.-I. *Intravascular Anatomy of Blood Cells in Man.* Basel: Karger, 1971.
52. BREISCH, E. A., S. R. HOUSER, R. A. CAREY, Y. F. SPANN, AND A. A. BOVE. Myocardial blood flow and capillary density in chronic pressure overload of the feline left ventricle. *Cardiovasc. Res.* 14: 469–475, 1980.
53. BREM, H., AND J. FOLKMAN. Inhibition of tumor angiogenesis mediated by cartilage. *J. Exp. Med.* 141: 427–439, 1975.
54. BREULL, W., D. REDEL, H. DAHNERS, J. SCHOTTE, AND H.

FLOHR. Myocardial blood flow in the left ventricular hypertrophy. *Bibl. Anat.* 11: 174–179, 1973.

55. BRODAL, P., F. INGJER, AND L. HERMANSEN. Capillary supply of skeletal muscle fibers in untrained and endurance-trained men. *Am. J. Physiol.* 232 (*Heart Circ. Physiol.* 1): H705–H712, 1977.
56. BROWN, M. D., M. A. COTTER, O. HUDLICKÁ, AND G. VRBOVÁ. The effects of different patterns of muscle activity on capillary density, mechanical properties and structure of slow and fast rabbit muscles. *Pfluegers Arch.* 361: 241–250, 1976.
57. BÜCHER, F. Qualitative morphology of heart failure. *Methods Achiev. Exp. Pathol.* 5: 60–120, 1971.
58. BULLER, A. J., J. C. ECCLES, AND R. M. ECCLES. Differentiation of fast and slow muscles in cat hind limb. *J. Physiol. London* 150: 399–416, 1960.
59. BULLOUGH, W. S., AND E. B. LAURENCE. Stress and adrenaline in relation to the diurnal cycle of epidermal mitotic activity in adult male mice. *Proc. R. Soc. London Ser. B* 154: 540–556, 1961.
60. BUZNEY, S. M., R. N. FRANK, AND W. G. ROBINSON, JR. Retinal capillaries: proliferation of mural cells in vitro. *Science* 190: 985–986, 1975.
61. BUZNEY, S. M., AND S. J. MASSICOTTE. Retinal vessels—proliferation of endothelium in vitro. *Invest. Ophthalmol. Vis. Sci.* 18: 1191–1195, 1979.
62. BYERLY, T. P. Studies in growth: suffocation effects in the chick embryo. *Anat. Rec.* 32: 249–270, 1920.
63. BYYNY, R. L., D. M. ORTH, AND S. COHEN. Epidermal growth factor: effects of androgenous and adrenergic agents. *Endocrinology* 95: 776–782, 1974.
64. CAMERON, D. P., M. AMHERDT, P. LEUENBERGER, L. ORCI, AND W. STAUFFACHER. Microvascular alterations in chronically streptozotocin-diabetic rats. *Adv. Metab. Disord. Suppl.* 2: 257–269, 1973.
65. CAMPBELL, A. C. P. Variation in vascularity and oxidase content in different regions of the brain of the cat. *Arch. Neurol. Psychiatry* 41: 223–242, 1939.
66. CAPLAN, B. A., AND C. J. SCHWARTZ. Increased endothelial cell turnover in areas of in vivo Evans blue uptake in the pig aorta. *Atherosclerosis* 17: 401–417, 1973.
67. CARLSON, B. M. *The Regeneration of Minced Muscles.* Basel: Karger, 1972, p. 16–23.
68. CARLSSON, S., A. LJUNGQVIST, G. TORNLING, AND G. UNGE. The reaction of the vascular pattern of the hypertrophied myocardium and increased cardiac volume load. *Acta Pathol. Microbiol. Scand. Sect. A* 86: 297–301, 1978.
69. CASSIN, S., R. D. GILBERT, C. E. BUNNELL, AND E. M. JOHNSON. Capillary development during exposure to chronic hypoxia. *Am. J. Physiol.* 220: 448–451, 1971.
70. CAVALLO, T., R. SADE, J. FOLKMAN, AND R. S. COTRAN. Tumor angiogenesis. Rapid induction of endothelial mitoses demonstrated by autoradiography. *J. Cell Biol.* 54: 408–420, 1972.
71. CHALKEY, H. W., C. H. ALGIRE, AND H. P. MORRIS. Effect of the level of dietary protein on vascular repair in wounds. *J. Natl. Cancer Inst.* 6: 363–372, 1946.
72. CHAPMAN, W. B. The effect of heart beat upon the development of the vascular system in the chick. *Am. J. Anat.* 23: 175–203, 1918.
73. CHEN, L. B., AND J. M. BUCHANAN. Mitogenic activity of blood components. I. Thrombin and prothrombin. *Proc. Natl. Acad. Sci. USA* 72: 131–135, 1975.
75. CLARK, D. R., AND P. SMITH. Capillary density and muscle fibre size in the hearts of rats subjected to simulated high altitude. *Cardiovasc. Res.* 12: 578–584, 1978.
76. CLARK, E. R. Observations on living, growing lymphatics in the tail of the frog larvae. *Anat. Rec.* 3: 183–198, 1909.
77. CLARK, E. R. Studies on the growth of blood vessels in the tail of the frog larvae. *Am. J. Anat.* 23: 37–88, 1918.
78. CLARK, E. R. Growth and development of function in blood vessels and lymphatics. *Ann. Intern. Med.* 9: 1043–1049, 1936.
79. CLARK, E. R. Intercellular substance in relation to tissue growth. *Ann. N.Y. Acad. Sci.* 46: 733–742, 1946.
80. CLARK, E. R., AND E. L. CLARK. Observations on living preformed blood vessels as seen in a transparent chamber inserted into the rabbit's ear. *Am. J. Anat.* 49: 441–477, 1932.
81. CLARK, E. R., AND E. L. CLARK. Observations on changes in blood vascular endothelium in the living animal. *Am. J. Anat.* 57: 385–438, 1935.
82. CLARK, E. R., AND E. L. CLARK. Observation on conditions affecting growth of cells and tissues from microscopic studies on living animals. *Biol. Bull.* 71: 405–406, 1936.
83. CLARK, E. R., AND E. L. CLARK. Microscopic observations on the growth of blood capillaries in the living mammal. *Am. J. Anat.* 64: 251–299, 1939.
84. CLARK, E. R., AND E. L. CLARK. Microscopic observations on the extraendothelial cells of living mammalian blood vessels. *Am. J. Anat.* 66: 1–49, 1940.
85. CLARK, E. R., W. J. HITCHLER, H. T. KIRBY-SMITH, R. O. REX, AND J. H. SMITH. General observations on the ingrowth of new blood vessels into standardized chambers in the rabbit's ear and the subsequent changes in the newly grown vessels over a period of months. *Anat. Rec.* 50: 129–168, 1931.
86. CLARK, J. F., K. L. JONES, D. GOSPODAROWICZ, AND G. SATO. Hormone dependent growth response of a newly established rat ovarian cell line. *Nature London New Biol.* 236: 180–183, 1972.
87. CLARK, R. A., R. D. STONEY, D. Y. K. LEUNG, I. SILVER, D. C. HOHN, AND T. K. HUNT. Role of macrophages in wound healing. *Surg. Forum* 27: 16–19, 1976.
88. CLIFF, W. J. Observations on healing tissue: a combined light and electron-microscopic investigation. *Philos. Trans. R. Soc. London Ser. B* 246: 305–325, 1963.
89. CLIFF, W. J. Kinetics of wound healing in rabbit ear chambers, a time lapse cinemicroscopic study. *Q. J. Exp. Physiol.* 50: 79–89, 1965.
90. CLIFF, W. J. The aortic tunica media in growing rats studied with the electron microscope. *Lab. Invest.* 17: 599–615, 1967.
91. CLIFF, W. J. *Blood Vessels.* New York: Cambridge Univ. Press, 1976.
92. COGAN, D. G. Vascularization of the cornea, its experimental induction by small lesions and a new theory of its pathogenesis. *Arch. Ophthalmol.* 41: 406–416, 1949.
93. COGAN, D. G., T. KUWABARA, AND E. FRIEDMAN. Retinal vasculature. *Microvasc. Res.* 1: 115–132, 1968.
94. CONVERSE, J. M., AND F. T. RAPPAPORT. The vascularization of skin autografts and homografts. An experimental study in man. *Ann. Surg.* 143: 306–315, 1956.
95. COOPER, J., AND O. HUDLICKÁ. Effect of the changes in the capillary bed induced by long-term stimulation on muscle fatigue (Abstract). *J. Physiol. London* 263: 155P–156P, 1976.
96. COTTER, M. A. A Study of the Interrelationships Between the Vascular Supply and Metabolism of Skeletal Muscle Fibres in the Course of Development and During Chronic Stimulation of Adult Muscles. Birmingham, UK: Univ. of Birmingham, 1975. Dissertation.
97. COTTER, M. The relationship between vascular and metabolic differentiation of fast and slow muscle during development (Abstract). *J. Physiol. London* 256: 82P–83P, 1976.
98. COTTER, M., AND O. HUDLICKÁ. Effects of chronic stimulation on muscles in aging rats (Abstract). *J. Physiol. London* 266: 102P–103P, 1977.
99. COTTER, M., AND O. HUDLICKÁ. Effect of different patterns of long-term stimulation on muscle performance (Abstract). *J. Physiol. London* 292: 20P–21P, 1979.
100. COTTER, M., O. HUDLICKÁ, AND G. VRBOVÁ. Growth of capillaries during long-term activity in skeletal muscle. *Bibl. Anat.* 11: 395–398, 1973.
101. CRAIGIE, E. H. Changes in vascularity in the brain stem and cerebellum of the albino rat between birth and maturity. *J. Comp. Neurol.* 38: 27–48, 1924.
102. CRANE, W. A. J., AND L. P. DUTTA. The influence of age on

the uptake of sulphate and ^{3}H-thymidine by the mesenteric arteries of rats with regenerating adrenal glands. *J. Pathol. Bacteriol.* 88: 291–301, 1969.

103. CROCKER, D. J., T. M. MURAD, AND J. C. GEER. Role of pericyte in wound healing. An ultrastructural study. *Exp. Mol. Pathol.* 13: 51–65, 1970.

103a. CUTTINO, J. T., JR., R. J. BARTUM, JR., N. K. HOLLENBERG, AND H. L. ABRAMS. Collateral vessel formation: isolation of a transferable factor promoting a vascular response. *Basic Res. Cardiol.* 70: 568–573, 1975.

104. D'AMORE, P. A., AND D. SHEPRO. Stimulation of growth and calcium influx in cultured bovine aortic endothelial cells by platelets and vasoactive substances. *J. Cell. Physiol.* 92: 177–184, 1977.

105. DBALÝ, J., B. OŠŤÁDAL, AND Z. RYCHTER. Development of the coronary arteries in rat embryos. *Acta Anat.* 71: 209–229, 1968.

106. DELORME, P. Différention ultrastructurale des jonctions intercellulaires de l'endothélium des capillaires télecephaliques chez l'embryon de poulet. *Z. Zellforsch. Mikrosk. Anat.* 133: 571–582, 1972.

107. DITZEL, J. The problem of tissue oxygenation in diabetes mellitus as related to the development of diabetic angiopathy. In: *Microcirculation,* edited by J. Grayson and W. Zingg. New York: Plenum, 1976, vol. 1, p. 263–274.

108. DODD, L., S. D. GRAY, O. HUDLICKÁ, AND E. M. RENKIN. Evaluation of capillary density in relation to fibre types in electrically stimulated rabbit fast muscles (Abstract). *J. Physiol. London* 301: 11P–12P, 1980.

109. DONAHUE, S., AND G. D. PAPPAS. The fine structure of capillaries in the cerebral cortex of the rat at various stages of development. *Am. J. Anat.* 108: 331–347, 1961.

110. DOWELL, R. T. Hemodynamic factors and vascular density as potential determinants of blood flow in hypertrophied rat heart. *Proc. Soc. Exp. Biol. Med.* 154: 423–426, 1977.

111. DUNNING, H. S., AND H. G. WOLFF. The relative vascularity of various parts of the central and peripheral nervous system of the cat and its relation to function. *J. Comp. Neurol.* 67: 433–450, 1937.

112. DYSON, S. E., D. G. JONES, AND W. L. KENDRICK. Some observations on the ultrastructure of developing rat cerebral capillaries. *Cell Tissue Res.* 173: 529–544, 1976.

113. EBNER, V. *Koelliker's Handbuch der Gewebelehre des Menschen.* Leipzig, Germany: Engelman, 1902, p. 664–674.

114. EBY, S. H., AND N. BANCHERO. Capillary density of skeletal muscle in Andean dogs. *Proc. Soc. Exp. Biol. Med.* 151: 795–798, 1976.

115. EDWARDS, J. L., AND R. E. KLEIN. Cell renewal in adult mouse tissues. *Am. J. Pathol.* 38: 437–453, 1961.

116. EDWARDS, R. H., S. S. SARMENTA, AND G. M. HASS. Stimulation of granulation tissue growth by tissue extracts. *Arch. Pathol.* 69: 286–302, 1960.

117. EISENSTEIN, R., S. B. GOREN, B. SCHUMACHER, AND E. CHOROMOKOS. The inhibition of corneal vascularization with aortic extracts in rabbits. *Am. J. Ophthalmol.* 88: 1005–1012, 1978.

118. EISENSTEIN, R., K. E. KUETTNER, C. NEAPOLITAN, L. W. SOBLE, AND N. SORGENTE. The resistance of certain tissues to invasion. III. Cartilage extracts inhibit the growth of fibroblasts and endothelial cells in culture. *Am. J. Pathol.* 81: 337–348, 1975.

119. EISENSTEIN, R., C. MEINEKE, B. SCHUMACHER, AND K. E. KUETTNER. Growth regulators in aorta (Abstract). *Am. J. Pathol.* 86: 26a–27a, 1977.

120. ENGERMAN, R. L., D. PFAFFENBACH, AND M. D. DAVIS. Cell turnover of capillaries. *Lab. Invest.* 17: 738–743, 1967.

121. ERIKSSON, E., AND H. A. ZAREM. Growth and differentiation of blood vessels. In: *Microcirculation,* edited by G. Kaley and B. M. Altura. Baltimore, MD: University Park, 1977, vol. 1, p. 393–418.

122. EVANS, H. J. On the development of the aorta, cardinal and umbilical veins and the other blood vessels of vertebrate embryos from capillaries. *Anat. Rec.* 3: 498–518, 1909.

123. EVANS, H. J. The development of the vascular system. In: *Manual of Human Embryology,* edited by F. Kleibel and F. P. Mall. Philadelphia PA: Lippincott, 1912, p. 570–709.

124. FAULKNER, J. A., L. C. MAXWELL, T. P. WHITE, AND J. H. NIEMEYER. Characteristics of autografted mammalian skeletal muscles. In: *Muscle Regeneration,* edited by A. Mauro. New York: Raven, 1979, p. 485–492.

125. FENSELAU, A., AND R. J. MELLO. Growth stimulation of cultured endothelial cells by tumor cell homogenates. *Cancer Res.* 36: 3269–3273, 1976.

126. FOLKMAN, J. Tumor angiogenic factor. *Cancer Res.* 34: 2109–2123, 1974.

127. FOLKMAN, J. Tumor angiogenesis: a possible control point in tumor growth. *Ann. Intern. Med.* 82: 96–100, 1975.

128. FOLKMAN, J., AND R. COTRAN. Relation of vascular proliferation to tumor growth. *Int. Rev. Exp. Pathol.* 16: 207–248, 1976.

129. FOLKMAN, J., AND H. P. GREENSPAN. Influence of geometry on control of cell growth. *Biochim. Biophys. Acta* 417: 211–231, 1975.

130. FOLKMAN, J., AND C. C. HAUDENSCHILD. Angiogenesis in vitro. *Nature London* 288: 551–556, 1980.

131. FOLKMAN, J., C. C. HAUDENSCHILD, AND B. R. ZETTER. Long-term culture of capillary endothelial cells. *Proc. Natl. Acad. Sci. USA* 76: 5217–5221, 1979.

132. FOLKMAN, J., E. MERLER, C. ABERNATHY, AND G. WILLIAMS. Isolation of a tumor factor responsible for angiogenesis. *J. Exp. Med.* 133: 275–288, 1971.

133. FOLKMAN, J., AND A. MOSCONA. Roll of cell shape in growth control. *Nature London* 273: 345–349, 1978.

134. FRANK, R. N., V. E. KINSEY, K. W. FRANK, K. MIKUS, AND A. RANDOLPH. In vitro proliferation of endothelial cells from kitten retinal capillaries. *Invest. Ophthalmol. Vis. Sci.* 18: 1195–1200, 1979.

135. FRAZER, R. A., E. M. ELLIS, AND A. L. STALKER. Experimental angiogenesis in the chorio-allantoic membrane. *Bibl. Anat.* 18: 25–27, 1979.

136. FRIST, S., AND M. B. STEMERMAN. Arterial growth and development. In: *Vascular Neuroeffector Mechanisms,* edited by J. A. Bevan, G. Burnstock, B. Johansson, R. A. Maxwell, and O. A. Nedergaard. Basel: Karger, 1976, p. 19–27. (Int. Symp. Odense, 2nd, 1975.)

137. FROMER, C. H., AND G. K. KLINTWORTH. An evaluation of the role of leukocytes in the pathogenesis of experimentally induced corneal vascularization. I. *Am. J. Pathol.* 79: 537–554, 1975.

138. FROMER, C. H., AND G. K. KLINTWORTH. An evaluation of the role of leukocytes in the pathogenesis of experimentally induced corneal vascularization. II. *Am. J. Pathol.* 81: 531–544, 1975.

139. FROMER, C. H., AND G. K. KLINTWORTH. An evaluation of the role of leukocytes in the pathogenesis of experimentally induced corneal vascularization. III. *Am. J. Pathol.* 82: 157–167, 1976.

140. FRY, D. L. Acute vascular endothelial changes associated with increased blood velocity gradients. *Circ. Res.* 22: 165–197, 1968.

141. FULTON, G. P., B. R. LUTZ, D. I. PATT, AND G. YERGANIAN. The cheek pouch of the Chinese hamster (*Cricetulus griseus*) for cinephotomicroscopy of blood circulation and tumor growth. *J. Lab. Clin. Med.* 44: 145–148, 1954.

142. GAJDUSEK, C., P. DICORLETTO, R. ROSS, AND S. M. SCHWARTZ. An endothelial cell-derived growth factor. *J. Cell Biol.* 85: 467–472, 1980.

143. GAUTIER, D., J. MARTINI, AND E. CORABOEUF. Étude comparative de la densité capillaire coronaire chez le rat et le cobaye. *J. Physiol. Paris* 50: 356, 1964.

144. GERDES, A. M., G. CALLAS, AND F. H. KASTEN. Differences in regional capillary distribution and myocyte sizes in normal and hypertrophic rat hearts. *Am. J. Anat.* 156: 523–531, 1979.

144a. GERDES, A. M., AND F. H. KASTEN. Morphometric study of endomyocardium and epimyocardium of the left ventricle in adult dogs. *Am. J. Anat.* 159: 389–394, 1980.

145. GIMBRONE, M. A., JR. Culture of vascular endothelium. *Prog. Hemostasis Thromb.* 3: 1–28, 1976.

146. GIMBRONE, M. A., JR., R. S. COTRAN, AND J. FOLKMAN. Human vascular endothelial cells in cultures, growth and DNA synthesis. *J. Cell Biol.* 60: 673–684, 1974.

147. GIMBRONE, M. A., JR., R. S. COTRAN, S. B. LEAPMAN, AND J. FOLKMAN. Tumor growth and neovascularization: an experimental model using the rabbit cornea. *J. Natl. Cancer Inst.* 52: 413–427, 1974.

148. GIMBRONE, M. A., S. B. LEAPMAN, R. S. COTRAN, AND J. FOLKMAN. Tumor dormancy in vivo by prevention of neovascularization. *J. Exp. Med.* 136: 261–276, 1972.

149. GIMBRONE, M. A., S. B. LEAPMAN, R. S. COTRAN, AND J. FOLKMAN. Tumor angiogenesis: iris neovascularization at a distance from experimental intracellular tumors. *J. Natl. Cancer Inst.* 50: 219–228, 1973.

149a. GLASER, B. M., P. A. D'AMORE, R. G. MICHELS, A. PATZ, AND A. FENSELAU. Demonstration of vasoproliferative activity from mammalian retina. *J. Cell Biol.* 84: 298–304, 1980.

150. GLICKMAN, F. S., AND Y. RAPP. Psoriatic angiogenic factor: evidence for its existence. *Arch. Dermatol.* 112: 1789, 1976.

151. GOLDMAN, R. Speculations on vascular changes with age. *J. Am. Geriatr. Soc.* 18: 765–779, 1970.

152. GOLDSTEIN, G. W., J. S. WOLINSKY, J. CSEJTEY, AND I. DIAMOND. Isolation of metabolically active capillaries from rat brain. *J. Neurochem.* 25: 715–717, 1975.

153. GOLLNICK, P. D., K. PIEHL, AND B. SALTIN. Selective glycogen depletion in skeletal muscle fibres after exercise of varying intensity and of varying pedalling rates. *J. Physiol. London* 241: 45–58, 1974.

154. GOLUBEW, A. Beiträge zur Kenntniss des Baues und der Entwicklungsgeschichte der Capillargefässe des Frosches. *Arch. Mikrosk. Anat. Entwicklungsmech.* 5: 49–89, 1869.

155. GONZALES-CRUSSI, F. Vasculogenesis in the chick embryo. An ultrastructural study. *Am. J. Anat.* 130: 441–459, 1971.

156. GOSPODAROWICZ, D. Humoral control of cell proliferation: the role of fibroblast growth factor in regeneration, angiogenesis, wound healing and neoplastic growth. In: *Membranes and Neoplasia: New Approaches and Strategies.* New York: Liss, 1976, p. 1–19.

157. GOSPODAROWICZ, D., H. BIALECKI, AND T. K. THAKRAL. The angiogenic activity of the fibroblast and epidermal growth factor. *Exp. Eye Res.* 28: 501–514, 1979.

158. GOSPODAROWICZ, D., K. D. BROWN, C. R. BIRDWELL, AND B. R. ZETTER. Control of proliferation of human vascular endothelial cells. Characterization of the response of human umbilical vein endothelial cells to fibroblasts growth factor, epidermal growth factor and thrombin. *J. Cell Biol.* 77: 774–788, 1978.

159. GOSPODAROWICZ, D., G. GREENBURG, AND C. R. BIRDWELL. Determination of cellular shape by the extracellular matrix and its correlation with the control of cellular growth. *Cancer Res.* 38: 4155–4171, 1978.

160. GOSPODAROWICZ, D., AND J. MORAN. Mitogenic effect of fibroblast growth factor on early passage cultures of human and murine fibroblasts. *J. Cell Biol.* 66: 451–457, 1975.

161. GOSPODAROWICZ, D., J. S. MORAN, AND H. BIALECKI. Mitogenic factors from the brain and the pituitary: physiological significance. In: *Growth Hormone and Related Peptides, Proc. Int. Symp. Growth Hormone, 3rd, Milan, Italy, 1975,* edited by A. Pecile and E. Müller. Amsterdam: Excerpta Med., 1976. (Int. Congr. Ser. 381.)

162. GOSPODAROWICZ, D., J. S. MORAN, AND D. L. BRAUN. Control of proliferation of bovine vascular endothelial cells. *J. Cell. Physiol.* 91: 377–386, 1977.

163. GOSPODAROWICZ, D., J. S. MORAN, D. L. BRAUN, AND C. R. BIRDWELL. Clonal growth of bovine vascular endothelial cells: fibroblast growth factor as a survival agent. *Proc. Natl. Acad. Sci. USA* 73: 4120–4124, 1976.

164. GOSPODAROWICZ, D., AND K. THAKRAL. The production of a corpus luteum angiogenic factor responsible for the proliferation of capillaries and the neovascularization of the corpus luteum. *Proc. Natl. Acad. Sci. USA* 75: 847–851, 1978.

165. GOSPODAROWICZ, D., I. VLODAVSKY, P. FIELDING, AND C. R. BIRDWELL. The effects of the epidermal and fibroblast growth factors upon cell proliferation using vascular and corneal endothelial cells as a model. In: *Birth Defects,* edited by J. W. Littlefield and J. DeGrouchy. Amsterdam: Excerpta Med., 1978, p. 233–271.

166. GRAHAM, R. C., AND S. L. SHANNON. Peroxidase arthritis. II. Lymphoid cell–endothelial interactions during a developing immunologic inflammatory response. *Am. J. Pathol.* 69: 7–24, 1972.

167. GRANDTNER, M., Z. TUREK, AND F. KREUZER. Cardiac hypertrophy in the first generation of rats native to simulated high altitude. *Pfluegers Arch.* 350: 241–248, 1974.

168. GRANT, R. T. Development of the cardiac coronary vessels in the rabbit. *Heart* 13: 261–272, 1926.

169. GRAY, S. D., P. F. MCDONAGH, AND R. W. GORE. Comparison of functional and total capillary densities in fast and slow muscles of the chicken. *Pfluegers Arch.* In press.

170. GRAY, S. D., AND E. M. RENKIN. Microvascular supply in relation to fiber metabolic type in mixed skeletal muscles of rabbit. *Microvasc. Res.* 16: 406–425, 1978.

171. GREENBLATT, M., K. V. P. CHONDARI, A. G. SANDERS, AND P. SHUBIK. Mammalian microcirculation in the living animals. Methodologic consideration. *Microvasc. Res.* 1: 420–432, 1969.

172. GREENBLATT, M., J. KAUFMAN, AND V. R. CHONDARI-KOMMINENI. Functioning heart homografts in hamsters. *Transplantation* 11: 50–55, 1971.

173. GREENBLATT, M., AND P. SHUBIK. Tumor angiogenesis: transfilter diffusion studies in the hamster by the transparent chamber technique. *J. Natl. Cancer Inst.* 41: 111–124, 1968.

173a. GROSS, J., R. G. AZIZKHAN, C. BISWAS, R. R. BRUNS, D. S. T. HSIEH, AND J. FOLKMAN. Inhibition of tumor growth, vascularization and collagenolysis in the rabbit cornea by medroxyprogesterone. *Proc. Natl. Acad. Sci. USA* 78: 1176–1180, 1981.

174. GULDNER, F. H., AND J. R. WOLFF. Seamless endothelium as indicators of capillaries developed from sprouts. *Bibl. Anat.* 12: 120–123, 1973.

175. HADFIELD, G. Granulation tissue. *Ann. R. Coll. Surg. Engl.* 9: 397–407, 1951.

176. HAKELIUS, L., AND B. NYSTRÖM. Blood vessels and connective tissue in autotransplanted free muscle grafts of the cat. *Scand. J. Plast. Reconstr. Surg.* 9: 87–91, 1975.

177. HAKKILA, J. Studies on the myocardial capillary concentration in cardiac hypertrophy due to training. *Ann. Med. Exp. Biol. Fenn. Suppl.* 10: 1–82, 1955.

178. HALL, M. *Essay on the Circulation of the Blood.* London: Seeley & Burnside, 1831.

179. HANNAH, R. S., AND E. J. H. NATHANIEL. The postnatal development of blood vessels in the substantia gelatinosa of the rat cervical cord. An ultrastructural study. *Anat. Rec.* 178: 691–710, 1974.

180. HARALDSON, S. The vascular pattern of a growing and full-grown human epiphysis. *Acta Anat.* 48: 156–167, 1962.

181. HASEN-SMITH, F. M., B. M. CARLSON, AND K. L. IRWIN. Revascularization of the freely grafted extensor digitorum longus muscle in the rat. *Am. J. Anat.* 158: 65–82, 1980.

182. HAUDENSCHILD, C. C. Growth control of endothelial cells in atherogenesis and tumor angiogenesis. *Adv. Microcirc.* 9: 226–251, 1980.

183. HAUDENSCHILD, C. C., R. S. COTRAN, M. A. GIMBRONE, AND J. FOLKMAN. Fine structure of vascular endothelium in culture. *J. Ultrastruct. Res.* 50: 22–32, 1975.

184. HAUDENSCHILD, C. C., D. ZAHNISER, J. FOLKMAN, AND M. KLAGSBRUN. Human vascular endothelial cells in culture: lack of response to serum growth factors. *Exp. Cell Res.* 98: 175–183, 1976.

185. HECHT, A. Zur Capillären Gefässversorgung der subendocardialen Muskelschichten im menschlichen Herzen. *Virchows*

Arch. Pathol. Anat. Physiol. 331: 26–35, 1958.

186. HENKIND, P. Ocular neovascularization. *Am. J. Ophthalmol.* 85: 287–301, 1978.
187. HENQUELL, L., AND C. R. HONIG. Intercapillary distances and capillary reserve in right and left ventricles. Significance for control of tissue Po_2. *Microvasc. Res.* 12: 35–41, 1976.
188. HENQUELL, L., C. L. ODOROFF, AND C. R. HONIG. Intercapillary distance and capillary reserve in hypertrophied rat hearts beating in situ. *Circ. Res.* 41: 400–408, 1977.
189. HERMANSEN, L., AND M. WACHTLOVÁ. Capillary density of skeletal muscle in well-trained and untrained men. *J. Appl. Physiol.* 30: 860–863, 1971.
190. HETZKO, D. Über die postnatale Zunahme des Capillarvolumens im Corpus callosum der Katze. *Z. Anat. Enwicklungsgesch.* 127: 138–144, 1968.
191. HIS, W. *Untersuchungen über die erste Anlage des Wirbeltierleibes.* Leipzig, Germany: Vogel, 1868.
192. HOFFMAN, H., B. MCAUSLAN, D. ROBERTSON, AND E. BURNETTE. An endothelial growth-stimulating factor from salivary glands. *Exp. Cell Res.* 102: 269–275, 1976.
193. HOFFMAN, J. I. E., E. D. VERRIER, G. VLAHARES, R. BAER, AND K. TURLEY. Intramyocardial pressures and regional myocardial blood flow. *Bibl. Anat.* 20: 480–492, 1981.
194. HOLLY, R. G., J. G. BARNETT, C. R. ASHMORE, R. G. TAYLOR, AND P. A. MOLÉ. Stretch-induced growth in chicken wing muscles: a new model of stretch hypertrophy. *Am. J. Physiol.* 238 (*Cell Physiol.* 7): C62–C71, 1980.
195. HOLM, J., P. BJÖRNTORP, AND T. SCHERSTÉN. Metabolic activity in human skeletal muscle. Effect of peripheral arterial insufficiency. *Eur. J. Clin. Invest.* 2: 321–325, 1972.
196. HOLTZ, G., W. R. RESTORFF, P. BARD, AND E. BASSENGE. Transmural distribution of myocardial blood flow and of coronary reserve in canine left ventricular hypertrophy. *Basic Res. Cardiol.* 72: 286–292, 1977.
197. HONIG, C. R. Hypoxia in skeletal muscle at rest and during the transition to steady work. *Microvasc. Res.* 13: 377–398, 1977.
198. HOPPELER, H., O. MATHIEU, R. KRAUER, H. CLAASEN, R. B. ARMSTRONG, AND E. R. WEIBEL. Structure-function correlation in the respiratory system. VI. Distribution of mitochondria and capillaries in various muscles. *Respir. Physiol.* 44: 87–112, 1981.
199. HOPPELER, H., O. MATHIEU, R. KRAUER, H. CLAASEN, R. B. ARMSTRONG, AND E. R. WEIBEL. Design of the mammalian respiratory system. VIII. Capillaries in skeletal muscles. *Respir. Physiol.* 44: 129–150, 1981.
200. HUDLICKÁ, O. Resting and postcontraction blood flow in slow and fast muscles of the chick during development. *Microvasc. Res.* 1: 390–420, 1969.
201. HUDLICKÁ, O. *Muscle Blood Flow: Its Relation to Muscle Metabolism and Function.* Amsterdam: Swets & Zeitlinger, 1973.
202. HUDLICKÁ, O. Effect of training on macro- and microcirculatory changes in exercise. *Exercise Sport Sci. Rev.* 5: 181–230, 1977.

202a. HUDLICKÁ, O., L. DODD, E. M. RENKIN, AND S. D. GRAY. Early changes in fiber profile and capillary density in long-term stimulated muscles. *Am. J. Physiol.* 243 (*Heart Circ. Physiol.* 12): H528–H535, 1982.

203. HUDLICKÁ, O., J. KOMAREK, AND A. J. A. WRIGHT. The effect of xanthine derivate, 1-(5′ oxohexyl)-3-methyl-7-propylxanthine, on heart performance and regional blood flow in dogs and rabbits. *Br. J. Pharmacol.* 72: 723–730, 1981.
204. HUDLICKÁ, O., D. PETTE, AND H. STAUDTE. The relation between blood flow and enzymatic activities in slow and fast muscles during development. *Pfluegers Arch.* 343: 341–356, 1973.
205. HUDLICKÁ, O., AND W. SCHROEDER. Factors involved in capillary growth in a normal adult skeletal muscle (Abstract). *Federation Proc.* 37: 314, 1978.
206. HUDLICKÁ, O., AND K. R. TYLER. Importance of different patterns of frequency in the development of contractile properties and histochemical characteristics of fast skeletal muscles (Abstract). *J. Physiol. London* 301: 10P–11P, 1980.
207. HUDLICKÁ, O., K. R. TYLER, AND T. AITMAN. The effect of long-term electrical stimulation on fuel uptake and performance in fast muscles. In: *Plasticity of Muscle*, edited by D. Pette. New York: de Gruyter, 1980, p. 401–408.

207a. HUDLICKÁ, O., K. R. TYLER, A. J. A. WRIGHT, AND A. M. ZIADA. The effect of long-term vasodilatation on capillary growth and performance in rabbit heart and skeletal muscle. *J. Physiol. London* 334: 49P, 1983.

208. HUGHES, A. F. W., AND L. DANN. Vascular regeneration in experimental wounds and burns. *Br. J. Exp. Pathol.* 22: 9–14, 1941.
209. HUNZIKER, O., S. ABDEL'AL, AND U. SCHULZ. The aging human cerebral cortex: a stereological characterization of changes in the capillary net. *J. Gerontol.* 34: 345–350, 1979.
210. ILLIG, L., AND U. HOLTZ. Die Blutgefäss-Reaktion bei der Psoriasis vulgaris. *Arch. Klin. Exp. Dermatol.* 226: 239–264, 1966.
211. IMRE, G. Studies on the mechanism of retinal neovascularization. *Br. J. Ophthalmol.* 48: 75–82, 1964.
212. INGJER, F. Effects of endurance training on muscle fibre ATPase activity, capillary supply and mitochondria content in man. *J. Physiol. London* 294: 419–432, 1979.
213. INGJER, F., AND P. BRODAL. Capillary supply of skeletal muscle fibres in untrained and endurance-trained women. *Eur. J. Appl. Physiol. Occup. Physiol.* 38: 291–299, 1978.
214. JAFFE, E. A., R. L. NACHMAN, C. G. BECKER, AND C. R. MINICK. Culture of human endothelial cells derived from umbilical veins. Identification of morphological and immunological criteria. *J. Clin. Invest.* 52: 2745–2756, 1973.
215. JAKOB, W., K. JENTZSCH, B. MAUERSBERGER, AND G. HEDER. The chick embryo chorioallantoic membrane as a bioassay for angiogenesis factors: reactions induced by carrier materials. *Exp. Pathol.* 15: 241–249, 1978.
216. JÄRVINEN, M. Healing of a crush injury in rat striated muscle 3. A microangiographical study of the effect of early mobilization and immobilization on capillary ingrowth. *Acta Pathol. Microbiol. Scand. Sect. A* 84: 85–94, 1976.
217. JENEY, A., AND E. TÖRÖ. Die Wirkungen von Aminosäuren und anderen biochemischen Produkten auf die Entwicklung des Hühnesembryos. *Virchows Arch. Pathol. Anat. Physiol.* 296: 471–479, 1935.
218. JOHNSON, R. C. Ultrastructure of developing ventricular endocardial endothelium in the avian embryo (Abstract). *Am. Zool.* 14: 1301, 1974.

218a. JOHNSTON, I. A. Capillarization, oxygen diffusion distances and mitochondrial content of carp muscles following acclimatization to summer and winter temperatures. *Cell Tissue Res.* 222: 325–337, 1982.

219. JORDAN, S. W., AND M. J. PERLEY. Microangiopathy in diabetes mellitus and aging. *Arch. Pathol.* 93: 261–265, 1972.
220. KAMINSKI, M., G. KAMINSKA, AND S. MAJEWSKI. Inhibition of new blood vessel formation in mice by systemic administration of human rib cartilage extract. *Experientia* 34: 490–491, 1978.
221. KARPER, H. E. Electron microscope study of developing chick embryo aorta. *J. Ultrastruct. Res.* 4: 420–454, 1960.
222. KASALICKÝ, J., J. RESSL, D. URBANOVÁ, J. WIDIMSKÝ, B. OŠŤÁDAL, V. PELOUCH, M. VÍZEK, AND J. PROCHÁZKA. Relative organ blood flow in rats exposed to intermittent high altitude hypoxia. *Pfluegers Arch.* 368: 111–115, 1977.
223. KELLY, P. J., R. L. SUDDITH, H. T. HUTCHINSON, K. WERRBACH, AND B. HABER. Endothelial growth factor present in tissue culture of CNS tumors. *J. Neurosurg.* 44: 342–346, 1976.

223a. KESSLER, D. A., R. S. LANGER, N. A. PLESS, AND J. FOLKMAN. Mast cells and tumor angiogenesis. *Int. J. Cancer* 18: 703–709, 1976.

224. KETCHUM, S. A., III, A. N. THOMAS, AND A. D. HALL. Angiographic studies on the effects of hyperbaric oxygen on burn wound revascularization. In: *Proc. Int. Congr. Hyperbaric*

Med., 4th, edited by J. Wada and T. Iwa. Tokyo: Igaku Shoin, 1970, p. 388.

225. KETY, S. S. The theory and applications of the exchange of inert gas at the lungs and tissues. *Pharmacol. Rev.* 3: 1–41, 1951.

226. KILO, C., N. VOGLER, AND J. R. WILLIAMSON. Muscle capillary basement membrane changes related to aging and to diabetes mellitus. *Diabetes* 21: 881–905, 1972.

226a. KISSUN, R. D., AND A. GARNER. Vasoproliferative properties of normal and hypoxic retinal tissues. *Br. J. Ophthalmol.* 61: 394–398, 1977.

226b. KISSUN, R. D., C. R. HILL, A. GARNER, P. PHILLIPS, S. KUMAR, AND J. B. WEISS. A low molecular weight angiogenic factor in cat retina. *Br. J. Ophthalmol.* 66: 165–169, 1982.

227. KIVISAARI, J., T. VIHERSAARI, S. RENVALL, AND J. NIINIKOSKI. Energy metabolism of experimental wounds at various oxygen environments. *Ann. Surg.* 181: 823–828, 1975.

228. KLAGSBRUN, M., D. KNIGHTON, AND J. FOLKMAN. Tumor angiogenesis activity in cells grown in tissue culture. *Cancer Res.* 36: 110–114, 1976.

229. KNOWER, H. M. E. Effects of early removal of the heart and arrest of the circulation on the development of frog embryos. *Anat. Rec.* 7: 161–165, 1907.

230. KOHLER, N., AND A. LIPTON. Platelets as a source of fibroblast growth promoting activity. *Exp. Cell Res.* 87: 297–301, 1974.

231. KRAMER, J., AND W. LIERSE. Die postnatale Entwicklung der Kapillarisation im Gehirn der Maus. *Acta Anat.* 66: 446–459, 1967.

232. KROGH, A. The supply of oxygen to the tissues and the regulation of the capillary circulation. *J. Physiol. London* 52: 457–474, 1919.

233. KROGH, A. *The Anatomy and Physiology of the Capillaries.* New Haven, CT: Yale Univ. Press, 1922.

234. KUNZ, J., AND V. KEIM. On the regeneration of aortic endothelium at different ages. *Mech. Ageing Dev.* 4: 361–369, 1975.

235. KUWABAVA, T., AND D. G. COGAN. Retinal vascular patterns. IV. Mural cells of the retinal capillaries. *Arch. Ophthalmol.* 69: 492–502, 1963.

235a. LAATKAINEN, L., AND R. K. BLACH. Behaviour of the iris vasculature in central retinal vein occlusion: a fluorescin angiographic study of the vascular response of the retina and the iris. *Br. J. Ophthalmol.* 61: 272–277, 1977.

236. LANGER, T., H. BREM, K. FALTERMAN, M. KLEIN, AND J. FOLKMAN. Isolation of a cartilage factor that inhibits tumor neovascularization. *Science* 193: 70–72, 1976.

237. LANGHAM, M. Observations on the growth of vessels into the cornea. Application of a new experimental technique. *Br. J. Ophthalmol.* 37: 210–222, 1953.

238. LANGHAM, M. E. The inhibition of corneal vascularization of triethylene thiophosphoamide. *Am. J. Ophthalmol.* 49: 1111–1117, 1960.

238a. LEINONEN, H., E. MATIIKAINEN, AND J. JUNTUNEN. Permeability and morphology of skeletal muscle capillaries in type 1 (insulin-dependent) diabetes mellitus. *Diabetologia* 22: 158–162, 1982.

239. LEWIS, L. J., J. C. HOAK, R. D. MACA, AND G. L. FRY. Replication of human endothelial cells in culture. *Science* 181: 453–454, 1973.

240. LEWIS, W. H. The outgrowth of endothelium and capillaries in tissue culture. *Bull. Johns Hopkins Hosp.* 48: 242–253, 1931.

241. LICATA, R. H. The human embryonic heart in the ninth week. *Am. J. Anat.* 94: 73–125, 1954.

242. LICATA, R. H. A continuation study of the development of the blood supply of the human heart. II. The deep or intramural circulation. *Anat. Rec.* 124: 326, 1956.

243. LICHNOVSKÝ, V., M. OBRUČNÍK, AND J. KRAUS. A quantitative morphometric study of capillary length and ventricular volume and surface area in the human embryonic and foetal heart. *Folia Morphol. Prague* 26: 187–193, 1978.

244. LIERSE, W. Die Kapillardichte in Wirbeltieren. *Acta Anat.* 54: 1–31, 1963.

245. LINDHE, J., AND P.-I. BRÅNEMARK. Observations on vascular proliferation in a granulation tissue. *J. Periodontal Res.* 5: 271–292, 1970.

246. LJUNGQVIST, A., AND G. UNGE. The finer intramyocardial vasculature in various forms of experimental cardiac hypertrophy. *Acta Pathol. Microbiol. Scand. Sect. A* 80: 329–340, 1972.

247. LJUNGQVIST, A., AND G. UNGE. The proliferation activity of the myocardial tissue in various forms of experimental cardiac hypertrophy. *Acta Pathol. Microbiol. Scand. Sect. A* 81: 233–240, 1973.

248. LJUNGQVIST, A., AND G. UNGE. Capillary proliferative activity in myocardium and skeletal muscle of exercised rats. *J. Appl. Physiol.: Respirat. Environ. Exercise Physiol.* 43: 306–307, 1977.

249. LJUNGQVIST, A., G. UNGE, AND S. CARLSSON. The myocardial capillary vasculature in exercising animals with increased cardiac pressure load. *Acta Pathol. Microbiol. Scand. Sect. A* 84: 244–246, 1976.

250. LOATS, J. T., A. H. SILLAU, AND N. BANCHERO. How to quantify skeletal muscle capillarity. *Adv. Exp. Med. Biol.* 94: 41–48, 1977.

251. LOEB, J. Ueber die Entwicklung von Fischemryonen ohne Kreislauf. *Pfluegers Arch. Gesamte Physiol. Menschen Tiere* 54: 525–531, 1893.

252. LUND, D. D., AND R. J. TOMANEK. Myocardial morphology in spontaneously hypertensive and aortic constricted rats. *Am. J. Anat.* 152: 141–147, 1978.

253. LUNDVALL, J. Tissue hyperosmolality as a mediator of vasodilatation and transcapillary fluid flux in exercising skeletal muscle. *Acta Physiol. Scand. Suppl.* 379: 1–142, 1972.

254. MAI, J. V., V. R. EDGERTON, AND R. J. BARNARD. Capillarity of red, white and intermediate muscle fibres in trained and untrained guinea pigs. *Experientia* 26: 1222–1223, 1970.

255. MANASEK, F. J. The ultrastructure of embryonic myocardial blood vessels. *Dev. Biol.* 26: 42–54, 1971.

256. MANDACHE, E., G. UNGE, L. E. APPLEGREN, AND A. LJUNGQVIST. The proliferative activity of the heart tissues in various forms of experimental cardiac hypertrophy studied by electron microscope autoradiography. *Virchows Arch. B* 12: 112–122, 1973.

257. MANDACHE, E., G. UNGE, AND A. LJUNGQVIST. Myocardial blood capillary reaction in various forms of cardiac hypertrophy. An electron microscopical investigation in the rat. *Virchows Arch. B* 11: 97–110, 1972.

258. MAUGH, T. H. Diabetic retinopathy: new ways to prevent blindness. *Science* 192: 539–540, 1976.

259. MAXWELL, L. C., D. S. CARLSON, J. A. MCNAMARA, JR., AND J. A. FAULKNER. Histochemical characteristics of the masseter and temporalis muscles of the Rhesus monkey. *Anat. Rec.* 193: 389–402, 1979.

259a. MAXWELL, L. C., J. A. FAULKNER, S. A. MUFTI, AND A. M. TUROWSKI. Free autografting of entire limb muscles in the cat: histochemistry and biochemistry. *J. Appl. Physiol.: Respirat. Environ. Exercise Physiol.* 44: 431–437, 1978.

260. MAXWELL, L. C., T. P. WHITE, AND J. A. FAULKNER. Oxidative capacity, blood flow and capillarity of skeletal muscles. *J. Appl. Physiol.: Respirat. Environ. Exercise Physiol.* 49: 627–633, 1980.

261. MCDONALD, R. I., D. SHEPRO, M. ROSENTHAL, AND F. M. BOOYSE. Properties of cultured endothelial cells. *Ser. Haematol.* 6: 469–478, 1973.

262. MCKINNEY, R. V. The structure of scorbutic regenerating capillaries in skeletal muscle wounds. *Microvasc. Res.* 11: 361–379, 1976.

263. MCKINNEY, R. V., D. H. DASHELY, AND B. B. SINGH. The permeability of wound capillaries (Abstract). *J. Cell Biol.* 67: 275a, 1975.

264. MCKINNEY, R. V., B. B. SINGH, AND P. D. BREWER. Fenestrations in regenerating skeletal muscle capillaries. *Am. J. Anat.* 150: 213–218, 1977.

265. MEDAWAR, P. B. The behavior and fate of skin autografts and

homografts in rabbits. *J. Anat.* 78: 176–199, 1944.

266. MERWIN, R. M., AND G. H. ALGIRE. The role of graft and host vessels in the vascularization of grafts of normal and neoplastic tissue. *J. Natl. Cancer Inst.* 17: 28–34, 1956.
267. MEYER, J. Ueber die Neubildung von Blutgefässen in plastischen Exudaten seröser Membranen und in Hautwunden. *Ann. Charité Berlin* 4: 41–140, 1852.
268. MICHAELSON, I. C. Mode of development of vascular system of the retina with some observations on its significance for certain retinal diseases. *Trans. Ophthalmol. Soc. UK* 68: 137–180, 1948.
269. MICHEL, G., H. BUCHWALD, AND H. SCHÖNHERR. Quantitative Untersuchungen zur Ausbildung der Muskelfasern und Kapillaren des Herzens bei einigen Haus- und Wildgeflügelenten. *Anat. Anz.* 132: 382–388, 1972.

269a. MICHEL, G., AND F. V. SALOMON. Quantitative Untersuchungen zum Eifluss motorischen Trainings auf die Muskelfasern und Kapillaren einiger Skelettmuskeln des Schweines. *Verh. Anat. Ges.* 71: 269–273, 1977.

270. MILLEN, F. V., AND A. HESS. The blood brain barrier: an experimental study with vital dyes. *Brain* 81: 248–257, 1958.
271. MILLER, A. M., AND J. E. MCWHORTER. Experiments on the development of blood vessels in the area pellucida and embryonic body of the chick. *Anat. Rec.* 8: 203–227, 1914.
272. MILLER, A. T., JR., AND D. M. HALE. Increased vascularity of brain, heart and skeletal muscle of polycythemic rats. *Am. J. Physiol.* 219: 702–704, 1970.
273. MINERVINI, R. Ueber die Neubildung der Blutgefässen. *Virchow Arch. Pathol. Anat. Physiol.* 204: 75–85, 1911.
274. MONSTER, A. W., H. C. CHAN, AND D. O'CONNOR. Activity patterns of human skeletal muscles: relation to muscle fiber type. *Science* 200: 314–316, 1978.
275. MOSSE, P. R. L. The distribution of capillaries in the somatic musculature of two vertebrate types with particular reference to teleost fish. *Cell Tissue Res.* 187: 281–303, 1978.
276. MOSSE, P. R. L. Capillary distribution and metabolic histochemistry of the lateral propulsive musculature of pelagic teleost fish. *Cell Tissue Res.* 203: 141–160, 1979.
277. MÜLLER, W. Subsarcolemmal mitochondria and capillarisation of soleus muscle fibres in young rats subjected to an endurance training. *Cell Tissue Res.* 174: 367–389, 1976.
278. MURPHY, M. E. Autoradiographic studies of basal lamina precursors in the developing endothelium of early chick embryos. *Anat. Rec.* 184: 486, 1976.
279. MURRAY, M., G. R. SCHRODT, AND H. F. BERG. Role of smooth muscle cells in healing of injured arteries. *Arch. Pathol.* 82: 138–146, 1966.
280. MYRHAGE, R. Capillary supply of the muscle fibre population in hindlimb muscles of the cat. *Acta Physiol. Scand.* 103: 19–30, 1978.
281. MYRHAGE, R., AND O. HUDLICKÁ. The microvascular bed and capillary surface area in rat extensor hallucis proprius muscle (EHP). *Microvasc. Res.* 11: 315–323, 1976.
282. MYRHAGE, R., AND O. HUDLICKÁ. Capillary growth in chronically stimulated adult skeletal muscle as studied by intravital microscopy and histological methods in rabbits and rats. *Microvasc. Res.* 16: 73–90, 1978.
283. NEES, S., B. WILLERSHAUSEN-ZÖNNCHEN, A. L. GERBES, AND E. GERLACH. Studies on cultured coronary endothelial cells. *Folia Angiologica* 28: 64–68, 1980.
284. NIINIKOSKI, J., A. RAJAMÄKI, AND E. KULONEN. Healing of open wounds: effects of oxygen, disturbed blood supply and hyperemia by infrared irradiation. *Acta Chir. Scand.* 137: 399–401, 1971.
285. NIMS, J. C., AND J. W. IRWIN. Technical report: chamber techniques to study the microvasculature. *Microvasc. Res.* 5: 105–118, 1973.
286. NISHIOKA, K., AND T. J. RYAN. The influence of the epidermis and other tissues on blood vessel growth in the hamster cheek pouch. *J. Invest. Dermatol.* 58: 33–45, 1972.
287. OGAWA, Y. Vascular pattern changes in the heart due to training. *Res. J. Physical Educ.* 17: 375–383, 1973.
288. OGAWA, Y. On the morphological bases of the microvascular beds. *J. Yokohama City Univ. Ser. Sport Sci. Med.* 3: 1–29, 1974.
289. OGAWA, Y. On the fine structural changes of the microvascular beds in the skeletal muscle. *J. Yokohama City Univ. Ser. Sport Sci. Med.* 6: 1–19, 1977.
290. O'KEEFE, D. D., J. E. HOFFMAN, R. CHEITLIN, M. J. O'NEIL, J. R. ALLARD, AND E. SHAPKIN. Coronary blood flow in experimental canine left ventricular hypertrophy. *Circ. Res.* 43: 43–51, 1978.
291. OLDENDORF, W. H., AND W. J. BROWN. Greater number of capillary endothelial cell mitochondria in brain than in muscle. *Proc. Soc. Exp. Biol. Med.* 149: 736–738, 1975.
292. OLIVETTI, G., P. ANVERSA, AND A. V. LOUD. Morphometric study of early postnatal development in the left and right ventricular myocardium of the rat. II. Tissue composition, capillary growth and sarcoplasmic alterations. *Circ. Res.* 46: 503–512, 1980.
293. OLIVETTI, G., P. ANVERSA, M. MELISSARI, AND A. V. LOUD. Morphometric study of early postnatal development of the thoracic aorta in the rat. *Circ. Res.* 47: 417–424, 1980.
294. OLIVETTI, G., P. ANVERSA, M. MELISSARI, AND A. V. LOUD. Morphometry of the renal corpuscle during postnatal growth and compensatory hypertrophy. *Kidney Int.* 17: 438–454, 1980.
295. OPITZ, E. Increased vascularization of the tissue due to acclimatization to high altitude and its significance for the oxygen transport. *Exp. Med. Surg.* 9: 389–403, 1951.
296. OŠŤÁDAL, B., Z. RYCHTER, AND O. POUPA. Qualitative development of the terminal coronary bed in the perinatal period of the rat. *Folia Morphol. Prague* 16: 116–123, 1968.
297. OŠŤÁDAL, B., Z. RYCHTER, AND O. POUPA. Comparative aspects of the development of the terminal vascular bed in the myocardium. *Physiol. Bohemoslov.* 19: 1–7, 1970.
298. OŠŤÁDAL, B., AND T. H. SCHIEBLER. Die Capillarenentwicklung im Rattenherzen. Elektronmikroskopische Untersuchungen. *Z. Anat. Entwicklungsgesch.* 133: 288–304, 1971.
299. OŠŤÁDAL, B., T. H. SCHIEBLER, AND Z. RYCHTER. Relations between development of the capillary wall and myoarchitecture of the rat heart. *Adv. Exp. Med. Biol.* 53: 375–388, 1975.
300. PARDO, V., E. PEREZ-STABLE, AND E. R. FISHER. Electron microscopic study of dermal capillaries in diabetes mellitus. *Lab. Invest.* 15: 1994–2005, 1966.
301. PAŘÍZKOVÁ, J., E. EISELT, S. SPRYNAROVÁ, AND M. WACHTLOVÁ. Body composition, aerobic capacity and density of muscle capillaries in young and old men. *J. Appl. Physiol.* 31: 323–325, 1971.
302. PAŘÍZKOVÁ, J., M. WACHTLOVÁ, AND M. SOUKUPOVÁ. The impact of different motor activity on body composition, density of capillaries and fibres in the heart and soleus muscles and cell's migration in vitro in male rats. *Int. Z. Angew. Physiol.* 30: 207–216, 1972.
303. PARRY, E. W., AND D. R. ABRAMOVICH. The ultrastructure of human umbilical vessel endothelium from early pregnancy to full term. *J. Anat.* 111: 29–42, 1972.
304. PATZ, A., S. BREM, D. FINKELSTEIN, C. H. CHEN, G. LUTTY, A. BENNETT, W. R. COUGHLIN, AND J. GARDNER. A new approach to the problem of retinal neovascularization. *Ophthalmology* 85: 626–637, 1978.
305. PEADON, A. M., AND M. SINGER. The blood vessels of the regenerating limb of the adult newt. *Triturus. J. Morphol.* 118: 79–90, 1966.
306. PERERA, P., K. KURBANA, AND J. T. RYAN. The development of the cutaneous microcircular system in the newborn. *Br. J. Dermatol.* 82, Suppl. 5: 86, 1970.

306a. PESSACQ, T. P., AND N. J. REISSENWEBER. Structural aspects of vasculogenesis in the central nervous system. *Acta Anat.* 81: 1–12, 1972.

307. PETRAKIS, N. L., M. DAVIS, AND S. P. LUCIA. The in vivo differentiation of human leukocytes into histocytes, fibroblasts and fat cells in subcutaneous diffusion chambers. *Blood* 17: 109–118, 1961.
308. PETRÉN, T., T. SJÖSTRAND, AND D. SYLVÉN. Der Einfluss des

Trainings auf die Häufigkeit der Kapillaren in Herz- und Skelettmuskulatur. *Arbeitsphysiologie* 9: 376–386, 1937.

309. Pette, D., M. E. Smith, H. W. Staudte, and G. Vrbová. Effect of long-term electrical stimulation on some contractile metabolic characteristics of fast rabbit muscles. *Pfluegers Arch.* 338: 257–272, 1973.
310. Pette, D., and K. R. Tyler. Quantitative changes in oxidative enzyme activity during chronic stimulation of rabbit fast muscles (Abstract). *J. Physiol. London* 317: 22P–23P, 1981.
310a. Phillips, P., P. Kumar, S. Kumar, and M. Woghe. Isolation and characterization of endothelial cells from rat and cow brain white matter. *J. Anat.* 129: 261–272, 1979.
311. Phillips, P., J. K. Steward, and S. Kumar. Tumor angiogenesis factor (TAF) in human and animal tumors. *Int. J. Cancer* 17: 549–558, 1976.
312. Pictet, R., and W. J. Rutter. Development of the embryonic endocrine pancreas. In: *Handbook of Physiology. Endocrinology*, edited by R. O. Greep and E. B. Astwood. Washington, DC: Am. Physiol. Soc., 1972, sect. 7, vol. I, chapt. 2, p. 25–66.
313. Platner, E. A. Einige Beobachtungen über die Entwicklung der Capillargefässe. *Müller's Arch. Anat. Physiol. Wiss. Med.*: 525–526, 1844.
314. Plyley, M. J., and A. C. Groom. Geometrical distribution of capillaries in mammalian striated muscle. *Am. J. Physiol.* 228: 1376–1383, 1975.
315. Polverini, P. J., R. S. Cotran, M. A. Gimbrone, and E. R. Unanue. Activated macrophages induce vascular proliferation. *Nature London* 269: 804–806, 1977.
316. Poole, J. C. F., A. G. Sanders, and H. W. Florey. The regeneration of aortic endothelium. *J. Pathol. Bacteriol.* 75: 133–143, 1958.
317. Poupa, O., B. Korecký, K. Krofta, K. Rakušan, and J. Procházka. The effect of anaemia during the early postnatal period on vascularization of the myocardium and its resistance to anoxia. *Physiol. Bohemoslov.* 13: 281–287, 1964.
318. Poupa, O., K. Rakušan, and B. Ošťádal. The effect of physical activity upon the heart of the vertebrates. *Med. Sport Basel* 4: 202–235, 1970.
319. Prendergast, F. J., J. K. McGeachie, R. H. Edis, and D. Allbrook. Whole-muscle reimplantation with microneurovascular anastomoses. *Ann. R. Coll. Surg. Engl.* 59: 393–400, 1977.
320. Rakušan, K. Quantitative morphology of capillaries of the heart. *Methods Achiev. Exp. Pathol.* 5: 272–286, 1971.
321. Rakušan, K., J. Jelínek, B. Korecký, M. Soukupová, and O. Poupa. Postnatal development of muscle fibres and capillaries in the rat heart. *Physiol. Bohemoslov.* 14: 32–37, 1965.
322. Rakušan, K., J. Moravec, and P. Y. Hatt. Regional capillary supply in the normal and hypertrophied rat heart. *Microvasc. Res.* 20: 319–326, 1980.
323. Rakušan, K., B. Ošťádal, and M. Wachtlová. The influence of muscular work on the capillary density in the heart and skeletal muscle of pigeon (*Columba livia dom.*). *Can. J. Physiol. Pharmacol.* 49: 167–170, 1971.
324. Rakušan, K., and O. Poupa. Capillaries and muscle fibres in the heart of old rats. *Gerontologia* 9: 107–112, 1964.
325. Rakušan, K., and O. Poupa. The relationship between the capillaries and protein nitrogen in the myocardium of the rat during postnatal development. *Physiol. Bohemoslov.* 14: 320–323, 1965.
325a. Rakušan, K., Z. Turek, and F. Kreuzer. Myocardial capillaries in guinea pigs native to high altitude (Junin, Peru, 4105m). *Pfluegers Arch.* 391: 22–24, 1981.
326. Ranvier, L. Note sur les vaisseaux sanguins et la circulation dans les muscles rouges. *C. R. Soc. Biol.* 26: 28–31, 1874.
327. Rasio, E., and M. Bendayan. Le métabolisme du tissu capillaire et ses anomalies au cours du diabète. *Diabete Metab.* 4: 57–62, 1978.
328. Reagan, F. R. Vascularization phenomena on fragments of embryonic bodies completely isolated from yolk sac entoderm. *Anat. Rec.* 9: 329–341, 1915.
329. Rebel, W., and T. Stegmann. Aktivitätsveränderungen der alkalischen Phosphatase des Herzmuskels bei tierexperimentell erzeugter Herzhypertrophie. *Virchows Arch. Pathol. Anat.* 357: 243–256, 1972.
330. Reitsma, W. Formation of new capillaries in hypertrophic skeletal muscle. *Angiology* 24: 45–57, 1973.
331. Remensnyder, J. P., and G. Majno. Oxygen gradients in healing wounds. *Am. J. Pathol.* 52: 301–323, 1968.
332. Ripoll, E., A. H. Sillau, and N. Banchero. Changes in the capillarity of skeletal muscle in the growing rat. *Pfluegers Arch.* 380: 153–158, 1979.
333. Roberts, J. T., and J. T. Wearn. Quantitative changes in the capillary muscle relationship in human hearts during normal growth and hypertrophy. *Am. Heart J.* 21: 617–633, 1941.
334. Roberts, L. N., M. Villanueva, B. C. Babacan, and G. P. Mason. A study of the effect of dipyridamole on the coronary circulation in man. *Can. Med. Assoc. J.* 98: 113, 1968.
335. Romanul, F. C. A. Capillary supply and metabolism of muscle fibers. *Arch. Neurol.* 12: 497–509, 1965.
336. Romanul, F. C. A. Reversal of enzymatic profiles and capillary supply of muscle fibres in fast and slow muscle after cross innervation. In: *Muscle Metabolism in Exercise*, edited by B. Pernow and B. Saltin. New York: Plenum, 1971, vol. 11, p. 21–32.
337. Romanul, F. C., and M. Pollock. The parallelism of changes in oxidative metabolism and capillary supply of skeletal muscle fibers. In: *Modern Neurology: Papers in Tribute to Derek Denny-Brown*, edited by S. Locke. Boston MA: Little, Brown, 1969, p. 203–213.
338. Ross, R., and E. D. Benditt. Wound healing and collagen formation. I. Sequential changes in components of guinea-pig skin wounds observed by electron microscope. *J. Biophys. Biochem. Cytol.* 11: 677–700, 1961.
339. Ross, R. J., B. Glomset, B. Kariya, and L. Harker. A platelet dependent serum factor that stimulates the proliferation of arterial smooth muscle cells in vitro. *Proc. Natl. Acad. Sci. USA* 71: 1207–1210, 1974.
340. Ross, R., and A. Vogel. The platelet-derived growth factor. *Cell* 14: 203–210, 1978.
340a. Rossini, A. A., and W. L. Chick. Microvascular pathology in diabetes. In: *Microcirculation*, edited by G. Kaley and B. M. Altura. Baltimore, MD: University Park, 1979, vol. 3, p. 245–271.
341. Rotter, W. Ueber die Bedeutung der Ernährungsstörung, insbesondere des Sauerstoffmangels, für die Prognose der Gefässwandveränderungen, mit besonderer Berücksichtigung der "Endarteritis obliterans" und der "Arteriosklerose." *Beitr. Pathol. Anat. Allg. Pathol.* 110: 46–102, 1949.
342. Rouget, C. Mémoirs sur le dévelopement des structures et les propriétés physiologique des capillaires sanguins et lymphatiques. *Arch. Physiol. Normal Pathol.* 5: 603–663, 1873.
343. Roux, W. Ueber die Verzweigungen der Blutgefässe des Menschen. *Jena. Z. Naturwiss.* 12: 205–206, 1878.
343a. Rowan, R. A., and D. S. Maxwell. Pattern of vascular sprouting in the postnatal development of the cerebral cortex of the rat. *Am. J. Anat.* 160: 247–256, 1981.
344. Rowinski, J., M. Nowak, and W. Sawicki. Proliferation kinetics in epithelium of guinea-pig colon. III. Distribution of blood capillaries along the crypt. *Cell Tissue Kinet.* 5: 237–243, 1972.
345. Rudland, P. S., W. Seifert, and D. Gospodarowicz. Growth control in cultured mouse fibroblasts: induction of the pleiotypic and mitogenic responses by a purified growth factor. *Proc. Natl. Acad. Sci. USA* 71: 2600–2604, 1974.
346. Ryan, T. J. Factors influencing the growth of vascular endothelium in the skin. *Br. J. Dermatol.* 82, Suppl. 5: 99–111, 1970.
347. Ryan, T. J. Microcirculation in psoriasis: blood vessels, lymphatics and tissue fluid. *Pharmacol. Ther.* 10: 27–64, 1980.
348. Ryan, T. J., and A. K. Kurban. New vessel growth in adult skin. *Br. J. Dermatol.* 82, Suppl. 5: 92–98, 1970.
349. Ryan, T. J., and A. T. Stockley. Mechanical versus bio-

chemical factors in angiogenesis (Abstract). *Microvasc. Res.* 20: 258–259, 1980.

350. RYCHTER, Z., AND B. OŠŤÁDAL. Mechanism of the development of coronary arteries in chick embryo. *Folia Morphol. Prague* 19: 113–124, 1971.
351. RYCHTEROVA, V. Formation of the terminal vascular bed in the chick embryo heart. *Folia Morphol. Prague* 25: 7–14, 1977.
352. RYTÖMAA, T. The chalone concept. *Int. Rev. Exp. Pathol.* 16: 155–206, 1976.
353. SABA, H. I., R. C. HARTMAN, AND S. R. SABA. Effects of polymorphonuclear leukocytes on endothelial cell growth. *Thromb. Res.* 12: 397–407, 1978.
354. SABA, S. R., AND R. G. MASON. Effect of platelets and certain platelet components on growth of cultured human endothelial cells. *Thromb. Res.* 7: 807–812, 1975.
355. SABIN, F. R. Healing of end-to-end intestinal anastomoses with specific reference to the regeneration of blood vessels. *Bull. Johns Hopkins Hosp.* 31: 289–300, 1920.
356. SABIN, F. R. Studies on the origin of blood vessels and of red corpuscles as seen in the living blastoderm of the chick during the second day of incubation. *Contrib. Embryol.* 9: 213–259, 1920.
357. SABIN, F. R. On the origin of the cells of the blood. *Physiol. Rev.* 2: 38–69, 1922.
358. SADE, R. M., J. FOLKMAN, AND R. S. COTRAN. DNA synthesis in endothelium of aortic segments in vitro. *Exp. Cell Res.* 74: 297–306, 1974.
359. SAIDKARIEV, B. K. K voprosu o vzaimootnoshenii myshechnykh volokon i kapillarov miokarda. *Arkh. Anat. Gistol. Embriol.* 60: 78–80, 1971.
360. SALMONS, S., AND G. VRBOVÁ. The influence of activity on some contractile characteristics of mammalian fast and slow muscles. *J. Physiol. London* 201: 535–549, 1969.
361. SALTIN, B., G. BLOMQVIST, J. H. MITCHELL, K. JOHNSON, K. WILDENTHAL, AND C. B. CHAPMAN. Response to exercise after bed rest and after training. *Circulation* 38, Suppl. 2: 1–78, 1968.
362. SANDISON, J. C. The transparent chamber of the rabbit's ear giving complete description of improved technic of construction and introduction, and general accounts of growth and behavior of living cells and tissues as seen with the microscope. *Am. J. Anat.* 41: 447–473, 1928.
363. SANDISON, J. C. Observations on the growth of blood vessels as seen in the transparent chamber introduced into the rabbit's ear. *Am. J. Anat.* 41: 475–496, 1928.
364. SANDISON, J. C. Contraction of blood vessels and observations on the circulation in the transparent chamber in the rabbit's ear. *Anat. Rec.* 54: 105–127, 1932.
365. SAVAGE, C. R., JR., T. INAGAMI, AND S. COHEN. The primary structure of epidermal growth factor. *J. Biol. Chem.* 247: 7612–7621, 1972.
366. SCHAPER, W., M. DEBRABANDER, AND P. LEWI. DNA synthesis and mitoses in coronary collateral vessels of the dog. *Circ. Res.* 28: 671–679, 1971.
367. SCHARRER, E. The regeneration of end-arteries in the opposum brain. *J. Comp. Neurol.* 70: 69–76, 1939.
368. SCHELLER, W., K. WELT, AND G. SCHIPPEL. Licht- und elektronenmikroskopische Untersuchungen zur postnatalen Entwicklung von Kapillaren im M. triceps brachii der weissen Ratte bis zum 20. Monat. *Verh. Anat. Ges.* 71: 701–705, 1977.
369. SCHMIDT-NIELSEN, K., AND P. PENNYCUIK. Capillary density in mammals in relation to body size and oxygen consumption. *Am. J. Physiol.* 200: 746–750, 1961.
370. SCHOEFL, G. I. Studies on inflammation. III. Growing capillaries: their structure and permeability. *Virchows Arch. Pathol. Anat. Physiol.* 337: 97–141, 1963.
371. SCHOEFL, G. I., AND G. MAJNO. Regeneration of blood vessels in wound healing. In: *Advances in Biology of Skin.* Oxford, UK: Pergamon, 1964, vol. V, p. 73–193.
372. SCHÜLER, R., AND W. LIERSE. Die Entwicklung der Kapillardichte nach der Geburt im Gehirn zweier Nestflüchter: eines Vogels (Haushuhn) und eines Säugers (Meerschweinchen). *Acta Anat.* 75: 453–465, 1970.
373. SCHWARTZ, S. M., AND E. P. BENDITT. Cell replication in the aortic endothelium: a new method for study of the problem. *Lab. Invest.* 28: 699–707, 1973.
374. SEIDEL, C. L., AND R. A. MURPHY. Changes in rat aortic actomyosin content with maturation. *Blood Vessels* 16: 98–108, 1979.
375. SHIPLEY, R. A., L. J. SHIPLEY, AND J. T. WEARN. Capillary supply in normal and hypertrophied hearts of rabbits. *J. Exp. Med.* 65: 29–42, 1937.
376. SHOLLEY, M. M., T. CAVALLO, AND R. S. COTRAN. Endothelial regeneration in acute inflammation. ^{3}H-thymidine studies in normal and severely leukopenic rats (Abstract). *Anat. Rec.* 178: 462–463, 1974.
377. SHOLLEY, M. M., AND R. S. COTRAN. Endothelial DNA synthesis in the microvasculature of rat skin during the hair growth cycle. *Am. J. Anat.* 147: 243–254, 1976.
378. SILLAU, A. H., L. AQUIN, M. V. BUI, AND N. BANCHERO. Chronic hypoxia does not affect guinea pig skeletal muscle capillarity. *Pfluegers Arch.* 386: 39–45, 1980.
379. SILLAU, A. H., AND N. BANCHERO. Skeletal muscle fibre size and capillarity. *Proc. Soc. Exp. Biol. Med.* 158: 288–291, 1978.
380. SMITH, A. R., AND L. WOLPERT. Nerves and angiogenesis in amphibian regeneration. *Nature London* 257: 224–225, 1975.
381. SMITH, R. S. The development of mast cells in the vascularized cornea. *Arch. Ophthalmol.* 66: 383–390, 1961.
382. SOBIN, S. S., AND H. M. TREMER. Three-dimensional organization of microvascular beds as related to function. In: *Microcirculation*, edited by G. Kaley and B. M. Altura. Baltimore, MD: University Park, 1977, vol. 1, p. 43–67.
383. SORGENTE, N., R. E. KUETTNER, L. W. SOBLE, AND R. EISENSTEIN. The resistance of certain tissues to invasion. II. Evidence for extractable factors in cartilage which inhibit invasion by vascularized mesenchyme. *Lab. Invest.* 32: 217–222, 1975.
384. SPAET, T., AND I. LEJNIEKS. Mitotic activity of the rabbit blood vessels. *Proc. Soc. Exp. Biol. Med.* 125: 1197–1201, 1967.
385. SPRARAGEN, S. C., V. P. BOND, AND L. K. DAHL. Role of hyperplasia in vascular lesions of cholesterol fed rabbits studied with thymidine-H^3 autoradiography. *Circ. Res.* 11: 329–336, 1962.

385a. STAUDTE, H. W., AND D. PETTE. Correlations between enzymes of energy supplying metabolism as a basic pattern of organization in muscle. *Comp. Biochem. Physiol. B* 41: 533–540, 1972.

386. STERE, A. J., AND A. ANTHONY. Myocardial Feulgen DNA levels and capillary vascularization in hypoxia-exposed rats. *J. Appl. Physiol.: Respirat. Environ. Exercise Physiol.* 42: 501–507, 1977.
387. STINGL, J. Architectonic development of the vascular bed of rat skeletal muscles in the early postnatal period. *Folia Morphol. Prague* 19: 308, 1971.
388. STOCKLAND, C. R. The origin of blood and vascular endothelium in embryos without a circulation of the blood and in the normal embryo. *Am. J. Anat.* 18: 227–327, 1915.
389. STOCKLEY, A. T. The chorioallantoic membrane as an assay for angiogenic factors. *Br. J. Dermatol.* 102: 738, 1980.
390. STOFER, A. R. Wirkung eines Herzextraktes auf die Kapillarisierung des Rattenherzens. *Cardiologia* 52: 241–245, 1968.

390a. STOKER, M. E., A. M. GERDES, AND J. E. MAY. Regional differences in capillary density and myocyte size in the normal human heart. *Anat. Rec.* 202: 187–191, 1982.

391. STUDITSKY, A. N. Dynamics of the development of myogenic tissue under conditions of explantation and transplantation. *Cinemicrography in Cell Biology*, edited by G. G. Rose. New York: Academic, 1963, p. 171–200.

391a. STURROCK, R. R. A quantitative and morphological study of vascularisation of the developing mouse spinal cord. *J. Anat.* 132: 203–222, 1981.

392. SUDDITH, R. L., P. J. KELLY, H. T. HUTCHINSON, E. A.

MURRAY, AND B. HUBER. In vitro demonstration of an endothelial proliferation factor produced by neural cell lines. *Science* 190: 682–684, 1975.

393. TANNOCK, I. F. Population kinetics of carcinoma cells, capillary endothelial cells and fibroblasts in a transplanted mouse mammary tumor. *Cancer Res.* 30: 2470–2476, 1970.
394. TANNOCK, I. F., AND S. HAYASHI. The proliferation of capillary endothelial cells. *Cancer Res.* 32: 77–84, 1972.
395. TAPPAN, D. V., B. REYNAFARJE, D., VAN R. POTTER, AND A. HURTADO. Alterations in enzymes and metabolites resulting from adaptation to low oxygen tensions. *Am. J. Physiol.* 190: 93–98, 1957.
396. TAUBENHAUS, M. Hormonal influences on granulation tissue formation. In: *The Healing of the Wounds*, edited by M. B. Williamson. New York: McGraw-Hill, 1957, p. 113–119.

396a. TAYLOR, S., AND J. FOLKMAN. Protamine is an inhibitor of angiogenesis. *Nature London* 297: 307–312, 1982.

397. THOMA, R. *Untersuchungen über die Histogenese und Histomechanik des Gefässsystems.* Stuttgart, Germany: Enke, 1893.
398. THOMA, R. Ueber die Histomechanik des Gefässsystems und die Pathogenese der Angiosklerose. *Virchows Arch. Pathol. Anat. Physiol.* 204: 1–74, 1911.
399. THOMSON, J. A., H. J. GREEN, AND M. E. HOUSTON. Muscle glycogen depletion patterns in fast twitch fibre subgroups of man during submaximal and supramaximal exercise. *Pfluegers Arch.* 379: 105–108, 1979.
400. TILLMANS, H., S. IKEDA, H. HANSEN, J. S. SARMA, J. M. FAUVEL, AND R. J. BING. Microcirculation in the ventricle of the dog and turtle. *Circ. Res.* 34: 561–569, 1974.
401. TODARO, G. J., G. K. LAZAR, AND H. GREEN. The initiation of cell division in a contact-inhibited mammalian cell line. *J. Cell. Comp. Physiol.* 66: 325–334, 1965.
402. TOMANEK, R. J. Effects of age and exercise on the extent of the myocardial capillary bed. *Anat. Rec.* 167: 55–62, 1970.

402a. TORNLING, G. Capillary neoformation in the heart of dipyridamole treated rats. *Acta Pathol. Microbiol. Scand. Sect. A* 90: 269–271, 1982.

403. TORNLING, G., J. ADOLFSSON, G. UNGE, AND A. LJUNGQVIST. Capillary neoformation in skeletal muscle of dipyridamole-treated rats. *Arzneim. Forsch.* 30: 791–792, 1980.
404. TORNLING, G., G. UNGE, J. ADOLFSSON, A. LJUNGQVIST, AND S. CARLSSON. Proliferative activity of capillary wall cells in skeletal muscle of rats during long-term treatment with dipyridamole. *Arzneim. Forsch.* 30: 622–623, 1980.
405. TORNLING, G., G. UNGE, L. SKOOG, A. LJUNGQVIST, S. CARLSSON, AND J. ADOLFSSON. Proliferative activity of myocardial capillary wall cells in dipyridamole-treated rats. *Cardiovasc. Res.* 12: 692–695, 1978.
406. TRAVERS, B. *The Physiology of Inflammation and the Healing Process.* London: Highley, 1844.
407. TUREK, Z., M. GRANDTNER, AND F. KREUZER. Cardiac hypertrophy, capillary and muscle fiber density, muscle fiber diameter, capillary radius and diffusion distance in the myocardium of growing rats adapted to a simulated altitude of 3500 m. *Pfluegers Arch.* 335: 19–28, 1972.
408. TUREK, Z., M. GRANDTNER, K. KUBÁT, B. E. RINGNALDA, AND F. KREUZER. Arterial blood gases, muscle fibre diameters and intercapillary distance in cardiac hypertrophy of rats with an old myocardial infarction. *Pfluegers Arch.* 376: 209–215, 1978.
409. TUREK, Z., M. TUREK-MAISCHEIDER, R. A. CLAESSENS, B. E. M. RINGNALDA, AND F. KREUZER. Coronary blood flow in rats native to simulated high altitude and in rats exposed to it later in life. *Pfluegers Arch.* 355: 49–62, 1975.
410. UNGE, G., S. CARLSSON, A. LJUNGQVIST, G. TORNLING, AND J. ADOLFSSON. The proliferative activity of myocardial capillary wall cells in variously aged swimming-exercised rats. *Acta Pathol. Microbiol. Scand. Sect. A* 87: 15–17, 1979.
411. VALDIVIA, E. Total capillary bed in striated muscle of guinea pigs native to the Peruvian mountains. *Am. J. Physiol.* 194: 585–589, 1958.
412. VALDIVIA, E., AND M. WATSON. Histologic alterations in muscles of guinea pigs during chronic hypoxia. *Arch. Pathol.* 69: 199–208, 1960.
413. VLODAVSKY, I., L. K. JOHNSON, AND D. GOSPODAROWICZ. Appearance in confluent vascular endothelial cell monolayers of a specific cell surface protein (CSP-60) not detected in actively growing endothelial cells or in cell types growing in multiple layers. *Proc. Natl. Acad. Sci. USA* 76: 2306–2310, 1979.
414. VOBOŘIL, Z., AND T. H. SCHIEBLER. Ueber die Entwicklung der Gefässversorgung des Rattenherzens. *Z. Anat. Entwicklungsgesch.* 129: 24–40, 1969.
415. VRACKO, R. Basal lamina layering in diabetes mellitus. Evidence for acceleration rate of cell death and cell regeneration. *Diabetes* 23: 94–104, 1974.
416. VRACKO, R., AND E. P. BENDITT. Basal lamina: the scaffold for orderly cell replacement. Observations on regeneration of injured skeletal muscle fibers and capillaries. *J. Cell Biol.* 55: 406–419, 1972.
417. WACHTLOVÁ, M., AND J. PAŘÍZKOVÁ. Comparison of capillary density in skeletal muscles of animals differing in respect of their physical activity—the hare (*Lepus europaeus*), the domestic rabbit (*Oryctolagus domesticus*), the brown rat (*Rattus norvegicus*) and the trained and untrained rat. *Physiol. Bohemoslov.* 21: 489–495, 1972.
418. WACHTLOVÁ, M., O. POUPA, AND K. RAKUŠAN. Quantitative differences in the terminal vascular bed of the myocardium in the brown rat (*Myotis myotis*) and the laboratory mouse (*Mus musculus*). *Physiol. Bohemoslov.* 19: 491–495, 1970.
419. WACHTLOVÁ, M., K. RAKUŠAN, AND O. POUPA. The coronary terminal vascular bed in the heart of the hare (*Lepus europeus*) and the rabbit (*Oryctolagus domesticus*). *Physiol. Bohemoslov.* 14: 328–331, 1965.
420. WACHTLOVÁ, M., K. RAKUŠAN, Z. ROTH, AND O. POUPA. The terminal vascular bed of the myocardium in the wild rat (*Rattus norvegicus*) and the laboratory rat (*Rattus norvegicus lab*). *Physiol. Bohemoslov.* 16: 548–554, 1967.
421. WAGNER, R. C. Endothelial cell embryology and growth. *Adv. Microcirc.* 9: 45–75, 1980.
422. WAGNER, R. C., AND M. A. MATTHEWS. Isolation and culture of capillary endothelium from epididymal fat. *Microvasc. Res.* 10: 286–297, 1975.
423. WALL, R. T., L. A. HARKER, L. J. QUADRACCI, AND G. E. STRICKER. Factors influencing endothelial cell proliferation in vitro. *J. Cell. Physiol.* 96: 203–213, 1978.
424. WARREN, B. A. The ultrastructure of capillary sprouts induced by melanoma transplants in the golden hamster. *J. R. Microsc. Soc.* 86: 177–187, 1966.
425. WARREN, B. A., AND P. SHUBIK. The growth of the blood supply to melanoma transplants in the hamster cheek pouch. *Lab. Invest.* 15: 464–478, 1966.
426. WELT, K., W. SCHELLER, K. SCHIPPEL, AND G. SCHIPPEL. Ueber die postnatale Entwicklung vom Kapillaren im Musculus triceps brachii der weissen Ratte. *Z. Mikrosk. Anat. Forsch.* 89: 327–339, 1975.
427. WELT, K., K. SCHIPPEL, G. SCHIPPEL, AND W. SCHELLER. Zur Ultrastruktur von Kapillaren im Skelettmuskel der weissen Ratte vom 19. Fetaltag bis zum 2. Tag post partum. *Z. Mikrosk. Anat. Forsch.* 88: 465–478, 1974.
428. WERTHEMANN, A. Ueber den Aufbau der Blutgefässwand in entzündlichen Neubildungen, insbesondere in Pleuraschwarten. *Virchows Arch. Pathol. Anat. Physiol.* 270: 605–666, 1929.
429. WHITE, J. F. Studies on the growth of blood vessels in vitro. I. The effect of initial pH on growth patterns. *Am. J. Anat.* 94: 127–169, 1954.

429a. WICKLER, S. J. Capillary supply of skeletal muscles from acclimatized white-footed mice *Peromyscus*. *Am. J. Physiol.* 241 (*Regulatory Integrative Comp. Physiol.* 10): R357–R361, 1981.

430. WIENER, J., G. GIACOMELLI, A. V. LOUD, AND P. ANVERSA. Morphometry of cardiac hypertrophy induced by experimental

renal hypertension. *Am. J. Cardiol.* 44: 919–929, 1979.

431. WILLIAMS, R. G. Experiments on the growth of blood vessels in thin tissue and in small autografts. *Anat. Rec.* 133: 465–485, 1959.
432. WILLIAMS, R. G. Microscopic studies in living mammals with transparent chamber methods. *Int. Rev. Cytol.* 3: 359–398, 1959.
433. WISLOCKI, G. B. The unusual mode of development of the blood vessels of the oppossum's brain. *Anat. Rec.* 74: 409–428, 1939.
434. WOLF, J. E., JR. A spectrum of cutaneous angiogenesis. *Bibl. Anat.* 16: 174–176, 1977.
435. WOLF, J. E., JR., AND R. G. HARRISON. Demonstration and characterization of an epidermal angiogenic factor. *J. Invest. Dermatol.* 61: 130–141, 1973.
436. WOLFF, J. R., AND T. BÄR. Seamless endothelia in brain capillaries during development of the rat's cerebral cortex. *Brain Res.* 41: 17–24, 1972.
437. WOODARD, W. C., AND C. M. POMERAT. The development of patent blood vessels from adult human rib marrow in tissue culture. *Anat. Rec.* 117: 663–683, 1953.
438. WRIGHT, A. J. A. The Effect of Chronic Bradycardial Pacing on Vascular Supply, Heart Performance and Coronary Blood Flow in the Rabbit. Birmingham, UK: Univ. of Birmingham, 1979. Dissertation.
439. WRIGHT, A. J. A., AND O. HUDLICKÁ. Capillary growth and changes in heart performance induced by chronic bradycardial pacing in the rabbit. *Circ. Res.* 49: 469–478, 1981.

439a. WRIGHT, A. J. A., AND O. HUDLICKÁ. Capillary density and coronary blood flow in hypertrophic bradycardially paced rabbit hearts. *Microvasc. Res.* 24: 236, 1982.

440. WRIGHT, A. J. A., O. HUDLICKÁ, K. R. TYLER, AND A. ZIADA. The effect of vasodilating drugs on capillary density and performance in skeletal muscles. *Bibl. Anat.* 20: 362–365, 1981.
441. WRIGHT, H. P. Endothelial mitosis around aortic branches in normal guinea pigs. *Nature London* 220: 78–79, 1969.
442. WRIGHT, H. P. Mitosis pattern in aortic endothelium. *Atherosclerosis* 15: 93–100, 1972.
443. YODAIKEN, R. E., L. YANKO, H. B. HERMAN, M. MENEFEE, AND E. DAVIS. Muscle capillaries and retinopathy among Israeli diabetics. With special reference to measurement techniques, relationship to age and the pericyte. *Bibl. Anat.* 16: 430–433, 1977.
444. ZACKS, S. G., Y. J. PEGUES, AND F. A. ELLIOT. Interstitial muscle capillaries in patients with diabetes mellitus. *Metabolism* 11: 381, 1962.

444a. ZAJICEK, G. The rodent incisor tooth proliferation. *Cell Tissue Kinet.* 9: 207–214, 1976.

445. ZAUBERMAN, H., I. C. MICHAELSON, F. BERGMANN, AND D. M. MAURICE. Stimulation of neovascularization of the cornea by biogenic amines. *Exp. Eye Res.* 8: 77–83, 1969.
446. ZETTER, B. R., T. SUNT, L. B. CHEN, AND J. M. BUCHANAN. Thrombin potentiates the mitogenic response of cultured fibroblasts to serum and other growth promoting agents. *J. Cell. Physiol.* 92: 253–240, 1977.

446a. ZICHE, M., J. JONES, AND P. M. GULLINO. Role of prostaglandins E_1 and copper in angiogenesis. *J. Natl. Cancer Inst.* 69: 475–482, 1982.

447. ZIKA, K., Z. LOJDA, AND M. KUČERA. Activities of some oxidative and hydrolytic enzymes in musculus biceps brachii of rats after some stress. *Histochemie* 35: 153–164, 1973.

CHAPTER 6

Blood flow in small tubes

SHU CHIEN

SHUNICHI USAMI

RICHARD SKALAK

Departments of Physiology and Civil Engineering and Engineering Mechanics, Columbia University, New York, New York

CHAPTER CONTENTS

Rheology of Tube Flow
- Definitions
- Steady flow of Newtonian fluids through unbranched tubes

Rheological Properties of Blood and Blood Cells
- Properties of blood
- Properties of blood cells
  - Erythrocytes
  - Leukocytes
  - Platelets

Microrheology of Cells in Narrow Tubes
- Cell velocity
- Cell concentration and cell migration
- Cell deformation and cell rotation
- Cell aggregation
- Interactions of cells with tube walls

Macrorheology of Red Cell Suspensions in Narrow Tubes
- Experimental studies
  - Flow in tubes >29 μm in diameter
  - Flow in tubes <29 μm in diameter
- Theoretical considerations
- Cell screening and plasma skimming
  - Relative velocity of cells and suspending medium
  - Pressure-flow relations
  - Semiempirical theories
  - Nonaxisymmetric flow

Effects of Alterations of Blood Cell Properties on Tube Flow
- Red cell deformability
- Red cell aggregation
- Leukocytes
- Platelets
- Generalized Fåhraeus effect

Pulsatile Flow
- Viscoelastic properties of blood
- Pulse wave propagation in microvessels

Flow of Cell Suspensions Through Branched Tubes
- Effects of discharge ratio on cell distribution
- Effects of blood cell eccentricity in feeding vessel on cell distribution
- Effects of entrance geometry and flow on cell distribution

Relevance to Blood Flow In Vivo

Summary

BLOOD IS A SUSPENSION of deformable cells in plasma that contains various proteins and other solutes. The flow behavior of this suspension depends on its composition, the flow conditions, and the boundary geometry. The circulatory system of the body is composed of a network of blood vessels with complicated geometry, including branching, curvature, and a wide range of diameters; in addition the vessel walls are viscoelastic. To analyze hemodynamic functions in the complex in vivo vascular system, one must first understand the flow behavior of blood in tubes with simple geometry in vitro. In this chapter we summarize the current experimental and theoretical knowledge on blood flow in tubes with diameters <0.5 mm. The discussion concentrates mainly on steady flow through straight tubes, but flow through branched tubes and pulsatile flow are also considered. Our purpose is to provide the reader with the basic information on blood flow through small tubes necessary to understand hemodynamic phenomena observed in the microcirculation in vivo (see the chapter by Zweifach and Lipowsky in this *Handbook*).

RHEOLOGY OF TUBE FLOW

Definitions

1. Pressure (P) in a fluid is the mean compressive force per unit area acting on fluid surfaces in directions normal to the surfaces at any point. Convenient units of pressure in blood flow are dynes per square centimeter and pascals; 1 Pa equals 1 N/m^2, 1 $kg \cdot m^{-1} \cdot s^{-2}$, or 10 dyn/cm^2. Pressure can also be expressed in terms of the equivalent height of a fluid column. At sea level 1 cmH_2O is equivalent to 98 Pa or 980 dyn/cm^2 and 1 mmHg is equivalent to 133.3 Pa or 1,333 dyn/cm^2.

2. Shear stress (σ) on a surface is the force acting on a unit area in a direction tangential to the surface. The units of shear stress are also pascals and dynes per square centimeter. In a fluid at rest, shear stresses are zero.

3. Shear rate ($\dot{\gamma}$) is the velocity gradient in a moving fluid. The units of $\dot{\gamma}$ are reciprocal seconds. For motion

in parallel layers, $\dot{\gamma}$ is the difference in velocity per unit distance of separation between adjacent layers.

4. Viscosity (η) is a measure of the resistance of the fluid to shearing when the fluid is in motion. For simple shear flows it is defined as the ratio of the shear stress to the shear rate

$$\eta = \sigma/\dot{\gamma} \quad (1)$$

A unit of viscosity is the poise (P), which is equal to 1 dyn·s·cm^{-2}; 1 cP is 0.01 P and equals 1 mPa·s. For simple, homogeneous fluids such as water or saline, σ varies linearly with $\dot{\gamma}$ and η is constant; such fluids are referred to as Newtonian fluids. Plasma is a Newtonian fluid. Blood, however, behaves as a non-Newtonian fluid: the stress σ is a nonlinear function of $\dot{\gamma}$. The ratio $\sigma/\dot{\gamma}$ for non-Newtonian fluids is sometimes referred to as the apparent viscosity (η_a) and varies with the shear rate. The apparent viscosity of blood decreases as σ and $\dot{\gamma}$ increase.

Steady Flow of Newtonian Fluids Through Unbranched Tubes

The pressure drop during the steady flow of an incompressible Newtonian fluid from point 1 to point 2 in a tube of variable cross section may be written [for a moderate Reynolds number (Re)] as

$$P_1 - P_2 = \eta A Q + \rho B Q^2 + \rho(\beta_2 \bar{V}_2^2 - \beta_1 \bar{V}_1^2)/2 + \rho g(h_2 - h_1) \quad (2)$$

where the subscripts 1 and 2 refer to the two points in the tube. The symbols A and B are coefficients (in units of cm^{-3} and cm^{-4}, respectively) that depend on geometric factors and some constants, Q is the volumetric flow (cm^3/s), ρ is fluid density (g/cm^3), $\bar{V}$ is the mean velocity (cm/s), g is the gravitational acceleration, and h is the height. The value of Q is equal to $\bar{V}$ times the cross-sectional area of the tube. The coefficients β_1 and β_2 depend on the velocity profiles and are in the range of 1–2 (flat and parabolic profile, respectively). According to Equation 2, the pressure drop along a tube can be attributed to the four terms on the right-hand side: laminar viscous dissipation (ηAQ), dissipation associated with inertial effects (ρBQ^2), change in kinetic energy, and difference in potential energy.

For two points at the same height ($h_1 = h_2$), the gravitational term $\rho g(h_2 - h_1)$ is zero. The kinetic energy difference between points 1 and 2, $\rho(\beta_2\bar{V}_2^2 - \beta_1\bar{V}_1^2)/2$, results mainly from a difference in tube diameter and can be neglected for a tube with a uniform diameter. The form of the dissipation terms ($\eta AQ + \rho BQ^2$) was suggested by Hagen (97). The ratio of the inertial loss term to the laminar loss term, $(\rho BQ^2)/(\eta AQ)$, is proportional to Re, which is dimensionless and is usually expressed as

$$\text{Re} = \rho \bar{V} d/\eta \quad (3)$$

where d is the tube diameter or other appropriate dimension. The lower the Re, the more predominant is the laminar viscous term, and fluid tends to move in laminae or layers with the fluid elements following smooth streamlines. The higher the Re, the more important is the inertial term; the flow paths of the fluid elements become increasingly tortuous and erratic, eventually leading to turbulent flow. For a fluid with known η and ρ, Re increases with increasing $\bar{V}$ and d. Both d and $\bar{V}$ are considerably lower in the microcirculation than in the large vessels, and the value of Re in the microcirculation is generally so low that the flow is laminar.

For steady laminar flow of a Newtonian fluid in a cylindrical tube with uniform radius r, the pressure drop (ΔP) between two points separated by a length l is given by Poiseuille's law, where A in Equation 2 is given as $8l/\pi r^4$ and B is zero; thus

$$\Delta P = 8l\eta Q/\pi r^4 \quad (4)$$

The ratio of pressure drop to volumetric flow is resistance (R). In laminar flow through a tube with uniform radius, the resistance is

$$R = 8l\eta/\pi r^4 \quad (5)$$

Equation 4 indicates the importance of tube radius (which enters to the 4th power) in determining viscous

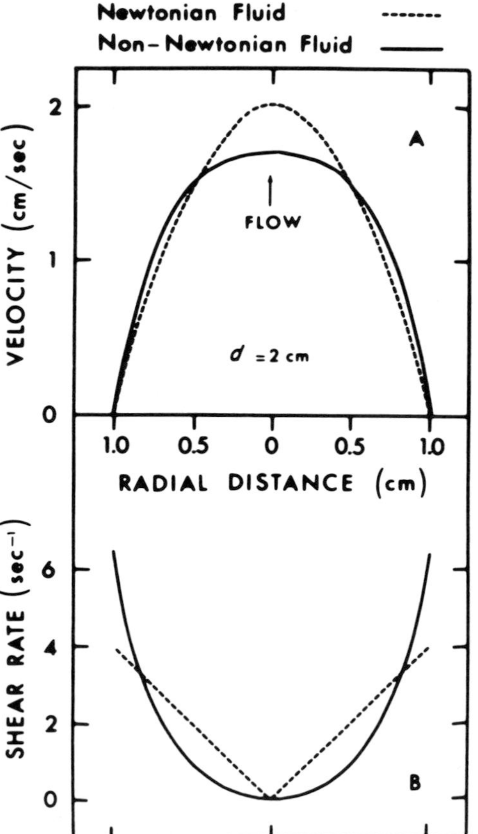

FIG. 1. *A*: velocity profile in cylindrical tube for Newtonian and non-Newtonian fluids. *B*: velocity gradient as function of radial distance for fluids in *A*. [From Chien (33).]

resistance. In laminar flow (Poiseuille flow) the velocity profile in the tube is parabolic, with a maximum velocity (V_{max}) in the center of the tube and a zero velocity at the tube wall (Fig. 1). In such a parabolic velocity profile, the maximum velocity is equal to twice the mean velocity ($\bar{V}$), i.e., $V_{max} = 2\bar{V}$. The shear rate in Poiseuille flow through a cylindrical tube varies from zero in the center to a maximum value at the wall. The wall shear rate ($\dot{\gamma}_w$) is equal to $4\bar{V}/r$ for Newtonian fluids. For non-Newtonian fluids the wall shear rate is usually higher (110), and $4\bar{V}/r$ may be regarded as an apparent wall shear rate ($\dot{\gamma}_{aw}$).

If there is a change in radius over a length of the tube (Fig. 2), the mean velocity at each cross section is

$$\bar{V} = Q/\pi r^2 \qquad (6)$$

Conservation of matter requires that $Q_1 = Q_2$ in a rigid, unbranched tube, and hence $\bar{V}$ is inversely proportional to r^2. When flow proceeds from a wide section, 1, to a narrow section, 2, of the tube, $\bar{V}$ increases, leading to an increase in kinetic energy ($\rho\bar{V}^2/2$) and a corresponding decrease of P at section 2 (Fig. 2). In a section of a tube where the radius changes abruptly, the change in velocity may be the dominant factor in determining the pressure drop, and the viscous term may be negligible over the short length in which the change occurs. Under these circumstances Equation 2 may be written as

$$P_1 - P_2 = \rho(\beta_2\bar{V}_2^2 - \beta_1\bar{V}_1^2)/2 + \rho g(h_2 - h_1) \qquad (7)$$

which is a form of Bernoulli's equation for inviscid flow. If $h_1 = h_2$, the term $\rho g(h_2 - h_1)$ vanishes in Equation 7 and

$$P_1 - P_2 = \rho(\beta_2\bar{V}_2^2 - \beta_1\bar{V}_1^2)/2 \qquad (8)$$

The velocity profile of such inviscid flow may be essentially flat, so that $\beta_1 = \beta_2 = 1$.

If the tube diameter is narrow in a short section followed by an expansion, as in a stenosis, the velocity profile in the region immediately beyond the minimum diameter is relatively flat. Downstream in the tube where the diameter is wider, flow gradually changes from the flat velocity profile to a fully developed laminar flow (parabolic velocity profile), with viscous friction dominant. In the transition region, the flow consists of a central free stream, where the velocity profile is flat, and a boundary layer in which the velocity decreases due to the presence of viscous friction (Fig. 3). In the expanding section of the tube, well-developed ring vortices might be present outside the core region (89). As flow proceeds along the length of the tube, the central core of inviscid flow decreases and the thickness of the boundary layer grows until the laminar flow profile is fully developed.

The velocity profile at the entrance to a small tube from a large reservoir or a large-diameter tube is also flat at high Re. For low Re (<1) flow a parabolic velocity profile occurs within one tube diameter from the entrance (53, 115).

RHEOLOGICAL PROPERTIES OF BLOOD AND BLOOD CELLS

Properties of Blood

This section briefly reviews the rheological behavior of blood during bulk flow as a basis for discussion of blood flow through narrow tubes. More detailed discussions of blood rheology can be found elsewhere (33, 46, 149, 178).

Because blood is a non-Newtonian fluid, its appar-

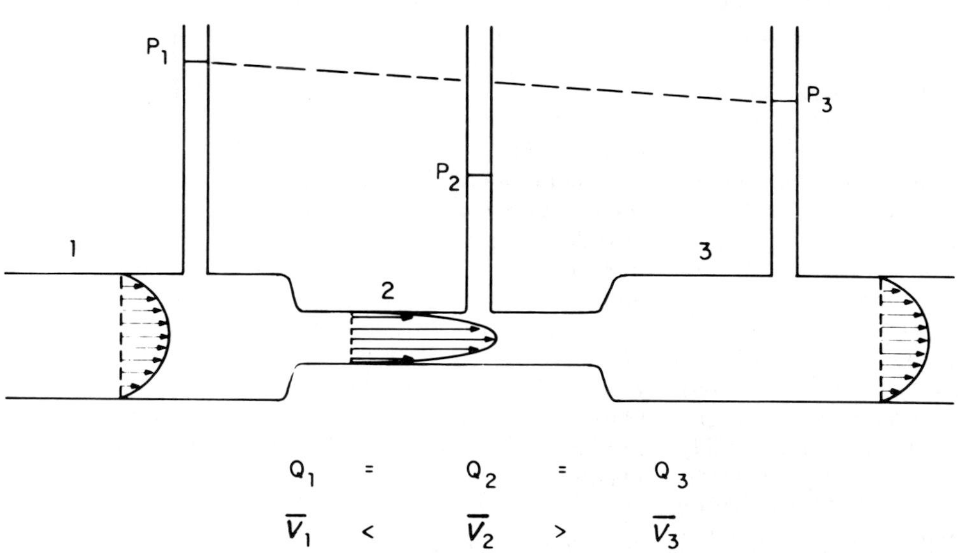

FIG. 2. Pressure readings (P_1, P_2, and P_3) in cylindrical tube with equal diameters in sections 1 and 3 and narrower diameter in section 2. Volumetric flow rates (Q_1, Q_2, and Q_3) through the 3 sections are equal; mean linear velocity in section 2 ($\bar{V}_2$) is faster than those in sections 1 ($\bar{V}_1$) and 3 ($\bar{V}_3$). Higher kinetic energy in section 2 is associated with pressure in that section (P_2) lower than the value expected from viscous dissipation alone (*dotted line* connecting P_1 and P_3).

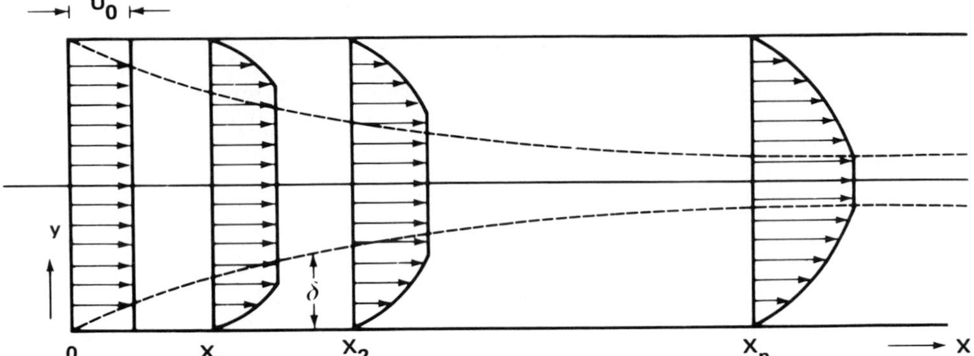

FIG. 3. Entry flow of fluid into tube. *Dotted lines* indicate boundary layer (δ); U_0 is the entrance velocity. [From Fung (71).]

ent viscosity should be measured under defined shear rates. Rotational viscometers (e.g., with a cone-plate or a coaxial-cylinder geometry) are most suitable for this purpose. Measurements show that η_a at a given temperature is a function of shear rate, cell concentration, plasma viscosity, cell deformability, and cell aggregation. Red blood cells (RBCs) constitute the largest percentage of cells in normal blood, and they are the primary cell species influencing the rheological properties of blood. The relationship between η_a and hematocrit (Hct, volume percent of RBCs) is nonlinear, with η_a rising at an increasing rate as Hct rises beyond the normal values of 40%–45% (Fig. 4). Blood plasma is a Newtonian fluid and the normal value of plasma viscosity (η_P) averages 1.2–1.3 cP at 37°C; η_P is primarily a function of the concentration of plasma proteins, especially large proteins with molecular asymmetry, like fibrinogen and some of the globulin fractions.

For a blood sample with a given Hct and η_P, the variation of η_a with $\dot{\gamma}$ (Fig. 5) is attributable to shear-dependent changes in cell deformation and cell aggregation (33). At low shear rates the bridging of adjacent cells by fibrinogen, globulins, or other macromolecules (19, 38) causes RBCs to aggregate and form rouleaux (49, 151, 180). The RBC aggregation represents an energy minimization at cell surfaces (36, 165) in which the macromolecular bridging energy is counterbalanced by the electrostatic repulsive energy of the negatively charged sialic acid on RBC membranes and the work done by the shear stress during flow. The net aggregation energy can be estimated from the shear stress required to disaggregate the rouleau (41) or changes in RBC membrane strain energy due to elastic deformation of cells in rouleaux (58, 164, 165). Although a small shear rate may enhance RBC aggregation by promoting cell-to-cell encounters (34), stresses >0.1 dyn/cm^2 cause rouleau disaggregation, which is a major factor for the shear-thinning behavior of η_a. An increase in shear stress also causes deformation of the dispersed RBCs and the alignment of their major axes with the direction of flow. Such cell deformation is another factor contributing to the shear-thinning behavior of blood.

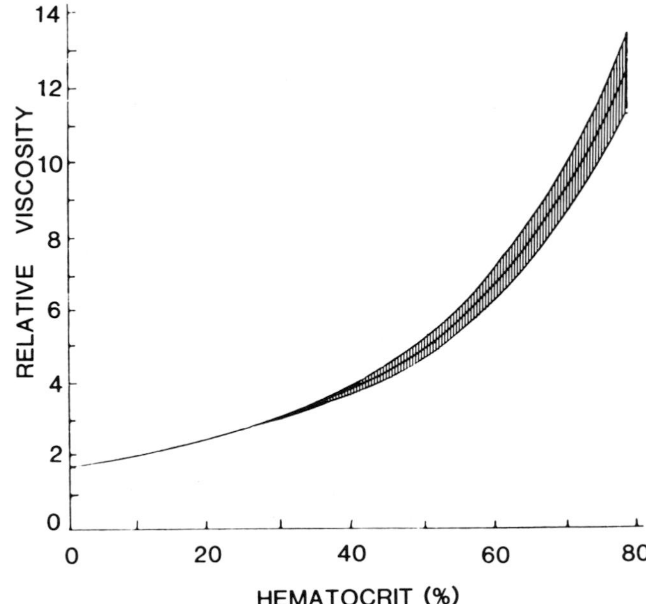

FIG. 4. Relative viscosity of blood (blood viscosity/water viscosity) flowing through large tubes ($d > 1$ mm). Shear rate is probably $>1{,}000$ s^{-1}. [Adapted from Whittaker and Winton (187).]

Blood possesses viscoelastic properties that are demonstrable by oscillatory rheological tests. The viscous component (η') and elastic component (η'') of the complex viscosity can be computed from the amplitude and phase of the response (39, 171, 173). In normal blood (Hct ~ 45%), η' predominates over η'', and the small value of η'', which is detectable at low frequencies of oscillation, is attributable to RBC aggregation. At high Hct values (80%–95%), both η' and η'' rise, and the viscoelastic behavior of the concentrated cell suspensions reflects the deformation of individual cells as they interact with closely packed neighbors.

Properties of Blood Cells

ERYTHROCYTES. The human RBC has a biconcave discoid shape at rest, with a major diameter of ~8 μm when suspended in an isotonic medium. The diameter

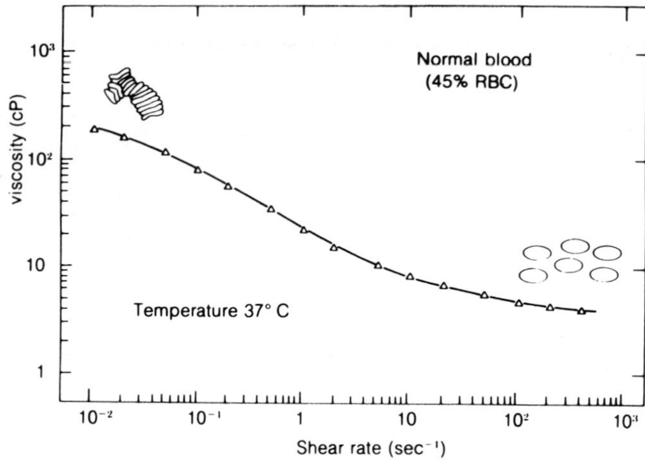

FIG. 5. Logarithmic relation between apparent viscosity and shear rate in normal human blood containing 45% RBCs by volume. *Insets* show RBC aggregation at low shear rates and RBC disaggregation and deformation at high shear rates.

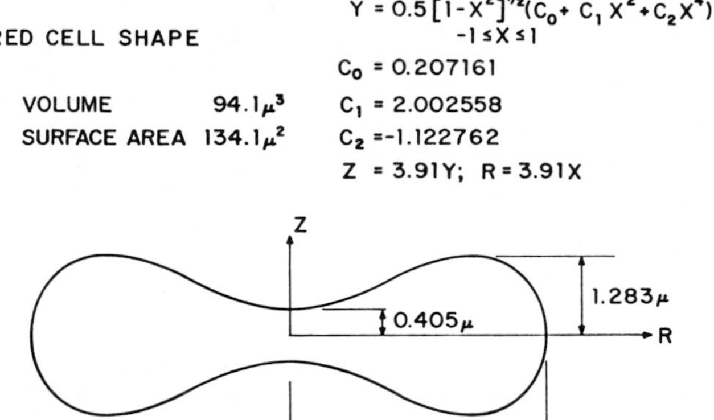

FIG. 6. Dimensions and shape of typical human RBC. [From Evans and Fung (59).]

decreases when the RBC is dried in a blood smear preparation. The dimensions of a typical human RBC are shown in Figure 6 (59). The mean corpuscular volume of an RBC is ~90 μm^3, and the cell surface area is ~140 μm^2, which is 44% in excess of that required to enclose a sphere of that volume.

The ability of the RBC to deform stems from *1*) the presence of the excess surface area for its volume, *2*) the fluidity of the internal contents, and *3*) the rheological properties of the membrane. The internal fluid is primarily a hemoglobin solution with a mean corpuscular hemoglobin concentration of ~33 g/dl. The corresponding internal viscosity is ~6–7 cP (42, 48). An increase in the mean corpuscular hemoglobin concentration or an alteration in the rheological properties of the hemoglobin (e.g., deoxygenation of sickle hemoglobin) can cause an increase in internal fluid viscosity and/or the transition to a viscoelastic gel, and hence a reduction of RBC deformability (35).

The RBC membrane is composed of a lipid bilayer and protein molecules. Some of the protein molecules are located on membrane surfaces and others extend into the hydrophobic core to different depths (158). The proteins spectrin and actin form a matrix on the endoface of the membrane. This endofacial matrix is connected to the glycoprotein molecules (e.g., band 3) that span the entire membrane thickness (109, 122, 167). The protein matrix, often referred to as the cytoskeleton, plays a major role in providing the stiffness of the membrane and in maintaining the shape of the RBC. The material properties of the RBC membrane make it easily deformed at a constant area but strongly resistant to any area expansion. The dilatational modulus of the RBC membrane during area expansion is several orders of magnitude greater than the shear modulus (or extensional modulus) at constant area (57, 163). The deformation of RBCs in vitro or in the circulation in vivo usually occurs at an essentially constant area. The presence of the excess membrane area, the low shear modulus of the membrane, and the fluidity of the internal content allow the normal RBC to deform into a variety of shapes without appreciable change in surface area or cell volume (93, 114, 137). The average normal RBC can pass through a cylindrical tube as narrow as 2.7–2.8 μm without areal stretching (Fig. 7). There are considerable variations in the geometric characteristics of individual RBCs in a given blood sample (70), and the minimum tube diameter for RBC transit may vary accordingly. The RBC cannot pass through a tube with less than the minimum diameter without areal stretching. Because the RBC membrane area can only expand a few percent (61), the application of high driving pressures results in RBC hemolysis (40). At a given cell volume and membrane area, alterations in RBC shape (e.g., echinocytes with spicules) may lead to a reduced cell deformability (124), but the minimum tube diameter for cell transit is probably not affected.

The RBC membrane has a surface viscosity that is important when the membrane is sheared in its own plane. The viscous stress is usually assumed to add to the elastic stress. The membrane is represented as a two-dimensional Kelvin solid. The principal tensions T_1 and T_2, which are expressed in dynes per centimeter (same as for surface tension), may be given in the form (60)

$$T_1 = \frac{\mu_m}{2}(\lambda_1^2 - \lambda_2^2) + K(\lambda_1\lambda_2 - 1) + 2\eta_m \frac{\dot{\lambda}_1}{\lambda_1} \tag{9}$$

$$T_2 = \frac{\mu_m}{2}(\lambda_2^2 - \lambda_1^2) + K(\lambda_1\lambda_2 - 1) + 2\eta_m \frac{\dot{\lambda}_2}{\lambda_2} \tag{10}$$

The coefficient μ_m is a shear modulus with a value of ~4 × 10^{-3} dyn/cm. In these equations the last term represents the viscous stress; the coefficient η_m is a surface viscosity equal to ~6 × 10^{-4} dyn·s·cm^{-1}. The coefficient K is an areal stiffness coefficient (or dila-

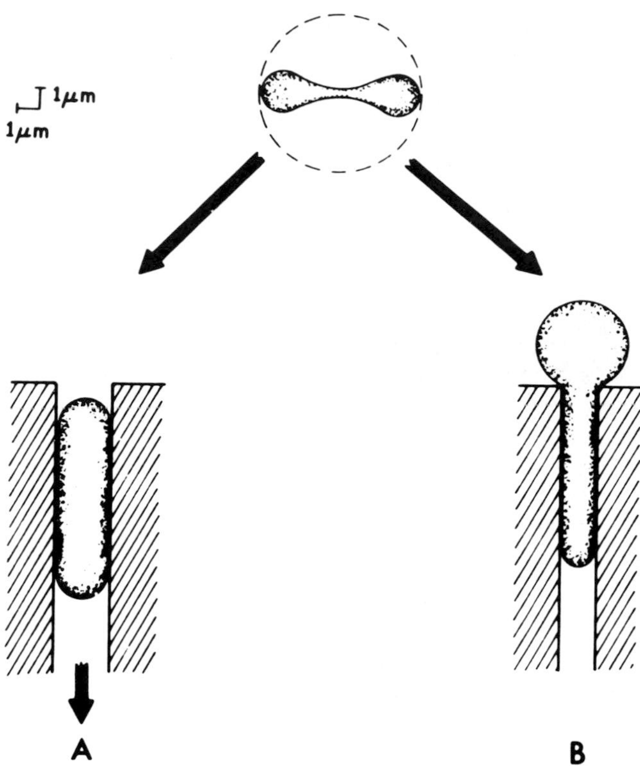

FIG. 7. Passage of normal human RBC (*top diagram*, top and side views of biconcave disk) through cylindrical channels with different diameters (*d*). *A*: $d = 3$ μm; *B*: $d = 2$ μm. Note that deformation of normal RBC allows passage through *A* but not *B*. [Adapted from Chien (33).]

tational modulus). It is typically much larger than μ_m. For the RBC, K has a value of ~4×10^2 dyn/cm. The stretch ratios λ_1 and λ_2 are the principal values defined as the ratio of the final length of a line element to its initial length. The symbol $\dot{\lambda}_1$ represents the derivative of λ_1 with respect to time. It follows that $\dot{\lambda}_1/\lambda_1$ is the strain rate in the principal direction, x_1. In a membrane with appreciable shear resistance, tensions T_1 and T_2 may be different. In most applications it is satisfactory to assume that the area of the membrane is always constant. This is expressed by

$$\lambda_1\lambda_2 = 1 \tag{11}$$

To model a membrane with constant area, the term involving K is replaced by an isotropic tension T_{iso}, which must be determined as part of the solution of a stress problem. This is satisfactory for blood flow in tubes because the changes in area are very small.

The RBC membrane also has appreciable bending resistance. This property causes the characteristically smooth surfaces of the RBC at rest. In reticulocytes, where the endofacial protein matrix is not yet completely formed, the bending stiffness is low and the cell shapes are more irregular.

The bending moments M_1 and M_2 in the principal directions may be expressed by (190)

$$M_1 = D(K_1 + \nu K_2)/\lambda_2 \tag{12}$$

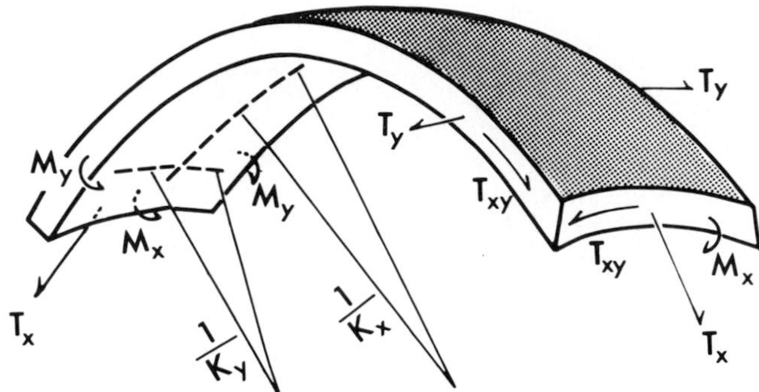

FIG. 8. Diagram showing membrane tensions (T) and bending moments (M) in piece of membrane with curvatures (K). [From Chien (35).]

$$M_2 = D(K_1 + \nu K_2)/\lambda_1 \tag{13}$$

where K_1 and K_2 are changes in the principal curvatures from the resting state (Fig. 8) and D is a bending stiffness coefficient. For the RBC, D is ~10^{-12} dyn/cm. The coefficient ν is a material property analogous to a Poisson ratio; in a homogeneous, incompressible material ν is equal to ½. To produce an isotropic bending moment, ν is assumed equal to 1; this is probably the most logical value for the RBC membrane.

These constitutive laws for the RBC membrane may be used in conjunction with equations of motion or equilibrium to derive the shape, stresses, and motion of RBCs in a variety of situations (60). Many experimental observations on RBC deformation have been made, and some deformed shapes have been computed theoretically (e.g., 161). Under resting conditions or at very low shear stresses, the elasticity and bending stiffness of the RBC membrane help maintain the biconcave discoid shape of the cell. In a flow channel (35, 102), shear stresses of the order of 1–10 dyn/cm^2 markedly deform the RBCs. At higher stresses the RBCs behave like flexible fluid-filled bags with a constant surface area. In many situations (especially in suspensions with high external viscosity or high Hct), the membrane rotates about its contents in a "tank-treading" motion (67, 152). In this motion the cell shape is steady and the membrane flows smoothly around it, imparting rotational motion to the cell interior. Theoretical analyses on a single cell, modeled as an ellipsoid, show that a given cell may either flip end-over-end as a rigid body or undergo rotational motion with stationary orientation, depending on the internal and external viscosities and the shape of the cell (107). Estimations of the dissipation in packed cell suspensions indicate that the minimum viscosity is achieved with a certain amount of membrane rotation in each cell, reducing the energy loss to below that for a rigid cell (154). The rotation of the cell is primarily caused by the asymmetric distribution of shear stresses on the cell.

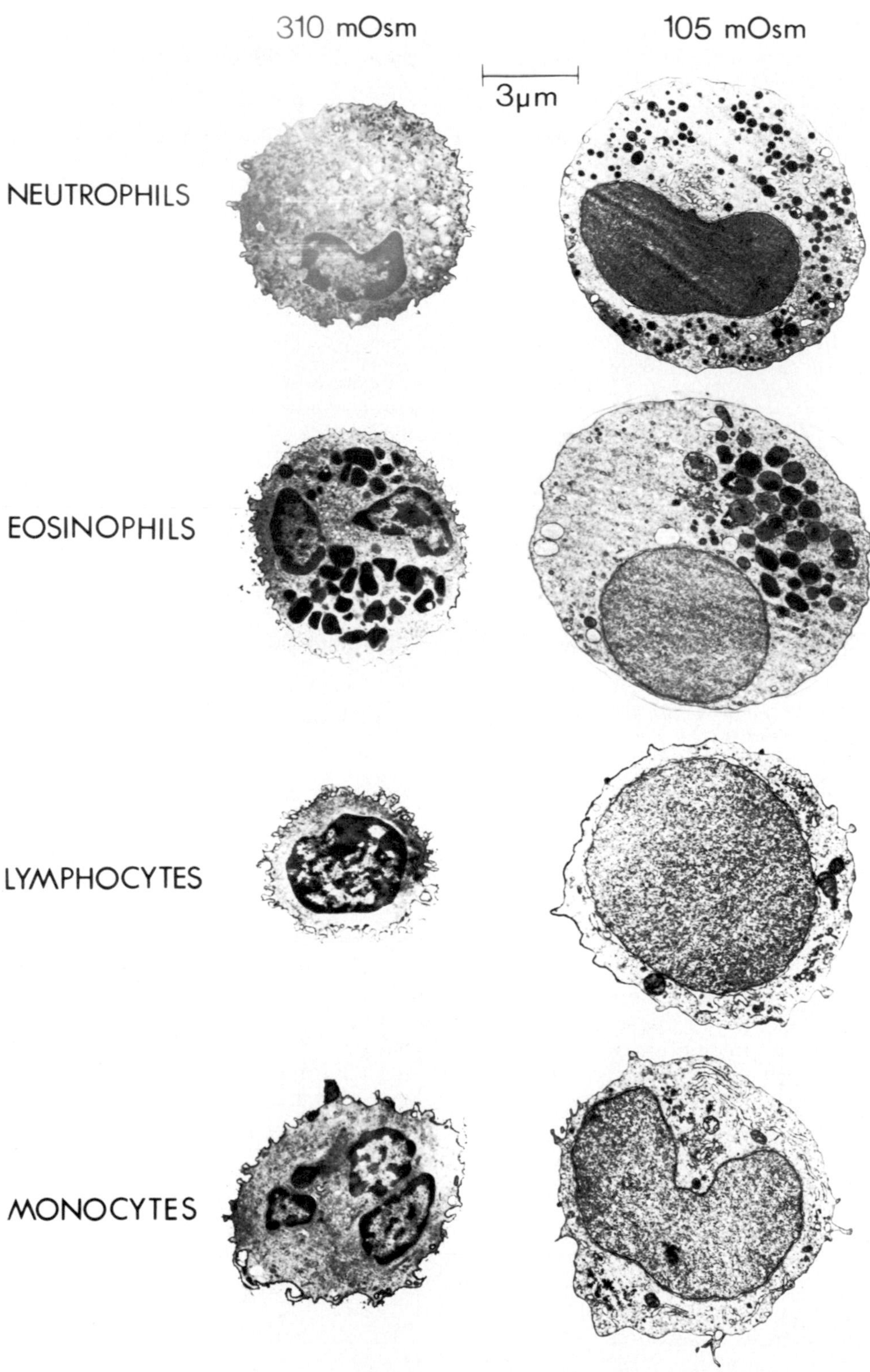

FIG. 9. Thin sections through human neutrophils, eosinophils, lymphocytes, and monocytes at 310 mosmol/kg (*left*) and 105 mosmol/kg (*right*). [From Schmid-Schönbein et al. (144).]

LEUKOCYTES. White blood cells (WBCs) constitute less than 1% of the total volume of blood cells in normal human subjects and exert little influence on the bulk rheological properties of normal blood in large vessels. The WBCs are generally spherical, but their surfaces are not usually smooth. Electron-microscopic examination has shown that the WBC membrane has many folds (Fig. 9), which provide a membrane area beyond that needed to encompass a smooth sphere of equal volume. The amount of excess membrane area is ~80% for neutrophils and ~130% for lymphocytes and monocytes (144).

Light-microscopic measurements of the diameters of human WBCs in an isotonic medium show that their mean diameter is 6.7 μm; stereological analysis of transmission electron micrographs yields a similar value (144). The latter study also shows that the mean diameter is only 6.2 μm for lymphocytes and varies from 7.0 to 7.5 μm for granulocytes. Segel et al. (155) found that lymphocytes have a mean volume of 210 μm^3, which corresponds to a mean diameter of 7.4 μm. The diameters of the WBCs in blood smears usually fall between 10 and 15 μm, a result of flattening the spheres into thin pancake shapes (0.5–1.5 μm thick) during smear preparation (143). Although the diameter of the WBC is not as large as the major diameter of the RBC, the spherical shape of the WBC results in a larger cell volume than that of the RBC. The mean cell volume is ~200 μm^3 for neutrophils, ~120 μm^3 for lymphocytes, and ~220 μm^3 for monocytes (144).

The WBC is much less deformable than the RBC. The stress required to cause the deformational entry of a small portion of the cell into a micropipette ($r \sim$ 1 μm) is 4–5 times greater for the WBC than for the RBC (37). Aspiration of a small portion of the WBC into the micropipette not only requires a greater stress but also takes longer, indicating that the WBC is more viscous than the RBC (144). The viscoelastic behavior of the WBC has been analyzed by use of a standard solid model with an elastic element in parallel with a Maxwell element, which is composed of an elastic element and a viscous element in series (144). Although these rheological elements have not been identified with the morphological constituents of the cell, the cytoplasm of the WBC apparently plays a more important role than its membrane. This is in contrast to the normal human RBC, where the contribution of the membrane is more significant. When rheological tests on WBCs are made with large deformation involving the whole cell (7, 116, 125), the nucleus may become an important factor in determining the viscoelastic behavior of the WBC.

When ethylenediaminetetraacetate (EDTA) is used to chelate Ca^{2+}, the viscoelastic properties of WBCs reflect their passive behavior. When heparin is used as an anticoagulant instead of EDTA, the WBCs undergo spontaneous, active deformation in the presence of Ca^{2+}. Micropipette aspiration tests under these conditions indicate that the projections of the WBC where membrane pleatings are unfolded are less deformable than the remainder of the cell (146).

In modeling the behavior of leukocytes we assume that the contents are incompressible and that the viscoelastic model of a standard solid applies to the behavior of a cell under shear (deviatoric stress). The stress deviator σ'_{ij} is defined as the stress tensor (σ_{ij}) minus mean normal stress ($\bar{\sigma}$); $\bar{\sigma} = -P$, where P is the pressure at any point. Thus the deviatoric stress is

$$\sigma'_{ij} = \sigma_{ij} + P\delta_{ij} \tag{14}$$

where δ_{ij} is the Kronecker delta symbol. A schematic diagram of the standard viscoelastic solid used to model leukocytes is shown in Figure 10. The corresponding equation for the behavior of the deviatoric stress is given by

$$\sigma'_{ij} + \frac{\eta_{cell}}{k_2}\frac{d\sigma'_{ij}}{dt} = k_1 e'_{ij} + \eta_{cell}\left(1 + \frac{k_1}{k_2}\right)\frac{de'_{ij}}{dt} \tag{15}$$

where e'_{ij} is the deviatoric part of the strain tensor. The coefficients k_1 and k_2 are elastic coefficients having the analogous roles shown in Figure 10, and η_{cell} is the coefficient of viscosity of the cell. In this model the contributions of the membrane and the cytoplasm are not separated, but it is expected that the membrane plays a minor role until it is stretched taut.

Using this model, Schmid-Schönbein et al. (147) derived coefficients for 75 neutrophils suspended in isotonic buffer (310 mosmol/kg, 7.4 pH, and 22°C) based on aspiration of a portion of a cell into a micropipette. The results show the following coefficients (mean ± SD): $k_1 = 275 \pm 119$ dyn/cm², $k_2 = 737 \pm 346$ dyn/cm², $\eta_{cell} = 130 \pm 54$ dyn·s·cm^{-2} (poise).

Additional tests by Sung et al. (168) show that the coefficients k_1 and k_2 are essentially constant in the temperature range of 9°C–40°C. The value of η_{cell} varies inversely with temperature. In the pH range of 5.4–8.4, the k_2 value remains essentially constant, but k_1 and η_{cell} increase with increasing pH. The most dramatic effect is due to changes in osmolalities. Over the range of 50–660 mosmol/kg, the values of k_1 and k_2 increase nearly exponentially with increasing os-

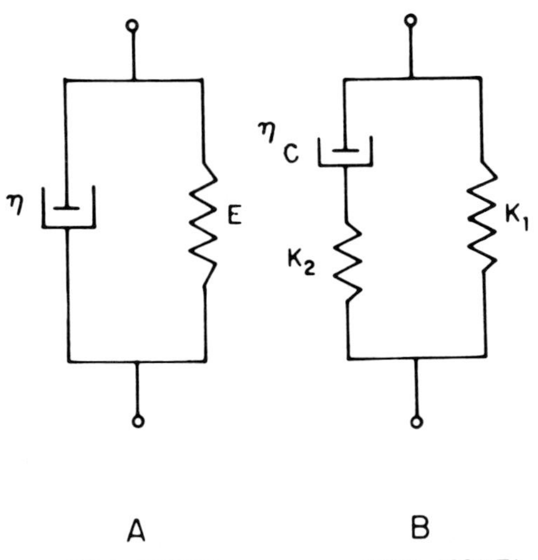

FIG. 10. Schematic drawing of viscoelastic models used for RBCs and WBCs. *A*: RBC model consists of elastic element (E) in parallel with viscous element (η). *B*: WBC model consists of elastic element (K_1) in parallel with Maxwell element, which is composed of another elastic element (K_2) in series with viscous element of cell (η_c).

molality. In hyperosmotic medium of 660 mosmol/kg, the η_{cell} value of neutrophils increases ~300-fold, from 10^2 P to 3×10^4 P. At osmolalities of 100 mosmol/kg or less, the surface foldings disappear and the neutrophil assumes the shape of a smooth sphere. The cells eventually become quite stiff despite the increased fluidity of the cell interior, due to the stress in the membrane as the cell becomes a smooth sphere.

PLATELETS. Human platelets are small corpuscles (~2 μm) with round or oval discoid shape. The platelets occupy even less of the blood volume than the WBCs and normally have little effect on the bulk viscosity of blood. Platelet adhesion to vessel surface and platelet aggregation, however, may affect viscous resistance to flow, especially in narrow tubes. Little information is available on the rheological properties of platelets, but they are probably not very deformable. Platelets are important in blood coagulation and thrombus formation, topics not treated here.

MICRORHEOLOGY OF CELLS IN NARROW TUBES

The distribution and deformation of blood cells in tubes can vary widely depending on cell properties, tube geometry, and flow conditions. In tubes with diameters comparable to those of arterioles and venules (30–200 μm), where there are many cells across the lumen section, the cells interact with and deform each other as a result of the velocity profile across the tube. Another important result of cell deformability is the tendency for RBCs to migrate away from the wall. These and other factors are discussed next.

Cell Velocity

Goldsmith and Marlow (90, 91) studied the microrheological behavior of human RBCs in flow through cylindrical tubes with diameters on the order of 100 μm. With the use of a microscope system in which the stage containing the tube can be moved in a direction opposite to that of the flow of the RBC suspension, the behavior of the individual RBCs can be tracked and photographed.

To visualize the flow behavior of RBCs at Hct of 40% or higher, Goldsmith and Marlow (91) studied suspensions of RBC ghosts in plasma containing a small fraction of normal or hardened RBCs. The ghosts are transparent to transmitted light, thus allowing analysis of the behavior of the tracer RBCs in an environment with rheological properties (179) similar to those of concentrated suspensions of normal RBCs.

In contrast to the Poiseuille parabolic velocity profile demonstrated for dilute RBC suspensions (90), the velocity profiles of the tracer RBCs in concentrated ghost suspensions are blunted in the tube center, with a corresponding steepening of the velocity gradient near the wall. For a given ghost cell concentration and tube diameter, the velocity distributions of the tracer particles, as a function of tube radial position, are identical for normal RBCs, hardened RBCs, and rigid latex spheres 1–4 μm in diameter. Therefore the velocity profile reflects primarily the behavior of the ghost cell suspension, which is probably a good model for a suspension of normal RBCs (91).

Careful mapping of the velocity distribution near the tube center indicates that the blunted velocity profile in concentrated suspensions is not exactly flat; small measurable velocity gradients exist near the tube center (91). For practical purposes, however, the core region is assumed to undergo plug flow with a uniform velocity. The blunting of the velocity profile can be qualitatively understood on the basis of the non-Newtonian behavior of blood. In the low-shear region in the center of the tube, the velocity gradient should decrease more sharply than the shear stress. Oka (128, 129) obtained theoretical solutions showing a blunted velocity profile by using a Casson fluid model.

An increase in cell concentration or cell aggregation, which enhances the non-Newtonian behavior of blood (33), also causes an increase in velocity blunting (91). An increase in flow rate causes a decrease in blood viscosity due to cell disaggregation and deformation (see *Properties of Blood*, p. 219), and this leads to a decrease in velocity blunting (91). An increase in tube diameter decreases the ratio of the particle diameter to the tube diameter and hence causes a decrease in blunting (91).

Cell Concentration and Cell Migration

The cell concentration is not uniform across a tube; it is greatest in the central portion of the tube and thins out to a small layer near the wall that contains relatively few cells (86). The presence of a peripheral particle-depleted layer contributes to blunting of the velocity profile. With normal cell concentrations, however, the cell-depleted layer is probably <5 μm thick (22, 150). The nonuniform distribution of particles across the tube, together with the nonuniformity of the velocity, leads to a lower mean particle concentration (Hct) in the tube than that in the feed reservoir (63, 64). (This Fåhraeus effect is discussed in MACRORHEOLOGY OF RED CELL SUSPENSIONS IN NARROW TUBES, p. 228.)

The nonuniformity of cell concentration across the tube is related to the radial migration of cells. Radial migration of small particles flowing in suspension in a tube was first demonstrated by Segré and Silberberg (156). They showed that, in a dilute suspension of rigid particles, particles near the wall of the tube migrate toward the axis and particles near the axis of the tube move toward the wall. This two-way migration results in the tubular pinch effect, with a maximum particle concentration at ~0.6 of the tube radius from the center. The radial migration of rigid particles at high flow rates depends on inertial effects. For blood flow in the microcirculation the velocities of interest and the Re are small enough that inertial effects can be neglected. Theoretically there is no migration at low Re for rigid spheres flowing in a circular tube (98). For flexible particles like RBCs, however, radial migration occurs even at a very low Re. This type of migration is related to cell deformation. Theoretical treatment by Rubinow and Keller (142) showed that a deformable sphere tends to migrate toward the axis in a parabolic velocity field. Gauthier et al. (82) and Schmid-Schönbein et al. (150) give numerical information on the extent of axial migration.

Particle interactions cause tracer RBCs in concentrated ghost suspensions to undergo random radial displacements during flow through tubes (91). These radial displacements are greater at an intermediate cell concentration (39%) than at either low (10%) or high (93%) cell concentrations; these displacements are enhanced by increasing shear rate. In tubes with a diameter of 79–155 μm and at a cell concentration of 40%, the largest radial displacements of RBCs occur in the region between 0.4 and 0.8 of the tube radius from the axis. Close to the tube wall the radial displacements cause frequent RBC collisions with the wall, a phenomenon that does not occur in dilute cell suspensions.

The RBCs are often not precisely axisymmetric in a narrow capillary with a diameter approximately the size of the RBC; the cells tend to seek some particular radial position and shape as they move down the capillary (5, 159). This implies that in capillary flow, as in flow in larger tubes, if a RBC is too close to the wall, it migrates slightly away from the wall. On the other hand, the axisymmetric position apparently is unstable if the capillary diameter is much larger than the cell diameter, and most of the blood cells flowing in capillaries are found in some nonaxisymmetric position. Theoretical computations on a two-dimensional model show a lower pressure drop for nonsymmetric cells (154).

Cell Deformation and Cell Rotation

The microrheological behavior of individual RBCs during flow through cylindrical glass tubes with diameters ranging from 60 to 200 μm was studied with dilute RBC suspensions at Hct below 2% (90). The flow rate and the suspending medium viscosity (η_o) were varied so that the tube's Re ranged from 10^{-3} to 10^{-1}. At low shear stresses ($\ll$1 dyn/cm^2), the normal RBCs behave like RBCs hardened in glutaraldehyde: they rotate with periodically varying angular velocities in close accord with the theory developed for rigid oblate spheroids by Jeffrey (103). When the shear stress is elevated above 1 dyn/cm^2 by increasing η_o with dextran, normal RBCs are aligned at a constant angle to the direction of flow, and the cell membrane rotates about the interior (67, 90), in a manner analogous to suspended fluid drops.

Direct observations of the microcirculation in vivo and in various devices in vitro show that RBCs at normal Hcts are regularly and extensively deformed at shear rates found in the microcirculation. [In vivo photographs of deformations of RBCs can be found in Brånemark's book (18).] Deformation of RBCs in concentrated suspensions in tubes with diameters of ~100 μm was observed by placing a few tracer cells in a suspension of ghost cells (89, 91). In contrast to the regular rotation of cells in a dilute suspension (90), normal RBCs in ghost cell suspensions with concentrations >20% rotate erratically as they interact with neighboring ghost cells. Deformation of RBCs becomes increasingly pronounced as the ghost cell concentration rises above 30%. At high shear rates (>100 s^{-1}) the deformed RBCs are elongated and aligned in the direction of flow while the membrane undergoes rotational motion.

In narrow capillaries RBCs tend to flow edgewise, and the pressure gradient in the capillaries squeezes the rear of the cell flat so that the hemoglobin bulges in the forward part of the cell (5, 159). In addition the cell may become asymmetric and shift toward the wall, resulting in a typical slipper shape (Fig. 11), and may exhibit a slow membrane rotation (73). Measurements of the deformation of RBCs in narrow glass capillaries were reported by Hochmuth et al. (101) and Sutera (169). As the velocity increases, the blood cells are increasingly deformed, resulting in a lower apparent viscosity.

Theoretical computations of RBC deformations are available only for capillary flow, assuming that the RBCs are initially at right angles to the axis of the tube and remain axisymmetric during flow. With the finite element method, the shape of the RBC during flow can be computed with the resting cell geometry and the rheological properties of the cell membrane (shear modulus and bending stiffness; see ERYTHROCYTES, p. 220). This leads to the so-called parachute shape illustrated in Figure 12 (162). A two-dimensional model (154) shows the occurrence of membrane rotation. The theoretical problem of computing the fluid motion of a bulk suspension with Hct on the order of 30% or 40% has not been solved in detail, even for rigid spheres, because of the complexity of the motion.

Cell Aggregation

Normal RBCs rapidly form rouleaux in the microcirculation if brought to a standstill (18). At very low velocities a rouleau may move as a rigid body down a microvessel.

Rouleau formation can be observed in vitro in small-diameter glass capillaries (90). Rouleaux of RBCs in plasma tumble end-over-end at low Hcts and low shear

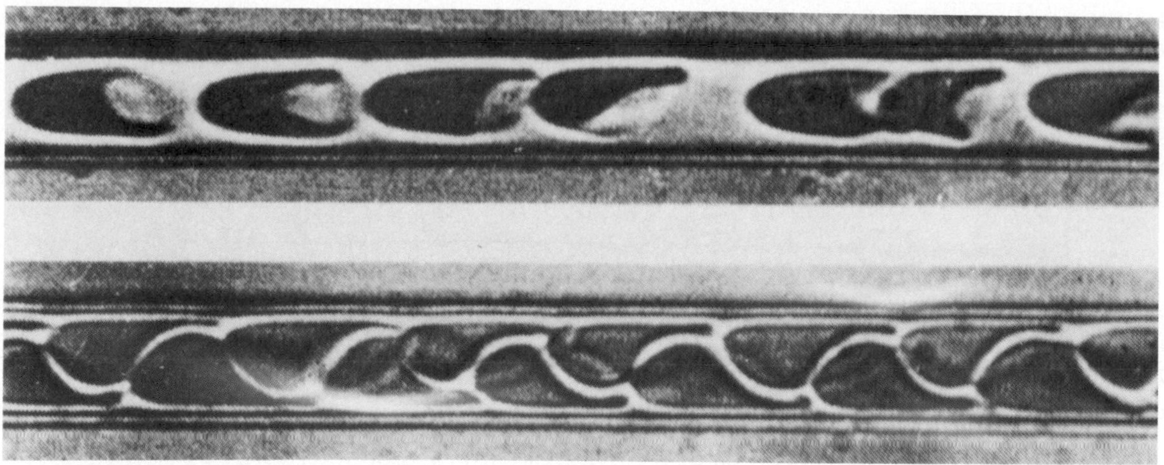

FIG. 11. Photomicrographs of RBCs in narrow tubes showing single-file (*top*) and two-file flow (*bottom*). [From Gaehtgens et al. (75).]

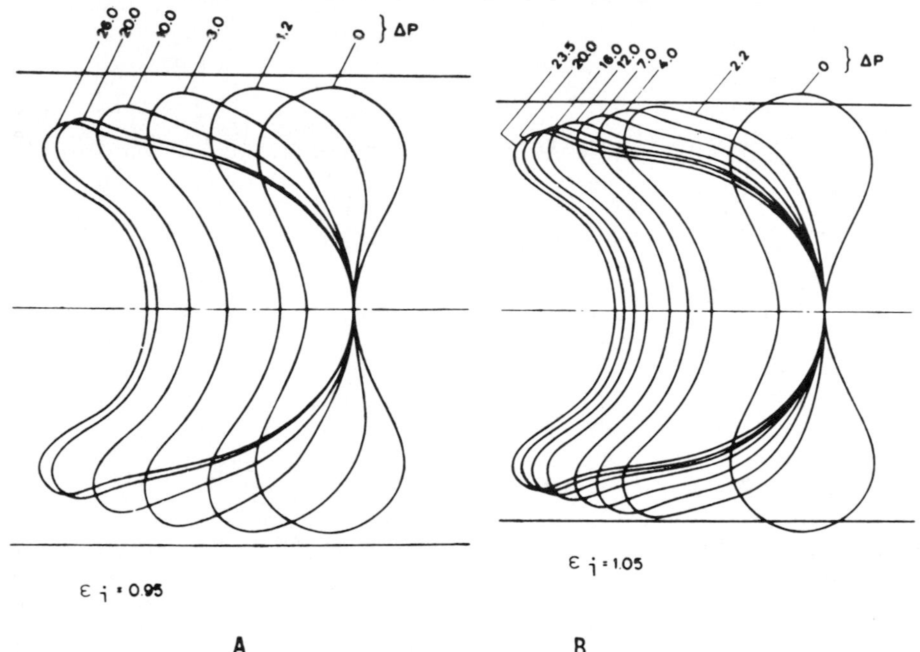

FIG. 12. Computed shapes of RBCs flowing axisymmetrically in capillary tube. (Unstressed shape of cells is shown in Fig. 6.) Pressure drop (ΔP in dyn/cm^2) shown is that over distance equal to spacing between cells. *A*: initial diameter ratio $\epsilon_i = 0.95$. *B*: $\epsilon_i = 1.05$. [From Skalak and Chien (161).]

rates. The rouleaux alternately undergo extension and compression during each rotation (90).

Interactions of Cells With Tube Walls

The interaction of RBCs with a vessel wall leads to radial migration; the exclusion of the cells by the wall leaves a zone at the wall with a lower cell concentration than that in the bulk suspension. The RBCs do not normally adhere to vessel walls, and their interaction is generally limited to radial migration. The WBCs may roll along the vessel wall, adhere to it, or even actively move along the wall against the flow (M. Wiedeman, personal communication), if there is local damage or if chemotactic agents are present. Another interesting aspect of blood rheology involving the vessel wall is the manner in which WBCs are brought in contact with the endothelium in the venular system. Microscopic observations show that WBCs adhere more regularly and in larger numbers in venules than in arterioles. Schmid-Schönbein et al. (148) have demonstrated that RBCs tend to overtake WBCs on leaving capillaries and entering venules and that, on passing the WBCs, the RBCs force the WBCs toward the vessel wall. A similar effect, described by Bagge and Karlsson (6), is that a WBC leaving a capillary and entering a venule at right angles is swept by the mainstream in the venule so that it tends to be pressed against the wall downstream of the capillary. When the flow rate is slow and RBC aggregation occurs, the WBCs are displaced toward the vessel wall by the rouleaux, thus reducing the WBC concentration in the central region. This is another mechanism by which WBCs are marginated. As a result of these mechanisms, WBCs frequently interact with the endothelial wall, possibly forming temporary bonds. The interaction of WBCs with the vessel wall can be an important mechanism in abnormally high resistance to blood flow in inflammation, shock, and other low-flow states (4, 121).

MACRORHEOLOGY OF RED CELL SUSPENSIONS IN NARROW TUBES

The Hct in most normal subjects is ~40%–45%. In comparison WBCs and platelets together occupy only ~0.5% of the volume concentration of blood. Therefore we first discuss the behavior of RBC suspensions in small tubes.

Experimental Studies

The classic work of Fåhraeus (64, 65) demonstrated changes in the flow behavior and the cell concentration of blood in tubes with $d < \sim 300\ \mu m$. The Fåhraeus-Lindqvist effect refers to the decrease in apparent viscosity of blood in these narrow tubes (65). The Fåhraeus effect indicates that the Hct in the capillary tube [tube Hct or dynamic Hct (H_T)] is lower than the discharge Hct (H_D) of the blood exiting from the tube (63, 64). The Fåhraeus effect ($H_T < H_D$) should be distinguished from the possibility that H_D may be lower than the Hct in the feed reservoir (H_F). Two mechanisms may lead to $H_D < H_F$. First, when the RBC size is close to the tube diameter, some of the RBCs may be screened out by the flow pattern at the tube entrance (steric hindrance). Second, H_D may also be less than H_F because of the cell-free layer at the wall of the feeding vessel, a phenomenon Krogh (112) termed "plasma skimming." The locations of H_F, H_T, and H_D are indicated in Figure 13.

Fåhraeus (63) based the reduction of H_T below H_D for narrow tubes on the difference between the mean velocities of RBCs and the suspending fluid. This difference is due to the nonuniform distribution of cells across the tube's lumen. The RBCs tend to travel near the center of the tube, where the velocity is higher than in the tube periphery. Consideration of the conservation of mass shows that, in a steady state, H_T must be lower than H_D when such concentration and velocity profiles exist.

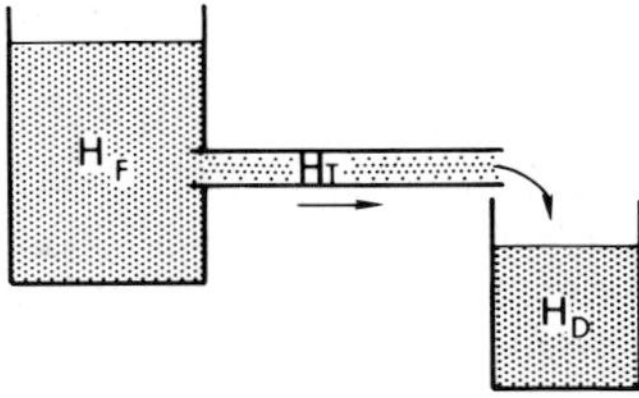

FIG. 13. Diagram showing locations of feed hematocrit (H_F), tube hematocrit (H_T), and discharge hematocrit (H_d) measurements. [From Skalak and Chien (161).]

FLOW IN TUBES >29 μM IN DIAMETER. Barbee and Cokelet (8, 9) investigated the quantitative relationship between the Fåhraeus and Fåhraeus-Lindqvist effects using glass capillary tubes with diameters varying from 29 to 221 μm. Determining the Hct values by centrifugation, they found that $H_D = H_F$ for these tubes and that the ratio H_T/H_D decreases monotonically with decreasing tube diameter (8). These latter data can be fitted with the equation

$$H_T/H_D = 0.218 \ln d - 0.130 \qquad (16)$$

where d is in micrometers. Equation 16 applies for $29 < d < 300\ \mu m$.

In tubes with $d < 100\ \mu m$, H_T/H_D at a given d tends to decrease with decreasing H_F. Barbee and Cokelet (8) found that the relationship of H_T/H_D versus d was independent of flow rate and of changes in suspending medium from plasma to isotonic saline. Gaehtgens et al. (74), however, reported that a reduction in flow velocity increased H_T/H_D.

From their pressure-flow data Barbee and Cokelet (8) plotted wall shear stress (σ_w) against the ratio $\bar{U}$ of blood bulk velocity to the tube diameter. Since $\bar{U} = \bar{V}/2r$ and the apparent wall shear rate $\dot{\gamma}_{aw} = 4\bar{V}/rr$, $\bar{U}$ is equal to $\dot{\gamma}_{aw}/8$. One such plot is shown in Figure 14.

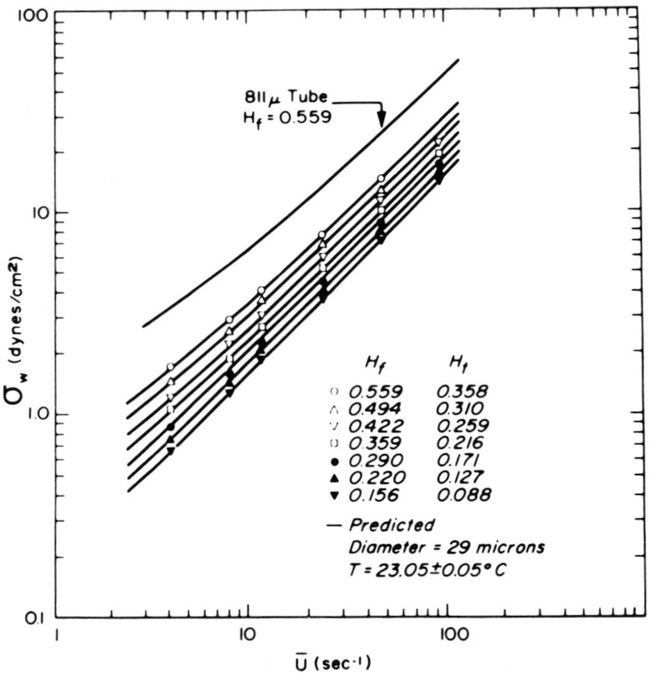

FIG. 14. Flow behavior of blood in 29-μm-diam tube. Symbols are actual flow data, recorded as σ_w, a shear stress, and $\bar{U}$, mean bulk velocity divided by tube diameter. *Solid curves* through *points* represent behavior of blood predicted from data obtained in 811-μm-diameter tube when average H_T is equal to that experimentally found in 29-μm tube. In 811-μm tube, $H_F = H_T$. [From Barbee and Cokelet (9).]

The point symbols represent data obtained for different H_F values, which are given together with the corresponding H_T values in each experiment (*inset*). Values of σ_w and $\bar{U}$ were also determined in a tube with $d = 811$ μm, which is sufficiently large that H_T, H_F, and H_D are all equal. The topmost curve represents the data for the 811-μm tube with $H_F = H_T = 0.559$, and a comparison of this curve with the open circles ($d = 29$ μm, $H_F = 0.559$, and $H_T = 0.358$) illustrates the viscosity reduction at the same H_F (Fåhraeus-Lindqvist effect). This comparison, however, was made at unequal H_T. Experiments were done with the 811-μm tube to obtain $\sigma_w - \bar{U}$ curves at various H_F values that match the H_T values observed in the experiments with the 29-μm tubes. The second solid curve from the top shows the relationship obtained in the 811-μm tube with $H_F = H_T = 0.358$. This curve fits the data obtained in the 29-μm tube at the same H_T of 0.358. Similarly the successive $\sigma_w - \bar{U}$ curves for the 811-μm tube agree with the data obtained for the 29-μm tube when the H_T values are matched (Fig. 14). These results indicate that the $\sigma_w - \bar{U}$ relationship of blood in narrow tubes can be predicted from their macrorheological properties determined in large tubes, provided that the proper H_T value is used (9). Cokelet (47) similarly analyzed data in the literature (e.g., 10, 12, 17, 64, 65, 99, 113) and found that the results support this conclusion. Therefore in tubes with $d =$ 29–300 μm the Fåhraeus-Lindqvist effect shows the same trend as the Fåhraeus effect.

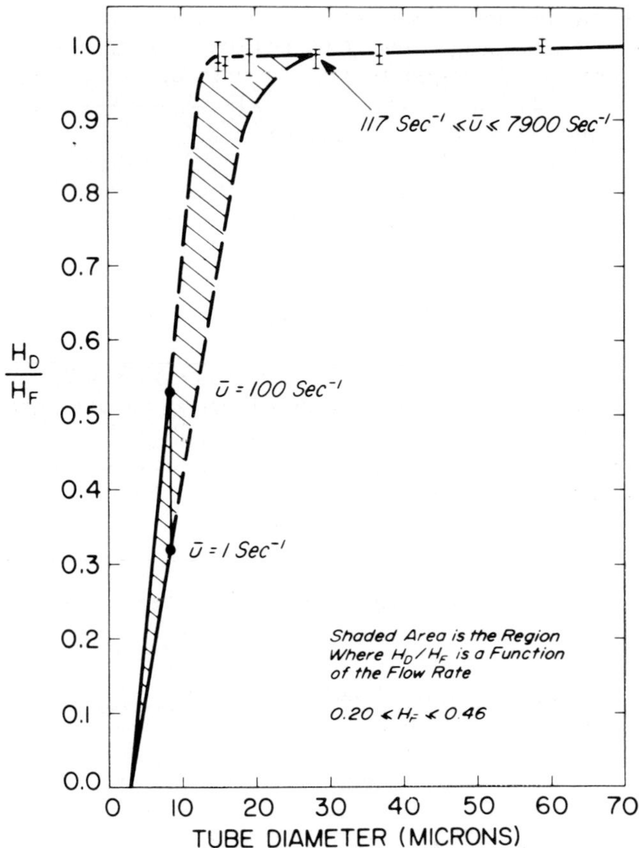

FIG. 15. Variation of H_D/H_F with tube diameter and velocity. $\bar{U}$ values (1 and 100 s^{-1}) noted for 8.1-μm tube are ratios of mean RBC velocities to tube diameter; $\bar{U}$ values for larger tubes are ratios of mean blood velocities to tube diameter. *Crossbars* indicate range and mean values of all data obtained with given tube size. [From Cokelet (47).]

FLOW IN TUBES <29 μM IN DIAMETER. When glass tubes with $d < 29$ μm are used, screening of RBCs at the tube entrance begin, as evidenced by the decrease in H_D/H_F (47). This effect is flow dependent; at high flow rates the deformation of the cells (44, 87) facilitates their entrance into the narrow tube and lessens the decrease of H_D/H_F. As shown in Figure 15, for $d = 8.1$ μm, $H_D/H_F = 0.32$ at a $\bar{U}$ value of 1.0 s^{-1}; it rises to 0.53 when $\bar{U}$ is increased to 100 s^{-1}. The magnitude of plasma skimming and/or cell screening is affected by the detailed geometric features and microscopic flow conditions at the entrance of the tube. Therefore results obtained from different experimental setups, even when compared under the same macroscopic flow conditions, may give different quantitative relationships between H_D/H_F and $\bar{U}$. Gaehtgens and Papenfuss (77) studied the influence of the location of the origin of capillary tubes ($d = 6.3$ μm) in the flow stream of a cylindrical feed channel ($d = 1.5$ mm) on H_D/H_F by comparing capillary tubes with their origin either at the wall or in the center stream of the feed channel (Fig. 16). Measurements of H_D/H_F were made over a wide range of capillary flow rates (tube flow Q_T from 0 to 10^{-4} mm^3/s) both at a constant perfusion flow through the feed channel ($Q_F = 30$ mm^3/s) and with this perfusion flow abruptly stopped ($Q_F = 0$). For $Q_F = 0$, H_D/H_F was slightly lower in the wall-origin capillary tubes (~0.74) than in the center-origin tubes (~0.88), and these H_D/H_F values were independent of variations in Q_T. At a constant Q_F of 30 mm^3/s, $H_D/H_F = 0$ or $\doteq 0$ at low Q_T in both cases, reflecting plasma skimming and/or cell screening at the capillary orifice; when Q_T is raised, H_D/H_F in the center-origin capillary tubes rises sharply and approaches the value of 0.88, but H_D/H_F in the wall-origin tubes increases only to ~0.3. These results suggest the presence of a peripheral cell-poor layer in the feed channel.

The Hct in very narrow tubes has not been determined by centrifugation; microphotography (1, 47) and photoelectric signal recording (1) have been used instead. With these techniques the average number of cells per unit tube length (n/l) is counted, and the average H_T is calculated from n/l, d, and the mean corpuscular volume of the RBCs. Photoelectric signal counting of RBCs can be applied only to tubes with single-file flow. When multifile flow occurs, microphotographic counting may present a problem because some cells are hidden from view by their neighbors (47). In tubes with $d <$ ~6 μm, RBCs travel through the tube in single file, but multifile flow may occur in

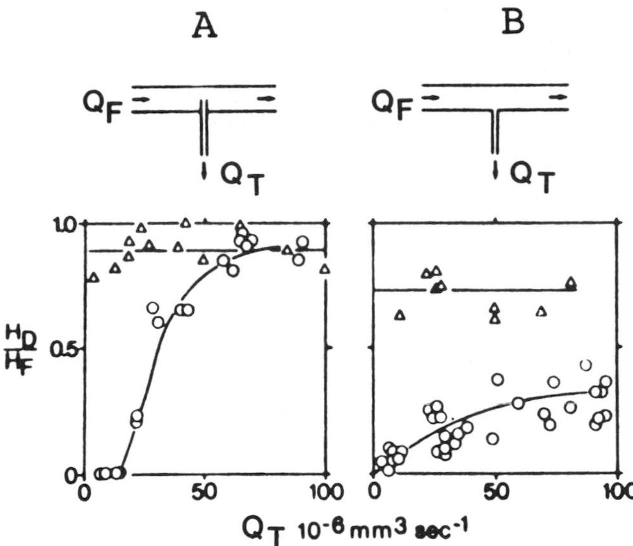

FIG. 16. Plasma skimming in 6.3-μm capillary tube with origins in center stream (*A*) and at wall (*B*) of the feed channel. Q_F and Q_T, volumetric flow in feed reservoir and tube, respectively. △, Q_F = 0; ○, Q_F = 30 mm^3/s. [From Gaehtgens and Papenfuss (77).]

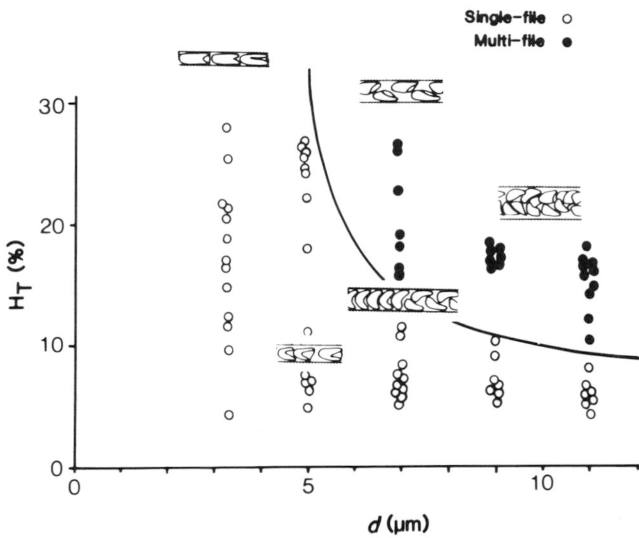

FIG. 17. H_T as function of tube diameter (*d*). *Insets* show 2 types of flow. Note transition from single-file flow at low H_T to multifile flow at high H_T for d = 7 μm. *Curved line* is drawn to show $H_T - d$ conditions for separation of single-file and multifile flows. Single-file flow occurs at small *d* and/or H_T values. [Adapted from Gaehtgens et al. (75).]

larger tubes (75). The transition from single-file to multifile flow pattern is favored by an increase in H_T as well as an increase in tube diameter (Fig. 17); e.g., in a 7-μm tube, single-file flow is observed when H_T < 0.15, but multifile flow occurs with H_T > 0.15 (75). These factors make accurate determinations of H_T difficult in tubes with d = 7–30 μm, especially when the Hct is high.

In the experiments by Cokelet (47) on tubes with d = 8.1–23.0 μm, H_T was determined by microphotography and H_D was determined by the centrifugation of collected outflow samples of blood. The decrease of H_T/H_D with reductions in tube diameter continues down to d = 10–20 μm, beyond which further reductions in tube diameter lead to a reverse in trend, i.e., H_T/H_D increases toward one. The tube diameter at which H_T/H_D is minimum varies inversely with the flow rate. Cokelet (47) suggests that this trend reversal of Fåhraeus effect occurs when multifile flow is changed into single-file flow. In single-file flow a decrease in tube diameter would increase the proportion of tube cross section occupied by the cell (32, 101) and reduce the difference between the cell velocity and the suspending medium velocity. For undeformed RBC $d_{cell} \doteq 8$ μm, and the minimum value an RBC can attain when deformed into a cylinder with hemispherical caps is d_{cell} = 2.7 μm (93, 114, 137). At slow flow rates that do not cause significant RBC deformation (e.g., $\bar{U}$ = 1 s^{-1}), H_T/H_D approaches unity as the diameter is reduced to 8 μm or less. For d = 2.7 μm, H_T/H_D approaches unity at all flow rates (33, 47). The ratio H_T/H_F increases with H_F in 8.1-μm tubes (47); when these data are converted by use of the corresponding H_D/H_F values, H_T/H_D also increases with H_D.

Albrecht et al. (1) determined H_T by microphotography and/or photoelectric signal recordings and computed H_D by the equation (cf. Eq. 18b)

$$H_D = \left[1 + \left(\frac{1}{H_T} - 1\right)\frac{\bar{V}_R}{\bar{V}_{cell}}\right]^{-1} \tag{17}$$

where $\bar{V}_{cell}$ is the mean cell velocity and $\bar{V}_R$ is the mean velocity of the suspending medium (buffered Ringer's solution) made visible with dye injection; both $\bar{V}_{cell}$ and $\bar{V}_R$ were determined by dual-slit photometry. Albrecht et al. (1) demonstrated the trend reversal of Fåhraeus effect in capillary tubes with d = 3.3–11.0 μm. At H_F = 0.35, the mean value of H_T/H_D increases from 0.67 in the 11.0-μm tube to 0.94 in the 3.3-μm tube. Gaehtgens (73) summarized the variations in H_T/H_D with tube diameter as determined by different investigators (3, 8, 47, 64, 74, 100) and concluded that the minimum H_T/H_D occurs at $d \doteq$ 15–20 μm (Fig. 18).

Albrecht et al. (1) found no significant effects of flow rate on H_T/H_D in tubes with d = 4.4 and 6.0 μm. This may be explained by the fact that the narrow tubes (4.4 μm) and the relatively high flow rates used in these studies are sufficient to cause a nearly maximum cell deformation.

In the study of Albrecht et al. (1), H_T/H_D is independent of H_D in tubes with d = 3.3, 4.4, and 6.0 μm, but it increases with H_D in tubes with d = 9.5 and 11.0 μm. The increase of H_T/H_D with H_D found in these 9.5- and 11.0-μm tubes by Albrecht et al. (1) and in 8.1-μm tubes by Cokelet (47) may be explained by the Hct-dependent transition from single-file to multifile flow (see Fig. 17). The change to multifile flow leads to a reduction in cell velocity, because the cells are closer to the wall, and hence to an increase in H_T/H_D. The Fåhraeus effect depends on both the velocity profile and the radial distribution of RBCs across the tube. The lack of a demonstrable effect of H_D on H_T/H_D in either larger tubes ($d > 100$ μm) or very small tubes ($d < 7$ μm) indicates that the matching of the velocity profile and radial distribution of the cells across tubes in which $d < 7$ μm or > 100 μm is not affected significantly by Hct changes in these cases.

Gaehtgens et al. (75) found the velocity profile of RBCs in 12-μm capillary tubes to be nearly parabolic when averaged over a time period of 1 s, although the velocity distribution can vary considerably on a shorter time scale due to interactions between cells. In narrow tubes ($d < 10$ μm) direct microphotographic studies (47, 101) have shown that the RBCs travel preferentially in the tube center and that the peripheral fluid sleeve (wall layer) widens as flow rate increases. For 8.1-μm tubes the wall layer thickness increases from ~0.1 to 0.4 μm as $\bar{U}$ is raised from 3 to 100 s^{-1} (47). Albrecht et al. (1) have computed the wall layer thickness from their H_T and velocity data obtained in tubes with $d = 3.3$–11.0 μm by the use of a two-phase model (76). In this model a central core containing all cells and some interspersed fluid is surrounded by a peripheral fluid sheath with a mean velocity one-half that in the core. The calculated values of the wall layer thickness, which vary directly with d, are in excellent agreement with the direct microphotographic measurements obtained by Hochmuth et al. (101) and Cokelet (47).

Determinations of pressure-flow relationships in an 8.1-μm capillary tube indicate that the apparent viscosity of the blood at high shear rates can be predicted from its macrorheological properties at the same H_T (47). Gaehtgens (72) has shown that the relative apparent viscosity (η_r) of human RBC suspensions continues to decrease with reducing tube diameter (Fåhraeus-Lindqvist effect) until $d \doteq 5$–7 μm. Further decreases in diameter then lead to an increase in η_r (Fig. 18). This trend reversal of the Fåhraeus-Lindqvist effect has been previously demonstrated in studies on flow of RBCs and model cells through various types of narrow channels (54, 84, 85, 93, 118, 188). The trend reversal of the Fåhraeus-Lindqvist effect occurs at a smaller tube diameter (5–7 μm) than that of the Fåhraeus effect (15–20 μm), which indicates that in the range of $d = 5$–20 μm, H_T is not the only determinant of η_r. With the use of cell membrane markers, Gaehtgens (73) has observed the rotation of RBC membrane in narrow tubes and also counterrotation of neighboring cells in two-file flow. The hemodynamic implications of these microscopic motions require further investigations.

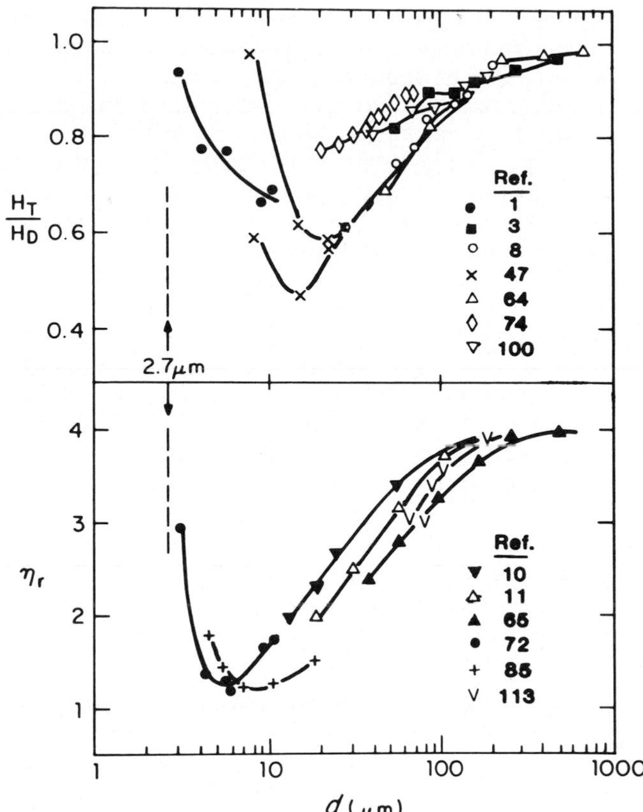

FIG. 18. Magnitude of Fåhraeus effect (*A*) and Fåhraeus-Lindqvist effect (*B*) in capillary tubes of various diameters. [Adapted from Gaehtgens (72, 73).]

Theoretical Considerations

Many experimental results may be understood on the basis of theoretical solutions of idealized cases. The number of directly pertinent theoretical solutions, however, is limited.

CELL SCREENING AND PLASMA SKIMMING. The decrease in H_D/H_F found experimentally in glass tubes <29 μm may be understood in terms of the detailed flow patterns in the entrance region of a glass capillary. No exact solution for a suspension of moderate Hct is available for this entrance region. However, the nature of the effect can be qualitatively understood in terms of streamlines and drag effects. When there is bulk flow past the entrance of the capillary, a disproportionate amount of flow entering the capillary may come from the cell-free layer near the wall of the reservoir. As a result it is expected that the flow into the capillary is also deficient in cells, leading to the decrease in H_D/H_F. This is the mechanism of plasma skimming first described by Krogh (112) and studied by others (e.g., 130, 132). An approximate theory (134) and experimental data obtained with glass capillaries (77) show that the H_D/H_F ratios in small side branches depend on flow.

Even when there is no bulk flow past the entrance of the capillary, cells near the boundary of the entrance to the capillary may be retarded by the presence of the boundary to a greater degree than the surrounding, suspending fluid flow. Although this effect may be appreciable only quite close to the boundary, if the tube is comparable in size to the particle, the domain influenced can be significant.

In the absence of particles, streamlines entering a capillary may resemble those of fluid entering an orifice (98). Dagan et al. (53) recently presented an exact solution for fluid entering a pore with finite length. When particles are present with a diameter comparable to that of the capillary, it is expected that the finite-sized particle does not exactly follow the streamlines of the suspending fluids, which may be considered to be composed of paticles with zero diameter. Dagan et al. (52) showed that a rigid sphere in a viscous flow at low Re may approach a pore and cross the streamlines of the suspending fluid, thus leading to the possibility of a screening effect. Exact solutions for situations in which more than one particle is present have not yet been obtained. The fact that RBC screening decreases at high velocities is due to cell deformability. That is, RBCs behave like smaller particles at high shear rates, whereas at low shear rates their elasticity tends to maintain their resting shape.

RELATIVE VELOCITY OF CELLS AND SUSPENDING MEDIUM. The Fåhraeus effect results from cells moving faster than the suspending medium. Consider any species of cells (or other suspended particles) with volumetric concentration C_T in a tube with a steady flow. The cell concentration in the discharge C_D is equal to the ratio of the cell flux to the total suspension flux through the tube (101)

$$C_D = \frac{C_T \bar{V}_{cell}}{\bar{V}} \tag{18}$$

The mean velocity of the suspension (or bulk velocity) can be calculated from $\bar{V}_{Cell}$, C_T, and $\bar{V}_R$, the mean velocity of the suspending medium

$$\bar{V} = C_T \bar{V}_{cell} + (1 - C_T)\, \bar{V}_R \tag{18a}$$

From Equations 18 and 18a it follows that

$$C_D = \left[1 + \left(\frac{1}{C_T} - 1\right) \frac{\bar{V}_R}{\bar{V}_{cell}}\right]^{-1} \tag{18b}$$

Equation 17 is Equation 18b written with H_D and H_T for RBCs in place of C_D and C_T, respectively.

A number of theoretical models of axisymmetric particles flowing in capillary tubes have been analyzed by exact and approximate methods. All these results show that for a solid particle located on the axis of the capillary, the particle velocity is always greater than the velocity of the suspending fluid. In addition the ratio of the two velocities depends primarily on the diameter ratio ϵ (ϵ = maximum particle diam/capillary diam). The simplest model is the so-called stacked-coins model dicussed by Whitmore (186), which consists of a train of circular disks stacked in the capillary to form a continuous concentric cylinder. The axial train of particles moves at constant velocity $\bar{V}_{cell}$; $\bar{V}_{cell}/\bar{V}$ of the suspension is given by

$$\frac{\bar{V}_{cell}}{\bar{V}} = \frac{2}{1 + \epsilon^2} \tag{19}$$

More exact analyses of axisymmetric disks were given by Bloor (15) and by Lew and Fung (115). Models consisting of spheres were analyzed by Wang and Skalak (183), and a train of spheroids was analyzed by Chen and Skalak (30). In all these solutions the approximate ratio of particle velocity to the mean velocity of flow is given by Equation 19. The limiting values given by Equation 19 are always valid: $\bar{V}_{cell}/\bar{V}$ attains a maximum value of 2 when ϵ approaches 0, and $\bar{V}_{cell} = \bar{V}$ when $\epsilon = 1$.

Some solutions have been given for rigid spheres located off the axis of the tube. For very small spheres the velocities of the particle and of the fluid at the same radial position in the capillary are equal. For large particles the presence of the boundary generally retards a particle near the wall (24). Particles that are not axisymmetrically located usually rotate or tumble (175).

Some solutions have been developed for flexible RBCs that are assumed to remain axisymmetric during flow through a narrow tube (154). In its deformed state, a flexible particle moving steadily in an axisymmetric form, with a deformed cell-to-tube diameter ratio of ϵ, behaves like a rigid particle with the same diameter ratio.

No theoretical three-dimensional solutions have been developed for RBCs that are not axisymmetrically located. It is expected that membrane rotation should occur as a result of the asymmetry of shear stresses. A two-dimensional model demonstrates this membrane rotation for an asymmetric cell in a narrow channel (154). Flexible particles sufficiently close to a wall in larger tubes travel at lower velocity than the average velocity of the suspension. As discussed previously (see *Cell Concentration and Cell Migration*, p. 225), cell migration away from the wall generally mitigates such wall retardation for RBCs and moves them to the faster streams nearer the tube's center, resulting in the Fåhraeus effect.

PRESSURE-FLOW RELATIONS. Most theoretical solutions for the flow of axisymmetric particles in uniform circular capillaries include a computation of the mean pressure gradient. The simplest method is the stacked-coins model (186) in which the apparent viscosity is given by

$$\eta_a = \eta_o \frac{1}{1 - \epsilon^4} \tag{20}$$

where η_o is the viscosity of the suspending fluid and η_a is the apparent viscosity for the continuous axial train of coins with a diameter ratio of ϵ. This expression forms an upper limit for the flow of any train of rigid or flexible particles of the same maximum diameter ratio. For any spaced train of particles, the pressure gradient between the particles is approximately that of Poiseuille flow, reducing the average pressure gradient over a long segment of capillary containing many particles. Solutions for rigid particles of the shape of RBCs were given by Skalak et al. (160). Figure 19 shows the relative apparent viscosity ($\eta_r = \eta_a/\eta_o$) computed as a function of Hct for several different diameter ratios and for cells either spaced singly or in rouleaux. One interesting aspect of these curves is that for closely fitting particles ($\epsilon \geq 0.95$) the relative apparent viscosity increases approximately linearly with Hct. This is because the fluid layer between the cell and the wall is the region of the major dissipation, and adding cells increases this effect. On the other hand, for cells with a diameter ratio of $\epsilon \sim 0.8$, there is an Hct range from ~30%–50% where the relative apparent viscosity does not change very much. This is because the added cells simply replace fluid that was trapped between adjacent cells and moving essentially as a rigid body. The curves shown in Figure 19 are also applicable to flexible cells at the same Hct, provided that the deformed diameter ratio is used as the effective diameter ratio. Thus the influence of detailed cell shape is minor, and the critical parameter is the thickness of the peripheral fluid layer between the cell and the wall. As the velocity increases, the flexible particles are increasingly deformed and the peripheral layer becomes thicker.

The results of some computations for flexible RBCs located axisymmetrically in a capillary tube are shown in Figure 20. These were computed with the resting geometry and material properties of the RBC discussed previously (see ERYTHROCYTES, p. 220). The various curves shown may be interpreted as resulting from variations in particle velocity, viscosity of the suspending fluid, and/or stiffness of the cell. The deformation parameter A* is given by

$$A^* = \eta_o \overline{V}_{cell}/\mu_m \qquad (21)$$

where μ_m is the shear elastic modulus (in dyn/cm) of the RBC membrane. The curve labeled A* = 0 corresponds to rigid cells or deformable cells moving at very low velocity. As the diameter ratio given on the abscissa in Figure 20 increases toward 1.0, the boundary of the cell approaches the wall of the capillary and the apparent viscosity rises toward infinity. Flexible cells may have an initial diameter ratio of >1.0, and thus they must be deformed in order to enter the capillary. The apparent viscosity is rather low for flexible particles flowing rapidly and comparatively high for stiff particles flowing slowly. The RBCs would have a fairly large value of the parameter A* at typical capillary velocities, so that theoretical computation

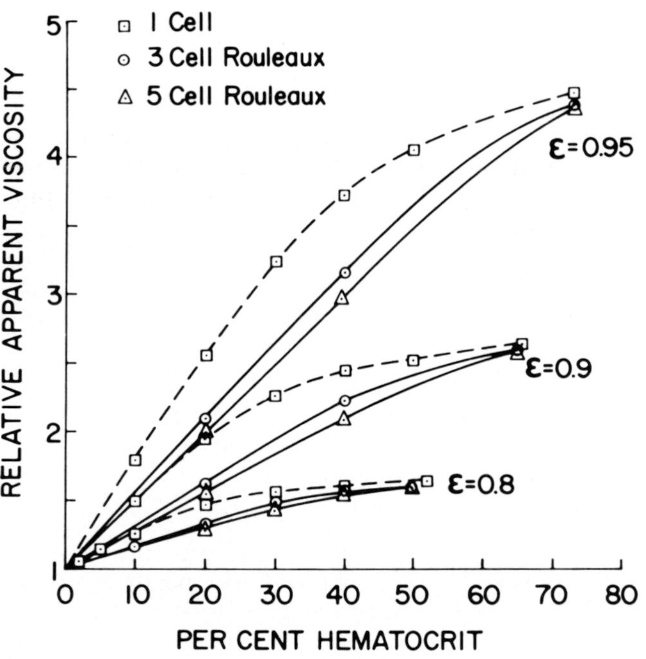

FIG. 19. Relative apparent viscosity for train of equally spaced rigid RBCs in capillary tube (*dashed curves*) and for rouleaux of 3 and 5 cells (*solid curves*) as a function of Hct (abscissa) and diameter ratio ϵ. [From Skalak, Chen, and Chien (160).]

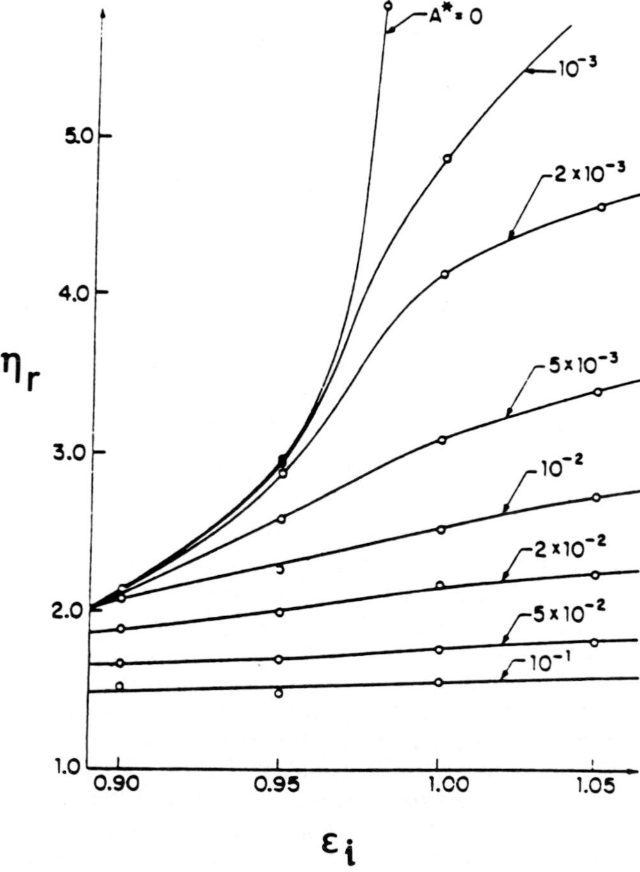

FIG. 20. Relative apparent viscosity (η_r) computed from line of RBCs at 26% Hct as a function of initial diameter ratio, ϵ_i, and the deformation parameter A*. [From Skalak and Tözeren (162).]

would predict a relative apparent viscosity in the range of 1.5–2.0 under normal conditions. The examples shown in Figure 20 have initial, undeformed diameter ratios (ϵ_i) in the vicinity of 1.0 and correspond to capillary diameters of ~8 μm. For larger capillary diameters the theory would predict that the relative apparent viscosity would be of the order of 1.5 or less. As indicated previously (see FLOW IN TUBES <29 μM IN DIAMETER, p. 229) the model of axisymmetric particles is probably not valid at these larger tube diameters because the cells form multifile flow and are not centered in the capillary. For smaller capillaries of the order of 3–6 μm, results similar to those shown in Figure 20 should be expected; these diameters correspond to an extension of the curves up to an initial diameter ratio >2. Theoretical computations have not been made in this range. Most likely the relative apparent viscosity at typical capillary conditions is still ~2.0 in these cases.

SEMIEMPIRICAL THEORIES. A number of theoretical approaches have been suggested in which blood is represented by a continuum fluid with properties defined by a semiempirical equation and with equations of motion integrated to derive the velocity profiles and pressure-flow relations. Such theories may be divided into two groups depending on the type of fluid used to represent the blood. *1*) For nonlinear fluids the shear stress is assumed to be some nonlinear function of the shear rate and Hct. *2*) In micropolar theories, in addition to the usual velocity vector at each point, a microrotation vector is introduced that is related to the angular velocity of the particle in suspension. These theories can be subdivided further depending on whether or not a peripheral fluid layer with flow properties different from those in the core is introduced.

An example of a model with a nonlinear fluid used to represent the blood is given by Oka (128, 129) and summarized by Fung (71). The assumed constitutive equation is the Casson equation (26) given by

$$\sqrt{\sigma} = \sqrt{\eta_C}\,\sqrt{\dot{\gamma}} + \sqrt{\sigma_y} \tag{22}$$

in which η_C is the Casson coefficient of viscosity and σ_y is a yield stress. According to this model $\dot{\gamma} = 0$ if $\sigma < \sigma_y$. The use of the Casson equation gives a flat velocity profile with some core radius r_{cr}, the magnitude of which depends on the flow conditions and σ_y. The discharge is a nonlinear function of the pressure drop, which may be approximated by an equation similar in form to that of a Bingham plastic. In applying this theory the Fåhraeus-Lindqvist effect can be incorporated by the choice of the parameters η_C and σ_y with appropriate dependence on the Hct.

The micropolar fluid theory is attractive because it allows the computation of particle rotation in addition to fluid velocity at each point, thus giving a more complete description of the blood flow. The applicability of the micropolar or other microstructure theories has not been conclusively demonstrated, however, either from first principles or experimentally. Moreover the boundary conditions that should be used are not entirely clear. Eringen (56), Ariman et al. (2), and Cowin (51) have written reviews of microstructure theories. Cowin (50), Popel et al. (136), Kang and Eringen (105), and Chaturani and Upadhya (27–29) have discussed applications to blood flow. Tözeren and Skalak (174) have discussed the difficulty of fitting boundary conditions at the wall.

The use of a thin cell-free layer at the wall of the vessel allows a certain degree of freedom in fitting velocity profiles. It is also realistic because the peripheral cell-free layer is known to exist experimentally. At present there is no theoretical way to derive the thickness of the peripheral fluid layer. The experimental data of Barbee and Cokelet (9) described previously (see *Experimental Studies*, p. 228) showed that the apparent viscosity obtained in large tubes is applicable to smaller vessels, provided that H_T is appropriately taken into account. This implies that the influence of the peripheral fluid layer on the resultant pressure-flow relation in capillary tubes with diameters as small as 29 μm is balanced by the influence of a slightly raised Hct in the core.

In the theories just discussed, blood is assumed to be a homogeneous fluid of two zones at most, i.e., the core and the peripheral fluid layer. In principle a single theory should be possible where the distribution of the concentration of cells across the tube is a fundamental variable computed by theory. Kang and Eringen (105), Popel et al. (136), and Quemada (138–140) have composed models of this type. In these theories some laws governing the particle concentration and the other flow variables are assumed. At present such laws must be regarded as semiempirical and not yet derived from the basic properties of the blood cells and plasma.

NONAXISYMMETRIC FLOW. Happel and Brenner (98), Bungay and Brenner (23), and Tözeren (175) have given some solutions for single particles located off the center in a cylindrical tube. These solutions, which are primarily for rigid spheres, show that nonaxisymmetric particles rotate in general as well as translate in the axial direction. This rotation may be regarded as a phenomenon similar to the membrane rotation of RBCs in capillaries (73). The results of the theory with respect to pressure distribution are limited but show that the pressure drop is not affected (at least to 1st order) by small variations in eccentricities of the particle center from the axis of the tube. This may be understood on a qualitative basis. At the side of the particle closest to the tube wall, the particle rotation tends to decrease the velocity gradient, whereas on the opposite side, where the fluid layer is wider, the rotation tends to increase the velocity gradient. As a result the mean rate of dissipation is not significantly affected. A reduction in pressure drop may result if the particle is asymmetric because the higher velocity gradient acts only on the shorter length (154).

EFFECTS OF ALTERATIONS OF BLOOD CELL PROPERTIES ON TUBE FLOW

Red Cell Deformability

Although the normal human RBC has a major diameter of ~8 μm, its ability to deform allows it to traverse tubes with diameters as small as ~2.7 μm (see ERYTHROCYTES, p. 220). The RBC deformability affects the cell distribution and apparent viscosity in tube flow (see *Cell Deformation and Cell Rotation*, p. 226). The influence of RBC deformability on apparent viscosity is velocity dependent because the degree of cell deformation and plasma gap thickness is velocity dependent. These effects were described theoretically by Lighthill (117) and Fitz-Gerald (68, 69) using a simple model of cell elasticity and by Tözeren and Skalak (176, 177) using a more exact and corrected treatment for elastic spheres. In any case, as the elastic cell velocity decreases toward zero, the cell expands to fill the capillary and the resistance increases. Using glass capillary arrays of various lengths, Lingard (119) showed experimentally that the resistance increases with decreasing velocities to attain a plateau level at low velocities.

A decrease in RBC deformability can be achieved by an alteration of membrane proteins, e.g., by heat (141) or diamide treatment (66). Changes in the tonicity of the suspending medium in either direction may reduce RBC deformability. In hypertonic media the internal fluid viscosity rises; in hypotonic media the internal viscosity decreases but the cell sphericity increases (35, 152).

Seshadri et al. (157) studied the effects of reduced RBC deformability by heat treatment in tubes with diameters ranging from 30 to 500 μm. The decreased deformability of the heated RBCs resulted in an increase in apparent viscosity that was more pronounced in smaller tubes. The Fåhraeus effect (reduction in H_T/H_D) for the heated RBC suspensions was found to be less than that for the normal RBC suspensions under comparable flow conditions. This indicates that the heated RBCs either do not migrate toward the tube center as much as the normal RBCs or that the velocity profile is flatter.

Measurements on H_D/H_F in a 5.6-μm capillary tube indicate that cell screening is enhanced (lower H_D/H_F) after osmotic treatment in either direction, the effect being more pronounced after hypertonic shrinkage than hypotonic swelling (77).

The RBCs subjected to hypotonic swelling show a maximum Fåhraeus effect (minimum H_T/H_D) at a tube diameter of 20 μm (16), which is at the upper end of the range of tube diameters (15–20 μm) at which the trend reversal of Fåhraeus effect occurs for normal RBCs (Fig. 18). Because the swollen cells are larger than normal cells, the ratio of the tube diameter at which trend reversal occurs to the effective cell diameter may be similar for these two types of RBCs.

A comparison of the microrheological behaviors of the nucleated avian RBC and human RBC illustrates the influence of cell deformability in flow through narrow tubes. The elliptical nucleated RBCs of turkeys (181), ducks (79), and several other nonmammals have larger corpuscular volume and membrane surface area than human RBCs. Calculation of the sphericity index, $4.84V^{2/3}/S$ (25), from the surface area (S) to volume (V) relationship shows that several types of nucleated RBCs have relatively more excess surface area for their volume compared with human RBCs (43), although the ratio V/S may be comparable (79). Viscometric and filterability measurements (43, 79, 181) as well as microscopic observations of cell deformation during flow in tubes with d = 25–50 μm (88) or 5–11 μm (79) indicate that the nucleated RBCs have a lower deformability. This low deformability can be attributed to the presence of the nucleus (43), the higher elastic modulus of the membrane (184), the rheological properties of the cytoplasm (43, 79), and the existence of microtubules just inside the membrane (45).

Normal, deformable human RBCs can undergo membrane rotation and maintain a remarkably stable orientation (usually more or less aligned with tube axis) during flow through tubes with diameters of 5–11 μm. In contrast the duck RBCs frequently exhibit a tumbling motion and are oriented at an angle relative to the tube axis [especially at low shear stresses and in 11-μm tubes (79)]. This type of microrheological behavior causes the duck RBCs to occupy a greater fraction of the tube cross section, leaving a small peripheral fluid layer. Consequently the duck RBCs exhibit less Fåhraeus effect (higher H_T/H_D) and a higher relative apparent viscosity at a given H_D or H_T (79, 80) compared with human RBCs (Fig. 21). Furthermore the slope of the line relating H_T/H_D to H_T or H_D is steeper for the duck RBCs, and H_T/H_D of duck RBCs becomes unity (disappearance of Fåhraeus effect) when H_T rises to 0.3–0.4.

The screening of duck RBCs at the tube entrance, as reflected by H_D/H_F, was studied in tubes with d = 5–11 μm (81). Screening is most pronounced during low flow, and H_D/H_F generally rises to a plateau as mean flow velocity increases. When H_F is raised above 0.4, the highest H_D observed is no more than 0.4, which probably reflects the limitation of packing efficiency of these less deformable RBCs in narrow tubes.

Red Cell Aggregation

In the presence of fibrinogen or other bridging macromolecules (e.g., dextrans), RBCs tend to aggregate and to form rouleaux at low shear rates (see *Properties of Blood*, p. 219). In blood flow through a tube the near-zero shear rate at the center favors aggregate formation. If the flow is slow, the aggregates become larger and the aggregated cells tend to occupy a larger centralized region in the tube.

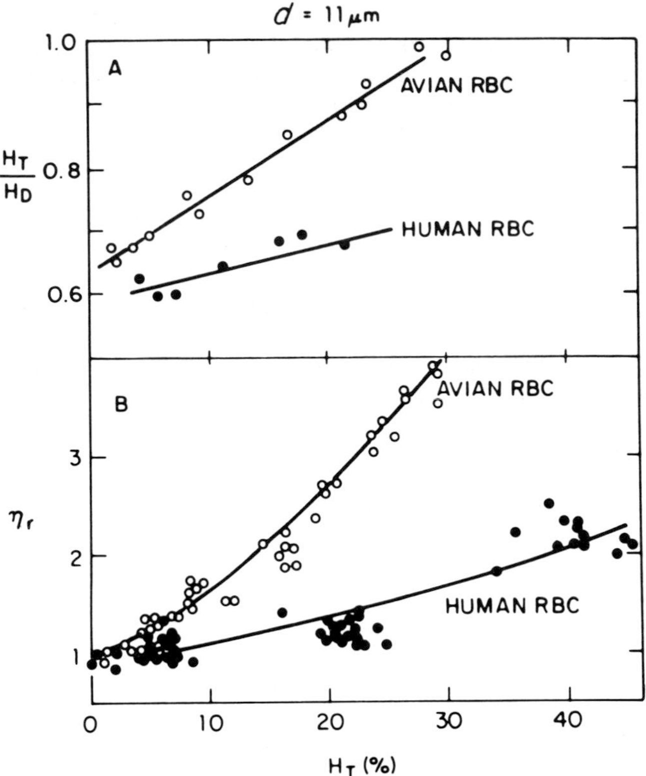

FIG. 21. *A*: ratio of H_T/H_D of avian (nucleated) and human RBC suspensions as a function of H_T in an 11-μm tube. *B*: relative apparent viscosity (η_r) of avian (nucleated) and human RBC suspensions as a function of H_T in an 11-μm tube. [Adapted from Gaehtgens et al. (79, 81).]

Studying the H_T/H_D ratios in tubes with d = 43–248 μm, Hochmuth and Davis (100) found that RBC suspensions in plasma had a lower ratio of H_T/H_D than RBC suspensions in saline, suggesting that RBC aggregation in plasma may accentuate the Fåhraeus effect.

Gaehtgens et al. (74) have systematically investigated the effects of RBC aggregation on cell screening and the Fåhraeus effect. They measured H_T, H_D, and H_F for human RBC suspensions in media containing a high-molecular-weight dextran (dextran 500, $\bar{M}_r \sim$ 511,000) during flow through glass capillaries with d = 15–75 μm. The flow rates were expressed in terms of a shear rate parameter $\bar{U}_{cell}$ equal to the cell velocity divided by the tube diameter: $\bar{U}_{cell} = V_{cell}/d$, where V_{cell} is the centerline velocity. Note that $\bar{U}_{cell}$ is 1–2 times the parameter $\bar{U}$, which equals $\dot{\gamma}_{aw}/8$ in Poiseuille flow. At high $\bar{U}_{cell}$ values (>500 s^{-1}) when RBCs are disaggregated by shear, dextran 500 does not cause significant RBC screening ($H_D/H_F \sim 1$) in tubes as narrow as 15 μm. A decrease in flow rate results in a reduction in H_D/H_F in tubes (increased screening) with $d \leq 60$ μm, and this effect is more pronounced in 15- to 30-μm tubes. Thus RBC aggregation by high-molecular-weight dextran causes cell screening in tubes where screening is negligible without RBC aggregation (e.g., 60 μm). In 15-μm tubes, cell screening is also observed in nonaggregating RBC suspensions at low flow rates (74), but the degree of screening is much greater in the presence of dextran (76).

In the high flow range ($\bar{U}_{cell}$ from 200 to 1,000 s^{-1}), the ratio H_T/H_D of RBC suspensions in high-molecular-weight dextran varies inversely with flow, in the same manner as that found for RBC suspensions in Ringer's solution (76). Under these conditions RBC aggregation is negligible and the enhancement of the Fåhraeus effect by flow is attributable to flow-induced deformation of RBCs, which increases their migration toward the axis. The slightly greater Fåhraeus effect in dextran suspension than in Ringer's suspension under these high-flow, nonaggregating conditions (76) may be explained by the greater degree of RBC deformation by the fluid of a higher viscosity (33). When the flow rate is reduced from $\bar{U}_{cell}$ = 200 s^{-1} to 20 s^{-1}, RBC aggregation probably occurs in dextran 500, and H_T/H_D decreases with the flow reduction (76). This is in opposition to the increase in H_T/H_D of nonaggregating RBC suspension observed with flow reduction in the same range (74). These results indicate that RBC aggregation enhances the Fåhraeus effect.

The ratio H_T/H_F reflects the combined effects of cell screening (H_D/H_F) and the Fåhraeus effect (H_T/H_D). During high flow, when aggregation is negligible, the H_T/H_F values of dextran suspensions are slightly lower than those of Ringer's suspensions because RBCs deform to a greater degree in a high-viscosity medium. As the flow rate is reduced to $\bar{U}$ = 20 s^{-1}, the progressive increase in RBC aggregation enhances both cell screening and the Fåhraeus effect, and therefore H_T/H_F values of dextran suspensions fall significantly below those of Ringer's suspensions (76).

Palmer and Jedrzejczyk (133) studied the effect of RBC aggregation on the flow behavior of RBC suspensions through capillary slits of 25 and 100 μm and through tubes with d = 400 μm and 1 mm. Normal human RBCs (30% Hct) were suspended in saline (0.9% NaCl) solution containing either dextran 40 ($\bar{M}_r \sim$ 40,000), 3.5 g/dl, which causes little RBC aggregation, or dextran 200 ($\bar{M}_r \sim$ 200,000), 2 g/dl, which causes marked RBC aggregation, especially at low shear rates. The two dextran media, though differing markedly in their ability to induce RBC aggregation, have the same viscosity (η_o). At the high $\dot{\gamma}_{aw}$ of 1,000 s^{-1}, when the shear stress is sufficient to prevent RBC aggregation, η_r is the same for the two dextran suspensions. At the low $\dot{\gamma}_{aw}$ of 20 s^{-1}, when significant RBC aggregation can occur in dextran 200, η_r in dextran 200 (2 g/dl) is significantly lower than that in dextran 40 (3.5 g/dl) or in dextran-free saline; the difference is the least in the 1-mm tube and the greatest in the 100-μm slit. These results indicate that RBC aggregation reduces apparent viscosity in channels with d <1 mm, and thus accentuates the Fåhraeus-Lindqvist effect as well as the Fåhraeus effect.

The results obtained with high-molecular-weight

dextrans (dextran 500 and 200) illustrate the effects of extensive RBC aggregation on flow through small tubes. Comparison between RBC suspensions in plasma and in saline indicates that the effects of RBC aggregation in normal blood are much less than those found with the use of high-molecular-weight dextrans.

In larger tubes, where the Fåhraeus effect is insignificant, RBC aggregation leads to an increase in apparent viscosity. The RBC aggregation causes the formation of a large core region, traveling almost as a plug flow, and an increase of shear rate in the tube periphery, thus increasing wall shear stress and pressure drop. In the region near the wall, where the aggregates are formed and continuously disrupted by the fluid shear, there may be an additional dissipation associated with the hysteresis of cell aggregation and disaggregation. For these reasons the presence of RBC aggregation at normal Hcts would increase the resistance to flow in larger tubes.

Leukocytes

Human WBCs are nearly spherical, and their diameters are similar to the major diameter of RBCs (see LEUKOCYTES, p. 223). The small protrusions and foldings on the surface of the WBC provide an excess membrane area that allows deformation at constant membrane area and cell volume. Micropipette tests show that WBCs are viscoelastic and less deformable than RBCs, due mainly to the difference in rheological properties of the contents of these cells (37, 116, 146).

There have been many studies on the rheological behavior of RBCs in flow through tubes but relatively few studies on WBCs. Vejlens (182) determined the concentrations of lymphocytes and granulocytes in tubes with diameters from 70 to 800 μm. The ratio of WBC concentration in the tube to that in the discharge blood ($C_{cell,T}/C_{cell,D}$) decreases as the tube diameter is reduced, reaching a value of ~0.6 in the 50-μm tube (Fig. 22) and demonstrating the Fåhraeus effect for WBCs. A comparison with the data on RBCs (Fig. 18) indicates that the Fåhraeus effect is more pronounced for WBCs in this range of tube diameter.

Nobis and Gaehtgens (127) determined the velocity of WBCs when human blood was perfused through glass tubes with diameters ranging from 8 to 50 μm. The WBCs were visualized by fluorescence microscopy after staining with acridine orange, and their velocity was determined by single-frame analysis from a television monitor. The ratio V/V_{cell} for WBCs increased as the tube diameter was reduced below 20–30 μm: i.e., the magnitude of the Fåhraeus effect decreased. At a tube diameter of 8 μm, V/V_{cell} rose to ~unity: i.e., the Fåhraeus effect disappeared.

Nobis and Gaehtgens (personal communication) investigated the effect of wall shear stress on the radial distribution of WBCs during perfusion of whole blood (cells in plasma) in glass tubes with diameters of 30–70 μm. With wall shear stress >10 dyn/cm^2, the WBC concentration is highest in the tube center. As wall shear stress is reduced below 10 dyn/cm^2, WBCs move out of the tube center toward the tube wall. The centralized location of WBCs at high shear stresses leads to an increase in the mean WBC velocity, causing decreases of V/V_{cell} and $C_{cell,T}/C_{cell,D}$ (Eq. 18), and thus an increased Fåhraeus effect for WBCs. The peripheral location of WBCs at low shear stresses, on the other hand, reduces the Fåhraeus effect for WBCs. Such shear-dependent variations in the degree of the Fåhraeus effect may explain the discontinuity of data

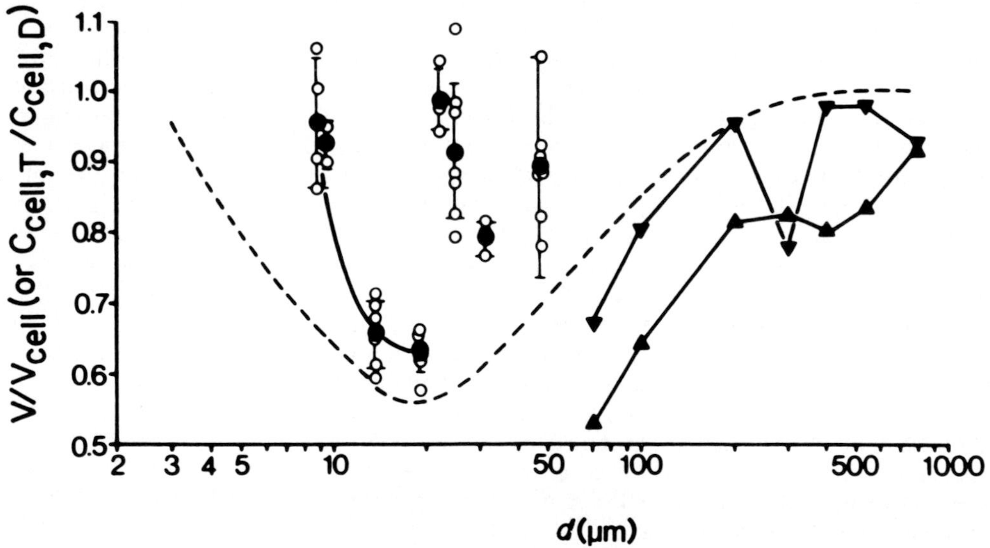

FIG. 22. Fåhraeus effect, expressed by velocity ratio between blood and WBCs (V/V_{cell}, which is equal to $C_{cell,T}/C_{cell,D}$ in steady state) as a function of tube diameter (*d*). ○, Data for WBCs in human whole blood obtained by Nobis and Gaehtgens (127). ●, Mean values and SDs are given. ▲, ▼, Results of Vejlens (182) for the Fåhraeus effect of WBCs in larger tubes. *Dotted line*, data from the literature on pure RBC suspensions.

reported by Nobis and Gaehtgens (127) (see Fig. 22). Possibly the wall shear stresses used in obtaining the data points for d between 8 and 20 μm were higher than those used for d between 20 and 50 μm, leading to a more pronounced Fåhraeus effect in the narrower tubes. Reductions of tube diameter would eventually lead to a trend reversal of the Fåhraeus effect for WBCs; the diameter at which this reversal occurs is a function of shear stress and RBC aggregation.

U. Nobis and P. Gaehtgens (unpublished observations) found that when RBC aggregation is eliminated by studying suspensions of RBCs and WBCs in saline, the shear-dependent change in the radial distribution of WBCs is significantly reduced. When RBC aggregation is enhanced by the use of high-molecular-weight dextran instead of plasma as the suspending medium, WBCs show a preferentially peripheral location, even at wall shear stresses as high as 22.5 dyn/cm^2.

Goldsmith and Spain (92) measured concentrations of WBCs during the flow of whole blood (20% and 40% Hct) through tubes with d = 100 μm. At high flow rates ($\bar{U} \geq 50\ s^{-1}$), when RBCs are mostly disaggregated, $C_{cell,T}/C_{cell,D}$ for WBCs is <1, indicating that the larger WBCs tend to be concentrated in the high-velocity regions near the center of the tube. At low flow rates ($\bar{U} < 5\ s^{-1}$), however, $C_{cell,T}/C_{cell,D}$ is >1; under these conditions RBCs aggregate to form rouleaux that occupy the tube center and displace the individual WBCs toward the low-velocity regions near the tube periphery.

These discussions indicate that RBCs can exert a significant influence on the Fåhraeus phenomenon for WBCs. In turn, WBCs also affect the flow of RBCs. In tubes with diameters not markedly larger than the WBC diameter, the presence of a WBC often causes the formation of a train of RBCs closely spaced behind the WBC (148). In tubes with diameters similar to or slightly larger than the WBC diameter, there is only a small clearance around the WBC, and it is difficult for RBCs to pass. Nobis and Gaehtgens (127) found that no RBC overtakes a WBC in an 8-μm glass tube. In tubes with larger diameters, some of the RBCs pass the WBC. In a 15-μm glass tube, 3% of the RBCs can pass the WBC, and the velocity of these single RBCs after passing the train is ~30% higher than that of the RBCs in the train behind the WBC. The reduction of RBC velocity in the train due to the presence of WBCs in narrow tubes decreases the Fåhraeus effect for the RBCs.

Determination of the pressure-flow relationship for cell suspensions indicates that an increase in WBC concentration in the feeding reservoir causes a strong elevation of flow resistance in the 8-μm tubes but no significant effect in the 12-μm tubes (127).

Platelets

When platelets are the only particulate species in the suspension, they tend to travel in the central region of the tube. Beck and Eckstein (13) showed this in experiments on the flow of human platelet-rich plasma through polyvinyl chloride tubing with an inner diameter of 178 μm. Over a wide range of flow ($\bar{U}$ from 10 to 1,200 s^{-1}), the ratio of platelet concentration in the tube ($C_{pl,T}$) to that in the feed reservoir ($C_{pl,F}$) was within the range 0.61–0.67. These values of $C_{pl,T}/C_{pl,F}$ are lower than expected based on studies of other particles. Because of the difficulties in handling platelets, further experiments on platelet-rich plasma are needed.

Studies on whole blood flowing through tubes with diameters from 40 to 635 μm indicate that the platelet concentration in the discharged blood ($C_{pl,D}$) is essentially the same as that in the feed reservoir, $C_{pl,D} \simeq C_{pl,F}$, and there is no significant screening of platelets in these tubes. However, $C_{pl,T}$ is higher than both $C_{pl,D}$ and $C_{pl,F}$ (13, 14). The finding of $C_{pl,T}/C_{pl,D}$ values >1 indicates that, in the presence of RBCs, the platelets travel preferentially in the low-velocity region near the wall of the tube. The $C_{pl,T}/C_{pl,F}$ value of human citrated whole blood at a Hct of 35% varies inversely with tube diameter, ranging from ~1 at d = 635 μm to 2 at d = 128 μm (13). This is in opposition to the Fåhraeus effect. There is no clear correlation of $C_{pl,T}/C_{pl,F}$ with flow rate ($\bar{U}$ from 1 to 1,500 s^{-1}) in these studies.

To eliminate the possibility of platelet adhesion to the tube wall, Beck and Eckstein (13) also studied suspensions of glutaraldehyde-hardened bovine platelets in saline in the presence of fresh bovine RBCs (35% Hct). In a tube with d = 302 μm, hardened bovine platelets behave like fresh human platelets; the ratio of $C_{pl,T}/C_{pl,F}$ is >1. This ratio increases from ~1.3 at $\bar{U} = 10\ s^{-1}$ to 2.0 at $\bar{U} = 60\ s^{-1}$. This may be related to the increasing deformation of RBCs at high shears (74). As the RBC concentration increases in the tube center with increasing shear stress, the platelets are displaced further toward the tube periphery. Beck and Eckstein (13) also studied hardened platelets in the presence of hardened RBCs; these data showed considerable scatter.

The behavior of suspensions containing platelets and RBCs is analogous to that of suspensions composed of WBCs and RBCs discussed in the previous section (see *Leukocytes*, p. 237). In the platelet-RBC system, the larger RBCs tend to concentrate in the tube center and the smaller platelets are preferentially located near the tube periphery.

Generalized Fåhraeus Effect

Particles flowing in a tube tend to migrate radially, generally toward the center of the tube. For rigid spheres, the migration depends on Re and becomes more pronounced as the particle diameter (d_{cell}) increases, i.e., as the diameter ratio $\epsilon = d_{cell}/d$ increases. For deformable particles the direction, rate, and extent of the migration are a function not only of d_{cell} but also of the shape and deformability of the particle.

For such deformable particles, relevant parameters are the diameter ratio and the ratio of the fluid shear stress to the particle stiffness, as measured by the deformation parameter A* defined for RBCs in Equation 21. For WBCs Equation 21 can be written as

$$A^* = \eta_o \; V_{cell}/d_{cell} \; E_c \qquad (23)$$

where E_c is a characteristic elastic modulus (in dyn/cm^2) of the particle interior. For particles in which all the elasticity of the cell resides in the membrane, as in the RBC, the combination $d_{cell}E_c$ is replaced by the membrane elastic modulus μ_m (dyn/cm) in Equation 21 (see p. 233). The effect of particle shape can probably be subsumed by defining ϵ' as the ratio of an effective diameter of the particle to the tube diameter, i.e., $\epsilon' = d_E/d$ where d_E is an equivalent spherical diameter taking into account the shape and deformation of the particle. One should expect universal curves of C_T/C_D and η_r versus d/d_E at low Re (Fig. 23).

When two different species of particles are present, their radial migration leads to a competition for the central position. Experiments on a mixture of RBCs and WBCs (see LEUKOCYTES, p. 223) have shown that, in the absence of RBC aggregation, the WBCs dominate and occupy the more central position in the tube. Although the major diameter of the discoid RBC is similar to the diameter of the spherical WBC, the more deformable RBC has a smaller equivalent diameter than the less deformable WBC. When RBCs form rouleaux they occupy the central position, leaving the now relatively smaller WBCs more concentrated near the wall. Similarly, in the presence of RBCs and WBCs, the smaller platelets migrate toward the wall; they are also found in greater abundance in smaller vessels.

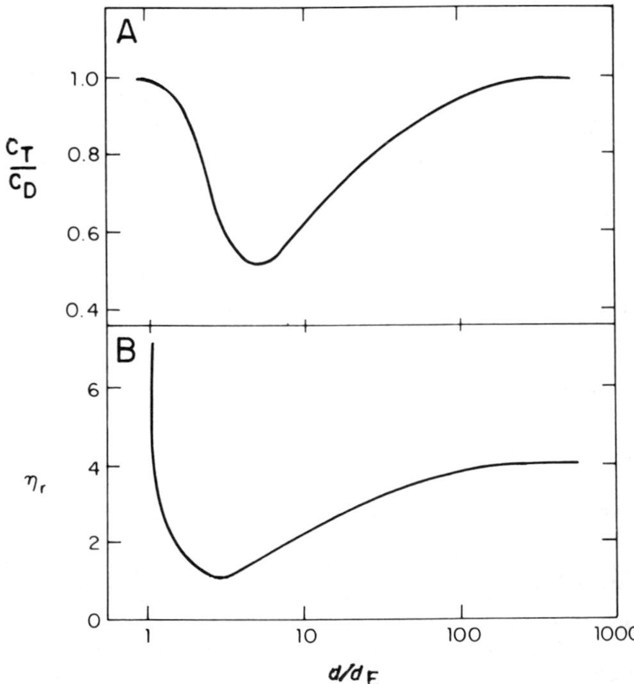

FIG. 23. Generalized plot of Fåhraeus (*A*) and Fåhraeus-Lindqvist (*B*) effects. C_T/C_D = ratio of tube concentration to discharge concentration.

The details of these phenomena must involve collisions of particles and their relative tendencies to migrate radially in the tube flow. The particles with the greatest tendency for radial migration predominates in the central position. The relative distribution of concentrations of the two species of particles (C_1/C_2) at low Re should be a universal function of the size and deformability ratios (i.e., ϵ_1'/ϵ_2' and A_1^*/A_2^*, respectively). Probably the size effect predominates in most cases, but the deformability plays a role in both migration and collision effects.

Collisions or close encounters are the mechanisms by which the different species of particles interact with one another. When two different-sized particles in close proximity collide, one particle may overtake the other or they may turn away from each other. This type of cell collision phenomena has been studied in small tubes with two rigid particles present (148). As a result of the many collisions and the preferential motion of one of the species toward or away from the center, there should eventually be a steady-state concentration distribution. The steady state should be derivable from an analysis of the statistical mechanics based on a large number of collisions. An alternate approach is to write field equations that involve the diffusion of each species, the tendency for radial migration, and interaction terms that represent the collisions. The solution of such differential equations would describe both the steady and transient states.

PULSATILE FLOW

Viscoelastic Properties of Blood

In the in vivo microcirculation, flow velocity fluctuates but usually does not reverse direction. The Fåhraeus-Lindqvist effect persists in such pulsatile flows (111, 123). By using glass tubes from 65 to 313 μm in diameter and sinusoidal variations of 50% of the mean flow at 1 and 2 Hz, it was shown that the relationship of mean flow rate to mean pressure drop is not appreciably affected by the presence of the pulsatile component. For the oscillatory component, or for purely oscillatory (reversing) flow, there is a further question concerning the phase of oscillatory flow compared with that of the oscillatory pressure. If these are not the same, the blood is said to show viscoelasticity and/or inertial effects.

Thurston (172) studied the rheological behavior of human blood (anticoagulated with citrate phosphate dextrose solution, 39%–71% Hct) under oscillatory flow (frequency = 2 Hz) in tubes with diameters from 400 μm to 4 mm. A wide range of wall shear rate ($\dot{\gamma}_w$) was obtained by changing the amplitude of the oscillation. Steady flow was also studied at comparable shear rates in the same tubes. The viscous and elastic components of the complex viscosity obtained in oscillatory flow (η' and η'', respectively), as well as the apparent viscosity determined in steady flow (η_s), are independent of $\dot{\gamma}_w$ below a critical level of $\dot{\gamma}_w^*$; above this critical level the viscosity coefficients η', η'', and η decrease with increasing $\dot{\gamma}_w$. The critical $\dot{\gamma}_w^*$ varies inversely with H_F and tube diameter (when $d \leq 800$ μm), and the value is generally on the order of 1 s^{-1}. The reductions of viscosity coefficients with increasing $\dot{\gamma}_w$ (above the critical level) have been interpreted as a reflection of shear disaggregation of RBC rouleaux. The viscosity coefficients determined in the low $\dot{\gamma}_w$ range (below the critical level) probably reflect primarily the behavior of RBC aggregates.

The effect of variations in tube diameter on the viscosity coefficients obtained in the low-shear range has been studied by Thurston (172) for H_F = 59%. Figure 24 shows an increase in steady-flow apparent viscosity (η_s) with increased tube diameter (up to 4 mm). In contrast, at high-shear rates (e.g., 65 s^{-1}), when RBCs are dispersed, the apparent viscosity in steady shear becomes essentially independent of d when $d > 400$ μm. That the η_s at low shear varies with d up to d as large as 4 mm probably reflects the large rouleau size (effective particle diameter) at the low $\dot{\gamma}_w$ levels studied. For the same blood sample (H_F = 59%) the oscillatory low-shear values of η' and η'' are nearly constant for $d > 800$ μm, but they decrease in the smaller tubes (Fig. 24). Singh and Coulter (158a) found a decrease in the η_a of blood during oscillatory flow with a decrease in d from 1,660 to 300 μm.

Thurston's results on viscosity coefficients at low-shear rates have been interpreted with the aid of a two-phase model consisting of a central core of aggregated cells and a boundary zone at the tube wall (172). In steady flow, the central core is assumed to form a plug, which is incapable of deformation, and the viscous flow is assumed in the boundary zone, which has a thickness t and a viscosity η_{bz}. Under these circumstances the apparent viscosity in steady flow is

$$\eta_a = d(\eta_{bz}/8t) \qquad (23)$$

Equation 23 is the leading term in a series expansion of Equation 20 for small t. In oscillatory flow, it is assumed that the core behaves viscoelastically with coefficients characterizing the blood in the bulk. In larger tubes the oscillatory flow is dominated by this bulk viscoelastic behavior, and the influence of the thin boundary zone is negligible. In small tubes, however, the radius of the viscoelastic core diminishes relative to the bondary zone thickness, and the oscillatory flow is dominated by the boundary zone. These two conditions are illustrated in Figure 25 where idealized velocity profiles for large and small tubes (A and B, respectively) are shown divided into three regions: *1*) the core with plug motion (cp), *2*) a core where there is viscoelastic deformation (cd), and *3*) the boundary zone (bz). The impedance per unit length in the cd zone ($Z_{cr,d}$) can be expressed as

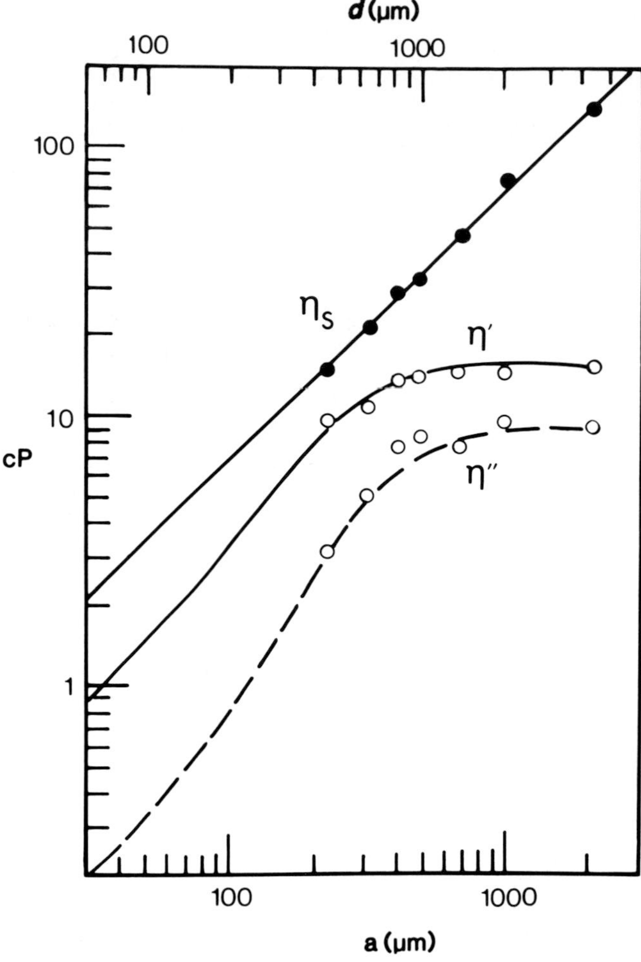

FIG. 24. Data points show dependence of apparent values of steady-flow viscosity η_s and components of oscillatory-flow viscosity η' and η'' on tube radius, a. Top abscissa scale shows tube diameter (d). Measurements of viscosity are for linear, low-flow-rate range. Blood Hct is 59%. *Lines* are theoretical values of η_s, η', and η'', as calculated by equations described in text. Here, thickness t = 0.0032 cm, blood density ρ = 1.05 g/ml, freq = 2 Hz, η'_{bz} = 0.035 P, η''_{bz} = 0.008 P, $\eta'_{cr,d}$ = 0.15 P, $\eta''_{cr,d}$ = 0.088 P, and (η_{bz}/t) = 28 P/cm. [Adapted from Thurston (172).]

$$Z_{cr,d} = (128\ \eta'_{cr,d}/\pi d^4) + i[(16\rho\omega/3\pi d^2) - (128\ \eta''_{cr,d}/\pi d^4)] \qquad (24)$$

where $\eta'_{cr,d}$ and $\eta''_{cr,d}$ are viscous and elastic components, respectively, of the complex viscosity in the core where viscoelastic deformation occurs, ρ is blood density, ω is the radian frequency, and i is an imaginary number. The impedance per unit length due to the oscillatory plug in the core moving on the boundary zone $Z_{cr,plug}$ can be expressed as

$$Z_{cr,plug} \simeq (16\ \eta'_{bz}/\pi d^3 t) + i[(4\rho\omega/\pi d^2) - (16\ \eta''_{bz}/\pi d^3 t)] \qquad (25)$$

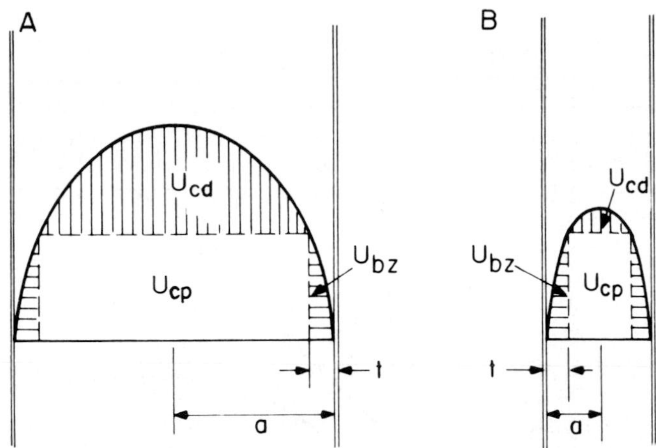

FIG. 25. Hypothetical velocity amplitude profiles for oscillatory flow in circular tubes. *A*: large tube (a = ~6t, where t = thickness of boundary zone). *B*: smaller tube (a ~2.5t). Regions of velocity profiles giving rise to volume flow components U_{cd}, U_{cp}, and U_{bz} are indicated, showing relative contributions to total flow by bulk deformation, pluglike motion, and boundary zone flow, respectively. [Adapted from Thurston (172).]

where η'_{bz} and η''_{bz} are viscous and elastic components, respectively, of the complex viscosity in the boundary zone. The overall impedance per unit length (Z) combining the deformation and plug effects can be calculated as

$$1/Z = [1 - (Q_{cr,d}/Q)]/Z_{cr,plug} + (Q_{cr,d}/Q)/Z_{cr,d} \quad (26)$$

where $Q_{cr,d}/Q$ is the fraction of total volume flow due to flow in the core. The above equations can be used to estimate η' and η'' under the condition that the magnitude of $(d/2)\ (\rho\omega/\eta^*)^{1/2}$ is <2, where η^* is the complex viscosity. By using the value of t = 32 μm, ρ = 1.05 g/cm^3, η'_{bz} = 3.5 cP, η''_{bz} = 0.8 cP, $\eta'_{cr,d}$ = 15 cP, $\eta''_{cr,d}$ = 8.8 cP, and η_{bz} = 8.96 cP, the experimental data obtained at oscillatory flow (frequency = 2 Hz) through tubes with diameters from 400 μm to 4 mm can be fitted with this theoretical model [Fig. 24; (172)]. As Thurston (172) pointed out, this analysis was simplified by assuming a boundary zone of prescribed thickness, but actually a gradual variation of properties probably occurs across the tube.

Pulse Wave Propagation in Microvessels

In the microcirculation the inertial terms of the equations of motion are small relative to viscous and pressure effects. Furthermore the total length of the microcirculation is short and the microvessels, compared with the major blood vessels, are quite stiff. All of these attributes lead to a situation in which the wave propagation velocity is high and the distances involved are short, so that the usual notion of an oscillating, propagating wave is not germane. Rather the microvascular dynamics are dominated by viscosity and may be considered without inertia. The equations governing the motion are then similar to the equations of diffusion or heat conduction. When the inertial terms are neglected, the governing equations are

$$\frac{\partial P}{\partial z} = -RQ \quad (27)$$

$$\frac{\partial Q}{\partial z} = -GP - C\frac{\partial P}{\partial t} \quad (28)$$

where G is a radial compliance of the blood vessel, Q is the rate of discharge, t is time, and z refers to the z-axis. Solutions of these equations for a number of different microcirculatory beds have been discussed by Gross (94) and Gross et al. (95). As expected from the diffusive character, there is a rapid decay in the pressure amplitude with distance downstream. This corresponds to the decay of the pulse wave observed through the microcirculation. Smaje et al. (166) recently gave an interesting application of the solution of this problem. In a blocked capillary the slight motion of RBCs observed may be interpreted in terms of wall motion and filtration through the walls.

FLOW OF CELL SUSPENSIONS THROUGH BRANCHED TUBES

Many investigators have observed and reported the nonuniform distribution of blood cells among capillaries in a microvascular network (64, 112, 126, 145). At any given time, the distribution of RBCs within the network appears patchy, with the RBCs unequally spaced in the capillaries. A given capillary may carry RBCs in groups at one time and only plasma and platelets at another time. Thus there are considerable spatial and temporal nonhomogeneities of blood cell distribution in the microcirculation. The flow velocity in capillary networks also exhibits significant spatial and temporal fluctuations (96, 185). Krogh (112) observed that the Hct in a daughter vessel of a divergent branch point varies with the rate of blood flow in the vessel and that the Hct in small side branches is lower than that in the larger vessel (plasma skimming). He pointed out that the flow behavior at divergent branches on the arteriolar side of the capillary network plays an important role in the nonhomogeneity of blood cell distribution. Studies on the microcirculation in vivo by several investigators (104, 106, 108, 147, 170) confirm that the relative Hct values entering the two daughter capillaries of a bifurcation are predominantly determined by the relative velocities of the daughter capillaries.

Effects of Discharge Ratio on Cell Distribution

In vitro studies on tubes with bifurcations allow the control of flow rates, cell concentration in the feeding fluid, and branch geometry. The results indicate that the distribution of blood cells in the daughter branches is affected by several conditions at the branch point, including relative tube diameter ratio, relative flow rates, and the cell concentration profile in the parent vessel (20, 21, 83, 130, 131). In most of these studies the diameters of the tubes were large compared with the size of the blood cells or simulating particles. Studying the distribution of spheres in a T-tube system with a tube-to-particle diameter ratio of ~10, Bugliarello and Hsiao (20) showed that the particle concentration in the side branch is nonlinearly related to the flow velocity and is a function of the cell concentration profile at the entrance to the branch, the Re, and the relative dimensions of the side branches to the parent tube.

Investigating the flow of spheres in a symmetrical bifurcation system with a tube-to-particle diameter ratio only slightly >1, Fung (70) showed that the branch with the faster flow (left-hand branch in Fig. 26) might not only get more particles but might get all of the particles. This can be understood by considering the resultants of the pressure force and shear stress acting on the sphere at the bifurcation point. In this symmetrical bifurcation the branch with higher flow rate has a higher pressure gradient. Thus the net force due to pressure and shear stresses (Fig. 26, *right*) draws the sphere into the high-flow branch. A perfectly centralized sphere arriving at the bifurcation may stop temporarily at the dividing point, and the suspending fluid may stream past the sphere. The

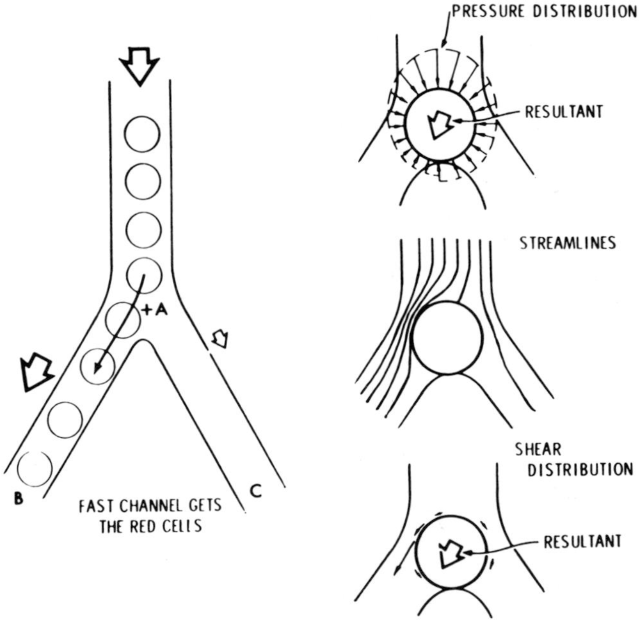

FIG. 26. At branch point of capillary tube system, branch with faster stream gets cells. *Left*: spherical balls flow in cylindrical tube that bifurcates into 2 equal branches. *Right*: forces acting on sphere at moment when it is located at point of bifurcation of vessel. Resultants of pressure forces (*top*) and shear stress (*bottom*) both point to faster stream. [From Fung (70).]

higher shear stress on the high-flow side pulls the sphere into that branch. Both the pressure distribution and the shear stress tend to pull the sphere into the faster stream, resulting in a strong dependence of particle distribution on the relative flow rates between the two branches. Yen and Fung (189) extended this above study with a large-scale model experiment in which flexible gelatin disks were used to simulate RBCs and the particle-to-tube diameter ratio was ~1. They found that the Hct ratio in the two daughter branches varied directly with the velocity ratio up to a critical velocity ratio, beyond which all particles entered the branch with the faster velocity. The critical velocity ratio is on the order of 2.5, with the exact value depending on the particle-to-tube ratio and the mechanical properties of the particle.

By the use of high-speed microcinephotography, Schmid-Schönbein et al. (145) have studied the distribution of RBCs and WBCs at capillary bifurcations in the rabbit ear chamber. These in vivo results confirm the nonlinear relationship between Hct ratio and velocity ratio and the existence of a critical flow ratio beyond which all cells enter the branch with the faster flow, as previously demonstrated in vitro. In addition they demonstrated that the degree of nonlinearity and the value of the critical flow ratio depend strongly on the radial location of the blood cells at the entrance to the branch point (see *Effects of Blood Cell Eccentricity in Feeding Vessel on Cell Distribution*, p. 243). Schmid-Schönbein et al. (145) also studied the effect of the entrance of a RBC or WBC into one branch of a bifurcation on the distribution of blood cells arriving subsequently at the branch point by using a simple network consisting of a parent capillary feeding two daughter capillaries of equal size, which join again at their downstream ends (i.e., two parallel daughter vessels with equal pressure drop and with a flow ratio that varies inversely with their resistance ratio). The entrance of a RBC into one branch causes an increase of resistance and a decrease of flow in that branch, and hence the next RBC enters the other branch. In this manner the RBCs arriving at the bifurcation alternate their entrance into the two branches, and the distribution of RBCs is automatically adjusted. When a WBC enters one branch, its lower deformability and larger effective cell diameter causes a greater increase in resistance than does the RBC. Therefore many subsequent RBCs are diverted into the other branch until the cumulative increase in resistance due to these additional RBCs matches that due to the single WBC; thereafter, the entering RBCs again alternate between the two sides. For a WBC with d_{cell}/d of 0.85, it may be equivalent to 20–30 RBCs in terms of resistance change. When the WBC exits the daughter vessel, the reduction in resistance in that branch causes the entry of many subsequent RBCs into it until the resistance is again equal between the two sides. Therefore the entry of WBCs into a capillary network has a large effect on the distribution of RBCs.

Effects of Blood Cell Eccentricity in Feeding Vessel on Cell Distribution

The relationship between the fractional cell flux into each daughter vessel as a function of the fractional bulk flow discussed previously (see *Effects of Discharge Ratio on Cell Distribution*, p. 241) may be defined as a cell distribution function (145). Studies on the microcirculation of the rabbit ear chamber indicate that the cell distribution function is strongly dependent on the transverse position (or degree of eccentricity) of the blood cells immediately upstream of the branch point (145). When the blood cells are evenly distributed across the parent vessel, the relative cell flux into the two daughter capillaries is almost a linear function of the relative flow rates, and the flow rate into one branch needs to be several times higher than that of the other side before all cells would enter only the fast-flow branch. In contrast, when most of the blood cells are centralized in the parent vessel, the cell distribution function is highly nonlinear, i.e., the relative cell flux into the two branches becomes very sensitive to differences in flow rates. Under such conditions all cells may enter only one branch, even with a small discrepancy in flow rates.

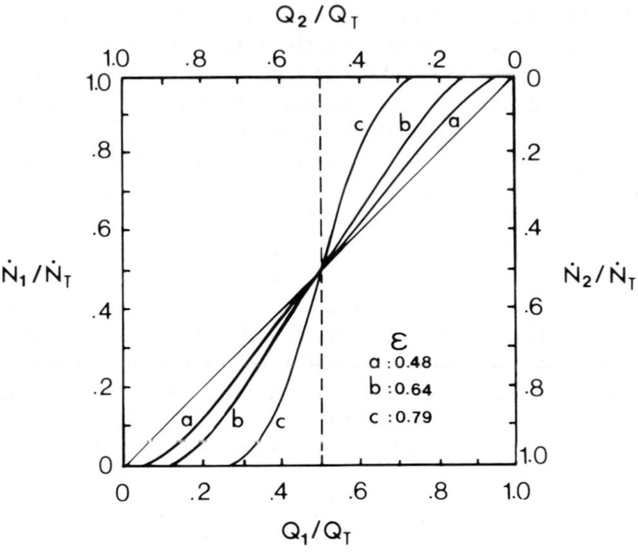

FIG. 27. Distribution functions for spherical particles. $\dot{N}_1/\dot{N}_T$ and $\dot{N}_2/\dot{N}_T$, fractional particle fluxes; Q_1/Q_T and Q_2/Q_T, fractional bulk flows. Limits of distribution functions are 45° line for diameter ratio $\epsilon \rightarrow 0$ and *dashed vertical line* at $Q_1/Q_T = Q_2/Q_T = 0.5$ for $\epsilon \rightarrow 1$.

The effects of particle-to-tube diameter ratio and particle eccentricity on the particle distribution function were studied in a large-scale model system in which rigid spheres (model WBCs) and flexible Silastic disks (model RBCs) flow through a symmetrical T-bifurcation (C. D. Tvetenstrand, M. A. F. Epstein, G. W. Schmid-Schönbein, and S. Chien, unpublished observations). For both types of particles, as ϵ increases from 0.3 to 0.8, the cell distribution function curve shifts from a nearly linear relation to a nonlinear S-shaped curve that approaches the limit of a vertical line at a fractional flow ratio of 0.5 as ϵ approaches 1 (Fig. 27). The effect of ϵ on particle distribution function is related to its influence on particle eccentricity. Small particles can closely approach the tube wall and have a relatively wide eccentricity distribution; because the center of a particle cannot approach the wall more closely than its radius, the centers of large particles are distributed primarily near the tube axis. For the same ϵ value, the eccentricity distribution for disks is wider than that for spheres, because the edge-on orientation of disks during transit through the bifurcation permits them to approach the tube wall more closely than spheres at the same ϵ. Yen and Fung (189) found that an increase in particle concentration reduces the nonlinearity of the particle distribution function of flexible disks; this may be explained by a wider distribution of particle eccentricity at high concentrations.

Effects of Entrance Geometry and Flow on Cell Distribution

When flow occurs from a large parent vessel into a small branch or from a reservoir into a small tube [e.g., in Fåhraeus's experiments (64)], the cell concentration entering the small branch may be affected by its size and the flow conditions at the entrance. First of all, because the small side branch draws blood mainly from the peripheral, cell-depleted layer of the parent vessel, the entering cell concentration would be lower. This is the plasma-skimming effect referred to earlier (see CELL SCREENING AND PLASMA SKIMMING, p. 231). The orientation of RBCs at the entrance of the small side branch can affect cell entry, which is easier when the RBCs are aligned with the entry section and more difficult if the RBCs are perpendicular.

Yen and Fung (188) studied the influence of the flow condition outside the entrance to a small tube on cell entry in model experiments. Neutrally buoyant, flexible gelatin disks (model RBCs) were allowed to flow through a glass tube ($d_{cell}/d = 0.37 - 1.13$) inserted into a reservoir in which the feed suspension was under a steady shear flow; the tube was placed perpendicular to the direction of this shear flow. The ratio of particle concentration in the discharge fluid to that in the feed reservoir (C_D/C_F) shows a bell-shaped relationship to the ratio of the mainstream velocity at the entrance of the tube to the mean velocity in the tube ($V_F/\bar{V}_T$). From a value <1 at $V_F = 0$, C_D/C_F rises to a maximum value of ~1 over a $V_F/\bar{V}_T$ range of 1–4, beyond which it declines again. Simultaneous determinations of C_T showed that the ratio C_T/C_D is also affected by the entrance condition ($V_F/\bar{V}_T$). These results indicate the complexity of the influence of the entrance condition on the entry of particles into small tubes and their subsequent flow behavior.

RELEVANCE TO BLOOD FLOW IN VIVO

Poiseuille's law (Eq. 4) indicates that the resistance to fluid flow through a cylindrical tube varies directly with the fluid viscosity and inversely with the fourth power of the tube diameter (Eq. 5). To a first approximation this relationship applies to the circulation in vivo. In the microcirculation, as the microvessel diameter decreases the flow resistance through the individual microvessel increases sharply (see the chapter by Zweifach and Lipowsky in this *Handbook*). The concomitant decreases in Hct (Fåhraeus effect) and the apparent blood viscosity (Fåhraeus-Lindqvist effect) as the microvessel diameter is reduced (121) minimize somewhat the increased resistance. The Fåhraeus effect is less pronounced for RBCs with reduced deformability (see *Red Cell Deformability*, p. 235). Therefore the normal RBC deformability leads to a reduction in the apparent blood viscosity in microvessels not only by decreasing the resistance contribution of each RBC but also by decreasing the RBC concentration in the vessel.

The Fåhraeus effect, in its fullest extent, can only reduce the Hct in the microvessel (H_{mv}) to one-half of the value in the large vessel (H_{LV}). The findings of H_{mv}/H_{LV} as low as 0.2 in the narrowest capillaries in vivo must be explained by other additional factors, e.g., preferential shunting of RBCs through some parts of the microvascular network (55, 106, 108, 121). Another effect that could lead to a reduced Hct, observed as a spatially averaged quantity, is the existence of a positive correlation between the Hct and velocity (135). Such a correlation is known to exist in vivo (62). A detailed discussion of this problem is given in the chapter by Zweifach and Lipowsky in this *Handbook*.

In tubes with $d < 10–20\ \mu m$, there is a trend reversal of the Fåhraeus effect, i.e., the ratio H_T/H_D begins to increase as the vessel diameter decreases (see FLOW IN TUBES <29 μM IN DIAMETER, p. 229). In these narrow vessels the RBCs occupy a greater fraction of the vessel cross-section a area, and the peripheral fluid layer near the wall becomes thinner. These changes would reduce the diffusion distance between the RBC and the interstitial fluid surrounding the narrow capillaries, thus facilitating O_2 delivery to tissues.

Red cell aggregation increases the effective particle size and accentuates the Fåhraeus effect (lowering of H_T/H_D) and the Fåhraeus-Lindqvist effect (lowering of η_a) in narrow tubes (see *Red Cell Aggregation*, p. 235). The lowering of η_a in narrow vessels is in opposition to the effect of RBC aggregation on η_a during bulk flow in large vessels. This provides a homeostatic mechanism to prevent an excessive rise in viscous resistance when RBC aggregation is enhanced by low-flow states or other causes.

There are frequent interactions among the different types of blood cells in the microvessels (see *Leukocytes*, p. 237). In high-flow states, when the RBCs are dispersed, the larger WBCs tend to occupy the central region of the tube. This increases the WBC velocity and reduces the WBC concentration in the tube. In low-flow states, the aggregation of RBCs increase their effective particle size, and WBCs tend to flow near the wall. Under such circumstances, the WBC velocity decreases and the WBC concentration in the tube increases. In convergent flow, WBCs entering from one branch tend to be pushed toward the wall by RBCs entering from the other branch (see *Interactions of Cells With Tube Walls*, p. 227). Such lateral displacement of WBCs by RBCs also occurs in a tube with gradually widening diameter. The postcapillary venules have the lowest shear rate in the circulation (31), are formed by converging capillaries, and have a gradually widening diameter; these factors contribute to the movement of WBCs toward the venular wall. Experiments indicate that ~95% of the WBCs in the postcapillary venule roll along the venular wall (148). This gives the WBCs a strategic location from which they can react to any chemotactic signal from the extravascular space. Furthermore their slow translational velocity in rolling along the venular wall facilitates the extravasation of the WBC in time of need.

Because of the lower deformability of WBCs than RBCs, the entrance of a WBC into one arm of a divergent branch causes the preferential entry of subsequently arriving RBCs into the other arm (*Effects of Discharge Ratio on Cell Distribution*, p. 241). This effect is seen on the arteriolar side of the capillary network. Hence the presence of WBCs modulates the temporal and spatial apportionment of RBCs in the capillary network, thereby influencing O_2 delivery to tissue cells.

In the presence of normal concentrations of RBCs, the platelets are located primarily near the tube wall. Platelets in the microvessels would have a lower relative velocity and exist in a higher concentration than in the large vessels. These hemodynamic effects on platelets may be significant in microvessel hemostasis.

The rheological behavior of blood cells in narrow tubes may have considerable implications in interpreting in vivo microcirculatory hemodynamics, metabolic transport, and phenomena such as chemotaxis and hemostasis. This discussion has centered on the flow behavior of the blood cells in vessels with given dimensions. In the microcirculation in vivo, neurohumoral influences may alter microvascular geometry and hemodynamic functions; these changes must be considered in conjunction with the rheological factors to develop a complete picture of the microcirculation.

SUMMARY

The rheological behavior of blood flow in tubes with $d < 500\ \mu m$ must be considered as the flow of a viscoelastic suspension rather than a uniform fluid. Like any other deformable particles, RBCs tend to migrate toward the center of the tube, leaving the fluid near the wall relatively depleted of RBCs. In large tubes ($d > 500\ \mu m$) this effect is not prominent because the relative thickness of the cell-depleted region near the wall is negligible when compared with the diameter. As the tube diameter is progressively reduced, the unequal distribution of RBCs along the radial direction of the tube becomes more prominent. Because the velocity is highest in the center and lowest near the wall, the RBCs, being preferentially located near the tube center, have a velocity (V_{cell}) higher than that of the suspending medium (V_P). This increase in V_{cell}/V_P leads to a decrease in H_T/H_D (the Fåhraeus effect) and a corresponding decrease in apparent viscosity (Fåhraeus-Lindqvist effect). With $d < 10$–$20\ \mu m$, the RBC occupies a greater cross section of the tube and V_{cell}/V_P rises toward 1.0 (trend reversal of Fåhraeus effect). In very narrow tubes the apparent viscosity also increases (trend reversal of Fåhraeus-Lindqvist effect), rising toward very high values as the limit for RBC passage is reached ($d \doteq 2.7\ \mu m$ for normal human RBCs).

The deformability of RBCs facilitates their migration toward the tube center, and a decrease in deformability causes reductions in V_{cell}/V_P and in the Fåhraeus effect. Aggregation of RBCs causes an increase in the effective particle size and a more prominent central migration, thus enhancing cell screening at the tube entrance and the Fåhraeus effect. The enhancement of the Fåhraeus effect by RBC aggregation can also be inferred from oscillatory studies at low shear rates.

The blood cells of different species with various tendencies for radial migration have different radial distributions in small tubes. Consequently there are corresponding species variations in the Fåhraeus and Fåhraeus-Lindqvist effects.

In the absence of RBC aggregation, the effectively larger WBCs occupy the more central position in the tube. When RBC aggregation occurs, the large rouleaux occupy the central position, leaving the now effectively smaller WBCs concentrated near the wall. Therefore the ratio of WBC concentration in the tube to that in the discharge fluid may change from <1 to >1 as RBC aggregation occurs. In the presence of RBCs and WBCs, the smaller platelets migrate toward the wall, leading to a high platelet concentration in small tubes. Therefore measurements of concentrations of WBCs or platelets in the tube may give results opposite to that of the Fåhraeus effect.

These findings may be generalized in the following manner. The mean velocity [and hence (C_T)] of a given type of blood cells depends on the interaction of their radial concentration profile with the velocity profile. The concentration profile of blood cells depends on their tendency for radial migration, which is a function of the effective cell diameter ratio ϵ' and the deformation parameter A^*. The larger the effective cell diameter and the greater the cell deformability, the more centralized the cell distribution in the tube and the lower the concentration of cells in the tube.

In divergent branches the distribution of blood cells into daughter branches is determined by the relative flow in the two branches and the radial location of the cells in the parent vessel. The entrance of an RBC into one branch raises the apparent viscosity and reduces the flow into that branch, favoring the entrance of the next cell into the other branch. Such effects are even stronger when a WBC enters a branch; this causes the preferential distribution of many subsequent RBCs into the other branch. In convergent branches the RBC-WBC interactions lead to a radial displacement of the WBC toward the tube wall.

The behavior of individual blood cells and their interactions provide the microrheological basis of the macrorheological properties of blood during flow through narrow tubes. The information gained from studies on the rheology of blood flow through narrow tubes is valuable in interpreting the hemodynamic and other functional data obtained on the microcirculation in vivo (see the chapter by Zweifach and Lipowsky in this *Handbook*).

We are grateful to Drs. Giles R. Cokelet, Peter Gaehtgens, and Harry L. Goldsmith for their valuable comments and discussions.

Our investigations were supported by National Heart, Lung, and Blood Institute Grant HL-16851.

REFERENCES

1. ALBRECHT, K. H., P. GAEHTGENS, A. PRIES, AND M. HEUSER. The Fåhraeus effect in narrow capillaries. *Microvasc. Res.* 18: 33–47, 1979.
2. ARIMAN, T., N. A. TURK, AND N. D. SYLVESTER. Microcontinuum fluid mechanics. A review. *Int. J. Eng. Sci.* 11: 905–930, 1973.
3. AZELVANDRE, F., AND C. OIKNINE. Effet Fåhraeus et effet Fåhraeus-Lindqvist: résultats expérimentaux et modèles théoretiques. *Biorheology* 13: 325–335, 1976.
4. BAGGE, U., B. AMUNDSON, AND C. LAURITZEN. White blood cell deformability and plugging of skeletal muscle capillaries in hemorrhagic shock. *Acta Physiol. Scand.* 108: 159–163, 1980.
5. BAGGE, U., P.-I. BRÅNEMARK, R. KARLSSON, AND R. SKALAK. Three-dimensional observations of red blood cell deformation in capillaries. *Blood Cells* 6: 231–239, 1980.
6. BAGGE, U., AND R. KARLSSON. Maintenance of white blood cell margination at the passage through small venular junctions. *Microvasc. Res.* 20: 92–95, 1980.
7. BAGGE, U., R. SKALAK, AND R. ATTEFORS. Granulocyte rheology: experimental studies in an in vitro micro-flow system. *Adv. Microcirc.* 7: 29–48, 1977.
8. BARBEE, J. H., AND G. R. COKELET. The Fåhraeus effect. *Microvasc. Res.* 3: 6–16, 1971.
9. BARBEE, J. H., AND G. R. COKELET. Prediction of blood flow in tubes with diameters as small as 29 μm. *Microvasc. Res.* 3: 17–21, 1971.
10. BARRAS, J. P. Blood rheology. General review. *Bibl. Haematol.* 33: 277–297, 1969.
11. BAYLISS, L. E. Rheology of blood and lymph. In: *Deformation and Flow in Biological Systems*, edited by A. Frey-Wissling.

Amsterdam: North-Holland, 1952, p. 354–418.

12. BAYLISS, L. E. The flow of suspensions of red blood cells in capillary tubes: changes in the "cell-free" marginal sheath with changes in the shearing stress. *J. Physiol. London* 179: 1-25, 1965.
13. BECK, M. R., JR., AND E. C. ECKSTEIN. Preliminary report on platelet concentration in capillary tube flows of whole blood. *Biorheology* 17: 455–464, 1980.
14. BLACKSHEAR, P. L., S. V. PATANKAR, R. W. HEIL, M. IVANDVIC, T. NIPPOLDT, AND A. ROSENSTEIN. *Fluid Dynamics of Blood Cells and Applications to Hemodialysis.* Springfield, VA: Natl. Tech. Inf. Serv., January 1978. (Rep. PB-288 587.)
15. BLOOR, M. I. G. The flow of blood in the capillaries. *Phys. Med. Biol.* 13: 443-450, 1968.
16. BRAASCH, D. Erythrocyte flexibility and blood flow resistance in capillaries with a diameter of less than 20 microns. *Bibl. Anat.* 9: 272–275, 1967.
17. BRAASCH, D., AND W. JENETT. Erythrocytenflexibilität, Hämokonzentration und Reibungswiderstand in Glascapillaren mit Durchmessern zwischen 6 bis 50 μm. *Pfluegers Arch.* 302: 245-254, 1968.
18. BRÅNEMARK, P.-I. *Intravascular Anatomy of Blood Cells in Man.* Basel: Karger, 1971.
19. BROOKS, D. E. Red cell interactions in low flow states. In: *Microcirculation*, edited by J. Grayson and W. Zingg. New York: Plenum, 1976, vol. 1, p. 33–52.
20. BUGLIARELLO, G., AND C. C. HSIAO. Phase separation in suspension flowing through bifurcations: a simplified hemodynamic model. *Science* 143: 469–471, 1964.
21. BUGLIARELLO, G., AND C. C. HSIAO. The mechanism of phase separation at bifurcations. *Bibl. Anat.* 7: 363–367, 1965.
22. BUGLIARELLO, G., AND J. SEVILLA. Velocity distribution and other characteristics of steady and pulsatile blood flow in fine glass tubes. *Biorheology* 7: 85–107, 1970.
23. BUNGAY, P. M., AND H. BRENNER. Pressure drop due to the motion of a sphere in proximity to the wall bounding a Poiseuille flow. *J. Fluid Mech.* 60: 81–96, 1973.
24. BUNGAY, P. M., AND H. BRENNER. The motion of a closely-fitting sphere in a fluid-filled tube. *Int. J. Multiphase Flow* 1: 25–56, 1973.
25. BURTON, A. C. Role of geometry, of size and shape, in the microcirculation. *Federation Proc.* 25: 1753–1760, 1966.
26. CASSON, N. A flow equation for pigment-oil suspensions of the printing ink type. In: *Rheology of Disperse Systems*, edited by C. C. Mill. London: Pergamon, 1959, p. 84–104.
27. CHATURANI, P., AND V. S. UPADHYA. A two-fluid model for blood flow through small diameter tubes. *Biorheology* 16: 109–118, 1979.
28. CHATURANI, P., AND V. S. UPADHYA. On micropolar fluid model for blood flow through narrow tubes. *Biorheology* 16: 419–428, 1979.
29. CHATURANI, P., AND V. S. UPADHYA. A two-fluid model for blood flow through small diameter tubes with non-zero couple stress boundary condition at interface. *Biorheology* 18: 245–254, 1981.
30. CHEN, T. C., AND R. SKALAK. Spheroidal particle flow in a cylindrical tube. *Appl. Sci. Res.* 22: 403–441, 1970.
31. CHIEN, S. Blood rheology and its relation to flow resistance and transcapillary exchange, with special reference to shock. *Adv. Microcirc.* 2: 89–103, 1969.
32. CHIEN, S. Present state of blood rheology. In: *Hemodilution, Theoretical Basis and Clinical Application*, edited by K. Messmer and H. Schmid-Schönbein. Basel: Karger, 1972, p. 1–40.
33. CHIEN, S. Biophysical behavior of red cells in suspensions. In: *The Red Blood Cell* (2nd ed.), edited by D. M. Surgenor. New York: Academic, 1975, vol. 2, p. 1031–1133.
34. CHIEN, S. Electrochemical interactions between erythrocyte surfaces. *Thromb. Res.* 8, Suppl. 2: 189–202, 1975.
35. CHIEN, S. Principles, and techniques for assessing erythrocyte deformability. *Blood Cells* 3: 71–99, 1977.
36. CHIEN, S. Aggregation of red blood cells: an electrochemical and colloid chemical problem. In: *Bioelectrochemistry: Ions, Surfaces, Membranes*, edited by M. Blank. Washington, DC: Am. Chem. Soc., 1980, p. 3–38.
37. CHIEN, S. Functional rheology of erythrocytes and leukocytes. In: *The Rheology of Blood, Blood Vessels, and Associated Tissues*, edited by D. R. Gross and N. H. C. Hwang; Amsterdam: Sijthoff & Noordhoff, 1981, p.118–136.
38. CHIEN, S., AND K.-M. JAN. Red cell aggregation by macromolecules: roles of surface adsorption and electrostatic repulsion. *J. Supramol. Struct.* 1: 385–409, 1973.
39. CHIEN, S., R. G. KING, R. SKALAK, S. USAMI, AND A. L. COPLEY. Viscoelastic properties of human blood and red cell suspensions. *Biorheology* 12: 341–346, 1975.
40. CHIEN, S., S. A. LUSE, AND C. A. BRYANT. Hemolysis during filtration through micropores: a scanning electron microscopic and hemorheologic correlation. *Microvasc. Res.* 3: 183–203, 1971.
41. CHIEN, S., A. L. SUNG, S. KIM, A. M. BURKE, AND S. USAMI. Determination of aggregation force in rouleaux by fluid mechanical technique. *Microvasc. Res.* 13: 327–333, 1977.
42. CHIEN, S., S. USAMI, AND J. F. BERTLES. Abnormal rheology of oxygenated blood in sickle cell anemia. *J. Clin. Invest.* 49: 623–634, 1970.
43. CHIEN, S., S. USAMI, R. J. DELLENBACK, AND C. A. BRYANT. Comparative hemorheology-hematological implications of species differences in blood viscosity. *Biorheology* 8: 35–57, 1971.
44. CHIEN, S., S. USAMI, R. J. DELLENBACK, AND M. I. GREGERSEN. Shear-dependent deformation of erythrocytes in rheology of human blood. *Am. J. Physiol.* 219: 136–142, 1970.
45. COHEN, W. D. Observations on the marginal band system of nucleated erythrocytes. *J. Cell Biol.* 78: 260–273, 1978.
46. COKELET, G. R. The rheology of human blood. In: *Biomechanics, Its Foundations and Objectives*, edited by Y. C. Fung, N. Perrone, and M. Anliker. Englewood Cliffs, NJ: Prentice-Hall, 1972, p. 63–103.
47. COKELET, G. R. Blood rheology interpreted through the flow properties of the red cell. In: *Microcirculation*, edited by J. Grayson and W. Zingg. New York: Plenum, 1976, vol. 1, p. 9–32.
48. COKELET, G. R., AND H. J. MEISELMAN. Rheological comparison of hemoglobin solutions and erythrocyte suspension. *Science* 162: 275–277, 1968.
49. COPLEY, A. L., R. G. KING, S. CHIEN, S. USAMI, R. SKALAK, AND C. R. HUANG. Microscopic observations of viscoelasticity of human blood in steady and oscillatory shear. *Biorheology* 12: 257–263, 1975.
50. COWIN, S. C. On the polar fluid as a model for blood flow in tubes. *Biorheology* 9: 23–25, 1972.
51. COWIN, S. C. The theory of polar fluids. *Adv. Appl. Mech.* 14: 279–347, 1974.
52. DAGAN, Z., R. PFEFFER, AND S. WEINBAUM. Theory and experiment on the three-dimensional motion of a freely suspended spherical particle at the entrance to a pore at low Reynolds number. *J. Fluid Mech.* 117: 143–170, 1982.
53. DAGAN, Z., S. WEINBAUM, AND R. PFEFFER. An infinite series solution for creeping motion through an orifice of finite length. *J. Fluid Mech.* 115: 505–523, 1982.
54. DINTENFASS, L. An inversion of the Fåhraeus-Lindqvist phenomenon in blood flow through capillaries of diminishing radius. *Nature London* 215: 1099–1100, 1967.
55. DULING, B. R., I. H. SARELIUS, AND W. F. JACKSON. Red cell flow, mass balance, hematocrit, and shunting in skeletal muscle microcirculation. *Int. J. Microcirc. Clin. Exp.* 1: 409–424, 1982.
56. ERINGEN, C. On bridging the gap between macroscopic and microscopic physics. *Recent Adv. Eng. Sci.* 6: 1–18, 1976.
57. EVANS, E. A. A new material concept for the red cell membrane. *Biophys. J.* 13: 926–940, 1973.
58. EVANS, E. A., AND K. BUXBAUM. Affinity of red blood cell membrane for particle surfaces measured by the extent of particle encapsulation. *Biophys. J.* 34: 1–12, 1981.
59. EVANS, E. A., AND Y. C. FUNG. Improved measurements of the erythrocyte geometry. *Microvasc. Res.* 4: 335–347, 1972.

60. EVANS, E. A., AND R. SKALAK. *Mechanics and Thermodynamics of Biomembranes.* Cleveland, OH: CRC, 1980.
61. EVANS, E. A., R. WAUGH, AND L. MELNIK. Elastic area compressibility modulus of red cell membrane. *Biophys. J.* 16: 585–595, 1976.
62. FAGRELL, B., M. INTAGLIETTA, AND J. ÖSTERGREN. Relative hematocrit in human skin capillaries and its relation to capillary blood flow velocity. *Microvasc. Res.* 20: 327–335, 1980.
63. FÅHRAEUS, R. Die Stromungsverhältnisse und die Verteilung der Blutzellen im Gefässystem. *Klin. Wochenschr.* 7: 100–106, 1928.
64. FÅHRAEUS, R. The suspension stability of blood. *Physiol. Rev.* 9: 241–274, 1929.
65. FÅHRAEUS, R., AND T. LINDQVIST. The viscosity of the blood in narrow capillary tubes. *Am. J. Physiol.* 96: 562–568, 1931.
66. FISCHER, T. M., C. W. M. HAEST, M. STÖHR-LIESEN, D. KAMP, AND B. DEUTICKE. Selective alteration of erythrocyte deformability by SH-reagents. Evidence for an involvement of spectrin in membrane shear elasticity. *Biochim. Biophys. Acta* 510: 270–282, 1978.
67. FISCHER, T. M., M. STÖHR-LIESEN, AND H. SCHMID-SCHÖNBEIN. The red cell as a fluid droplet: tank tread-like motion of the human erythrocyte membrane in shear flow. *Science* 202: 894–896, 1978.
68. FITZ-GERALD, J. M. Implications of a theory of erythrocyte motion in narrow capillaries. *J. Appl. Physiol.* 27: 912–918, 1969.
69. FITZ-GERALD, J. M. Mechanics of red-cell motion through very narrow capillaries. *Proc. R. Soc. London Ser. B* 174: 193–227, 1969.
70. FUNG, Y.-C. Stochastic flow in capillary blood vessels. *Microvasc. Res.* 5: 34–48, 1973.
71. FUNG, Y.-C. *Biomechanics, Mechanical Properties of Living Tissues.* New York: Springer-Verlag, 1981.
72. GAEHTGENS, P. Flow of blood through narrow capillaries: rheological mechanisms determining capillary hemotocrit and apparent viscosity. *Biorheology* 17: 183–189, 1980.
73. GAEHTGENS, P. *In vitro* studies of blood rheology in microscopic tubes. In: *The Rheology of Blood, Blood Vessels, and Associated Tissues*, edited by D. R. Gross and N. H. C. Hwang. Amsterdam: Sijthoff & Noordhoff, 1981, p. 257–275.
74. GAEHTGENS, P., K. H. ALBRECHT, AND F. KREUTZ. Fåhraeus-effect and cell screening during tube flow of human blood. I. Effect of variation of flow rate. *Biorheology* 15: 147–154, 1978.
75. GAEHTGENS, P., C. DÜHRSSEN, AND K. H. ALBRECHT. Motion, deformation, and interaction of blood cells and plasma during flow through narrow capillary tubes. *Blood Cells* 6: 799–817, 1980.
76. GAEHTGENS, P., F. KREUTZ, AND K. H. ALBRECHT. Fåhraeus-effect and cell screening during tube flow of human blood. II. Effect of dextran-induced cell aggregation. *Biorheology* 15: 155–161, 1978.
77. GAEHTGENS, P. A. L., AND H. D. PAPENFUSS. Effects of bifurcation on hematocrit reduction in the microcirculation. II. Experimental studies in narrow capillaries. *Bibl. Anat.* 18: 53–55, 1979.
78. GAEHTGENS, P., A. R. PRIES, AND K. H. ALBRECHT. Model experiments on the effect of bifurcations on capillary blood flow and oxygen transport. *Pfluegers Arch.* 380: 115–120, 1979.
79. GAEHTGENS, P., F. SCHMIDT, AND G. WILL. Comparative rheology of nucleated and non-nucleated red blood cells. I. Microrheology of avian erythrocytes during capillary flow. *Pfluegers Arch.* 390: 278–282, 1981.
80. GAEHTGENS, P., G. WILL, AND F. SCHMIDT. Comparative microrheology of avian and mammalian blood. In: *Advances in Physiological Sciences. Respiration*, edited by I. Hutas and L. A. Debreçzeni. Budapest: Akad. Kiado, 1981, vol. 10, p. 171–176.
81. GAEHTGENS, P., G. WILL, AND F. SCHMIDT. Comparative rheology of nucleated and non-nucleated red blood cells. II. Rheological properties of avian red cell suspensions in narrow capillaries. *Pfluegers Arch.* 390: 283–289, 1981.
82. GAUTHIER, F. J., G. L. GOLDSMITH, AND S. G. MASON. Flow of suspensions through tubes. X. Liquid drops as models of erythrocytes. *Biorheology* 9: 205–224, 1972.
83. GELIN, L. E. A method for studies of aggregation of blood cells, erythrostasis, and plasma skimming in branching capillary tubes. *Biorheology* 1: 119–127, 1963.
84. GERBSTADT, H. Blutviskositätswirksame Veränderungen mechanischer Kenngrössen der Erythrozyten. *Gefässwand Blutplasma* 4: 169–171, 1972.
85. GERBSTADT, H., C. VOGTMANN, P. RUTH, AND E. SCHONTUBE. Die Scheinviskosität von Blut in Glaskapillaren kleinster Durchmesser. *Naturwissenschaften* 53: 526, 1966.
86. GOLDSMITH, H. L. The microrheology of red blood cell suspensions. *J. Gen. Physiol.* 52, Suppl.: 5S–27S, 1968.
87. GOLDSMITH, H. L. Deformation of human red cells in tube flow. *Biorheology* 7: 235–242, 1971.
88. GOLDSMITH, H. L., AND S. CHIEN. Comparative microrheology: species difference in red cell flow behavior (*Abstract*). *Microcirc. Soc., 19th Annu. Meet., 1971.*
89. GOLDSMITH, H. L., AND T. KARINO. Physical and mathematical models of blood flow: experimental studies. In: *Erythrocyte Mechanics and Blood Flow*, edited by G. R. Cokelet, H. J. Meiselman, and D. E. Brooks. New York: Liss, 1980, p. 165–194.
90. GOLDSMITH, H. L., AND J. C. MARLOW. Flow behavior of erythrocytes. I. Rotation and deformation in dilute suspensions. *Proc. R. Soc. London Ser. B* 182: 351–384, 1972.
91. GOLDSMITH, H. L., AND J. C. MARLOW. Flow behavior of erythrocytes. *J. Colloid Interface Sci.* 71: 383–407, 1979.
92. GOLDSMITH, H. L., AND S. SPAIN. Distribution of human leucocytes in blood flowing through tubes. *Microvasc. Res.* 23: 254–255, 1982.
93. GREGERSEN, M. I., C. A. BRYANT, W. HAMMERLE, S. USAMI, AND S. CHIEN. Flow characteristics of human erythrocytes through polycarbonate sieves. *Science* 157: 825–827, 1967.
94. GROSS, J. F. The significance of pulsatile microhemodynamics. In: *Microcirculation*, edited by G. Kaley and B. Altura. Baltimore, MD: University Park, 1977, vol. 1, p. 365–390.
95. GROSS, J. F., M. INTAGLIETTA, AND B. W. ZWEIFACH. Network model of pulsatile hemodynamics in the microcirculation of the rabbit omentum. *Am. J. Physiol.* 246: 1117–1123, 1974.
96. GUEST, M. M., T. P. BOND, R. G. COOPER, AND J. R. DERRICK. Red blood cells: change in shape in capillaries. *Science* 142: 1319–1321, 1963.
97. HAGEN, G. Über die Bewegung des Wassers in engen cylindrischen Röhren. *Ann. Phys. Chem. Poggendorf.* 46: 423–442, 1839.
98. HAPPEL, J., AND H. BRENNER. *Low Reynolds Number Hydrodynamics.* Leiden, The Netherlands: Noordhoff, 1973.
99. HAYNES, R. H., AND A. C. BURTON. Role of the non-Newtonian behavior of blood in hemodynamics. *Am. J. Physiol.* 197: 943–950, 1959.
100. HOCHMUTH, R. M., AND D. O. DAVIS. Changes in hematocrit for blood flowing in narrow tubes. *Bibl. Anat.* 10: 59–65, 1969.
101. HOCHMUTH, R. M., R. N. MARPLE, AND P. SUTERA. Capillary blood flow. I. Erythrocyte deformation in capillaries. *Microvasc. Res.* 2: 409–419, 1970.
102. HOCHMUTH, R. M., N. MOHANDAS, AND P. L. BLACKSHEAR, JR. Measurement of the elastic modulus for red cell membrane using a fluid mechanical technique. *Biophys. J.* 13: 747–762, 1973.
103. JEFFREY, G. B. On the motion of ellipsoidal particles immersed in a viscous fluid. *Proc. R. Soc. London Ser. A* 102: 161–179, 1922.
104. JOHNSON, P. C., J. BLASCHKE, K. S. BURTON, AND J. H. DIAL. Influence of flow variations on capillary hematocrit in mesentery. *Am. J. Physiol.* 221: 105–112, 1971.
105. KANG, C. K., AND A. C. ERINGEN. The effect of microstructure on the rheological properties of blood. *Bull. Math. Biol.* 38: 135–159, 1976.
106. KANZOW, G., A. R. PRIES, AND P. GAEHTGENS. Analysis of the hematocrit distribution in the mesenteric microcirculation.

Int. J. Microcirc. Clin. Exp. 1: 67–79, 1982.
107. KELLER, S. R., AND R. SKALAK. Motion of a tank-treading ellipsoidal particle in a shear flow. *J. Fluid Mech.* 120: 27–47, 1982.
108. KLITZMAN, B., AND P. C. JOHNSON. Hematocrit, diameter, red cell flux, velocity, and flow: correlations and heterogeneities in striated muscle capillaries. *Bibl. Anat.* 20: 144–148, 1981.
109. KOPPEL, D. E., M. P. SHEETZ, AND M. SCHINDLER. Matrix control of protein diffusion in biological membranes. *Proc. Natl. Acad. Sci. USA* 78: 3576–3580, 1981.
110. KRIEGER, I. M. Shear rates in the Couette viscometer. *Trans. Soc. Rheol.* 12: 5–11, 1968.
111. KRISHNAKUMAR, C. K., A. A. ROVICK, AND Z. LAVAN. The effect of pressure pulsations on the Fåhraeus-Lindqvist effect. *Microvasc. Res.* 15: 245–249, 1978.
112. KROGH, A. *The Anatomy and Physiology of Capillaries.* New Haven, CT: Yale Univ. Press, 1922.
113. KUMIN, K. Bestimmung des Zähigkeitskoeffizienten für Rinderblut bei Newtonscher Strömung in verschieden weiten Röhren und Capillaren bei physiologischer Temperatur. Bern: Universität Bern, 1949. Dissertation.
114. LACELLE, P. L. Alteration of membrane deformability in hemolytic anemias. *Semin. Hematol.* 7: 355–371, 1970.
115. LEW, H. S., AND Y. C. FUNG. Entry flow blood vessels at arbitrary Reynolds number. *J. Biomech.* 3: 23–38, 1970.
116. LICHTMAN, M. A. Rheology of leukocytes, leukocyte suspensions and blood in leukemia. *J. Clin. Invest.* 52: 350–358, 1973.
117. LIGHTHILL, M. J. Pressure forcing of tightly fitting pellets along fluid-filled elastic tubes. *J. Fluid Mech.* 34: 113–143, 1968.
118. LINGARD, P. S. Capillary pore rheology of erythrocytes. IV. Effect of pore diameter and hematocrit. *Microvasc. Res.* 13: 59–77, 1977.
119. LINGARD, P. S. Capillary pore rheology of erythrocytes. V. The glass capillary array: effect of velocity and hematocrit in long bore tubes. *Microvasc. Res.* 17: 272–289, 1979.
120. LIPOWSKY, H. H., S. KOVALCHECK, AND B. W. ZWEIFACH. The distribution of blood rheological parameters in the microvasculature of cat mesentery. *Circ. Res.* 43: 738–349, 1978.
121. LIPOWSKY, H. H., S. USAMI, AND S. CHIEN. *In vivo* measurements of "apparent viscosity" and microvessel hematocrit in the mesentery of the cat. *Microvasc. Res.* 19: 297–319, 1980.
122. LUX, S. Dissection of the red cell membrane skeleton. *Nature London* 281: 426–429, 1979.
123. MCCOMIS, W. T., S. E. CHARM, AND G. KURLAND. Pulsing blood flow in capillary tubes. *Am. J. Physiol.* 212: 49–53, 1967.
124. MEISELMAN, H. J. Rheology of shape-transformed human red cells. *Biorheology* 15: 225–237, 1978.
125. MILLER, M. E., AND K. A. MYERS. Cellular deformability of the human peripheral blood polymorphonuclear leukocyte: method of study, normal variation, effects of physical and chemical alterations. *J. Reticuloendothel. Soc.* 18: 337–345, 1975.
126. MONRO, P. A. G. The appearance of cell-free plasma and "grouping" of red blood cells in normal circulation in small blood vessels observed *in vivo*. *Biorheology* 1: 239–246, 1963.
127. NOBIS, U., AND P. GAEHTGENS. Rheology of white blood cells during blood flow through narrow tubes. *Bibl. Anat.* 20: 211–214, 1981.
128. OKA, S. Theoretical considerations on the flow of blood through a capillary. In: *Proc. Int. Congr. Rheol., 4th, Providence, Rhode Island 1963* (Pt. 4: Symp. Biorheol.), edited by A. L. Copley. New York: Interscience, 1965, p. 89–102.
129. OKA, S. *Rheology and Biorheology* [in Japanese, English summary]. Tokyo: Syokabo, 1974.
130. PALMER, A. A. Axial drift of cells and partial plasma skimming in blood flowing through glass slits. *Am. J. Physiol.* 209: 1115–1122, 1965.
131. PALMER, A. A. Platelet and leukocyte skimming. *Bibl. Anat.* 9: 300–303, 1967.
132. PALMER, A. A., AND W. H. BETTS. The influence of gravity on plasma skimming and axial drift of red cells. *Bibl. Anat.* 11: 63–68, 1973.
133. PALMER, A. A., AND H. J. JEDRZEJCZYK. The influence of rouleaux on the resistance to flow through capillary channels at various shear rates. *Biorheology* 12: 265–270, 1975.
134. PAPENFUSS, H. D., AND P. A. L. GAEHTGENS. Effect of bifurcations on hematocrit reduction in the microcirculation. *Bibl. Anat.* 18: 50–52, 1979.
135. POPEL, A. S. Effect of heterogeneity of capillary flow on the capillary hematocrit. In: *1979 Biomechanics Symposium*, edited by W. C. van Buskirk. New York: Am. Soc. Mech. Eng., 1979, p. 83–84.
136. POPEL, A. S., S. A. REGIRER, AND P. I. USICK. A continuum model of blood flow. *Biorheology* 11: 427–437, 1974.
137. PROTHERO, J., AND A. C. BURTON. The physics of blood flow in capillaries. III. Pressure required to deform erythrocytes. *Biophys. J.* 2: 213–222, 1962.
138. QUEMADA, D. Rheology of concentrated disperse systems and minimum energy principle. I. Viscosity concentration relationship. *Rheol. Acta* 16: 82–94, 1977.
139. QUEMADA, D. Rheology of concentrated disperse systems. II. A model for non-Newtonian shear viscosity in steady flows. *Rheol. Acta* 17: 632–642, 1978.
140. QUEMADA, D. Rheology of concentrated disperse systems. III. General features of the proposed non-Newtonian model. Comparison with experimental data. *Rheol. Acta* 17: 643–653, 1978.
141. RAKOW, A. L., AND R. M. HOCHMUTH. Thermal transition in the human erythrocyte membrane: effect on elasticity. *Biorheology* 12: 1–3, 1975.
142. RUBINOW, S. I., AND J. B. KELLER. Flow of a viscous fluid through an elastic tube with applications to blood flow. *J. Theor. Biol.* 35: 299–313, 1972.
143. SCHMID-SCHÖNBEIN, G. W., AND S. CHIEN. Deformation and damage of leukocytes on a hematological blood film. *Federation Proc.* 40: 754, 1981.
144. SCHMID-SCHÖNBEIN, G. W., Y. Y. SHIH, AND S. CHIEN. Morphometry of human leukocytes. *Blood* 56: 866–875, 1980.
145. SCHMID-SCHÖNBEIN, G. W., R. SKALAK, S. USAMI, AND S. CHIEN. Cell distribution in capillary networks. *Microvasc. Res.* 19: 18–44, 1980.
146. SCHMID-SCHÖNBEIN, G. W., K. L. P. SUNG, AND S. CHIEN. Human leukocytes in the passive and active state. *Microvasc. Res.* 21: 256–257, 1981.
147. SCHMID-SCHÖNBEIN, G. W., K. L. P. SUNG, H. TÖZEREN, R. SKALAK, AND S. CHIEN. Passive mechanical properties of human leukocytes. *Biophys. J.*, 36: 243–256, 1981.
148. SCHMID-SCHÖNBEIN, G. W., S. USAMI, R. SKALAK, AND S. CHIEN. The interaction of leukocytes and erythrocytes in capillary and postcapillary vessels. *Microvasc. Res.* 19: 45–70, 1980.
149. SCHMID-SCHÖNBEIN, H. Microrheology of erythrocytes, blood viscosity, and the distribution of blood in the microcirculation. In: *Cardiovascular Physiology II*, edited by A. C. Guyton and A. W. Cowley, Jr. Baltimore, MD: University Park, 1976, vol. 9, p. 1–62.
150. SCHMID-SCHÖNBEIN, H., T. FISCHER, G. DREISSEN, AND H. RIEGER. Microcirculation. In: *Quantitative Cardiovascular Studies*, edited by N. H. C. Hwang, D. R. Gross, and D. J. Patel. Baltimore, MD: University Park, 1979, p. 353–417.
151. SCHMID-SCHÖNBEIN, H., P. GAEHTGENS, AND H. HIRSCH. On the shear rate dependence of red cell aggregation in vitro. *J. Clin. Invest.* 47: 1447–1454, 1968.
152. SCHMID-SCHÖNBEIN, H., AND R. WELLS. Fluid drop-like transition of erythrocytes under shear. *Science* 165: 288–291, 1969.
153. SECOMB, T. W., AND R. SKALAK. Rheology of highly concentrated red blood cell suspensions. In: *Advances in Bioengineering*, edited by D. C. Viano. New York: Am. Soc. Mech. Eng., 1981, p. 143–148.
154. SECOMB, T. W., AND R. SKALAK. A two-dimensional model for capillary flow of an asymmetric cell. *Microvasc. Res.* 24:

194–203, 1982.

155. SEGEL, G. B., G. R. COKELET, AND M. A. LICHTMAN. The measurement of lymphocyte volume: importance of reference particle deformability and counting solution tonicity. *Blood* 57: 894–899, 1981.
156. SEGRÉ, C. T., AND A. SILBERBERG. Behavior of macroscopic rigid spheres in Poiseuille flow. *J. Fluid Mech.* 14: 115–157, 1962.
157. SESHADRI, V., C. MCKAY, AND M. Y. JAFFRIN. The effect of red blood cell flexibility on blood flow through tubes with diameters in the range 30 to 500 microns. *Biorheology* 16: 473–483, 1979.
158. SINGER, S. J. Architecture and topography of biological membranes. In: *Cell Membranes: Biochemistry, Cell Biology and Pathology*, edited by G. Wasserman and R. Claiborne. New York: Hosp. Practice, 1975, p. 35.
158a. SINGH, M., AND N. A. COULTER, JR. Fåhraeus-Lindqvist effect in oscillatory flow. *Biorheology* 16: 119–120, 1979.
159. SKALAK, R., AND P.-I. BRÅNEMARK. Deformation of red blood cells in capillaries. *Science* 164: 717–719, 1969.
160. SKALAK, R., P. H. CHEN, AND S. CHIEN. Effect of hematocrit and rouleaux on apparent viscosity in capillaries. *Biorheology* 9: 67–82, 1972.
161. SKALAK, R., AND S. CHIEN. Capillary flow: history, experiments and theory. *Biorheology* 18: 307–330, 1981.
162. SKALAK, R., AND H. TÖZEREN. Flow mechanics in the microcirculation. In: *Mathematics of Microcirculation Phenomena*, edited by J. F. Gross and A. Popel. New York: Raven, 1980, p. 17–40.
163. SKALAK, R., A. TÖZEREN, P. R. ZARDA, AND S. CHIEN. Strain energy function of red blood cell membranes. *Biophys. J.* 13: 245–264, 1973.
164. SKALAK, R., P. R. ZARDA, K. M. JAN, AND S. CHIEN. Theory of rouleau formation. In: *Cardiovascular and Pulmonary Dynamics*, edited by M. Y. Jaffrin. Paris: INSERM, 1978, p. 299–308.
165. SKALAK, R., P. R. ZARDA, K. M. JAN, AND S. CHIEN. Mechanics of rouleau formation. *Biophys. J.* 35: 771–781, 1981.
166. SMAJE, L. H., P. A. FRASER, AND G. CLOUGH. The distensibility of single capillaries and venules in the cat mesentery. *Microvasc. Res.* 20: 358–370, 1980.
167. STECK, T. L. The band 3 protein of the human red cell membranes: a review. *J. Supramolec. Struct.* 8: 311–324, 1978.
168. SUNG, K. L. P., G. W. SCHMID-SCHÖNBEIN, R. SKALAK, G. B. SCHUESSLER, S. USAMI, AND S. CHIEN. Influence of physicochemical factors on rheology of human neutrophils. *Biophys. J.* 39: 101–106, 1982.
169. SUTERA, S. P. Red cell motion and deformation in the microcirculation. In: *Cardiovascular and Pulmonary Dynamics*, edited by M. Y. Jaffrin. Paris: INSERM, 1978, p. 221–241.
170. SVANES, S. R., AND B. W. ZWEIFACH. Variations in small blood vessel hematocrits produced in hypothermic rats by micro-occlusion. *Microvasc. Res.* 1: 210–221, 1968.
171. THURSTON, G. B. Viscoelasticity of human blood. *Biophys. J.* 12: 1205–1217, 1972.
172. THURSTON, G. B. The viscosity and viscoelasticity of blood in small diameter tubes. *Microvasc. Res.* 11: 133–146, 1976.
173. THURSTON, G. B. Rheological parameters for the viscosity, viscoelasticity and thixotropy of blood. *Biorheology* 16: 149–162, 1979.
174. TÖZEREN, A., AND R. SKALAK. Micropolar fluids as models for suspensions of rigid spheres. *Int. J. Eng. Sci.* 15: 511–523, 1977.
175. TÖZEREN, H. Torque on eccentric spheres flowing in tubes. *J. Appl. Mech.* 49: 279–283, 1982.
176. TÖZEREN, H., AND R. SKALAK. The steady flow of closely fitting incompressible elastic spheres in a tube. *J. Fluid Mech.* 87: 1–16, 1978.
177. TÖZEREN, H., AND R. SKALAK. Flow of elastic compressible spheres in tubes. *J. Fluid Mech.* 95: 743–760, 1979.
178. USAMI, S. Physiological significance of blood rheology. *Biorheology* 19: 29–42, 1982.
179. USAMI, S., AND S. CHIEN. Shear deformation of red cell ghosts. *Biorheology* 10: 425–430, 1973.
180. USAMI, S., R. G. KING, S. CHIEN, R. SKALAK, C. R. HUANG, AND A. L. COPLEY. Microcinephotographic studies on red cell aggregation in steady and oscillatory shear—a note. *Biorheology* 12: 323–325, 1975.
181. USAMI, S., V. MAGAZINOVIĆ, S. CHIEN, AND M. I. GREGERSEN. Viscosity of turkey blood: rheology of nucleated erythrocytes. *Microvasc. Res.* 2: 489–499, 1970.
182. VEJLENS, G. The distribution of leukocytes in vascular system. *Acta Pathol. Microbiol. Scand. Suppl.* 33: 11–239, 1938.
183. WANG, H., AND R. SKALAK. Viscous flow in a cylindrical tube containing a line of spherical particles. *J. Fluid Mech.* 38: 75–96, 1969.
184. WAUGH, R., AND E. A. EVANS. Viscoelastic properties of erythrocyte membranes of different vertebrate animals. *Microvasc. Res.* 12: 291–304, 1976.
185. WAYLAND, H., AND P. C. JOHNSON. Erythrocyte velocity measurement in microvessels by two-split photometric method. *J. Appl. Physiol.* 22: 333–337, 1967.
186. WHITMORE, R. L. A theory of blood flow in small vessels. *J. Appl. Physiol.* 22: 767–771, 1967.
187. WHITTAKER, S. R. F., AND F. R. WINTON. The apparent viscosity of blood flowing in the isolated hindlimb of the dog and its variation with corpuscular concentration. *J. Physiol. London* 78: 339–369, 1933.
188. YEN, R. T., AND Y. C. FUNG. Inversion of Fåhraeus effect and effect of mainstream flow on capillary hematocrit. *J. Appl. Physiol.: Respirat. Environ. Exercise Physiol.* 42: 578–586, 1977.
189. YEN, R. T., AND Y. C. FUNG. Effect of velocity distribution on red cell distribution in capillary blood vessels. *Am. J. Physiol.* 235 (*Heart Circ. Physiol.* 4): H251–H257, 1978.
190. ZARDA, P. R., R. SKALAK, AND S. CHIEN. Elastic deformation of red blood cells. *J. Biomech.* 10: 211–221, 1977.

CHAPTER 7

Pressure-flow relations in blood and lymph microcirculation

BENJAMIN W. ZWEIFACH | *AMES-Bioengineering, University of California, San Diego, La Jolla, California*

HERBERT H. LIPOWSKY | *Department of Physiology, College of Physicians and Surgeons, Columbia University, New York City*

CHAPTER CONTENTS

Microvessel Pressures
- Background
  - Modular configuration of network
  - Terminology
- Microvessel pressure measurement
- Systemic pressure dissipation
  - Effect of vessel dimensions
  - Branching considerations
  - Pressure distribution in successive segments
  - Venous vessels
- Microvessel pressure variability
- Systemic pressure versus microvessel pressure
- Capillary pressure
  - Early measurements
  - Isogravimetric pressures
  - Pressure drop within capillary network
  - Local regulation of capillary pressure
  - Microvessel pressure and fluid exchange
  - Capillary pressure in humans
- Shunts
- Anesthesia and microvessel pressure
- Hypertension

Microvessel Blood Flow
- General considerations
- Velocity relationships
- Flow distribution
- Capillary flow
- Capillary flow in humans
- Microvessel number
- Capillary recruitment

Microvascular Control Mechanisms
- Vascular tone
- Central versus local
- Myogenic adjustments
- Vasomotion
- Oxygen tension and local adjustments
- Ancillary factors
- Blood rheology
- Sympathetic innervation

Rheological Behavior of Blood Flow in the Microcirculation
- Background
  - Conceptual framework
  - Rheological properties of blood
  - Macrocirculatory studies of in vivo blood rheology
- Network distributions of hemodynamic parameters
  - Intravascular pressure
  - Volumetric flow rates
  - Ratio of precapillary resistance to postcapillary resistance
- Hemodynamics in individual microvessels
  - Pressure gradients
  - Resistance versus luminal diameter
  - Apparent viscosity
  - Microvessel hematocrit
  - Phenomena related to shear rate
  - Branch points and bifurcations
- Mathematical modeling of network hemodynamics
  - Lumped-parameter models
  - Distributive models
  - Discrete-network models

Pressure-Flow Relations in Extravascular Systems
- Interstitium
- Terminal lymphatics
- Lymphatic pressures
- Interstitial transport
- Tissue pressure
- Extravascular flow system

MODULATION OF THE MICROCIRCULATION to match the changing metabolic needs of the parenchymal cells requires integrated adjustments of the driving hydraulic pressure in conjunction with the selective distribution of the bloodstream. Such locally directed adjustments involve both structural and functional features that are unique to the extreme peripheral portion of the vascular tree and operate through a series of feedbacks that is linked either directly or indirectly to the biochemical activities of the tissue. Activation of these control systems is related not only to the delivery of essential substrates for oxidative processes but to the accumulation of by-products of cell metabolism that under steady-state conditions are continuously removed or degraded to a biologically inert form. Recent evidence indicates participation of a coupled series of reactions concerned with the formation and removal of specific vasoactive substances. The structural entity around which such controls operate is the most peripheral portion of the arterial tree, the arterioles. Inasmuch as these minute vessels represent the bridge between the large systemic arteries and the microscopic precapillaries and the capillaries proper, the arterioles are involved in two sets of

branches. As a consequence of the predominantly parallel deployment of the precapillary and capillary vessels, the overall impact of their high individual resistances is substantially reduced (251, 303).

The main exchange vessels, the true capillaries, arise directly from the precapillaries, each of which delivers 3–5 capillaries. Two types of transition are seen from the precapillary arterioles into the capillaries proper (302). As the successive arterioles branch dichotomously, the smooth muscle layer becomes progressively attenuated until in the A4 arterioles smooth muscle cells are no longer present. On the other hand the transverse arterioles distribute numerous side-arm branches along which the smooth muscle coat is terminated abruptly, but not until several muscle cells have encircled the proximal portion of the lateral offshoot for 20–30 μm. In skeletal muscle as many as 4–8 of these lateral branches are given off. The direct continuation of the parent arteriole finally terminates by dividing into two capillary-sized extensions. Smooth muscle cells do not reappear in the microvascular network until the 25- to 30-μm venules are formed.

By virtue of this general design, local controls can have a selective action on the small muscular vessels just proximal to and distal to the key set of exchange vessels, the network of true capillaries. Because of their small size and favorable ratio of wall thickness to lumen, the microscopic arterioles are capable of vasomotor changes that range from complete closure to maximal diameters 1.5–2.0 times greater than that prevailing under steady-state conditions.

Because the dimensions of the smallest microvessels and those of the blood cells are approximately of the same order in a given species, the flow properties of the blood itself become an increasingly important determinant of the distribution of red blood cells and the frictional resistance encountered. The rheological properties of the blood and its cellular components are discussed in detail in the chapter by Chien, Usami, and Skalak in this *Handbook.*

Microvascular topology thus represents a basic determinant of the distribution of pressure and flow. Superimposed onto these structural constraints are active adjustments that affect not only pressure and/or flow but the number of exchange vessels actively perfused. In an analysis of the optimal design of microvascular networks, Mayrovitz and Roy (250) concluded that the overall arrangement in the bat wing and the rat cremaster muscle made volumetric flow (Q) everywhere proportional to the cube of the vessel radius r ($Q = kr^3$) to provide optimal exchange per unit of flow, a relationship Murray (265) originally postulated.

Microvessel Pressure Measurement

Microvessel pressures have been measured in two ways, by direct intubation of capillary-sized vessels (101, 215, 359, 361) and indirectly by mechanical obstruction and release until flow appears under known pressures (3, 4). The resurgence of direct measurements in recent years was due largely to the development and refinement of an electrical-null method that used saline-filled glass micropipettes as sensors (171, 178, 368).

The earliest numerical estimates for pressure distribution were obtained by Roy and Brown (313), who used a transparent distensible bag that could be inflated under a known head of pressure and attached to the microscope objective so that the effect on flow in the surface microvessels could be observed as pressure was applied and released (Fig. 2). Hill (159) and Algire (3) used a similar approach and estimated vessel pressures in a transparent skin chamber inserted into the back of mice. By noting the points at which flow resumed when pressure was released from an inflated bag and at which flow stopped as pressure was elevated, values were obtained for vessels ranging from 6- to 8-μm capillaries to 100-μm arteries and veins. Such estimates are flawed by errors introduced by the need to deform not only overlying supporting structures but also vessels with different wall thicknesses. Algire's data compare reasonably well with more recent measurements obtained by direct intubation of the vessels in the subcutaneous tissue of the bat wing by Nicoll (ref. 272; Table 1).

In his pioneering studies on pressure-related aspects

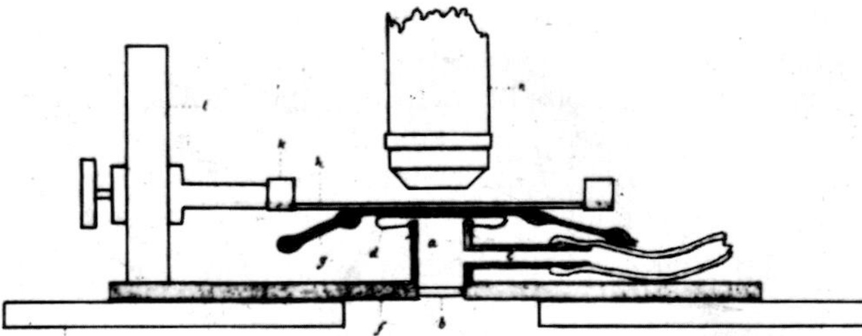

FIG. 2. Transparent bag originally used by Roy and Brown (313) in 1888 to mechanically occlude microvessel flow under a known head of air pressure. Stoppage or onset of red cell movement was observed via the microscope coincident with the application of pressure and its release. [From Krogh (210).]

TABLE 1. *Estimates of Microvessel Pressure*

	Diameter, μm	Micropressure, mmHg	
		Mouse skin*	Bat wing†
Small artery	70	70–95	65–80
Arteriole	30	60–70	50–60
Precapillary	8	35–50	40–50
Capillary	5	20–25	20–30
Postcapillary	10	10–17	16–21
Venule			
Small	20	16–18	14–16
Large	40	10–14	23‡
Small vein	50	8–10	20‡

* Data from Algire (3, 4), transparent-capsule method. † Data from Nicoll (272), micropipette intubation. ‡ Displays active vasomotion.

of fluid exchange across the capillary wall, Landis (215, 216) obtained estimates of micropressures by a hydraulic linkage with a micropipette inserted into these vessels; he observed the pressure needed to force dyed fluid into the selected microvessels (Table 2).

In an attempt to improve the accuracy and time characteristics of the micropipette pressure sensors, Rappaport et al. (298) and Levasseur et al. (227) devised modifications in which the signal was processed electrically. The tendency to drift and problems of calibration made these systems impractical. Another modification by Nicoll (272) provided spot measurements of short duration in bat wing microvessels. Not until the development of the electrical-null micropipette sensor by Wiederhielm et al. (360) and its improvement by Intaglietta et al. (172, 175) did acceptable micropressure information become available under steady-state conditions and following specific perturbations. This system has provided serial measurements of micropressures in mesentery (109, 124), omentum (175, 180), skin (228), skeletal muscle (39, 104, 105, 374), pial surface of the brain (323, 335), intestinal wall (37, 38), frog lung (248), and the heart (340, 341).

Systemic Pressure Dissipation

The contractile action of the heart provides the driving force for the bloodstream. This force is transmitted along the vascular tree as a pressure wave that is gradually dissipated by resistance encountered as the vessels subdivide and narrow. Maximal pressure drop across the microcirculatory network does not occur at a fixed anatomical position but may be shifted according to the functional state of the network. The greatest part of this pressure reduction occurs in vessels <100 μm in diameter. Even in the supply arteries 100–150 μm wide that actually penetrate the tissue, pressures are essentially the same as in the major arterial pipelines of the vascular tree. On the other hand pressures in the capillary network average 20–25 mmHg, a net reduction in arterial hydrostatic pressure of ~75%–80%. It is significant that irrespective of organ size and function, pressures in the precapillary and capillary vessels fall into essentially the same range in the various tissues used for intravital

TABLE 2. *Mesentery Blood Pressure*

	Aorta	Artery	Arteriole	Capillary	Postcapillary	Venule
Rat						
Average	97	96	50.5	30	1.7	14.5
Highest	108	110	52	34	20	15
Lowest	88	70	40	22	15	12
Guinea pig						
Average	110	106	76	38.5	17	12.5
Highest	115	118	97	49	19.5	14
Lowest	98	90	60	31	13	10

Values in cmH_2O. [Adapted from Landis (215).]

microscopy. Such an equilibration occurs despite the fact that input pressures in different regions of a given species may range from 90 mmHg in skeletal muscles of the limb to 60 mmHg for muscles in the shoulder region. On the venous side of the microcirculation the pressure gradient is much shallower, except for the mechanical differences imposed by gravitational factors in dependent structures during the upright position.

Dissipation of the hydrostatic force driving the bloodstream is mainly due to frictional losses encountered in moving the blood through progressively narrower conduits. For the network as a whole, vessel number, length, diameter, and branching characteristics are the primary features involved. Small differences in any one of these structural attributes are sufficient to shift pressure and flow distribution in particular tissues. In addition the ratios of wall thickness to lumen and the elastin content (factors determining compliance of arteriolar and venular vessels) contribute to the overall reduction in pressure and flow. The capillaries are relatively nondistensible despite their thin walls and act as tunnels in a gel (64, 108). The capillary network proper thus contributes to the degradation of pressure by virtue of the narrow caliber and large number of the vessels. Capillary diameters range from 4.0 μm in the omentum of mammals to ~7.0–7.5 μm in the skin; diameters as low as 3.1–3.5 μm are based on histological cross sections and are suspect because of fixation artifacts.

Blood hematocrit is much lower in capillary-sized vessels, the concentration of red blood cells being one-third of that in systemic levels. Blood leukocytes that are larger and much less deformable than the erythrocytes frequently block flow in individual capillaries from 5–10 s up to several minutes. A combination of these factors contributes to the shifting red cell velocity and the variable distribution of cells even under normal steady-state flow (188, 193, 194, 197).

Representative pressure values are shown in Table 3 for different modular patterns. Part A compares several in-series types of beds and part B compares pressure levels in four of the muscles commonly used for intravital microscopy. The total pressure drop across a given module is essentially the same (60% and 64%) for the two splanchnic tissues in which complete pressure distributions have been mapped out. The differences in the micropressure profiles for skeletal muscle and the omentum or mesentery are mainly due to anatomical peculiarities. Interestingly, any given segment of the skeletal muscle network shows almost the same pressures as those measured in the mesentery (327).

EFFECT OF VESSEL DIMENSIONS. Generally the pressure gradient within the network is a function of the diminishing diameter of the successive branching orders, with the sharpest fall occurring in the region of the narrowest arterioles—the A3 arterioles and their

TABLE 3. *Microvessel Pressure Distribution*

	A. Two-Dimensional Arrays								
	Arterial diameter, μm				Venous diameter, μm				Ref.
	40–50	30	20	10	15	20	30	40–50	
Rabbit omentum	51	38	33	28	27	24	22	20	238
Cat mesentery	67	50	38	33	30	28	26	24	370
Cat brain (pia mater)	72	55	45						323
Bat wing	69	46	36	19	16	14	*	*	272
	B. Skeletal Muscle								
	A1	A2	A3	A4	V4	V3	V2	V1	Ref.
Rat spinotrapezius	66	43	30	24	16	13	10	5	374
Rat cremaster	90	39	28	24	22	17	12	9	39
Rat anterior gracilis	90	55	43	26			10		156
Cat tenuissimus	93	84	68	39	24	18	15	12	105

Values are mean pressures in mmHg. Arterial (A) and venous (V) dichotomous branchings numbered beginning with sector that feeds the arteries. * Region of active venous vasomotion.

A4 precapillary branches. A logarithmic plot of micropressure versus diameter in rabbit omentum can be fitted by a regression line that follows the exponential relationship predicted by the Poiseuille-Hagen formulation for flow in single large vessels (Fig. 3). Thus despite the involvement of a complex array of factors that includes vessel length, diameter, branching, in-series versus in-parallel deployment, blood rheological variants, and possible inertial factors, the flow for the network as a whole has the characteristics of a Newtonian fluid.

The pressure drop along the length of larger microvessels (>30 μm) averages 0.1–0.2 cmH_2O/100 μm. In narrower vessels (e.g., 18- to 20-μm terminal arterioles), $\Delta P/\Delta l$ increases 50%–70% to 0.3–0.4 cmH_2O/100 μm. In 6- to 9-μm capillaries dP/dl ranges from 0.6 to 1.2 cmH_2O/100 μm depending on the exact diameter. Figure 4 shows that the pressure drop is 8 times greater along individual capillaries than in the 50-μm arterioles. However, due to their short length and simple branching, capillary pressures decrease more gradually than on the precapillary side. On the venous side $\Delta P/\Delta l$ values remain comparatively high until the region of the large muscular venules, primarily because of blood rheological factors combined with the low flow rate in these vessels.

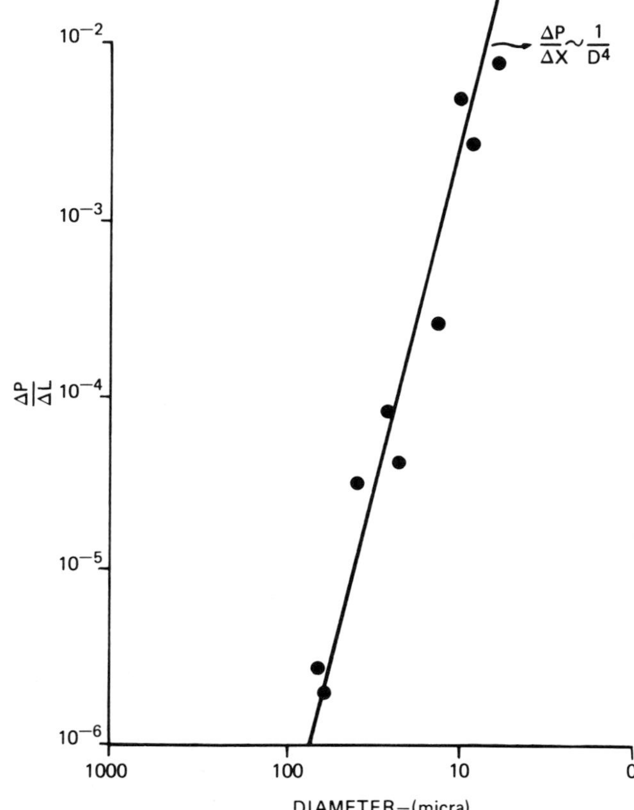

FIG. 3. Pressure versus vessel length relationships across the microvascular network plotted with log coordinates. An essentially linear distribution is seen in which the slope of the fitted regression line can be represented by an exponential function of diameter as predicted by the Poiseuille equation. [Data from Intaglietta and Zweifach (180), by permission of the American Heart Association, Inc.]

BRANCHING CONSIDERATIONS. The major site of peripheral resistance, determined from direct measurements of flow and pressure, is located in the precapillary portion of the microvascular network. Most of this resistance is encountered in the region of the A4 type of vessel. Branching of the larger vessels occurs primarily by repeated dichotomous division into two vessels (daughters) of essentially the same diameter. At such junctions there is no significant impediment to the movement of blood. In contrast the long muscular A3 arterioles have numerous side-arm offshoots that are usually much narrower than the parent arteriole. Because of the presence of spirally arranged muscle in both the parent stem and the lateral offshoot, entrance into the daughter is restricted by foldings of the vessel wall and a necklike pinching of the junctional segment. Several branchings are shown for the rat mesentery (Fig. 5). Junctions of this type are characteristic of precapillary sphincters. The in-

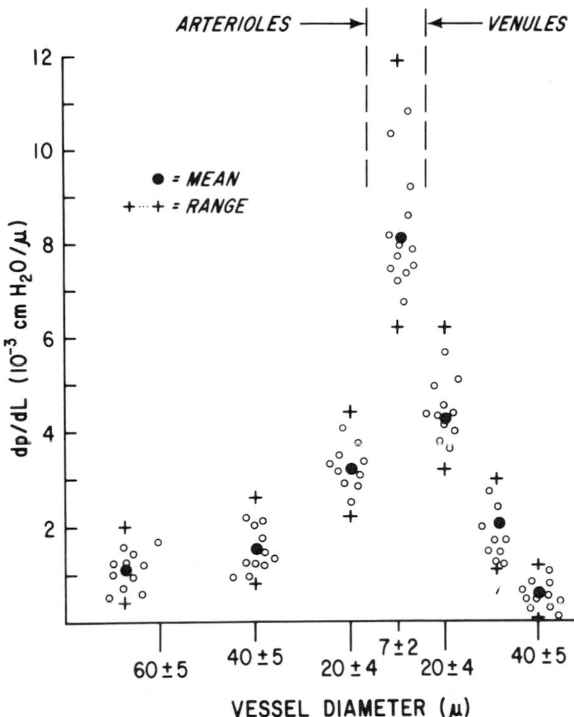

FIG. 4. Plot of the pressure drop in cat mesentery across successive branchings of decreasing diameter. Note the sharp increase in resistance encountered along vessels ≤20 μm wide. Capillary dp/dL is 4 times the dp/dL for the 40-μm arteriole. [From Zweifach (371), by permission of the American Heart Association, Inc.]

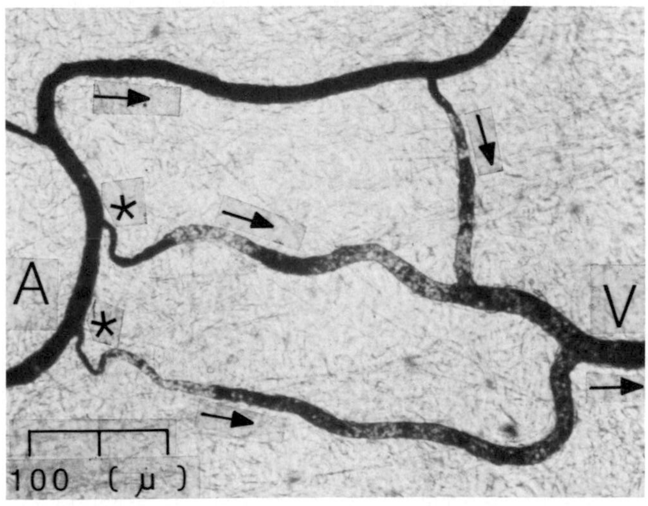

FIG. 5. In vivo photograph of rat mesenteric microvessels after intravenous injection of colloidal carbon. Precapillary sphincter deployment of side-arm branches with necklike strictures at immediate junction (*). Capillary portion of vessels then becomes progressively wider toward venous end. *V*, venous; *A*, arterial. *Arrows*, direction of flow. × 100. [From Zweifach (371).]

creased resistance encountered in this structural configuration sharply reduces pressure and flow, and consequently the vessel shows a gradual increase in diameter as it courses toward the venous side.

Inasmuch as both the parent and daughter are invested with smooth muscle, such entry conditions can be modified actively in both directions. Individual differences in the spontaneous vasomotion of the two vessels can result in a partial narrowing of the parent arterioles while the daughter is narrowed to the point of flow stoppage. The high resistance at these points is made physically evident by the distortion of red blood cells as they traverse the entrance to the daughter.

TABLE 4. *Pressure Drop Across Arteriole-Precapillary Branching Configuration*

	Diameter, μm	Pressure, mmHg	Ratio, d_p/d_d*	Drop, %
Parent	22	41	2.1	15
Daughter	11	35		
Parent	47	56	2.4	18
Daughter	19	46		
Parent	43	53	3.3	25
Daughter	13	40		

* Ratio of parent diameter to daughter diameter. [Adapted from Vawter, Fung, and Zweifach (345).]

Vawter, Fung, and Zweifach (345) analyzed in detail the pressure drop across branching configurations. At the region of the A3 arterioles where side-arm branches are usually only one-third as wide as the parent (branching ratio of 0.2–0.3), pressure in the daughter is 25%–30% lower than in the parent stem. Thus the pressure drop across such lateral branching points is much greater than the pressure dissipation by frictional interaction across the entire length of even a 6-μm-wide capillary. In the latter $\Delta P/\Delta l$ is ~1.0–1.5 mmHg/200 μm. The pressure drop in unbranched arteriolar vessels 50–100 μm wide and as long as 1,500 μm is <1 mmHg. In the majority of cases the parent-to-daughter vessel diameter ratio is > 2.0, so that the resulting fall in pressure is substantially greater (Table 4). The narrow neck in the precapillary branch further exaggerates the pressure drop, and a slight narrowing of the branch frequently results in a complete stoppage of flow into the side-arm branch. The absolute pressure drop across a given branching configuration is linearly related to the pressure level in the feeding vessel (345). Such muscular branching complexes allow adjustments to be made in either or both components and thus provide a greater degree of control for local blood pressure adjustments than that afforded by the Poiseuille lr^4 relationship for flow along a simple tube.

PRESSURE DISTRIBUTION IN SUCCESSIVE SEGMENTS. As arterial vessels subdivide in the tissue they interconnect to form arcading structures that by virtue of their interlocking pattern demarcate circumscribed masses of tissue (102). The accompanying veins go through similar end-to-end anastomoses. Discrete sectors are thus bounded on their periphery by an arcade of paired arterioles and venules 40–60 μm in diameter. These circumscribed areas vary in size from 2.5×10^4

to 8.1 × 10^4 μm^2 (102) and are vascularized by a network supplied by two or three terminal arterioles and collecting venules. An arcading pattern of arteriole-to-arteriole and venule-to-venule interconnections tends to balance out pressure differences in the feeding and effluent vessels for a particular area.

In a tissue such as mesentery, pressures in the larger microvessels (50–150 μm) on the arterial side are directly proportional to those in the superior mesenteric artery. Gore (124) found essentially a 1:1 relationship between experimental perturbations in central arterial pressure and pressures in the larger arterioles (diam >65 μm) of the isolated cat mesentery. Once the terminal branching pattern is introduced, pressure is not only reduced sharply but also falls within a comparatively narrow range dictated by the structural peculiarities of the final muscular branches. In different tissues these vessels are designated as terminal arterioles, metarterioles, or precapillaries (367, 372). Diameters of individual vessels vary by up to 30%–40% in any given branching order, making it necessary to take into account their actual distribution because the diameter factor by itself strongly influences the hydraulic hindrance (d^2).

Detailed measurements of physical dimensions are available for microvessels of rabbit omentum (180), cat mesentery (158, 159, 238, 239), bat wing (275, 358, 359), and for several skeletal muscles in the rat (374, 376) and cat (103, 105). Table 5 shows diameter data for the omentum, mesentery, and bat wing as examples of a dichotomous type of microvessel deployment. The cremaster and spinotrapezius muscle beds represent patterns with a larger number of in-parallel branchings in the A3 and A4 regions. It is only in the capillaries and immediately contiguous precapillaries (A4) and postcapillaries (V4) that vessel diameters are reasonably similar for the different tissues.

Substantial differences in systemic arterial pressure encountered in any population are not reflected in the absolute levels of hydraulic pressures in the complex of microvessels ≤25 μm in diameter. Micropressure in a particular vessel fluctuates over a comparatively narrow range (±3–4 mmHg). The range of differences in individual precapillary and postcapillary vessels appears to reflect variations that occur over a comparatively long time (~10–15 min). These variations include speeding and slowing of red cell velocity, changes in distribution of red blood cells, and even stopping and restarting of flow. Spontaneous variability of this magnitude is quite characteristic of the microcirculation in normal tissues studied by intravital microscopy.

Although contiguous branching orders of the microcirculation show some overlap in pressure levels, the actual decline in hydraulic pressure is significantly steeper across the arteriolar-precapillary portion of the network (Fig. 6). A much broader range of pressures is encountered on the arteriolar-precapillary side of the bed. Absolute pressures are shown for the mesentery in Table 6 and also as a percent of the total drop at successive anatomical cross sections. Maximal pressure drop is encountered during the transition from the long terminal arterioles to the precapillaries and from the latter to the capillaries. The capillary network proper and the postcapillary vessels contribute only a comparatively small fraction of the total drop. Local perturbations induced with either a topical constrictor (norepinephrine) or a topical dilator (papaverine) had their greatest effect on precapillary pressure (105), presumably because of the much greater length of the proximal arterioles. Capillary and venular pressure was affected proportionately much less than the pressure in the feeding vessels.

VENOUS VESSELS. The postcapillary side of the microvascular network is formed by the successive confluence of capillary-sized vessels that display no active vasomotor reactions. Because the capillaries converge to join one another in rapid succession, the diameter of postcapillary vessels is increased by up to 20–30 μm over a comparatively short distance. Although the postcapillary vessels display no active vasomotor reactions, they are more distensible than the true capillaries (304). With the progressive decrease in resistance, the velocity of the blood increases substantially from 1,000 μm/s in the capillaries to 3,000–3,500 μm/s in the muscular venules. Pressures, however, decrease much more gradually on the venous side, with values in the larger venules (40–60 μm) only 2–3 mmHg lower than those in the postcapillaries proper (Fig. 7).

Microvessel Pressure Variability

Microvessel pressure variability has both temporal and spatial characteristics. Temporally related factors include systolic-diastolic fluctuations as well as

TABLE 5. *Microvessel Diameter*

	Diameter, μm									Ref.
	A1	A2	A3	A4	Capillary	V4	V3	V2	V1	
Rabbit omentum	46–60	16–29	10–18	8–12	7–10	12–16	18–35	50–60	71–79	180
Cat mesentery	51–65	25–35	15–23	10–14	8–10	11–16	18–24	30–40	50–65	237
Bat wing	78	49	34	18	7.0	15	26	37	55	272
Rat cremaster	80–90	40–50	12–15	8–12	5–6	9–12	20–28	45–50	100–120	38
Rat spinotrapezius	70–100	30–55	12–22	6–10	5–6.5	7–10	12–18	35–60	100–170	374

Arterial (A) and venous (V) dichotomous branchings numbered beginning with sector that feeds the arteries.

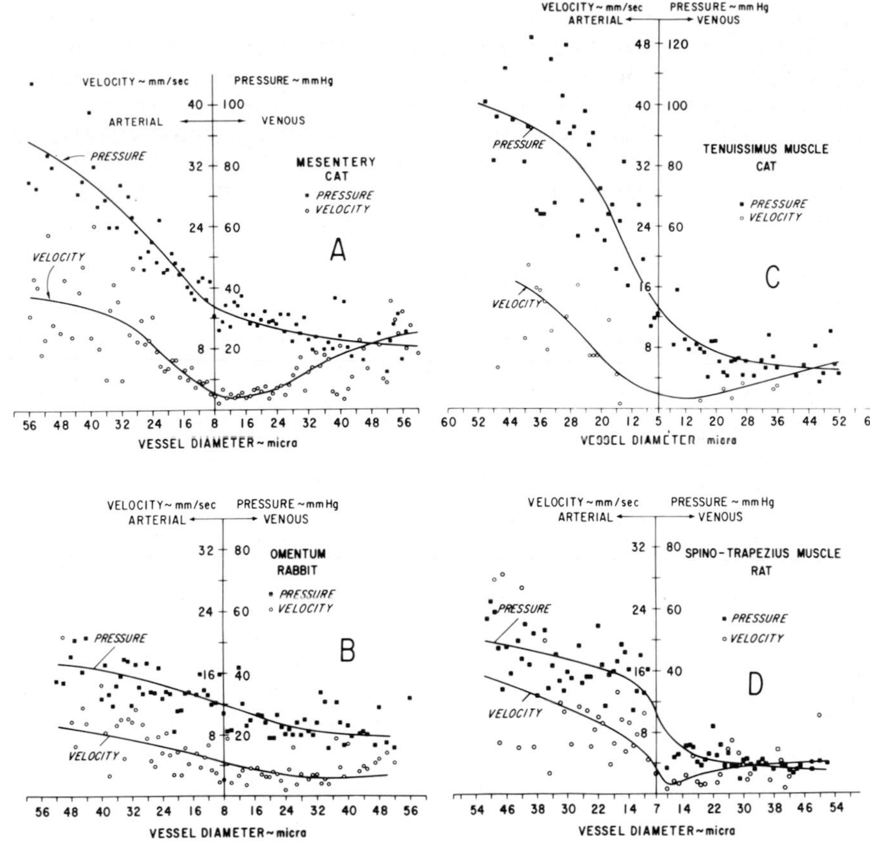

FIG. 6. Arteriovenous distribution of intravascular pressures (servo-null method) and red cell velocities (two-slit photometric technique) as a function of microvessel luminal diameter. Diameter indicated as an index of position of a given vessel network hierarchy. *A*: mesentery [data from Zweifach and Lipowsky (375)]; *B*: omentum [data from Zweifach and Lipowsky (375)]; *C*: tenuissimus muscle [data from Fronek and Zweifach (105)]; and *D*: spinotrapezius muscle [data from Zweifach et al. (374)].

TABLE 6. *Pressure Drop Across Successive Segments of Microcirculation*

	Diameter, μm	Pressure, mmHg	Pressure Drop, mmHg	$\frac{P_A - P_x}{P_A - P_V}$, %
Arteriole	25–35	60 ± 11		
Precapillary	15–25	47 ± 12	13	38
Capillary	8–12	33 ± 11	14	41
Postcapillary	15–25	29 ± 10	4	12
Collecting venule	35–45	26 ± 8	3	9

Data from 93 normotensive cats. Pressure values are means ± SD. P_A, arteriolar pressure; P_V, collecting venule pressure; P_x, pressure at given segment. [From Zweifach (371).]

changes in pressure associated with variations in both the rate and amplitude of spontaneous vasomotion. Variations in pressure and flow are especially striking in vessels ≤20 μm in diameter. Pressure fluctuations that develop more slowly (5- to 10-min intervals) occur in the larger arterioles (>25 μm).

Spatially related variations in the microcirculatory network involve numerous factors. Each microvascular module has several arteriolar inputs and venular outputs. Diameter and length differences among individual vessels, together with their branching frequency, are other important determinants of pressure distribution and its dissipation. As indicated, the pressure drop along a given capillary averages only 1.0–1.5 mmHg. Because of these small pressure differences even slight changes associated with blood rheological factors lead to continuous redistribution of the bloodstream.

Frictional resistance encountered in the successive branchings of the arterial tree dampens the pulse pressure but does not completely eliminate it; even recordings of capillary pressure show a pulse pressure of 1.0–2.0 cmH_2O (Fig. 8). On the venous side the pressure wave is again pulsatile with variations of 3–4 mmHg in venules where mean pressures are as low as 8–10 mmHg. The presence of pressure oscillations may reflect some form of shunting, although other explanations are possible. Even in skeletal muscle where capillary paths are 350–400 μm and longer, a clearly discernible pulse persists in postcapillaries and venules as narrow as 20–30 μm (103, 109, 110, 374).

Systemic Pressure Versus Microvessel Pressure

Because the driving force for the entire cardiovascular tree originates with the ejection of the blood into the aorta and pulmonary artery, obviously the systemic pressure in these vessels directly affects the pressures in the various microvessels. A number of studies suggest that microvessel pressures in the individual branching orders show a constant relationship to the level of the systemic arterial pressure (335).

Gore and Bohlen (124, 126) measured pressures by

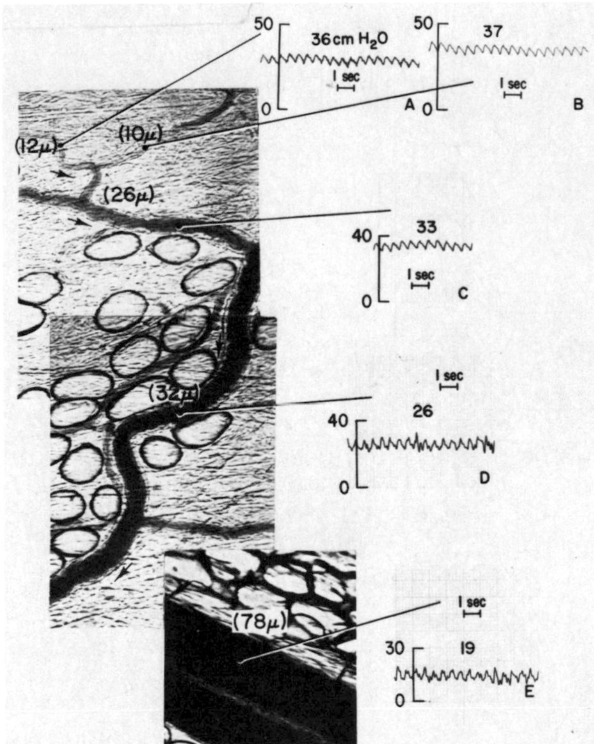

FIG. 7. Pressure gradient on venous side of cat mesentery is much shallower than on precapillary portion of the network, with only a small pressure difference between successive confluences. Pressures recorded directly by insertion of sharpened micropipette. [From Zweifach (370, 371), by permission of the American Heart Association, Inc.]

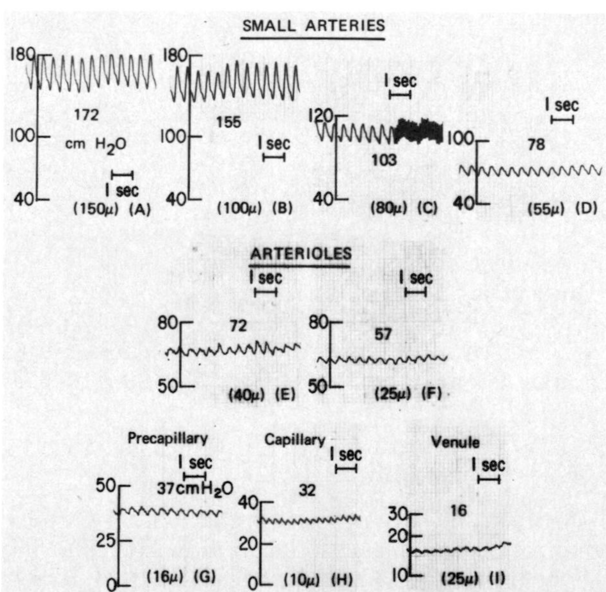

FIG. 8. Pulsatile nature of the pressure waveform is attenuated as the bloodstream moves through arteriolar and precapillary branchings but is not completely abolished in any of the microvessels, including the narrow true capillaries. Tracings from cat mesenteric network. [From Zweifach (370), by permisssion of the American Heart Association, Inc.]

direct intubation of the microvessels in cat mesentery and found a linear relationship between the pressure change in a comparatively large artery and that in the arterioles. They did not, however, explore the relationship within the successive branchings leading into the capillaries proper. Gore and Bohlen (38, 126) also advanced a somewhat similar conclusion based on studies of the cremaster muscle of normotensive and hypertensive rats. As shown in a pressure plot (Fig. 9*A*), when micropressures are expressed as a fraction

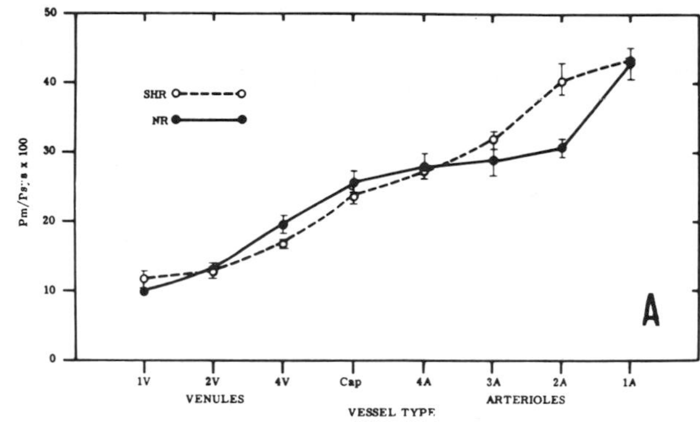

RAT CREMASTER MUSCLE

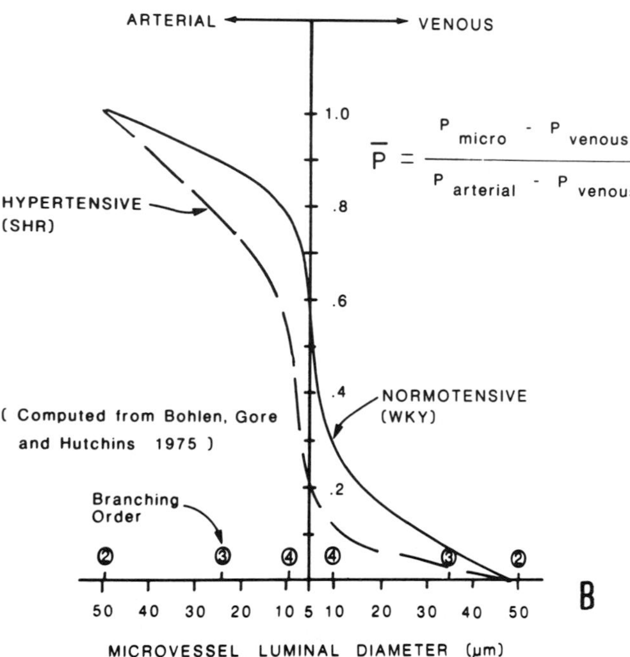

FIG. 9. *A*: microvessel pressure (Pm) normalized against systemic blood pressure (Psys) in spontaneously hypertensive rats (SHR) and in normotensive controls (NR). Ratio of the two pressures appears to be a constant fraction of Psys in cremaster muscle microcirculation. Some divergence is seen in the A2 and A3 regions (terminal arterioles and precapillaries). [From Bohlen et al. (39).] *B*: same data plotted as a fraction of total pressure drop across the microvascular network. Note that pressure drop is significantly greater in SHR microvessels than in normotensive (WKY) microvessels, reinforcing the independent activity of the successive branching orders.

of systemic pressure the curves appear to follow a similar relationship irrespective of whether the animals are normotensive or hypertensive. However, the same data plotted as the pressure drop across the microvascular network proper (Fig. 9*B*) show that the pressure gradients are distinctly different in normotensive and hypertensive preparations. The pressure drop in hypertensives is much steeper in the region of the A3 arterioles and their precapillary branches, reflecting the impact of local regulatory mechanisms.

In Figure 10 the relationship of small vessel pressures is compared with systemic arterial pressures along successive segments of the microcirculation of the cat mesentery. It shows that the slope of the regression line fitted for the successively smaller microvessels is gradually flattened until in the postcapillaries the regression line has virtually no positive slope. The fact that a positive correlation coefficient is found in microvessels >40–50 μm wide, whereas the relationship no longer holds at the capillary level, supports physiological concepts of the independence

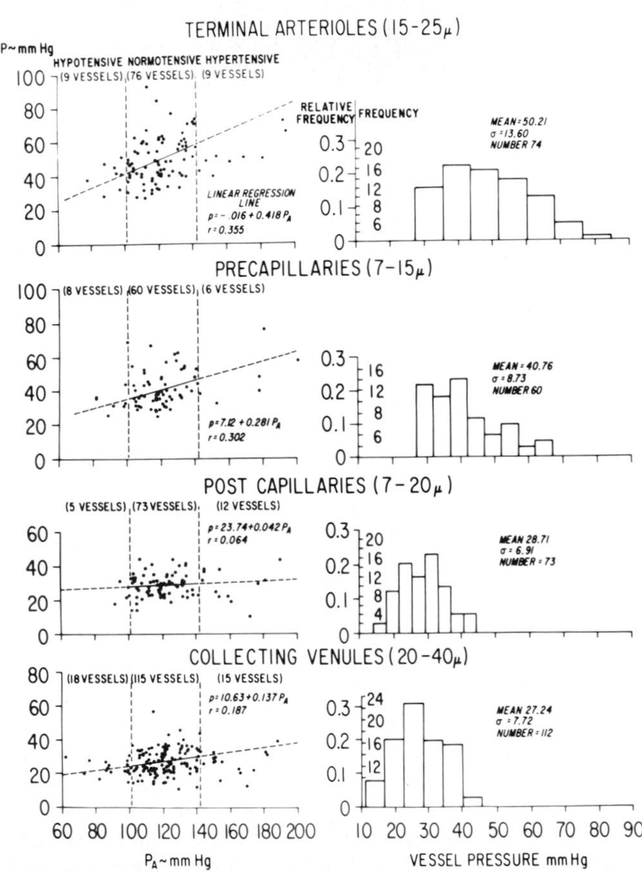

FIG. 10. Distribution pressure levels in the successive branchings of the cat mesenteric network plotted as a function of systemic pressure. Regression lines fitted to data show a progressive flattening of the slope, indicating that micropressures become relatively independent of systemic pressures in the smaller subdivisions of the microcirculation. [From Zweifach (370, 371), by permission of the American Heart Association, Inc.]

of microcirculatory function. Moment-to-moment adjustments of pressure in the microvascular network are maintained by a combination of local factors.

Capillary Pressure

EARLY MEASUREMENTS. The narrow caliber of true capillaries in mammalian tissues has made it difficult to directly measure capillary pressure (P_c) without interfering with blood flow. Most measurements of this kind reflect either arteriolar pressure (P_A) or venular outflow pressures (P_V) depending on the direction of the pipette opening. Estimates of capillary pressure have also been obtained by occlusion of upstream or downstream vessels or by extrapolating from precapillary to postcapillary values. Table 7 shows that indirect estimates for cat mesentery tend to be 2–3 mmHg higher than those based on direct intubation of side-arm branches of the true capillaries.

Landis (215) undertook pioneering experiments to determine pressure levels in the exchange portion of the microvascular network, making it possible to analyze the interaction of the key variables in the Starling equation for transcapillary fluid exchange. The wide capillaries in the frog mesentery were comparatively easy to intubate with fine micropipettes for direct recording of pressure (Fig. 11), whereas only a few spot measurements could be obtained in mammalian tissues where capillary width was only 5–6 μm. Capillary pressure values in skeletal muscle have mostly been determined by extrapolating from postcapillary or precapillary recordings or from fluid exchange data.

In mesenteric vessels of various mammals, mean capillary pressures are consistently higher than plasma oncotic pressures by some 4–6 mmHg (373, 378). Pressures in individual capillaries fluctuate in both a cyclic and irregular pattern so that they are above plasma oncotic pressure at one time (25–30 mmHg) and below it at another (10–15 mmHg), providing a time-dependent sequence alternatively favoring filtration and then absorption. Details of the mechanisms that modulate such activity to balance fluid exchange are not well documented (133), particularly with respect to different organs.

TABLE 7. *Capillary Pressure in Cat Mesentery Estimated by Different Methods*

	Number of Vessels	Pressure, mmHg
Topographical average for complete network	19	29.4 ± 5.6
Numerical average in different animals	396	31.7 ± 6.4
Average of arteriolar and venular pressures	93	33.7 ± 6.2
Microobstruction	23	28.2 ± 5.7

All values are means ± SD. [From Zweifach (368).]

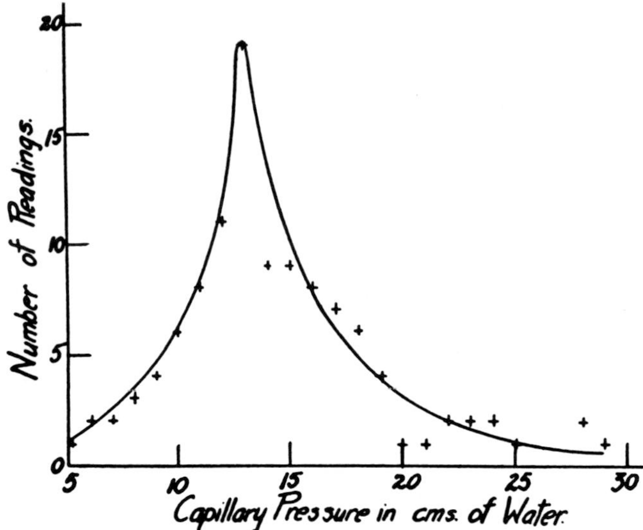

FIG. 11. Capillary pressures recorded directly with micropipettes by using a hydraulic linkage to a water manometer. Distribution plot for capillaries in frog mesentery shows a range of 5–29 cmH_2O with an average of 14.5 cmH_2O. [From Landis (215).]

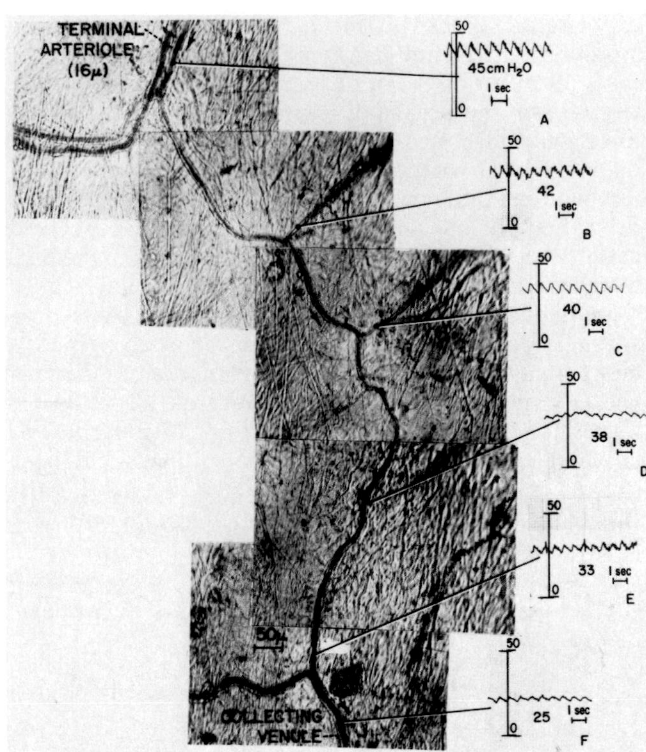

FIG. 12. Pressure drop along successive branchings of true capillary network in cat mesentery. Micropipettes inserted into side-arm branchings so as not to interfere with flow in parent channels. Net pressure drop along these 6- to 8-μm capillaries varies mainly with length. [From Zweifach (370, 371), by permission of the American Heart Association, Inc.]

ISOGRAVIMETRIC PRESSURES. When isolated hindlimbs are perfused under controlled pressure, it is possible to calculate the average pressures at the level of the exchange vessel during fluid equilibrium as determined by the continuous measurement of limb volume or weight (289, 292). Isogravimetric pressures result from intravascular and extravascular forces that contribute to net fluid flux. Such values are substantially lower than directly measured pressures (15–20 mmHg vs. 25–28 mmHg). This is probably because water movement from blood to interstitium occurs not only across the capillaries but also across the postcapillaries where hydrostatic pressures are 5–6 mmHg below those of the most proximal capillaries.

PRESSURE DROP WITHIN CAPILLARY NETWORK. The actual distribution of capillary pressures can be obtained in special circumstances (371). Serial measurements of pressure in the successive branchings of the capillary portion of the microvascular network in cat mesentery show a fairly uniform drop of 0.6–1.0 mmHg/100 μm for capillaries 7.5–9.0 μm wide. In a representative protocol (Fig. 12) capillary pressure falls from 42 mmHg on the arterial side to 33 mmHg on the venous side, a 9-mmHg drop that averages 0.7–0.8 mmHg/100 μm in cat mesentery.

LOCAL REGULATION OF CAPILLARY PRESSURE. Irrespective of the actual head of pressure in the distributive arteries, pressures are lowered to a common level in the capillaries of tissues where the microcirculation serves primarily a nutritive function. Direct measurements in four separate muscles—cat tenuissimus, rat spinotrapezius and cremaster, and rat anterior gracilis—show pressures in the most peripheral feeding artery to be 80–85 mmHg in the tenuissimus and 50–60 mmHg in the cremaster, with other muscles falling between these two extremes. In the splanchnic viscera (omentum and mesentery) the venous outflow drains into the portal venous system, and consequently capillary pressures tend to be 5–8 mmHg higher than in skeletal muscle. In the bat wing and the hamster cheek pouch, direct steady-state measurements show capillary pressure levels of ~22 mmHg. Some form of local vasomotor adjustment must be activated to bring this broad array of arterial pressures into a given range in the exchange portion of nutritive microvascular networks.

Evidence for this type of selective action is obtained in spontaneously hypertensive animals where pressures in the terminal arterioles and precapillaries are brought down to normotensive levels despite the fact that pressures in the distributing arteries of skeletal muscle are 50%–60% higher than in controls. In experiments where local vasodilation was induced with papaverine, micropressures throughout the network were increased in proportion to the prevailing systemic pressure of the spontaneously hypertensive animals. Similarly, capillary pressure was increased 6–8 mmHg (depending on systemic pressure level) in normotensive individuals in which local adjustments were counteracted by topically applied dilator agents.

No well-documented evidence associates acute perturbations in capillary blood flow with changes in endothelial cell shape or disposition. Endothelial cell nuclei frequently encroach on the vessel lumen of capillaries to reduce luminal cross-section area by 50% or more. It is not known whether this deformation is the result of an active response involving the endothelial cell or is passively induced by differences in transmural or interstitial pressure. In most capillaries, particularly in skeletal muscle (86, 87, 89), the endothelial cell cytoplasm forms a thin rim ~1–2 μm thick except for the nuclear bulges at 60- to 70-μm intervals. Individual capillary vessels maintain remarkably uniform luminal cross sections and outside dimensions. In some tissues capillary length and diameter are more variable, especially the mesentery where thoroughfare channels may be as wide as 10–12 μm at their distal end (see *Shunts*, p. 264).

Reports based on intravital microscopy of particular organs [e.g., liver (255) and retina of eye (212)] describe a narrowing of the capillary lumen produced by a spontaneous inbulging of the endothelial cell nucleus that can also be induced by electrical or chemical stimulation. These deformations are accompanied by a slowing or diversion of the bloodstream to other vessels. Similar endothelial perturbations have not been seen in other mammalian tissues in response to discrete stimulation.

Numerous investigators have explored endothelial cell contractility since the provocative observations of Rouget (312) and Krogh (210). Recent evidence (27) that capillary endothelial cells in mammals do contain actin filaments and heavy meromyosin has rekindled interest in some form of endothelial contractility. Others have found specialized endothelial cells at capillary branchings in frog mesentery (1, 349). These cells restrict the vessel lumen through nuclear protrusion after electrical stimulation. Current consensus is that if changes do occur in vessel diameter with standard constrictor stimuli, they are too small in mammals to have an observable effect on capillary flow. McCuskey (255) believes that active changes in the disposition of endothelial cells forming the lining of the liver sinusoids can contribute to flow redistribution within that organ.

The possibility has been raised that endothelial cell contraction contributes to the increased permeability of venules to macromolecules after topical introduction of bradykinin, histamine, and prostaglandins (198, 246). The gaps between contiguous endothelial cells have been interpreted as defects resulting from mechanical separation of the cell surfaces, a phenomenon that can be blocked by agents with an affinity for β_2-adrenergic receptors. The issue is whether such evidence by itself indicates endothelial cell contractility or whether interaction with β_2-adrenergic receptors might simply lead to a disturbance in cation exchange and give rise to endothelial swelling or to a modification of the surface-to-surface binding forces. The fact remains that short of disrupting the integrity of the endothelial wall as a permeability barrier, muscle cell agonists do not directly affect capillary vessel diameter. It is possible, however, that active changes in cell contour in certain organs (liver, retina of eye) may lead to an inbulging of the endothelial nucleus into the lumen sufficient to impede blood flow distal to that point.

MICROVESSEL PRESSURE AND FLUID EXCHANGE. The continuous flux of fluid across the blood-capillary barrier is governed by the interaction of hydraulic and colloid osmotic pressures within the blood and interstitial compartments. The principal variable in the microcirculation proper is the capillary pressure gradient. The pressure drop across the 600- to 1,200-μm path from precapillary to postcapillary is comparatively small, at most 3–5 mmHg for different microvascular networks. It is therefore unlikely that a fall in capillary pressure by itself would be sufficient to allow for anything but marginal control of fluid exchange.

Direct observations suggest a somewhat different mechanism. Because of periodic fluctuations in pressure, capillary perfusion is highly periodic, and consequently during maximal flow the hydrostatic pressures are well above the 20–25 mmHg exerted by the colloids of the blood. On the other hand, during reduced flow the average capillary pressures fall as low as 10–15 mmHg, particularly in skeletal muscle. The picture that emerges is one of alternating periods of filtration and absorption across the entire exchange network. Instead of structural dissipation of pressure, fluid balance is achieved through temporal variations associated with vasomotion (possibly the reaction of vascular smooth muscle to changes in wall tension coincident with fluctuations in transmural pressure).

CAPILLARY PRESSURE IN HUMANS. Among the earliest direct measurements of capillary pressure in humans were those made in the digits of the upper and lower extremities by Danzer and Hooker (75), Landis (217), Carrier and Rehberg (54), and Eichna and Bordley (83). Recent studies with more accurate microsensors have been made by Mahler and co-workers (245) and Levick and Michel (228) (Table 8). Figure 13 shows the unusual nature of capillary pressure pulsations in

TABLE 8. *Microvessel Pressure in Nailfold Capillaries of the Human Finger*

Condition	Pressure, mmHg	
	Mean	Range
Heart level		
Room temperature, 21°C	31.5	14–55
Room temperature, 31°C	41	25–39
Skin temperature, 25°C	13	18.8–7.6
Skin temperature, 35°C	44	50–38
Elevated venous pressure		
+30 mmHg	43	
+50 mmHg	58	

Pressures from arterial limb of capillary. [Data from Mahler et al. (245) and Levick and Michel (228).]

174, 176, 177, 233, 374). Much of the current data on flow in individual branchings of the microcirculation was obtained with adaptations of the dual-slit, cross-correlation procedure.

Net flow across the entire microvascular network or localized areas of tissue has been calculated either by arterial-to-venous transit times for various markers (364) or by microsphere distribution relative to cardiac output measurements (249, 264, 269). Such data are valuable largely because of their applicability to regional or peripheral resistance measurements or in providing a frame of reference for the integrative effect of the flow levels in individual branching orders (152, 196, 368).

Velocity Relationships

Because blood is essentially a suspension of cells in a protein fluid, it moves along the vascular conduits nonuniformly with much higher velocity in the center of the tube (see the chapter by Chien, Usami, and Skalak in this *Handbook*). The velocity profile is influenced under normal and abnormal conditions by factors such as driving force, vessel size, and blood hematocrit.

Schmid-Schoenbein and Zweifach (318) have shown that the average hematocrit in the 8-μm-wide capillaries of the omentum is 17.2% compared with a systemic hematocrit of 38.5%. About 10% of the capillaries contain no red blood cells. Much of the data analyzing the effect of changes in vessel hematocrit has been obtained in vitro by using glass or plastic tubes as small as 15–20 μm in diameter, although some data exist for tubes 3–5 μm in diameter (see the chapter by Chien, Usami, and Skalak in this *Handbook*).

Details of flow velocity profiles for individual microvessels, however, have been worked out by examining single frames of high-speed cine recordings (315, 318). Because of the unsteady nature of red blood cell velocity and uneven vessel contours, the velocity profiles in both the microscopic arterioles and venules are not only asymmetric but are more blunted than would be expected from Poiseuille profiles (Fig. 15). Maximum blunting of the velocity profiles occurs in the narrow arteriolar vessels (15–20 μm wide). As a direct consequence of the blunted velocity profiles the shear rates at the vessel wall are comparatively high, leading to higher resistance than predicted from simple calculations.

Most on-line measurements of velocity are made with sensor diodes smaller than the projected image of the microvessels, so that centerline velocity is actually being recorded. Velocity falls off gradually in the initial branchings of the arterioles (A1 to A2, A2 to A3) with little change in the contours of the tracing. The asymmetric nature of the velocity profiles makes it difficult to calculate bulk flow on the basis of simple Poiseuille relationships. On the precapillary side the shear rates for vessels 20–60 μm in diameter are on the order of 1,000 s^{-1}, whereas on the postcapillary side the shear rates are as low as 100 s^{-1}. For precise measurements the calculations of mean velocity in vessels of different sizes should be normalized with the maximum velocity (see Table 9 for data on the omentum).

On the basis of in vitro measurements in 150- to 100-μm glass tubes Baker and Wayland (20) adopted a 1.6 correction to bring centerline flow rates down to bulk flow values. Corrections of a similar order of magnitude were found to be applicable in intravital studies of pressure-flow relations in cat mesentery (240, 241).

The pulsatile nature of the velocity recordings remains clearly evident at all levels of the microcirculatory network in cat mesentery (112, 116). The peak-to-valley amplitude is blunted by only 15% in the

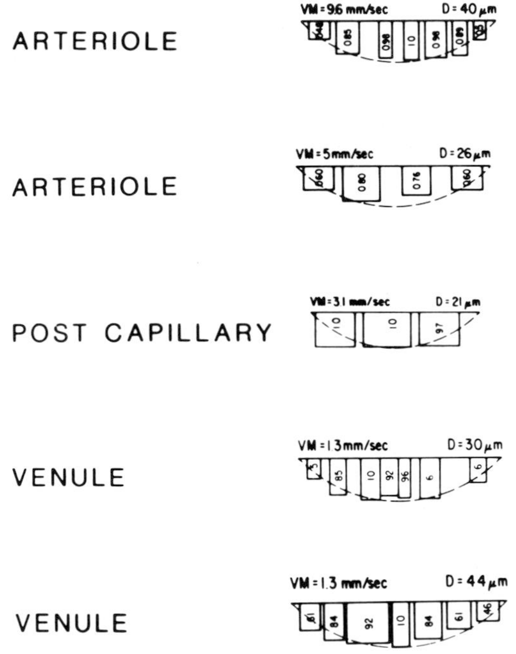

FIG. 15. Reconstruction of velocity profile from high-speed motion picture recording of mesenteric vessels. Note blunting of the profile in arteriolar branchings, a feature that affects the calculation of bulk flow from such recordings. VM, maximum velocity; D, diameter. [From Schmid-Schoenbein and Zweifach (318).]

TABLE 9. *Normalized Velocities for Rabbit Omentum*

	Diameter, μm	Average Mean Velocity, mm/s
Large arteriole	≥100	0.66
Arteriole	43–29	0.77
	25–18	0.78
Postcapillary	16–27	0.80
Venule	30–40	0.74
	40–53	0.72

Velocities from two-dimensional profile. [Adapted from Schmid-Schoenbein and Zweifach (318).]

precapillaries, with little or no phase shift between systemic and micropressure records (304).

Flow Distribution

The volume of blood in the microvascular network proper is distributed unequally—about 70% in the postcapillaries and venules and only about 30% in the arterioles and true capillaries. Because the capillaries can be considered comparatively rigid tubes, dilation of the arterioles does not increase the volume of blood in individual capillaries but leads to an increase in the velocity of the bloodstream. Fluctuations in movement of the blood appear to be related to the type of spontaneous vasomotor activity present in the different arteriolar branchings. Inasmuch as vasomotor activity of this kind is highly variable, blood flow appears to shift almost randomly (344).

The importance of network pattern or topography to the distribution of blood is best illustrated by comparing distributions for tissues with different vascular patterns. Figure 16 shows typical velocity distributions for cat mesentery and tenuissimus muscle. It can be seen that capillary velocities are an order of magnitude lower than velocities in the A1 arterioles. Some 10%–15% of the capillaries have flows 3–4 times faster than the remainder of the network. Detailed information of this kind is available for mesentery (196, 197, 237, 378), omentum (238), and skeletal muscle (374).

Because capillaries are relatively nondistensible under normal conditions, changes in blood velocity are a good index of flow through this portion of the terminal vascular bed. The range of capillary velocities has been documented for most of the intravital preparations used for direct microscopy (Table 10). Because capillary velocity fluctuates over such a wide range in single vessels, mean values have only limited use. These variations in the nonmuscular capillary channels must therefore be a consequence of factors other than active dimensional changes in these vessels. Flow changes are associated not only with the interdiction of precapillary and postcapillary dilation or constriction but also with the flow properties of blood, i.e., the distribution and deformability of the blood cells.

The extent to which the distribution of flow in the microcirculation depends on the progressive reduction in vessel diameter is reflected by the parabolic shape of the curves (Fig. 17). The lowest flow rates (0.5×10^{-4} mm^3/s) are encountered in the region where the capillaries become confluent and form the 10- to 14-μm postcapillaries. The variance in flow is strongly influenced by the frequency of branching in the network. The multiplicity of interconnections in the network tends to keep the flow rates within a narrow range, in contrast to the much broader range of microvascular pressures.

Tissues with a predominantly in-series arrangement of the microvessels (e.g., omentum) have a much more shallow flow gradient than that in skeletal muscle, where microvessel deployment has a predominantly in-parallel arrangement. Unfortunately the precise mechanisms that tie together pressure-dependent and flow-dependent processes are only sketchily understood.

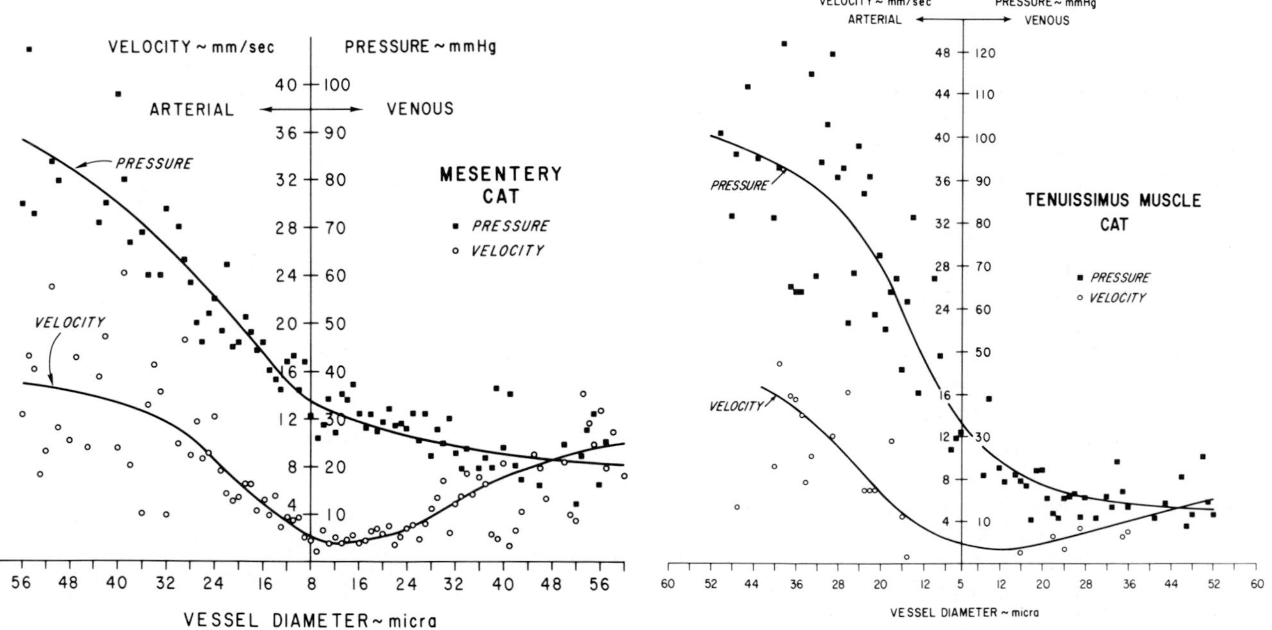

FIG. 16. Velocity profiles in cat mesentery and tenuissimus muscle largely determined by the topography of the microvascular network. Plots show both pressure and flow distributions in the same set of vessels. Range of pressure fluctuations is greater than that for velocity. [From Lipowsky and Zweifach (237, 238).]

Capillary Flow

The flow pattern in the true capillaries varies considerably, ranging from highly erratic excursions to nearly identical periodicities in adjacent capillaries. The similarity of flow in groups of capillaries is particularly striking in skeletal muscle where the vessels are aligned in parallel array with as many as 4–6 adjacent capillaries having a common origin in a given transverse arteriole (Fig. 18).

Capillary flow patterns (Fig. 19) have been described (120, 196, 197, 203, 332) as either continuous (having wide fluctuations in rate) or intermittent (stop-and-go flow). The irregular pattern appears in vessels with high flow rates and is highly correlated with the spontaneous vasomotion of the proximal arterioles. The on-off pattern is associated with the vasomotor excursions of A3 and A4 precapillaries, the only vessels in which narrowing is sufficient to obliterate the vessel lumen. Myogenic adjustments in the arteriolar region have also been found to contribute to the periodicity of flow in individual capillaries (187, 191, 197).

TABLE 10. *Flow Velocity in Vessels*

	Velocity, mm/s	Ref.
Capillary vessels		
Cat mesentery	0.0–1.2	197
	0.5–1.0	187
	≤1.7	110
Cat sartorius	0.38	51
Frog pectoralis	0.33 ± 0.19	120
Cat tenuissimus	0.0–1.5	89
	≤10.0	176
Rabbit omentum	1.0–1.5	176
Human nailfold	0.3–2.35	40
Cat sartorius	0.28 ± 0.02	193
Rat anterior gracilis	0.26 ± 0.05	156
Rat spinotrapezius	0.25 ± 0.10	374
Rabbit tenuissimus	0.29 ± 0.14	231
Larger-diameter microvessels		
Cat mesentery		
<30 μm	8.65 ± 1.79	109
>30 μm	5.65 ± 1.04	109
Cat omentum		
20 μm	10.0	176
20–80 μm	0.1–2.38	303
Cat mesentery, 7–25 μm	0.7–12.00	375
Mouse pia mater arterioles	1.88–6.0	308
Rat brain		
78.9 μm	12.4	286
55.0 μm	14.7	286
Mouse brain, 13–46 μm	2.0–26	308
Rat cremaster, 20 μm	2.36 ± 0.29	296
Cat tenuissimus precapillaries	3.8 ± 1.0	105

Adapted from Fronek and Zweifach (105) and Palmer (286).

An analysis by Lindbom et al. (231) of red blood cell velocity in adjacent capillaries of rabbit tenuissimus muscle showed that patterns could be altered by changing the oxygen tension of the fluid used to bathe the exteriorized tissue. When the partial pressure of oxygen (Po_2) of the fluid is increased by as little as 5–10 mmHg, red blood cell velocities decrease, and at oxygen tensions of 55–60 mmHg capillary flow is almost completely curtailed. The effect of variations in the oxygen tension of the suffusion fluid was most striking in preparations where red cell velocity periodically underwent spontaneous adjustments. Hippensteele and co-workers (161) found that the level of the partial pressure of carbon dioxide (Pco_2) of the solution bathing the rat cremaster muscle strongly influenced the degree of constriction induced by elevated levels of oxygen. When pH was lowered by excess CO_2, the constrictor response of the terminal arterioles was almost completely suppressed and the local control of blood flow was shifted to the larger supply arterioles. It is readily appreciated that calculations of capillary density can be strongly biased by various combinations of these factors.

Prewitt and Johnson (296) found a close correlation between the lack of response to changes in oxygen tension of suffusion fluid and the presence or absence of spontaneous vasomotion. Muscle preparations in which Po_2 tension was maintained above normal (>20 mmHg) showed prominent vasomotion (167).

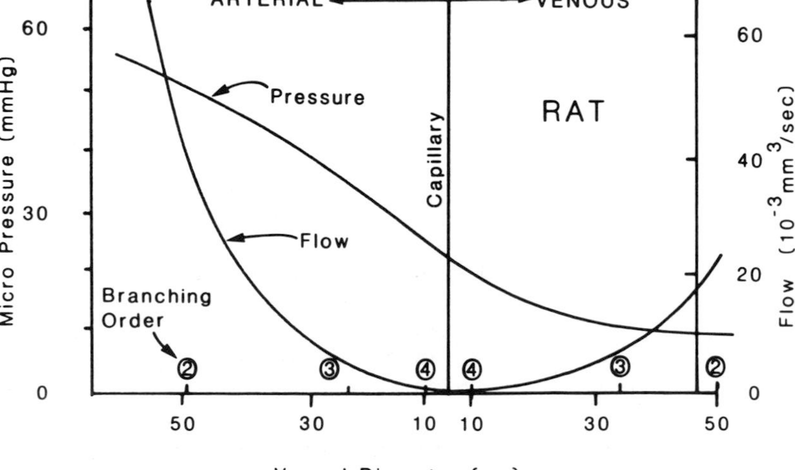

FIG. 17. Flow distribution in microvessels of cat mesentery. Compare with Fig. 30 for rat spinotrapezius muscle. Sharper drop in flow in muscle due to more numerous branchings in the A3 and A4 regions. Lines plotted from 250 individual velocity readings in each tissue. [Adapted from Zweifach et al. (374).]

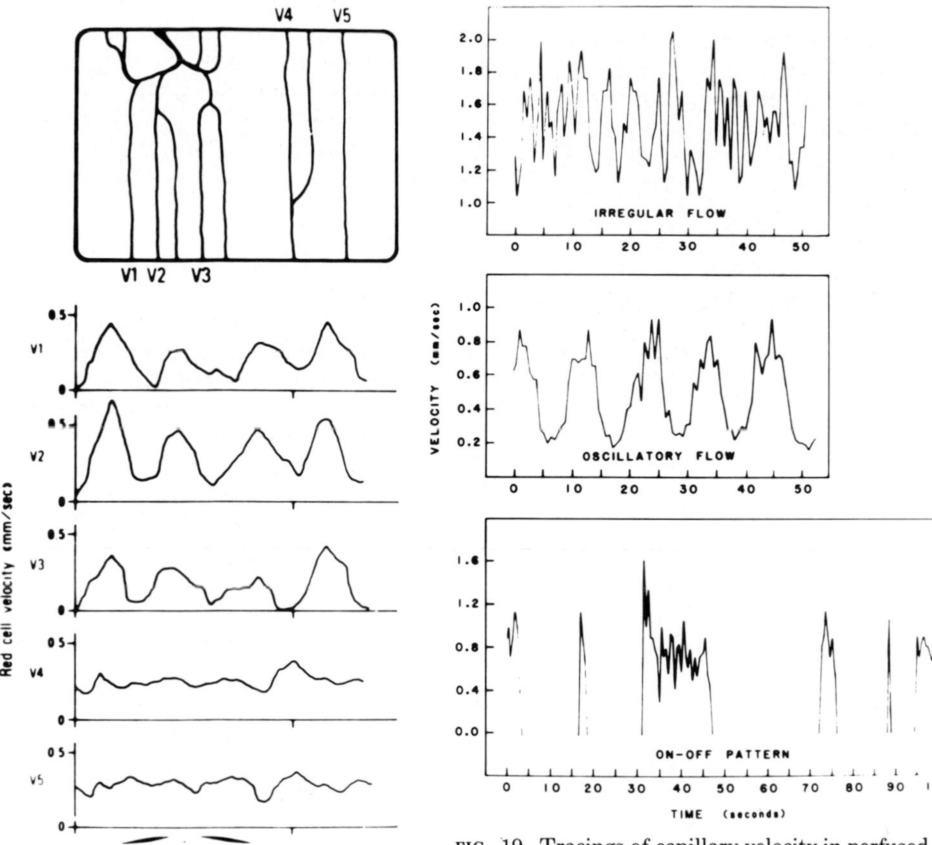

FIG. 18. Contiguous capillaries in rabbit tenuissimus arising from a common parent arteriole showing similar fluctuations in flow but differing in absolute level of flow. This is due to differences in vessel length, red cell hematocrit, and size of the postcapillary into which the vessels drain. [From Lindbom et al. (231).]

FIG. 19. Tracings of capillary velocity in perfused cat mesentery showing a variety of patterns varying from periodic changes to erratic random fluctuations. Multiple factors contribute to these diverse patterns. [From Johnson and Wayland (197).]

Capillary Flow in Humans

Although incidental measurements of microvessel velocity have been made in the retina (49, 84, 204, 206, 226, 337), repeated measurements under well-defined conditions have been obtained primarily in the nailfold vessels of the digits.

Bollinger et al. (40) and Fagrell et al. (93) measured red blood cell velocity in the nailfold capillaries by dual-slit photometric procedures and reported average values of 0.4–0.7 mm/s. As with pressure, the flow pattern is wavelike with intervals of 6–20 s interspersed with periods of complete stoppage of flow (Fig. 20). Recordings at both the arterial and venous ends of the capillary loops in the nailfold showed cardiac pulsatility in addition to the more slowly developing rhythmic changes. These fluctuations in red blood cell velocity were associated with a periodic rise and fall in vessel hematocrit. An analogue recording of red blood cell velocity for the arterial loop in the nailfold of the finger (Fig. 21) shows fluctuations in velocity of 0.47–0.84 mm/s. As with pressure, flow relationships varied with skin temperature and could be shifted by the position of the extremity relative to the level of the heart.

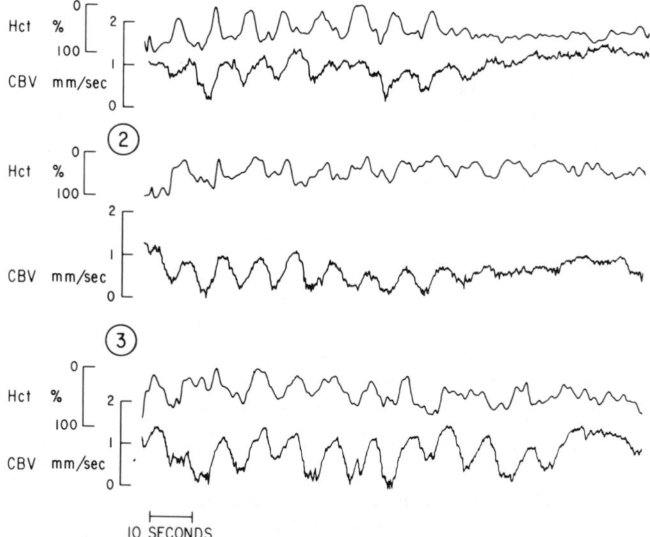

FIG. 20. Simultaneous tracings of red blood cell velocity (CBV) and relative hematocrit (Hct) in several adjacent capillaries of the nailfold of human digits. Tracings show close correspondence of periodic fluctuations. [From Fagrell et al. (93).]

Brånemark (47) recorded details of capillary blood flow in a special transparent chamber inserted into pedicle skin flaps of the arm. The data were especially

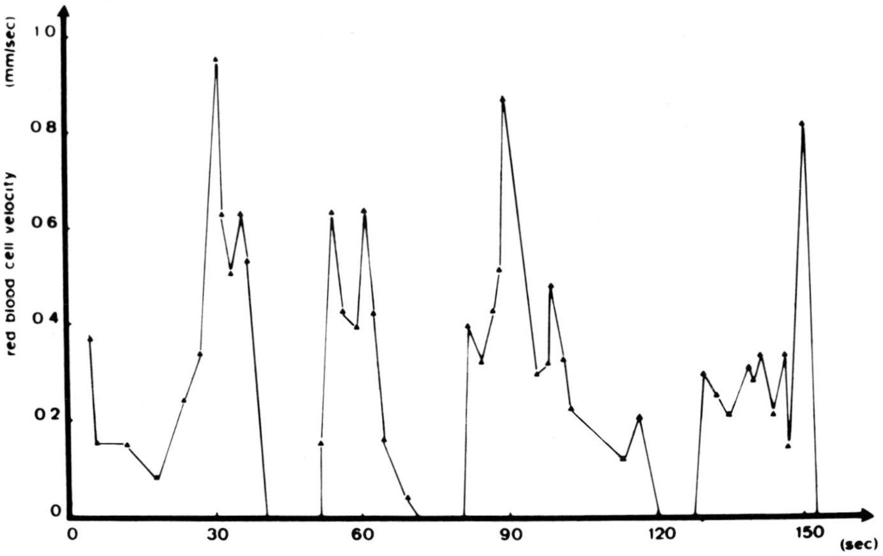

FIG. 21. Intermittent flow patterns in capillaries of human nailfold demonstrating 3 recognizable patterns. Various patterns develop randomly and reflect the erratic vasomotor excursions of parent arterioles. [From Bollinger et al. (40).]

useful in the analysis of the factors affecting the flow properties of blood introduced by changes in red blood cell hematocrit and leukocyte entrapment.

Microvessel Number

The number of vessels at the successive cross sections of the microcirculation is difficult to establish by direct visualization. In flat, essentially two-dimensional arrays direct counts have been made after intravenous injection of filler materials much as latex (118, 168), carbon (333), or silicone (328, 329). Serial vessel counts have been documented in the cremaster muscle and different mesenteries (158, 168). The methods are laborious and subject to error because of incomplete filling. Other approaches have compared the calculated flow rate in the major feeder vessels with that recorded in individual vessels at different branching orders. The ratio of the two flow rates reasonably estimates the total number of microvessels at a given branching order that would be required to carry the volume of blood introduced by the feeding artery. Calculations of this kind are based on the assumption that the distribution of flow values is symmetrical and that the vessel population for each branching order is fairly homogeneous. Most muscles are a mixture of red and white fibers that have different metabolic requirements and hence are supplied by different numbers of vessels in these regions (266). Furthermore the conditions under which these measurements are made must be carefully examined because tissue oxygen tension, tissue handling, and anesthetic procedure significantly affect the number of actively perfused vessels.

Table 11 shows tenuissimus muscle vascularity based on volume flow ratios; somewhat different numbers can be obtained from the data in Figure 31. Calculations of this kind approximate a capillary density of 1,000/mm^2 for a flat skeletal muscle such as the tenuissimus (89) after vasodilation. On this basis

TABLE 11. *Vascularity of Cat Tenuissimus Muscle*

	Diameter, μm	Flow, × 10^{-3} mm^3/s	Q_p/Q_d	Total Vessels*
Feeding artery, A1	50	51		1
Arcading arteriole, A2	40	15	1/3.4	3
Transverse arteriole, A3	20	2.8	1/5.3	53
Precapillary, A4	9	0.33	1/8.5	466
Capillary	5	0.10	1/3.3	1,487

* Assumed all parent flow (Q_p) feeds into successive daughters (Q_d). [Adapted from Fronek and Zweifach (105).]

estimated flow under steady-state conditions averages 6.0 × 10^{-6} ml/min. Indirect measurements of blood flow in intact limbs indicate that flow at rest utilizes only a fraction of the total capillary population, with active perfusion of as few as 20% of the available capillaries. Lindbom et al. (231) estimate that flow in rabbit tenuissimus muscle can be varied from 5.6 to 7.5 ml·min^{-1}·100 g^{-1} by simply shifting from high to low oxygen levels in the ambient air surrounding the exteriorized preparation.

Capillary Recruitment

Measurements of capillary flow and vessel number make it possible to calculate total blood flow per unit muscle mass. The number of perfused capillaries or their density, however, varies considerably. The 5- to 12-fold difference in blood flow for resting muscle as opposed to that in working muscle has been interpreted in different ways (220).

Through the use of systemic injections of carbon particles followed by fixation and histological sectioning, Krogh (209) developed the concept of capillary recruitment. As shown in Figure 22 adapted from his monograph (210), the number of open or actively perfused microvessels in diaphragm muscle increases 12-fold under stimulation. More recent intravital studies of rabbit tenuissimus muscle and rat cremaster

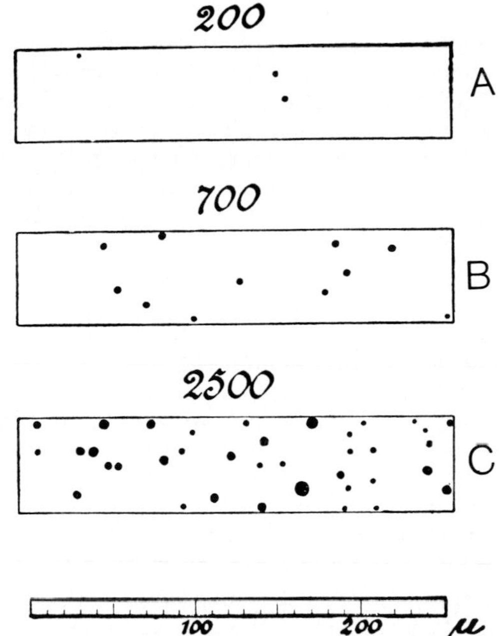

FIG. 22. Cross sections of guinea pig muscle after intravenous injection of carbon particles. From results of capillary counts Krogh advanced the concept of capillary recruitment with muscle work. Sections show an almost 12-fold increase in number of perfused microvessels after repeated muscle stimulation. [From Krogh (210).]

and spinotrapezius muscles have led to different interpretations. Some investigators believe that essentially all capillaries are always being actively perfused. Differences in flow requirements at work and at rest are met by modification in individual vessel flow rate (87). Other workers claim that in humans only 10%–20% of the available capillaries in skeletal muscle are perfused at rest (201, 220). Observations on exteriorized skeletal muscle preparations reveal that even under steady-state conditions flow is intermittent in spatially separated groups of capillaries (372, 376). This alternating sequence suggests that 20%–30% of capillaries may be perfused at any given time but that a shifting pattern of stop-and-go flow equalizes flow to different portions of the network. During muscle work spontaneous vasomotion of the arterioles is greatly reduced, leading to more uniform flow and distribution of red cells through all of the available capillaries.

Direct comparisons of capillary recruitment in experimental animals and in humans are difficult to make because of different flow requirements associated with the higher metabolic needs of skeletal muscle in small animals; their oxygen consumption (V_{O_2}) is 5 times greater. Further complication in extrapolating from one species to another arises because the derecruitment phenomenon after hyperemia in a muscle such as the myocardium has a different time base in humans or large experimental animals than in small animals used for intravital microscopy (153).

Burton and Johnson (51) in studies on perfused cat mesentery were unable to demonstrate capillary recruitment during reactive hyperemia. It should be pointed out that much of the negative evidence for capillary recruitment was obtained in exteriorized tissues in which precise physiological status is uncertain because they are studied under a set of arbitrary experimental conditions (123). It is possible that inadequate control of factors such as anesthesia and oxygen tension may bias the data and not reflect true steady-state values in a highly active tissue such as skeletal muscle.

MICROVASCULAR CONTROL MECHANISMS

Adjustments of the circulation that are tied to systemic phenomena such as blood pressure are handled by centrally mediated reflex pathways (100, 373, 374). The peripheral vasomotor component of such central adjustments is usually identified in a loose way as the precapillary arteriole, a somewhat ambiguous classification even from a functional point of view. Locally directed adjustments are then attributed to the microcirculation where again boundaries are only loosely defined. The separation of local and systemic mechanisms is obviously not absolute, and there is overlap in the region of the 50- to 75-μm supply vessels. Although the behavior of the small, more distal arterioles is increasingly dominated by environmental factors, neurogenic mechanisms continue to contribute to local adjustments. In the tissues the overriding influences of pH, P_{O_2}, and P_{CO_2}, as well as of chemicals of local origin, afford the microcirculatory portion of the system a considerable degree of independence from the circulation as a whole. Because all of these materials have direct access to vascular smooth muscle, they not only modulate flow by action on spontaneous vasomotor behavior but also affect the number of actively perfused exchange vessels.

Total blood flow to the tissue has a strong correlation with the level of metabolic activity. This commitment is met by changing the caliber of the supply arterioles proximal to the microcirculation in line with continuously shifting levels of tissue metabolism. In addition there is a need to distribute the available volume of blood among a sufficiently large number of capillaries so as to maximize the surface area across which exchange can occur, a feature accomplished by the microcirculation proper. The actual number of capillaries and their physical spacing in particular tissues is proportional to the level of oxygen consumption. This dependence is seen in the capillarization of red versus white muscle fibers (266), with the red or slow-twitch fibers having a 50%–70% greater capillary density.

Vascular Tone

Structural features normally have an essentially invariable influence on microvascular dynamics. On the other hand the variable reactivity of the terminal hierarchy of arterioles represents the keystone for the active control of pressure and flow in the tissue. The relative contribution of active adjustments as opposed to passive adjustments depends on the state of tone (degree of shortening) under which the microvascular smooth muscle is being maintained in the different organ systems of the body. The selective nature of the tissue perfusion depends strongly on the state of vascular smooth muscle tone. When this tone has been superseded by inducing local vasodilation, flow distribution is dictated largely by geometrical considerations.

In regions where vascular tone is high (skin, skeletal muscle, intestinal wall), pressure and flow fluctuate widely. An open-ended question is whether particular adjustments are geared to pressure regulation or whether they have a nutritional or metabolic basis. In view of the need to confine both variables to a narrow range, more than a casual interdependence must exist between the two apparently disparate sensing systems (259, 291).

Interdependence of pressure and flow was examined systematically by Johnson et al. (186, 190, 191, 193) in mesentery by manipulating pressure with a cuff placed around the superior mesenteric artery. When systemic pressure was lowered in such perfused preparations, the pulsatile component of capillary pressure tracings was reduced more than that of arteriole and venule pressures, presumably because of the high viscous losses in the narrow capillaries (304). It should be kept in mind that most perturbations leading to a dilation of arterioles in mesentery are associated with a reduction in both pressure and flow, so that autoregulation of flow cannot be readily attributed to either metabolic or myogenic mechanisms alone (324).

Reactive hyperemia, induced by local occlusion of flow for 10–30 s, leads to increased capillary flow even when the Po_2 of the bathing medium for the muscle preparation has been raised to 40 mmHg (343). Observations of this kind have led a number of investigators to postulate that two types of responses are associated with reduced flow. Short periods of occlusion produce an increase in capillary flow presumably based on a myogenic response, whereas longer periods of occlusion introduce a metabolic reaction of smooth muscle (188).

Central Versus Local

Autoregulatory phenomena were first described at the level of whole-organ systems, but more recently it has been possible to document comparable reactions in the microcirculatory system through intravital microscopy. The concept was originally applied to the microcirculation in the gracilis muscle (97, 185–187) on the basis of local adjustments of capillary blood flow that developed when systemic blood pressure was manipulated. The specific event that triggers such localized autoregulatory responses has not been fully elucidated. There is convincing evidence that adjustments of local flow may be mediated through some chemical product linked to tissue metabolism or through a direct myogenic reaction to disturbances in transmural pressure. Both processes are probably involved. Not only are metabolic and myogenic factors interrelated, but they represent time-dependent processes. Their relative contributions can vary under different circumstances. Furthermore there is good evidence that the sympathetic nervous system may also contribute to the local feedback because adjustments of arteriolar caliber and flow in response to the elevation of venous pressure can be modified by agents that affect neurogenic mediation (16).

Local microvascular responses to fluctuations in blood pressure are more pronounced in those in situ preparations that exhibit well-defined spontaneous vasomotion. The time-dependent aspects of the autoregulatory response are quite characteristic. For example, a short period of arterial occlusion in a muscle preparation is followed primarily by rapid dilation of the supply arterioles. After release from longer periods of arterial occlusion (up to several minutes), muscles undergo sustained reactive hyperemia. Increased blood flow has been attributed to local hypoxia set up by the interruption of arterial inflow, and the height and duration of the hyperemia response are proportional to the period of stasis (35).

Inasmuch as comparable degrees of reactive hyperemia can be induced in exteriorized tissues even when immersed in fluids with oxygen tensions above normal (132, 187), it is unlikely that oxygen levels per se affect local distribution through direct action on vascular smooth muscle.

Models of the microvascular network in the conjunctiva of the human eye have been developed by compiling precise measurements of diameter, length, and branching (96). They show that the network design tends to keep capillary pressures within a 2.0- to 2.5-mmHg range, whereas flow values may vary almost threefold in different capillaries. Short-term fluctuations in overall flow rate that are observed in different preparations can be traced back to the vasomotor activity of the precapillary arterioles, with additional variations superimposed by the continuous shifting of hematocrit in small vessels and by temporary leukocyte obstruction.

Although the highly periodic nature of capillary blood flow under steady-state conditions is blunted during the readjustment to reduction in arterial pressure (Fig. 23), periodicity can be restored by increasing venous pressure. These experiments led Johnson and Wayland (197) to conclude that myogenic adjustments set up by shifts in arteriolar wall tension are a major factor responsible for the periodicity of capillary flow.

Myogenic Adjustments

The term *myogenic* is used to describe an adjustment in smooth muscle of the contractile machinery

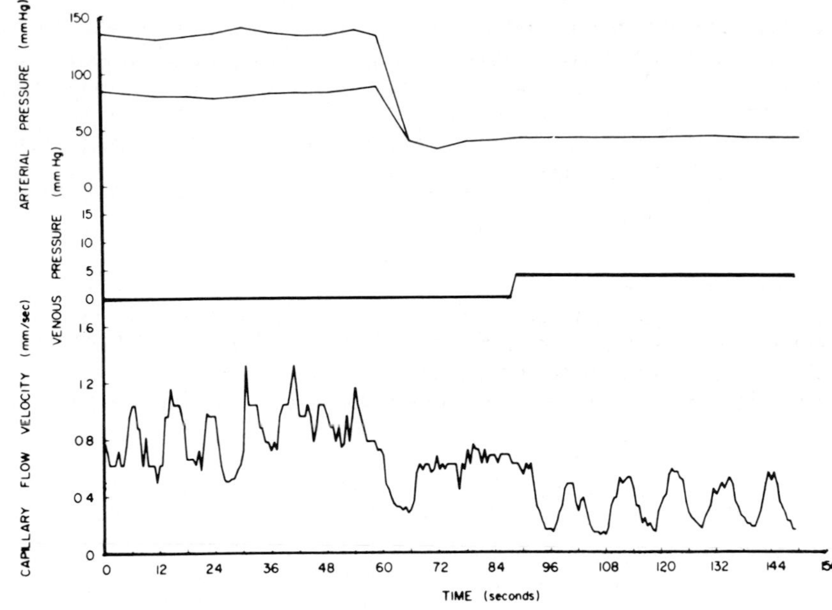

FIG. 23. In vivo experiments on perfused gracilis muscle demonstrate the myogenic contribution to autoregulatory responses after a reduction in perfusion pressure. Loss of flow periodicity was counteracted by elevating venous pressure during arterial occlusion. Restoration of flow periodicity supports the idea of myogenic involvement in these alterations. [From Johnson and Wayland (197).]

that is set in motion by mechanical forces acting directly on the muscle cell. The response is presumably activated in situ by the variable wall tension set up by the prevailing transmural pressure (13, 50, 97, 258, 259, 355). Myogenic responses occur even after the removal of neurogenic and blood-borne humoral influences. A basic implication of the myogenic concept is that pressure is the fulcrum around which local arteriolar adjustments are made (187). An equally plausible case can be made for metabolic activation of local vascular adjustments (324). The latter concept presupposes that a flow-dependent variable is being sensed and monitored (35).

Connective tissue elements in the walls of the large arterioles and their parent arteries take up a substantial portion of the strain created by the distending intravascular pressure, whereas the layer of smooth muscle that makes up the wall of the transverse arterioles (A3) and precapillaries (A4) provides the predominant physical support for counteracting the outward action of the transmural pressure (44). For this reason the smooth muscle cells in the smallest vessels are continuously subjected to a proportionately greater stretch-and-release action than those in larger vessels.

The structural alignment of the smooth muscle in the terminal arterioles optimizes the mechanical effects on lumen dimensions of changes in length of smooth muscle. Microvascular adjustments to changes in arterial blood flow usually develop in stages; the terminal arterioles show an immediate change in diameter that persists for several minutes and then undergoes a gradual secondary readjustment. This type of autoregulation is readily demonstrated when venous pressure is elevated by any of several means (189, 191, 195, 196). Within 60–90 s the initial perturbation is followed by a narrowing of the precapillaries delivering blood to this particular network. Although *myogenic* by definition implies that the response of vascular smooth muscle is triggered by changes in transmural pressure, the reaction can be attenuated by β-adrenergic factors of both neural and humoral origin (32, 127, 128, 192).

Myogenic accommodations appear to develop differently depending on the rate of change in transmural pressure. Grände et al. (128, 129) studied the myogenic reaction in hindlimb preparations and found that response to a dynamic perturbation is ~6–8 times greater than the static response to slow loading of skeletal muscle circulation (Fig. 24). Muscle tone in these distal arterioles appears to be spike generated (128, 129). There is no substantive information concerning the molecular basis for mechanically induced myogenic responses in smooth muscle.

The extent to which myogenic as opposed to metabolic factors predominate in autoregulatory responses varies with the particular tissue (191, 196, 202, 203). Davis et al. (77) found that in hamster cheek pouch arterioles myogenic behavior represents the major factor in local adjustments, whereas in pulmonary arterioles little or no myogenic activity can be demonstrated.

Vasomotion

The characteristic intermittency of capillary pressure and flow under steady-state conditions is greatly reduced in preparations where the arterioles and precapillaries do not exhibit spontaneous vasomotion. Some flow irregularity still exists in these preparations because of the uneven distribution of blood cells among the network vessels and the recurring obstruction of capillary flow during the slowed passage of the numerous leukocytes. Changes in both the frequency and amplitude of vasomotion minimize blood flow

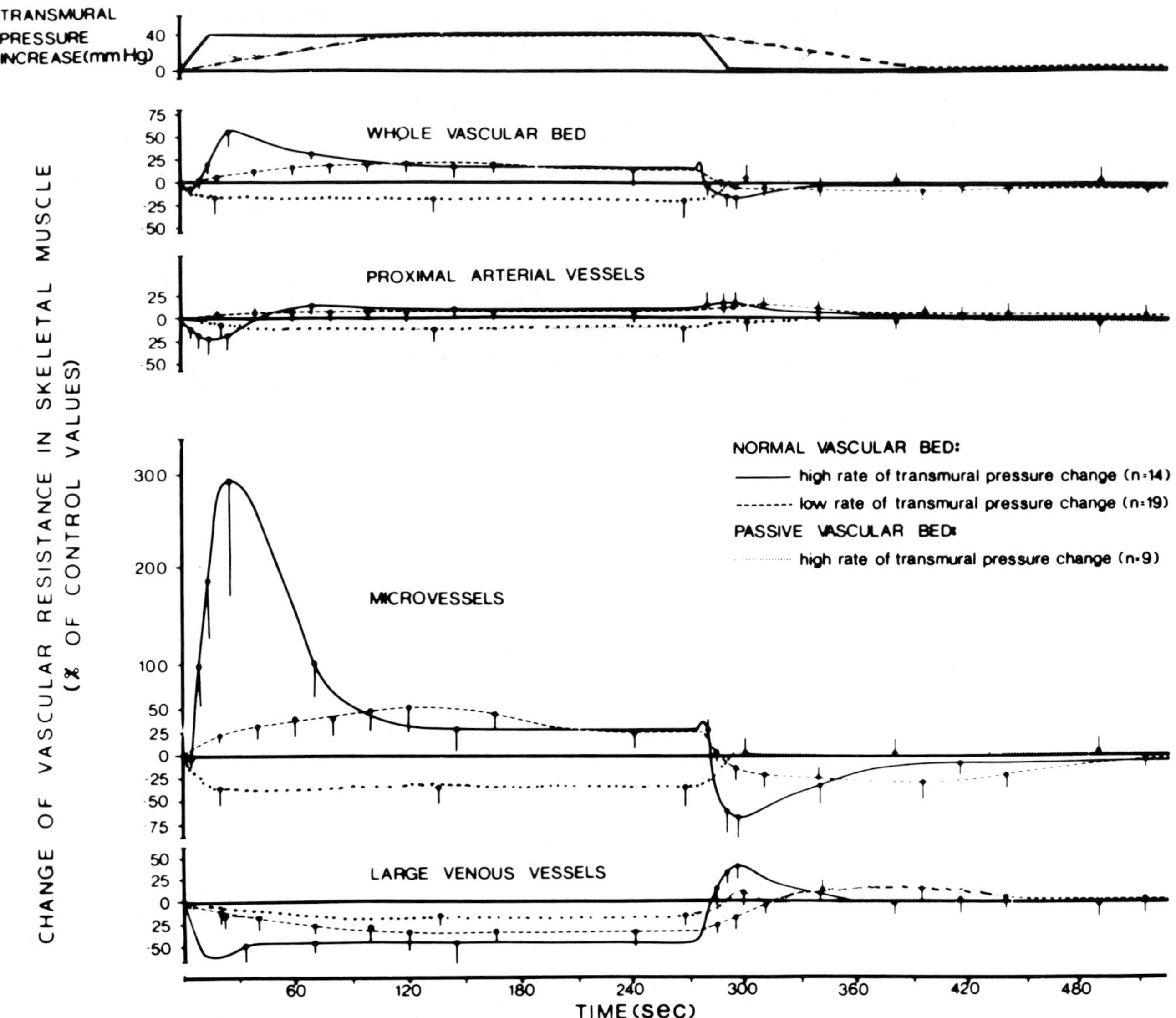

FIG. 24. Isolated hindlimb experiments demonstrate the relative contribution of dynamic as opposed to static or passive changes in transmural pressure. A dynamic load resulted in a change in microvessel resistance 6 times greater than a comparable load induced at a low rate. Venous vessels were much less reactive. [From Grände et al. (129).]

fluctuations in small vessels in the face of perturbations of systemic pressure. The basic feedback underlying these temporal adjustments is presumed to be changes in the chemical makeup of the tissue milieu accompanying either an excess or diminished flow (194, 197, 367). In general, substrates and by-products of general metabolism act to relax vascular smooth muscle; an exception is oxygen, which in concentrations above normal produces arteriolar and precapillary narrowing (231). There is increasing evidence that the cyclic generation and destruction of specific vasoactive agents of both the polypeptide and prostaglandin classes may be involved (261). Models of spontaneous vasomotion based on intravital measurements in rat spinotrapezius muscle (42, 43) suggest that the periodicity of the phenomenon can be accounted for by assuming the local release of a slowly diffusing vasoactive substance.

Oxygen Tension and Local Adjustments

Spontaneous vasomotor activity becomes exaggerated in preparations where ambient tissue oxygen concentration is increased by bringing the superfusion solution into equilibrium with gas mixtures containing 20% or more oxygen. With these above-normal oxygen tensions the mean diameters of the A2 and A3 arterioles in skeletal muscle are reduced by 20%–50%. The stimulatory action of high oxygen tension is much greater in metabolically active tissue such as skeletal muscle than in mesentery, where a comparable increase in oxygen tension results in only minor narrowing of these arterioles. The increase in smooth muscle tone with increased oxygen in the suffusion fluid is associated with an enhanced myogenic response to standardized shifts in transmural pressure (52).

The magnitude of response to a given change in oxygen tension varies with vessel size. Larger supply arterioles (>40 μm) show less of a change in diameter than the smaller arterioles and precapillaries. A stepwise adjustment of capillary flow to successive increments of oxygen tension occurs in skeletal muscle prepared for vital microscopy (Fig. 25). Similar responses have been reported in a number of species (e.g., rabbit, rat, cat, and dog) after an increase in oxygen in the fluid bathing the exteriorized muscle. At P_{O_2} levels of ~30–40 mmHg capillary flow is drastically reduced and nearly stopped in rabbit tenuissimus muscle and rat spinotrapezius and cremaster muscles (61, 78, 231, 296). The response to oxygen is especially striking in the transverse arterioles and precapillaries that frequently narrow to obliterate the vessel lumen. The resulting perturbations were reversible, with the vessels returning to control conditions within 15–20 s after oxygen tension returned to control levels.

Höper and Kessler (165) have obtained evidence in several tissues for the presence of an oxidase enzyme system at the mitochondrial level that responds to a fall in tissue oxygen tension by reducing the oxidative requirements of the cell. They postulate that such sensor enzymes in endothelial cells or smooth muscle cells provide a feedback mechanism for adjusting pressure and blood flow in accordance with extracellular oxygen levels.

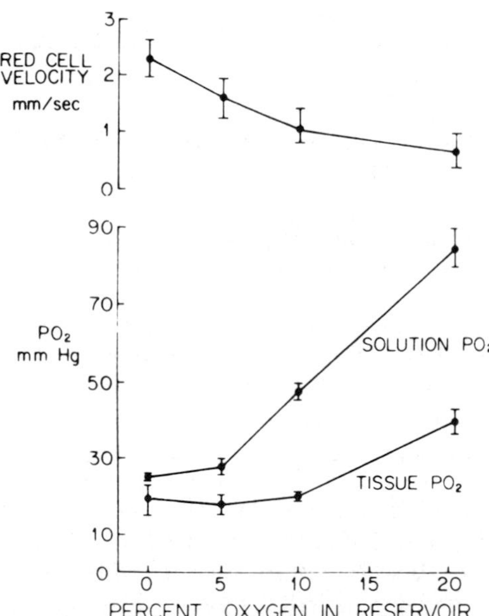

FIG. 25. Changes in oxygen content of fluid suffusing the surface of exteriorized tissues substantially affect diameter and flow in the microcirculation. As indicated for rat cremaster muscle an increase in P_{O_2} from 15 to 90 mmHg reduces red cell velocity in 20-μm arterioles to one-third of the control rate. Tissue P_{O_2} increases significantly when solution P_{O_2} > 50 mmHg. [From Prewitt and Johnson (296).]

Ancillary Factors

Vessels on the venous side of the microvascular bed of most tissues show only minor spontaneous vasomotor activity and much less of a response to known smooth muscle agonists than on the arterial side. Striking exceptions are the veins in the bat wing (275, 347, 355), a highly specialized structure that because of its size requires venomotor activity to ensure venous return. Differences in arterial and venous vessel behavior appear to be due to differences in overall reactivity of smooth muscle cells and to specific receptor characteristics (99).

The introduction of local adjustments in the face of centrally mediated reflexes is exemplified by the response to graded hemorrhage; until systemic pressure falls below 40–50 mmHg, capillary flow rates in the rat spinotrapezius muscle are maintained near normal despite narrowing of the precapillary arterioles. Capillary velocity then becomes highly erratic, with periods of no flow or even retrograde flow. In turn, venular flow rates fall off substantially to less than 20% of control values, with only a moderate venoconstriction (162, 373). In other organs such as the skin, venomotor responses are much greater in response to hypovolemia or hypoxia (76, 99, 132).

When systemic pressure is restored to normal levels in animals subject to hemorrhage, the reinfusion of the volume of shed blood results in rapid and plethoric flow throughout the microcirculation. This mechanical advantage is not sustained even though systemic pressure remains at 70–85 mmHg, presumably because of an uncoupling of local adjustment mechanisms (88, 169, 277). When hypotension is allowed to persist for several hours, capillary pressure is maintained near normal but flow is greatly reduced because of widespread arterial vasoconstriction (368). Microvascular adjustments also intervene during perturbations that involve an increase in systemic pressure. For example, capillary blood flow in skeletal muscle of hypertensive rats is adjusted to essentially normal levels despite substantial elevation in blood pressure (374).

Blood Rheology

Under steady-state conditions the non-Newtonian properties of blood become more important at the low shear rates seen on the venous side of the microcirculation. Red blood cells are distributed among the branchings of the microvascular network in line with the pressure drop across them. Because the A4 precapillaries, capillaries, and postcapillaries often are narrower than the red cell diameter, the hematocrit in these vessels is significantly lower than the systemic hematocrit and in many capillaries is reduced to as low as 10%. As a consequence of this heterogeneity, the greater frictional loss in the vessels with higher hematocrit decreases their flow rate. Both the rate and direction of flow in the capillary network proper are continuously changing, even when inflow pressures remain fairly stable.

Entrance of a leukocyte into a narrow capillary results in temporary slowing of blood flow because of the greater resistance of these cells to mechanical deformation (135, 252). When the pressure difference across the entrapped leukocyte in the capillary is not large enough to dislodge the obstructing cell, flow may be interrupted for up to several minutes (8, 9, 11, 280).

Under induced hypotension the surface forces involved in the adhesion of the leukocyte to the endothelial wall may be strong enough to resist cell displacement, and capillary flow is interrupted for long periods. In view of the comparatively large number of circulating leukocytes this phenomenon is a potential hazard contributing to microcirculatory inefficiency in various states of low flow and ischemia (10).

Sympathetic Innervation

There is considerable structural and functional evidence pointing to direct innervation of the microvascular network by the sympathetic nervous system (34, 38, 98, 100, 148, 149, 242, 325). Both α- and β-receptors have been demonstrated for the arteriolar and venular vessels (16, 243), but no convincing evidence has been provided either from physiological or structural observations that the true capillaries receive motor innervation. Baez and co-workers (16, 17) have shown that even myogenic reactions involve a neurogenic component and can be modified by agents that block α- and β-receptor sites. Honig and associates (163, 164) described what they believe to be neuronlike cells adjacent to the terminal arterioles and suggested that they could serve as possible sensors for local readjustment mechanisms.

Lundvall and Järhult (243) found that stimulation of the regional sympathetic nerves supplying skeletal muscle substantially reduces blood flow (from 8.9 ± 0.2 ml·min^{-1}·100 g^{-1} to <2.0 ml·min^{-1}·100 g^{-1}). Because the pressure of small arteries was elevated to near systemic levels, the vasoconstriction appears to reside primarily with arterioles (Fig. 26). The net result was an almost 500% increase in total vascular resistance. Inasmuch as the curve depicting the pressure drop during stimulation of the sympathetic nervous system was similar to that obtained under steady-state conditions, these investigators concluded that the relative increase in resistance during stimulation was approximately the same in the different parts of the vascular tree. Local differences in the successive segments of the microcirculatory network may then represent secondary adjustments.

A secondary relaxation of the arterioles during sympathetic nerve stimulation has been observed in the tenuissimus muscle preparation (87). Some investigators believe this to be secondary to the accumulation of dilator metabolites, but others have suggested that a neurogenically mediated β-adrenergic dilation may be the mechanism responsible for the phenomenon (242, 243).

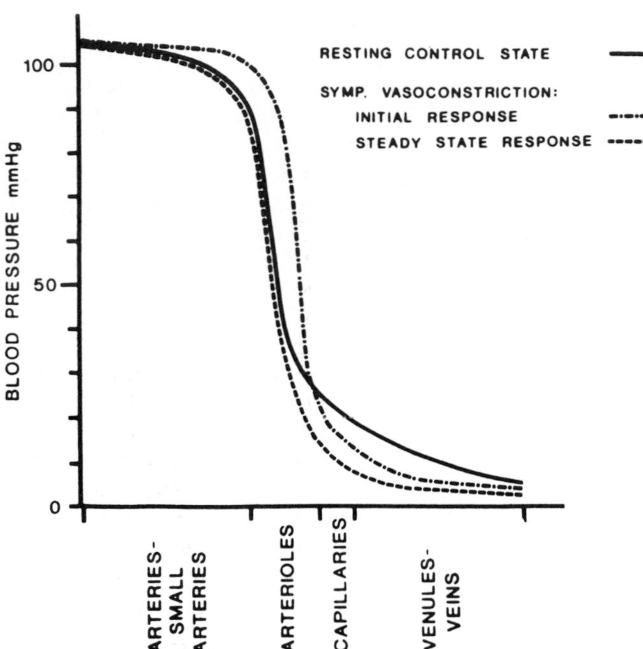

FIG. 26. Effect of direct stimulation of the sympathetic nervous system on cat hindlimb muscles. Pressure drop shown for successive segments of the microvasculature compared with the resting control state. [From Lundvall and Järhult (243).]

The efferent pathways for baroreceptor reflexes operate via the larger arterioles to maintain systemic blood pressure within a given range. This modulating action is accomplished through variable α-adrenergic mediation of vascular smooth muscle tone. In the more distal ramifications of the arterial tree there is steepening of the downward pressure gradient as the bloodstream courses through the fine transverse arterioles (A3) and their precapillary branches (A4). Although these minute vessels come increasingly under the control of local mechanisms (myogenic and metabolic), their behavior can still be modified by sympathetic nervous activity. A continuous barrage of neurogenic stimuli is responsible for a substantial portion of the tone of the A1, A2, and A3 arterioles because surgical section of the nerves leads to a 30%–40% increase in vessel diameter (259). However, the induced dilation does not persist. Denervated vessels resume their tonic state within 15–20 min, presumably through the intervention of myogenic and/or metabolically linked factors (including oxygen tension). It is highly likely that local adjustments in this portion of the vascular system involve the interaction of both local and systemic factors to some degree.

Spontaneous or extrinsically induced active adjustments of pressure and flow in the microcirculation appear to operate primarily via the precapillary side of the network, with finer control achieved by selective changes in the 8- to 20-μm terminations of the arterioles. In some tissues such as skeletal muscle the most prominent spontaneous vasomotor activity is seen in the A4 precapillaries. Activity at this network cross section controls small groups of capillaries, as few as one or two in mesentery. This contrasts with the situation in skeletal muscle, where vasomotor adjustments of the transverse arterioles act collectively on flow through as many as 10–20 capillaries.

RHEOLOGICAL BEHAVIOR OF BLOOD FLOW IN THE MICROCIRCULATION

Background

CONCEPTUAL FRAMEWORK. It is generally acknowledged that the mechanisms of control and regulation of blood flow in the microcirculation are principally manifest as alterations in the resistance to blood flow in individual microvessels, as well as throughout specific functional segments of the network. For the flow of a Newtonian fluid (i.e., one with constant viscosity) the relationship between pressure, flow, and geometry (vessel length and luminal diameter) is readily understood in terms of the classic Poiseuille-Hagen (145, 295) relationship, $Q = (\pi/128\ \eta)\Delta P d^4/l$. In the microvascular network for flow with low Reynolds number ($\sim 10^{-3}$–10^{-2}), it is not too difficult to apply this relationship to an ensemble of interconnected tubes to elucidate the distribution of pressure and flow throughout successive divisions (237). In practice, however, departures from such ideal fluid behavior and complexities in network geometry result in substantially nonlinear pressure-flow relationships that obscure the relative roles of blood rheology and network topography as determinants of microvascular perfusion.

In general the rheological behavior of blood embodies the relationship between pressure gradient and mean velocity of cells and plasma for a specific microvessel geometry. The network topography encompasses the number of vessels at a specific position in the network available to carry off the total flow of the network, their relative deployment in terms of an arrangement of serial and/or parallel vessels, and the configuration of their cross sections. In the framework of the forces that propel blood (pressure gradients) of a specific viscosity through the network, it is the branching pattern of the network that dictates the fraction of the overall arteriovenous (AV) pressure drop that appears across any local segment. Hence if the relationship between pressure gradient, vessel geometry, and blood viscosity is nonlinear, the branching pattern may interact with rheological determinants of resistance in the blood to produce rheological equilibrium throughout the network.

Attempts to evaluate microvascular pressure-flow relationships in terms of the relative contributions of rheological and vascular factors have formed a recurrent theme in microvascular research. An exemplary approach to this problem has been given by Landis (218), who used the Poiseuille-Hagen relationship to compute the pressure gradients in individual microvessels of frog mesentery. With values of apparent viscosity obtained by in vitro methods (tube viscometer) and values of red cell velocity measured in vivo (215), he applied the Poiseuille-Hagen equation to obtain $\Delta P/l$. By comparing these with pressure gradient values obtained in his earlier studies (215), Landis concluded that Poiseuille's law was not directly applicable to the microcirculation. Although present studies (233) suggest that under certain conditions the Poiseuille-Hagen equation only approximates the relationship between resistance and luminal diameter, i.e., $R \sim 1/d^4$, Landis' studies remain a prime example of the means by which one may evaluate the rheological basis of microvascular blood flow.

Drawing on a broader base of macrocirculatory experimental observations, Lamport (214) proposed that the summated effects of rheological and topographical factors may be described by defining the total resistance to blood flow for a given organ or region of tissue as the product of a geometrical hindrance (Z) and effective blood viscosity (η) such that $R = Z\eta$. Attempts to determine Z for an ensemble of microvessels in terms of their individual hindrances [from Poiseuille's law $Z = 128l/\pi d^4$; (180)] have been useful. However, the major difficulty in applying this representation to a given network has been to decipher the topography of the constituent microvessels in light of their serial or parallel deployment. Although the hindrance of n serial elements is computed easily from the electrical analogue as $Z = nZ_i$ and for parallel vessels as $Z = 1/\Sigma\ (1/Z_i)$, it is not possible to represent the network in terms of serial or parallel microvessels in all but the simplest cases. To overcome these difficulties numerous applications of the techniques of electrical network analysis have appeared to assess the contribution of network topography.

To shed some light on these facets of in vivo rheological behavior of blood in the microcirculation, this section reviews some of the salient features of the mechanisms and determinants of viscous behavior of blood and their contribution to microvascular function overall. To accomplish this the following sections briefly examine the pertinent features of blood rheology, interpretations of microvascular function obtained by indirect macrovascular studies, specific functional themes common to microvascular hemodynamics in general, and the determinants and expressions of in vivo blood rheology.

RHEOLOGICAL PROPERTIES OF BLOOD. Rheology (Greek *rheos* "anything flowing" and *logia* "study") is traditionally concerned with the ability of a fluid to deform at a particular rate under specific shear stresses. In engineering the viscosity of a fluid is rigorously defined only for a homogeneous fluid, i.e., a continuum (66), and hence in the case of a particulate suspension such as blood the term *apparent viscosity* is commonly used. For example, when blood flows in a small-bore tube of given luminal diameter and length, measurement of the pressure drop and volumetric flow rate provides sufficient information to calculate the viscosity of the medium from the Poiseuille-Hagen relationship. However, this value for apparent viscosity, based on a continuum equation, reveals a material property (η) that may not be applicable to the description of pressure-flow relationships in other flow situations such as at bifurcations or in tubes of irregular cross section. With these limitations on the applicability of continuum concepts to describe blood flow, considerable caution must be exercised in attempting to describe flow in many organs, for example, liver sinusoids and pulmonary capillaries.

In an attempt to place the rheological behavior of blood on a firm quantitative foundation numerous studies have elucidated the principal determinants of apparent viscosity in large-scale viscometric instruments. There are several reviews that delineate the major developments to date (23–26, 66, 69, 79, 257, 301). As a result of these studies it is generally accepted that the principal determinants of apparent blood viscosity are hematocrit and shear rate. For hematocrits below ~30%, η varies nearly linearly with hematocrit, whereas for higher hematocrit values η rises exponentially to reach a value ~50 times that of plasma viscosity at 50% hematocrit. It has also been shown that shear rate may be important; red cells form aggregates as shear rate is reduced below ~200 s^{-1}, where η may increase some 60-fold. Thus to evaluate the in vivo expression of these overall features of rheological blood behavior it is desirable to give considerable attention to the distribution of hematocrit and shear rates throughout the entire microvascular network.

In addition much attention has been given to the rheological properties of the blood's cellular elements insofar as they may contribute to the apparent viscosity of the suspension. As a result of these studies erythrocyte deformability has been shown to be a major determinant of η (45, 59, 60, 69, 320). Also the pioneering studies of Fåhraeus (94) demonstrated that the hematocrit of blood flowing in small-bore tubes diminished compared with its feed reservoir value as tube diameter was decreased to ~40 μm (the Fåhraeus effect) and that apparent viscosity was reduced as well [the Fåhraeus-Lindqvist effect (95)]. Hence considerable information has been obtained to describe the behavior of blood in small-bore tubes comparable in size to microcirculation vessels (see refs. 21, 22, 67, 68, 346, and the chapter by Chien, Usami, and Skalak in this *Handbook*). The pertinent contribution of these studies is that microvessel hematocrit, by virtue of the strong dependency of η on hematocrit, may indeed be the main determinant of in vivo apparent viscosity at the microvascular level during normal flow (i.e., without excessive red cell aggregation). The interface between blood and endothelium has also been proposed as an important determinant of in vivo η because of the possibility that macromolecules can coat the endothelium (e.g., fibrin) and lessen the apparent viscosity of blood (70, 71); blood cellular elements [leukocytes (315) and erythrocytes (155)] may also adhere to the vascular wall, obstructing the vessel lumen and increasing flow resistance. With these facets of microvascular rheology in mind, the numerous studies aimed at unraveling its mysteries are now explored.

MACROCIRCULATORY STUDIES OF IN VIVO BLOOD RHEOLOGY. Information on in vivo blood rheology in the microcirculation has been obtained mostly from macrocirculatory studies of pressure-flow relationships of both isolated organs and extremities and specific segments of the systemic circulation. This situation has prevailed due to both a general interest in the overall expression of the summated (systemic) effects of blood viscosity at the microvascular level and a lack of suitable instrumentation and techniques for direct in situ quantitation of microvascular blood behavior. Although recent advances in instrumentation have aided direct examination of in vivo blood rheology, macrocirculatory studies are still an important tool for evaluating microvascular events and their contribution to systemic circulation. To set the stage for the more detailed features seen at the microcirculatory level and their correlation with macrocirculatory behavior, a brief review of the significant findings of these studies follows.

The classic work of Whittaker and Winton (352) is the basic model for studies of microvascular blood rheology. Alternate perfusion of the isolated dog hindlimb with Ringer's solution and whole blood facilitated the computation of in vivo apparent viscosity from the product of the ratio of flow resistance (blood: Ringer's) and viscosity of Ringer's solution. Network topography was assumed to remain unchanged. As shown in Figure 27 these studies revealed that the in vivo η was 50% lower than that obtained in an in vitro tube viscometer. This result was interpreted as a consequence of the Fåhraeus effect; thus the lower microvessel hematocrits (analogous to the lower hematocrits found by Fåhraeus in small-bore glass tubes) resulted in a lower apparent viscosity (as in the Fåhraeus-Lindqvist effect found in vitro). Similar results have been obtained for perfusion of the isolated rabbit ear (160), rat tail artery (211), isolated calf muscle of the cat (10, 80), and the isolated dog lung (2). In addition to the lower in vivo apparent viscosity of blood, Whittaker and Winton's studies brought to light departures from a linear relationship between pressure drop and flow as pressure drop fell below 20

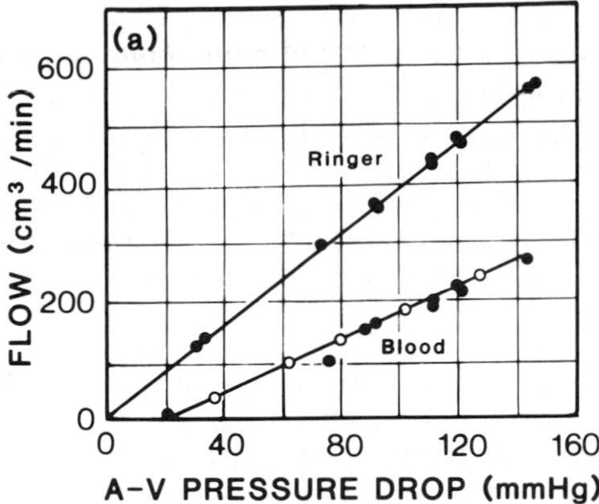

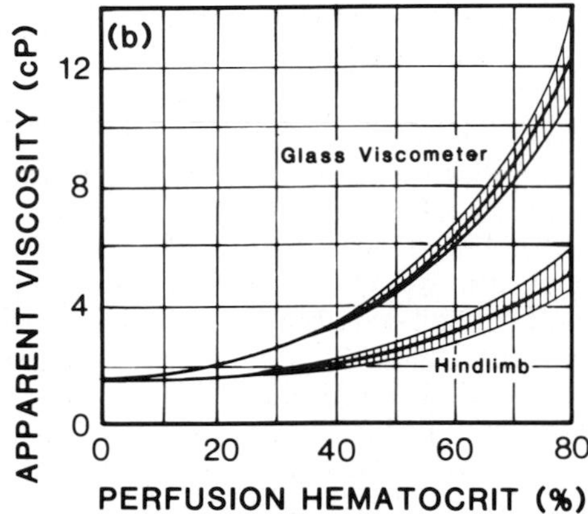

FIG. 27. *A*: flow versus arteriovenous (AV) pressure drop for isolated dog hindlimb. *B*: in vivo apparent viscosity (η) versus perfusion hematocrit. Values of η were attributed to Fåhraeus and Fåhraeus-Lindqvist effects in the microcirculation proper. [From Whittaker and Winton (352).]

mmHg (Fig. 27*A*). Subsequent studies have also demonstrated the occurrence of zero flow at a positive pressure drop, which has been attributed to increased η with decreased shear rates as well as with vasoconstriction (80, 98, 148, 162, 201, 229, 281, 322). These studies have also described departures from a linear Q versus ΔP_{av} curve attributable to vasomotion that may be eradicated during vasodilation (229). Other studies of these nonlinearities have suggested the importance of inertial losses in relatively large vessels outside the microcirculation proper (29–31) that may contribute as much as 40% of the total AV pressure drop for perfusion with cell-free Ringer's solution. This value diminishes to 5% for perfusion with blood at 50% hematocrit. Contrary evidence has also suggested that the presence of inertial losses may be insignificant (85) because they do not appear to be present in the maximally dilated network.

Macrocirculatory studies have also attempted to separate the total organ resistance into its precapillary (arteriolar) and postcapillary (venular) components to establish the physiological role of the ratio of precapillary resistance (R_{pre}) to postcapillary resistance (R_{post}) as a determinant of the capillary hydrostatic pressure (148, 149, 162, 277, 292). The approach taken has been to utilize the isogravimetric method of Pappenheimer and Soto-Rivera (292), or variations thereof, to calculate the effective capillary hydrostatic pressure (P_c') that contributes to the balance of the Starling forces. From simultaneous measurements of arterial (inflow) and venous (outflow) pressures, P_a and P_v, respectively, $R_{pre}/R_{post} = (P_a - P_c')/(P_c' - P_v)$. As is shown in the following sections such indirect measurements may not compare well with in situ measurements, primarily because the isogravimetrically determined capillary hydrostatic pressure may have been measured at a point distal to the microvessels that were anatomically determined to be true capillaries.

Network Distributions of Hemodynamic Parameters

INTRAVASCULAR PRESSURE. Direct in situ measurements of intravascular pressure [servo-null method (171, 172, 175, 360)] and red cell velocity [two-slit photometric technique (171, 174, 342, 347)] have provided a wealth of in vivo data that characterizes their distribution throughout successive microvascular divisions in many tissues. Evaluation and interpretation of the results of these studies have usually pursued the relationship between network structure (branching patterns) and functional behavior in light of the needs of the parenchymal tissue (i.e., convective transport and transcapillary exchange of water and solutes). With the basic goal of relating network stucture to function, the principal theme has been to quantitatively evaluate network hemodynamics by examining commonalities between networks of various configurations and their departures from the norm under pathophysiological conditions. Some of the general features of microhemodynamics are illustrated by the hemodynamic parameters in four apparently dissimilar networks, two splanchnic and two skeletal muscle beds, various features of which have already been discussed.

Figure 6 presents the AV distributions of intravascular pressures and red cell velocities versus luminal diameter [obtained by image-shearing method (179)]. The latter relationship may be interpreted as an index of position in the overall hierarchy of microvessels in mesentery (375), omentum (375), spinotrapezius muscle (B. W. Zweifach, unpublished data), and tenuissimus muscle (105). All measurements were obtained for the normal resting state of these tissues. Individual pressures and velocities have been averaged over 3–5 cardiac cycles. It is evident that each network has a distribution pattern characteristic of its topography, overall AV pressure drops, flows, and properties of blood rheology. Similarities in the function of each network may be gleaned from these distributions by a suitable normalization of the data. Specifically, if one

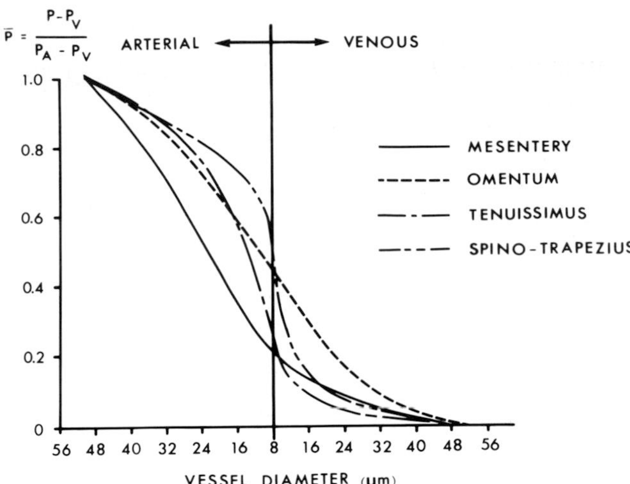

FIG. 28. Arteriovenous distribution of normalized microvascular pressure for the 4 networks of Fig. 6. Intravascular pressure is normalized with respect to arterial (P_A) and venous (P_V) pressures in 50-μm vessels. $\overline{P} = (P - P_V)/(P_A - P_V)$.

assumes that the distribution of intravascular pressures has been sampled in sufficiently large numbers (which appears satisfied by the 300–500 measurements for each tissue), the attendant variation of intravascular pressure with diameter may indicate how the total network flow is apportioned by a succession of serial resistances between each functional division (arterioles and precapillaries). The normalized value for intravascular pressure ($\overline{P}$) with respect to the arteriolar and venular pressures has been proposed to represent the fraction of the total overall network resistance distal to a microvessel of any size and position in the network (304)

$$\overline{P} = (P - P_V)/(P_A - P_V) \tag{2}$$

The resultant AV distributions of $\overline{P}$ computed for P_A and P_V, corresponding to pressures in 50-μm arterioles and venules, respectively (Fig. 28), clearly demonstrate the similar manner in which pressure declines throughout each network. The fraction of total network resistance required to attenuate arteriolar pressure to its value in true capillaries ranges from ~0.2 for mesentery and tenuissimus muscle to ~0.45 for omentum and spinotrapezius preparations. Although the numerical value of $\overline{P}$ at the level of the true capillaries is determined mainly by the magnitude of arteriolar pressure (equilibration of the Starling forces dictates that capillary pressure does not vary widely from one tissue to another), the mechanisms that incur these reductions are affected by the network topography. Similar analyses of other tissues under pathological conditions, for example, cremaster network in spontaneously hypertensive rats (39), demonstrate shifts in $\overline{P}$ consistent with the concept of increased arteriolar-to-capillary resistance (see Fig. 9*B*).

The AV distribution of the resistance to total flow of each network can be visualized more clearly by examining the slopes of P or $\overline{P}$ in Figures 6 and 28 (240). Specifically, if one treats the abscissas of Figure 6 as axes of rightward-running coordinates with negative diameters for the arterioles and positive diameters for the venules (i.e., as coordinate systems where $x = d_c - d$ for arterioles and $x = d - d_c$ for venules), then the slope of pressure or flow may be computed from dP/dx or dQ/dx, respectively, noting that $d/dx = d/dd$. Figure 29 presents the AV distributions of dP/dd as obtained for these four networks. The negative of dP/dd is plotted because the monotonically decreasing pressure distribution yields a negative slope. This representation of the network pressure gradients delineates the specific location of the major sites of resistance to flow throughout the ensemble of microvessels and agrees fairly well with topographical features previously discussed. For example, the mesentery shows maximum network resistance in the precapillary microvessels ranging in diameter from 15 to 35 μm, which is consistent with observations on the arcaded modular structure of this network (102). The omentum, however, shows a maximum pressure gradient at the level of the true capillaries consistent with its nearly dichotomous branching pattern (180). The two skeletal muscle beds indicate a maximum fall in pressure in the region of the precapillary vessels, which may be identified with small arterioles that run transverse to the muscle fibers prior to the final ramification at the true capillaries (89, 105).

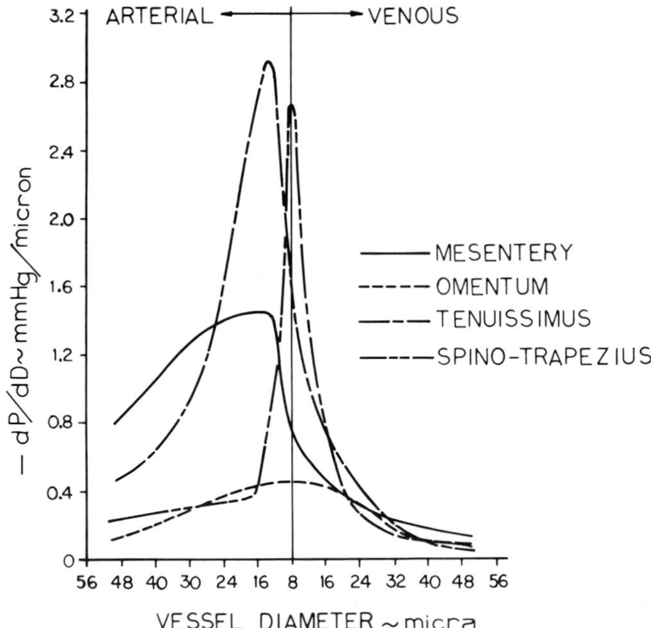

FIG. 29. Arteriovenous distribution of network pressure gradient. Pressure gradient throughout successive divisions computed from slopes of pressure curves in Fig. 6, calculated for an arbitrary length scale as illustrated in Fig. 35. dP/dD, change in pressure as a function of change in diameter.

VOLUMETRIC FLOW RATES. Although the AV distributions of P and $\overline{P}$ indicate the relative deployment of network resistances, it is the AV distribution of flow that gives insight into the relative number of microvessels that are effectively in parallel at each division to carry off the total flow of the network. Using the empirical relationships between red cell velocity and mean velocity ($\overline{V}$) (20, 213, 241), one can compute the bulk volumetric flow as $Q = \overline{V}\pi d^2/4$ and plot its AV distribution as in Figure 30. In light of the limited variation of red cell velocity (Fig. 6) relative to d^2 it appears that microvessel cross-sectional area dominates the AV distribution of flow, thus yielding a parabolic distribution. In these four preparations the minimum flow appears to fall in the postcapillary microvessels immediately following the true capillaries.

The relative number of vessels at each position in the network may be assessed from the distributions of Figure 30 by calculating the number of distal microvessels required to carry off the stream for a given large arteriole (e.g., diam 50 μm) as the ratio of flow in a 50-μm arteriole to flow in a microvessel. Figure 31 shows the resultant distributions of this ratio for these networks. It is evident that the omentum, mesentery, and spinotrapezius networks have 90–110 true capillaries per 50-μm arteriole, whereas the tenuissimus muscle has 165 capillaries per 50-μm arteriole (~60% higher). It should be emphasized that the interpretation of these flow ratios as relative capillary densities is made on a functional basis rather than an anatomical one. Purely anatomical estimates suggest, for example, in the case of the omentum (180) that there are ~10 true capillaries for each 20-μm arteriole. The corresponding ratio derived from the network flow distributions (Fig. 6) reveals on the order of only 6 capillaries per 20-μm arteriole, or ~40% fewer actively flowing capillaries. These differences may represent a functional reserve of capillaries to meet higher metabolic demands of the tissue in nonresting states.

Although the relative flow ratios of Figure 31 offer a means of quantitating flow distribution relative to a major feeding arteriole, a clearer perspective on the apportionment of flow throughout successive microvascular divisions can be obtained from the slopes of the AV distributions of Figure 30. After calculating the slopes of the smoothed data (dQ/dd) the commonalities in flow apportionment become more striking, as shown in Figure 32 for these four networks. It is evident that although branching patterns may vary considerably, the rates at which flow varies with respect to the diameters of the constituent vessels of the network are similar for each tissue. The similarities of trends such as these have been analyzed in the context of an optimal network design (250) based on the principle of minimum work (265). It was shown that the branching pattern of the microvascular network may be configured to facilitate perfusion of the true capillaries for the least amount of energy expended in overcoming vascular resistance (250).

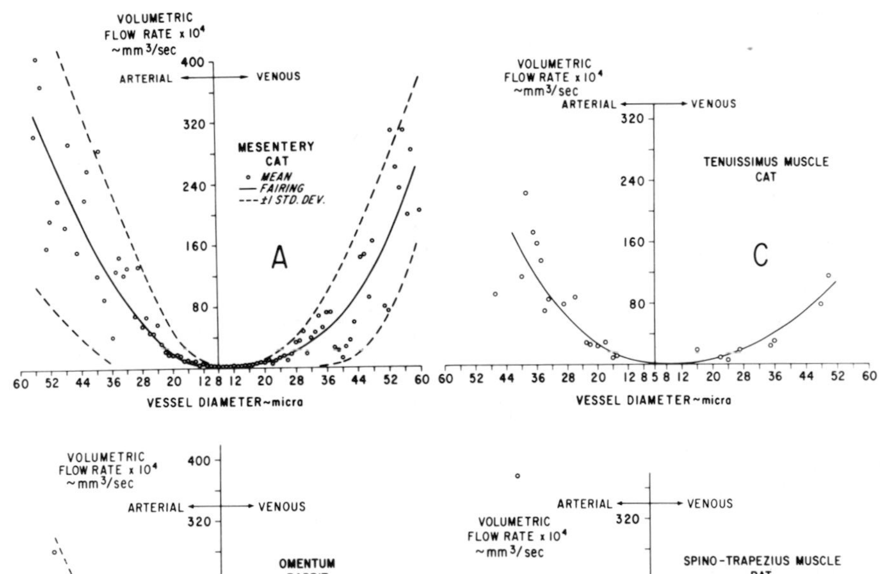

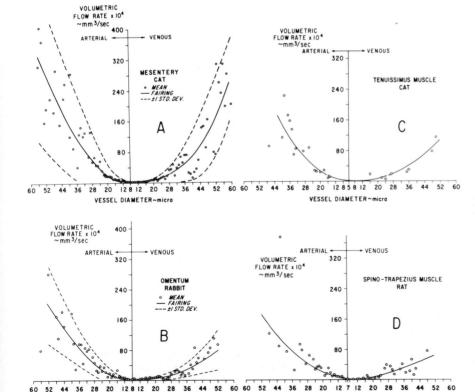

FIG. 30. Arteriovenous distribution of intravascular volumetric flow rates computed by the product of mean flow velocity and vessel cross-section area.

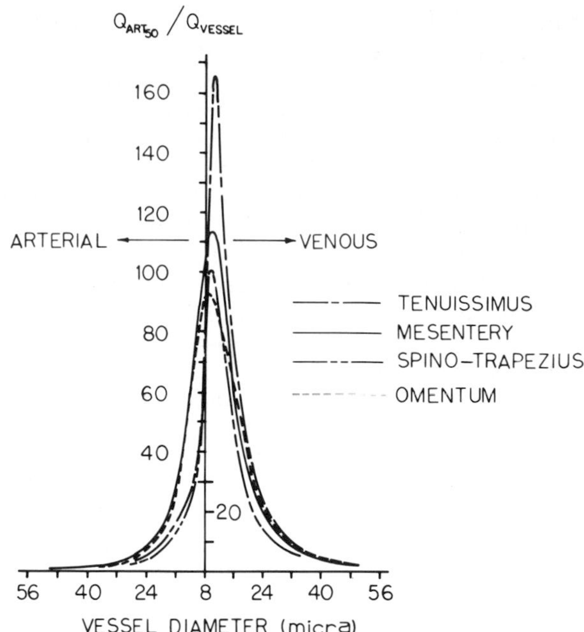

FIG. 31. Relative flow distribution throughout the network computed as the ratio of flow in an arteriole with diam 50 μm ($Q_{ART_{50}}$) to that in its distal microvessels (Q_{VESSEL}). If the network is composed of *n* parallel vessels at each successive division, then $Q_{ART_{50}}/Q_{VESSEL}$ may be interpreted as the number of distal vessels necessary to carry off the arteriolar stream.

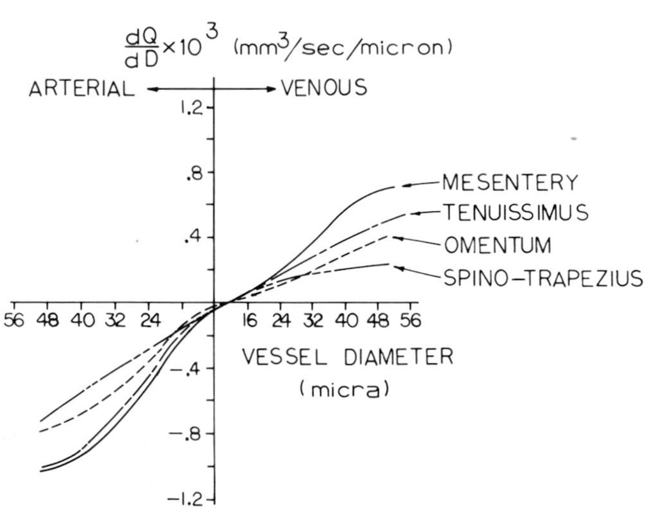

FIG. 32. Network distribution of flow gradient. Each curve is computed in a manner similar to that of the network pressure gradient (Figs. 29 and 35) and represents the rate at which flow varies between adjacent network divisions.

RATIO OF PRECAPILLARY RESISTANCE TO POSTCAPILLARY RESISTANCE. Another parameter of interest that can be obtained from the network distributions of pressure and flow is R_{pre}/R_{post}, usually defined from macrocirculatory measurements of AV pressure drop and isogravimetrically determined capillary hydrostatic pressure as $(P_a - P_{c,i})/(P_{c,i} - P_v)$. Although macrocirculatory measurements take advantage of the equivalency of total flow through arteries and veins as measured from one inlet to the corresponding outlet of the intervening vascular bed, microvascular measurements must proceed on the functional equivalency in flow magnitude between specific arterioles and venules (104). This situation is schematized in Figure 33 where arteriolar and venular pressures may be measured at hierarchical positions of equivalent flows. With this criterion satisfied one may evaluate R_{pre}/R_{post} at different positions throughout the network by choosing Q as the independent variable. Clearly as Q becomes very large the one-to-one correspondence between inlet and outlet should agree with macrocirculatory measurements.

Numerical computations of R_{pre}/R_{post} for the four tissues under consideration are presented in Figure 34 as a function of the Q value chosen for the estimate. At large Q values these curves should approach the macrocirculatory values found in the literature. At lesser Q values the computation reveals a characteristic trend peculiar to each network, until the point where a precapillary vessel cannot be identified with

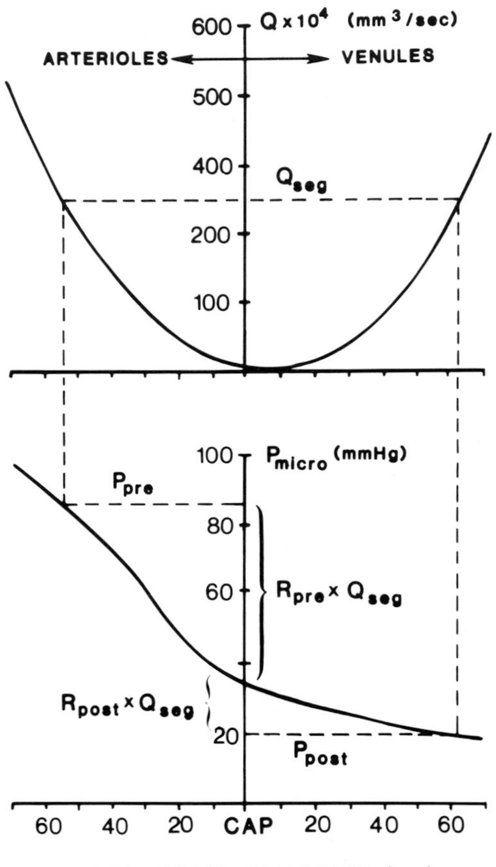

FIG. 33. Schema by which the ratio of precapillary resistance (R_{pre}) to postcapillary resistance (R_{post}) may be computed from the AV distribution of intravascular pressure. The R_{pre}/R_{post} may be computed as the ratio of pressure drops from arteriolar and venular segments to anatomical capillaries for segments bounded by arterioles and venules of equal flows. Q_{seg}, flow in a segment; P_{pre}, precapillary pressure; P_{micro}, microvessel pressure; P_{post}, postcapillary pressure.

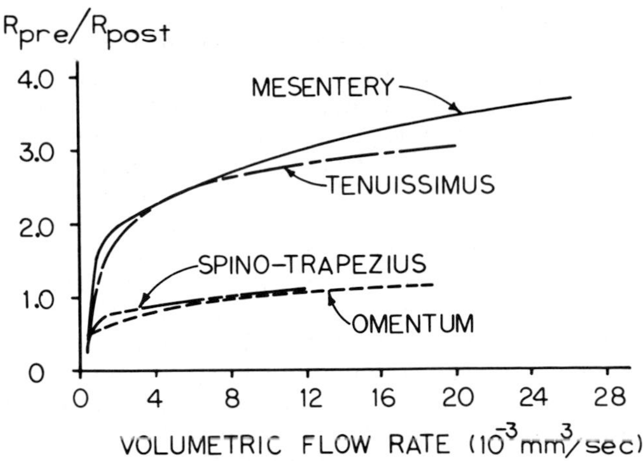

FIG. 34. Computed R_{pre}/R_{post} according to schema of Fig. 33. Abscissa represents magnitude of volumetric flow rates in arterioles and capillaries bounding a finite segment of the network. At larger flows arterioles and venules approach those of the outer network boundaries and should asymptotically approach the single inflow-outflow obtained in the whole-organ approach.

a postcapillary vessel of equivalent flow due to the flow minima occurring in the postcapillary vessels of the network. It should be emphasized that along the curves of Figure 34 the diameters of arterioles and venules vary according to the pattern delineated in Figure 6.

The trends of R_{pre}/R_{post} shown in Figure 34 reveal an asymptotic increase with progressive increase in flow of the arteriole-venule pairs; the major variations of R_{pre}/R_{post} occur in vessels smaller than 25 μm. Precise quantitative agreement with estimates of R_{pre}/R_{post} acquired by the whole-organ isogravimetric approach is not readily apparent. Between the extremes of the mesenteric and tenuissimus networks, for example, a maximal R_{pre}/R_{post} on the order of 3.0–3.5 is found from a direct computation with anatomical capillary pressures of 34 and 32 mmHg, respectively. In contrast, isogravimetric estimates of the intestinal loop [$P_c' \sim 15$ mmHg (190)] and the hindlimb [$P_c' \sim 21$ mmHg (339)] yield R_{pre}/R_{post} values of 4.5 and 5.6, respectively. These differences between the direct and indirect methods appear to result mainly from the lower isogravimetrically determined capillary hydrostatic pressure compared with the anatomical capillary pressure. Recalculation of R_{pre}/R_{post} for the hindlimb studies (339) by using a capillary pressure of 32 mmHg yields a R_{pre}/R_{post} value on the order of 2.5. In addition to these disparities the isogravimetric approach is subject to uncertainties in the delineation of the particular vascular region being studied and the state of vascular tone throughout the network. In the original studies of Pappenheimer and Soto-Rivera (292) measurements of R_{pre}/R_{post} for the hindlimb yielded values on the order of 10 in the resting state. Removal of the skin in subsequent hindlimb studies (339) yielded 50% lower values, attributable to the deletion of the passive dilation of the veins of the skin that tends to mask venous resistance changes in the muscle.

Because of these difficulties in characterizing the distribution of resistance throughout the microvascular network, the isogravimetric approach has not been widely used to evaluate the effect of the rheological behavior of blood. Studies attempting to assess the differences between precapillary and postcapillary apparent viscosities (277) have demonstrated that the effective viscosity during normal flow is higher in the precapillary microvessels (i.e., proximal to the site where P_c' is measured) than in the distal postcapillary network. The studies show that these trends are reversed during low flow where postcapillary viscosity exceeds its precapillary counterpart. This behavior during normal flow is contrary to theoretical expectations (i.e., lower venular shear rates should yield greater postcapillary viscosity) and also in contrast to direct in situ measurements (233) as discussed in the following section concerning the contribution of individual microvessels to the overall network resistance.

Hemodynamics in Individual Microvessels

PRESSURE GRADIENTS. From the rheological behavior of blood one knows that the pressure gradient along the length of an individual microvessel ($\Delta P/l$) determines flow for a given luminal diameter and a specified magnitude of apparent blood viscosity. The network pressure gradient presented in the preceding section is a functional parameter (rather than a physical one) that expresses the variability of a hemodynamic parameter with respect to specific anatomical landmarks (e.g., arterioles and precapillaries). In general the agreement between the network pressure gradient and that corresponding to an individual microvessel can be achieved only under very specific conditions of network topography. These conditions are that a particular anatomical site (e.g., vessel of a given diameter) can be represented by a finite number of parallel vessels through which the total flow of the network must pass and that the number of these parallel vessels is given by the ratio of the total flow to the flow in an individual vessel, Q/Q_i. The pressure gradients of the network and individual vessels are shown in Figure 35*A* and *B*, respectively. The network gradients are the same as those shown in Figure 29 with the addition of the arbitrary abscissa transformation used to calculate $dP/dd(= dP/dx)$, assuming that all vessels of a given diameter do not appreciably vary in length. Pressure gradients of individual vessels (Fig. 35*B*) were obtained by in vivo measurement of the upstream-to-downstream pressure drop divided by the vessel length (233).

Note that the following analyses of microhemodynamics are performed on time-averaged values (over 3–5 cardiac cycles) of pressure drop and flow. The effects of pulsatility on apparent blood viscosity (72) and the resistance to flow in large-bore (207) and

ship of increased blood viscosity to elevated hematocrit and the flux of red cells to the capillary bed. Theoretical considerations of the resistance-viscosity relationship make it conceivable that increases in viscosity attendant to elevations in perfusion hematocrit may negate the advantage of higher red cell concentrations (oxygen-carrying capacity) by reducing perfusion. This concept had been explored in the framework of an optimal hematocrit for maximum red cell flux and hence oxygen delivery to tissue (74, 113, 181, 262). For H_{sys} values (i.e., H_D) of 0.3–0.4 the volumetric flux of red cells through the entire network may be maximized by the nonlinear relationship between blood viscosity and hematocrit (256).

Microcirculatory studies of the flux of red cells during systemic hemodilution and/or concentration have revealed a general invariance of red cell velocity in rat mesentery over a wide range (0.3–0.6) of H_{sys} values (82). The precise relationships between microvascular hematocrit, red cell flux, and systemic hematocrit are undetermined.

PHENOMENA RELATED TO SHEAR RATE. Characterization of the rheological behavior of blood both in vitro and in vivo requires the specification of shear rates imposed on the suspension. To satisfy this requirement it is common to characterize microvessel shear rates in terms of the wall shear rate of a Newtonian fluid flowing with an equivalent mean velocity for a given tube diameter. Under these conditions the wall shear rate may be derived from the Navier-Stokes equations as $8\bar{V}/d$. From a rheological standpoint the representation of effective shear rates imposed on a fluid can be improved somewhat for a homogeneous non-Newtonian fluid (66); however, in view of the particulate nature of blood such refinements have given way to the empiricism of an equivalent Newtonian wall shear rate. Although some blood rheologists have preferred the characterization of blood shear rates for tube flow in terms of the reduced velocity [$\bar{V}/d$ (21, 22)], the utility of using $8\bar{V}/d$ is equally justified by the conceptual advantages of an effective Newtonian value.

Wall shear rates throughout the microvasculature can be easily calculated from the AV distribution of red blood cell velocity (V_{RBC}) with diameter by using the empirical relationship $V_{RBC}/\bar{V} = 1.6$ (20, 213, 241). Applying this to the mesenteric network yielded arteriolar wall shear rates of ~1,400 s^{-1} in 50-μm arterioles and a maximum value of ~1,800 s^{-1} in 25-μm precapillary vessels. Values steadily declined to a minimum of 500 s^{-1} in the 20-μm postcapillary venules but rose to 800 s^{-1} in 50-μm venules (233). Wall shear rates for 10- to 60-μm microvessels averaged 1,200 s^{-1} in the arterioles and 850 s^{-1} in the venules, with an overall average of 1,330 s^{-1}. These wall shear rates are considerably higher than those usually studied in vitro (66), mainly because the relationship between apparent viscosity and wall shear rate becomes invariant (asymptotically) for wall shear rates >1,000 s^{-1} at physiological hematocrits.

It should be emphasized that these shear rates are derived from continuum concepts as the slope of the velocity profile at the tube wall. In situ observations of the velocity profile of red cells flowing in 16- to 43-μm arterioles and venules in rabbit omentum (318) have revealed considerable blunting of the radial velocity profile. These studies have also demonstrated that for red cells flowing in close proximity to the endothelium (<1 μm away) with velocities on the order of 0.5 mm/s, shear rates as high as 16,400 s^{-1} can be calculated assuming a linear shear field between the blood cell and vessel wall.

Based on the in vitro behavior of η versus wall shear rate, the high shear rates in the mesenteric circulation suggest an invariance of in vivo apparent viscosity. In contrast there appears to be a 40% rise in η corresponding to the 30% decrease in the in vivo wall shear rate. To evaluate the potential for effects of velocity (shear rate) in individual microvessels, curves of flow versus upstream-to-downstream pressure drop have been obtained in vivo (233). As typified in Figure 40*A*

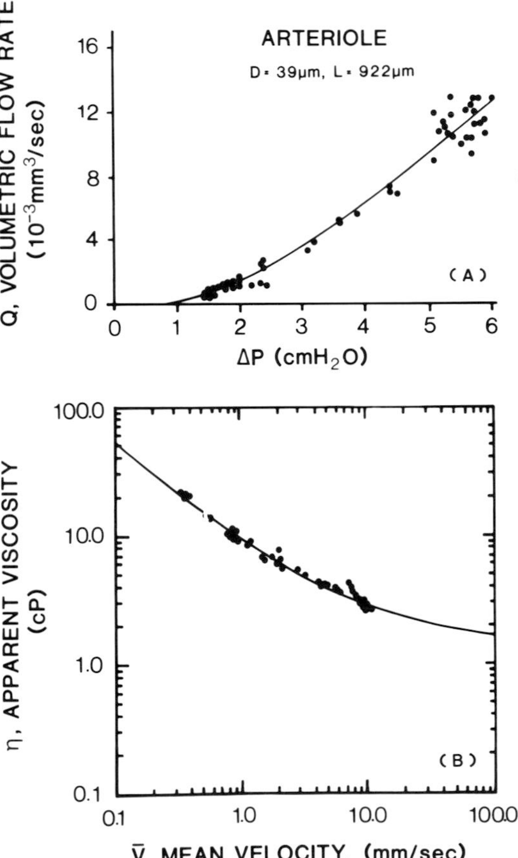

FIG. 40. Pressure drop and flow relationships in a single unbranched mesenteric arteriole during cessation of flow by clamping of the superior mesenteric artery. *A*: volumetric flow rate (Q) versus pressure drop (ΔP). [From Lipowsky, Kovalcheck, and Zweifach (233).] *B*: apparent viscosity (η) as a function of mean blood velocity ($\bar{V}$). [From Lipowsky and Zweifach (238).]

a nonlinear variation of Q with ΔP (obtained by occlusion of the superior mesenteric artery) suggests dramatic elevations of η as the mean velocity of the flow is reduced (Fig. 40*B*). The shape of these curves as well as the zero-flow intercept on the ΔP axis is similar in nature to whole-organ measurements of Q versus ΔP obtained for the isolated intestinal loop (322). For the 39-μm arteriole in Figure 40, a rise in η from ~3 cP during normal flow to 20 cP is obtained as flow velocity is reduced to 0.3 mm/s.

These elevations in apparent blood viscosity during reductions in shear rates may arise either from red cell aggregation, as suggested by in vitro studies (319, 320), or by leukocyte-endothelium adhesion, as evidenced by in vivo observations (315). Study of the effects of red cell aggregation has mostly relied on the whole-organ approach due to a lack of suitable instrumentation for its in situ quantitation. However, conflicting assessments of the effect of red cell aggregation on in vivo η have not yielded definitive results. Some studies with high-molecular-weight dextrans have shown no significant rise in η (160), whereas others have shown a substantial effect (80, 141, 142).

BRANCH POINTS AND BIFURCATIONS. Variability of hemodynamic parameters throughout the microvascular network, discussed so far on the basis of increasing vascularity (i.e., numbers of microvessels), has also been examined in light of the flow behavior of blood at a branching site. In most networks that have the configuration of a succession of branching tubes (e.g., muscle and splanchnic beds), the sequential division of arterioles into branches of smaller diameter may be characterized as a bifurcation involving a parent and two daughter branches. Although substantial departures from this schema are present in many tissues (e.g., lung and liver), most analyses of branch flow processes have centered around bifurcations. As a result three major characteristics of branch hemodynamics have been explored: *1*) attenuation of intravascular pressure, *2*) intermittency of flow, and *3*) hematocrit variations.

The reduction of intravascular pressure at bifurcations in the arteriolar network has been measured for parent arterioles 50–20 μm in diameter (370). The ratios of parent pressure to daughter pressure were found to increase substantially with the diminishing ratio of their respective diameters (d_d/d_p), rising from 5% to 40% as d_d/d_p decreased from 0.9 to 0.1. Because of the technical difficulties in making these measurements without disturbing the flow field, more detailed information on this process has been derived from theoretical analyses. It has been shown that the specific geometry of the orifice of the side-arm branch may greatly influence the pressure drop incurred as flow enters the branch (344). Irregularities at the orifice, conceptualized as a precapillary sphincter (357) that may obstruct the inlet by as much as 80%, can produce pressure drops on the order of 20–30 times greater than those present without a constriction. Because of difficulties in evaluating these geometric factors by intravital microscopy, the relative contribution of this process to the overall AV distribution of intravascular pressure remains obscure.

Intermittent flow at a branch has also been studied, although mostly on a qualitative basis. It is thought to result from the transient plugging of capillaries by the less deformable leukocytes (280, 283) and transients in plasma skimming arising from randomly placed plasma gaps in the parent vessel (283). The degree of intermittency has been shown to increase dramatically in the region of the true capillaries (6, 7, 154) where stochastic effects may influence the apportionment of red cells from parent to daughter microvessels (107, 316). Theoretically it has been illustrated that the distribution of cells to either of two daughter branches at a bifurcation is a function of the balance of hydrodynamic forces on the particle; red cells are drawn into the branch with the greatest flow (107). This can result in intermittent flow through increases in η in a branch that has received additional red cells. The resultant increase in branch resistance may lower the pressure gradient and flow at the orifice of the branch and thus swing the balance of forces to favor admission of cells to the contralateral branch (316). Analyses of stochastic events at the capillary level in terms of their frequencies of occurrence have shown that they are greatly overshadowed by the pulsatility that is synchronous with heart rate (314).

Apportionment of red cells at a bifurcation has received considerably more attention than either pressure drop or transient flow variations. The concept of plasma skimming introduced by Krogh (210) and the comparatively low capillary hematocrits have prompted an examination of the conservation laws governing red cell flux at a bifurcation. Two cases have been studied: a sizable arteriole feeding a capillary side-arm branch and a bifurcation of a vessel with a diameter near that of a capillary. In the arteriole-capillary branch, nonuniformities in the radial distribution of hematocrit and the presence of a marginal zone of plasma along the arteriole wall have been ascribed as the principal factors in the dilution of the side-arm branch hematocrit (284). Theoretical (287) and in vitro studies of blood flow in small-bore glass tubes (117) have stressed the importance of diameter and flow velocity of the daughter branch as determinants of its hematocrit. The greater the branch diameter and flow, the further into the parent stream the dividing streamline protrudes relative to the plasma layer of the parent vessel. This behavior has been examined in the arteriolar network of the mesentery, where measurements of preferentially higher hematocrits have been correlated with higher velocities in daughter branches (189).

Detailed studies of blood cell distributions at a bifurcation with all branch diameters comparable to those of capillaries have emphasized the roles of both the balance of hydrodynamic forces and blood cell deformability (both erythrocytes and leukocytes) as determinants of cell concentrations in daughter branches (316, 362). The net hydrodynamic forces steering a cell into a particular side-arm branch have been shown to be a direct function of the relative ratio of the branch flow (i.e., the sum of the two daughter branch flows) to the parent flow (363). In situ observations of the rabbit ear chamber (316) have shown that in parent vessels with sparse cell concentrations, the position of the blood cell (either erythrocyte or leukocyte) with respect to the dividing streamline (i.e., radial eccentricity of the cell position) is the principal determinant of which branch the cell may enter. The position of the dividing streamline is in turn affected by the ratio of daughter-to-parent vessel bulk flow.

In addition to velocity factors the forces required to deform a blood cell so it can enter a capillary also dictate the relative distribution of cells at a bifurcation. Modeling experiments have demonstrated that if the size of an undeformed blood cell is larger than the branch diameter, then it is possible for seizure of cells to occur in the capillary network (362). The seizure of cells in capillary branches may thus increase capillary hematocrit above that of the feeding arteriole and lead to an inversion of the Fåhraeus effect.

The expression of these hemodynamic processes on the scale of the entire network has been studied in both the arterioles and venules of mesentery (234) and the capillary bifurcations of cremaster muscle (203). These studies examined the conservation of red cell flux at bifurcations as a function of the relative flows in the daughter branches. Specifically, conservation of volumetric flow at a bifurcation must satisfy the following relationships for bulk flow of cells plus plasma in the daughter and parent vessels, Q_d and Q_p, respectively, as well as for the volumetric flux of red cells, Q_{RBC}

$$Q_{d1} + Q_{d2} = Q_p \tag{3}$$

and

$$Q_{RBC_{d1}} + Q_{RBC_{d2}} = Q_{RBC_P} \tag{4}$$

where the volumetric flux of red cells is given by the product of bulk flow and the discharge hematocrit (QH_D) for each branch. These relationships must be satisfied whether or not plasma skimming or other factors favor a preferential distribution of red cells into a branch. However, comparison of the ratio of daughter QH_D to parent QH_D with the flow ratio Q_d/Q_p should reveal a linear relationship only if the red cells are uniformly distributed without preferential shunting into a branch. Figure 41 presents representative plots of these ratios of red cell flux versus bulk flow from parent to daughter branches for the capillaries of the cremaster network (Fig. 41*A*), and the arterioles and venules of the mesenteric network (Fig. 41*B*). The deviation of the capillary distributions from a linear relationship is small but statistically significant, whereas the deviation from a linear relationship in the arterioles and venules is not significant. Hence it appears that the effects of plasma skimming do not contribute greatly to a nonuniform distribution of blood throughout successive microvascular divisions when parent vessels feed daughters of comparable size.

In situations where arterioles supply substantially smaller branches the ensuing plasma skimming may result in a slight hemoconcentration in the parent branch (285). It has been proposed that such a process may enhance the transit time of red cells through the network by contributing to the axial streaming of red cells, and hence it may be partly responsible for the

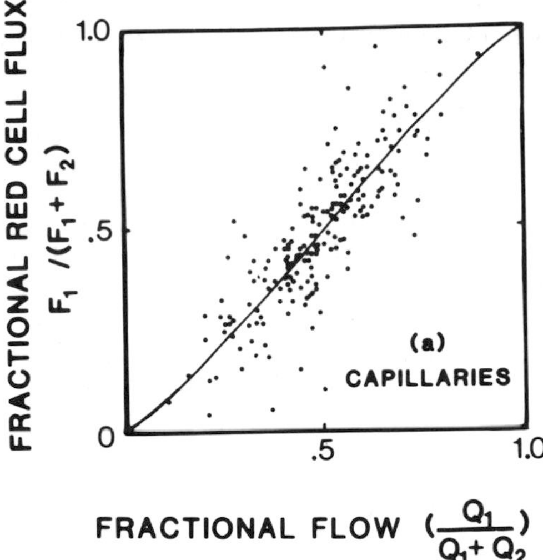

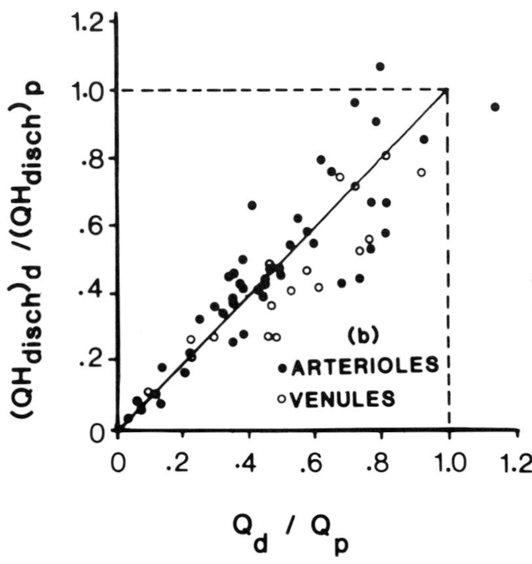

FIG. 41. Red cell flux at bifurcation. *A*: ratio of red cell flux from daughter to parent versus corresponding bulk flow ratio in capillaries of cremaster muscle. *B*: volumetric flux ratio (computed as product of bulk flow and discharge hematocrit between daughter and parent) versus the corresponding ratio of their bulk flows of cells plus plasma (Q_d/Q_p) for arterioles and venules in mesentery. [*A* from Klitzman and Johnson (203); *B* from Lipowsky et al. (234).]

15% faster transit time observed by the whole-organ approach (138) and by direct in situ observations (306, 308–311).

Mathematical Modeling of Network Hemodynamics

In view of the many architectural and hemodynamic parameters that affect the distribution of pressure and flow throughout the microvasculature, the formulation of mathematical models and numerical simulations has become an important tool in the analysis of microvascular structure and function. Three basic approaches have emerged in an attempt to elucidate the relationships between microvascular pressure and flow distributions and network topography: *1)* lumped-parameter models that describe microhemodynamics in terms of fundamental microvascular divisions, i.e., arterioles, capillaries, and venules; *2)* distributive geometric models that rely on idealizations of a specific network configuration; and *3)* discrete-network analyses of specific topographical patterns. These studies, varying in both complexity and sophistication, have examined microhemodynamics in light of network topography and blood rheology and as a tool for the interpretation of data acquired by intravital microscopy. Each of these three classes of modeling is briefly described in terms of its basic assumptions and applications.

LUMPED-PARAMETER MODELS. Although many lumped-parameter models have appeared in the literature with the objective of examining the function of the macrocirculation (143), few have dealt with the detailed workings of the microcirculation proper. Granger and Shepherd (132) formulated an exemplary application of these modeling techniques in their attempt to analyze the mechanisms of the control of oxygen delivery to tissue. Employing a greatly simplified representation of the anatomical features of the microvascular network (arterioles, precapillary sphincters, capillaries, and venules), this study sought to examine the feedback mechanisms regulating arteriolar resistance, capillary density, and intracellular oxygen tensions in the surrounding parenchymal tissue. Although this approach may be characterized more precisely as an exercise in systems analysis, the model itself embraces the major role of the resistance in blood flow — as a determinant of network perfusion. By incorporating into the model the mechanisms that may modulate resistance through arteriolar vasodilation or recruit additional parallel capillaries by the opening of precapillary sphincters, the model demonstrates the relationship between decreased oxygen levels in the tissue and the attendant demand for increased network perfusion.

Feedback equations have been employed that postulate that arteriolar resistance (R_A) is directly proportional to the time-integrated difference between tissue (cellular) oxygen tension (Po_{2_t}) and its required value (Po_{2_r})

$$R_A = R_{A_0} + K_R \int (Po_{2_t} - Po_{2_r})dt \qquad (5)$$

A similar equation for the number of actively flowing capillaries (n) was also used to describe the effect of capillary recruitment by the opening of precapillary sphincters

$$n = n_0 + K_n \int (Po_{2_r} - Po_{2_t})dt \qquad (6)$$

The coefficients K_R and K_n are system constants and R_{A_0} and n_0 are initial or resting state values. Under these conditions it has been shown that as metabolic stresses become greater, the principal site of microvascular control moves from the normally more powerful sphincters to the upstream arterioles. Granger and Shepherd (133) also considered more detailed analyses of the dynamics and control of the microcirculation that examine the processes of cellular metabolism, nervous regulation, and transcapillary fluid balance.

Applications of lumped-parameter models are also an important tool in the analysis and interpretation of experimental data, for example, in determining the vascular components involved in the response to specific microvascular regulatory maneuvers. To this end Nellis and Zweifach (268) have characterized the microvasculature in terms of an analogous electrical circuit composed of six generalized resistance segments (Fig. 42*A*): arterial resistance, venous resistance, microvascular resistance, and three resistances associated with the flow in any localized area. The three local resistances are upstream resistance, downstream resistance, and that of the local segment under study. Measurement of intravascular pressures and flow velocities in an individual microvessel proximal and distal to the site of an induced occlusion (with a blunt probe) facilitated computation of the resistances of the analogue model. This procedure utilized the analogy between the mechanical manipulation of flow (vessel occlusion) and the creation of an open circuit in an electrical network. From the data of individual microvessels in Figure 42*B* the effective upstream and downstream resistances on either side of the occlusion probe during flow cessation were determined from the flow-versus-pressure slopes.

In physical terms the upstream and downstream resistances reflect the relative deployment of a given microvessel with respect to contiguous vessels. For example, at the level of the true capillaries with numerous parallel pathways, occlusion of any capillary has a relatively minor effect on intravascular pressure and hence upstream and downstream resistances are fairly large. However, in larger microvessels with fewer effectively parallel neighbors (e.g., a large arteriole) occlusion of the vessel yields relatively large increases in pressure proximal to the occluding probe. Similarly, large decreases in pressure distal to the probe that

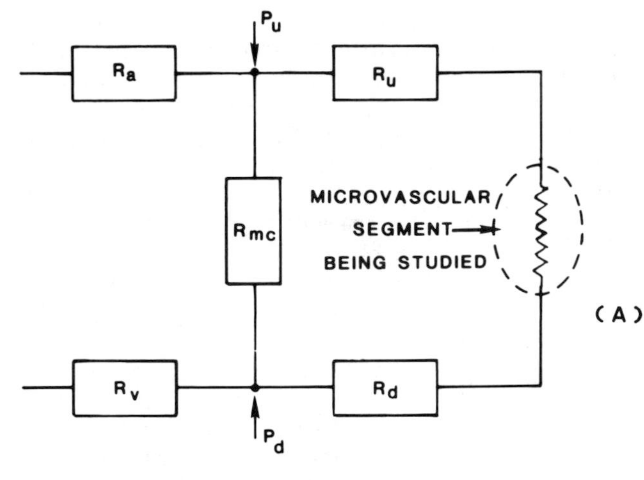

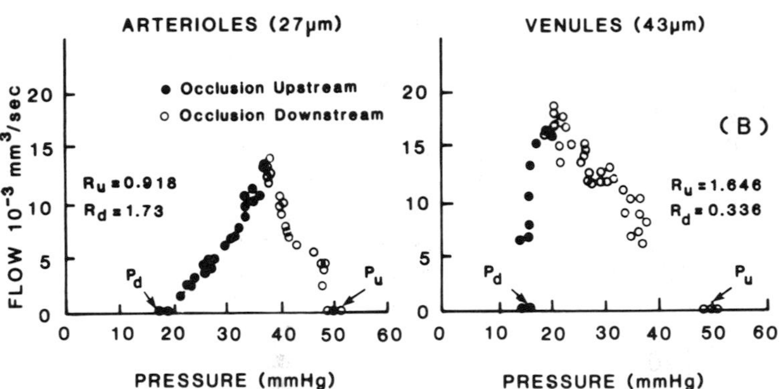

FIG. 42. Techniques of electrical network analysis employed to characterize pressure and flow relationships of specific segments of microvasculature. By measuring variation of intravascular pressure and flow proximal and distal to an occluding probe, proximal and distal segmental resistances can be computed. P_u, P_d : upstream and downstream pressures; R_a, R_v, R_{mc}, R_u, and R_d : arterial, venous, microvascular, upstream, and downstream resistances. [From Nellis and Zweifach (268), by permission of the American Heart Association, Inc.]

reflect a drop in arteriolar pressure toward venous values are incurred. These alterations in pressure and the attendant flow variation are indicative of lower values for the impedance or segmental (upstream and downstream) resistances. With this formulation at hand the hemodynamic role of the distributing vessels in rabbit omentum were evaluated both at rest and in response to vasoactive agents.

DISTRIBUTIVE MODELS. Analysis of microhemodynamics by formulating detailed network models has received considerably more attention than other techniques. The general approach has been to characterize the branching pattern of the network in terms of a simplified schematic representation of the overall hierarchy of microvessels or specific portions of a given network. In the simplest case these models have used analogies to electrical networks, which relate the resistance throughout the network by a succession of serial and/or parallel elements. The resistance of an individual microvessel of circular cross section may be estimated from the Poiseuille-Hagen equation. For example, early attempts to describe convective transport throughout the microvasculature (300) used morphological models obtained from anatomical studies in amphibians (57) to describe capillary clearance of solutes. The model network was composed of an array of parallel and serial microvessels interposed between arcading arterioles and venules (300). More realistic representations of the distribution of geometric parameters affecting microhemodynamics have been examined for rabbit omentum (180). In this study the network was characterized by the distribution of hydraulic hindrance from arteriole to venule as a succession of serial resistances. Each network is composed of a specified number of parallel vessels from each branching order in the network.

Simplified network representations based on combinations of purely serial and parallel elements have also been used to study the distribution of mean transit times of red cells (223, 225) for comparison with direct in situ measurements in the mesenteric circulation (267). By incorporating characteristics of the mesenteric modular network (102) a representative module was postulated as a rectangular area of tissue bounded on four sides by paired arterioles and venules (223). The connection of the arterial and venous segments of the module perimeter with vessels of various diameters arranged like rungs of a ladder modeled the deployment of arterioles, precapillaries, capillaries, and venules. Distribution of volumetric flow rate throughout the network was then computed.

Descriptions of microhemodynamics have also been achieved by the synthesis of hypothetical networks on a much larger scale (319). In this study a composite series network was proposed from morphometric data of the vascular topography (lengths and diameters) in fixed canine mesentery (247) and from in situ observations of the microvasculature in bat wing (354). By piecing together a serial network from aorta to vena cava with successive divisions composed of a specified number of parallel elements, dynamic parameters such as pressure, pressure gradient, and wall shear stress were estimated.

Figure 43 shows a more sophisticated approach to network modeling proposed by Mayrovitz et al. (251, 253, 254). In vivo data obtained from the bat wing (354) supplied measurements of vessel length, diameter, and number at each successive division, and a representative geometric configuration of the network was mapped out (Fig. 43*A*). Corresponding to this topographical pattern, an analogous electrical network was synthesized in terms of the average resistance of the *j*th segment of an *i*th-order vessel. As shown in Figure 43*B* for an individual *i*th-order microvessel, each vessel is modeled by a network with as many T sections as there are branches. The pressure and flow velocity were easily computed from equations derived for the electrical network corresponding to this configuration (254). Successful applications of this approach have provided an assessment of the effects of altered luminal diameter (vasomotion) on the overall distribution of network parameters (253) and the computation of network pressure distributions corresponding to in situ measurements of red cell velocity (251).

Most of these network models have examined transport throughout the network, but a few have also dealt with the rheological behavior of blood and the fluid mechanics peculiar to a specific network pattern. For example, modeling of the ladderlike pattern of true capillaries has highlighted the implications of the nonlinear rheological behavior of blood (28). It has been demonstrated that flow may cease in portions of the network when pressure gradients are insufficient to overcome the minimum value necessary to initiate flow as embodied in the rheological concept of a yield stress.

Modeling has also been performed to elucidate the hemodynamics in topographical patterns strikingly different from an ensemble of tubes of circular cross section, as in the lung (282, 288, 351). An elegant analysis of flow through the pulmonary capillary bed (sheet-flow model) described the geometric determinants of resistance in these very short capillaries (288). Analysis of the patchiness of pulmonary capillary blood flow observed in vivo has also been facilitated by modeling the pulmonary capillary bed as a highly reticulated meshwork of capillaries (351). By using a nonlinear rheological model for blood designed to illustrate the effects of blood yield stress or cell-to-cell interaction (e.g., red cell aggregation and eryth-

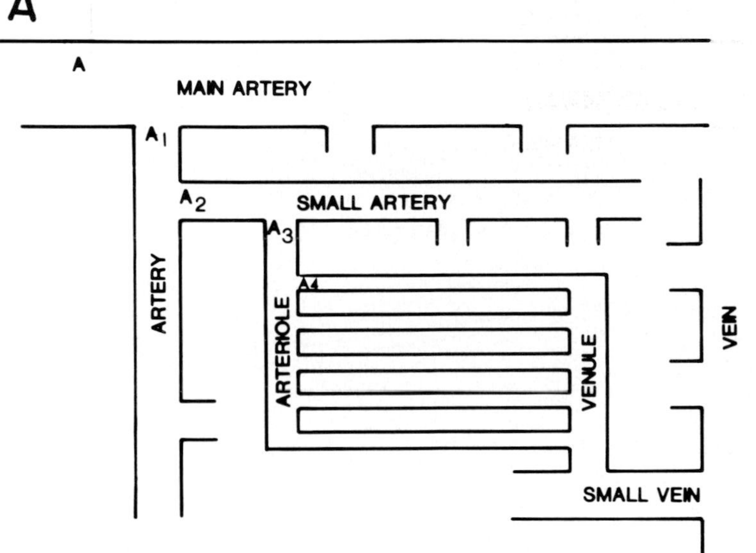

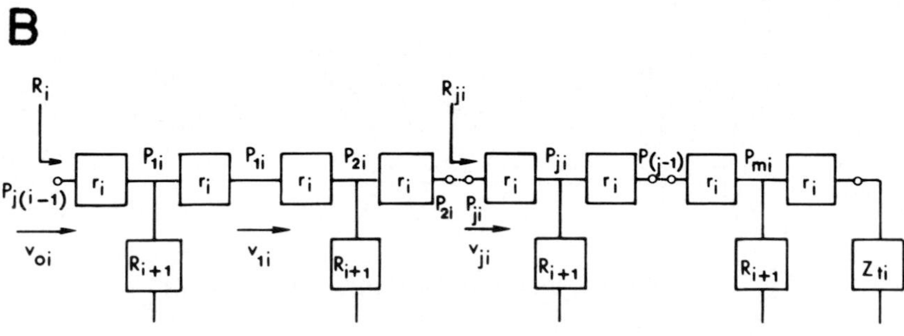

FIG. 43. Representative network model of bat wing microvasculature for analysis of the distribution of resistance (*A*) throughout successive divisions employing a repetitive pattern of distributed resistances (*B*). For the *j*th segment of an *i*th order microvessel: R_{ji}, average resistance; P_{ji}, pressure; V_{ji}, flow velocity. [From Mayrovitz et al. (253).]

rocyte-endothelium adhesion), West et al. (351) described the flow dependency of perfusion heterogeneities. The results demonstrated that flow could be reversed during stepwise increases in perfusion pressure. Modeling of the pulmonary capillary bed has also served as the basis for assessing the applicability of pleural capillary pressure measurements to a description of hemodynamics throughout the whole lung (282).

In addition, applications of network modeling have examined the propagation of pressure pulsatility throughout successive microvascular divisions (139, 140). With a representative network model consisting of several levels of parallel vessels from small arteries to small veins, pulsatile effects were described by a passive-diffusion equation. The diffusion coefficient was determined by the dimensions and mechanical properties of the constituent microvessels. The amplitudes of the pulsatile components of pressure and flow decreased along with an increase in their phase difference in accordance with increasing vascular compliance as blood traversed the network.

DISCRETE-NETWORK MODELS. In contrast to the preceding models of the microvasculature, a few studies have performed network computations based on the comparatively exact network topography (237, 240, 316). This approach applied the techniques of electrical network analysis to compute the distribution of pressure and flow throughout a discrete network of microvessels (237). A photographic map of the network under consideration was obtained by intravital microscopy, as shown in Figure 44*A* for the mesenteric modular network. Measurements of the lengths and diameters of all microvessels in the field permitted the schematic description of the network (Fig. 44*B*) in

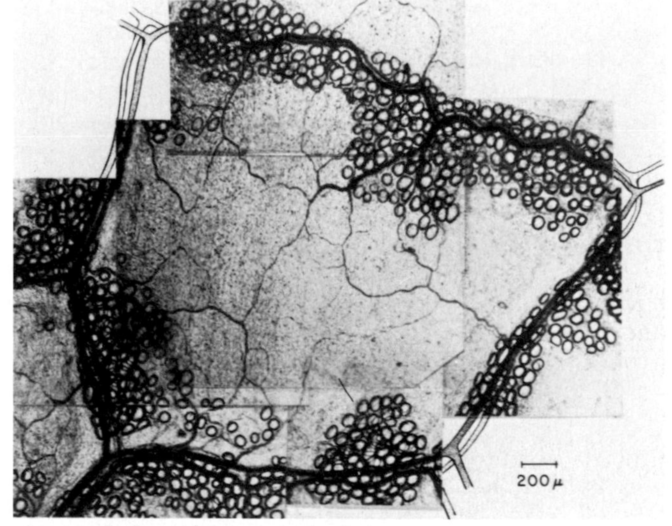

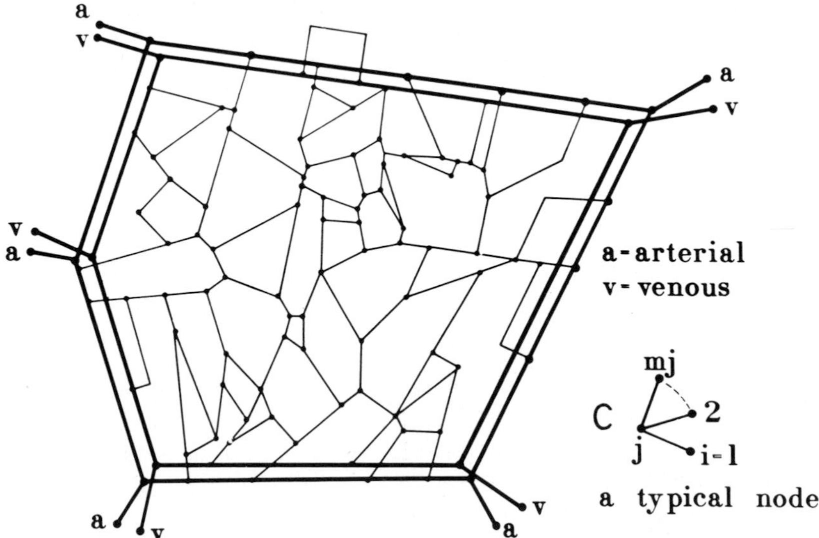

FIG. 44. Network analysis of blood flow in mesenteric circulation. From an in situ photomontage (*A*) all vessel lengths and diameters were measured to construct a network schematic for a mathematical network analysis employing the techniques of electrical network theory (*B*). To perform the analysis, each microvessel was labeled as the *i*th vessel emanating from node j for up to mj vessels at any node (*C*). [From Lipowsky and Zweifach (237).]

which each junction or branch point (node) is assigned a number. Each microvessel was thus characterized as an element of the network running from node i to node j, with constant diameter and length. For specified levels of intravascular pressure at the arterial and venous boundary nodes on the network perimeter (a and v, respectively, Fig. 44*B*), the distribution of intravascular pressures throughout the interior of the network was computed by using the electrical engineering technique of node-voltage analysis. This applies the laws of mass-flow conservation at each node point (Fig. 44*C*), which dictate that the sum of all flows into a node (taken as positive) and all flows exiting a node (taken as negative) must equal zero, $\Sigma Q_{ij} = 0$.

By expressing the pressure-flow relationship in each individual microvessel with the Poiseuille-Hagen law, $Q_{ij} = (\pi/128\eta_{ij})\Delta P_{ij}G_{ij}$ where the conductance (inverse of hindrance) is $G_{ij} = d_{ij}/l_{ij}$, the network flow distribution was evaluated in light of a specific rheological model for η. In the case of constant viscosity ($\eta_{ij} = \eta$ = constant) for a network of n nodes with m boundary pressures, this approach led to the solution of $n - m$ stimultaneous linear algebraic equations that for the network of Figure 44 was on the order of 100. Solution of these equations by high-speed digital computer with sparse-matrix methods provided rapid computation of hemodynamic parameters throughout the entire network.

The results of these techniques for computing pressure and flow during constant blood viscosity have shown reasonable agreement with in vivo measurements of the AV distribution of intravascular pressure (237). Simulations of the effects of non-Newtonian blood rheology have also revealed trends that agree with experimental data (239). With an equation established for the in vivo variation of η with blood velocity in single microvessels, the distribution of pressure and flow throughout the network was computed (233). Comparisons of the total flow of the network (i.e., the sum of all arteriolar inflows) with measurements of flow in the isolated intestinal loop (322) showed remarkably similar trends. Schmid-Schoenbein et al. (316) utilized the technique to describe the distribution of red cells throughout the terminal vascular network of omentum. They showed that alterations in flow resistance due to cells entering and leaving individual capillaries resulted in significant heterogeneities of hematocrit distribution throughout the omental capillaries.

PRESSURE-FLOW RELATIONS IN EXTRAVASCULAR SYSTEMS

Physical transport of blood by the microcirculation represents only one step in the maintenance of tissue homeostasis. The actual distribution of nutritive and waste materials is accomplished by what is referred to as the extravascular flow system. To gain access to the parenchymal cell population, materials must first move across the blood-capillary barrier and then through a layer of interstitial tissue of variable thickness and physicochemical composition. Provision has to be made for the return of materials from the tissue to the systemic circulation. For protein and other macromolecules movement from the interstitium to the blood must occur against a concentration gradient, a problem that is handled by the participation of the lymphatic system (247). Analyses of blood-tissue exchange must therefore address two separate entities—the microvascular flow system and the extravascular flow system. This section deals with the properties of the latter component, although it is obvious that the two flow systems are interlocked at the blood capillary-interstitium interphase.

The fluid exchange aspects of blood-tissue homeostasis are determined by hydrostatic and osmotic factors as formulated by the Starling equation, which concerns the movement of water between two fluid compartments separated by a semipermeable barrier. These conditions are not actually duplicated in situ unless the interstitium is depicted as a thick membrane interposed between the fluid blood and lymph. Measurements of pressure and flow or conductivity in the interstitium proper, however, are difficult to make.

Interstitium

Properties of the interstitium are those of a structure with two phases: a solid, essentially immobile phase and a fluid-rich phase that provides aqueous channels for the transport of materials (131, 146, 150, 151). The solid phase contains a framework of collagen fibers that are the major structural struts supplying mechanical support for the tissue as a whole (Fig. 45). Interspersed is a gel made of 5%–15% proteoglycans (358, 379).

Plasma proteins in transit from the bloodstream to the parenchymal elements, together with immobile macromolecules of the hyaluronic acid class, endow the interstitium with a colloid osmotic force of ~8–10 mmHg. Variations in this potential force have a substantial influence on fluid fluxes into and out of the interstitium.

Terminal Lymphatics

A number of approaches can be taken in studying the terminal or end lymphatics. They can be considered an integral part of the interstitium (essentially a continuation of the fluid phase). Measurements of hydrostatic pressures in these terminal lymphatics would therefore reflect the pressure prevailing in the interstitium proper (150, 379). Alternatively a model can be envisaged in which boundary restrictions at the lymphatic wall lead to selective passage of materials; for example, tight intercellular junctions or vesicular transport against a concentration gradient (55).

If the first assumption is correct, the interstitium

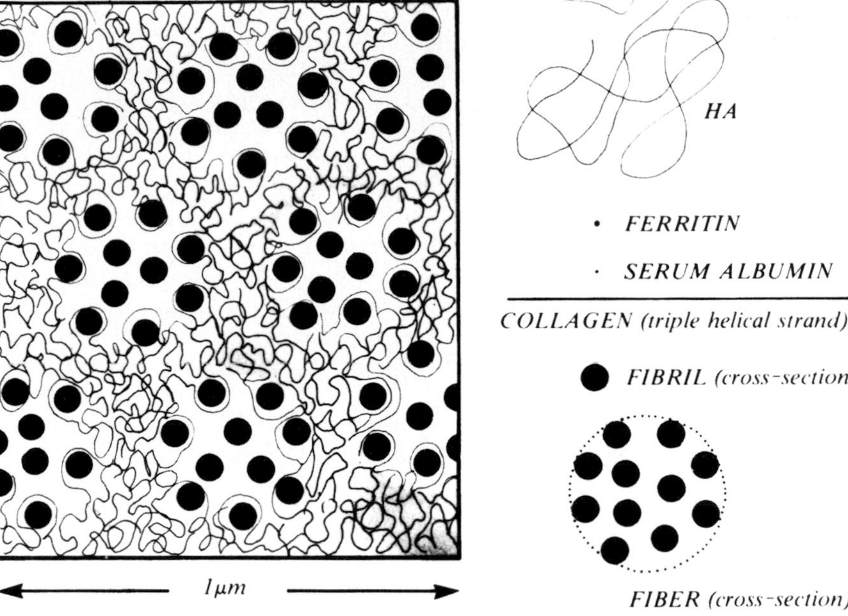

FIG. 45. Model of the interstitium based on data from Wharton's jelly. Coiled long-chain hyaluronic acid (HA) molecules interwoven with collagen fibers that are made up of 8–12 fibrils. Ferritin and serum albumin molecules depicted to indicate ability of these macromolecules to penetrate the fluid-filled spaces between the HA meshes. [From Zweifach and Silberberg (379).]

and lymph fluids should have the same composition of ions, plasma proteins, and other water-soluble materials. Exchange between the interstitium and terminal lymphatic pool would then occur by diffusive processes if concentration gradients were upset. These perturbations could result either from variations in transcapillary flux or from extrinsic mechanisms that move lymph fluid via convective bulk flow into the collecting lymphatic channels.

Other investigators have concluded that a model depicting the lymphatic wall as a selective barrier more accurately conforms with their data on blood-interstitium-lymph exchange. Casley-Smith (55) envisages a lymphatic terminal barrier that can change its selective properties, particularly with respect to protein movement from the interstitium to the lymph. The indirect nature of the evidence makes it difficult to distinguish between these different models of the system.

Lymphatic Pressures

Movement of fluid into the lymphatic capillaries is based on relatively small shifts in tissue pressure and osmotic forces. Direct recordings of pressure in the terminal lymphatics range from subatmospheric (−1.0 to 0.5 cmH_2O) to just above atmospheric (1.0–2.0 cmH_2O) (66, 144, 151, 152). In contrast, pressures in the larger collecting lymphatics range from 2.0 cmH_2O to as high as 12 cmH_2O. These measurements show a stepwise increase in lymphatic pressure in the successive intervalve segments (Fig. 46). Lymph transport against a pressure gradient of this kind is made possible by generation of a centrally directed contraction wave in the large collecting channels. Pressures in the blind-end lymphatic terminals are affected indirectly during the centripetal displacement of fluid by the contractions of the collecting lymphatics. Reports on bat wing lymphatics (273, 274) have described spontaneous contractions of the entire system including the bulb-shaped terminal endings. Comparable contractions of the terminal ends of the lymphatic system, however, have not been seen in other tissues or species (278).

Vasomotor excursions of the large lymphatic vessels appear to be related to some type of myogenic behavior, because contractions can be induced by a slight increase in intraluminal pressure (130, 134, 151, 273). In addition passive movements of the tissue, respiratory movements, contraction of skeletal muscle, and peristaltic contractions of the intestinal wall compress the terminal lymphatics and thereby facilitate the transport of lymphatic fluid (12, 338). In specialized structures such as the intestinal villi mechanical obstruction of the central lymphatic duct leads to an increase in terminal lymphatic pressure of 20%–30% and actually nullifies the slight pressure gradient involved in fluid transport [Table 13; (224)].

Because pressures in the terminal lymphatic capillary can also be shifted upward or downward by appropriate manipulation of blood pressure or colloid osmotic pressure of plasma, it is probable that these vessels are functionally an integral part of the interstitium (359). Pressures in the initial or terminal lymphatic capillaries remain fairly constant over several minutes in the mesentery where no spontaneous contractions are seen. The pulsatile character of the pressure in the precapillary or capillary blood vessels is not transmitted across the interstitial tissue compartment.

Acute perturbations that raise lymphatic flow and

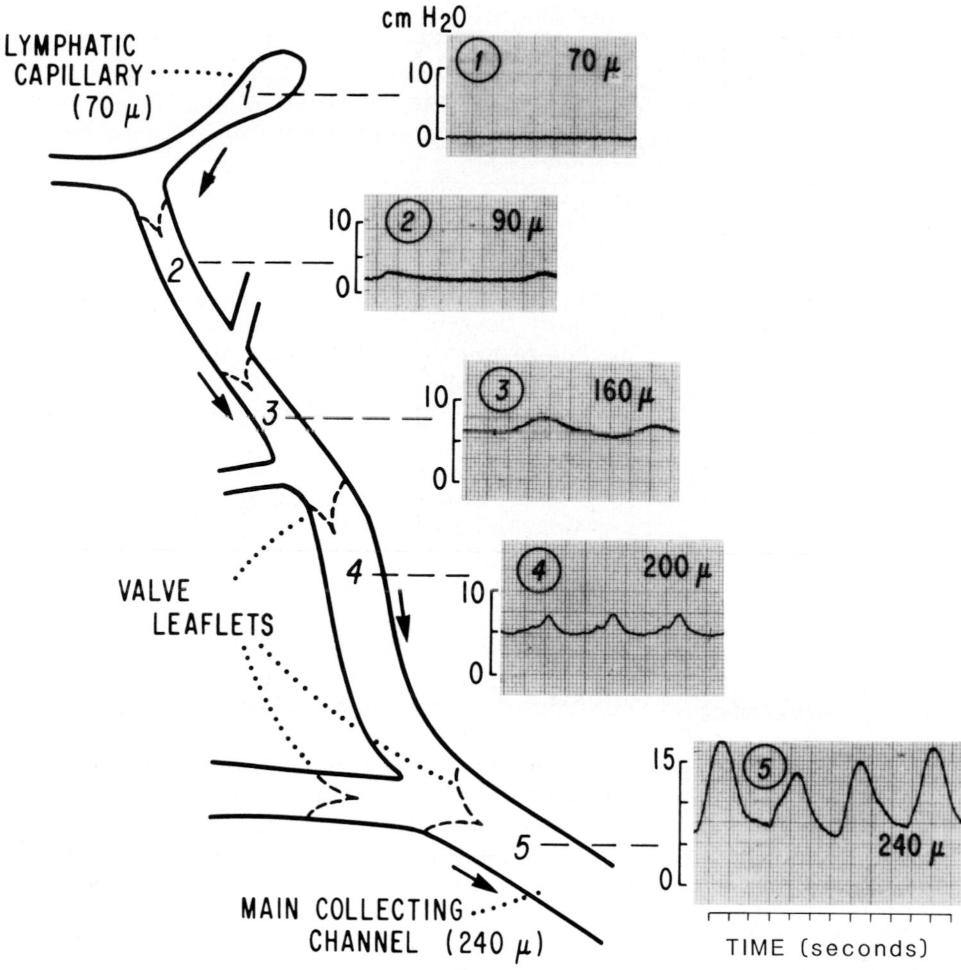

FIG. 46. Terminal lymph capillary in cat mesentery and its associated collecting channel. Successive recordings of lymphatic pressure shown for sequence of segments between valves of the system. Pressure tracings in larger collecting vessels (*3–5*) show wavelike patterns due to opening and closing of the valve leaflets brought on by peristaltic movements of intestinal wall proper. [From Hargens and Zweifach (150, 151).]

TABLE 13. *Intestinal Lymph Capillary Pressure Under Various Conditions*

	Lymphatic Obstruction	Pressure, cmH_2O	Number of Villi
In vivo	Without	1.4 ± 0.5	23
	With	1.7 ± 0.4	21
In vitro	Without	1.1 ± 0.4	72
	With	1.1 ± 0.6	43

From Lee (224).

pressure tend to bring terminal lymphatic pressure into the positive range (up to 5–10 cmH_2O), whereas those that reduce lymph flow bring lymphatic pressure only marginally into the negative range (−0.5 to −1.0 cmH_2O). Clough and Smaje (65) recorded negative lymphatic pressure in the terminal lymphatics of cat mesentery when the surface of the exteriorized tissue was covered with an osmotically inert material (fluorocarbon). Even under extreme conditions of this kind lymphatic pressure falls to only −1.0 to −2.0 cmH_2O.

Interstitial Transport

Movement of materials within the extravascular compartment depends on hydraulic and osmotic pressure gradients. Except for the bloodstream proper, hydraulic pressures are comparatively low in the various exchange compartments. The net flux set up by the balance of forces favoring fluid filtration as opposed to transcapillary absorption is a periodic phenomenon rather than a steady state. Because blood flow is several orders of magnitude higher than lymph flow, a concentration gradient is maintained in the direction of the lymphatic terminals. Fluid transport between blood and lymph can be schematized as in Figure 47 with only a small fraction of the net fluid flux involving lymphatic uptake. Irrespective of the absolute level of tissue pressure, the gradient of tissue and lymphatic pressures is such that lymph is moved at an appropriate rate. Once the lymph reaches the valve-containing segments of the collecting lymphatics, active contractions as well as passive compression

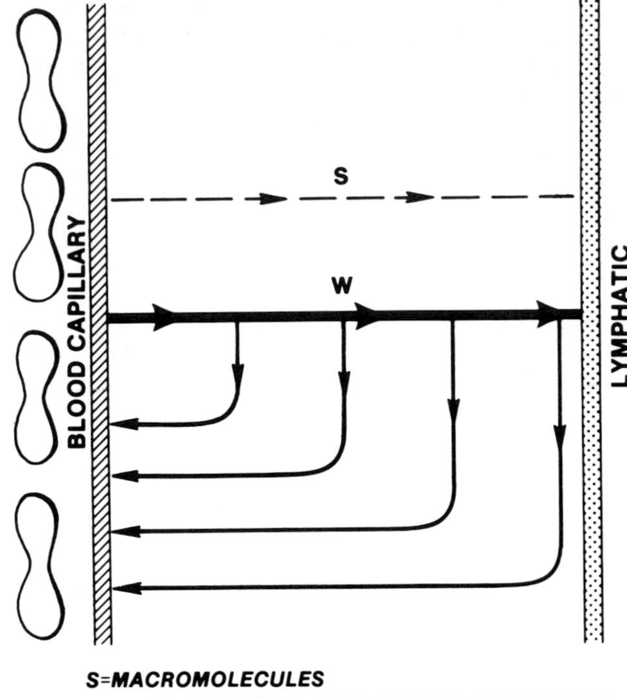

FIG. 47. Water movement (W) in interstitium associated with capillary filtration. Note that most of fluid is returned by the capillary network and only a residual fraction is taken up by the lymphatics. *Broken line* shows that macromolecules such as protein (S) are returned to the circulation by the lymphatics. [From Zweifach and Silberberg (379).]

move the fluid centrally in a peristaltic wave (130, 131).

The principal mobile macromolecules responsible for osmotic gradients in the blood-tissue compartments are the plasma proteins. Although both the interstitial fluid and lymph are diluted plasma, sufficient plasma proteins are present to set up physiologically significant osmotic forces, particularly because only small gradients are needed to account for the observed movements.

In experiments where excised slabs of tissue are immersed in a fluid that has the same osmotic properties as the lymph, the tissue swells and after several hours the protein solute and the water are distributed through the tissue as a whole (130, 134, 263). In situ, however, the capillary filtrate moves through the tissue at a faster rate than the tissue can swell.

The fulcrum for balancing net fluid movement is the concentration of plasma proteins in the interstitium. Presumably, under physiological conditions plasma proteins move into the interstitium at a fairly constant rate. The variable then is the amount of fluid filtered by the network of blood capillaries that dilutes the pool of interstitial plasma protein and thereby shifts the net osmotic force exerted by these macromolecules (58).

Vasomotion of the arterioles and precapillaries provides the intermittency needed for alternate periods of filtration and absorption of fluid. Depending on the number of capillaries involved in such transients, fixed quanta of fluid can be shifted back across the temporarily stagnant capillaries even when the transient is as short as 2–3 s.

Tissue Pressure

The precise level of pressure in the fluid phase of the interstitium has remained a controversial issue primarily because of the questionable nature of the methods available for measuring this force (199). Although the issue has been thoroughly reviewed recently (46, 92, 143, 359, 379), a real consensus does not exist.

Measurements of the physical or hydraulic pressure in different tissues range from subatmospheric (−2.0 to −6.0 mmHg) to essentially atmospheric (0.5–1.5 mmHg). Under abnormal conditions where tissue damage has occurred, comparable measurements give uniformly high values of 4.0–5.0 mmHg for tissue pressure (379). Terminal lymphatic pressures in the latter experiments are also high (3.0–4.0 mmHg). Substitution of fluorocarbon for the Krebs solution used routinely to suffuse the surface of the exteriorized mesentery shifts the lymphatic pressure distribution plot toward the lower end of the pressure scale with a much higher incidence of subatmospheric readings (Fig. 48). Although these experiments were designed

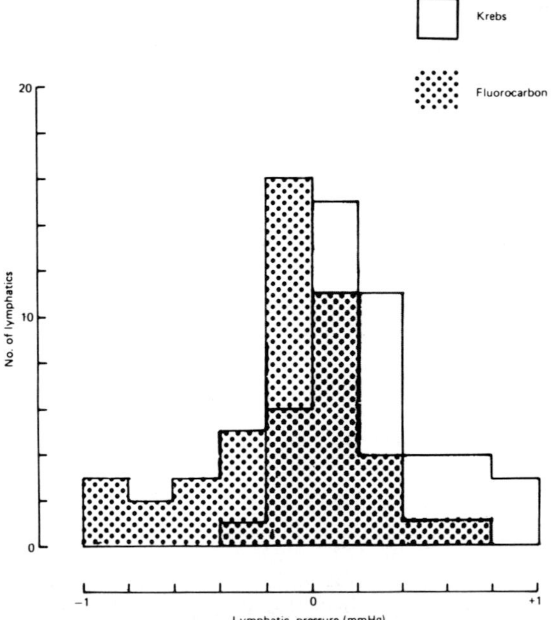

FIG. 48. Effect of change in external bathing medium on terminal lymphatic pressure in cat mesentery. Osmotic effects of the conventional Krebs electrolyte mixture tend to shift lymphatic pressures into the atmospheric (slightly positive) range. In the presence of an osmotically inert fluorocarbon, lymphatic pressure falls into the slightly subatmospheric range. [From Clough and Smaje (65).]

to eliminate possible osmotic effects of the Krebs solution used conventionally, they introduce an abnormal, nonhydrophilic interphase not present in situ.

For tissue pressure to remain negative some active process must be involved to continuously remove fluid from the interstitium, in effect preventing a fluid buildup that in time would result in tissue swelling. Movement of fluid from the interstitium to the lymphatic terminal requires a gradient in that direction. If a gradient in hydraulic pressure were involved, terminal lymphatic pressures would have to be even more negative than in the interstitium proper. An alternative would be for some type of suction force to be provided by the contraction of the valve-containing collecting lymphatics, making capillary-interstitium gradients of secondary importance in this regard.

Extravascular Flow System

A number of models have been developed to account for the operational characteristics of the extravascular flow system (358, 379). Mass transport across the interstitium involves two major components, flow of water and flow of macromolecules. The maintenance of the water potential in the interstitium appears to be the fulcrum around which extravascular controls operate. Additional mechanisms maintain the chemical potential of mobile protein. The gel component of the interstitium (primarily a skeleton of hyaluronic acid molecules) is constrained by being threaded through numerous collagen fibers. Response of this gel phase to concentration levels fixes the volume of the tissue space in steady state.

The dilute blood filtrate of the capillary is forced into the interstitium at a rate such that only minimal potential gradients are superposed on the interstitial steady state. The flux leaves the interstitium by two possible escape routes. The first is the lymphatic system, which is also the major pathway available to the plasma proteins. The second is reabsorption of fluid directly back into the microvascular network by the Starling mechanism. Mainly this latter process is responsible for the level of the water potential; the flow of lymph takes care of the macromolecular potential, being actively aided by a pumping or suction action developed in the collecting lymphatic channels.

These two mechanisms interact to stabilize tissue volume. A dynamic control process of this kind is much more flexible under pathological conditions than is a system operated solely by mechanical constraints. Uncertainties still exist because of the absence of definitive data for the reflection coefficient of the tissue compartment, the contribution of the capillary basement membrane, and the properties of the interstitium–terminal lymphatic barrier.

This work was supported in part by National Institutes of Health Research Grants HL-10881, HL-16851, and HL-28381 and Research Career Development Award HL-00594.

REFERENCES

1. ADDICKS, K., H. WEIGELT, G. HAUCK, D. W. LÜBBERS, AND H. KNOCHE. Light- and electronmicroscopic studies with regard to the role of intraendothelial structures under normal and inflammatory conditions. *Bibl. Anat.* 17: 21–35, 1979.
2. AGARWAL, J. B., R. PALTOO, AND W. H. PALMER. Relative viscosity of blood at varying hematocrits in the pulmonary circulation. *J. Appl. Physiol.* 29: 866–871, 1970.
3. ALGIRE, G. H. Blood pressure measurements and changes in peripheral vascular bed in unanesthetized mice (Abstract). *Federation Proc.* 8: 349, 1949.
4. ALGIRE, G. H. Determination of peripheral blood pressure in unanesthetized mice during microscopic observation of blood vessels. *J. Natl. Cancer Inst.* 14: 865–873, 1957.
5. APPELGREN, K. L. Effect of perfusion pressure and hematocrit on capillary flow and transport in hyperemic skeletal muscle of the dog. *Microvasc. Res.* 4: 231–246, 1972.
6. ASANO, M. On plasma skimming observed in cutaneous microcirculation in man and rabbits. *J. Phys. Soc. Jpn.* 35: 424–425, 1973.
7. ASANO, M., K. YOSHIDA, AND K. TATAI. Microphotoelectric plethysmography using a rabbit ear chamber. *J. Appl. Physiol.* 20: 1056–1062, 1965.
8. ATHERTON, A., AND G. V. BORN. Effect of blood flow velocity on the rolling of granulocytes in venules (Abstract). *J. Physiol. London* 231: 35P–36P, 1973.
9. ATHERTON, A., AND G. V. BORN. Relationship between the velocity of rolling granulocytes and that of the blood flow in venules. *J. Physiol. London* 233: 157–165, 1973.
10. BAECKSTRÖM, P., B. FOLKOW, E. KENDRICK, B. LOFVING, AND B. ÖBERG. Effects of vasoconstriction on blood viscosity in vivo. *Acta Physiol. Scand.* 81: 376–384, 1971.
11. BAECKSTRÖM, P., B. FOLKOW, A. G. B. KOVACH, B. LOFVING, AND B. ÖBERG. Evidence of plugging of the microcirculation following acute hemorrhage. In: *Proc. Eur. Conf. Microcirc., 6th, Aalborg, 1970.* Basel: Karger, 1970, p. 16–23.
12. BAEZ, S. Flow properties of lymph. A microcirculatory study. In: *Flow Properties of Blood and Other Biological Systems*, edited by A. L. Copley and G. Stainsby. New York: Pergamon, 1960, p. 398–411.
13. BAEZ, S. Bayliss response in the microcirculation. *Federation Proc.* 27: 1410–1415, 1968.
14. BAEZ, S. A method for in-line measurement of lumen and wall of microscopic vessels in vivo. *Microvasc. Res.* 5: 299–308, 1973.
15. BAEZ, S. An open cremaster muscle preparation for the study of blood vessels by in vivo microscopy. *Microvasc. Res.* 5: 384–394, 1973.
16. BAEZ, S., S. M. FELDMAN, AND P. M. GOOTMAN. Central neural influence on precapillary microvessels and sphincter. *Am. J. Physiol.* 233 (*Heart Circ. Physiol.* 2): H141–H147, 1977.
17. BAEZ, S., Z. LAIDAW, AND L. R. ORKIN. Localization and measurement of microvascular and microcirculatory responses to venous pressure elevation in the rat. *Blood Vessels* 11: 260–276, 1974.
18. BAKER, C. H., D. L. DAVIS, AND E. T. SUTTON. Arteriolar capillary and venular FITC-dextran time concentration curves and plasma flow velocities. *Proc. Soc. Exp. Biol. Med.* 161: 370–377, 1979.
19. BAKER, C. H., D. L. DAVIS, AND E. T. SUTTON. Microvascular plasma velocity and indicator dispersion with hemorrhage. *Circ. Shock* 6: 61–74, 1979.
20. BAKER, M., AND H. WAYLAND. On-line volumetric flow rate and velocity profile measurement for blood in microvessels. *Microvasc. Res.* 7: 131–143, 1974.

21. BARBEE, J. H., AND G. R. COKELET. The Fahraeus effect. *Microvasc. Res.* 3: 6–16, 1971.
22. BARBEE, J. H., AND G. R. COKELET. Prediction of blood flow in tubes with diameters as small as 29 μm. *Microvasc. Res.* 3: 17–21, 1971.
23. BARRAS, J. P. Blood rheology–general review. *Bibl. Haematol. Basel* 33: 277–297, 1969.
24. BARRAS, J. P. Blood viscosity and rheology: physiological introduction. *Schweiz. Med. Wochenschr.* 101: 1761–1766, 1971.
25. BAYLISS, L. E. Rheology of blood and lymph. In: *Deformation and Flow in Biological Systems*, edited by A. Frey-Wyssling. New York: Interscience, 1952, p. 355–418.
26. BAYLISS, L. E. The anomalous viscosity of blood. In: *Flow Properties of Blood and Other Biological Systems*, edited by A. L. Copley and G. Stainsby. New York: Pergamon, 1960, p. 29–62.
27. BECKER, C. G., AND S. R. SHUSTAK. Contractile proteins in endothelial cells: comparison of cerebral capillaries with those in heart and skeletal muscle and with liver sinusoids (Abstract). *Circulation* 45/46, Suppl. 2: 87, 1972.
28. BENIS, A. M., AND J. LACOSTE. Distribution of blood flow in vascular beds: model study of geometrical, rheological, and hydrodynamic effects. *Biorheology* 5: 147–161, 1968.
29. BENIS, A. M., S. USAMI, AND S. CHIEN. Effect of hematocrit and intertial losses on pressure-flow relations in the isolated hindpaw of the dog. *Circ. Res.* 27: 1047–1068, 1970.
30. BENIS, A. M., S. USAMI, AND S. CHIEN. Evaluation of viscous and inertial pressure losses in isolated tissue with a simple mathematical model. *Microvasc. Res.* 4: 81–93, 1972.
31. BENIS, A. M., S. USAMI, AND S. CHIEN. A reappraisal of Whittaker and Winton's results on the basis of inertial losses. *Biorheology* 11: 153–161, 1974.
32. BENITEZ, D., AND S. BAEZ. Venous-arteriolar response in striated cremaster muscle in the rat. *Microvasc. Res.* 1: 115, 1976.
33. BERMAN, H. J., AND R. L. FUHRO. Effect of rate of shear on the shape of the velocity profile and orientation of red cells in arterioles. *Bibl. Anat.* 10: 32–37, 1969.
34. BERMAN, H., W. MCNARY, D. AUSPRUNK, E. LEE, S. WEAVER, AND R. SOPOUR. Innervation and fine structure of the precapillary sphincter in the frog retrolingual membrane. *Microvasc. Res.* 4: 51–61, 1972.
35. BERNE, R. M. Myocardial blood flow: metabolic determinants. In: *The Peripheral Circulation*, edited by R. Zelis. New York: Grune & Stratton, 1975, p. 117–129.
36. BLOCH, E. H. A quantitative study of the hemodynamics in the living microvascular system. *Am. J. Anat.* 110: 125–146, 1962.
37. BOHLEN, H. G., AND R. W. GORE. Preparation of rat intestinal muscle and mucosa for quantitative microcirculatory studies. *Microvasc. Res.* 11: 103–110, 1976.
38. BOHLEN, H. G., AND R. W. GORE. Comparison of microvascular pressures and diameters in the innervated and denervated rat intestine. *Microvasc. Res.* 14: 251–264, 1977.
39. BOHLEN, H. G., R. W. GORE, AND P. M. HUTCHINS. Comparison of microvascular pressures in normal and hypertensive rats. *Microvasc. Res* 13: 125–130, 1977.
40. BOLLINGER, A., P. BUTTI, J. P. BARRAS, H. TRACHLER, AND N. SIEGENTHALER. Red blood cell velocity in nailfold capillaries of man, measured by a television microscopy technique. *Microvasc. Res.* 7: 61–72, 1974.
41. BOND, T. P., M. M. GUEST, T. D. KIRSKEY, AND J. R. DERRICK. High speed cinematographic studies of the microcirculation in the human subject (Abstract). *Physiologist* 9: 142, 1966.
42. BORDERS, J. Vasomotion Patterns in Skeletal Muscle in Normal and Hypertensive Rats. San Diego: Univ. of California Press, 1980. Dissertation.
43. BORDERS, J., AND B. W. ZWEIFACH. Vasomotor patterns of skeletal muscle circulation in normal and hypertensive rats (Abstract). *Microvasc. Res.* 17: 361, 1979.
44. BOUSKELA, E., AND C. A. WIEDERHIELM. Microvascular myogenic reaction in the wing of the intact unanesthetized bat. *Am. J. Physiol.* 237 (*Heart Circ. Physiol.* 6): H59–H65, 1979.
45. BRAASCH, D. Red cell deformability and capillary blood flow. *Physiol. Rev.* 51: 679–701, 1971.
46. BRACE, R. A. Progress toward resolving the controversy of positive vs. negative interstitial fluid pressure. *Circ. Res.* 49: 281–297, 1981.
47. BRÅNEMARK, P.-I. *Intravascular Anatomy of Blood Cells in Man.* Basel: Karger, 1971, p. 1–80.
48. BRÅNEMARK, P.-I., AND I. JONSSON. Determination of velocity of corpuscles in blood capillaries. A flying spot device. *Biorheology* 1: 143–146, 1963.
49. BULPITT, C. J., E. M. KOHNER, AND C. T. DOLLERY. Velocity profiles in the retinal microcirculation. *Bibl. Anat.* 11: 448–452, 1973.
50. BURROWS, M. E., AND P. C. JOHNSON. The response of cat mesenteric arterioles to arterial pressure reduction. *Arch. Int. Pharmacodyn. Ther.* 236: 290–291, 1978.
51. BURTON, K. S., AND P. C. JOHNSON. Reactive hyperemia in individual capillaries of skeletal muscle. *Am. J. Physiol.* 223: 517–524, 1972.
52. CARDON, S. Z., C. F. OESTERMEYER, AND E. H. BLOCH. Effect of oxygen on cyclic red blood cell flow in unanesthetized striated muscle as determined by microscopy. *Microvasc. Res.* 2: 67–76, 1970.
53. CARRIER, E. B. Observations of living cells in the bat's wing. In: *Physiol. Papers Dedicated to A. Krogh.* Copenhagen: Levin & Munksgaard, 1926, p. 1–9.
54. CARRIER, E. B., AND P. B. REHBERG. Capillary and venous pressure in man. *Scand. Arch. Physiol.* 44: 20–31, 1923.
55. CASLEY-SMITH, J. R. Lymph and lymphatics. In: *Microcirculation*, edited by G. Kaley and B. M. Altura. Baltimore, MD: University Park, 1977, vol. 2, p. 423–502.
56. CASTENHOLZ, A. Microkymography and its applications in microcirculatory investigations. *Adv. Microcirc.* 2: 24–36, 1969.
57. CHAMBERS, R., AND B. W. ZWEIFACH. Topography and function of the mesenteric circulation. *Am. J. Anat.* 75: 173–205, 1944.
58. CHEN, H. I., H. J. GRANGER, AND A. E. TAYLOR. Interaction of capillary interstitial and lymphatic forces in the canine hindpaw. *Circ. Res.* 39: 245–254, 1976.
59. CHIEN, S. Biophysical behavior of red cells in suspensions. In: *The Red Blood Cell* (2nd ed.), edited by D. Surgenor. New York: Academic, 1975, vol. 2, p. 1031–1133.
60. CHIEN, S. Principles and techniques for assessing erythrocyte deformability. *Blood Cells* 3: 71–99, 1977.
61. CHILDS, C. M., K. E. ARFORS, R. TUMA, AND F. N. MCKENZIE. Continuous capillary red cell velocity measurements in the tenuissimus muscle under changing local oxygen tensions. *Bibl. Anat.* 13: 153–154, 1975.
62. CLARK, E. R., AND E. L. CLARK. Observations on changes in blood vascular endothelium in the living animal. *Am. J. Anat.* 57: 385–438, 1935.
63. CLARK, E. R., AND E. L. CLARK. Caliber changes in minute blood vessels observed in the living mammal. *Am. J. Anat.* 73: 215–250, 1943.
64. CLOUGH, G., P. A. FRASER, AND L. H. SMAJE. Compliance measurements in single capillaries of the cat mesentery (Abstract). *J. Physiol. London* 240: 98P, 1974.
65. CLOUGH, G., AND L. H. SMAJE. Simultaneous measurement of pressure in the interstitium and the terminal lymphatics of the cat mesentery. *J. Physiol. London* 283: 457–468, 1978.
66. COKELET, G. R. The rheology of human blood. In: *Biomechanics: Its Foundations and Objectives*, edited by Y. C. Fung, N. Perrone, and M. Anliker. Englewood Cliffs, NJ: Prentice-Hall, 1972.
67. COKELET, G. R. Macroscopic rheology and tube flow of human blood. In: *Microcirculation*, edited by J. Grayson and W. Zingg. New York: Plenum, 1976, vol. 1, p. 9–32.
68. COKELET, G. R. Rheology and hemodynamics. *Annu. Rev. Physiol.* 42: 311–324, 1980.

69. COKELET, G. R. Dynamics of red blood cell deformation and aggregation, and in vivo flow. In: *Erythrocyte Mechanics and Blood Flow*, edited by G. R. Cokelet, H. J. Meiselman, and D. E. Brooks. New York: Liss, 1980, p. 141–148.
70. COPLEY, A. L. Hemorheological aspects of the endothelium-plasma interface. *Microvasc. Res.* 8: 192–212, 1974.
71. COPLEY, A. L., AND G. W. SCOTT-BLAIR. Comparative observations on adherence and consistency of various blood systems in living and artificial capillaries (Abstract). *Rheol. Acta* 1: 170, 1961.
72. COULTER, N. A., AND M. SINGH. Frequency dependence of blood viscosity in oscillatory flow. *Biorheology* 8: 115–124, 1971.
73. CRANDALL, E. D., AND R. W. FLUMERFELT. Effects of time-varying blood flow on oxygen uptake in the pulmonary capillaries. *J. Appl. Physiol.* 23: 944–953, 1967.
74. CROWELL, J. W., AND E. E. SMITH. Determinant of the optimal hematocrit. *J. Appl. Physiol.* 22: 501–504, 1967.
75. DANZER, C. S., AND D. R. HOOKER. Determination of the capillary blood pressure in man with the microcapillary tonometer. *Am. J. Physiol.* 52: 136–167, 1920.
76. DAVIS, M. J., J. P. GILMORE, AND W. L. JOYNER. Responses of pulmonary allograft and cheek pouch arterioles in the hamster to alterations in extravascular pressure in different oxygen environments. *Circ. Res.* 49: 133–140, 1981.
77. DAVIS, M. J., W. L. JOYNER, AND J. P. GILMORE. Microvascular pressure distribution and responses of pulmonary allografts and cheek pouch arterioles in the hamster to oxygen. *Circ. Res.* 49: 125–132, 1981.
78. De LANO, F. A., AND B. W. ZWEIFACH. Anesthesia and microvascular dynamics in spontaneously hypertensive rats. *Am. J. Physiol.* 241 (*Heart Circ. Physiol.* 10): H821–H828, 1981.
79. DINTENFASS, L. *Blood Microrheology: Viscosity Factors in Blood Flow and Ischaemia and Thrombosis.* London: Butterworths, 1971.
80. DJOJOSUGITO, A. M., B. FOLKOW, B. OBERG, AND S. WHITE. A comparison of blood viscosity in vitro and in a vascular bed. *Acta Physiol. Scand.* 78: 70–84, 1970.
81. DOTY, D. B., AND M. H. WEIL. Comparison of the microcirculatory and central hematocrit as a measure of circulatory shock. *Surg. Gynecol. Obstet.* 124: 1263–1266, 1967.
82. DRIESSEN, G. K., H. HEIDTMANN, AND H. SCHMID-SCHÖNBEIN. Effect of hemodilution and hemoconcentration on red cell flow velocity in the capillaries of the rat mesentery. *Pfluegers Arch.* 380: 1–6, 1979.
83. EICHNA, L. W., AND J. BORDLEY. Capillary blood pressure in man: direct measurements in the digits of normal and hypertensive subjects during vasoconstriction and vasodilation. *J. Clin. Invest.* 21: 711–729, 1942.
84. EINAV, S., H. J. BERMAN, R. L. FUHRO, P. R. DIGIOVANI, S. FINE, AND J. D. FRIEDMAN. Measurement of velocity profiles of red blood cells in the microcirculation by laser Doppler anemometry (LDA). *Biorheology* 12: 207–219, 1975.
85. ELIASSEN, E., B. FOLKOW, AND B. OBERG. Are there any significant inertial losses in the vascular bed? *Acta Physiol. Scand.* 87: 567–569, 1973.
86. ERIKSON, L. E., E. ERICSSON, AND B. JOHANSSON. Morphological aspects of the microvessels in cat skeletal muscle. *Adv. Microcirc.* 4: 62–79, 1972.
87. ERIKSSON, E., AND B. LISANDER. Changes in precapillary resistance in skeletal muscle vessels studied by intravital microscopy. *Acta Physiol. Scand.* 84: 295–305, 1972.
88. ERIKSSON, E., AND B. LISANDER. Low flow states in the microvessels of skeletal muscle in the cat. *Acta Physiol. Scand.* 86: 202–210, 1972.
89. ERIKSSON, E., AND R. MYRHAGE. Microvascular dimensions and blood flow in skeletal muscle. *Acta Physiol. Scand.* 86: 211–222, 1972.
90. EVERTT, N. B., B. SIMMONS, AND E. P. LASHER. Distribution of blood (^{59}Fe) and plasma (^{131}I) volumes of rats determined by liquid nitrogen freezing. *Circ. Res.* 4: 419–424, 1956.
91. FABER, J. E., AND P. D. HARRIS. Depression of arteriolar vasomotion in skeletal muscle of decerebrate rats by urethane-chloralose anesthesia. In: *Proc. Eur. Conf. Microcirc., 11th, Garmisch, 1980.* Basel: Karger, 1980, p. 60.
92. FADNES, H. O., R. K. REED, AND K. AUKLAND. Interstitial fluid pressure in rats measured with a modified wick technique. *Microvasc. Res.* 14: 27–36, 1977.
93. FAGRELL, B., M. INTAGLIETTA, AND J. OSTERGREN. Relative hematocrit in human skin capillaries and its relation to capillary blood flow velocity. *Microvasc. Res.* 20: 327–335, 1980.
94. FÅHRAEUS, R. The suspension stability of the blood. *Physiol. Rev.* 9: 241–274, 1929.
95. FÅHRAEUS, R., AND T. LINDQVIST. The viscosity of the blood in narrow capillary tubes. *Am. J. Physiol.* 96: 562–568, 1931.
96. FENTON, B. M. Topographical Simulation of the Blood Vessels in the Human Bulbar Conjunctiva and Application to Pressure-Flow Relations. San Diego: Univ. of California Press, 1980. Dissertation.
97. FOLKOW, B. Intravascular pressure as a factor regulating the tone of the small blood vessels. *Acta Physiol. Scand.* 86: 211–222, 1949.
98. FOLKOW, B., O. LUNDGREN, AND I. WALLENTIN. Studies on the relationship between flow resistance, capillary filtration coefficient and regional blood volume in the intestine of the cat. *Acta Physiol. Scand.* 57: 270–283, 1963.
99. FOLKOW, B., AND E. NEIL. *Circulation.* London: Oxford Univ. Press, 1971, chapt. 16, p. 185–306.
100. FOLKOW, B., R. R. SONNENSCHEIN, AND D. L. WRIGHT. Loci of neurogenic and metabolic effects on precapillary vessels of skeletal muscle. *Acta Physiol. Scand.* 81: 459–471, 1971.
101. FOX, J. R., AND C. A. WIEDERHIELM. Characteristics of the servo-controlled micropipet pressure system. *Microvasc. Res.* 5: 324–335, 1973.
102. FRASHER, W. G., AND H. WAYLAND. A repeating modular organization of the microcirculation of cat mesentery. *Microvasc. Res.* 4: 62–76, 1972.
103. FRONEK, K., AND B. W. ZWEIFACH. The effect of vasodilator agents on microvascular pressures in skeletal muscle. *Angiologia Italy* III: 35–39, 1974.
104. FRONEK, K., AND B. W. ZWEIFACH. Pre- and postcapillary resistances in cat mesentery. *Microvasc. Res.* 7: 351–361, 1974.
105. FRONEK, K., AND B. W. ZWEIFACH. Microvascular pressure distribution in skeletal muscle and the effect of vasodilation. *Am. J. Physiol.* 228: 791–796, 1975.
106. FRY, D. L. Acute vascular endothelial changes associated with increased blood velocity gradients. *Circ. Res.* 22: 165–197, 1968.
107. FUNG, Y. C. Stochastic flow in capillary blood vessels. *Microvasc. Res.* 5: 34–48, 1973.
108. FUNG, Y. C. Structural mechanics of microvasculature. In: *Mathematics of Microcirculation Phenomena,* edited by J. Gross and A. Popel. New York: Raven, 1979, p. 1–16.
109. GAEHTGENS, P. Pulsatile pressure and flow in the mesenteric vascular bed of the cat. *Pfluegers Arch.* 316: 140–151, 1970.
110. GAEHTGENS, P. Hemodynamics of the microcirculation: physical characteristics of blood flow in the microvasculature. In: *Handbuch der allgemeinen Pathologie. Mikrozirkulation,* edited by H. Meessen. Berlin: Springer-Verlag, 1977, vol. 3/7, p. 231–287.
111. GAEHTGENS, P., K. H. ALBRECHT, AND K. U. BENNER. Velocity dependence of the dynamic hematocrit in capillaries. *Arzneim. Forsch.* 26: 1231–1232, 1976.
112. GAEHTGENS, P., K. U. BENNER, S. SCHICKENDANTZ, AND K. H. ALBRECHT. Method for simultaneous determination of red cell and plasma flow velocity in vitro and in vivo. *Pfluegers Arch.* 361: 191–195, 1976.
113. GAEHTGENS, P., F. KREUTZ, AND K. H. ALBRECHT. Optimal hematocrit for canine skeletal muscle during rhythmic isotonic exercise. *Eur. J. Appl. Physiol.* 41: 27–39, 1979.
114. GAEHTGENS, P., H. J. MEISELMAN, AND H. WAYLAND. Evaluation of the photometric double slit velocity measuring method in tubes 25 to 130 microns in bore. *Bibl. Anat.* 10: 571–578, 1969.
115. GAEHTGENS, P., H. J. MEISELMAN, AND H. WAYLAND. Veloc-

ity profiles of human blood at normal and reduced hematocrit in glass tubes up to 130 microns in diameter. *Microvasc. Res.* 2: 13–23, 1970.

116. GAEHTGENS, P., H. J. MEISELMAN, AND H. WAYLAND. Erythrocyte flow velocities in mesenteric microvessels of the cat. *Microvasc. Res.* 2: 151–162, 1970.
117. GAEHTGENS, P., AND H. D. PAPENFUSS. Effect of bifurcations on hematocrit reduction in the microcirculation. II. Experimental studies in narrow capillaries. *Bibl. Anat.* 18: 53–55, 1979.
118. GANNON, R. J. Vascular casting. In: *Principles and Techniques of Scanning Electron Microscopy*, edited by M. A. Hayat. New York: Van Nostrand Rheinhold, 1978, vol. 9, p. 170–193.
119. GATTI, R. A. Hematocrit values of capillary blood in the newborn infant. *J. Pediatr.* 70: 117–119, 1967.
120. GENTRY, R. M., AND P. C. JOHNSON. Reactive hyperemia in arterioles and capillaries of frog skeletal muscle following microocclusion. *Circ. Res.* 31: 953–965, 1972.
121. GIBSON, J. G., A. M. SELIGMAN, W. C. PEACOCK, J. C. AUB, J. FINE, AND R. D. EVANS. The distribution of red cells and plasma in large and minute vessels of the normal dog, determined by radioactive isotopes of iron and iodine. *J. Clin. Invest.* 25: 848–857, 1946.
122. GOLDSMITH, H. L., AND R. SKALAK. Hemodynamics. In: *Annual Review of Fluid Mechanics*, edited by M. Van Dyke, W. G. Vincenti, and J. V. Wehausen. Palo Alto, CA: Annual Reviews, 1975, vol. 7, p. 213–247.
123. GORCZYNSKI, R. J., AND B. R. DULING. Role of oxygen in arteriolar functional vasodilation in hamster striated muscle. *Am. J. Physiol.* 235 (*Heart Circ. Physiol.* 4): H505–H515, 1978.
124. GORE, R. W. Pressures in cat mesenteric arterioles and capillaries during changes in systemic arterial blood pressure. *Circ. Res.* 34: 581–591, 1972.
125. GORE, R. W. Wall stress: a determinant of regional differences in response of frog microvessels to norepinephrine. *Am. J. Physiol.* 222: 82–91, 1972.
126. GORE, R. W., AND H. G. BOHLEN. Pressure regulation in the microcirculation. *Federation Proc.* 34: 2931–2937, 1975.
127. GRÄNDE, P. O. Influence of neural and humoral beta-adrenoreceptor stimulation on dynamic microvascular reactivity in cat skeletal muscle. *Acta Physiol. Scand.* 106: 457–465, 1979.
128. GRÄNDE, P. O., P. BORGSTRÖM, AND S. MELLANDER. On the nature of basal vascular tone in cat skeletal muscle and its dependence on transmural pressure stimuli. *Acta Physiol. Scand.* 107: 365–376, 1979.
129. GRÄNDE, P. O., J. LUNDVALL, AND S. MELLANDER. Evidence for a rate-sensitive regulatory mechanism in myogenic microvascular control. *Acta Physiol. Scand.* 99: 432–477, 1977.
130. GRANGER, H. J., S. KOVALCHECK, B. W. ZWEIFACH, AND G. E. BARNES. Quantitative analysis of lymph formation and propulsion. In: *Proc. Computer Simulation Conf., 1977, La Jolla.* La Jolla, CA: Simulation Council, 1977, p. 562–569.
131. GRANGER, H. J., J. OHAR, AND H. I. CHEN. Structure and function of the interstitium. In: *Proc. NIH Workshop on Albumin, 1975, La Jolla*, edited by J. T. Sgouris and A. Rene. La Jolla, CA: Simulation Council, 1975, p. 114–124.
132. GRANGER, H. J., AND A. P. SHEPHERD, JR. Intrinsic microvascular control of tissue oxygen delivery. *Microvasc. Res.* 5: 49–72, 1973.
133. GRANGER, H. J., AND A. P. SHEPHERD, JR. Dynamics and control of the microcirculation. In: *Advances in Biomedical Engineering*, edited by J. H. Brown. New York: Academic, 1979, vol. 7, p. 1–63.
134. GRANGER, H. J., AND B. W. ZWEIFACH. Mechanics of active lymphatic pumping in rat mesentery (Abstract). *Federation Proc.* 38: 851, 1978.
135. GRANT, L. The sticking and emigration of white blood cells in inflammation. In: *The Inflammatory Process* (2nd ed.), edited by B. W. Zweifach, L. Grant, and R. T. McCluskey. New York: Academic, 1973, vol. 2, p. 205–249.
136. GRANT, R. T., AND H. P. WRIGHT. Further observations on the blood vessels of skeletal muscle (rat cremaster). *J. Anat.* 103: 553–565, 1968.
137. GRAY, S. D. Rat spinotrapezius muscle preparation for microscopic observation of the terminal vascular bed. *Microvasc. Res.* 5: 395–400, 1973.
138. GROOM, A. C., W. B. MORRIS, AND S. ROWLANDS. The difference in circulation times of plasma and corpuscles in the cat. *J. Physiol. London* 136: 218–225, 1957.
139. GROSS, J. F., AND M. INTAGLIETTA. Effect of morphology and structural properties on microvascular hemodynamics. *Bibl. Anat.* 11: 532–539, 1973.
140. GROSS, J. F., M. INTAGLIETTA, AND B. W. ZWEIFACH. Network model of pulsatile hemodynamics in the microcirculation of the rabbit omentum. *Am. J. Physiol.* 226: 1117–1123, 1974.
141. GUSTAFSSON, L., L. APPELGREN, AND H. E. MYRVOLD. The effect of polycythemia on blood flow in working and non-working skeletal muscle. *Acta Physiol. Scand.* 109: 143–148, 1980.
142. GUSTAFSSON, L., L. APPELGREN, AND H. E. MYRVOLD. Blood flow and apparent viscosity in working and non-working skeletal muscle of the dog after high and low molecular weight dextran. *Circ. Res.* 48: 465–469, 1981.
143. GUYTON, A. C., H. J. GRANGER, AND A. E. TAYLOR. *Circulatory Physiology: Dynamics and Control of Body Fluids.* Philadelphia, PA: Saunders, 1975.
144. HADDY, F. J., AND R. B. GILBERT. Relation of a venous-arteriolar reflex to transmural pressure and radius in small and large systemic vessels. *Circ. Res* 4: 25–32, 1956.
145. HAGEN, G. Über die Bewegung des Wassers in engen zylindrischen Röhren. *Ann. Phys. Chem.* 46: 423–442, 1839.
146. HALJAMÄE, H., A. LINDE, AND B. AMUNDSON. Comparative analyses of capsular fluid and interstitial fluid. *Am. J. Physiol.* 227: 1199–1205, 1974.
147. HAMMERSEN, F. The terminal vascular bed in skeletal muscle with special regard to the problem of shunts. In: *Capillary Permeability*, edited by C. Crone and N. A. Lassen. Copenhagen: Munksgaard, 1970, p. 351–365. (Alfred Benzon Symp. 2.)
148. HANSON, K. M., AND P. C. JOHNSON. Evidence for local arteriovenous reflex in intestine. *J. Appl. Physiol.* 17: 509–513, 1962.
149. HANSON, K. M., AND P. C. JOHNSON. Vascular resistance and arterial pressure in autoperfused dog hind limb. *Am. J. Physiol.* 203: 615–620, 1962.
150. HARGENS, A. R., AND B. W. ZWEIFACH. Transport between blood and peripheral lymph in intestine. *Microvasc. Res.* 11: 89–101, 1976.
151. HARGENS, A. R., AND B. W. ZWEIFACH. Contractile stimuli in collecting lymph vessels. *Am. J. Physiol.* 233 (*Heart Circ. Physiol.* 2): H57–H65, 1977.
152. HARRIS, P. D. Quantification of capillary RBC flow. *Bibl. Anat.* 9: 155–159, 1967.
153. HARRIS, T. R., C. A. GERVIN, D. BURKS, AND P. CUSTER. Effects of coronary flow reduction on capillary-myocardial exchange in dogs. *Am. J. Physiol.* 234 (*Heart Circ. Physiol.* 3): H679–H689, 1978.
154. HAUCK, G., AND H. SCHRÖDER. Stability of the postcapillary bloodstream (Abstract). *Pfluegers Arch.* 312: R38, 1969.
155. HEBBEL, R. P., O. YAMADA, C. F. MOLDOW, AND H. S. JACOB. Abnormal adherence of sickle erythrocytes to cultured vascular endothelium. *J. Clin. Lab. Invest.* 65: 154–160, 1980.
156. HENRICH, H., AND A. HECKE. A gracilis muscle preparation for quantitative microcirculatory studies in the rat. *Microvasc. Res.* 15: 349–356, 1978.
157. HENRIKSEN, O. Local nervous mechanism in regulation of blood flow in human subcutaneous tissue. *Acta Physiol. Scand.* 97: 385–391, 1976.
158. HERTEL, R., R. ASSMANN, AND H. HENRICH. Structural differences in the mesentery microcirculation between normotensive and spontaneously hypertensive rats. *Pfluegers Arch.* 375: 153–159, 1978.

159. HILL, L. The pressure in the small arteries, veins, and capillaries of the bat's wing. *Proc. Physiol. Soc. J. Physiol. London* 54: 24–25, 1920.
160. HINT, H. C. The flow properties of erythrocyte suspensions in isolated rabbit's ear: the effects of erythrocyte aggregation, hematocrit and perfusion pressure. *Bibl. Anat.* 4: 112–118, 1964.
161. HIPPENSTEELE, J. R., P. D. HARRIS, D. L. WIEGMAN, AND I. G. JOSHUA. Effect of altered bath oxygen and carbon dioxide tension on cremasteric arteriolar diameters in decerebrate rats (Abstract). *Microvasc. Res.* 21: 245, 1981.
162. HOLLENBERG, N. K., AND M. NICKERSON. Changes in pre- and postcapillary resistance in pathogenesis of hemorrhagic shock. *Am. J. Physiol.* 219: 1483–1489, 1970.
163. HONIG, C. R., J. L. FRIERSON, AND J. L. PATTERSON. Comparison of neural controls of resistance and capillary density in resting muscles. *Am. J. Physiol.* 218: 937–942, 1970.
164. HONIG, C. R., C. L. ODOROFF, AND J. L. FRIERSON. Capillary recruitment in exercise: rate, extent, uniformity, and relation to blood flow. *Am. J. Physiol.* 238 (*Heart Circ. Physiol.* 7): H31–H42, 1980.
165. HÖPER, J., AND M. KESSLER. Na^+ and Po_2 dependent flow changes in the isolated perfused rat liver (Abstract). *Microvasc. Res.* 17, Suppl.: S54, 1979.
166. HUGUES, J. Contribution à l'étude des facteurs vasculaires et sanguins dans l'hémostase spontanée. *Arch. Int. Physiol.* 61: 565–571, 1953.
167. HUTCHINS, P. M. Participation of oxygen in local control of skeletal muscle microvasculature. *Circ. Res.* 34: 85–93, 1974.
168. HUTCHINS, P. M., AND A. E. DARNELL. Observation of a decreased number of small arterioles in spontaneously hypertensive rats. *Circ. Res.* 34/35, Suppl. 1: 161–165, 1970.
169. HUTCHINS, P. M., J. GOLDSTONE, AND R. WELLS. Effects of hemorrhagic shock on the microvasculature of skeletal muscle. *Microvasc. Res.* 5: 131–140, 1973.
170. HYMAN, C. Independent control of nutritional and shunt circulation. *Microvasc. Res.* 3: 89–94, 1971.
171. INTAGLIETTA, M. Microvascular pressure measurements by cannulation: independency of concentration gradients and deviations in micro-servonulling. *Microvasc. Res.* 3: 396–399, 1971.
172. INTAGLIETTA, M. Pressure measurements in the microvasculature with active and passive transducers. *Microvasc. Res.* 5: 317–323, 1973.
173. INTAGLIETTA, M. The measurement of pressure and flow in the microcirculation: application to physiological and clinical problems. *Med. Prog. Technol.* 4: 55–60, 1976.
174. INTAGLIETTA, M. Measurement of flow dynamics in the microcirculation. *Med. Instrum. Baltimore* 11: 149–152, 1977.
175. INTAGLIETTA, M., R. F. PAWULA, AND W. R. TOMPKINS. Pressure measurements in the mammalian microvasculature. *Microvasc. Res.* 2: 212–220, 1970.
176. INTAGLIETTA, M., D. R. RICHARDSON, AND W. R. TOMPKINS. Blood pressure, flow, and elastic properties in microvessels of cat omentum. *Am. J. Physiol.* 221: 922–928, 1971.
177. INTAGLIETTA, M., N. R. SILVERMAN, AND W. R. TOMPKINS. Capillary flow velocity measurements in vivo and in situ by television methods. *Microvasc. Res.* 10: 165–179, 1975.
178. INTAGLIETTA, M., AND W. R. TOMPKINS. Micropressure measurement with 1 micron and smaller cannulae. *Microvasc. Res.* 3: 211–214, 1971.
179. INTAGLIETTA, M., AND W. R. TOMPKINS. Microvascular measurements by video shearing and splitting. *Microvasc. Res.* 5: 309–312, 1973.
180. INTAGLIETTA, M., AND B. W. ZWEIFACH. Geometrical model of the microvasculature of rabbit omentum from in vivo measurements. *Circ. Res.* 28: 593–600, 1971.
181. JAN, K.-M., AND S. CHIEN. Effect of hematocrit variations on coronary hemodynamics and oxygen utilization. *Am. J. Physiol.* 233 (*Heart Circ. Physiol.* 2): H106–H113, 1977.
182. JAY, A. W. L., S. ROWLANDS, AND L. SKIBO. The resistance to blood flow in the capillaries. *Can. J. Physiol. Pharmacol.* 50: 1007–1013, 1972.
183. JENDRUCKO, R. J., AND J. S. LEE. The measurement of hematocrit of blood flowing in glass capillaries by microphotometry. *Microvasc. Res.* 6: 316–331, 1973.
184. JENDRUCKO, R. J., AND J. S. LEE. Hematocrit measurement in cat arterioles by microphotometry (Abstract). *Federation Proc.* 33: 313, 1974.
185. JOHNSON, P. C. Autoregulatory responses of cat mesenteric arterioles measured in vivo. *Circ. Res.* 22: 199–212, 1968.
186. JOHNSON, P. C. Renaissance in the microcirculation. *Circ. Res.* 31: 817–823, 1972.
187. JOHNSON, P. C. The microcirculation and local and humoral control of the circulation. In: *Cardiovascular Physiology I*, edited by A. Guyton and C. E. Jones. Baltimore, MD: University Park, 1974, vol. 1, p. 163–196. (Int. Rev. Physiol. Ser.)
188. JOHNSON, P. C. The myogenic response and the microcirculation. *Microvasc. Res.* 13: 1–18, 1977.
189. JOHNSON, P. C., J. BLASCHKE, K. S. BURTON, AND J. H. DIAL. Influence of flow variations on capillary hematocrit in mesentery. *Am. J. Physiol.* 221: 105–112, 1971.
190. JOHNSON, P. C., AND K. M. HANSON. Effect of arterial pressure on arterial and venous resistance of intestine. *J. Appl. Physiol.* 17: 503–508, 1962.
191. JOHNSON, P. C., AND H. A. HENRICK. Metabolic and myogenic factors in local regulation of the microcirculation. *Federation Proc.* 34: 2020–2024, 1975.
192. JOHNSON, P. C., D. L. HUDNALL, AND J. H. DIAL. Measurement of capillary hematocrit by photometric techniques. *Microvasc. Res.* 5: 351–356, 1973.
193. JOHNSON, P. C., AND M. INTAGLIETTA. Autoregulation in arterioles of sartorius muscle (Abstract). *Physiologist* 18: 266, 1975.
194. JOHNSON, P. C., AND M. INTAGLIETTA. Contributions of pressure and flow sensitivity to autoregulation in mesenteric arterioles. *Am. J. Physiol.* 231: 1686–1698, 1976.
195. JOHNSON, P. C., AND D. R. RICHARDSON. The influence of venous pressure on filtration forces in the intestine. *Microvasc. Res.* 7: 296–306, 1974.
196. JOHNSON, P. C., AND H. WAYLAND. Oscillatory flow pattern in single mesenteric capillaries. *Bibl. Anat.* 9: 164–168, 1967.
197. JOHNSON, P. C., AND H. WAYLAND. Regulation of blood flow in single capillaries. *Am. J. Physiol.* 212: 1405–1415, 1967.
198. JOHNSTON, M. G., J. B. HAY, AND J. Z. MOVAT. The modulation of enhanced vascular permeability by prostaglandins through alterations in blood flow (hyperemia). *Agents Actions* 6: 705–711, 1976.
199. KATZ, M. A. Validity of interstitial fluid hydrostatic pressure measurements in hollow porous polyethylene capsules. *Microvasc. Res.* 16: 316–326, 1978.
200. KINTER, W. B., AND J. R. PAPPENHEIMER. Role of red blood corpuscles in regulation of renal blood flow and glomerular filtration rate. *Am. J. Physiol.* 185: 399–406, 1956.
201. KJELLMER, I. The effect of exercise on the vascular bed of skeletal muscle. *Acta Physiol. Scand.* 62: 18–30, 1964.
202. KLITZMAN, B., AND B. R. DULING. Microvascular hematocrit and red cell flow in resting and contracting striated muscle. *Am. J. Physiol.* 237 (*Heart Circ. Physiol.* 6): H481–H490, 1979.
203. KLITZMAN, B., AND P. C. JOHNSON. Capillary network geometry and red cell distribution in the hamster cremaster muscle. *Am. J. Physiol.* 242 (*Heart Circ. Physiol.* 11): H211–H219, 1982.
204. KOHNER, E. M., C. T. DOLLERY, M. SHAKIB, P. HENKIND, J. W. PATTERSON, L. N. F. DE OLIVEIRA, AND C. J. BULPITT. Experimental retinal branch vein occlusion. *Am. J. Ophthalmol.* 69: 778–825, 1970.
205. KOYAMA, R., H. MISHINA, AND T. ASAKVRA. A study of the effects of hypoxia and hypercapnia on the capillary blood flow of frog web by using laser Doppler microscope. *Bull. Res. Inst. Appl. Electr. Jpn.* 28: 21–26, 1976.
206. KOZUKA, T. Experimental studies on the effect of the intra-

CHAPTER 8

Mechanics and thermodynamics of transcapillary exchange

FITZ-ROY E. CURRY | *Department of Human Physiology, University of California School of Medicine, Davis, California*

CHAPTER CONTENTS

I. Background
II. Diffusion
  A. Stochastic description of diffusion coefficients
  B. Hydrodynamic description of diffusion coefficients
  C. Diffusion across thin membranes
  D. Diffusion with superimposed convective solute transport
  E. Partition of solute flux into convective and diffusive components
III. Thermodynamic Principles
  A. Entropy generation and dissipation of free energy
  B. Entropy generation and fluxes and forces across membranes
  C. Onsager's law—thermodynamic relations for passive solute and water flows across membranes
  D. Molecular viewpoint—some elementary statistical mechanical concepts
    1. Entropy change as ideal solute mixes with water
    2. Chemical potential
    3. Thermodynamic equilibrium
IV. Membrane Transport
  A. Staverman-Kedem-Katchalsky equations
    1. Transformation of membrane flux-force relations
    2. Volume flow
    3. Solute flow
  B. Thermodynamic equations within membranes
    1. Background
    2. Solute flow
    3. Volume flow
    4. Relation to mechanical models of transport
  C. Application of membrane-transport equations to steady-state ultrafiltration
  D. Experimental demonstration of reciprocity
V. Pore Theory
  A. Poiseuille's law
    1. Water flow in pores
    2. Critique of application of Poiseuille's law in pores of molecular dimensions
    3. Calculations and units
  B. Pore diffusion
    1. Diffusion coefficients of spherical solutes within cylindrical pores
    2. Diffusion in membranes penetrated by cylindrical pores
    3. Restricted diffusion in artificial membranes
  C. Pore theory
    1. Restricted diffusion in capillary beds
    2. Discrepancy between equivalent pore radii from restricted diffusion and Poiseuille flow
    3. Molecular sieving in cylindrical pores
  D. Solvent drag
    1. Introduction of new concept
    2. New hydrodynamic theory of solvent drag
    3. Solvent-drag reflection coefficients in artificial membranes
  E. Pore theory of ultrafiltration
    1. Experimental evaluation
    2. Intermediate-sized solutes at capillary walls
    3. Blood-to-lymph ultrafiltration of macromolecules
    4. Parallel-pathway model
    5. Membrane solvent-drag reflection coefficients in heterogeneous membranes
  F. Osmotic flow
    1. Osmotic reflection coefficient in pores
    2. Flow in semipermeable membranes
    3. Mechanics of osmotic flow
    4. Anderson-Malone model
    5. Experimental evaluation of pore theory for osmotic reflection coefficients
    6. Parallel-pathway model of osmotic flow
    7. Osmotic and solvent-drag reflection coefficients in heteroporous membranes
  G. Slit geometry
  H. Overview
VI. Fiber-Matrix Model
  A. Introductory concepts
  B. Spaces within fibrous networks
  C. Steric exclusion
  D. Restricted diffusion
  E. Exclusion and diffusion in hyaluronic acid networks
  F. Permeability coefficients of membranes containing fibrous networks
  G. Water flow through fibrous networks
    1. Hydrodynamic-drag model
    2. Hydraulic-radius model
  H. Reflection coefficients in fibrous networks
  I. Pore and fiber-matrix models applied to capillary transport
VII. Charge
  A. Donnan distribution
  B. Donnan potential and osmotic pressure
  C. Critique of Donnan-distribution calculations
  D. Concentration and potential profiles near membranes
  E. Interaction of charged solutes in cylindrical pores
  F. Effect of charge on selectivity of capillary wall
VIII. Vesicle and Lipophilic-Solute Transport
  A. Vesicular exchange—transcytosis
  B. Vesicle filling
    1. Equilibrium partition
    2. Kinetics
  C. Movement of vesicles within cytoplasm
  D. Measurement of transcapillary exchange—vesicle transport versus ultrafiltration

$$J_s/S = V_{s,imp} \left[\frac{C_1 - C_2 \exp\left(-\dfrac{V_{s,imp}}{V_{s,dif}}\right)}{1 - \exp\left(-\dfrac{V_{s,imp}}{V_{s,dif}}\right)} \right] \quad (2.29)$$

The ratio of imposed velocity to diffusion velocity of the solute is dimensionless and is called the Péclet number (Pe) for diffusion with superimposed convective transport

$$Pe = \frac{V_w \chi \Delta x}{D} \quad (2.30)$$

The derivation of the equation ignores a very small velocity imparted to the solute by a hydrostatic pressure difference (ΔP) across the membrane. Pressure diffusion is described further in V. PORE THEORY (see Eq. 5.49a and 5.49b, p. 327).

Equation 2.28, often called the Hertzian equation, is closely related to the expression for the flux of a charged species down its electrochemical-potential gradient. A potential difference across the membrane will impart a velocity to an ion (charge, z) equal to the product of the electrostatic force acting on the solute per mole ($zF\mathrm{d}\psi/\mathrm{d}z$) and the molar mobility (D/RT)

$$V_{s,imp} = \left(\frac{DzF}{RT}\right)\left(\frac{\mathrm{d}\psi}{\mathrm{d}x}\right) \quad (2.31)$$

where F is the Faraday constant, and ψ is the electrical potential. Substitution of Equation 2.31 into Equation 2.25 gives

$$J_s/S = D\left[\frac{\mathrm{dC}}{\mathrm{d}x} - \left(\frac{zFC}{RT}\right)\left(\frac{\mathrm{d}\psi}{\mathrm{d}x}\right)\right] \quad (2.32)$$

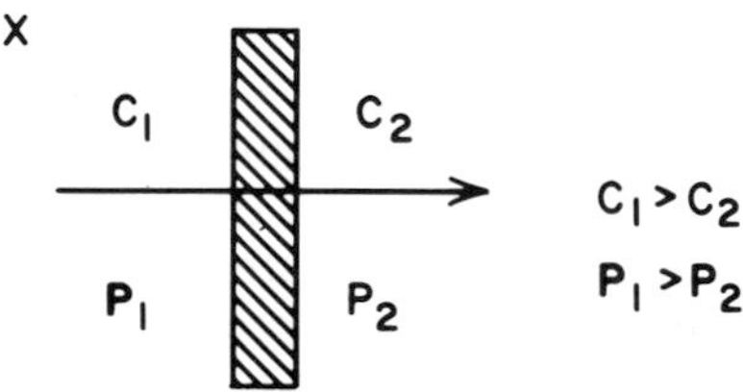

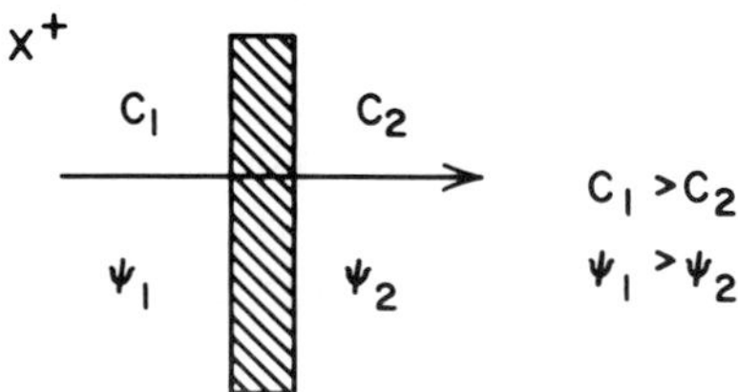

FIG. 2.3. Sign convention for diffusive fluxes in presence of imposed solute velocity. All fluxes are positive from left to right. *A*: diffusion of a neutral solute (X) in presence of water flow down a pressure gradient. *B*: diffusion of cation (X^+) down a gradient of electric potential.

which is the Nernst-Planck equation. When $\mathrm{d}\psi/\mathrm{d}x$ is assumed to be constant throughout the membrane (constant electric field), the integrated form of Equation 2.32 is

$$J_s/S = -\left(\frac{Dz_iF\Delta\psi}{RT\Delta x}\right)\left[\frac{C_1 - C_2 \exp\left(\dfrac{zF\Delta\psi}{RT}\right)}{1 - \exp\left(\dfrac{zF\Delta\psi}{RT}\right)}\right] \quad (2.33)$$

where $\Delta\psi$ is measured as $\psi_2 - \psi_1$.[1] Equation 2.33 is the Goldman or constant-field flux equation widely used to describe ion flow across thin membranes. For cation flow across a membrane with $C_1 > C_2$ and $\psi_1 > \psi_2$, $\Delta\psi$ is negative and z is positive—Equation 2.33 has the same form as Equation 2.29. Specifically, $DzF\Delta\psi/RT\Delta x$ is the imposed velocity (Eq. 2.31), and the exponent is the ratio of the imposed velocity to the diffusion velocity. The exponent is therefore a Péclet number for diffusion in an electric field. In the Goldman equation the physical process that determines the imposed velocity is simple diffusion (Eq. 2.31), whereas in the Hertzian equation the imposed velocity is determined by the hydrodynamic slip coefficient and the mean water velocity. The relation between the water velocity and the driving force for water flow through the pathway shared with the diffusive process is described by a separate relation. For example, in Poiseuille flow

$$\bar{V}_w = \frac{r_p^2 \Delta P}{8\eta\Delta x} \quad (2.34)$$

where r_p is the channel radius [see V. PORE THEORY (p. 327) for further development].

In the same way as investigators have used the current-voltage relations described by the constant-field equation to study the ionic conductivities of cellular and epithelial membranes, capillary physiologists have used the solute flux–water flow relation (Eq. 2.28) to study the porous pathways for water and solute transport across the capillary wall. The most common approach has been to partition the flux into so-called diffusive and convective components. Some of the limitations of this approach are reviewed next.

E. Partition of Solute Flux Into Convective and Diffusive Components

When the water velocity is zero, Equation 2.28 reduces to Fick's first law. The concentration gradient is constant across the membrane. If $V_w \neq 0$, the solute concentration gradient is nonlinear. Thus the magnitudes of the diffusive component in Equation 2.25 ($D\mathrm{dC}/\mathrm{d}x$) and of the convective component ($V_w\chi C$) vary across the membrane. The two components can

[1] In electrophysiology C_2 is designated C_{inside}, and C_1 is designed $C_{outside}$.

be described unequivocally only at the interface at which fluid enters the membrane. When water flows from high to low solute concentration, the concentration gradient (convective component of flux entering membrane) is $V_w \chi C_1$, where C_1 is the concentration of the solute just outside the membrane entrance. Equation 2.28 can be rearranged to identify the convective component of flux entering the membrane as a separate term

$$J_s/S = \left[\frac{D}{\Delta x}(C_1 - C_2)\right]\{Pe/[\exp(Pe) - 1]\} + (V_w \chi C_1) \tag{2.35a}$$

$$J_s/S = \left[\frac{D}{\Delta x}(C_1 - C_2)\right]\left[\frac{Pe}{2}\left(\coth\frac{Pe}{2} - 1\right)\right] + (V_w \chi C_1) \tag{2.35b}$$

Equations 2.35a and 2.35b are mathematically identical to Equation 2.28. They may also be obtained from expressions previously described by Patlak et al. (110), Bresler et al. (14), and Perl (112). The term Pe/[exp(Pe) − 1] or its equivalent, (Pe/2)[coth(Pe/2) − 1], has an intuitively simple meaning. It is the ratio of the solute concentration gradient at the channel entrance in the presence of water flow, $(dC/dx)_0$, to its value in the absence of water flow, $\Delta C/\Delta x$. This is most easily seen by examining the concentration profile within the membrane shown in Figure 2.4. As the Péclet number increases, the concentration gradient at the membrane interface falls from $(C_1 - C_2)/\Delta x$ toward zero. Values of Pe/[exp(Pe) − 1] are plotted as a function of Pe in Figure 2.5. This term may be evaluated by expanding the term coth(Pe/2) in Equation 2.35b as a Taylor series. The result is

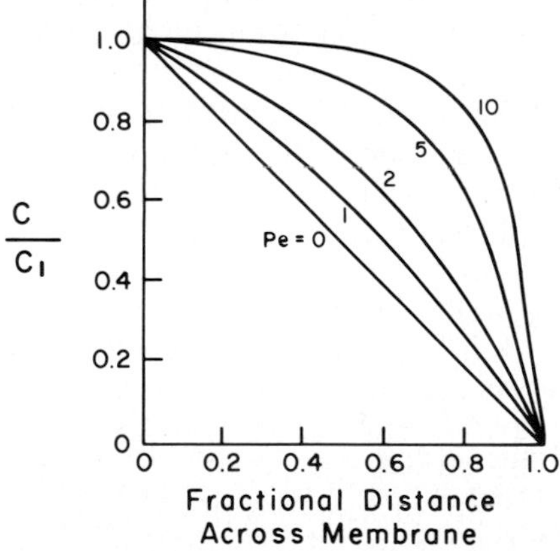

FIG. 2.4. Solute concentration profiles within membrane. Ordinate, solute concentrations (C) are expressed relative to concentration entering membrane (C_1). Distance across membrane is expressed relative to membrane thickness. Péclet number (Pe) measures imposed solute velocity relative to diffusion velocity of solute. As Pe increases, concentration gradient at membrane entrance approaches zero.

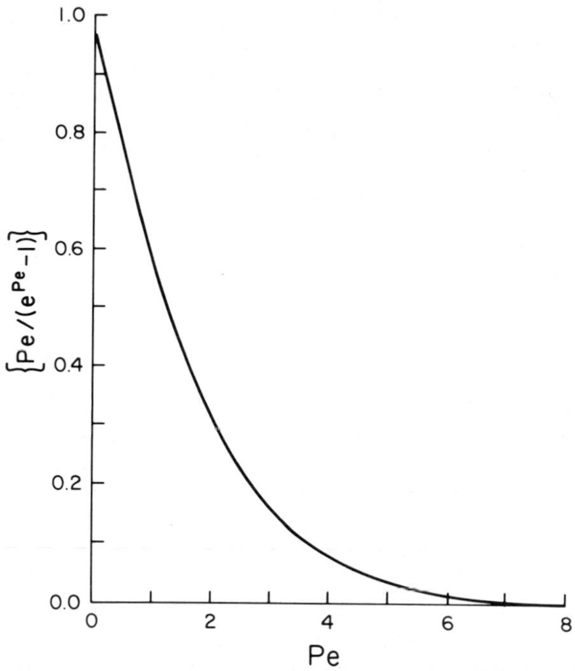

FIG. 2.5. Fractional reduction in solute concentration gradient at the membrane entrance as Péclet number (Pe) increases (see Fig. 2.4) is measured by Pe/[exp(Pe) − 1] and plotted on ordinate.

$$\begin{aligned} Pe/(\exp^{Pe} - 1) &= Pe/2 \coth(Pe/2) - (Pe/2) \\ &= 1 - (Pe/2) + (Pe^2/12) - (Pe^4/720) \end{aligned} \tag{2.36}$$

Figure 2.5 shows that the magnitude of the diffusive component falls rapidly as Pe increases. When Pe = 3.6 the concentration gradient at the membrane entrance is only 10% of that expected in the absence of flow. With larger Pe values the magnitude of the diffusion term approaches zero. This is not because the process of molecular diffusion ceases, but rather because the gradient of solute concentration at the pore entrance falls toward zero. The random bombardment of solute, which is responsible for diffusion, ceases only at absolute zero. In the limit of high Péclet numbers ($Pe > 5$)

$$J_s/S = V_w \chi C_1 \tag{2.37}$$

Conversely, with very low Péclet numbers ($Pe \ll 1$) the term Pe/[exp(Pe) − 1] in Figure 2.5 approaches 1. Equations 2.35a and 2.35b reduce to a simple superposition of the elementary diffusive flux and convective flux entering the membrane

$$J_s/S = \frac{D}{\Delta x}(C_1 - C_2) + V_w \chi C_1 \tag{2.38}$$

An equation like Equation 2.38 was introduced by Pappenheimer and colleagues (109) and used to develop expressions for ultrafiltration. For a Péclet number of 0.2, the term $(D/\Delta x)(C_1 - C_2)$ overestimates the diffusive component by 10%. A good correction factor for Péclet numbers ranging from 0.2 to 1 is obtained by retaining the first term of the series expansion in Equation 2.36 and writing Equations 2.35a and 2.35b in the reduced form

$$J_s/S = \frac{D}{\Delta x}(C_1 - C_2)\left(1 - \frac{Pe}{2}\right) + V_w\chi C_1 \quad (2.39)$$

An expression like Equation 2.39 has not been used in transport theory. Rather Equation 2.38 has been rearranged into the identical form

$$J_s/S = \frac{D}{\Delta x}(C_1 - C_2) + V_w\chi\left(\frac{C_1 + C_2}{2}\right) \quad (2.40)$$

Equation 2.40 has correctly been recommended by several authors as a good approximation of Equations 2.35a and 2.35b for $Pe^2/12 \ll 1$ (81, 112). However, the term $V_w\chi(C_1 + C_2)/2$ has been identified as the convective component of solute flux within the membrane, based on its superficial resemblance to an approximate form of the Kedem-Katchalsky equations. This interpretation is incorrect. Equation 2.39 should be used instead of Equation 2.40; the term $1 - (Pe/2)$ in Equation 2.39 is then understood as a first-order correction for reduction of the solute concentration gradient at the membrane entrance from the value of $\Delta C/\Delta x$ expected when there is no flow through the membrane. The convective component of flux entering the membrane is $V_w\chi C_1$.

The general principles introduced in this section are widely used to describe the transport of water and solute across the capillary wall. A direct comparison between the equations derived in this section and those derived from the principles of irreversible thermodynamics is developed in III. THERMODYNAMIC PRINCIPLES (this page) and IV. MEMBRANE TRANSPORT (p. 320).

III. THERMODYNAMIC PRINCIPLES

TABLE 3.1. *Principal Relations and Nomenclature for III. Thermodynamic Principles*

	Relation	
1.	$dG = TdS_{int}$	(3.12)
2.	$\frac{TdS}{dt} = \Sigma\Delta\mu_i J_{s,i}/S$	(3.18)
3a.	$J_s/S = L_{ss}\Delta\mu_s + L_{sw}\Delta\mu_w$	(3.27)
3b.	$J_w/S = L_{ws}\Delta\mu_s + L_{ww}\Delta\mu_w$	(3.28)
3c.	$L_{ws} = L_{sw}$	(3.29)
4.	$\Delta S_{ideal} = k \ln\left[\frac{(N_w + N_s)!}{N_w! N_s!}\right]$	(3.30, 3.31)
5.	$C_{i,1} = C_{i,2}\exp(-\Delta E_i/RT)$	(3.45)

Nomenclature

C	concentration (M)
e	amount of charge (C)
E	internal energy (cal) (1 cal = 4.18 joul)
E_i	energy per mole associated with potential fields (cal/mol)
f	activity coefficient
F	Faraday constant (C/equivalent)
G	Gibbs free energy (cal)
J_s/S	solute flux ($mol \cdot cm^{-2} \cdot s^{-1}$)
J_w/S	water flux ($mol \cdot cm^{-2} \cdot s^{-1}$)
k	Boltzmann constant (R/N_A)
L_{sw}, L_{ws}	thermodynamic conductances
n	number of moles (mol)
P	pressure (dyn/cm^2)
R	gas constant ($1.99\ cal \cdot °K^{-1} \cdot mol^{-1}$)
S	surface area (cm^2)
S	entropy (cal/°K)
T	temperature (°K)
t	time (s)
V	volume (cm^3)
x	mole fraction
z	valency
δ	change in magnitude of extensive variable (variable)
μ	chemical potential (cal/mol)
$\tilde{\mu}$	electrochemical potential (cal/mol)
ν	fractional increase (Eq. 3.30)
ψ	electrical potential (V)

Numbers in parentheses refer to text equations.

The relation between the dissipation of free energy stored in a gradient of electrochemical potential and the generation of entropy is the starting point for the thermodynamic analysis of transcapillary exchange. Table 3.1 shows one form of the relation (entry 1) derived from the first and second laws of thermodynamics. Classic thermodynamics is also used to derive a general relation between the rate of entropy generation and the product of the driving forces and the flows of solute and water across a membrane (entry 2). The classic thermodynamic description of the energetics of membrane transport was extended by Onsager, who used statistical thermodynamic principles. Onsager's law applies for small driving forces and flows of solute and water in which entropy generation conforms to the general relation in entry 2. A set of transport equations is derived from Onsager's law (entry 3); these relations are developed further in IV. MEMBRANE TRANSPORT (p. 320). A brief introduction to some statistical mechanical concepts as applied to entropy, chemical potential, and equilibrium distributions of solutes (entries 4 and 5) is given to extend the molecular viewpoint introduced in II. DIFFUSION (p. 310).

Schultz (132) has presented an excellent general review of the thermodynamics of membrane transport that has influenced the development in this section. The standard reference for the application of irreversible thermodynamic principles to membrane transport is the monograph by Katchalsky and Curran (68).

A. *Entropy Generation and Dissipation of Free Energy*

The entropy of a system is a property of state—values depend only on the initial and final state of the system and not on the way the system changes. The change in entropy is therefore the same if the system undergoes a spontaneous (irreversible) process, such as diffusive transfer, or an idealized (reversible) process. For a reversible process the change in entropy (dS) is defined from the second law of thermodynamics as

$$dS = \frac{dQ}{T} \tag{3.1}$$

where dQ is the amount of heat exchanged with the surroundings, and T is the absolute temperature. For an irreversible process the heat exchanged (dQ_{ext}) is less than that for a reversible process. Therefore

$$dS > \frac{dQ_{ext}}{T} \tag{3.2}$$

The additional entropy indicated by the inequality in Equation 3.2 represents entropy created during the irreversible process and is designated dS_{int}. The inequality can then be replaced by the equality

$$dS = dS_{ext} + dS_{int} \tag{3.3}$$

where $dS_{ext} = dQ_{ext}/T$. The relation between the amount of entropy created and the change in free energy is now derived from the definition of free energy. The Gibbs free energy (G) is also a property of state

$$G = E + PV - TS \tag{3.4}$$

where E is total internal energy, P is pressure, and V is volume. For a process occurring at constant temperature and pressure the change in free energy is

$$dG = dE + PdV - TdS \tag{3.5}$$

Substituting for dS from Equation 3.3

$$dG = dE + PdV - T(dS_{ext} + dS_{int}) \tag{3.6}$$

Because $TdS_{ext} = dQ$ from Equation 3.3

$$dG = TdS_{int} + (dE + PdV - dQ) \tag{3.7}$$

The second term on the right of Equation 3.7 is simply interpreted in terms of the first law of thermodynamics

$$\begin{aligned} dE &= dQ - dW \\ &= dQ - PdV + \psi de + \Sigma\mu_i dn_i \end{aligned} \tag{3.8}$$

The work performed by the system (dW) consists of pressure-volume work (PdV), the work of transferring an amount of positive charge (de) against an electrical potential (ψ), and the work of transferring a number of moles (dn_i) into the system, which has a chemical potential of μ_i. Thus $dE + PdV - dQ$ equals the work performed by the system other than pressure-volume work. Equation 3.7 may be rewritten

$$dG = TdS_{int} + \psi de + \Sigma\mu_i dn_i \tag{3.9}$$

If the only carriers of charge in the system are ions, $de = \Sigma z_i F dn_i$, where z_i is the charge on an ion. Equation 3.9 is then written

$$dG = TdS_{int} + \Sigma\tilde{\mu}_i dn_i \tag{3.10}$$

where $\tilde{\mu}_i$ is the electrochemical potential, i.e.

$$\tilde{\mu}_i = \mu_i + z_i\psi F \tag{3.11}$$

When applied to an open system, Equation 3.10 shows that some of the free energy gained when material is added to a system is lost as the result of the generation of internal entropy. When applied to a closed system in which no material crossed the boundary and $\Sigma dn_i = 0$, Equation 3.10 shows that all free energy stored in the system will be dissipated as internal entropy

$$dG = TdS_{int} \tag{3.12}$$

An example of a closed system for which Equation 3.12 applies is shown in Figure 3.1. The system consists of a container separated into two compartments by a membrane. Solute and water cross the membrane from one compartment to the other, but neither solute nor water crosses the walls of the container. The relation between the entropy generation and the fluxes and forces across the membrane is developed further below.

B. *Entropy Generation and Fluxes and Forces Across Membranes*

The chemical potential (Eq. 3.8) is the partial molar free energy, i.e., the free energy per mole of substance in the absence of electrical forces

$$\mu_i = \left(\frac{\partial G}{\partial n_i}\right) \tag{3.13}$$

When electrical and pressure work terms contribute to the potential energy of the solute

$$\tilde{\mu}_i = \left(\frac{\partial G}{\partial n_i}\right) \tag{3.14}$$

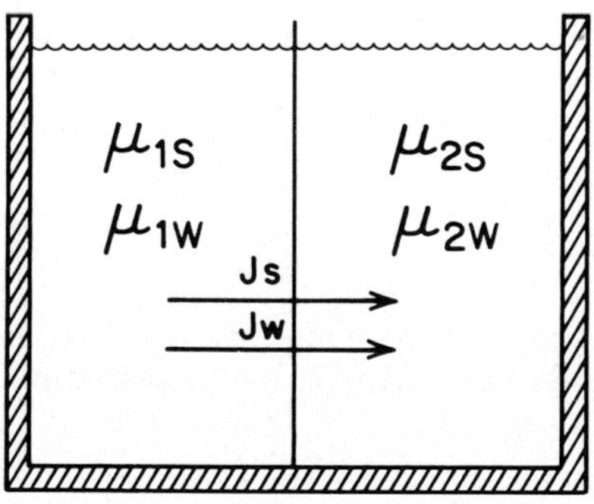

FIG. 3.1. Closed system consisting of 2 compartments, containing water and solute, separated by membrane permeable to both. When solute and water are transported between compartments at constant temperature, rate of entropy generation is described by Eqs. 3.12, 3.17, and 3.26.

The change in free energy that occurs when dn_i moles move from side 1 of the membrane (electrochemical potential, $\tilde{\mu}_{i,1}$) to side 2 (electrochemical potential, $\tilde{\mu}_{i,2}$) is

$$dG_i = dn_i(\tilde{\mu}_{i,1} - \tilde{\mu}_{i,2}) \quad (3.15)$$

Therefore the total change in free energy resulting from the transfer of several species is

$$dG = \Sigma\Delta\tilde{\mu}_i dn_i \quad (3.16)$$

Equations 3.12 and 3.16 together give

$$TdS_{int} = \Sigma\Delta\tilde{\mu}_i dn_i \quad (3.17)$$

Because the flux of each species ($J_{s,i}/S$) across a unit area of membrane is dn_i/dt, Equation 3.17 can be rewritten

$$T\frac{dS_{int}}{dt} = \Sigma\Delta\tilde{\mu}_i(J_{s,i}/S) \quad (3.18)$$

which states that the rate of formation of entropy is determined by the product of the flux of a substance across the membrane ($J_{s,i}/S$) and its corresponding driving force ($\Delta\tilde{\mu}_i$). Equation 3.18 is quite general; furthermore it has exactly the form that leads via Onsager's law to the phenomenological equations for membrane transport.

C. Onsager's Law—Thermodynamic Relations for Passive Solute and Water Flows Across Membranes

The relation between entropy generation and chemical potential described in the previous subsection is a direct expression of the underlying molecular properties. A simple statistical derivation of the entropy change as an ideal solute mixes into solution is given near the end of this subsection. On the basis of statistical mechanical arguments, Onsager (102) extended the classic thermodynamic arguments for a system that is close to thermodynamic equilibrium.

In this derivation the small changes in magnitude of extensive variables (e.g., concentration, pressure) from their equilibrium values are designated δ_i. The corresponding increase in entropy can be written as a Taylor series expansion about the equilibrium values

$$\Delta S_{int} = \Sigma\left(\frac{\partial S}{\partial \delta_i}\right)\delta_i + \Sigma\frac{1}{2}\left(\frac{\partial^2 S}{\partial\delta_i\partial\delta_j}\right)\delta_i\delta_j \quad (3.19)$$

Because the expansion is about the equilibrium values at which entropy is maximum, $(\partial S/\partial\delta_i) = 0$. For small values of δ

$$\Delta S_{int} = \frac{1}{2}\Sigma\left(\frac{\partial^2 S}{\partial\delta_i\partial\delta_j}\right)\delta_i\delta_j \quad (3.20)$$

Onsager's law states that *1*) if the fluxes are chosen as the time derivatives of the state variables

$$J_i/S = \frac{\partial\delta_i}{\partial t} \quad (3.21)$$

and *2*) if the thermodynamic forces (X_i) are chosen so that

$$\frac{X_i}{T} = \left(\frac{\partial S_i}{\partial\delta_i}\right) \quad (3.22)$$

then Equation 3.20 can be written

$$T\frac{dS_{int}}{dt} = \Sigma(J_{s,i}/S)(X_i) \quad (3.23)$$

and the fluxes can be written as linear functions of the forces

$$J_1/S = L_{1,1}X_1 + L_{1,2}X_2 + \ldots L_{1,n}X_n \quad (3.24)$$

and

$$J_n/S = L_{1,n}X_1 + L_{n,2}X_2 + \ldots L_{nn}X_{nn} \quad (3.25)$$

where $L_{i,j} = L_{j,i}$. Equation 3.23 has exactly the same form as Equation 3.18. The L coefficients are thermodynamic variables whose magnitudes generally depend on the extensive variables. Equations 3.24 and 3.25 and the L coefficients are of little value until their range of validity has been established experimentally. The analysis of passive solute and water transport across membranes in terms of Equations 3.24 and 3.25 was introduced at about the same time that capillary physiologists began detailed quantitative analysis of restricted diffusion and ultrafiltration at the capillary wall (109, 119). For the membrane in Figure 3.1, Staverman (144) wrote Equation 3.17 (or Eq. 3.23) as

$$T\Delta S = \Delta\mu_s n_s + \Delta\mu_w n_w \quad (3.26)$$

where n_s and n_w are the amounts of solute and water transferred (mmol). The reference equilibrium state occurs when solute and water concentrations on both sides of the membrane are equal. Because $J_s/S = dn_s/dt$ and $J_w/S = dn_w/dt$, application of Onsager's law leads to the following linear phenomenological equations

$$J_s/S = L_{ss}\Delta\mu_s + L_{sw}\Delta\mu_w \quad (3.27)$$

$$J_w/S = L_{ws}\Delta\mu_s + L_{ww}\Delta\mu_w \quad (3.28)$$

where

$$L_{sw} = L_{ws} \quad (3.29)$$

The usefulness of the L coefficients in Equations 3.27 and 3.28 as characteristics of membrane-solute and membrane-solvent interactions is examined in IV. MEMBRANE TRANSPORT (p. 320). The linear relations and the reciprocity condition, $L_{sw} = L_{ws}$, apply when the approximation of Equation 3.20 is valid (small perturbations from equilibrium). The restriction to linear form is also examined in IV. MEMBRANE TRANSPORT. The forces and flows in Equations 3.27 and 3.28

are defined precisely in accordance with Onsager's law. They cannot be criticized in the same way as many applications of irreversible thermodynamics that do not take Equations 3.21 and 3.22 into account when defining forces and fluxes (150). Experimental and theoretical tests of Equations 3.27, 3.28, and 3.29 and the relation derived from each are considered throughout this chapter.

D. Molecular Viewpoint—Some Elementary Statistical Mechanical Concepts

The thermodynamic relations are based on kinetic events at the molecular level. The examples given next are based on a stochastic theory and provide a brief introduction to the important contributions of statistical mechanics to the understanding of membrane phenomena.

1. ENTROPY CHANGE AS IDEAL SOLUTE MIXES WITH WATER. Suppose a number (N_s) of molecules of an ideal solute are added to N_w molecules of water. The random spread of the solute molecules between the water molecules increases the number of the ways solute and water molecules can be arranged. The total number of ways that any group of N molecules can be arranged is $N(N-1)(N-2)\ldots 3\cdot 2\cdot 1$, written as $N!$ (factorial N). Assuming ideal molecules with no restrictions on arrangements the fractional increase (ν) in the number of ways solute and water molecules can be arranged as a result of dissolving solute in water is

$$\nu = \frac{(N_s + N_w)!}{N_s!N_w!} \qquad (3.30)$$

The corresponding change in the entropy of the system, calculated from the Boltzmann relation, is

$$\Delta S_{\text{ideal}} = R \ln \nu \qquad (3.31)$$

where R is the gas constant. For very large numbers, $\ln N! = N(\ln N) - N$. With this approximation Equations 3.30 and 3.31 can be reduced to the form (62, 116)

$$\Delta S_{\text{ideal}} = R(X_s \ln X_s + X_n \ln X_w) \qquad (3.32)$$

where

$$X_s = N_s/(N_s + N_w)$$
$$X_w = N_w/(N_s + N_w) \qquad (3.33)$$

X_i is the mole fraction. The quantity ΔS in Equation 3.32 is the change in internal entropy as described for a closed system in Equation 3.12. The derivation can be extended to demonstrate the mechanistic connection between entropy generation and changes in chemical potential described by Equation 3.17 (see Eq. 3.34).

2. CHEMICAL POTENTIAL. From Equation 3.12 the change in free energy (ΔG_{ideal}) resulting from the intermixing of solute and water is $T\Delta S_{\text{ideal}}$. Therefore

$$\Delta G_{\text{ideal}} = RT(X_s \ln X_s + X_w \ln X_w) \qquad (3.34)$$

$$G = G^\circ + RT(X_s \ln X_s + X_w \ln X_w) \qquad (3.35)$$

where G° is the free energy of the pure substances. The chemical potential is the partial molar free energy (Eq. 3.13). In the absence of electrical forces

$$\mu_s = \left(\frac{dG_s}{dn_s}\right)_{n_w,T,P} = \mu_0(s) + RT \ln X_s \qquad (3.36)$$

$$\mu_w = \left(\frac{dG_w}{dn_w}\right)_{n_s,T,P} = \mu_0(w) + RT \ln X_w \qquad (3.37)$$

where $\mu_0(s)$ and $\mu_0(w)$ are the standard chemical potentials for pure substances (usually equal to zero). These derivations are based on idealized conditions and show that the expressions for the chemical potential of a solute in dilute solution are derived directly from the tendency of a solute to distribute uniformly throughout the solvent.

For systems that are not ideal the intermolecular forces reduce the number of possible configurations. Equation 3.35 can be written

$$G = G^\circ - T\Delta S + \Delta G_{\text{mix}} \qquad (3.38)$$

where ΔG_{mix} is a measure of the change in intermolecular forces between solute and water. Detailed descriptions of modern solution theory that relate ΔG_{mix} to molecular properties are given in references 62, 95, and 116. In classic thermodynamics, ΔG_{mix} is accounted for by the activity coefficient, f

$$\mu = \mu_0 + RT \ln(X_s f) \qquad (3.39)$$

3. THERMODYNAMIC EQUILIBRIUM. For most purposes the procedure used to define an electrochemical potential (Eq. 3.11) is generalized for potential fields arising from electrical, pressure, magnetic, surface tension, or intermolecular forces

$$\mu_i = \mu_0 + RT \ln X_i + E_i \qquad (3.40)$$

where E_i is energy per mole associated with the potential fields. Two parts of a system are in equilibrium when their free energies are equal. For a system involving exchange between phases, the condition $dG = 0$ requires that $\Delta\mu_i = 0$, or

$$\mu_{i,1} = \mu_{i,2} \qquad (3.41)$$

In the presence of electrical and other forces acting on the solutes, this can be written

$$\mu_0 + RT \ln X_{i,1} + E_{i,1} = \mu_0 + RT \ln X_{i,2} + E_{i,2} \qquad (3.42)$$

or

$$RT \ln\left(\frac{X_{i,1}}{X_{i,2}}\right) = -\Delta E_i \qquad (3.43)$$

where ΔE_i is the difference in potential energy, other than chemical, acting on the two solutes. When ΔE_i is only from electrical potential, Equation 3.43 is the

Nernst equation. For a dilute binary solution, $N_s \ll N_w$. Then from Equation 3.33

$$\frac{X_{i,1}}{X_{i,2}} = \frac{C_{i,1}}{C_{i,2}} \tag{3.44}$$

where C is the solute molar concentration. Thus from Equation 3.43

$$C_{i,1} = C_{i,2} \exp(-\Delta E_i/RT) \tag{3.45}$$

which states that at equilibrium the solutes are distributed according to Boltzmann's law—the random thermal motions that tend to equalize concentrations are modified by the potential energy stored in electrical (ion-ion interaction), pressure (pressure-volume work), and body force (e.g., steric exclusion) fields. The equilibrium distribution is simply the most probable distribution of particles undergoing thermal motion in the presence of external forces. At any time a particle may have a velocity and position very different from its neighbors. This observation leads to the idea that some of the properties of a system that is not too far from equilibrium may be described in terms of the properties of a system at equilibrium. This idea was developed by Onsager (102) in the formulation of the linear phenomenological relations (Eqs. 3.27 and 3.28). Modern developments of this theory are discussed in references 72 and 73.

IV. MEMBRANE TRANSPORT

The quantitative analysis of the transport of substances across the capillary wall is based on the measurement and interpretation of membrane coefficients that characterize the principal barriers to the diffusion of solute and the flow of water. Perhaps one of most important roles of membrane-transport equations is their use as a basis for the careful design of experiments to measure membrane coefficients. The problem with the three phenomenological coefficients L_{ss}, L_{sw}, and L_{ww} (Eqs. 3.27 and 3.28) is that their values are not constant; they depend strongly on the conditions of the experiment. For example, the value of L_{ss} depends on the solute concentration because $\Delta\mu_s$ is a logarithmic function of the ratio of solute concentrations bathing the two sides of the membrane. To overcome this problem Equations 3.27 and 3.28 must be rearranged to obtain expressions for the fluxes of water and solute across the membrane that can be used over a wider range of experimental conditions. The solution to the problem is far from solved, and further developments to refine current theory and develop new analyses are required. Two approaches are described in this section (Table 4.1). The first approach, introduced by Staverman (144) and developed by Kedem and Katchalsky (69–71), expresses the differences in chemical potentials directly in terms of the differences in concentration and pressure (Table 4.1, entries 1 and 2). The Kedem-Katchalsky equations provide a complete description of solution flow across the membrane in terms of the membrane hy-

TABLE 4.1. *Principal Relations and Nomenclature for IV. Equations of Membrane Transport*

Relation

	Relation	Eq.
1.	$J_v/S = L_P(\Delta P - \sigma_d \Delta \Pi)$	(4.13)
2.	$J_s/S = P\Delta C + J_v/S(1 - \sigma_f)C^*$	(4.26)
3a.	$L_P = \left(\frac{J_v/S}{\Delta P}\right)_{\Delta\pi=0}$ or $\left(\frac{J_v/S}{\sigma_d \Delta \Pi}\right)_{\Delta P=0}$	(4.14a)
3b.	$\sigma_d = \left(\frac{\Delta P}{\Delta \Pi}\right)_{J_v=0}$ or $\left(\frac{J_v/S}{L_P \Delta \Pi}\right)_{\Delta P=0}$	(4.14b)
3c.	$P = \left(\frac{J_s/S}{\Delta C}\right)_{J_v=0}$	(4.20)
3d.	$(1 - \sigma_f) = \left(\frac{J_s}{J_v C_1}\right)_{(dC/dx)_o=0}$	(4.22)
4a.	$J_s/S = \Omega_{ss}\frac{d\mu_s}{dx} + \Omega_{sw}\frac{d\mu_w}{dx}$	(4.32)
4b.	$J_w/S = \Omega_{ws}\frac{d\mu_s}{dx} + \Omega_{ww}\frac{d\mu_w}{dx} \quad \Omega_{sw} = \Omega_{ws}$	(4.33)
5.	$J_s/S = P(C_1 - C_2)\{Pe/[\exp(Pe) - 1]\} + J_v/S(1 - \sigma_f)C_1$	(4.49)
6.	$C_2/C_1 = \frac{1 - \sigma_f}{1 - \sigma_f \exp(-Pe)}$	(4.55)

Nomenclature

A_p	area for exchange in membrane (cm^2)
C	concentration (M)
C*	ratio ($\Delta\mu/\Delta\pi$) when $\Delta P = 0$ (M)
E_i	energy/mole (cal/mol)
F_{sw}, F_{sm}, F_{wm}	molar friction coefficients (dyn·s·cm^{-1}·mol^{-1})
J_D	volume flow of solute relative to solvent (exchange flow) (cm^3/s)
J_v	volume flow of solution (cm^3/s)
L_P	hydraulic conductivity (cm^3·dyn^{-1}·s^{-1})
L_{PD}, L_{DP}, L_D	nonhydraulic volume flow conductivities (cm^3·dyn^{-1}·s^{-1})
P	pressure (dyn/cm^2)
P	permeability coefficient (cm/s)
Pe	Péclet number
Q	weighted molar friction coefficient (dyn·s·cm^{-1}·mol^{-1})
RT	gas constant × absolute temperature (19.34 mmHg/mM)
S	entropy (cal/°K)
S	surface area (cm^2)
V	velocity (cm/s)
v	partial molar volume (cm^3/mol)
x	distance (cm)
α	fractional area
μ	chemical potential (cal/mol)
χ	slip coefficient
Π	osmotic pressure (dyn/cm^2)
σ_d	osmotic reflection coefficient
σ_f	solvent-drag reflection coefficient
ϕ	partition coefficient
Ω	specific thermodynamic conductance (dyn·s·cm^{-2}·mol^{-1})

Numbers in parentheses refer to text equations.

draulic conductivity and osmotic reflection coefficients. However, they provide only a limited description of solute flow across the membrane. The membrane transport coefficients are defined by the Kedem-Katchalsky approach (entry 3). A new constraint is imposed on the definition of the solvent-drag reflection coefficient. Some of the limitations of the Kedem-Katchalsky approach are overcome when the transmembrane differences in the chemical potentials for water and solute are replaced by the gradients of chemical potential within the membrane (entry 4; see refs. 83, 112, 138). Although the intramembrane equations can presently be integrated only under restricted conditions, the resulting equations provide a more complete description of solute flow and ultrafiltration in the membrane. The new expressions for transmembrane solute flux and for ultrafiltration across the membrane are nonlinear (entries 5 and 6).

A. *Staverman-Kedem-Katchalsky Equations*

1. TRANSFORMATION OF MEMBRANE FLUX-FORCE RELATIONS. This topic is dealt with in a comprehensive review by Ogston and Michel (99). The difference in chemical potential of water across the membrane is expressed exactly in terms of differences in osmotic and hydrostatic pressure, $\Delta\Pi$ and ΔP, respectively

$$\Delta\mu_w = \upsilon_w(\Delta P - \Delta\Pi) \quad (4.1)$$

where υ_w is the partial molar volume of water. No equivalent general substitution is possible for expressing the difference in chemical potential of solute in terms of ΔP and $\Delta\pi$. From Equations 3.36 and 3.40

$$\Delta\mu_s = \upsilon_s\Delta P + RT\,\Delta\ln X_s \quad (4.2)$$

Kedem and Katchalsky (69) forced this equation into a form containing the solute concentration difference. Assuming a dilute solution, $\Delta\ln X_s$ (Eq. 4.2) can be replaced by $\ln(C_1/C_2)$ (cf. Eq. 3.44), and the expression for $\Delta\mu_s$ is written

$$\Delta\mu_s = \upsilon_s\Delta P + RT\Delta C\left[\frac{\ln(C_1/C_2)}{\Delta C}\right] \quad (4.3)$$

where the solute concentration difference is introduced into the expression for the chemical potential by multiplying both numerator and denominator by ΔC. The quantity $\Delta C/\ln(C_1/C_2)$, designated C^*, is a mean concentration in the membrane that arises from the definition of chemical potential, not from any mechanistic description of the concentration profile in the membrane. Equation 4.3 can therefore be expressed

$$\Delta\mu_s = \upsilon_s\Delta P + RT\Delta C/C^* \quad (4.4)$$

For $1 < (C_1/C_2) < 3$, $\ln(C_1/C_2)$ can be approximated by the first term of a Taylor Series expansion for a natural logarithm

$$\ln(C_1/C_2) = \frac{2(C_1/C_2 - 1)}{(C_1/C_2) + 1} = \frac{\Delta C}{(C_1 + C_2)/2} \quad (4.5)$$

Therefore C^* can be approximated by $(C_1 + C_2)/2$ for $1 < (C_1/C_2) < 3$. By substituting Equation 4.1 into Equation 3.29, and Equation 4.4 into Equation 3.30, expressions for the volume flux of solution (J_v/S), and the so-called exchange flux (J_D/S) are obtained in terms of ΔP and $\Delta\Pi$

$$J_v/S = L_P\Delta P + L_{PD}\Delta\Pi \quad (4.6)$$

$$J_D/S = L_{DP}\Delta P + L_D\Delta\Pi \quad (4.7)$$

where

$$J_v - J_w\upsilon_w + J_s\upsilon_s \quad (4.8)$$

$$J_D = J_s/C^* - J_w\upsilon_w \quad (4.9)$$

and J_D/S has the units of volume flow per unit area. The new L coefficients in Equations 4.6 and 4.7 may be described exactly in terms of the L coefficients in Equations 3.27 and 3.28

$$L_P = L_{ww}\upsilon_w^2 + 2L_{ws}\upsilon_s\upsilon_w + L_{ss}\upsilon_s^2 \quad (4.10)$$

$$L_{PD} = L_{DP} = \left[L_{ss}\frac{\upsilon_s}{C^*} - L_{sw}\upsilon_w\left(\upsilon_s - \frac{1}{C^*}\right) - L_{ww}\upsilon_w^2\right] \quad (4.11)$$

$$L_D = \frac{L_{ss}}{C^{*2}} - 2L_{sw}\frac{\upsilon_w}{C^*} + L_{ww}\upsilon_w^2 \quad (4.12)$$

According to Equation 4.11 the reciprocity of the cross coefficients is retained and expressed as $L_{PD} = L_{DP}$. Equations 4.10, 4.11, and 4.12 are similar to those derived from the exact formulation of the equations for J_v and J_D at a point within the membrane (99). In the exact local expressions, $1/C^*$ is replaced by $C_w\upsilon_w/C_s$, where C_w is water concentration and C_s is solute concentration; there is no restriction on the range of C_s. In contrast, for the whole membrane formulation, the form of Equation 4.11 depends on the dilute solution approximation (Eq. 4.3), and the reciprocity relation is valid only when the latter approximation is satisfied. Equality of L_{PD} and L_{DP} has been demonstrated in a porous glass membrane (139).

2. VOLUME FLOW. The coefficients L_P, L_{DP}, L_{PD}, and L_D have units of hydraulic conductivity. Furthermore each coefficient approaches a single value, L_P, when the membrane is semipermeable (69). For all cases in which solute penetrates the membrane

$$|L_{PD}| < |L_P|$$

and Equation 4.6 is written without approximation

$$J_v/S = L_P(\Delta P - \sigma_d\Delta\Pi) \quad (4.13)$$

where $\sigma_d = -L_{PD}/L_P$ and is the osmotic reflection coefficient. Equation 4.14 defines the membrane coefficient in terms of measurable quantities

$$L_P = \left[\frac{J_v/S}{\Delta P}\right]_{\Delta\Pi=0} \quad \text{or} \quad \left[\frac{J_v/S}{\sigma_d \Delta\Pi}\right]_{\Delta P=0} \tag{4.14a}$$

$$\sigma_d = \left[\frac{\Delta P}{\Delta\Pi}\right]_{J_v=0} \quad \text{or} \quad \left[\frac{J_v/S}{L_P \Delta\Pi}\right]_{\Delta P=0} \tag{4.14b}$$

Figure 4.1 shows three different experimental applications of Equation 4.13. In Figure 4.1*A* the volume flow across a glass Vycor membrane was measured in the presence of successively increasing concentration differences of the permeable solute raffinose across the membrane. The slope of the relation between J_v/S and ΔP (equal to L_P) is constant over the range of concentrations studied. The intercept on the pressure axis is $\sigma_d\Delta\Pi$. Similar experiments have been carried out on capillary membranes. Experiments on individually perfused capillaries in frog mesentery are shown in Figures 4.1*B* and 4.1*C*. In both figures a control experiment measured L_P from the filtration rate at capillary pressures between 10 and 50 cmH_2O. In Figure 4.1*B* the osmotic reflection coefficient to sucrose was measured by setting up a 100-mM concentration difference of the solute across the capillary wall (35). Figure 4.1*C* is a modern demonstration of the Starling hypothesis. When the capillary was perfused with a solution containing 3 g/100 ml γ-globulin, the capillary filtered at all applied hydrostatic pressures. When the same capillary was perfused with a solution containing 9 g/100 ml albumin, reabsorption of fluid occurred at all pressures below 45 cmH_2O. An estimate of the coefficient to albumin was obtained by dividing the intercept (45 cmH_2O) by the measured colloid osmotic pressure of the perfusate (54 cmH_2O)—σ_d for albumin equaled 0.83.

3. SOLUTE FLOW. Equation 4.7, which describes an exchange flux, has not been used for experimental investigations. To overcome the experimental difficulties of working with the flux J_D, a form of the solute flux equation that abandons the symmetry of Equations 4.6 and 4.7 must be accepted. From Equation 4.9

$$J_s = J_D C^* + J_w v_w C^* \tag{4.15}$$

Substituting for $J_w v_w$ from Equation 4.8

$$J_s = (J_v + J_D)\frac{C^*}{1 + v_s C^*} \tag{4.16}$$

If J_D is expressed in terms of J_v by substituting for ΔP in Equation 4.7 using Equation 4.6, then

$$J_D = L_{DP}\left[\frac{J_v - L_{PD}\Delta\Pi}{L_P}\right] + L_D\Delta\Pi \tag{4.17}$$

Combining Equations 4.16 and 4.17 yields

$$J_s/S = \frac{J_v/S}{1 + v_s C^*}\left(1 + \frac{L_{PD}}{L_P}\right)C^* + \frac{C^*}{(1 + v_s C^*)}\left(\frac{L_D L_P - L_{PD} L_{DP}}{L_P}\right)\Delta\Pi \tag{4.18}$$

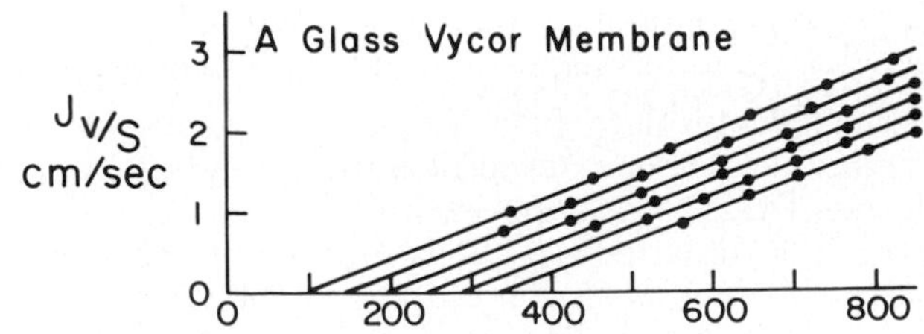

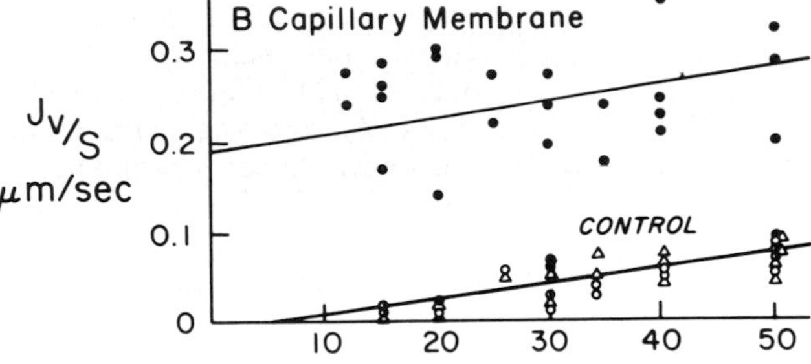

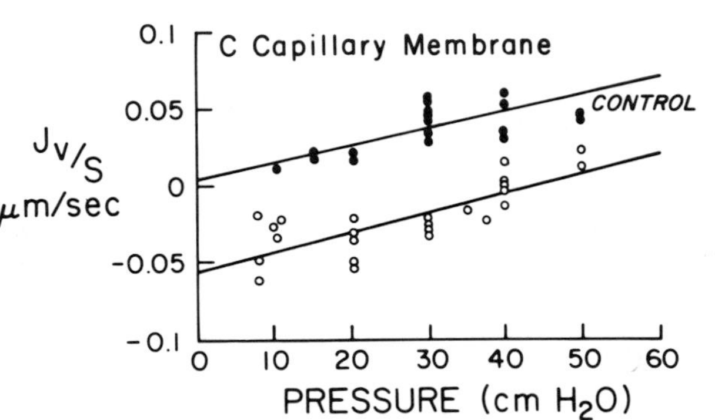

FIG. 4.1. Relation between initial volume flux across selective membrane (J_v/S) and hydrostatic pressure difference across membrane (ΔP) in presence of permeant solute. Slope of relation is hydraulic conductivity of membrane (L_P), and intercept on pressure axis is $\sigma_d\Delta\Pi$. Three applications of Eq. 4.13 are shown. *A*: glass Vycor membrane; test solute, raffinose. Both L_p and σ_d are practically independent of concentration over range studied (138). *B*: single perfused capillary of frog mesentery. *Lower points* represent data obtained when tissue was superfused with Ringer solution. Three determinations of filtration coefficient, measured as slopes of regression line through *points* indicated by *symbols*, were 1.54×10^{-7}, 1.89×10^{-7}, and 1.89×10^{-7} $cm \cdot s^{-1} \cdot cmH_2O^{-1}$. *Line* has slope of mean filtration coefficient and cuts abscissa at pressure of 4 cmH_2O. *Upper points* are measurements of initial filtration rate on same capillary when tissue was superfused with frog Ringer solution containing sucrose (20 mM). *Line* drawn through these *points* has slope equal to mean filtration coefficient. Osmotic reflection coefficient to sucrose measured from increased filtration rate in presence of sucrose is 0.22 (35). *C*: single perfused capillary of frog mesentery. *Closed circles* represent measurements made in presence of low perfusate-colloid osmotic pressure (3 g bovine γ-globulin/100 ml; $\Pi = 3.6$ cmH_2O); *open circles* represent measurements in presence of high perfusate osmotic pressure (9.0 g albumin/100 ml; $\Pi = 57$ cmH_2O). Values of L_p, derived from slopes of regression lines through data, are 1.08×10^{-7} and 1.27×10^{-7} $cm \cdot s^{-1} \cdot cmH_2O^{-1}$, respectively. Intercept of $\sigma_d\Delta\Pi$ on pressure axis is 45 cmH_2O.

Two limiting cases of Equation 4.18 are recognized. First, when $J_v = 0$

$$J_s/S = \left(\frac{RTC^*}{1 + v_s C^*}\right)\left(\frac{L_P L_D - L_{DP} L_{PD}}{L_P}\right)\Delta C \tag{4.19}$$

The proportionality constant between J_s/S and ΔC is a solute permeability coefficient, P. Therefore Equation 4.19 is usually rewritten

$$J_s/S = (P\Delta C)_{J_{v=0}} \tag{4.20}$$

Interpretation of Equation 4.20 as a simple relation with a constant permeability coefficient fails to take into account all the information in Equation 4.19. These thermodynamic constraints on the value of P in Equation 4.20 are discussed next. Because $\sigma_d = -L_{PD}/L_P$ and $L_{PD} = L_{DP}$, the permeability coefficient in Equation 4.20 is equal to $RTC^*(L_D - \sigma_d^2 L_P)/(1 + v_s C^*)$. When $\sigma_d = 1$, $L_D = L_P$ and the permeability coefficient equals zero as expected for a semipermeable membrane. For a partially selective membrane ($0 < \sigma_d < 1$) the permeability coefficient defined by Equation 4.20 is intrinsically concentration dependent because of the term $\sigma_d^2 L_P C^*$. When $\sigma_d < 0.2$, the contribution of the term $\sigma_d^2 L_P C^*$ is small; but as σ_d approaches 1 and L_D approaches L_P in magnitude the coupling between osmotically induced volume flows and diffusion down the gradient of solute concentration will make the permeability coefficient concentration dependent. These processes have been neglected in the study of large-solute transport across the capillary wall and deserve more careful investigation. Generally the permeability coefficient should be designated as concentration dependent.

The second limiting case (from Eq. 4.18) occurs when $\Delta C = 0$. Then

$$J_s/S = \frac{J_v/S}{1 + v_s C^*}\left(1 + \frac{L_{DP}}{L_P}\right) C^* \tag{4.21}$$

From Equation 4.5, when $\Delta C = 0$, C^* equals the actual solute concentration entering the membrane (C_1). The quantity $J_s/(J_v C^*)$ is the ratio of the flux carried through the membrane to the flux carried up the membrane. The solvent-drag reflection coefficient (σ_f) is defined

$$\sigma_f = 1 - \left(\frac{J_s}{J_v C_1}\right)_{\Delta C=0} \tag{4.22}$$

From Equation 4.21

$$\sigma_f = 1 - \left(\frac{1}{1 + v_s C^*}\right)\left(\frac{L_{DP}}{L_P} + 1\right) \tag{4.23}$$

Because $\sigma_d = -L_{PD}/L_P$ and $L_{DP} = L_{PD}$ for dilute solutions ($n_s \ll n_w$), the reciprocity relation

$$\sigma_d = \sigma_f \tag{4.24}$$

applies with the additional restriction that $v_s C^* \ll 1$. For a dilute solution Equation 4.21 can therefore be written

$$J_s/S = [(J_v/S)(1 - \sigma_f)C^*]_{\Delta C=0} \tag{4.25}$$

where C is the solute concentration bathing both sides of the membrane. All real ultrafiltration experiments give rise to a concentration difference across the membrane because of sieving of the solute. Both diffusion and solvent drag then contribute to the flux. It is shown later in this section that an experimentally measurable convective component of flux can be identified in ultrafiltration experiments if the condition $\Delta C = 0$ (Eq. 4.25), imposed for the whole membrane, is replaced by the condition $(dC/dx) = 0$ at the entrance to the membrane. In both cases the total solute flux is measured under conditions at which the diffusive flux is zero. Before describing this alternative approach some restrictions on the use of Equation 4.18 are discussed.

Substitution of Equations 4.20 and 4.25 into Equation 4.18 yields

$$J_s/S = P\Delta C + (J_v/S)(1 - \sigma_f)C^* \tag{4.26}$$

If $L_P\sigma_d^2 C^*$ is a small term relative to $L_D C^*$ and if $1 < (C_1/C_2) \leq 3$ so that the approximation in Equation 4.8 is valid, then for the flux across a membrane, Equation 4.26 reduces to

$$J_s/S = P(C_1 - C_2) + (J_v/S)(1 - \sigma_f)\frac{C_1 + C_2}{2} \tag{4.27}$$

where P is a concentration-independent permeability coefficient, and the thermodynamic mean concentration has been replaced by an arithmetic mean concentration within the membrane. Table 4.2 summarizes the assumptions made in this derivation. Provided all these assumptions are valid, Equation 4.27 is a good description of the total flux across the membrane. Nevertheless its use as a practical equation has produced many difficulties. The most persistent and troublesome question has been whether the components $P(C_1 - C_2)$ and $(J_v/S)(1 - \sigma_f)C^*$ (identified in Eqs. 4.20 and 4.25 under limiting conditions as diffusive and solvent-drag components of transport) retain their identity in the presence of both a concentration gradient and a net volume flow (13, 14).

One of the principal theses of this chapter is that, although Equation 4.27 is a valid expression for the whole solute flux across the membrane, the compo-

TABLE 4.2. *Assumptions in Derivation of Equations 4.26 and 4.27 (Thermodynamic Relation for Diffusive and Convective Transport of Water)*

Assumption	
The fluxes of solute and water across the membrane are small so that Onsager's law applies across the whole membrane	(3.20)
Ideal-solution theory	(4.2)
Dilute-solution theory	(4.3)
Linearization of natural logarithm, $1 < C_1/C_2 < 3$	(4.5)
Solute volume small relative to solution volume, $v_s C \ll 1$	(4.25)
Permeability coefficients are concentration independent, $C^*\sigma_d^2 L_P \ll C^* L_D$	(4.20)

Numbers in parentheses refer to text equations.

nents $P\Delta C$ and $(J_v/S)(1 - \sigma_f)C^*$ do not generally represent the diffusive and convective components of transport. This conclusion cannot be reached by thermodynamic arguments; it is reached by comparing Equation 4.27 with the expression for free diffusion in the presence of superimposed water flow. To demonstrate, Equation 4.27 may be rewritten

$$J_s/S = P(C_1 - C_2) - P(J_v/S) \cdot \frac{(1 - \sigma_f)(C_1 - C_2)}{2P} + (J_v/S)(1 - \sigma_f)C_1 \tag{4.28}$$

or

$$J_s/S = P(C_1 - C_2)\left(1 - \frac{\text{Pe}}{2}\right) + (J_v/S)(1 - \sigma_f)C_1 \tag{4.29}$$

where Pe is a modified Péclet number with exactly the same meaning as in Equations 2.29 and 2.30. Here

$$\text{Pe} = \frac{(J_v/S)(1 - \sigma_f)}{P} \tag{4.30}$$

Equation 4.29 is recognized as almost identical in form to Equation 2.39. Using the simple diffusion model as a guide, the quantity $(J_v/S)(1 - \sigma_f)C_1$ (Eq. 4.29) is taken as a measure of the convective component of solute flux entering the membrane, and the quantity $P(C_1 - C_2)(1 - \text{Pe}/2)$ (Eq. 4.29) is taken as the diffusive component entering the membrane. The term $1 - \text{Pe}/2$ is a first-order correction for the reduction of the solute concentration gradient at the membrane interface below its value in the absence of volume flow, $\Delta C/\Delta X$. This interpretation differs from the usual approach, which equates $(J_v/S)(1 - \sigma_f)(C_1 + C_2)/2$ with the convective-component solvent drag. Quite large errors arise in the analysis of ultrafiltration experiments if $(J_v/S)(1 - \sigma_f)(C_1 + C_2)/2$ is incorrectly identified as the convective component of solute flux. From the arguments developed in the case of free diffusion, Equation 4.29 can be shown to be a linearized form of a more general nonlinear relation describing solute flow in the presence of volume flow. These modifications cannot be accommodated within the Staverman-Kedem-Katchalsky development and a more detailed description is given next.

B. *Thermodynamic Equations Within Membranes*

1. BACKGROUND. Applying Onsager's law to the expression for the local entropy production at any position within the membrane

$$\frac{d}{dx}\left(T\frac{dS}{dt}\right) = \Sigma \frac{d\mu_i}{dx} dn_i \tag{4.31}$$

gives a set of phenomenological equations within the membrane

$$J_s/S = \Omega_{ss}\frac{d\mu_s}{dx} + \Omega_{sw}\frac{d\mu_w}{dx} \tag{4.32}$$

$$J_w/S = \Omega_{ws}\frac{d\mu_s}{dx} + \Omega_{ww}\frac{d\mu_w}{dx} \tag{4.33}$$

where Ω is a specific conductance, and $\Omega_{sw} = \Omega_{ws}$ (99). These equations may also be derived from the general friction model of membrane transport. In its simplest form the free energy stored in the gradient of chemical potential is assumed to be dissipated by friction as solute and water move relative to the membrane

$$-\frac{d\mu_s}{dx} = F_{sm,c}(V_s - V_m) + F_{sw,c}(V_s - V_w) \tag{4.34}$$

$$-\frac{d\mu_w}{dx} = F_{wm,c}(V_s - V_m) + F_{ws,c}(V_w - V_s) \tag{4.35}$$

where $F_{sw,c}$, $F_{sm,c}$, and $F_{wm,c}$ are concentration-dependent molar friction coefficients, and V_s and V_w are measured relative to a stationary membrane matrix ($V_m = 0$). These equations were originally introduced as an intuitive generalization of Einstein's hydrodynamic description of diffusion (cf. Eq. 2.19) (69, 112, 143), but it is now recognized that they can be derived directly from Onsager's law (138). For example, these equations can be arranged into a form identical to Equations 4.32 and 4.33

$$J_s/S = V_sC_s = -\frac{C_s}{Q}\left[(F_{wm,c} + F_{ws,c})\frac{d\mu_s}{dx} + F_{sw,c}\frac{d\mu_w}{dx}\right] \tag{4.36}$$

$$J_w/S = V_wC_w = -\frac{C_w}{Q}\left[F_{ws,c}\frac{d\mu_s}{dx} + (F_{sm,c} + F_{wm,c})\frac{d\mu_w}{dx}\right] \tag{4.37}$$

where

$$Q = (F_{wm,c} + F_{ws,c})(F_{sm,c} + F_{sw,c}) - F_{ws,c}F_{sm,c} \tag{4.38}$$

The reciprocity relation $\Omega_{sw} = \Omega_{ws}$ reduces, for the binary solution interaction, to describe $C_sF_{sm,c} = C_wF_{ws,c}$ as expected from Newton's law of action and reaction.

In Equations 4.36 and 4.37 the membrane is assumed to be homogeneous so that $J_s/S = V_sC_s$, where V_s is expressed per unit of membrane area. A distinction is needed between the general relation $J_s/S = V_sC_s$, where V_s is the solute velocity from all forces, and the case $J_s/S = V_wC_s$ (Eq. 2.37, $\chi = 1$), where $V_s = V_w$ and the solute velocity arises from momentum transfer from water to solute. When solute penetrates only a fractional area (α^*) of membrane area

$$J_s/S = \alpha^* V_sC_s \tag{4.39}$$

The integration of Equations 4.36 and 4.37 across a porous membrane has been described in detail by Perl (112) and Lightfoot et al. (83). The development by

Perl is the most complete because it specifically sets out the assumptions at each step of the integration procedure. The alternate development by Lightfoot et al. clarifies important questions relating to appropriate frames of reference; however, for dilute solutions the more complicated expressions from Lightfoot et al. are the same as Equations 4.40–4.51, which are derived next using Perl's analysis.

Equations 4.36 and 4.37 can be rearranged to give an exact expression for the pressure gradient within the membrane

$$-\frac{dP}{dx} = F_{sm,c}J_s + F_{wm,c}J_w \qquad (4.40)$$

The exact relation for the concentration gradient within the membrane is

$$\left[\frac{RT(1 - \upsilon_s C_s)}{1 - (\upsilon_s - \upsilon_w C_s)}\right]\left(\frac{dC_s}{dx}\right) = [F_{sw,c} + F_{sm,c}(1 - \upsilon_s C_s)^2] + [F'_{wm,c}\upsilon_s C_s(1 - \upsilon_s C_s]J_s + [F'_{wm,c}(1 - \upsilon_s C_s)]J_v C_s \qquad (4.41)$$

where $F'_{wm,c} = F_{wm,c}\upsilon_s/\upsilon_w$. For a dilute solution, $C_s\upsilon_s \ll 1$ and the equation reduces to

$$RT\frac{dC_s}{dx} = -(F_{sw} + F_{sm})J_s/S + (F_{sw} + F'_{wm})C_sJ_v/S \qquad (4.42)$$

The frictional coefficients are assumed to be concentration independent. Equations 4.40 and 4.42 provide the soundest theoretical basis to date for the logical extension of the binary hydrodynamic analysis (see II. DIFFUSION, p. 310) to the description of coupled solute and water flows through porous membranes.

A relation between solute concentration and pressure in the bulk solution and the corresponding variables just inside the membrane is also required. For this purpose the solute or water in bulk solution (subscript o) is assumed to be in equilibrium at the membrane–bulk solution interface with solute or water just inside the membrane (subscript i) (86). For a dilute solution

$$\frac{C_i}{C_o} = \phi = \exp -\left(\frac{\Delta E}{RT}\right) \qquad (4.43)$$

where ΔE is the energy barrier to be overcome by the solute to enter the membrane (see Eq. 3.45), and ϕ is the membrane partition coefficient. The forces on water are assumed to be identical inside and outside the membrane.

The membrane coefficients can be defined directly from Equations 4.40, 4.41, and 4.43 without the need to integrate for the general case in which water flow is superimposed on diffusion. The resulting expressions are

$$P = \frac{RT}{\Delta x}\left(\frac{\phi}{F_{sw} + F_{sm}}\right) \qquad (4.44)$$

$$1 - \sigma_d = \phi\left(\frac{F_{sw} + F'_{wm}}{F_{sw} + F_{sm}}\right) \qquad (4.45)$$

$$1 - \sigma_f = \phi\left(\frac{F_{sw} + F'_{wm}}{F_{sw} + F_{sm}}\right) \qquad (4.46)$$

$$L_P = \frac{RT}{\Delta x F_{wm}} \qquad (4.47)$$

where Δx is the membrane thickness. For the dilute solution, $\sigma_d = \sigma_f$ as derived by Kedem and Katchalsky.

2. SOLUTE FLOW. Integration of Equation 4.42 to obtain J_s/S in terms of the concentration of solute on the two sides of the membrane and the volume flow yields (110, 143)

$$J_s/S = J_v/S(1 - \sigma_f)\left[\frac{(C_1 - C_2)\exp(-Pe)}{1 - \exp(-Pe)}\right] \qquad (4.48)$$

which is almost identical in form to the expression for diffusive flux with superimposed volume flow (Eq. 2.28). For a dilute solution, J_v/S is approximately equal to $\upsilon_w J_w/S$ or V_w. In addition a precise hydrodynamic relation is developed between the slip coefficients (χ) and $1 - \sigma_f$ with the pore theory described in V. PORE THEORY (p. 327).

Equation 4.48 can be partitioned into convective and diffusive components entering the membrane (see Eq. 2.28)

$$J_s/S = P(C_1 - C_2)\{Pe/[\exp(Pe) - 1]\} + (J_v/S)(1 - \sigma_f)C_1 \qquad (4.49)$$

where $Pe/(\exp^{Pe} - 1)$ has the same intuitive meaning as described for Equation 2.35a. Figure 2.5 describes the change in magnitude of $Pe/(\exp^{Pe} - 1)$ as Pe increases from 0 to >5. By the same argument that led to Equation 2.39, Equation 4.49 reduces to the limiting form derived from the Staverman-Kedem-Katchalsky relations for low Pe values

$$J_s/S = P(C_1 - C_2)(1 - Pe) + (J_v/S)(1 - \sigma_f)C_1 \qquad (4.50)$$

Even though Equations 4.48 and 4.49 provide a more complete description of solute flux than the Staverman-Kedem-Katchalsky equations, the large number of assumptions required to derive Equations 4.48 and 4.49 must be recognized. These assumptions and the equations in which they are applied are summarized in Table 4.3. The studies by Lightfoot et al. (83) and Perl (112) provide additional information about this subject.

3. VOLUME FLOW. Equation 4.40 is integrated to obtain the volume flow relation across the membrane in terms of differences in hydrostatic and osmotic pres-

TABLE 4.3. *Assumptions in Derivation of Equations 4.48 and 4.49 (Nonlinear Thermodynamic Relations for Diffusive and Convective Transport of Solute)*

Assumption	
Ideal-solution theory	(4.41, 4.42)
Thermodynamic equilibrium at membrane interfaces	(4.43)
Channel interfaces are symmetrical	(4.43)
Channel interior is uniform	(4.41, 4.42)
Friction coefficients are concentration independent	(4.42)
Hydraulic conductivity is measure of resistance of channel to pure water flow, ignoring volume occupied by solute and effect of solute on solution viscosity	(4.47)
Bulk solutions are dilute	(4.43)
Solution inside channel is dilute	(4.42, 4.43)
Frames of reference for solution flow and diffusion can be specified independently	(4.41, 4.42)

Numbers in parentheses refer to text equations.

sure. If Equation 4.48 is used to substitute for J_s, the resultant equation for J_v in terms of ΔP and $\Delta \Pi$ is highly nonlinear. If the low Péclet number approximation (Eq. 4.50) is used instead to describe J_s, the result can be written

$$J_s/S = L_P(\Delta P - \sigma_d \Delta \Pi) \tag{4.51}$$

which is the Starling relation (see Eq. 4.13). The restraint that this equation is only valid when $(Pe^2/12) \ll 1$ has not been generally recognized but was noted independently by Lightfoot et al. (83). Preliminary calculations for plasma protein transport in transcapillary pathways suggest that, in channels in which the solute Péclet number might exceed one, the osmotic pressure contribution to total transcapillary filtration pressure is very small. Thus the nonlinearities in Equation 4.51 are not expected to be a source of error in the analysis of transcapillary volume flows.

4. RELATION TO MECHANICAL MODELS OF TRANSPORT. When there is no volume flow through a membrane channel, either Equation 4.48 or Equation 4.49 reduces to the modified form of Fick's first law of diffusion

$$J_s = PS(C_1 - C_2) \tag{4.52}$$

where

$$PS = \frac{A_p}{\Delta x} \cdot \phi \cdot \frac{RT}{F_{sw} + F_{sm}} \tag{4.53}$$

The term $A_p/\Delta x$ is the membrane area available for the exchange of solute per unit membrane thickness, and $RT/(F_{sw} + F_{sm})$ is the solute diffusion coefficient within the membrane, which may be calculated with the pore (hydrodynamic) or fiber-matrix (stochastic) models outlined in V. PORE THEORY (p. 327) and VI. FIBER-MATRIX MODEL (p. 351).

C. Application of Membrane-Transport Equations to Steady-State Ultrafiltration

A special case of Equation 4.48 is of particular importance to transcapillary exchange studies; it describes steady-state ultrafiltration. In the steady state a simple mass balance on the solute on the low pressure side of the homogeneous membrane (side 2) requires that

$$J_s = J_v C_2 \tag{4.54}$$

If C_2 (Eq. 4.48) is set equal to J_s/J_v, then the equation may be rearranged to yield

$$\frac{C_2}{C_1} = \frac{1 - \sigma_f}{1 - \sigma_f \exp(-Pe)} \tag{4.55}$$

Alternatively Equation 4.49 yields

$$\frac{C_2}{C_1} = \frac{PS\{Pe/[\exp(Pe) - 1]\} + J_v(1 - \sigma_f)}{PS\{Pe/[\exp(Pe) - 1]\} + J_v} \tag{4.56}$$

Both of the equations state that in a homogeneous membrane C_2/C_1 falls toward a limiting value of $1 - \sigma_f$ as Pe increases. A valid estimate of $1 - \sigma_f$ can be made even though there is a concentration difference across the membrane. The reason is easily determined from Equation 4.56. As Pe increases, the solute concentration gradient of the pore entrance falls toward zero and solute enters the membrane solely by convective transport. An example illustrating the use of Equation 4.55 to analyze an ultrafiltration experiment is given next.

Figure 4.2 shows the ultrafiltration of sucrose, raffinose, and glucose on Visking cellulose (119). Renkin previously analyzed these data with an early version of the pore theory (see V. PORE THEORY, p. 327). The current analysis illustrates the importance of using the nonlinear relations (Eq. 4.55 or 4.56) rather than

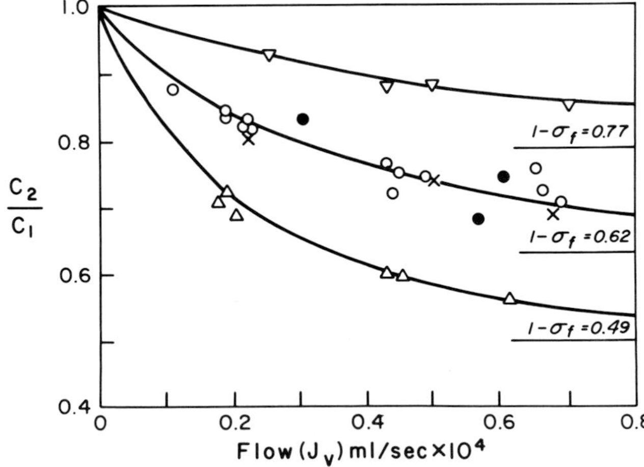

FIG. 4.2. Steady-state ultrafiltration of glucose (▽), sucrose (○, ●, and ×), and raffinose (△) on dialysis membrane, fitted by using the nonlinear steady-state relation in Eqs. 4.55 and 4.56. Limiting value of $C_2/C_1 = (1 - \sigma_f)$ is given for each solute. [Data from Renkin (119).]

their linear approximations. For each solute a preliminary estimate of $1 - \sigma_f$ was made from the value of C_2/C_1 at the highest flow rate measured. For example, C_2/C_1 at a flow of 0.62×10^{-4} cm^3/s is 0.56 for raffinose. If $1 - \sigma_f$ is set equal to 0.56, the Pe value corresponding to a measured permeability–surface area product for the membrane (2.16×10^{-5} cm^3/s for raffinose) is 1.6. This Pe value is substituted into Equation 4.55, and the equation is solved for a revised estimate: $1 - \sigma_f = 0.49$. The whole curve, constructed from Equation 4.55 and the newly derived parameters, fits the data for raffinose, as judged by eye. The data for glucose and sucrose were analyzed in the same way to construct the curves shown in Figure 4.2 and to estimate σ_f. The estimated Pe value at the highest flow is 1.2 for sucrose and 0.85 for glucose. In all cases the nonlinear analysis is required. Errors would arise if the alternate form of Equation 4.50 (see Eq. 2.40)

$$J_s = PS(C_1 - C_2) + J_v(1 - \sigma_f)\frac{C_1 + C_2}{2} \quad (4.57)$$

is used to analyze the data. For example, the steady-state ultrafiltration relation corresponding to Equation 4.57 (112) is

$$\frac{C_2}{C_1} = \frac{PS + \frac{1}{2}(1 - \sigma_f)J_v}{PS + \frac{1}{2}(1 + \sigma_f)J_v} \quad (4.58)$$

The limiting value of C_2/C_1 at high filtration rates is predicted to be $(1 - \sigma_f)/(1 + \sigma_f)$ instead of $(1 - \sigma_f)$. For the raffinose experiment illustrated in Figure 4.1, the limiting value of C_2/C_1 is predicted to be 0.33 instead of 0.49.

D. Experimental Demonstration of Reciprocity

In Figure 4.3 the values of σ_f, estimated by applying the above analysis to ultrafiltration experiments, are plotted against independently measured values of σ_d measured for the same solute-membrane combinations (40). The equality of σ_d and σ_f shown in the figure is an experimental verification of global reciprocity.

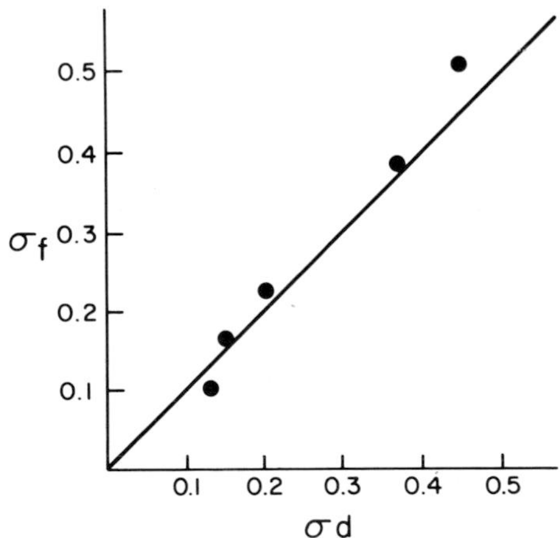

FIG. 4.3. Experimental test of $\sigma_d = \sigma_f$ for porous cellulose membranes. *Solid line* is line of equality.

V. PORE THEORY

The striking similarity between the sieving of macromolecules by artificial porous membranes and the ultrafiltration of plasma proteins at the capillary wall led to the pore theory of capillary permeability. Table 5.1 summarizes the principal relations from hydrodynamic pore theory developed in this section. The first two entries are based on the use of Poiseuille's law to describe water flow in cylindrical pores of molecular dimensions. The third entry is the application of Boltzmann's law to describe the equilibrium partition of solute between bulk and pore water. The Stokes-Einstein hydrodynamic model of free diffusion is extended to describe restricted diffusion in a cylindrical pore with the principles discussed in III. THERMODYNAMIC PRINCIPLES (p. 316) and IV. MEMBRANE TRANSPORT (p. 320) (entries 4–6). These principles are also used to describe ultrafiltration and osmotic flow in a pore. New developments in the pore theory of solvent drag are also based on an expression for the forces acting on a sphere as it moves through a water-filled channel (entry 7). A new hydrodynamic description of osmotic flow within a cylindrical pore provides an expression for the osmotic reflection coefficient without needing to assume reciprocity (entry 8). The very limited conditions under which global reciprocity appears to apply for a cylindrical pore may be deduced by comparing entry 7a and entry 8. There appear to be multiple pathways for solute and water transport across the capillary wall. Ultrafiltration across a membrane is described in entry 9. Solvent-drag and osmotic reflection coefficients for a membrane with multiple pore pathways are described in entries 10 and 11.

Pore theory has been described in previous reviews by Pappenheimer (107), Renkin and Pappenheimer (127), Landis and Pappenheimer (75), Crone and Lassen (27), Michel (90), Bean (7), Renkin and Curry (124), Renkin (121), and Crone and Christensen (24).

A. Poiseuille's Law

1. WATER FLOW IN PORES. The principal assumption in the derivation of the pore equations of membrane transport is that the hydrodynamic relations describing flow and viscous drag forces in macroscopic flow systems are applicable in channels of molecular dimensions. A brief review of the physics of very slow viscous water flow and its application in water-filled channels is given. Figure 5.1 shows a fluid element in a rectangular channel through which steady flow of an incompressible fluid is occurring. The forces acting on the fluid element are body forces caused by the pressure gradient in the axial direction and viscous forces (X_{sh}) described by Newton's law of viscosity

TABLE 5.1. *Principal Relations and Nomenclature for V. Pore Theory*

	Relation	
1.	$J_v/S = \frac{A_p r_p^2}{S\Delta x 8\eta} \Delta P$	(5.11)
2.	$L_P = (J_v/S)/\Delta P = \frac{A_p r_p^2}{S\Delta x 8\eta}$	(5.12)
3.	$\phi_p = (1-\alpha)^2$	(5.22, 5.27)
4a.	$\frac{D_p}{D_{fr}} = F(\alpha)$	(5.16)
4b.	$F(\alpha) = 1 - 2.10444\alpha + 2.08877\alpha^3 - 0.94813\alpha^5 - 1.372\alpha^6 + 3.87\alpha^8 - 4.19\alpha^9$	(5.17)
5.	$J_s/S = \frac{A_p}{S\Delta x} \phi D_p \Delta C$	(5.19, 5.28)
6.	$P = (J_s/S)\Delta C = \frac{A_p}{S\Delta x} \phi_p D_p$	(5.29)
7a.	$\sigma_f = 1 - [1-(1-\phi)^2]G(\alpha) - \frac{v_s P}{RTL_P}$	(5.49b)
7b.	$G(\alpha) = \frac{1 - \frac{2}{3}\alpha^2 - 0.20217\alpha^5}{1 - 0.75851\alpha^5}$	(5.51)
7c.	$\sigma_f = \frac{16}{3}\alpha^2 - \frac{20}{3}\alpha^3 + \frac{7}{3}\alpha^4 - \frac{v_s P}{RTL_P}$	(5.54)
8.	$\sigma_d = (1-\phi)^2$	(5.80)
9.	$\frac{C_2}{C_1} = \frac{PS\{Pe/[\exp(Pe) - 1]\} + J_v(1-\sigma_f)}{PS\{Pe/[\exp(Pe) - 1]\} + J_v}$	(5.60)
10.	$\overline{(1-\sigma_f)}\left(\frac{dC_i}{dx}\right)_{0}^{=0} = \frac{\Sigma J_{v,i}(1-\sigma_f)_i}{\Sigma J_{v,i}}$	(5.68)
11.	$\bar{\sigma}_d = \frac{\Delta J_v/S}{\bar{L}_P RT\Delta C} = \frac{\Sigma L_{P,i}A_i\sigma_i}{\Sigma L_{P,i}A_i}$	(5.89)

Nomenclature	
a_e	solute radius (cm)
A_p	area for water diffusion and flow (cm^2)
A_{sd}, A_{wd}	virtual area for diffusion of solute and water (cm^2)
A_{sf}, A_{wf}	virtual area for diffusion of solute and water during ultrafiltration (cm^2)
C	integration constant
C	concentration (M)
D	diffusion constant (cm^2/s)
E	potential energy (cal/mol)
F(α)	term describing modified drag on a sphere in a cylinder
G(α)	term accounting for solute velocity relative to centerline water velocity in a cylinder
I	integration constant
J_s/S	solute flux (mol·cm^{-2}·s^{-1})
J_v/S	solution flux (cm/s)
J_L	lymph flow (cm^3/s)
L_P	hydraulic conductivity (cm^3·dyn^{-1}·s^{-1})
N/S	pore density (cm^{-2})
n	number of moles
P	pressure (dyn/cm^2)
P	permeability coefficient (cm/s)
Pe	Péclet number
r_p	radius of pore (cm)
R_{uf}	ultrafiltration ratio C_2/C_1
R	gas constant (0.082 atm·°K^{-1}·M^{-1})
S	surface area (cm^2)
T	absolute temperature (°K)
V_s, V_w	velocity of solute or water (cm/s)
x	distance (cm)
X	force (dyn/cm^2)
α	ratio a/r_p
η	viscosity (dyn·s·cm^{-2})
σ_d	osmotic reflection coefficient
σ_f	solvent-drag reflection coefficient
ϕ	partition coefficient
Subscripts and superscripts	
s	solute
w	water
sp	small pore
lp	large pore

Numbers in parentheses refer to text equations.

$$X_{sh} = \eta \frac{dV}{dr} \qquad (5.1)$$

where r is the coordinate at right angles to the axial direction and η is the water viscosity. A force balance on the fluid element yields

$$\frac{dP}{dx} = \eta \frac{d^2V}{d^2r} \qquad (5.2)$$

which is a simplified version of the Navier-Stokes equation, the equation of motion for Newtonian fluid flow. In cylindrical coordinates Equation 5.2 becomes

$$\frac{dP}{dx} = \frac{\eta}{r}\frac{d}{dr}\left(r\frac{dV}{dr}\right) \qquad (5.3)$$

The velocity profile in a cylindrical pore is obtained by integrating this equation with the following boundary conditions

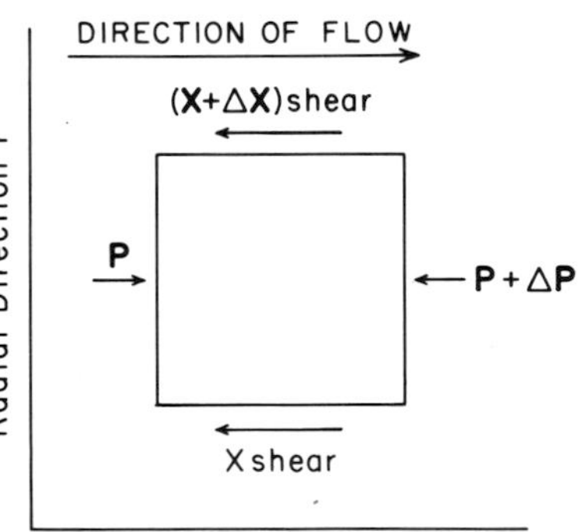

FIG. 5.1. Forces acting on element of Newtonian fluid in rectangular channel. Direction of flow is positive.

$$\frac{dV(r)}{dr} = 0 \quad \text{at} \quad r = 0 \tag{5.4}$$

and

$$V = 0 \quad \text{at} \quad r = r_p \tag{5.5}$$

where r_p is the radius of the pore. The first condition requires that the velocity profile be symmetrical about the axis. The second condition requires that there be no slip between the water at the wall and the material forming the channel boundary. Integration of Equation 5.3 with respect to r yields

$$\frac{r^2}{2\eta}\left(\frac{dP}{dx}\right) + I_1 = r\frac{dV}{dr} \tag{5.6}$$

where I_1 is a constant of integration. Dividing both sides by r

$$\frac{dV}{dr} = \frac{r}{2\eta}\left(\frac{dP}{dx}\right) + \frac{I_1}{r} \tag{5.7}$$

For the first boundary condition (Eq. 5.4) to be met, I_1 must be zero. A second integration with respect to r yields

$$V(r) = \left(\frac{dP}{dx}\right)\frac{r^2}{4\eta} + I_2 \tag{5.8}$$

The second boundary condition (Eq. 5.5) allows I_2 to be evaluated and an expression for the water velocity at any radial position in the pore to be obtained

$$V(r) = \left(\frac{dP}{dx}\right)\frac{r_p^2}{4\eta}(1 - r^2/r_p^2) \tag{5.9}$$

The total flow through a cylindrical channel is

$$\int_0^r V(r)2\pi r dr$$

Evaluation of the integral gives the total volume flow of pure water through a pore of length Δx caused by a pressure difference ΔP

$$J_v = \frac{\pi r_p^4}{8\eta}\left(\frac{\Delta P}{\Delta x}\right) \tag{5.10}$$

For a number (N) of pores in parallel in area S, the quantity $N\pi r_p^2$ is the area for water exchange, A_p. The volume flow per unit area is

$$J_v/S = \frac{A_p r_p^2}{S\Delta x 8\eta}\Delta P \tag{5.11}$$

The quantity $J_v/\Delta P$ is a measure of the hydraulic conductivity of the membrane multiplied by the total surface area of the membrane (L_pS). This quantity is always measured in experiments on whole organs and is often referred to as the filtration coefficient (K_f) with units of $ml \cdot min^{-1} \cdot mmHg^{-1} \cdot 100\ g^{-1}$ of tissue. When an independent measurement of the surface area of the capillary bed is available, the hydraulic conductivity (L_p) of the capillary wall is K_f/S. Equation 5.11 leads to an expression for the hydraulic conductivity of a membrane with a population of uniform cylindrical pores

$$L_p = (J_v/S)/\Delta P = \frac{A_p r_p^2}{S\Delta x 8\eta} = \frac{N_p \pi r^4}{S\Delta x 8\eta} \tag{5.12}$$

The term A_p/S is the fraction of the membrane surface area occupied by porous pathways, and N_p/S is the pore density. The quantity A_p/S is identical to the quantity α^* (Eq. 4.39). The length of the water pathway is assumed to be equal to the membrane thickness. The quantity $A_p/\Delta x$ is measured directly from the diffusion of water; it is also calculated from the area available for diffusion of small hydrophilic solutes, assuming there is no additional pathway for water. When this assumption is valid, there is no justification for distinguishing between A_p and the area available for diffusion of water, which is often designated A_w.

Pappenheimer and colleagues (109) rearranged Equation 5.11 to yield an expression for an equivalent pore radius ($r_{p,eq}$) characteristic of the frictional resistance to water flow through the channels in a porous membrane

$$r_{p,eq} = \sqrt{\left(\frac{J_v/S}{\Delta P}\right)\left(\frac{8\eta}{A_p/\Delta x}\right)} \tag{5.13a}$$

Alternatively from Equation 5.12

$$r_{p,eq} = \sqrt{L_p \frac{8\eta}{A_p/(\Delta x S)}} \tag{5.13b}$$

2. CRITIQUE OF APPLICATION OF POISEUILLE'S LAW IN PORES OF MOLECULAR DIMENSIONS. The equivalent radius calculated from Equation 5.13 is probably not characteristic of membrane structure if the viscous forces in the membrane described by Equation 5.1 are modified by long-range structuring of water within the channels or if radial velocity gradients at the pore wall differ from those described by the no-slip condition (Eq. 5.5). Pappenheimer (107) addressed the first problem. He reviewed experiments that demonstrate that the flow of solvent through artificial porous membranes is inversely proportional to the solvent viscosity measured in bulk solutions. These observations conform to the hypothesis that the fluid viscosity in the pore is equal to the bulk fluid viscosity.

Until recently the second problem was addressed rather indirectly. Pappenheimer (107) showed that the equivalent pore radius from Equation 5.13 is close to the equivalent radius estimated from three independent methods applied to artificial porous membranes: *1*) the pressure required to balance the surface tension of immiscible fluids within the channels of the membrane, *2*) the upper limit of solute size that will just penetrate the membrane, and *3*) the channel size estimated by the earliest attempts to measure channel dimensions in an artificial membrane by electron microscopy. These results demonstrate that the equivalent pore radius calculated from Poiseuille's law can be used to predict the physical properties of the membrane for a variety of processes. Nevertheless it must be emphasized that the physical basis for this remarkable internal consistency remains poorly understood because the ultrastructure of the artificial membranes studied to date consists of randomly oriented, multiply connected regions whose geometry cannot be simply described.

A more direct comparison between the predictions of macroscopic flow relations and the flow mechanisms through microscopic pores can be made with channels etched into mica membranes irradiated with a γ-ray source (7, 8). Table 5.2 compares the pore radius calculated from water flow through mica membranes with three independent estimates of channel dimension: *1*) one-half the diameter of the rhomboidal etched pore observed in the scanning electron microscope, *2*) the channel radius calculated from restricted diffusion of solutes, and *3*) the channel radius calculated from the flow of air through the membrane in which the slip of gas molecules at the wall is taken into account. Overall, the close correspondence between pore radii is the best experimental support currently available for the application of macroscopic equations to pores as small as 60 Å in radius. For smaller pore radii there is conflicting evidence about the application of Poiseuille's law. In six out of eight experiments on etched mica membranes described by Beck and Schultz (8), the pore radius obtained by assuming that water flow is described by Poiseuille's law was larger than that obtained from air flow measurements. Beck and Schultz suggest that the discrepancy is caused by an adsorbed layer of water on the mica during the experiments with air. An alternative suggestion is that there is some slip of the water at the wall. Calculations by Iberall and Schindler (64) indicated that in pores as small as 40 Å in radius,

TABLE 5.2. *Comparison of Directly Measured Pore Radii in Etched Membranes With Values Calculated From Hydrodynamic Theory*

Direct Observation	Water Flow	Restricted Diffusion	Air Flow	Ref.
148 ± 6	135 ± 8	147 ± 3		7
66.5 ± 8.8	68	67.5	62.5	8
155 ± 15	178 ± 2.6	145		152

All values in Å.

Equations 5.13a and 5.13b overestimate the pore radius by up to 25%. These conclusions are not supported by computer dynamic simulation of water flow in small pores, which suggests Poiseuille's law would apply in pores as small as 10 Å in radius (80). Further research on this topic with well-characterized membranes of small size is required.

3. CALCULATIONS AND UNITS. The example used here is based on the published values for capillary 6 in Table 3 of reference 29. The hydraulic conductivity of the capillary wall at 16°C is 3.14×10^{-7} cm·s^{-1}·cmH$_2$O^{-1}, or 3.20×10^{-10} cm^3·s^{-1}·dyn^{-1} (1 cmH$_2$O = 980 dyn/cm^2). The hydraulic conductivity of a second pathway, assumed to represent flow across the endothelial cells, was estimated to be 0.11×10^{-10} cm^3·s^{-1}·dyn^{-1}. The area for water exchange per unit area of capillary wall per unit of membrane thickness ($A_p/S\Delta x$) was estimated for this vessel from the measured permeability coefficients to NaCl and sucrose as 22.3 cm^{-1}. At 16°C the viscosity of water is 0.014 dyn·s·cm^2 (poise). Substituting these values into Equation 5.13a yields

$$r_{p,eq} = \sqrt{3.1 \times 10^{-10}\frac{\text{cm}^3}{\text{dyn}\cdot\text{s}} \times 8 \times 0.014\frac{\text{dyn}\cdot\text{s}}{\text{cm}^2} \times \frac{1\ \text{cm}}{22.3}}$$

$$= 1.26 \times 10^{-6}\ \text{cm} \quad \text{or} \quad 126\ \text{Å}$$

The relation between pore radii calculated from Poiseuille's law and independent estimates of pore radii is discussed at the end of this section.

B. Pore Diffusion

1. DIFFUSION COEFFICIENTS OF SPHERICAL SOLUTES WITHIN CYLINDRICAL PORES. The assumption underlying the pore theory of restricted diffusion is that all the frictional force on a spherical solute diffusing within a pore can be described in terms of the viscous drag on the solute. There is no direct friction between membrane and solute. Consider a spherical solute (radius, a) moving at a velocity V_s along the axis of a cylinder (radius, r_p) as in Figure 5.2. If water flow in the cylinder is Poiseuillean, with the water velocity along the axis V_0, then the drag force on the sphere is given by (59)

$$X_{s,d} = \frac{6\pi\eta a}{F(\alpha)}[V_s - G(\alpha)V_0] \tag{5.14}$$

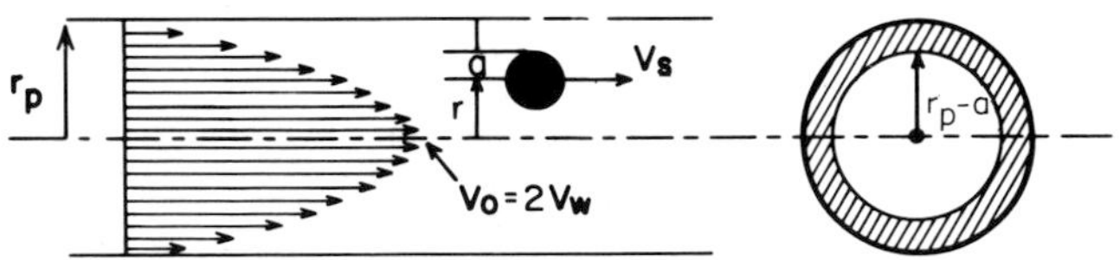

FIG. 5.2. Uncharged sphere (radius, a) moves at velocity V_s inside cylinder (radius, r_p). The region $r_p - a < r < r_p$ is unavailable to solute center. Undisturbed water velocity profile is parabolic.

where α is the ratio a/r_p. The term $F(\alpha)$ is the principal term in the theory of restricted diffusion, and the term $G(\alpha)$ forms the basis of the modern theory of ultrafiltration. For example, for a very small solute moving on the axis of a cylinder, $F(\alpha)$ approaches a value of 1.0, and the drag force on the sphere is nearly equal to the Stokes drag. As $\alpha \rightarrow 1$, $F(\alpha)$ decreases toward zero and the drag force on the sphere increases. The term $G(\alpha)$ accounts for the difference between the solute velocity and the water velocity. It is closely related to the slip coefficient (χ) (see II. DIFFUSION, p. 310) and is discussed further with reference to the pore theory of the solvent-drag reflection coefficient later in this section (see Eq. 5.44).

In the absence of water flow the mobility of the solute on the pore axis ($X_{s,d}/V_s$) is $6\pi\eta a/F(\alpha)$ (Eq. 5.14). Thus from the Stokes-Einstein description of diffusion the pore diffusion coefficient (D_p) on the axis is

$$D_p = \frac{RTF(\alpha)}{N_A 6\pi\eta a} \quad (5.15)$$

From the Stokes-Einstein expression for D_{fr} (Eq. 2.18)

$$\frac{D_p}{D_{fr}} = F(\alpha) \quad (5.16)$$

Accurate values of $F(\alpha)$ are given in Table 5.3 (103). The value $F(\alpha)$ is usually expressed as a power series in α (45)

$$F(\alpha) = 1 - 2.10444\alpha + 2.08877\alpha^3 - 0.94813\alpha^5 - 1.372\alpha^6 + 3.87\alpha^8 - 4.19\alpha^9 \quad (5.17)$$

TABLE 5.3. *Centerline Values of Hydrodynamic Functions F(α) and G(α)*

α	$F(\alpha)$	$G(\alpha)$	α	$F(\alpha)$	$G(\alpha)$
0.00	1.00000	1.00000	0.46	0.20795	0.86062
0.02	0.95791	0.99973	0.48	0.18721	0.84863
0.04	0.91593	0.99894	0.50	0.16780	0.83626
0.06	0.87415	0.99756	0.52	0.14969	0.82347
0.08	0.83266	0.99573	0.54	0.13285	0.81033
0.10	0.79158	0.99333	0.56	0.11727	0.79684
0.12	0.75098	0.99040	0.58	0.10291	0.78303
0.14	0.71096	0.98693	0.60	0.08972	0.76892
0.16	0.67162	0.98293	0.62	0.07767	0.75452
0.18	0.63305	0.97840	0.64	0.06672	0.73986
0.20	0.59530	0.97333	0.66	0.05681	0.72492
0.22	0.55849	0.96773	0.68	0.04791	0.70985
0.24	0.52266	0.96160	0.70	0.03998	0.69454
0.26	0.48789	0.95494	0.72	0.03294	0.67904
0.28	0.45433	0.94776	0.74	0.02674	0.66338
0.30	0.42174	0.94006	0.76	0.02135	0.64751
0.32	0.39047	0.93184	0.78	0.01670	0.63164
0.34	0.36045	0.92312	0.80	0.01273	0.61558
0.36	0.33171	0.91389	0.82	0.00940	0.59942
0.38	0.30428	0.90417	0.84	0.00665	0.58316
0.40	0.27819	0.89397	0.86	0.00443	0.56680
0.42	0.25343	0.88330	0.88	0.00268	0.55036
0.44	0.23002	0.87218	0.90	0.00135	0.53382

which is a good approximation of the values in Table 5.1 for $\alpha \leq 0.6$.

This analysis does not account for the drag forces on the sphere when the solute center is off axis. Bean (7), with $F(\alpha)$ values for solute position in the range $r_p - a < r < 0$, concluded that the mean diffusion coefficient in the pore was close to one-half that calculated from the axial value. Bean's result is based on an incorrect averaging procedure and overestimates the reduction in diffusion coefficient (4). A detailed analysis of off-axis diffusion is given by Brenner and Gaydos (12), who combined hydrodynamic pore theory with a statistical mechanics model of Brownian diffusion in a cylindrical pore to obtain

$$\frac{D_p}{D_{fr}} = \frac{1 - 1.25\alpha \ln \alpha - 1.539\alpha}{(1 - \alpha)^2} \quad (5.18)$$

The analysis leading to this equation is valid only when $0 < \alpha < 0.2$; the equation predicts D values that are 20% less than those obtained with the axial value in Equation 5.16. The averaging is carried out over the area available to solute alone, not over the whole pore area. This is required for the mechanical interpretation of the diffusion coefficients to be consistent with both the statistical and the hydrodynamic relations for the diffusion coefficient described in II. DIFFUSION (p. 310).

2. DIFFUSION IN MEMBRANES PENETRATED BY CYLINDRICAL PORES. Very few direct measurements of the diffusion coefficients in porous structures have been made. Experimental tests of the pore theory are based on the measurement of total flow (J_s) when the volume flow across the membrane is zero. From Equations 4.52 and 4.53

$$J_s = \frac{A_p}{\Delta x} \phi D_p \Delta C \quad (5.19)$$

where ϕ is the pore partition coefficient, and $A_p/\Delta x$ is the area for exchange per unit path length. Although Equation 5.19 was introduced into the original description of the pore theory of permeability (109), the formal derivation of this relation (beginning with Eq. 5.14) has been described only recently (5, 7, 81, 83, 153). The derivation is based on the recognition of Equation 5.14 as a particular form of the equations of membrane transport within the cylindrical pore. When the gradient of solute chemical potential within the pore is set equal to the drag force on a sphere moving on the axis of the cylindrical pore, Equation 5.14 can be rewritten

$$\frac{d\mu_{s,p}}{dx} = \frac{6\pi\eta a}{F(\alpha)} \bar{V}_s - \frac{6\pi\eta a G(\alpha)}{F(\alpha)} 2\bar{V}_w \quad (5.20)$$

where the mean water velocity $\bar{V}_w$ is one-half of the maximum water velocity on the axis. Equation 5.20 is identical in form to the general friction-model equation (Eq. 4.34). A development exactly parallel to the one that leads from Equation 4.34 to 4.42 allows Equation 5.20 to be reduced in the absence of net volume flow ($J_v = 0$)

$$J_{s,p} = \pi r_p^2 \left[\frac{RT\overline{F}(\alpha)}{6\pi\eta a}\right]\left(\frac{dC_{s,p}}{dx}\right) \tag{5.21}$$

where $J_{s,p}$ is the flux through a single pore. The quantity $RT\overline{F}(\alpha)/6\pi\eta a$ is equal to the diffusion coefficient within the pore (D_p) averaged over the area available to solute. When Equation 5.21 is integrated across the membrane and the solute concentration just within the pore is set equal to ϕC_{bulk}, Equation 5.21 for N_p pores in parallel yields

$$J_s = \frac{A_p}{\Delta x}\,\phi D_p \Delta C$$

which is Equation 5.19 with $A_p = N_p \pi r_p^2$.

The magnitude of ϕ is determined by the steric exclusion of solute at the channel walls. For a spherical solute, ϕ is simply the pore area available to solute $\pi(r_p - a)^2$ relative to the total pore area πr_p^2

$$\phi = (1 - \alpha)^2 \tag{5.22}$$

The same result is obtained if Boltzmann's law is used to describe the radial distribution of solute concentration [$C(r)$] in the pore at equilibrium

$$C(r) = C_{bulk} \exp[-E(r)/RT] \tag{5.23}$$

The hard-sphere exclusion at the cylinder wall is described by the following distribution of the interaction potential $E(r)$

$$\begin{aligned} E(r) &= 0 \qquad 0 < r \leq r_p - a \\ E(r) &= \infty \qquad r_p - a < r \leq r_p \end{aligned} \tag{5.24}$$

$$\phi = \frac{\int_0^{r_p} C(r)\, 2\pi r dr}{C_{bulk}} \tag{5.25}$$

Substituting from Equation 5.23 and integrating yields

$$\begin{aligned} \phi &= \frac{1}{\pi r_p^2}\int_0^{r_p} \exp[-E(r)/RT] 2\pi r dr \\ &= \frac{1}{\pi r_p^2}\int_0^{r_p - a} 1\,(2\pi r dr) \end{aligned} \tag{5.26}$$

$$= (1 - \alpha)^2 \tag{5.27}$$

The ability to independently specify the interaction potential between solute and membrane at the channel entrance (Eq. 5.24) and the forces of the solute within the channel (Eq. 5.20) means that the pore theory is one of the best understood mechanical molecular models available to study passive membrane transport.

The quantity $J_s/\Delta C$ (Eq. 5.19) is equal to the solute permeability coefficient (P) multiplied by the surface area (S) of the membrane

$$J_s/\Delta C = PS \tag{5.28}$$

The permeability–surface area product (PS) is the primary measurement of permeability in whole organs. Values of P are calculated from an independent measure of the surface area for exchange

$$P = (J_s/S)/\Delta C = \frac{A_p}{S\Delta x}\,\phi D_p \tag{5.29}$$

Because $A_p = N_p \pi r_p^2$, Equation 5.29 can also be written

$$P = \frac{N_p \pi r_p^2}{S\Delta x}\,\phi D_p \tag{5.30}$$

The specific steric and hydrodynamic forces described by the pore theory have been conveniently described by writing Equation 5.19 as

$$J_s = \frac{A_p}{\Delta x}(1 - \alpha)^2 \left(\frac{D_p}{D_{fr}}\right) D_{fr} \Delta C \tag{5.31a}$$

Alternatively the permeability coefficient is described as

$$P = \frac{J_s}{S\Delta C} = \frac{A_p}{S\Delta x}(1 - \alpha)^2 \left(\frac{D_p}{D_{fr}}\right) D_{fr} \tag{5.31b}$$

where A_p/S has the same meaning as in Equation 5.14. Several of the terms in Equations 5.31a and 5.31b form part of the basic vocabulary in pore-theory applications. The product $(1 - \alpha)^2(D_p/D_{fr})$ is usually designated A_s/A_p, and the product $[(A_p/\Delta x)(1 - \alpha)^2(D_p/D_{fr})]$ is designated $A_s/\Delta x$; A_s can be thought of as a virtual area for the free diffusion of solute. As $\alpha \rightarrow 0$, $A_s \rightarrow A_p$ and Equation 5.31a describes free diffusion; as $\alpha \rightarrow 1$, A_s falls toward 0. Experimental tests of the pore theory of restricted diffusion compare the measured value of A_s/A_p (or $A_s/\Delta x$) with the value of A_s/A_p calculated from pore theory with the following relations (75, 119) (see Eq. 5.17)

$$A_s/A_p = (1 - \alpha)^2(1 - 2.104\alpha + 2.09\alpha^3 - 0.95\alpha^5) \tag{5.32a}$$

using the centerline approximation, or

$$A_s/A_p = 1 - 1.25 \ln \alpha - 1.539\alpha \qquad \alpha < 0.2 \tag{5.32b}$$

from the analysis by Brenner and Gaydos (12). From experimental data, $A_s/\Delta x$ is calculated as PS/D_{fr}. When the permeability–surface area product of the membrane to water is also measured

$$A_s/A_p = \frac{(PS/D)_s}{(PS/D)_w} \tag{5.33}$$

The quantity $A_p/\Delta x$ may be calculated from $A_s/\Delta x$ when an estimate of pore radius is given.

3. RESTRICTED DIFFUSION IN ARTIFICIAL MEMBRANES. The two parts of Figure 5.3 compare experimental and calculated values of A_s/A_p as a function

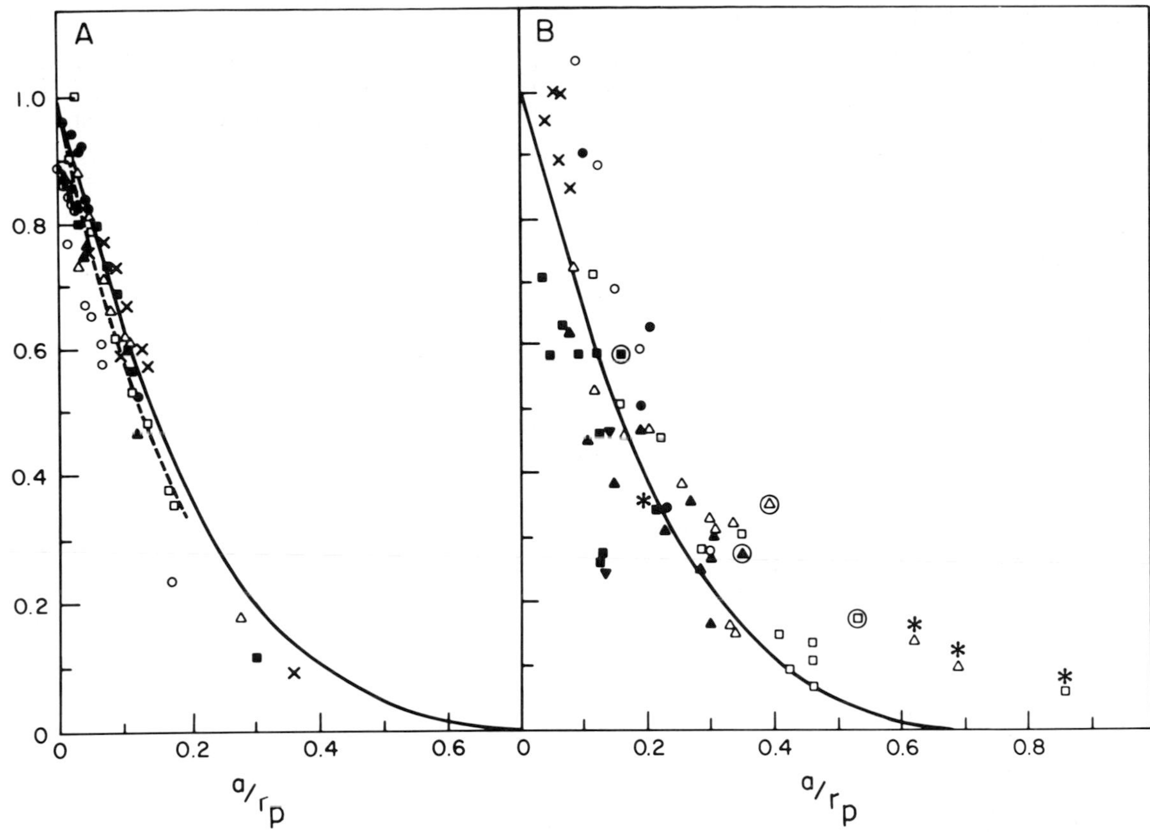

FIG. 5.3. Restricted diffusion and exclusion of small hydrophilic solutes in porous membranes as function of solute radius. Solute radius is expressed relative to pore radius calculated from Poiseuille's law. *A*: etched mica membranes with reasonably well-defined pore geometries. *Solid line* is relation between A_s/A_p and a/r_p calculated from centerline approximation (Eq. 5.32a). *Broken line* is off-axis relation (Eq. 5.32b). *Symbols* represent different pore radii: ◑, 306 Å; ○, 119 Å; ▲, 172 Å; ●, 169 Å; △, 75 Å; ■, 68.5 Å; ×, 50 Å; □, 45.7 Å. [Data from Beck and Schultz (8).] *B*: cellulose and cross-linked polymer membranes with an internal structure that is less well defined. *Solid line* is centerline approximation. *Symbols* represent different membranes: □, Cuprophan 150 PM, cellulose; △, Bard PCM, polycarbonate; ▲, Celanese CA2-3, cellulose acetate; ■, Rhone-Poulenc RP-AN69, polyacrylonitrile; ●, Visking cellulose; ○, Dupont cellophane; ×, Sylvania viscose wet gel. *Points* circled indicate vitamin B_{12} as test solute; *points* asterisked indicate [^{14}C]methoxyinulin as test solute. [Data from Renkin (119) and Wendt et al. (159).]

of the ratio a/r_p in artificial membranes. Overall, the experimental data conform to the remarkable prediction of the pore theory that the flux of solute across a membrane is reduced to ~60% of that expected from free diffusion through the same area when the solute radius is only 10% of the pore radius. The data shown in Figure 5.3*A* were measured on etched mica membranes with a quite narrow distribution of pore radii (8). The solid line is calculated from Equation 5.32a with an axial value for F(α). The latter relation may underestimate the restriction to solute diffusion because twice as many experimental values of A_s/A_p fall below the predicted curve as fall on or above the predicted curve. In the range $0 < \alpha < 0.2$, which includes 70% of the data, experimental values are distributed uniformly about the broken line derived from Brenner and Gaydos (12; see Eq. 5.32b). The difference between the two curves is never greater than 8%. No major discrepancy in the interpretation of experimental data from capillary membranes is likely to be resolved by further refinements in pore theory for a/r_p values < 0.2. On the other hand there is virtually no experimental data describing restricted diffusion in pores with well-defined geometry in which the solute radius is >30% of the pore radius. Further experimental and theoretical investigations of the transport of larger solutes in pores 40–100 Å in radius are required.

The data in Figure 5.3*B* show diffusion measurements in porous membranes with an internal structure that is more complicated and less well defined. The equivalent pore radius calculated from Poiseuille's law is used as a measure of the pore radius through which the test solute diffuses. The data include the diffusion studies by Renkin (119) on cellulosic membranes and more recent data from newer dialysis membranes (74, 159). The solid line is A_s/A_p plotted as a function of a/r_p with the axial value for F(α) (Eq. 5.32a). Although there is more scatter than in Figure 5.3*A*, the data in Figure 5.3*B* conform to the hypothesis that the equivalent pore radius calculated from Poiseuille's law can be used to characterize the frictional resistance to solute diffusion in porous membranes. The physical basis for the internal consistency is not as well understood.

One consistent observation from the data (159) is that values of A_s/A_p measured with vitamin B_{12} and isotopically labeled inulin are larger than predicted from pore theory. These two solutes are often used as test solutes in capillary membranes. Clearly a careful characterization of test probes used in capillary membrane studies is needed. These control experiments must be carried out on membranes such as those in Figures 5.3*A* and 5.3*B*.

C. Pore Theory

1. RESTRICTED DIFFUSION IN CAPILLARY BEDS. The measurement of permeability coefficients to small solutes in the capillary wall in both whole organs and single capillaries is a difficult procedure. Measurements of permeability properties are compromised whenever transcapillary concentration differences cannot be measured directly. Further uncertainties arise because of the heterogeneity of blood flow and permeability properties within the organ, osmotic buffering, and compliance in the vascular and interstitial spaces (see the chapters by Crone and Levitt, Bassingthwaighte and Goresky, and Renkin in this *Handbook*).

In Figure 5.4, $A_s/\Delta x$ values measured in the continuous capillaries of skeletal muscle and skin in mammalian hindlimb (circles) and human forearm (triangles) are plotted against the solute Stokes-Einstein radius. The solid circles are the isogravimetric data from Pappenheimer et al. (109), recalculated with estimates of the osmotic reflection coefficient as described by Renkin and Curry (124). If Figure 5.4 is compared with the equivalent figure in the Landis-Pappenheimer review (75), it will be seen that $A_p/\Delta x$ values are an order of magnitude smaller for solutes <10 Å in radius. The values are smaller because the osmotic reflection coefficients used by Renkin and Curry to calculate $A_s/\Delta x$ from the original estimates of $A_s\sigma_d/\Delta x$ are close to 0.1 for small solutes, whereas values close to 1.0 were used by Pappenheimer et al. (see the chapter by Crone and Levitt in this *Handbook* for details). Two solid lines in Figure 5.5 are calculated for pore radii of 40 and 50 Å, respectively, with $A_p/\Delta x$ set equal to 0.15 × 10^5 cm/100 g (124). With the exception of one result for inulin (a_e, 12–15 Å), the data conform quite closely to the hypothesis that the frictional interaction of hydrophilic solutes within the size-limiting structures in the capillary wall can be described in terms of restricted diffusion through cylindrical channels 40–50 Å in radius. Of particular note in Figure 5.4 is the result that the measured

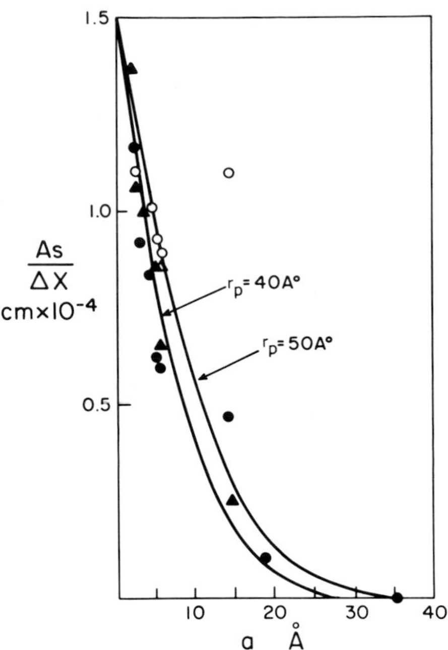

FIG. 5.4. Restricted diffusion and exclusion of small hydrophilic solutes across walls of continuous capillaries as function of solute radius: ●, cat hindlimb (109); ○, dog hindlimb (38); ▲, human forearm (149). *Solid lines* show relation between $A_s/\Delta x$ and solute radius for pore radii of 40 and 50 Å; $A_p/\Delta x$ is 1.5 × 10^{-4} cm (124).

values of $A_s/\Delta x$ for myoglobin (a_e, 19 Å) from the isogravimetric experiments are very similar to predicted values. This result removes a large discrepancy in earlier analyses of the isogravimetric data (75) in which the values of $A_s/\Delta x$ for myoglobin predicted from the pore theory were much larger than the measured values. Apparently the measured $A_s/\Delta x$ value for myoglobin is consistent with the smaller $A_p/\Delta x$ value calculated by Renkin and Curry (124). Not all whole-organ measurements of permeability coefficients in continuous capillaries are consistent with restricted diffusion (see the chapter by Crone and Levitt in this *Handbook*). However, recent experiments on individually perfused capillaries of frog mesentery demonstrate restricted diffusion for solutes as small as 15 Å in radius (33, 78, 79). These experiments avoid many of the complications arising from heterogeneity in whole-organ experiments. Further experiments in single capillaries and whole organs with solutes of different size, shape, and charge are required to identify systematically the physical and chemical nature of transcapillary pathways.

Perhaps the most important investigations of restricted diffusion across the capillary involve comparison of two different measurements of permeability—from transient blood-to-tissue exchange and from steady-state determinations of blood-to-lymph transport. In Figure 5.5 the values of $A_s/\Delta x$, measured for both blood-to-tissue and blood-to-lymph transport in hindlimb, heart, lung, and intestine, are plotted as a function of molecular size; both scales are logarithmic.

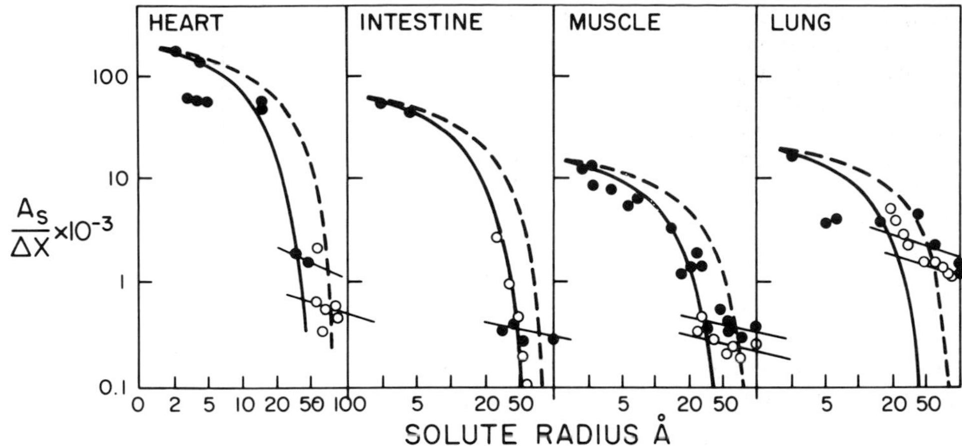

FIG. 5.5. Restricted diffusion and exclusion of hydrophilic solutes ranging in size from 2.3 to 100 Å in radius at walls of continuous and fenestrated capillaries. Both scales are logarithmic. *Solid curve* fitted to muscle data is theoretical relation between $A_s/\Delta x$ and solute size, assuming $A_p/\Delta x = 1.5 \times 10^4$ cm with a pore radius of 50 Å. *Curve* was traced onto transparency and fitted to data for each organ by superimposing *points* representing NaCl permeability (a_e = 2.3 Å). *Broken curves* are calculated for pore radii of 100 Å. Values of $A_s/\Delta x$ calculated from macromolecule permeability coefficients (●, plasma proteins; ○, dextrans) diverge from predictions for 50-Å pore as indicated by *short thin lines* for solutes greater than 20 Å in radius. *Solid line* fitted to muscle data is plotted on linear coordinates in Fig. 5.4. (Data from Tables 2, 3, and 4 of ref. 121).

The heavy solid line is the theoretical relation between $A_s/\Delta x$ and solute size as calculated for a pore radius of 50 Å. This relation describes data in hindlimb muscle and skin, heart, and intestine. It cannot be fitted to lung data. The broken line in Figure 5.5 corresponds to a pore radius of 100 Å.

In all organs the $A_p/\Delta x$ values measured for solutes with equivalent radii of 40–100 Å are inconsistent with a single pathway across the capillary wall for both small solutes and macromolecules. A series of short straight lines were drawn by hand on the figure to indicate the existence of a second pathway or pathways for macromolecules. Transport mechanisms in larger pores are also described in this section; macromolecule transport via vesicles is discussed in VIII. VESICLE AND LIPOPHILIC-SOLUTE TRANSPORT (p. 363).

It has been suggested that the structures determining the size selectivity shown in Figure 5.5 might reside within the interstitium and not at the capillary wall (which is assumed to include the basement membranes associated with endothelial cells; see the chapter by Bert and Pearce in this *Handbook*). There is evidence against this view from the hindlimb data in Figure 5.5. The $A_s/\Delta x$ value measured for myoglobin (a_e, 19 Å) is 1.25×10^3 cm. Because it was estimated from transient osmotic water flows across the capillary wall, the value probably represents diffusion and selectivity mechanisms at the capillary wall. It is smaller than the $A_s/\Delta x$ values for dextrans with effective solute radii of 22 and 24 Å (1.68 and 2.08 nm, respectively) calculated from the concentration difference of the solutes between plasma and lymph draining the tissue. Exactly the opposite result would be expected if there were a significant resistance to the movement of test solutes (up to 48 Å in diam) within the tissue.

2. DISCREPANCY BETWEEN EQUIVALENT PORE RADII FROM RESTRICTED DIFFUSION AND POISEUILLE FLOW. When the estimate of $A_p/S\Delta x$ for hindlimb capillaries is combined with the measured hydraulic conductivity of the capillary wall in hindlimb skin and muscle capillaries, the equivalent pore radius estimated from Poiseuille's law is 75 Å. This estimate is much larger than the pore radius estimated from restricted diffusion. The same type of discrepancy was noted in a number of other organ beds (32) and in single capillaries of frog mesentery (34). The hypothesis that the discrepancy results from transport through structures such as a fibrous network within the principal water pathways is discussed in VI. FIBER-MATRIX MODEL (p. 351); however, other factors may contribute to the discrepancy. For example, it is now recognized that up to 25% of the measured hydraulic conductivity in hindlimb capillaries can be accounted for by the combined L_P values of two additional water pathways across the capillary wall: *1*) a semipermeable pathway from which solute is excluded (35, 41) and *2*) a large-pore pathway that may contribute to large-molecule transport (128, 147). In the hindpaw the equivalent pore radii estimated from restricted diffusion and Poiseuille's law are brought closer together if the total capillary hydraulic conductivity is partitioned so that only 75% of the transcapillary water flux occurs through the principal pathways for small hydrophilic solutes.

3. MOLECULAR SIEVING IN CYLINDRICAL PORES. The capillary wall acts as a molecular sieve; large

plasma proteins are retained within the capillary lumen, whereas small molecules cross the capillary wall. Until 1972 it was assumed that the selectivity properties of a porous channel during ultrafiltration were determined by the same hydrodynamic factors that describe restricted diffusion. However, it is now recognized that separate hydrodynamic terms describe diffusion and the coupling of solute flux to water flow in a pore; this is referred to as solvent drag. These important new developments in pore theory are reviewed with earlier theories, and a development of the new theory of solvent drag in porous membranes is given next.

D. Solvent Drag

1. INTRODUCTION OF NEW CONCEPT. Figure 5.6 shows an idealized porous membrane. The solution within the pore is assumed to flow as a plug; i.e., the velocity of the fluid is the same at all radial positions. Furthermore the solute, a sphere of radius a, is assumed to be identical to water except for its size. If J_v is the volume flow through the cylinder, the solute flow through the pore (J_s), expressed as a fraction of the total solute carried up to the pore (J_vC_1), is determined solely by the area available to solute relative to the area available to water

$$\left(\frac{J_s}{J_vC_1}\right)_{\Delta C=0} = \frac{\text{area available to solute}}{\text{area available to water}} = (1-\alpha)^2 \quad (5.34)$$

The quantity

$$1 - \left(\frac{J_s}{J_vC_1}\right)_{\Delta C=0}$$

is the solvent-drag reflection coefficient (see Eq. 4.22), and the quantity $(1 - \alpha)^2$ is the solute partition coefficient, ϕ. Thus from Equation 5.34

$$\sigma_{f,pl} = 1 - \phi \quad (5.35)$$

where $\sigma_{f,pl}$ is the solvent-drag reflection coefficient for plug flow. This derivation ignores the frictional interaction of solute and water within the pore. Both the presence of a parabolic velocity profile and the frictional forces acting on the sphere within the cylinder must be accounted for in a real pore.

Ferry (46) accounted for the presence of the parabolic velocity profile by assuming that solute in the pore moved at the local water velocity

$$\left(\frac{J_s}{J_vC_1}\right)_{\Delta C=0} = \frac{1}{\pi r_p^2}\int_0^{r_p-a}(1 - r^2/r_p^2)2\pi r dr \quad (5.36)$$

The integral in this equation yields

$$1 - \sigma_{f,Ferry} = [2(1-\alpha)^2 - (1-\alpha)^4] \quad (5.37)$$

which can be reduced to a simple expression for σ_f in terms of the partition coefficient

$$\sigma_f = 1 - 2(1-\alpha)^2 + (1-\alpha)^4 = [1 - (1-\alpha)^2]^2 \quad (5.38)$$

That is

$$\sigma_{f,Ferry} = (1-\phi)^2 \quad (5.39)$$

The term $2(1 - \alpha)^2 - (1 - \alpha)^4$ in Equation 5.37 has been described as a filtration entry condition by a number of investigators (7, 28, 81, 119), but the simple rearrangement of Equation 5.37 to yield Equation 5.39 has not been widely recognized. Equation 5.39 is important because it is identical to the expression for the osmotic reflection coefficient derived considering only steric exclusion of the solute (see Eq. 5.80). A potential problem with Equation 5.39 is that it does not account for frictional forces acting on the solute in the pore. An appropriate solution to this problem is the main contribution of the new theory.

Pappenheimer and associates (109) described frictional resistance to solute movement in the pore during volume flow by replacing the real area terms in Equation 5.34 with the virtual area for diffusion from restricted diffusion theory

$$\left(\frac{J_s}{J_vC_1}\right)_{\Delta C=0} = \frac{\text{virtual area for solute diffusion}}{\text{virtual area for water diffusion}} \quad (5.40)$$

The virtual area for solute (A_s) is described by Equation 5.32a. Pappenheimer et al. (109) treated water as if it were a hard-sphere solute; substitution into Equation 5.40 gave

$$\left(\frac{J_s}{J_vC_1}\right)_{\Delta C=0} = (A_s/A_w)_D = \frac{(1-\alpha_s)^2F(\alpha_s)}{(1-\alpha_w)^2F(\alpha_w)} \quad (5.41)$$

where α_w is the ratio of the radius of the water molecule to the pore radius. The subscript D refers to the use of a diffusive entry condition that does not take into account the presence of a parabolic profile. Renkin (119) combined both the Ferry term accounting for the parabolic profile and the virtual area terms to obtain

$$\left(\frac{J_s}{J_vC_1}\right)_{\Delta C=0} = \frac{[2(1-\alpha_s)^2 - (1-\alpha_s)^4]F(\alpha_s)}{[2(1-\alpha_w)^2 - (1-\alpha_w)^4]F(\alpha_w)} \quad (5.42)$$

The right side of this equation was interpreted to be the ratio of virtual areas for solute and water transport

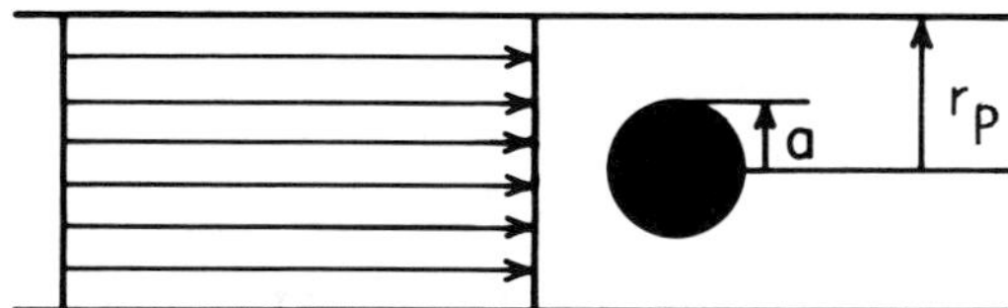

FIG. 5.6. Idealized ultrafiltration experiment. Solute moves at water velocity in region $0 < r < r_p - a$. Water velocity is independent of radial position and cylinder is frictionless (plug flow); r_p, pore radius.

during ultrafiltration and was designated $A_{s,f}/A_{w,f}$. Renkin used the equation to interpret the ultrafiltration data in Figure 4.2 in terms of pore theory. In addition, Durbin (140) used it to interpret osmotic reflection coefficients measured on cellulose membranes assuming $\sigma_d = \sigma_f$

$$\sigma_d = \sigma_f = 1 - (A_{s,f}/A_{w,f}) \qquad (5.43)$$

In spite of the fact that Equations 5.42 and 5.43 provide a reasonably consistent description of early experimental data on the selectivity of cellulose membranes, it is now recognized that the use of the concept of a virtual area for diffusion to describe ultrafiltration is incorrect. Two problems have been identified. *1*) There is a fundamental inconsistency in the use of the continuum theory to distinguish betwen the virtual area available to water and the total pore area (28). This objection is easily overcome by setting the denominator in Equation 5.40 equal to the actual pore area available for water. *2*) The term F(α) (Eq. 5.41) should be replaced by the term G(α) [Eq. 5.14; (7, 153)]. One form of the new relation for the solvent-drag reflection coefficient is

$$1 - \sigma_f = [2(1 - \alpha)^2 - (1 - \alpha)^4]G(\alpha) \qquad (5.44)$$

which predicts a relation between σ_f and α that is quite different from that described by Equation 5.43. A formal development of this relation, beginning with Eq. 5.14, which describes the force on a sphere moving within a cylindrical pore, is given next.

2. NEW HYDRODYNAMIC THEORY OF SOLVENT DRAG. The starting point for the derivation of the expression for the solvent-drag reflection coefficient in terms of the pore theory is Equation 5.14. When the drag force is set equal to the gradient of chemical potential, Equation 5.14 may be expressed in the following form (see Eq. 5.20)

$$\frac{d\mu_s}{dx} = \frac{6\pi\eta a}{F(\alpha)}[\bar{V}_s - 2G(\alpha)\bar{V}_w] \qquad (5.45)$$

In the absence of a solute concentration gradient, the gradient of chemical potential ($d\mu_s/dx$) is determined solely by the pressure gradient (i.e., $d\mu_s/dx = v_s dP/dx$, where v_s is the partial molar volume of the solute). Substitution of this relation into Equation 5.45 yields an expression for the solute velocity when dC/dx is zero

$$\bar{V}_s = v_s\left(\frac{dP}{dx}\right)\left[\frac{F(\alpha)}{6\pi\eta a}\right] + 2G(\alpha)\bar{V}_w \qquad (5.46)$$

The first term on the right side of this equation is the velocity of the solute resulting directly from the potential energy in the pressure gradient; thus it describes the component of pressure diffusion in the porous channel. In a pore, Poiseuille's law can be used to describe dP/dx in terms of $\bar{V}_w$ (see Eqs. 5.10 and 5.12)

$$\left(\frac{dP}{dx}\right)_p = \frac{\bar{V}_w}{L_P\Delta x} \qquad (5.47)$$

where Δx is the pore length. Equation 5.15 allows the first term on the right side of Equation 5.46 to be rewritten as $\bar{V}_w(v_s D_p)/(RTL_P\Delta x)$.

The second term on the right side of Equation 5.46 identifies G(α) as a measure of the solute velocity relative to the water velocity on the axis of the pore. The velocity of a small solute traveling on the axis of the pore will approach a local water velocity that is twice the mean water velocity for Poiseuille flow, and G(α) will be very close to 1. On the other hand a solute with a radius approximately equal to the radius of the pore will travel at the mean water velocity, and G(α) will approach a lower limit of 0.5. To describe the total flux carried through the membrane, the values of G(α) at off-axis positions must be known. On the basis of model experiments, Bean (7) concluded that the value of G(α) for an axial position was a good approximation to the ratio of the local solute-to-water velocity at all axial positions available to the solute. Thus the total solute flow through the pore, expressed as a fraction of the total solute carried up to the membrane, is given as

$$\left(\frac{J_s}{J_v C_1}\right)_{\Delta C=0} = \frac{1}{\pi r_p^2}\left[\frac{v_s D_p}{RTL_P\Delta x}\int_0^{r_p-a} 2\pi r dr + G(\alpha)\int_0^{r_p-a}(1 - r^2/r_p^2)2\pi r dr\right] \qquad (5.48)$$

which was also derived by Verniory et al. (153). The integrals in this equation yield

$$1 - \sigma_f = [2(1 - \alpha)^2 - (1 - \alpha)^4] \cdot G(\alpha) + \frac{v_s P}{RTL_P} \qquad (5.49a)$$

or

$$\sigma_f = \{1 - [1 - (1 - \phi)^2]G(\alpha)\} + \frac{v_s P}{RTL_P} \qquad (5.49b)$$

The pressure-diffusion term ($v_s P/RTL_P$) has been evaluated from pore theory assuming the partial molar volume of the solute is $(4/3)N_A\pi a^3$ (7, 28)

$$\frac{v_s P}{RTL_P} = \frac{16}{9}\alpha^2(1 - \alpha)^2 F(\alpha) \qquad (5.50)$$

Values of $v_s P/RTL_P$ calculated from this equation are given in Table 5.4 (column 2). In a cylindrical pore the contribution of pressure diffusion increases as solute size increases up to $\alpha = 0.30$ because the solute volume increases more rapidly than the resistance to diffusion. Thereafter the mobility of the solute falls more rapidly than the volume increases, and the pressure diffusion approaches zero for $\alpha > 0.06$.

The term containing G(α) in Equations 5.49a and

TABLE 5.4. *Summary of Calculations for Pore Theory of Solvent-Drag Reflection Coefficient*

α	$\dfrac{\bar{v}_s P}{RTL_P}$ [a]	$(1-\phi)^2$ [b]	$[(1-\alpha)^2 - (1-\alpha)^4]\,G(\alpha)$ [c]	σ_f [d]	σ_f [e]
0.0	0.000	0.000	0.000	0.000	0.000
0.1	0.011	0.036	0.043	0.031	0.034
0.2	0.027	0.129	0.152	0.125	0.138
0.3	0.033	0.260	0.304	0.271	0.286
0.4	0.029	0.409	0.472	0.441	0.458
0.5	0.019	0.562	0.634	0.615	0.627
0.6	0.009	0.705	0.773	0.764	0.773
0.7	0.003	0.828	0.878	0.875	0.884
0.8	0.0006	0.921	0.951	0.950	0.955
0.9	0.0002	0.980	0.989	0.989	0.991
1.0	0.0000	1.000	1.000	1.000	1.000

[a] Pressure-diffusion term (Eq. 5.50). [b] Value of σ_f when steric terms alone are considered (Eqs. 5.38 and 5.39). [c] Value of σ_f based on centerline approximation for G(α), no pressure-diffusion term. [d] Value of σ_f based on centerline approximation for G(α), including pressure-diffusion term from column 2. [e] Value of σ_f based on radial variation of G(α), including pressure-diffusion term from column 2.

5.49b is the principal determinant of the solvent-drag reflection coefficient in a pore. Accurate values for G(α) are given in Table 5.3. These values may be described, for $\alpha \leq 0.6$, by the relation

$$G(\alpha) = \frac{1 - (2/3)\alpha^2 - 0.20217\alpha^5}{1 - 0.75851\alpha^5} \qquad (5.51)$$

which predicts G(α) values slightly larger than those given in Table 5.3 for $\alpha > 0.6$. For example, G(α) converges to a value of 0.544 at $\alpha = 1$, instead of 0.5. A summary of calculations based on Equation 5.49 is given in Table 5.4. Anderson and Quinn (5) also derived Equation 5.49 but neglected the pressure-diffusion term (cf. columns 4 and 5 in Table 5.4).

Curry (28) and Levitt (81) examined the off-axis variation of G(α), designated by the term G(α,r), in more detail. Happel and Brenner (59) and Haberman and Sayre (57) give

$$G(\alpha,r) = 1 - (2/3)\alpha^2 - r^2/r_p^2 \qquad (5.52)$$

as a first approximation. The solvent-drag reflection coefficient is calculated by averaging G(α,r) over the area available to solute rather than by calculating a flow-weighted value of G(α) (cf. Eq. 5.49). The analysis by Curry yields

$$1 - \sigma_f = \frac{v_s P}{RTL_P} + (1-\alpha)^2[1 + 2\alpha + (7/3)\alpha^2] \qquad (5.53)$$

The second term may be expanded, retaining terms up to α^4

$$\sigma_f = \frac{16}{3}\alpha^2 - \frac{20}{3}\alpha^3 + \frac{7}{3}\alpha^4 - \frac{\bar{v}_s P}{RTL_P} \qquad (5.54)$$

which approaches the limit 1 as $\alpha \rightarrow 1$. Values of σ_f calculated from this equation are given in Table 5.4 (column 6). They are very close to values calculated from Equation 5.49 with Equation 5.51 used to describe G(α). A number of variations of Equation 5.54 have been published, and there is some confusion over their use in the literature. The pressure-diffusion term was not included in the analysis by Levitt (81). At $\alpha = 0.3$ in a cylindrical pore, the pressure diffusion would account for 5.4% of the solute flux through the membrane. Levitt also dropped the α^4 term in Equation 5.54. The expression no longer converges to 1 as $\alpha \rightarrow 1$. Drake and Davis (39) included the α^4 term in the equation, and Wangensteen (156) added a term in α^5, which is often quoted

$$\sigma_f = \frac{16}{3}\alpha^2 - \frac{20}{3}\alpha^3 + \frac{7}{3}\alpha^4 - 0.354\alpha^5 \qquad (5.55)$$

This expression closely describes σ_f for $\alpha \leq 0.7$; it reaches a maximum value at $\alpha = 0.75$ and then falls toward an unsatisfactory limit of 0.646 at $\alpha = 1$. There is no advantage gained from the addition of the α^5 term. In summary, two expressions provide the most complete description of σ_f: either Equation 5.49 based on a flow-averaged value of the axial G(α) or Equation 5.54 based on an area-averaged radially dependent G(α,r).

3. SOLVENT-DRAG REFLECTION COEFFICIENTS IN ARTIFICIAL MEMBRANES. Most of the σ_f values in Figure 5.7 were obtained from the reanalysis of Renkin's (119) ultrafiltration experiments in Figure 4.2. Additional values were obtained from the ultrafiltration experiments by Wendt et al. (159), who analyzed their data with Equation 4.55. The equivalent pore radius for each membrane was calculated from Poiseuille's law. (No experiments have been reported on membranes containing etched pores.) The lower solid line (curve A) in Figure 5.7 is calculated from the area-averaged value of G(α,r) (Eq. 5.54). Immediately above this solid line is a broken line (curve B) calculated from the flow-averaged relation (Eq. 5.49). The lower broken line (curve C) is the limiting relation $\sigma_f = (1-\phi)^2$ (Eq. 5.39). Two relations predicted from the earlier theory are also shown on the curve. The upper solid line (curve D) is one limit of the relation proposed by Durbin (40) and obtained by replacing A_w (Eq. 5.43) with A_p so that $\sigma_f = 1 - A_{s,f}/A_p$. The upper broken line (curve E) is the relation $\sigma_f = 1 - A_{s,f}/A_{w,f}$ (Eq. 5.43) for an equivalent pore radius of 23 Å. Overall, the experimental data for small α values conform more closely to the quadratic relation predicted from the new theory than to the relation of the previous theory. Nevertheless systematic deviations from the predicted curve in a number of experiments indicate the need for further refinements in the new theory. For example, there is an indication that at least in smaller pores the new theory underestimates the value of σ_f. More data from solutes with radii greater than 20% of the equivalent pore radius are required to evaluate the theory.

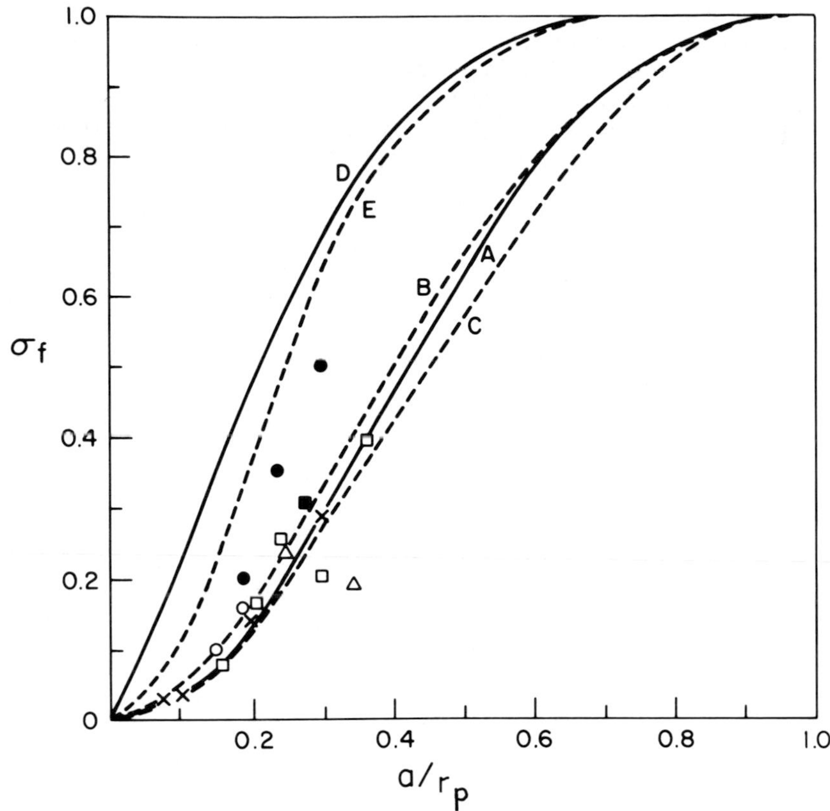

FIG. 5.7. Solvent-drag reflection coefficients as function of solute size. Solute size expressed relative to equivalent pore radius. *A*: new hydrodynamic formulation (Eq. 5.54). *B*: new hydrodynamic formulation based on center-line approximation (Eq. 5.49). *C*: limiting form of new formulation (Eq. 5.39). *D*: modified Durbin relation ($\sigma_f = 1 - A_s/A_p$). *E*: Durbin relation ($\sigma_f = 1 - A_{s,f}/A_{w,f}$) for dialysis tubing. Experimental values derived from analyses of Renkin ultrafiltration data (see Fig. 4.2 and ref. 159). Membranes and symbols are as in Fig. 5.3*B*.

E. Pore Theory of Ultrafiltration

Pappenheimer and associates (75, 109, 127) divided the transcapillary solute flux through capillary pores into a convective component entering the membrane, $J_v(A_{s,f}/A_{w,f})C_1$, and a diffusive component, $D(A_s/\Delta x)(C_1 - C_2)$

$$J_s = D(A_s/\Delta x)(C_1 - C_2) + J_v(A_{s,f}/A_{w,f})C_1 \quad (5.56)$$

where $A_s/\Delta x$ and $A_{s,f}/A_{w,f}$ were calculated from the pore theory of restricted diffusion. Rearranging Equation 5.56 leads to the ultrafiltration relation derived by Pappenheimer

$$\frac{C_2}{C_1} = \frac{\dfrac{A_{s,f}}{A_{w,f}} + \dfrac{DA_s}{J_v\Delta x}}{1 + \dfrac{DA_s}{J_v\Delta x}} \quad (5.57a)$$

which can also be written

$$\frac{C_2}{C_1} = \frac{\dfrac{A_{s,f}}{A_{w,f}} + \dfrac{PS}{J_v}}{1 + \dfrac{PS}{J_v}} \quad (5.57b)$$

by using the definition of A_s (see Eq. 5.31b et seq.).

On the basis of these new hydrodynamic concepts, $1 - \sigma_f$ calculated from the revised pore theory of solvent drag should be used instead of $A_{s,f}/A_{w,f}$, and Equation 5.56 should be written

$$J_s = PS(C_1 - C_2) + J_v(1 - \sigma_f)C_1 \quad (5.58)$$

The corresponding ultrafiltration relation is

$$\frac{C_2}{C_1} = \frac{(1 - \sigma_f) + \dfrac{PS}{J_v}}{1 + \dfrac{PS}{J_v}} \quad (5.59)$$

For a homogeneous membrane this equation is valid only for very small volume flows or very high diffusion fluxes because Equation 5.58 is the very low Péclet number approximation of the expression for diffusive flux in the presence of convective flow (see Eq. 2.38). The term $J_v(1 - \sigma_f)C_1$ correctly describes the solute flux entering the membrane by solvent drag under all conditions. On the other hand, $PS(C_1 - C_2)$ overestimates the diffusive component of transport at Péclet numbers larger than 0.2 because it fails to take into account the decrease in solute concentration gradient at the membrane entrance as flow increases. The diffusive component of flux entering the membrane is properly described by the complete expression for solute flux in the presence of a superimposed water flow (see discussion of Eqs. 2.35 and 4.49).

The relative importance of convective and diffusive transport at the channel entrance depends on the

Péclet number. The magnitude of the term Pe/($\exp^{Pe} - 1$) as a function of Pe is exactly the same as described in Figure 2.5. In steady-state ultrafiltration, Equation 4.49 applied to a cylindrical pore leads to a new expression for the concentration ratio across a membrane

$$\left(\frac{C_2}{C_1}\right)_p = \frac{(1 - \sigma_f) + \left(\frac{PS}{J_v}\right)\left[\frac{Pe}{\exp(Pe) - 1}\right]}{1 + \left(\frac{PS}{J_v}\right)\left[\frac{Pe}{\exp(Pe) - 1}\right]} \tag{5.60}$$

which, applied to a homogeneous population of pores, provides a complete description of ultrafiltration. In the limit of $Pe > 5$, it reduces exactly to the limiting form discussed earlier (see Eq. 4.56)

$$\left(\frac{C_2}{C_1}\right)_p = (1 - \sigma_f)_p \tag{5.61}$$

Equation 5.60 has not been applied to pore theory. Perl (113) recognized the need to account for the nonlinear form of the flux equation. His approach leads to an expression mathematically identical to Equation 5.60

$$\left(\frac{C_2}{C_1}\right)_p = \frac{PS[Pe(\coth Pe/2 - 1)/2] + J_v(1 - \sigma_f)}{PS[Pe(\coth Pe/2 - 1)/2] + J_v} \tag{5.62}$$

Perl applied the first-order approximation, $(Pe/2)(\coth Pe/2 - 1) = 1 - Pe/2$ (see Eq. 2.35), which is valid for $Pe < 1$, to derive Equation 4.58 for a pore model.

More recently a number of investigators (see ref. 14 for review) have recognized the errors that arise when Equation 4.58 is applied to analyze ultrafiltration in large pores at high Péclet numbers and have correctly used the pore equivalent of Equation 4.55. Equations 4.55, 5.60, and 5.62 are mathematically identical.

1. EXPERIMENTAL EVALUATION. Figure 5.8 shows the ultrafiltration experiments from Renkin's 1954 paper (119) reanalyzed with the modern hydrodynamic pore theory. For each solute the *PS* and σ_f values were estimated from Equations 5.29 and 5.54, respectively. The predicted curves were calculated from Equation 4.55. The analysis showed that the ultrafiltration of raffinose, sucrose, and glucose on Visking cellulose may be described in terms of solute and water flows through equivalent channels 12–16 Å in radius. Very similar equivalent radii were found in the original analysis of these data with Equation 5.57. This result is quite fortuitous. Apparently the underestimate of convective flux that results from the use of $A_{s,f}/A_{w,f}$ instead of $1 - \sigma_f$ (Eq. 5.56) is largely offset by an overestimate of diffusive flux by using *PS* instead of $PS\{Pe/[\exp(Pe) - 1]\}$ (Eq. 5.56).

It is instructive to compare analyses of the same experimental data (Figs. 4.2 and 5.8) with the same

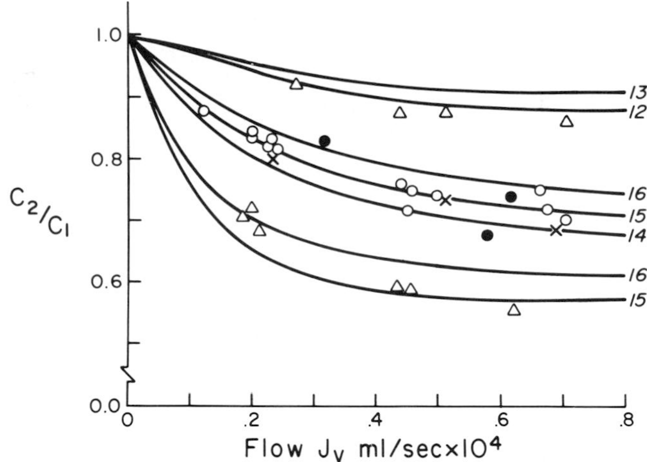

FIG. 5.8. Pore-theory analysis of ultrafiltration experiments in Fig. 4.2; membrane is Visking cellulose. *Solid curves* were calculated with nonlinear ultrafiltration theory (Eq. 4.55). Permeability–surface area products were calculated from pore theory (Eq. 5.29) with $(A_p/S)/\Delta x = 19\ cm^{-1}$. Solvent-drag reflection coefficients were calculated from Eq. 5.54. Relations for pore radii of 12–16 Å are shown.

relation between C_2/C_1 and flow across the membrane (Eq. 4.55, 5.60, 5.62) but with different constraints imposed on the way the membrane coefficients might vary. In the analysis described in Figure 4.2, *PS* was measured directly in diffusion experiments, and σ_f was chosen without constraints on its value. In the analysis in Figure 5.8, *PS* and σ_f must vary in relation to one another as described by pore theory. For sucrose transport through a 15-Å pore, the values of *PS* and σ_f estimated from pore theory are $0.22 \times 10^{-4}\ cm^3/s$ and 0.31, respectively, whereas the measured *PS* and estimated σ_f are $0.363 \times 10^{-4}\ cm^3/s$ and 0.38, respectively. The discrepancy may be caused by the tendency of the modern form of the pore theory of ultrafiltration to underestimate σ_f in the membrane and thus overestimate the solvent-drag component. A lower estimate of *PS* results from the need to compensate for an overestimate of solvent-drag convective flux. The discrepancy is in a direction opposite to that in the original Renkin analysis (119) of the data in which the solvent-drag component of flux was underestimated.

The resolution of discrepancies such as those described above lies not only in further development of pore ultrafiltration theory but also in more refined experimental design. For example, it is possible to test whether the estimates of σ_f (see Fig. 4.2) provide a consistent description of the transport system by increasing flow rates until the value of C_2/C_1 is truly constant. Similarly it is possible to test the prediction of pore theory that the C_2/C_1 value for raffinose has reached a limiting value at flow rates of 0.6×10^{-4} cm/s by increasing flow.

2. INTERMEDIATE-SIZED SOLUTES AT CAPILLARY

WALLS. The predictions of the pore theory of ultrafiltration can be tested in a quite remarkable way with an ultrafiltration experiment on mammalian hindlimb described by Pappenheimer et al. (109). At a steady filtration rate of 0.72 $ml \cdot min^{-1} \cdot 100\ g^{-1}$ of tissue, the mean tissue-to-plasma inulin concentration ratio was found to be 0.71. If the PS_{inu} values of 10.0×10^{-3} $cm^3 \cdot s^{-1} \cdot 100\ g^{-1}$ and σ_{inu} values of 0.375 (subscript inu denotes inulin) estimated by Renkin and Curry (124) are substituted in Equation 5.60, the predicted ratio of C_2/C_1 is 0.75. The agreement between predicted and measured values is encouraging; further experiments with intermediate-sized solutes could provide useful new data on the selectivity of the capillary wall.

From the steady-state condition $J_s = J_v C_2$ applied to a population of uniform pores, the fraction of total flux entering the membrane by convective transport during steady-state ultrafiltration is $(1 - \sigma_f)/R_{uf}$, where $R_{uf} = C_2/C_1$. In the example of inulin ultrafiltration given above, $1 - \sigma_f = 0.625$ and $R_{uf} = 0.75$. Therefore 0.625/0.75 or 83% of the flux is carried by convective transport. Contrary to the conclusion in the original analysis, this result shows that convective transport does play a significant role in steady ultrafiltration of molecules as small as inulin across the capillary wall. It is important to note that this conclusion is not inconsistent with the observation that diffusion is the predominant mechanism of transport for small solutes (including inulin) after a change in plasma solute concentration. Solute distribution to the interstitial space maintains a large transcapillary concentration difference.

3. BLOOD-TO-LYMPH ULTRAFILTRATION OF MACROMOLECULES. Figure 5.9 shows the ultrafiltration of individual plasma proteins across the blood-to-lymph barrier in skeletal muscle and skin capillaries in the dog paw. The data are taken from Renkin et al. (126); steady state is assumed. In addition the concentration of proteins in the prenodal lymph is assumed to represent the protein concentration on the tissue side of the capillary wall. The capillary wall is therefore assumed to be the principal barrier to transport. The ratio (R_{uf}) of protein concentration in lymph (C_L) to protein concentration in plasma (C_P) falls as lymph flow is increased from a normal level of $\sim 1 \times 10^{-4}$ ml/min per limb to values up to 800% of normal values produced by venous congestion. Furthermore the experimental values of R for albumin, γ-globulin, and fibrinogen approach a constant value as lymph flow increases—the larger solutes approach their limiting value at lower lymph flow rates. The following analysis of these results is based on the assumption that R, at a lymph flow of 6×10^{-4} ml/min, approaches the high Péclet number limit for $C_2/C_1 = \overline{1 - \sigma_f}$. This assumption is equivalent to the proposition that only porous pathways contribute to macromolecule solute flux. It specifically excludes solute flux via a pathway with no water flow. In fact the condition $C_2/C_1 = \overline{1 - \sigma_f}$ represents a limit of the relation derived in VIII. VESICLE AND LIPOPHILIC-SOLUTE TRANSPORT (p. 363; see Eq. 8.17) for ultrafiltration across a membrane containing porous and nonporous pathways.

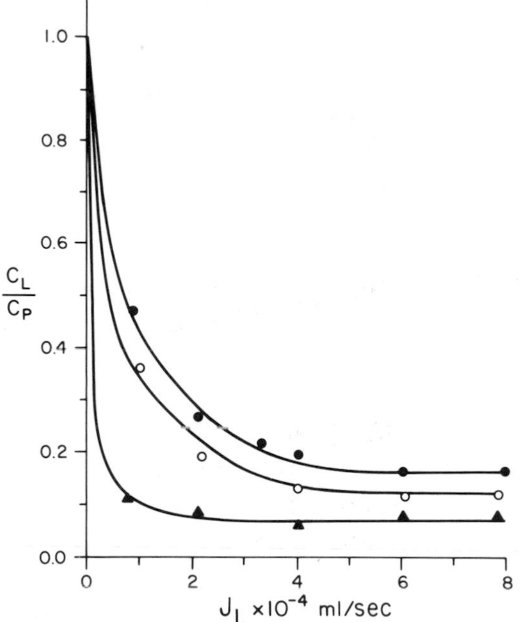

FIG. 5.9. Ultrafiltration of albumin (●), γ-globulin (○), and fibrinogen (▲) across blood-to-lymph barriers in dog hindlimb skeletal muscle and skin capillaries. *Solid curves* were fitted to the data by hand. For analysis in Table 5.5*A*, values of capillary membrane solvent-drag reflection coefficients ($\overline{1 - \sigma_f}$) were estimated from value of C_L/C_P at lymph flow of 6.16×10^{-4} ml/s. [Data from Renkin et al. (126).]

Values of $\overline{1 - \sigma_f}$ set equal to R_{uf} at a lymph flow of 6×10^{-4} ml/s are listed in Table 5.5*A* (row 2); corresponding values of $\overline{\sigma_f}$ for the whole membrane are given in row 3. Assuming that the membrane is homoporous, $\overline{PS}$ for the membrane was calculated by rearranging Equation 4.55

$$\overline{PS} = \frac{J_L(\overline{1 - \sigma_f})}{\ln\left[\dfrac{R\sigma_f}{R - (\overline{1 - \sigma_f})}\right]} \tag{5.63}$$

where J_L is the total lymph flow. Values of $\overline{PS}$ are in row 4 of Table 5.5*A*. Péclet numbers $[J_L(\overline{1 - \sigma_f})/\overline{PS}]$ corresponding to a lymph flow of 6×10^{-4} ml/s are given in row 5 of Table 5.5*A*. The numbers indicate an inconsistency in the analysis of these data; the Péclet numbers for albumin and γ-globulin (1.85 and 2.1, respectively) are significantly less than values (>5) required to accept R_{uf} as an estimate of $\overline{1 - \sigma_f}$. It is shown in the next section that a homoporous membrane model is inconsistent with the derived membrane parameters. An extended analysis of these parameters is given as an example of pore theory applications. Many of the concepts were introduced by Renkin and Taylor and their collaborators (9, 10, 126, 128, 147). The analysis provides a theoretical frame-

TABLE 5.5. *Convection and Diffusion of Macromolecules: Pore Analysis*

	Conditions	Albumin	γ-Globulin	Fibrinogen/ Macroglobulin
A. Homogeneous Membrane Analysis				
1.	a_e	35.5	56.0	100
2.	$\overline{1 - \sigma_f}$ [a]	0.165	0.115	0.08
3.	$\overline{\sigma_f}$	0.835	0.885	0.92
4.	$\overline{PS} \times 10^4$ (cm^3/s) per paw[b, c]	0.541	0.34	0.15
5.	$\overline{Pe}$ [c]	1.85	2.08	7.39
B. Two-Pathway Analysis: Limiting Values at High Péclet Numbers				
1.	σ_{lp} [d]	0.084	0.238	0.556
2.	$(1 - \sigma_f)_{lp}$	0.916	0.768	0.444
3.	$PS_{lp} \times 10^4$ (cm^3/s) per paw [e]	0.155	0.091	0.005
4.	Pe_{lp} [c]	6.38	9.11	95.6

C. Two-Pathway Analysis: Partition of Water Fluxes

	1 $J_L \times 10^4$, ml/s [f]	2 $(\Delta P_f)_{lp}$, mmHg [g]	3 $J_{v,lp} \times 10^4$, ml/s [h]	4 $(\Delta P_f)_{sp}$, mmHg [g]	5 $J_{v,sp} \times 10^4$, ml/s [i]	6 $\left(\frac{J_{v,lp}}{J_L}\right)$ [j]	7 R_{uf} [f] (Albumin)	8 Pe_{lp} [k] (Albumin)	9 R_{uf} [f] (γ-Globulin)	10 Pe_{lp} [k] (γ-Globulin)	11 R_{uf} [f] (Fibrinogen/Macroglobulin)	12 Pe_{lp} [k] (Fibrinogen/Macroglobulin)
1.	0.77	13.9	0.34	5.5	0.85	0.285	0.469	2.00	0.358	2.86	0.188	30.1
2.	2.21	21.4	0.52	10.6	1.64	0.240	0.294	3.07	0.203	4.38	0.124	46.1
3.	3.29	28.8	0.70	17.4	2.69	0.207	0.236	4.13	0.156	5.90	0.098	62.1
4.	4.00	35.0	0.85	23.4	3.62	0.189	0.223	5.02	0.154	7.17	0.085	75.4
5.	6.16	44.0	1.08	32.8	5.08	0.175	0.165	6.38	0.121	9.11	0.074	95.6
6.	7.89	56.7	1.37	45.1	6.98	0.165	0.159	8.09	0.119	11.5	0.074	121.0

D. Two-Pathway Analysis: Partition of Solute Flux

	1 $J_L \times 10^4$, ml/s [f]	2 % CF [l] (Albumin)	3 % DF [m] (Albumin)	4 % NP [n] (Albumin)	5 % CF [l] (γ-Globulin)	6 % DF [m] (γ-Globulin)	7 % NP [n] (γ-Globulin)	8 % CF [l] (Fibrinogen/Macroglobulin)	9 % DF [m] (Fibrinogen/Macroglobulin)	10 % NP [n] (Fibrinogen/Macroglobulin)
1.	0.77	55.6	6.9	37.5	61.05	4.9	33.6	67.3	0.3	32.4
2.	2.21	74.7	5.6	19.7	90.7	3.4	5.9	85.9	0.2	13.9
3.	3.29	80.3	3.5	16.2	101.7	2.2	−3.9	93.7	0.1	6.2
4.	4.00	77.6	2.7	19.7	93.0	1.7	4.6	98.7		
5.	6.16	97.1	1.3	0	111.0	1.3		105.0		
6.	7.89	95.0	1.0	4	106.0	1.1		99.0		

[a]Estimated as value of R_{uf} when lymph flow is 6×10^{-4} ml/s in Fig. 5.9. [b]Calculated from Eq. 5.63. [c]Calculated for lymph flow of 6×10^{-4} ml/s. [d]Calculated from Eq. 5.53; $r_p = 200$ Å. [e]Calculated from estimate of $L_{P,lp}$; Eq. 5.31b (see text for details). [f]Experimental values from Renkin et al. (126, 128). [g]ΔP_f = capillary pressure $P_c - \sigma_d \Delta\Pi$; $\Delta\Pi$ calculated from plasma and lymph protein concentrations ($P_c = 15 + 0.8 \times$ venous pressure). [h]Calculated from Eq. 5.67a. [i]Calculated from Eq. 5.67b. [j]Calculated from Eq. 5.67c. [k]Calculated as $J_{v,lp}(1 - \sigma_f)_{lp}/PS_{lp}$; PS_{lp} is given in row 3 of *B*. [l]Calculated as convective flux (CF) in large pore $[J_{v,lp}(1 - \sigma)_{lp}C_p]$ expressed as percent of total flux ($J_L C_L$); values are given for each solute. [m]Calculated as diffusive flux (DF) in large pore $[PS_{lp}(C_p - C_L)]$ expressed as percent of total flux. [n]NP, nonporous; calculated as (measured flux − total calculated large-pore flux)/(measured flux).

work for applications of ultrafiltration theory to other organs as described in the chapter by Taylor and Granger in this *Handbook*.

4. PARALLEL-PATHWAY MODEL. The σ_f values in Table 5.5 are inconsistent with ultrafiltration through a population of uniform pores. A σ_f value for albumin (a_e 35.5 Å) of 0.835 corresponds to transport through uniform pores of 53-Å radius; this pathway would not allow passage of γ-globulin or fibrinogen. On the other hand, a σ_f value of 0.93 for fibrinogen corresponds to a pore radius of 140 Å for which σ_{alb} (subscript alb denotes albumin) would be 0.27. The explanation of these problems may lie in the multiplicity of pathways for water flow and solute ultrafiltration in the capillary wall. A description of ultrafiltration through a membrane with more than one pathway is developed in this subsection. The solute flux through each porous pathway is given by Equation 4.49. If the Péclet number in each porous pathway is >5, Pe/[exp(Pe) − 1] is close to zero [$(dC/dx)_0$ at the pore entrance is close to zero], and the solute flux through the membrane can be described by

$$J_s = \Sigma J_{v,i}(1 - \sigma_i)C_1 \quad (5.64)$$

where the subscript i refers to individual pathways. The simplest application of this equation is for pores permeable to macromolecules (large-pore pathway, designated lp) in parallel with a porous pathway that excludes macromolecules (small-pore pathway, designated sp, in which σ_f for albumin is assumed to be one). Then

$$J_s = J_{v,lp}(1 - \sigma_{f,lp})C_1 \quad (5.65a)$$

or

$$J_s = J_L \left(\frac{J_{v,lp}}{J_L} \right) (1 - \sigma_{f,lp}) C_1 \quad (5.65b)$$

It is easy to show that in the steady state there is always net filtration through a membrane consisting of a semipermeable channel and a leaky channel in parallel. There can be no steady-state reabsorption (see the chapter by Michel in this *Handbook*). Thus from Equations 5.64–5.65b it can be seen that the solvent-drag reflection coefficient of the membrane, $\overline{1 - \sigma_f}$ [measured as $J_s(J_L C_1)$], is given by

$$(1 - \sigma_f)_{Pe>5} = \left(\frac{J_{v,lp}}{J_L} \right) (1 - \sigma_{f,lp}) \quad (5.66)$$

Figure 5.10 shows a graphical method of solving Equation 5.66 for the ratio J_v/J_L and the pore size that accounts for the change of $\overline{1 - \sigma_f}$ with solute size. The analysis was introduced by Renkin et al. (128). Values of $1 - \sigma_{f,lp}$ as a function of solute size for pore radii of 100, 200, and 300 Å were calculated from Equation 5.54 and plotted as broken lines in Figure 5.10 with a logarithmic scale for the ordinate. The broken lines, transferred to transparent overlays, were superimposed over estimated values of $\overline{1 - \sigma_f}$ (see Table 5.5*A*, row 2) to determine the ratio $J_{v,lp}/J_L$ and the pore size that best fitted the data.

Pores 200 Å in radius, which account for 18% of the volume flow at a lymph flow of 6×10^{-4} ml/s ($J_{v,lp} = 1.08 \times 10^{-4}$ ml/s), are consistent with the data. Values of $\sigma_{f,lp}$ calculated for a 200-Å channel (Eq. 5.53) are given in row 1 of Table 5.5*B*. These are significantly different from the whole-membrane values. To calculate the Péclet number in the large pore (Pe_{lp}) the permeability–surface area product for the channel (PS_{lp}) was calculated in three steps. *1*) The hydraulic conductivity–surface area product $(L_pS)_{lp}$ was calculated as $J_{v,lp}/\Delta P_f$, where ΔP_f is the effective filtration pressure (see Table 5.5*C*): $(L_pS)_{lp} = 0.19 \times 10^{-8}$ $cm^5 \cdot s^{-1} \cdot dyn^{-1}$ per paw. *2*) The value of $(A_p/\Delta x)_{lp}$ was calculated from Equation 5.12 (pore radius, 200 Å). *3*) The *PS* value was calculated from Equation 5.31b (see row 3 of Table 5.5*B*). Values of Pe_{lp} are given in row 4 of Table 5.5*B*. These values conform to the hypothesis that convective flow is the principal transport mechanism in the large pores when the lymph flow is 6.0×10^{-4} ml/s or greater. The partitioning of fluxes of water and solutes at lower capillary pressures is calculated as follows.

The volume flow across each pathway is calculated by applying the Starling equation to each pathway. The results are summarized in Table 5.5*C*

$$J_{v,lp} = (L_pS)_{lp}(\Delta P - \sigma_{d,lp}\Delta\Pi) \quad (5.67a)$$

$$J_{v,sp} = (L_pS)_{sp}(\Delta P - \Delta\Pi) \quad (5.67b)$$

$$J_L = J_{v,lp} + J_{v,sp} \quad (5.67c)$$

Net filtration pressure (ΔP_f) is equal to $\Delta P - \sigma_d\Delta\Pi$; ΔP_f is larger across the large-pore system than across the small-pore system because the osmotic reflection coefficient is smaller in the large-pore pathway. Estimates of ΔP_f for large- and small-pore systems are listed in columns 2 and 4, respectively, of Table 5.5*C*.

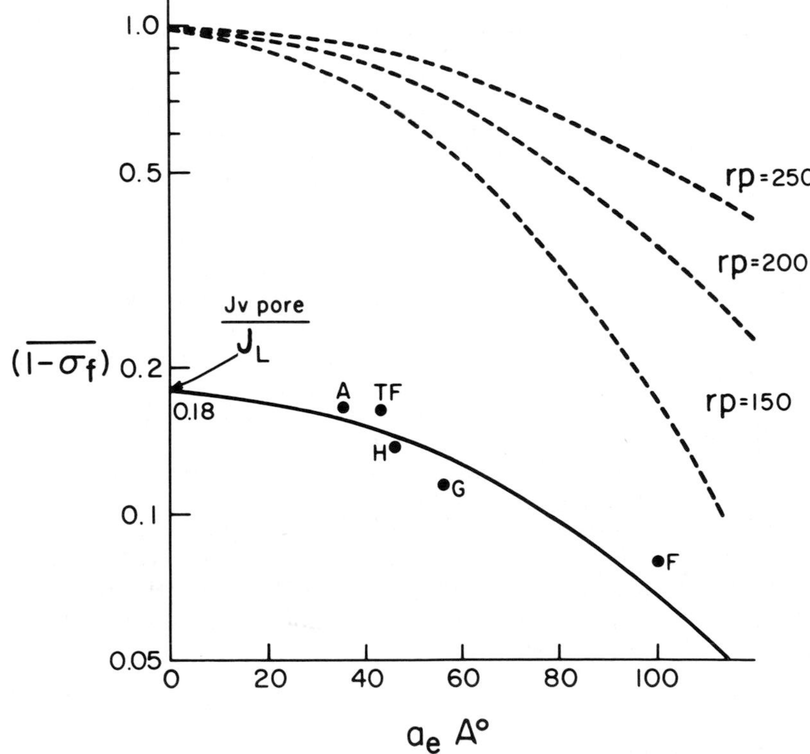

FIG. 5.10. Hydrodynamic pore analysis of convective pathway transport of macromolecules in skeletal muscle and skin capillaries of dog hindlimb. Experimental points are for albumin (A), transferrin (TF), haptoglobulin (H), γ-globulin (G), and fibrinogen plus macroglobulin (F). Semilogarithmic plot is graphical solution of parallel-pathway model (Eq. 5.66). *Broken lines* are theoretical relation between 1 − σ_f and solute radius (Eq. 5.54) for spherical molecules in cylindrical pores. *Solid curve* is for pore radius of 200 Å, displaced downwards. [Adapted from Renkin et al. (128).]

The hydraulic conductivity of the small-pore pathway $(L_pS)_{sp}$ was calculated as the small-pore volume flow $J_{v,sp} = J_{v,L} - J_{v,lp}$ divided by the effective filtration pressure across the small pores $(\Delta P_f)_{sp}$ at a lymph flow of 6×10^{-4} ml/s: $(L_pS)_{sp} = 1.16 \times 10^{-8}$ $cm^5 \cdot s^{-1} \cdot dyn^{-1}$ per paw. Values of $J_{v,lp}$ and $J_{v,sp}$ at all other lymph flows were calculated from Equations 5.67a and 5.67b (columns 3 and 5, respectively). These calculations emphasize that a complex interplay of hydrostatic and osmotic forces determines the distribution of water flow between the pathways. Values of $J_{v,lp}$ expressed as a fraction of total water flow $(J_{v,lp} + J_{v,sp})$ are in Table 5.5*C* (column 6). It should be emphasized that $\Delta\Pi$ is a function of transcapillary water flux (see the chapter by Michel in this *Handbook*).

As filtration pressure across the large pores is reduced from 56.7 mmHg (high capillary pressure) to 13.9 mmHg (control pressure), the fraction of total lymph flow passing through the large pores increases from 18% to 28.5%. The ratio of $J_{v,lp}/J_L$ is not constant as assumed in earlier analyses of these data (128). The consequences of this observation in terms of solute flux through the large pore are calculated next. Experimental values of R for each solute are listed in columns 7, 9, and 11 of Table 5.5*C*. Values of the Péclet number at each lymph flow are given in columns 8, 10, and 12 of Table 5.5*C*.

The analysis of solute flux is summarized in Table 5.5*D*. The convective flux through the large pore equals $J_{v,lp}(1 - \sigma_{f,lp})C_P$. The total flux through the membrane equals J_LC_L. The ratio of convective to total flux therefore equals $(J_{v,lp}/J_L)(1 - \sigma_{lp})/R$. Calculated values are given for each solute in Table 5.5*D* (columns 2, 5, and 8). This preliminary analysis indicates that >50% of the flux of macromolecules is coupled to water flow entering the membrane through the large pores. This result differs from the interpretation of these data published by Renkin et al. (128). In the previous analysis it was assumed that water flow through the large-pore pathway was a constant proportion of total water flow. As demonstrated in Table 5.5*C*, this assumption is incorrect for a heteroporous membrane and leads to an underestimate of convective solute transport at all low lymph flows.

Whereas almost all macromolecule flux is coupled to water flow at high capillary pressure, close to 50% is not coupled to water flow at normal capillary pressure. The additional diffusion flux is not accounted for by diffusion in the large-pore pathway (see columns 3, 6, and 9 of Table 5.5*D*). The fractional diffusive flux is $PS_{lp}(1 - R)/J_L$. The maximum contribution is 7% of the total flux for albumin. The analysis indicates that at normal capillary pressures 30%–40% of macromolecule flux crosses the capillary wall via a separate nonporous pathway (see columns 4, 7, and 10 of Table 5.5*D*). The present analysis is the first step in an iterative process that will provide better estimates of the partitioning of water and solute fluxes and enable more refined experimental studies of this important problem. A more extended analysis must take into account the contribution to macromolecule flux of nonporous pathways (vesicle shuttle, vesicle exchange, specific binding and/or diffusion in the plasma membrane). Vesicle transport is discussed in VIII. VESICLE AND LIPOPHILIC-SOLUTE TRANSPORT (p. 363). It is shown (Eq. 8.17) that R does not generally approach $1 - \sigma_f$ at high Péclet numbers when nonporous pathways are present.

5. MEMBRANE SOLVENT-DRAG REFLECTION COEFFICIENTS IN HETEROGENEOUS MEMBRANES. Equation 5.66 is a particular form of the relation that follows directly from Equation 5.64

$$\overline{(1 - \sigma_f)}_{\left[\left(\frac{dC_i}{dx}\right)_0 = 0\right]_{**}} = \frac{\Sigma J_{v,i}(1 - \sigma_{f,i})}{\Sigma J_{v,i}} \tag{5.68}$$

where the double asterisk indicates the condition for all pathways. This equation has been derived before (71, 112), but the constraints are new. Previously $1 - \sigma_f$ was defined for the condition $\Delta C = 0$. Equation 5.68, defined for the condition that dC/dx at the membrane entrance is zero, removes the apparent inconsistency that a solvent-drag reflection coefficient is measured under conditions of a concentration difference across the membrane.

It is emphasized that the partition of flux into convective and diffusive components is made only at the entrance to the membrane. This assumption is sufficient to reach the conclusions drawn above. Within the pore the solute concentration gradients appear. It is confusing to talk about the convective and diffusive components of flux across the membrane because the relative importance of each component will change at every point within the membrane.

F. Osmotic Flow

1. OSMOTIC REFLECTION COEFFICIENT IN PORES. Until recently no mechanistic model to describe osmotic flow in a pore permeable to the solute was available. The osmotic reflection coefficient was described assuming $\sigma_d = \sigma_f$ (4, 7, 28, 40). Anderson and Malone (4) extended the description of osmotic flow in a porous semipermeable membrane to a partially selective pore. The osmotic flow in a semipermeable membrane is considered before a simplified version of the analysis by Anderson and Malone is developed.

2. FLOW IN SEMIPERMEABLE MEMBRANES. The excellent review of the mechanics and thermodynamics of osmotic flow through porous semipermeable membranes by Mauro (89) emphasizes the importance of distinguishing between transmembrane and intramembrane events. The six parts of Figure 5.11 show a rigid porous membrane separating compartment 1 (containing an aqueous solution of an impermeant

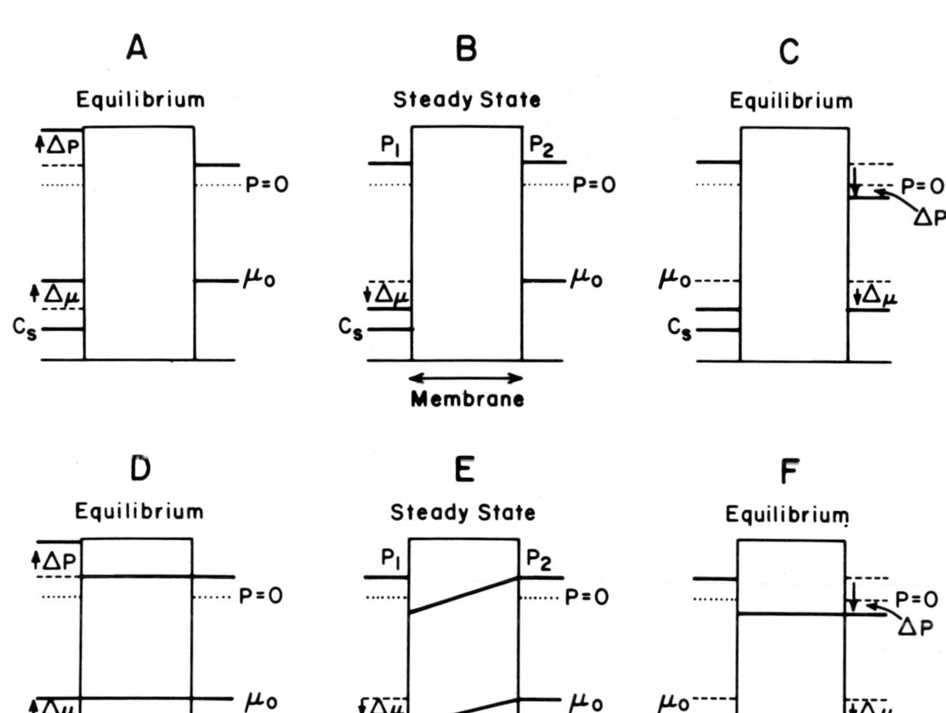

FIG. 5.11. Thermodynamic analysis of osmosis in porous membrane. *A–C*: profiles of thermodynamic variables in external phase to left and right of membrane. Zero pressure (P) is indicated by *fine dotted line.* Concentration of impermeant solute in external phase is shown by C_s. *D–F*: profiles of thermodynamic variables extended throughout membrane phase. Linear profiles for steady state reflects assumption that hydraulic conductance is constant. [From Mauro (89).]

solute: pressure, P_1; chemical potential of water, μ_1) from compartment 0 (containing pure water: pressure, P_0; chemical potential, μ_0). As described in III. THERMODYNAMIC PRINCIPLES (p. 316; Eqs. 3.31–3.37) the addition of solute to the water lowers the chemical potential of the water—in Figure 5.11*B* this amount is shown as $\Delta\mu$. As long as the concentration difference is maintained, a steady osmotic flow of water occurs across the membrane. The usual way to prevent osmotic flow and to achieve osmotic equilibrium is to raise the pressure on the solution by an amount (ΔP) sufficient to equalize the potential energy of water on each side of the membrane (Fig. 5.11*A*). From Equation 3.41 the equilibrium condition $\mu_1 = \mu_0$ is expressed as

$$v_w(P_0 + \Delta P) + RT \ln X_{w,1} = v_w P_0 + RT \ln X_{w,0} \tag{5.69}$$

The steps required to simplify this relation to the well-known expression for the osmotic pressure of a dilute solution are given below. For pure water $X_{w,0} = 1$, therefore

$$\Delta P = \frac{RT}{v_w} \ln X_{w,1} \tag{5.70}$$

Substitute for $X_{w,1}$ from Equation 3.33

$$\Delta P = -\frac{RT}{v_w} \ln\left(1 - \frac{n_s}{n_s + n_w}\right) \tag{5.71}$$

If $n_s/(n_s + n_w)$ is small, $\ln[1 - n_s/(n_w + n_s)] \sim n_s/(n_w + n_s)$ and

$$\Delta P = \frac{RT}{v_w}\left(\frac{n_s}{n_w + n_s}\right) \tag{5.72}$$

Furthermore for $n_s \ll n_w$

$$\Delta P = \frac{RTn_s}{v_w n_w} = RTC_s \tag{5.73}$$

where C_s is the molar concentration. The value of RT is 23 atm·mol^{-1}·liter^{-1} at 25°C (1 atm = 760 mmHg).

A second equilibrium position is obtained with a reduced pressure on the solvent (Fig. 5.11*C*). If the solute concentration is greater than 1/23 moles (43 mM), ΔP in Figure 5.11*C* is greater than 1 atm. Thus the water in the channel is under tension. To extend the analysis to the fluid inside the membrane, the water in the channel is assumed to be a finite phase in which the bulk solution thermodynamic expressions apply. The water just inside the membrane is also assumed to be very close to equilibrium with the water in compartment 1. The profiles within the membrane for the equilibrium case are shown in Figures 5.11*D* and 5.11*F*, corresponding to parts *A* and *C*, respectively.

The final step in the development of the thermodynamic description of osmotic flow is to determine the profile of pressure and chemical potential within the membrane as steady-state osmotic flow occurs

(Fig. 5.11*B*). The profiles shown (Fig. 5.11*E*) are based on the additional assumption that the water just inside the membrane is in equilibrium with water in solution at the interface, even though there is water flow. Water molecules at the interface are assumed to remain close to equilibrium because of the very small distances involved, perhaps only a few molecular diameters. If P_m is the pressure just inside the membrane at the interface between solution and water in the membrane and P is the atmospheric pressure on the solution, the condition $\mu_{w,1} = \mu_w$ just inside the membrane yields

$$v_w P_1 + RT \ln X_{w,1} = v_w P_m \tag{5.74}$$

Therefore

$$(P_m - P_1) = \frac{RT}{v_w} \ln X_{w,1} \tag{5.75}$$

Because $X_{w,1} < 1$, ln $X_{w,1}$ is negative indicating that P_m falls below P_1. The result shows that flow occurs within the membrane down a gradient of hydrostatic pressure. Both the water and the channel must be able to support the tensile stress that may develop. Experimental results from Mauro (see ref. 89 for review) conform to the hypothesis that tension is developed within the channel.

3. MECHANICS OF OSMOTIC FLOW. Thermodynamic, experimental, and statistical mechanical arguments have been presented recently (61, 88) that soundly reject the Scholander-Hammel concept that water in solution is under tension from solute bombardment of solution-free surface (58); tension is developed only within the membrane. Further refinements in the statistical mechanical description of the fluid state can be expected to provide new insights into the interfacial region during osmotic flow. Ultimately a description of the interface between solution and solvent, analogous to the statistical mechanical interpretation of the Donnan equilibrium interface described in VII. CHARGE (p. 358) (Fig. 7.2), is required.

4. ANDERSON-MALONE MODEL. The region of the pore from which solute is excluded is represented by the shaded regions in Figure 5.12*A* for a semipermeable membrane and Figure 5.12*B* for a partially selective cylindrical pore. For a solute of radius a in a pore of radius r_p, solute is excluded from the region $r_p - a < r < r_p$. If the pore radius is small compared with the pore length, a one-dimensional model assuming radial equilibrium can be applied (4). The same argument, applied to the solution-water interface in a semipermeable membrane to derive the relation $\Delta P = RTC_s$ (Eq. 5.61), can be applied to the interface at $r = r_p - a$, where water from which solute is assumed to be excluded is in equilibrium with water in solution. A radial distribution of pressure is thereby defined

$$\begin{aligned} P &= P_0 \qquad 0 < r \le r_p - a \\ P &= P_0 - RTC_x \qquad r_p - a < r \le r_p \end{aligned} \tag{5.76}$$

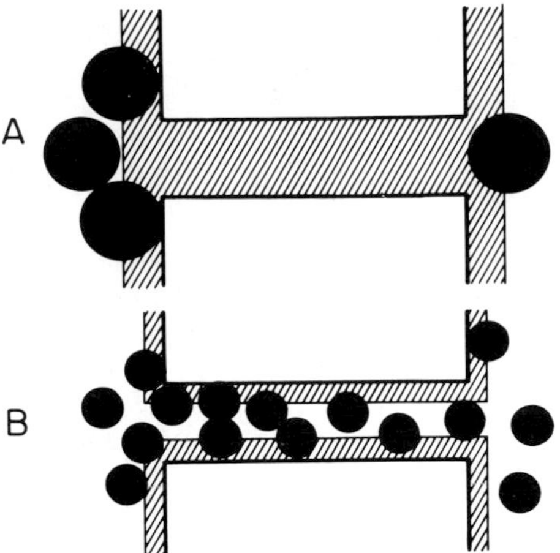

FIG. 5.12. Region of pore from which solute is excluded (*shaded*) in semipermeable membrane (*A*) and partially selective membrane (*B*).

where C_x is solute concentration at axial position x along the pore. When there is a solute gradient (dC_x/dx) within the pore, an axially directed pressure gradient will be present in the region $r_p - a < r < r_p$ with magnitude $RTdC_x/dx$.

The osmotic flow is calculated by integrating the flow equations in a pore with a radially distributed pressure at any position along the pore. The procedure is almost identical to that leading to Poiseuille's law (Eqs. 5.3–5.9). The resultant volume flow through a pore is

$$J_{v,p} = \frac{\pi r_p^4}{8\eta \Delta x} \{\Delta P - [1 - 2(1-\alpha)^2 - (1-\alpha)^4] RT\Delta C\} \tag{5.77}$$

Because $r_p^2/8\eta\Delta x$ is the hydraulic conductivity of a cylindrical pore, this can be rewritten

$$J_v/S = L_P(\Delta P - \sigma_d RT\Delta C) \tag{5.78}$$

where

$$\sigma_d = 1 - 2(1-\alpha)^2 + (1-\alpha)^4 \tag{5.79}$$

Therefore Equation 5.77 is a statement of the Starling equation for a homoporous membrane. By direct comparison with Equation 5.38, Equation 5.79 yields

$$\sigma_d = (1 - \phi_{st})^2 \tag{5.80}$$

where the subscript st denotes steric forces. Equation 5.80 is identical to the expression for the solvent-drag reflection coefficient when only steric forces act on a solute carried in a parabolic profile. Equality of σ_d and σ_f demonstrates global reciprocity for this simple case. The difference between σ_d described by Equation 5.80 and σ_f described by the more complete theory of the solvent-drag reflection coefficient (Eq. 5.54) is expressed by the difference between curves A and B in Figure 5.7. No theory of osmotic flow is available for the more general case in which the frictional forces on the solute within the membrane are taken into account. Anderson and Malone (4) show that the velocity profile in the pore corresponding to the pressure distribution in Equation 5.76 is not parabolic. Thus the solvent drag will not be described by the same values of σ_f as determined for a fully developed parabolic profile.

5. EXPERIMENTAL EVALUATION OF PORE THEORY FOR OSMOTIC REFLECTION COEFFICIENTS. Figure 5.13 shows osmotic reflection coefficients from artificial membranes plotted as a function of the ratio of solute radii to pore radii (131). The data in Figure 5.13*A* were measured on etched mica membranes. Most of the experimental values of σ_d are larger than those predicted by Equation 5.80, although the range of values measured at one value of a/r_p is also very large. Osmotic reflection coefficients for cellulosic membranes are shown in Figure 5.13*B*; the equivalent pore radius was calculated from Poiseuille's law. The solid line is the relation $\sigma_d = (1 - \phi)^2$; the broken line is calculated from Equation 5.54 assuming $\sigma_d = \sigma_f$. In all the membranes that were studied, the predicted relation underestimated σ_d for values of α greater than 0.15. The source of this discrepancy has not been investigated. One deficiency in Equation 5.80, that it does not account for frictional forces on the solute within the pore, is likely to result in an underestimate of σ_d. Another deficiency is that Equation 5.80 does not take into account electrostatic, adsorptive, and more complex steric interactions that might determine the distribution of solute in the pore. Anderson (2) has recently proposed that

$$\Delta J_v/S = L_P(1 - \phi_{st})^2 \Delta\Pi \tag{5.81}$$

is a quite general description of osmotic flow through porous membranes. Equation 5.81 describes the osmotic flow calculated for channels and solutes with a wide range of configurations. The results suggest that Equation 5.80 has a generality beyond its derivation for a uniform cylindrical pore. Further study on the factors determining the partitioning of solutes into membranes may provide insight into the discrepancies found in Figure 5.13.

6. PARALLEL-PATHWAY MODEL OF OSMOTIC FLOW. This subsection illustrates the application of the pore theory of the osmotic reflection coefficient to the interpretation of reflection coefficients measured in single perfused capillaries (35, 93). The solid line in Figure 5.14 is the predicted relation for the reflection

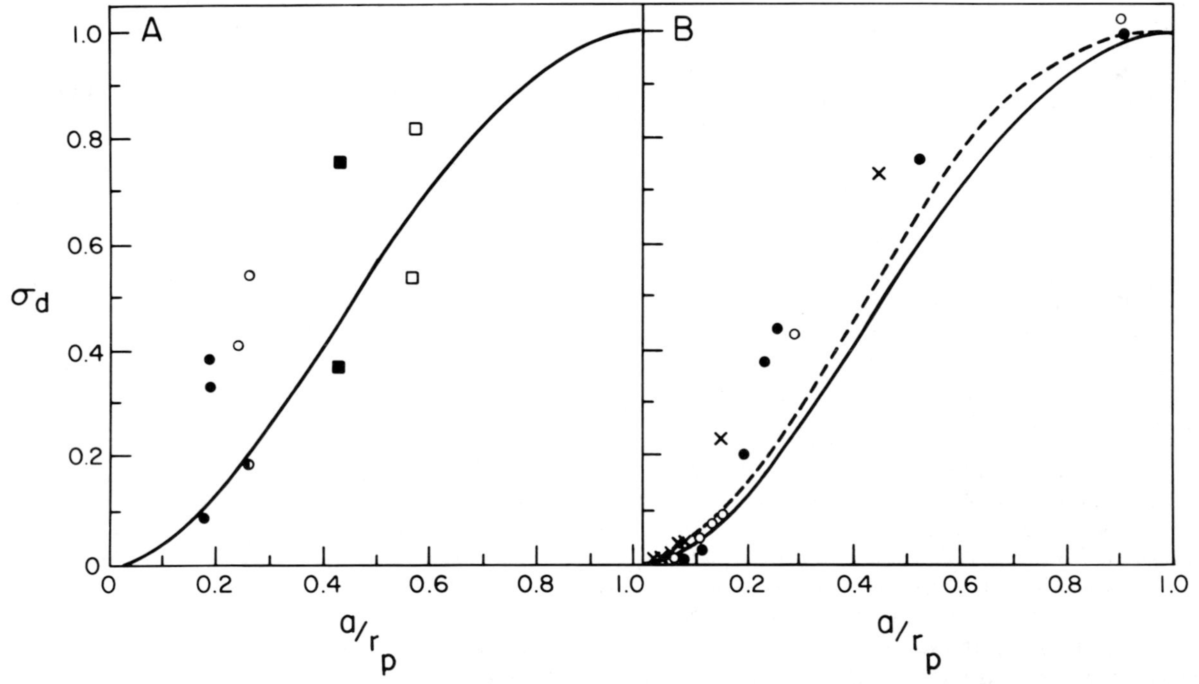

FIG. 5.13. Osmotic reflection coefficients of hydrophilic solutes as function of solute radius. Solute radius is expressed relative to pore radius. *A*: etched pores. *Solid line* is relation $\sigma_d = (1 - \phi)^2$. ○, Albumin, 4 g/100 ml in pores of nominal diam 300 Å (measured radii, 141–151 Å); ●, albumin, 4 g/100 ml in pore of nominal diam 500 Å (measured radii, 204–210 Å); ◐, albumin, 8 g/100 ml in 140-Å pore; □, γ-globulin, 10 g/100 ml in pores of nominal diam 300 Å (measured radii, 98 Å); ■, globulin, 10 g/100 ml, in pores of nominal diam 500 Å (measured radii, 131–132 Å). Plasma proteins apparently adsorb onto walls of water channel reducing effective channel dimensions. Measured equivalent pore radii calculated from Poiseuille's law and water flow in presence of solute. [Data from Schultz et al. (131).] *B*: cellulose membranes. *Solid line* is relation $\sigma_d = (1 - \phi)^2$; *broken line* is calculated assuming $\sigma_d = \sigma_f$, with σ_f described by Eq. 5.54. Data for small hydrophilic solutes and albumin on cellulose membranes; ●, Visking cellulose; ○, Dupont cellophane; ×, Sylvania sucrose wet gel. [Data from Durbin (40).]

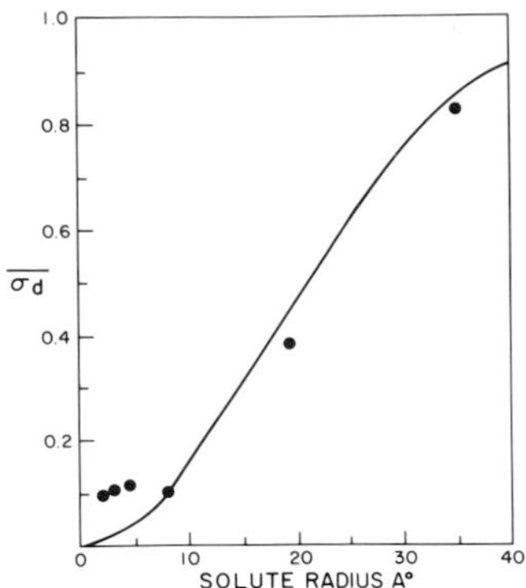

FIG. 5.14. Osmotic reflection coefficients (σ_d) as a function of solute radius measured in single perfused capillaries of frog mesentery. *Solid line* is calculated for pore radius of 50 Å from $\sigma_d = (1 - \phi)^2$. [Data from Curry et al. (35).]

coefficient of solutes in a 50-Å-radius pore as solute size increases. Measured values of the osmotic reflection coefficients for NaCl, glucose, sucrose, vitamin B_{12}, myoglobin, and albumin in individually perfused capillaries of frog mesentery are shown. The experimental values for myoglobin and albumin are reasonably consistent with transport through 50-Å pores, but the measured reflection coefficients for solutes with Stokes radii <10 Å are too large to be described by transport through 50-Å pores. For example, the reflection coefficient of NaCl is 0.12, which is >500% of the value predicted for a 50-Å pore. An equivalent pore radius of 12 Å would account for this σ_{NaCl} value but would be inconsistent with the observed reflection coefficients for solutes with Stokes radii >12 Å. Thus these data are inconsistent with a single porous pathway for osmotic flow.

The experimental data for small solutes conform to the hypothesis introduced by Pappenheimer (108) and formulated explicitly for the capillary wall by Lifson (82) and by Tosteson (148) that some of the osmotic water flow crosses the capillary wall via a pathway that excludes small hydrophilic solutes (35). Figure 5.15 illustrates the parallel-pathway hypothesis. A semipermeable pathway for water flow across the capillary wall has a hydraulic conductivity $L_{P,1}$ and occupies a fraction A_1 of the total membrane area. It lies in parallel with a porous pathway with a hydraulic conductivity $L_{P,2}$ and a fractional area A_2. The hydraulic conductivity of the whole membrane $\bar{L}_P$ is the area-weighted sum of individual hydraulic conductivities (71)

$$\bar{L}_P = L_{P,1}A_1 + L_{P,2}A_2 \tag{5.82}$$

The total osmotic flow $\Delta J_v/S$ across a unit area of membrane that is caused by a concentration difference of test solute (ΔC) is

$$\Delta J_v/S = L_{P,1}A_1RT\Delta C + L_{P,2}A_2\sigma_pRT\Delta C \tag{5.83}$$

The partitioning of osmotic flows depends on the relative values of L_P, A, and σ_p. Consider the case in which $L_{P,2}A_2$ is 10 times larger than $L_{P,1}A_1$. The latter ratio appears to be representative of some capillary beds (35, 49, 124). When the osmotic solute has dimensions that approach those of the pore pathway and $\sigma_p \rightarrow 1$, 90% of the osmotic flow occurs via the pore pathway. However, when the solute reflection coefficient of the pore pathway is ~0.1, the osmotic flows will be distributed equally between the semipermeable and porous pathways. Finally, when the solute osmotic reflection coefficient of the pore pathway is 0.01, only 10% of the flow occurs through the pore pathway.

In the limit where $\sigma_p = 0$, $\Delta J_v/S = L_{P,1}A_1RT\Delta C$, and the osmotic reflection coefficient of the whole membrane ($\bar{\sigma}_d$) is described by (see also Eq. 4.13)

$$\bar{\sigma}_d = \frac{L_{P,1}}{\bar{L}_P} A_1 \qquad \sigma_p = 0 \tag{5.84}$$

According to this, $\bar{\sigma}_d$ for small solutes is determined by *1*) the magnitude of the hydraulic conductivity of the semipermeable pathway relative to the whole-membrane conductivity ($L_{P,1}/\bar{L}_P$) and *2*) the fractional area occupied by the semipermeable pathway, A_1. Curry et al. (35) suggested that the semipermeable pathway may represent a pathway across the endothelial cells, which occupy >99.9% of the membrane surface; they therefore interpreted the product $\bar{L}_P\bar{\sigma}$ for small solutes as the hydraulic conductivity of the endothelial cells in frog mesentery and calculated a mean value of ~0.2×10^{-7} $cm \cdot s^{-1} \cdot cmH_2O^{-1}$. This value may be an overestimate because the osmotic contribution from the porous pathway has been excluded. This omission can be corrected if the definition of the osmotic reflection coefficient (Eq. 4.14b) is applied to Equation 5.83

$$\bar{\sigma}_d = \frac{L_{P,1}A_1}{\bar{L}_P} (1 - \sigma_p) + \sigma_p \tag{5.85}$$

This equation has been used to describe the osmotic reflection coefficients plotted in Figure 5.14 in terms of water flow through cylindrical pores 55 Å in radius in parallel with a semipermeable pathway accounting for 10% of the total membrane hydraulic conductivity (92). The graph analysis applied in Figure 5.10 for solvent-drag reflection coefficients can be used to confirm this result. Equation 5.85 may be rearranged to yield

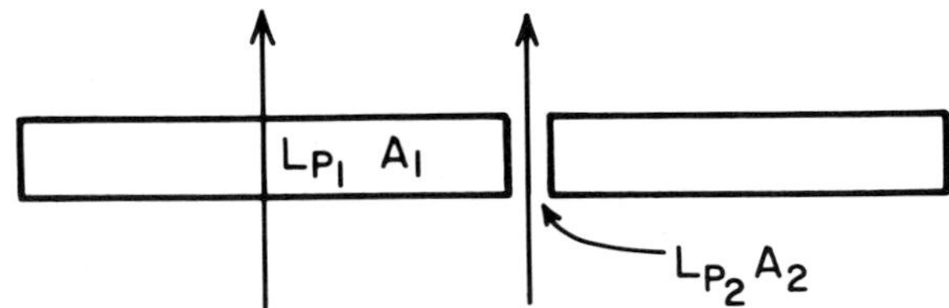

FIG. 5.15. Parallel-pathway model of water flow across capillary wall. Hydraulic conductivities of both pathways are expressed per unit area of whole membrane. A_1 and A_2 are fractional areas. Pathway 1 is semipermeable, $\sigma_d = 1$; for pathway 2, $\sigma_d < 1$.

$$\overline{1 - \sigma_d} = \frac{L_{P,2}A_2}{\bar{L}_P}(1 - \sigma_p) \quad (5.86)$$

A family of curves describing the relation between $1 - \sigma_p$ and solute size was generated for a range of pore radii and plotted on semilogarithmic paper. Superposition of the curves for a pore radius of 55 Å on the experimental data is shown in Figure 5.16. An intercept of 0.90 on the ordinate measures the fraction of total hydraulic conductivity from pores 55 Å in radius.

The analyses in Figures 5.15 and 5.16 are based on mean values of the osmotic reflection coefficient and the hydraulic conductivity and fail to account for the observed heterogeneity in L_P and σ. In frog mesenteric capillaries the L_P values may vary from as low as 0.3 to >10 × 10^{-7} cm·s^{-1}·cmH_2O^{-1}. If the ratio $L_{P,1}A_1/L_P$ remains constant as L_P varies, $\bar{\sigma}$ will be independent of $\bar{L}_P$. On the other hand, if only $L_{P,1}A_1$ remains constant, Equation 5.85 indicates that a plot of $\bar{\sigma}_d$ versus $1/L_P$ will be linear with a slope of $L_{P,1}A_1(1 - \sigma_p)$ and an intercept of σ_p. The results of Curry et al. (35) are consistent with the latter interpretation. The results suggest that $L_{P,1}A_1$ is constant; changes in the number of pores, measured as small changes in A_2, appear to be responsible for changes in $\bar{L}_P$. A model with an extracellular pathway for water that occupies less than 0.1% of the total membrane area in parallel with a water pathway across the endothelial cells is consistent with the data.

7. OSMOTIC AND SOLVENT-DRAG REFLECTION COEFFICIENTS IN HETEROPOROUS MEMBRANES. Equation 5.85 is a special case of the expression for the osmotic reflection coefficient of a heteroporous membrane and is derived as shown here

$$\Delta J_v/S = \Sigma L_{P,i}A_i\sigma_{d,i}RT\Delta C \quad (5.87)$$

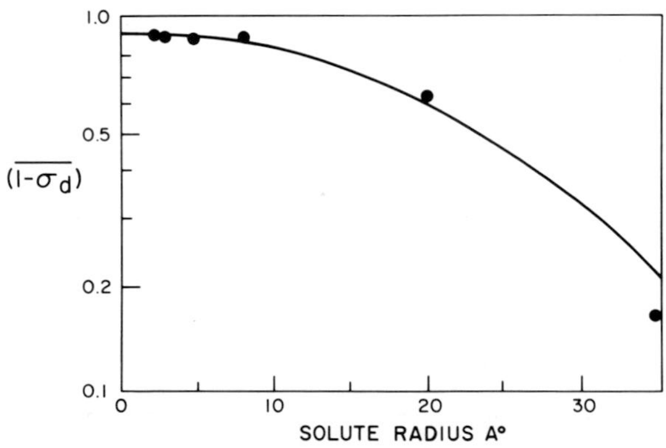

FIG. 5.16. Hydrodynamic pore analysis for partitioning of water flow between transcapillary pathways. Data are values of $1 - \sigma_d$ (Fig. 5.14). Semilogarithmic plot is graphical solution of parallel-pathway model of transcapillary osmotic water flow (Eq. 5.86). Family of curves (not shown; cf. Fig. 5.10) describing $1 - \sigma_d$ as a function of solute radius was generated from Eq. 5.80. *Solid line* is curve for pore radius of 55 Å, displaced down to superimpose on experimental data.

and

$$L_P = \Sigma L_{P,i}A_i \quad (5.88)$$

Therefore

$$\bar{\sigma}_d = \frac{\Delta J_v/S}{\bar{L}_P RT\Delta C} = \frac{\Sigma L_{P,i}A_i\sigma_{d,i}}{\Sigma L_{P,i}A_i} \quad (5.89)$$

A simple generalization of Equation 5.67 substituted into Equation 5.68 yields

$$(1 - \sigma_f) = \frac{\Sigma L_{P,i}S_i(\Delta P - \sigma_{d,i}\Delta\Pi)(1 - \sigma_{f,i})}{\Sigma L_{P,i}S_i(\Delta P - \sigma_{d,i}\Delta\Pi)} \quad (5.90)$$

For the condition $\Delta P \gg \sigma_{d,i}\Delta\pi$

$$(\overline{1 - \sigma_f}) = \frac{1 - \Sigma L_{P,i}S_i\sigma_{f,i}}{\Sigma L_{P,i}S_i} \quad (5.91)$$

Therefore

$$\overline{\sigma_f} = \frac{\Sigma L_{P,i}S_i\sigma_{f,i}}{\Sigma L_{P,i}S_i} = \frac{\Sigma L_{P,i}A_i\sigma_{d,i}}{\Sigma L_{P,i}A_i} \quad (5.92)$$

which is identical to Equation 5.89.

The form of Equations 5.68 and 5.90 is determined by the mass balance during steady-state ultrafiltration: $C_2 = J_s/J_v$. Ogston and Michel (99) argue that equality of σ_d and σ_f is more fundamentally derived from the reciprocity relation $\bar{L}_{PD} = \bar{L}_{DP}$ for a heteroporous membrane. Equation 5.90 shows that such reciprocity may be demonstrated experimentally only under the particular experimental conditions in which the driving forces (in this case effectively ΔP only) are the same for all pathways (in this case $\Delta P \gg \sigma_{d,i}\Delta\pi$).

G. Slit Geometry

It appears more realistic in some studies of capillary permeability to consider flow through a rectangular channel. For parallel channel walls a distance $2w$ apart

$$L_{P,slit} = \frac{w^2}{3\eta\Delta x} \quad (5.93)$$

$$P_{slit} = \frac{A_p}{\Delta x}(1 - \alpha_s)F(\alpha)_{slit} \quad (5.94)$$

and

$$\sigma_{f,slit} = \frac{2\alpha_s^2}{3}(1 - \alpha_s)F(\alpha)_{slit} + (1 - \alpha_s)\left(\frac{2}{3} + \frac{2\alpha_s}{3} + \frac{7\alpha_s^2}{12}\right) \quad (5.95)$$

where $\alpha_s = a/w$, and $F(\alpha)_{slit}$ is the centerline approximation for the ratio D_{slit}/D_{fr} (28)

$$F(\alpha)_{slit} = 1.0 - 1.004\alpha_s + 0.418\alpha_s^3 + 0.210\alpha_s^4 - 0.1696\alpha_s^5 \quad (5.96)$$

Equation 5.95 was derived by Curry (28).

H. Overview

The analysis of restricted diffusion (Figs. 5.4 and 5.5), ultrafiltration of macromolecules (Fig. 5.9), and the osmotic reflection coefficients to small hydrophilic solutes (Fig. 5.16) demonstrates that the frictional resistance to passive transport of water and solutes across the capillary wall cannot be described in terms of a uniform population of porous channels. At least three pathways are indicated: *1)* a very small pore pathway that is permeable to water but that excludes all hydrophilic solutes, *2)* a pathway permeable to water and solutes up to the size of albumin, and *3)* a large-pore pathway permeable to solutes up to 100 Å in radius. The chemical and physical nature of these pathways remains poorly understood.

Further information about each pathway must come from experiments with test probes of various sizes, shapes, charges, and chemical compositions. Much information can be gained by identifying systematic deviations from the predictions of the pore model. An example of an analysis of water and solute exchange in which this approach is developed is given next.

Figure 5.17*A* shows measured values of the osmotic reflection coefficient to albumin in individually perfused capillaries of frog mesentery (91). The striking feature of these data is the relative constancy of σ_{alb} in capillaries with a 10-fold range of hydraulic conductivity. According to Equation 5.80, the equivalent pore radius corresponding to σ_{alb} = 0.82 is 52 Å. Changes in the hydraulic conductivity must be caused by variation in the number of porous channels and not by changes in pore size. The factors that might determine pore numbers have received relatively little attention—variation in the length of intercellular junction that is permeable to solute has been suggested (25, 77, 111).

If real cylindrical pores 52 Å in radius are present in the capillary wall, the value of $A_p/\Delta x$ required to account for the observed L_P values can be calculated from Poiseuille's law (Eq. 5.12). If the same area is assumed to be available for diffusion, then a permeability coefficient can be predicted from Equation 5.31b. The solid line in Figure 5.17*B* is the locus of values of sucrose permeability (P_{su}) expected as the number of pores 52 Å in radius increases. The solid

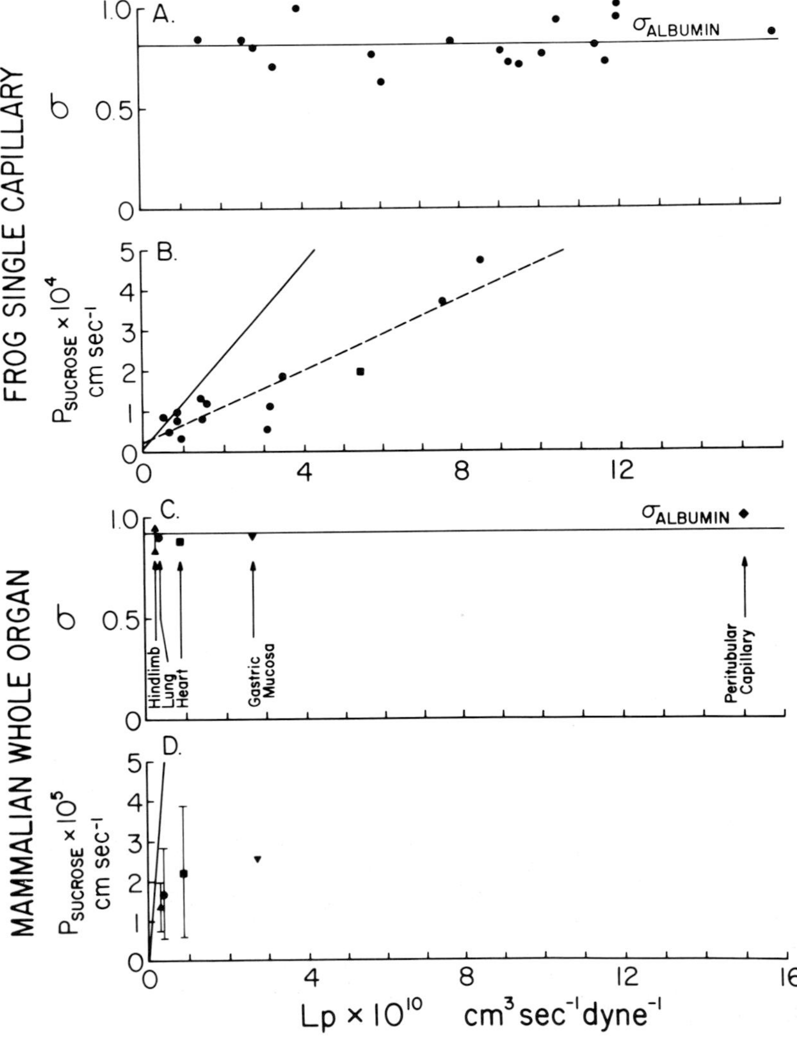

FIG. 5.17. Hydrodynamic pore analysis of permeability properties of single perfused capillaries of frog mesentery (*A* and *B*) and mammalian organs (*C* and *D*). See text for details. [From Curry and Huxley (32).]

points in Figure 5.17*B* are P_{su} values measured in single capillaries of frog mesentery in which L_P is also determined. The square is an independent measure of P_{su} calculated from the mean potassium permeability coefficient (P_{K^+}), assuming $P_{su} = P_{K^+}D_{su}/D_{K^+}$. In all but two vessels, the measured P_{su} values fall below the value predicted from pore theory. Nevertheless the regression of P_{su} on L_P (broken line) indicates a constant proportion between change in L_P and the corresponding changes in P_{su}. The results conform to the hypothesis that the number of pores, not pore size, changes from capillary to capillary. However, the pore size that accounts for the selectivity of the capillary wall to albumin fails to account for the transcapillary flows of water and small solutes.

A similar conclusion is drawn when data from mammalian capillary beds is analyzed in the same way. As shown in Figure 5.17*C* the measured osmotic reflection coefficients to albumin are reasonably constant over a >10-fold range of hydraulic conductivities. These data are mean values determined from all capillaries in an organ—values for the fenestrated capillaries of dog gastric mucosa and renal peritubular capillaries are included. The mean σ_{alb} is 0.92; the corresponding equivalent radius is 44 Å. In four of the organs (hindlimb, heart, lung, and gastric wall) the permeability coefficients to sucrose have also been measured. Figure 5.17*D* was constructed in the same way as Figure 5.17*B*. For hindlimb, lung, and heart the mean P_{su} values from many determinations fall below predicted values by at least one standard deviation. The single value for gastric wall shows a similar large discrepancy. The same capillary surface area was used to calculate P_{su} and L_P; the discrepancies in Figure 5.17*D* do not depend on the estimate of total surface area. Furthermore the discrepancies do not depend solely on some failure of pore theory to adequately describe σ_{alb}. The same inconsistency can be demonstrated if a 50-Å pore is calculated from restricted diffusion instead of from the osmotic reflection coefficient.

One source of the discrepancies may involve the partitioning of water flows between pathways (111) that do not contribute significantly to the flux of small hydrophilic solutes. An alternative hypothesis is that structures other than pores with regular geometry determine the selectivity of the capillary wall. This idea is explored in more detail in the next section.

TABLE 6.1. *Principal Relations and Nomenclature for VI. Fiber-Matrix Model*

	Relation	
1.	$\phi_f = \exp\left[-(1-\epsilon)\left(\frac{2a}{r_f} + \frac{a^2}{r_f^2}\right)\right]$	(6.10b)
2.	$D_f = D_{fr}\exp\left[-(1-\epsilon)^{1/2}\left(1 + \frac{a}{r_f}\right)\right]$	(6.20)
3.	$P = \frac{A}{S\Delta x}\phi_f D_f$	(6.24)
4a.	$L_P = \left(\frac{A}{\Delta x}\right)\frac{3r_f^2\epsilon}{4\eta(1-\epsilon)}$ drag model	(6.30, 6.31)
4b.	$L_P = \frac{1}{S}\left(\frac{A}{\Delta x}\right)\frac{r_f^2\epsilon^3}{4Gn(1-\epsilon)^2}$ hydraulic-radius model	(6.39)
5.	$\sigma_d = \sigma_f = (1-\phi_f)^2$	(6.44, 6.45)

Nomenclature

a	solute radius (cm)
A_{net}	area of exchange in membrane (cm^2)
C_f	fiber concentration (g/cm^3)
C	solute concentration (M)
$\bar{d}$	one-dimensional mean displacement (cm)
D	diffusion coefficient (cm^2/s)
G	Kozeny coefficient
J_s/S	solute flux (mol·s^{-1}·cm^{-2})
J_v/S	volume flux (cm/s)
K_{av}	volume fraction of network available to solute
l	fiber length per unit volume (cm/cm^3)
L_P	hydraulic conductivity (cm·s^{-1}·cmH$_2$O^{-1})
N_c	number of collisions or contacts
P	permeability coefficient (cm/s)
P	pressure (dyn/cm^2)
r_f	fiber radius (cm)
r	spherical radius (cm)
r_h	hydraulic radius (cm)
Re	Reynolds number
S	surface area (cm^2)
V_w	velocity of water (cm/s)
v_f	partial specific volume of fiber (cm^3/g)
x	distance (cm)
X	force (dyn/cm^2)
ϵ	void volume
λ	three-dimensional displacement step (cm)
κ	frequency (s^{-1})
η	viscosity (dyn·s·cm^{-2})
ν	number of fibers per unit volume (cm^{-3})
σ_d	osmotic reflection coefficient
σ_f	solvent-drag reflection coefficient
ϕ	partition coefficient
Φ	probability

Numbers in parentheses refer to text equations.

VI. FIBER-MATRIX MODEL

Michel (91, 93) recently reintroduced the hypothesis that a three-dimensional network of fibrous molecules in the endothelial cells may be the principal determinant of the selectivity of the capillary wall. To provide a quantitative basis to test the fiber-matrix hypothesis, Curry and Michel (34) developed relations to describe the capillary membrane transport coefficients in terms of the fiber radius and fractional fiber volume of a network of molecules within the principal exchange pathways.

The first two entries in Table 6.1 describe the solute partition coefficient and solute diffusion coefficient within a fibrous network. The third entry describes the permeability coefficient of a membrane with channels filled with a fiber matrix. The two parts of the fourth entry are expressions for the hydraulic conductivity of a fibrous network, derived from a drag model of water flow (entry 4a) or the hydraulic-radius model

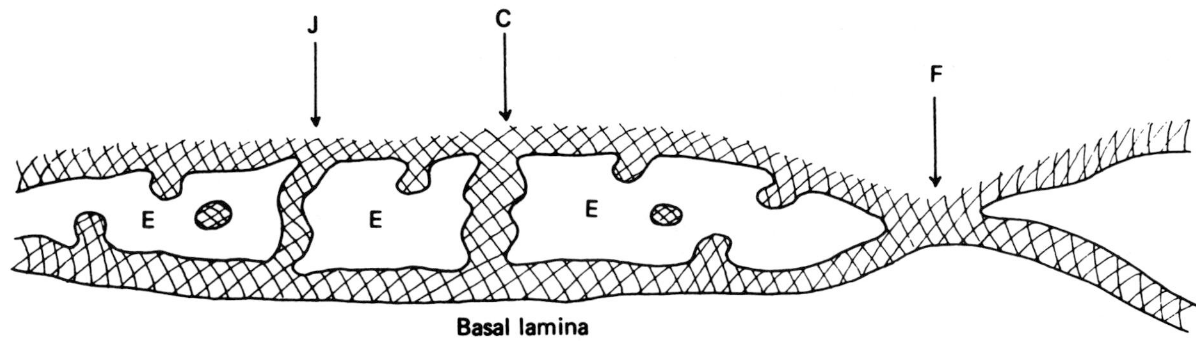

FIG. 6.1. Fiber-matrix model of capillary permeability. Endothelium (E) is traversed by intercellular junctions (J), transendothelial channels (C), and fenestrations (F). Dimensions and numbers of these channels determine area of permeable regions of capillary wall, but molecular sieving properties are endowed on capillary by size of interstices of fiber matrix enveloping cell surface and filling channels that penetrate it. [From Michel (93).]

(entry 4b). The osmotic reflection coefficients for a fibrous network are described in entry 5.

In the fiber-matrix model the resistance to transport is assumed to lie completely within the network. Therefore the selectivity of each of the hypothetical pathways indicated in Figure 6.1 is the same; selectivity does not depend on the geometry of the channel. Furthermore the permeability and hydraulic conductivity depend on the total area for exchange and on membrane thickness but are also independent of specific channel geometry.

A. Introductory Concepts

Within the fibrous network the collision of the solute with the fibers restricts the volume of the network available to the solute and reduces the solute diffusion coefficient. The starting point for the description of both exclusion and diffusion is an expression for the number of tangential contacts (dN_c) that a hypothetical spherical surface makes with fibers in the network as it expands a differential amount from a radius of r to a radius of $r + dr$. An expression for this quantity was derived by Ogston (98)

$$dN_c = 2\pi rl dr \qquad (6.1)$$

where l is the total length of fibers in a unit volume of the network. The interesting and useful property of the distribution in Equation 6.1 is the result that, as a spherical surface expands within a network of fibers, the number of tangential contacts per unit increase in surface area of the sphere is a constant equal to $l/4$. The result is easily derived by writing the number of tangential contacts per unit surface area (dN_c/dS) in terms of dN_c/dr. From Equation 6.1

$$\frac{dN_c}{dS} = \left(\frac{dN_c}{dr}\right)\left(\frac{dr}{dS}\right) \qquad (6.2)$$

For a spherical surface, $dr/dS = 1/(8\pi r)$. Therefore

$$\frac{dN_c}{dS} = \frac{2\pi rl}{8\pi r} = \frac{l}{4} \qquad (6.3)$$

B. Spaces Within Fibrous Networks

The size of spaces within the network is defined by taking the arbitrary origin in Figure 6.1 and expanding a spherical space until it reaches the nearest fiber. The probability that a spherical space lies between r and $r + dr$ is the combined probability that no contact occurs between the origin and r and at least one contact occurs between r and $r + dr$.

Suppose the changes in surface area as r expands from 0 to r are divided into equal increments (δS) of magnitude S/N. Then the probability ($\delta\Phi$) that there are no contacts in N consecutive increments in S and one contact in the $(N + 1)$th increment is given by the binomial distribution

$$\delta\Phi = \left(1 - \frac{l}{4}\,\delta S\right)^N \left(\frac{l}{4}\right) \delta S \qquad (6.4)$$

Because $\delta S = S/N$, Equation 6.4 can be written

$$\delta\Phi = \left(1 - \frac{lS}{4N}\right)^N \left(\frac{l}{4}\right) \delta S \qquad (6.5)$$

In the limit of very large N, the binomial distribution in Equation 6.5 reduces to a Poisson distribution

$$d\Phi = \frac{l}{4} \exp\left(-\frac{l}{4}\,S\right) dS \qquad (6.6)$$

To express the distribution in terms of the radius r rather than S, substitute for S and dS from Equation 6.3

$$\frac{d\Phi}{dr} = 2\pi rl \exp(-\pi lr^2) \qquad (6.7)$$

This result was derived by Ogston (98) from a different geometrical argument. If end-on contacts are also considered, Equation 6.7 becomes (98)

$$\frac{d\Phi}{dr} = (2\pi rl + 4\pi r^2 N_{f,V}) \cdot \exp[-\pi lr^2 + (4/3)\,\pi N_{f,V} r^3] \qquad (6.8)$$

where $N_{f,V}$ is the number of fibers per unit volume. For $l \gg r$, the contribution of end-on contacts to the total number of contacts is very small, and Equation 6.7 is a very good approximation to Equation 6.8.

C. Steric Exclusion

A spherical molecule of radius a is excluded from a network if there is at least one fiber contact in the region $0 < r < a + r_f$. The fiber radius (r_f) is included in the effective radius of the space because the development of Equation 6.7 ignores a finite fiber size. On the other hand the extent to which a solute penetrates a network is determined by the probability distribution of spaces with effective radii larger than $a + r_f$. The fraction of network volume that will accommodate a solute of radius a is the probability that r (Eq. 6.7) is greater than $a + r_f$. The fraction of network volume available to solute is usually represented as K_{av}. Therefore

$$K_{av} = \int_{a+r_f}^{\infty} \frac{d\Phi}{dr}\,dr = \exp[-\pi l(a + r_f)^2] \tag{6.9}$$

Michel (personal communication) gives an alternative derivation of Equation 6.9. Fibers of radius r_f will exclude a solute of radius a from a volume of $\pi(a + r_f)^2$ per unit length. If the fibers are arranged in an ordered geometry, $K_{av} = 1 - \pi l(a + r_f)^2$. On the other hand, if the fibers are arranged randomly, a first-order Poisson distribution will describe K_{av} as a function of l. The result is Equation 6.9 (cf. Eq. 8.2).

The partition coefficient (ϕ_f) is defined as the space available to a solute of radius a relative to the space available to water ($a = 0$). Therefore

$$\phi_f = \frac{\exp[-\pi l(a + r_f)^2]}{\exp(-\pi l r_f^2)} \tag{6.10a}$$

or

$$\phi_f = \exp\left[-(1 - \epsilon)\left(\frac{2a}{r_f} + \frac{a^2}{r_f^2}\right)\right] \tag{6.10b}$$

where ϵ is the fractional void volume

$$\epsilon = 1 - \pi r_f^2 l \tag{6.11}$$

The partition coefficient (Eqs. 6.10a and 6.10b) is used in expressions for the permeability coefficient and the osmotic reflection coefficient of the capillary wall (see Eqs. 6.24 and 6.44, respectively).

D. Restricted Diffusion

The quantitative description of diffusion in a three-dimensional fibrous network is a direct extension of the stochastic model of diffusion described in II. DIFFUSION (p. 310). In a network the unit step may be in any direction—the resultant expression for the diffusion coefficient is

$$D = \frac{1}{6}\lambda^2\kappa \tag{6.12}$$

The unit step λ is related to the unit step d in the one-dimensional model of diffusion (Eq. 2.10) by the relation

$$\lambda^2 = \frac{\overline{d^2}}{3} \tag{6.13}$$

In free diffusion the unit step is always completed. To describe restricted diffusion in the network, solute is imagined to lie within a space of radius $\frac{1}{2}\lambda$. A particle that steps through a distance λ without collision ends in an adjacent space, whereas a particle that collides with a fiber remains in its original space. The fractional reduction in the free-diffusion coefficient is equal to the probability of a successful step corresponding to the transport of solute between two adjacent regions within the network. This probability is one minus the probability of a collision with the fibers. An expression for the probability of a collision was derived by Ogston et al. (100).

A simple extension of the geometrical arguments that led to Equation 6.1 describes the number of tangential contacts (dN_c) when a sphere of radius a moves through a distance dx in any direction (100)

$$dN_c = \frac{1}{2}\pi l a\,dx \tag{6.14}$$

This equation ignores a finite fiber radius. According to Equation 6.14, the number of contacts per unit distance (dN_c/dx) is a constant ($\frac{1}{2}\pi la$) and, from the argument developed in Equations 6.4–6.7, the probability that there are no collisions in moving a distance x but at least one collision in moving from x to $x + dx$ is

$$d\Phi = \frac{1}{2}\pi la\exp\left(-\frac{1}{2}\pi lax\right)dx \tag{6.15}$$

Thus the probability of collision with a fiber during a unit step of size $\Phi(\lambda)$ is

$$\int_0^{\lambda} d\phi dx$$

that is

$$\Phi(\lambda) = 1 - \exp\left(-\frac{1}{2}\pi la\lambda\right) \tag{6.16}$$

On the basis of the argument following Equation 6.13, $\Phi(\lambda)$ is a measure of D_{net}/D_{fr}, where D_{net} is the diffusion coefficient of the network. The magnitude of the fractional reduction depends on an appropriate choice of λ.

Ogston and colleagues (100) chose λ to be twice the root mean square radius of spaces defined by Equation 6.1, that is

$$\lambda = 2(\pi l)^{-1/2} \tag{6.17}$$

Substitute for λ in Equation 6.16

$$\frac{D_{net}}{D_{fr}} = \exp[-(\pi l)^{1/2}a] \tag{6.18}$$

To account for a finite fiber size, the fiber radius is added to the solute size. Thus

$$\frac{D_{net}}{D_{fr}} = \exp[-(\pi l)^{1/2}(a + r_f)] \tag{6.19}$$

A useful alternative form of this equation is obtained with the substitution $\epsilon = 1 - \pi r_f^2 l$ (Eq. 6.11)

$$\frac{D_{net}}{D_{fr}} = \exp[-(1 - \epsilon)^{1/2}(1 + a/r_f)] \tag{6.20}$$

Experimental studies to evaluate the expression for diffusion and exclusion in a network are outlined below.

E. *Exclusion and Diffusion in Hyaluronic Acid Networks*

Figure 6.2*A* shows experiments that measure the fraction of a network of hyaluronic acid available to solutes with Stokes-Einstein radii between 0.39 and 9.7 nm. The hyaluronic acid concentration is 0.145 g/100 ml. From Equation 6.9

$$\ln K_{av} = -(1 - \epsilon)(1 + a/r_f)^2 \tag{6.21}$$

When $a/r_f \gg 1$, a plot of $\ln K_{av}$ against the square of solute radius should be linear with a slope of $-(1 - \epsilon)/r_f^2$.

The experimental data in Figure 6.2*A* conform to the linear relation predicted from Equation 6.9. The magnitude of $1 - \epsilon$, the fiber volume, is $C_f v_f$, where C_f is the fiber concentration in g/cm^3 and v_f is the effective partial specific volume of the fibers in cm^3/g. For hyaluronic acid, v_f is 0.65 cm^3/g (100). The slope of the relation in Figure 6.2*A* corresponds to a fiber radius of 0.4 nm.

The diffusion of ovalbumin, albumin, and γ-globulin in hyaluronic acid, and a sulfated proteoglycan is shown in the three parts of Figure 6.2*B*. The solid line describes the relation between D_{net}/D_{fr} and fiber concentration given by Equation 6.20

$$\ln\left(\frac{D_{net}}{D_{fr}}\right) = -v_f^{1/2}(1 + a/r_f) \tag{6.22}$$

which predicts that a plot of ln (D_{net}/D_{fr}) against $C^{1/2}$ should be linear with a slope of $-v_f^{1/2}(1 + a/r_f)$. The experimental points fall on a line with a slope very close to that predicted for a partial specific volume of 0.65 cm^3/g and a fiber radius of 0.5 nm. However, in all experiments the measured value of D_{net}/D_{fr} is larger than predicted values by ~10%. The source of this discrepancy remains to be determined.

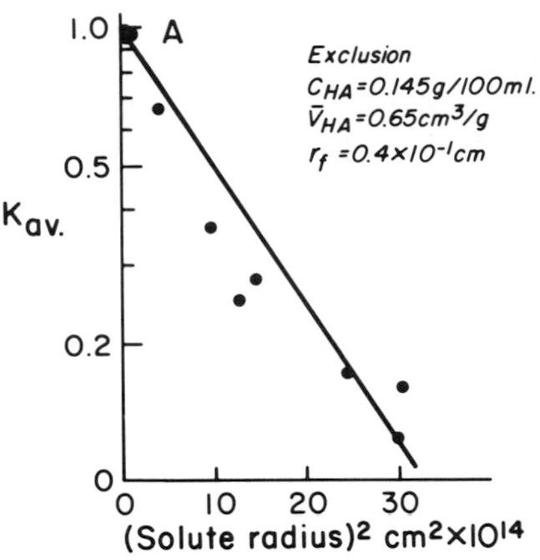

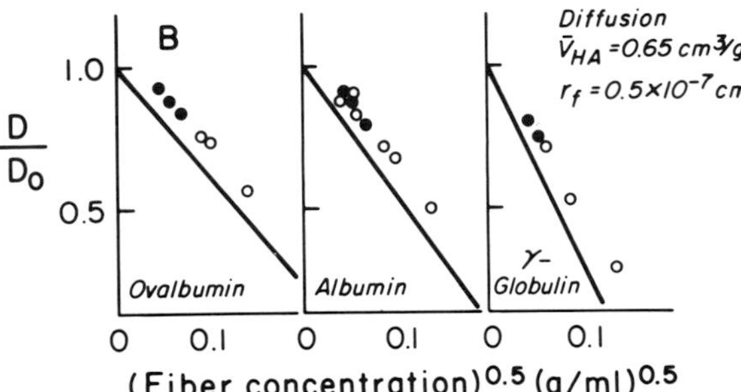

FIG. 6.2. Experimental evaluation of expressions for exclusion and diffusion in 3-dimensional random network. *A*: exclusion. Hyaluronic acid concentration is 0.145×10^{-3} g/cm^3, fractional fiber volume is 0.094%. Semilogarithmic plot shows fraction of network volume available to solutes as function of square of solute radius. Slope of linear relation [Eq. 6.21; $a/r_f \gg 1$] corresponds to fiber radius of 0.4 mm. *B*: diffusion. Fractional reduction in diffusion coefficient as function of square root of fiber concentration for ovalbumin (a = 2.8 nm), albumin (a = 3.55 nm), and γ-globulin (a = 5.55 nm). Slope of linear relation (Eq. 6.22) corresponds to fiber radius of 0.5 mm. ●, Hyaluronate; ○, sulfated proteoglycan. [Data from Ogston et al. (100).]

F. *Permeability Coefficients of Membranes Containing Fibrous Networks*

The total flux through a membrane containing channels filled with a network of fibrous molecules, in the absence of water flow, is given by the fiber-matrix form of Equation 4.52

$$J_s = \frac{A_{net}}{\Delta x_{net}} \phi_{net} D_{net} \Delta C \tag{6.23}$$

Substitution of Equations 6.10a and 6.20 into Equation 6.23 yields an expression for the permeability coefficient of a membrane penetrated by channels filled with a network of fibrous molecules

$$P = \frac{1}{S}\left(\frac{A}{\Delta x}\right)_{net} \exp\left[-(1 - \epsilon)\left(\frac{2a}{r_f} + \frac{a^2}{r_f^2}\right)\right] \cdot D_{fr} \exp\left[-(1 - \epsilon)^{1/2}\left(1 + \frac{a}{r_f}\right)\right] \tag{6.24}$$

The term A_{net}/S is the fraction of the total membrane area occupied by the fibrous membrane. The network is assumed to be the same thickness as the membrane. Application of fiber-matrix theory to describe transport across the capillary wall is described at the end of this section.

G. *Water Flow Through Fibrous Networks*

The theoretical basis for the description of water flow through a network of fibrous molecules is less well developed than the stochastic theory of exclusion and diffusion. Two theories are outlined below—a hydrodynamic-drag model and a hydraulic-radius model.

1. HYDRODYNAMIC-DRAG MODEL. The assumption underlying the drag model is that the pressure drop from flow through a fibrous network is determined by the drag forces exerted by the fibers. The fibers are assumed to be sufficiently dilute so that there is no interaction between fibers. A model based on these assumptions was developed by Iberall (63). For flow parallel to the fibers the drag force per unit length of fibers is (43)

$$X_{dr} = 4\pi\eta V_w \tag{6.25}$$

If the fiber length per unit volume is l, the drag force per unit volume is $4\pi\eta V_w l$, which also equals the pressure drop per unit length. For randomly distributed fibers the contribution to the total pressure drop per unit length of fiber network from flow parallel to the fibers is one-third of that given in Equation 6.25

$$\left(\frac{\Delta P}{\Delta x}\right)_{pf} = \frac{1}{3}\,(4\pi\eta V_w l) \tag{6.26}$$

where the subscript pf denotes parallel flow. The contribution to the total pressure drop from flow perpendicular to the fibers is two-thirds of the pressure drop calculated for flow perpendicular to the fibers (59)

$$\left(\frac{\Delta P}{\Delta x}\right)_{pe} = \frac{2}{3}\left(\frac{4\pi\eta V_w l}{2 - \ln Re}\right) \tag{6.27}$$

where the subscript pe denotes perpendicular flow and Re is a fiber Reynolds number. Linear supposition yields the total pressure drop per unit length

$$\frac{\Delta P}{\Delta x} = \frac{4\pi\eta V_w l}{3}\left(\frac{4 - \ln Re}{2 - \ln Re}\right) \tag{6.28}$$

At the very low Reynolds numbers associated with transcapillary flow ($Re < 10^{-5}$), ln Re is a negative number greater than 5 and the quantity $(4 - \ln Re)/(2 - \ln Re)$ is very close to unity. Therefore

$$\frac{\Delta P}{\Delta x} \sim \frac{4\pi\eta V_w l}{3} \tag{6.29}$$

Because $l = (1 - \epsilon)/\pi r_f^2$ and $V_w = J_v/\epsilon A_{net}$ (see Eqs. 6.37 and 6.38), Equation 6.29 may be rearranged

$$J_v/S = \left(\frac{A}{\Delta x}\right)_{net}\left(\frac{3r_f^2}{4\eta}\right)\left(\frac{\epsilon}{1 - \epsilon}\right)\Delta P \tag{6.30}$$

which may also be written

$$J_v/S = \frac{1}{S}\left(\frac{A}{\Delta x}\right)_{net}\frac{\kappa}{\eta}\,\Delta P = L_P\Delta P \tag{6.31}$$

where κ is a specific hydraulic conductivity of the network with units of cm^2. The specific hydraulic conductivity is a property of fiber radius, fiber volume, and the geometrical constants. From Equations 6.30 and 6.31

$$\kappa = \frac{3r_f^2}{4}\left(\frac{\epsilon}{1 - \epsilon}\right) \tag{6.32}$$

With $1 - \epsilon$ (fractional fiber volume) set equal to $C_f\bar{v}_f$, κ can be expressed in terms of fiber concentrations

$$\kappa = \frac{3r_f^2}{4}\,\frac{(1 - Cv)_f}{(Cv)_f} \tag{6.33}$$

which predicts an inverse relation between κ and fiber concentration when $Cv \ll 1$. This prediction has not been systematically tested.

2. HYDRAULIC-RADIUS MODEL. Equation 6.31 is the Darcy equation for the viscous flow of water through a porous medium. One specific geometrical interpretation of κ is obtained by comparing Darcy's law with Poiseuille's law (Eq. 5.12). This comparison shows that $\kappa = R^2/8$ for a cylindrical pore. A further generalization of the geometrical interpretation of κ is provided by the hydraulic-radius concept. The hydraulic radius (r_h) is defined as the volume available for water flow within the porous material divided by the surface area in contact with the water. For a cylindrical pore, $r_h = R/2$. Both Equation 6.31 and Equation 5.12 can be written

$$J_v/S = \left(\frac{A}{S}\right)\left(\frac{1}{\Delta x}\right)\frac{r_h^2}{G\eta}\,\Delta P \tag{6.34}$$

where G is a geometric constant, often called the Kozeny constant, characteristic of the geometry of the porous material. For a cylindrical pore, $G = 2$ and Equation 6.34 reduces to Poiseuille's law.

The hydraulic-radius model of water flow through a fibrous network is an application of the definition of a hydraulic radius to a network of random fibers. The development in terms of r_h is quite precise, but the choice of a value of G is more empirical. Appropriate values of G are best determined experimentally (see Eq. 6.41 and its discussion).

Curry and Michel (33) used the theory of Sullivan and Hertel (146) to describe water flow through a fibrous network within the principal water pathway of the capillary wall. The volume available to water in the network is assumed to be the fractional void volume ϵ. The surface area in contact with water in a network of fibers (radius, r_f; length, l) per unit volume is $2\pi r_f l$. The hydraulic radius for water flow through the network is

$$r_{h,net} = \frac{\epsilon}{2\pi r_f l} \tag{6.35}$$

Using Equation 6.11, this is rewritten

$$r_{h,net} = \frac{\epsilon r_f}{1 - \epsilon} \tag{6.36}$$

Substitution of Equation 6.36 into Equation 6.34 yields an expression for the water flow through a network of thickness Δx and area A_w available to water

$$J_v/S = \frac{A_w r_f^2 \epsilon^2}{\Delta x S(1 - \epsilon)^2 4G\eta} \Delta P \tag{6.37}$$

In a fibrous network the ratio of area available for water flow to total network area (A_{net}) is equal to the void volume ϵ. Therefore Equation 6.37 is written

$$J_v/S = \frac{A_{net} r_f^2 \epsilon^3}{\Delta x S(1 - \epsilon)^2 4G\eta} \Delta P \tag{6.38}$$

Thus the hydraulic conductivity of a membrane consisting of channels filled with a network of fibrous molecules is

$$L_P = \frac{A_{net} r_f^2 \epsilon^3}{\Delta x S(1 - \epsilon)^2 4G\eta} \tag{6.39}$$

The term A_{net}/S is the fractional membrane area occupied by the fibrous network. From Equation 6.39 and the argument developed for Equations 6.32 and 6.33, it can be seen that the specific hydraulic conductivity of a network depends on fiber concentration according to

$$\kappa = \frac{r_f^2(1 - Cv)_f^3}{4G(Cv)_f^2} \tag{6.40}$$

When $Cv \ll 1$, this equation predicts an inverse relation between κ and the square of the fiber concentration.

For most regular shapes, Carman (16) calculated Kozeny constants between 2 and 3. These calculations assume the streamlines within the channel are straight. Sullivan and Hertel (146) found experimentally that $G = 3.07$ when flow is parallel to bundles of glass fibers with a void volume of 0.82; but G increases to 6.04 when the flow is perpendicular to the fibers. In a random network an average of two-thirds of the fibers will lie at right angles to the direction of flow and one-third will lie parallel to flow. An appropriately weighted value of G is $(2/3 \times 6) + (1/3 \times 3) = 5.0$. The average value of G for a wide range of randomly packed beds with $\epsilon \leq 0.90$ is ~5. The increase in the value of G from 2–3 to an average of ~5 has been attributed to the increase in the path length (tortuosity) as fluid flows around the obstacles in the porous media. Modern hydrodynamic models evaluating G support the use of a value of ~5 for void volumes between 0.5 and 0.9 (59).

A difficulty with the application of the hydraulic-radius model to capillary membranes is that preliminary estimates of void volumes within proposed transcapillary channels are greater than 0.9 (30, 33). Experimental and theoretical studies of macroscopic systems show that G is not constant but increases in magnitude as the void volume increases above 0.90 (59, 146). If the same phenomenon were found in microscopic networks, the hydrodynamic-radius approach would be of limited value. However, there is evidence that the hydraulic-radius concept is applicable at much higher void volumes in systems composed of fibers of molecular dimensions. Ogston and colleagues (101) have applied the hydraulic-radius concept to describe the sedimentation of macromolecules at $\epsilon \leq 0.98$. The Kozeny constant used in these sedimentation studies was 2.7. Preliminary results for water flow through hyaluronic acid networks have been obtained in my laboratory (1). The specific hydraulic conductivity was measured from the initial rate of filtration of buffered saline through hyaluronic acid. Measurement of initial flow is required to avoid piling up of hyaluronic acid and fibers against the restraining membranes. The concentration of hyaluronic acid ranged from 0.1 to 2.0 g/100 ml. Taking the effective partial specific volume of hyaluronic acid as 0.65 cm^3/g, the corresponding void volumes range from 0.993 to 0.970. The experimental results for hyaluronic acid concentrations in the range 0.3 to 2 g/100 ml were described by the relation

$$\kappa = \frac{r_f^2}{8C^2v^2} \tag{6.41}$$

which is the low concentration limit of Equation 6.40 when $r_f = 0.5$ nm, $v_s = 0.65$ cm^3/g, and $G = 2$. Both the slope of the predicted relation and the magnitude of the predicted κ values conform more closely to the experimental data than values from the drag model. The significance of a geometric factor of two, rather than five as found for macroscopic fibers, remains to be investigated in more detail with a range of fiber types and a larger range of fiber volumes. One interpretation is that at the high void volumes used in the experiments a correction for tortuosity is not required, and a geometric constant characteristic of cylindrical pores ($G = 2$) provides an adequate description of the channels for water flow through the network.

H. Reflection Coefficients in Fibrous Networks

The simplest expression for the solvent-drag reflection coefficient (σ_f) in a fibrous network is obtained if the water velocity profile between fibers is assumed to be flat. For such a case the argument that led to Equation 5.34 yields

$$(J_s)_{\Delta C=0} = J_v \phi_f C_1 \qquad (6.42)$$

and

$$\sigma_{f,pl} = \left(1 - \frac{J_s}{J_v C_1}\right)_{\Delta C=0} = 1 - \phi_f \qquad (6.43)$$

If the velocity profile between fibers is curved, this equation will overestimate σ_f. The exact profile for water flow in the network is unknown. However, the result that a hydraulic-radius model describes water flow indicates that flow between fibers can be described in a first approximation as pseudo-Poiseuillean. Within a cylindrical pore with Poiseuillean flow the appropriate form of the solvent-drag reflection coefficient is given by Equation 5.39. The corresponding relation within a fibrous network is

$$\sigma_f = (1 - \phi_f)^2 \qquad (6.44)$$

No experimental test of this equation for a network of fibers has been made.

An expression identical to Equation 6.44 was suggested by Curry and Michel (33) to describe the osmotic reflection coefficient in a fibrous network

$$\sigma_d = (1 - \phi_f)^2 \qquad (6.45)$$

which is a further generalization of Equations 5.80 and 5.81 as suggested by Anderson (2). In this case the channel geometry is the complex pathway through a fibrous network. The form of Equations 6.44 and 6.45 depends on the presence of a velocity profile that bears a quadratic relation to the cross-sectional coordinate. No experimental test of Equation 6.45 has been made. However, the analysis given next of transcapillary exchange with the fiber-matrix model demonstrates the potential of the model to resolve some of the inconsistencies in the current pore-theory analyses.

I. Pore and Fiber-Matrix Models Applied to Capillary Transport

Figure 6.3 shows the analysis of the data from single-capillary and whole-organ studies (Fig. 5.17) with both the pore and fiber-matrix models of capillary permeability (30, 32). In each an apparent κ measured as $(L_P \eta D)/P$ is plotted on the ordinate, and σ_{alb} is plotted on the abscissa. The broken lines in Figures 6.3*A* and 6.3*C* show how the magnitude of these two variables changes as pore radius is increased from 4 to 14 nm. Pore-theory calculations use Equations 5.12 and 5.31b for L_P and P, respectively, and Equation 5.54 for σ_{alb}. The solid lines in Figures 6.3*B* and 6.3*D* show how specific hydraulic conductivity and σ_{alb} vary when the fiber radius is held constant and the fractional fiber volume is varied from 2% to 8% (void volume varies from 98% to 92%). Fiber-

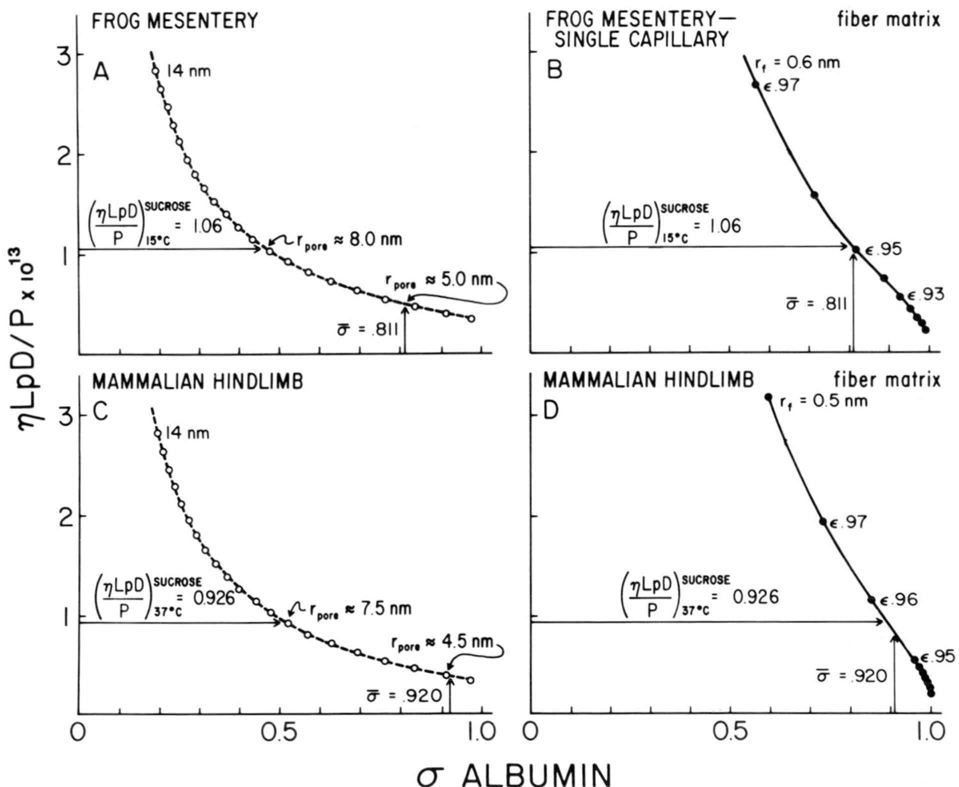

FIG. 6.3. Analysis of permeability data (Fig. 5.17) with pore and fiber-matrix models of capillary permeability. Apparent specific hydraulic conductivity measured as $L_P \eta D/P$ (in cm^2) is plotted on ordinate and albumin osmotic reflection coefficient is plotted on abscissa of each graph. *A* and *B* show data from single capillaries of frog mesentery for pore and fiber-matrix analyses, respectively. *C* and *D* show mammalian hindlimb data for pore and fiber-matrix analyses, respectively. [From Curry and Huxley (32).]

matrix calculations use Equations 6.31 and 6.24 to calculate L_P and P, respectively, and Equation 6.45 to calculate σ_{alb}.

The analysis in Figure 6.3*A* is another way of illustrating the inconsistency in the pore analysis described in Figure 5.17. The pore radius that accounts for the measured specific hydraulic conductivity is 8 nm, which is 60% larger than the radius that accounts for the albumin reflection coefficient. In contrast a network of fibers 0.6 nm in radius that occupies 5% of the total network volume (Fig. 6.3*B*) accounts for the hydraulic conductivity, sucrose permeability, and osmotic reflection coefficient of the capillary wall to albumin (30, 35). The striking feature of the analysis of mammalian hindlimb capillaries (Figs. 6.3*C* and 6.3*D*) is that the pore and fiber parameters describing the data are very similar to those found for mesenteric capillaries. In the hindlimb the pore radius estimated from the specific hydraulic conductivity is 7.5 nm, which is 70% larger than the pore radius that accounts for the reflection coefficient to albumin in these vessels. In terms of the fiber-matrix model, fibers 0.5 nm in radius that occupy 4.5% of the network volume describe the data. Similar values of fiber radius and fiber volume describe data for the mammalian lung. In the heart, smaller fibers 0.3 nm in radius that occupy 3% of the network describe the data. The reflection coefficient of the fenestrated capillaries is accounted for by fibers 0.5 nm in radius that occupy 5% of the network volume, but these fiber parameters predict a specific hydraulic conductivity that is smaller than that calculated from the data in Figure 5.17.

The L_P and *PS* values in mammalian hindlimb are usually one order of magnitude smaller than the corresponding values in frog mesentery. The analysis in Figure 6.4 confirms previous analyses that differences in the magnitudes of L_P and *PS* in the two types of vessels are not caused by fundamental differences in the structure of the size-limiting barriers in the two capillaries (29, 93). In fact, comparison of Figures 6.4*B* and 6.4*D* suggests that a network of fibrous molecules with radii close to those measured for sulfated proteoglycans will account for the permeability characteristics (100). The differences in magnitude of L_P and P must depend on the area and thickness of fiber-filled pathway available for exchange. The geometry of the porous pathway need not be specified if the fibrous network is rate limiting.

VII. CHARGE

Charge plays a significant role in transcapillary exchange because electrostatic contributions to osmotic pressure account for nearly one-third of the normal colloid osmotic pressure exerted by plasma proteins at pH 7.4 (75). The effect of electrostatic interactions between charged solutes and the capillary wall on exclusion and diffusion has just begun to be systematically studied and is not well understood.

Table 7.1 summarizes the principal relations describing the interaction of charged particles with the capillary wall. The first entry is a modified expression for the Donnan distribution of ions across the capillary wall when protein is present on both sides of the membrane. Entry 2 is the expression for the Donnan potential difference across the capillary membrane, and entry 3 is an expression for the osmotic pressure of albumin as a function of both solute concentration and charge. In addition to the classic Donnan contribution to osmotic pressure, the virial coefficients in the series expansion of solute concentrations are charge dependent. Entry 4 shows the application of

TABLE 7.1. *Principal Relations and Nomenclature for VII. Charge*

Relation

	Relation	
1.	$C_2^+(C_2^+ - zC_P) = C_1^+C_1^-$	(7.13)
2.	$\psi_{DP} = \dfrac{RT}{zF}\ln\left(\dfrac{C_2^+}{C_1^+}\right)$	(7.9)
3.	$\Pi_P = RT\left[2\left(\dfrac{zC_P^*}{2M_P} + C_2^2\right)^{0.5} - 2C_2\right] + \dfrac{RT}{M_P}(C_P^* + A_2C_P^{*2} + A_3C_P^{*3})$	(7.17)
4.	$\left(\dfrac{F}{RT}\right)\left[\dfrac{d^2\psi(x)}{dx^2}\right] = \dfrac{1}{l_D^2}\left[\sinh\dfrac{\psi(x)F}{RT} - \dfrac{zC_P}{2C_2(\infty)}\right)$	(7.24, 7.25)
5.	$\alpha^* = \dfrac{a + l_D}{r_p - l_D}$	(7.27)

Nomenclature

A_2, A_3	virial coefficients
C	concentration (M)
C*	concentration (g/dl)
E	potential energy/mole (cal/mol)
F	Faraday constant (C/equivalent)
l_D	Debye length (cm)
M	molecular weight
P	pressure (dyn/cm²)
r	radial distance (cm)
r_p	radius of pore (cm)
R	gas constant (1.99 cal·°K⁻¹·mol⁻¹)
T	absolute temperature (°K)
v	partial molar volume (cm³/mol)
x	distance coordinate (cm)
X	mole fraction
y	dimensionless ratio
z	valency
α^*	modified ratio of solute/pore radius
ϵ	dielectric constant (C·V⁻¹·cm⁻¹)
ρ	charge density (C/cm³)
ϕ	partition coefficient
Π	osmotic pressure (dyn/cm²)
ψ	electrical potential (V)
Subscripts and superscripts	
+	cation
−	anion
1, 2	compartment designation
P	protein
∞	bulk solution

Numbers in parentheses refer to text equations.

the Boltzmann distribution and Poisson equation to describe the potential profile at a charged interface—the Debye length (l_D) is a measure of the extent of charge interactions within the capillary pathways. In entry 5 the Debye length is used to increase the radius of the solute and decrease the radius of a cylindrical pore. The modified solute and pore dimensions provide a crude approximation to the magnitude of charge interactions.

A. Donnan Distribution

A Donnan equilibrium distribution of ions is established across the capillary wall as a result of the retention of negatively charged plasma proteins in the lumen of the capillary. Generally a gel or any cross-linked structure with a fixed charge will give rise to a distribution of mobile ions. The characteristics of a system with a Donnan equilibrium are *1*) an asymmetric distribution of diffusible ions between two solutions separated by a membrane or gel, *2*) an electrical potential difference between the phases, and *3*) an osmotic pressure between the phases. Detailed analyses of the Donnan distribution are given by Sten-Knudsen (145) and by Finkelstein and Mauro (47).

The starting point in the thermodynamic development of expressions for the Donnan equilibrium distribution of ions between the luminal fluid (side 1) and tissue fluid (side 2) is the condition for thermodynamic equilibrium on each of the ions in solution (Eq. 3.41). For example, the equilibrium distribution of monovalent cations (partial molar volume, v^+) between solutions with pressures P_1 and P_2 and potentials ψ_1 and ψ_2 is calculated from the following statement of thermodynamic equilibrium

$$\mu_0 + P_1 v^+ + RT \ln X_1^+ + F\psi_1 = \mu_0 + P_2 v^+ + RT \ln X_2^+ + F\psi_2 \quad (7.1)$$

where F is the Faraday constant. Rearranging with the dilute-solution theory yields

$$(P_1 - P_2)v^+ + F(\psi_1 - \psi_2) = RT \ln \frac{C_2^+}{C_1^+} \quad (7.2)$$

For anions the same argument gives

$$(P_1 - P_2)v^- - F(\psi_1 - \psi_2) = RT \ln \frac{C_2^-}{C_1^-} \quad (7.3)$$

The second step in the development introduces the requirement for electroneutrality on both sides of the membrane. If C_P is the concentration of plasma protein, valency z, electroneutrality on the luminal side requires

$$C_1^+ = C_1^- + zC_{P,1} \quad (7.4)$$

Similarly the condition for electroneutrality on the tissue side requires

$$C_2^+ = C_2^- + zC_{P,2} \quad (7.5)$$

which differs from the usual statement of Donnan equilibrium by including the protein concentration of the tissue side. Some calculations accounting for the effect of a nonzero protein concentration on the tissue side of the capillary wall are given after Equation 7.13. Addition of Equations 7.2 and 7.3 yields

$$\ln\left(\frac{C_2^+C_2^-}{C_1^+C_1^-}\right) = \frac{(P_1 - P_2)(v^+ + v^-)}{RT} \quad (7.6)$$

For pressures in the range of 10–50 mmHg, partial molar volumes of ions on the order of 100 cm^3/mol, and RT equal to 19.3 × 10^6 mmHg·cm^3·mol^{-1}, the right side of this equation is very small. Therefore it is closely approximated by the result

$$C_1^+C_1^- = C_2^+C_2^- \quad (7.7)$$

which is the familiar expression for the Donnan distribution of ions. Therefore

$$\frac{C_1^+}{C_2^+} = \frac{C_2^-}{C_1^-} \quad (7.8)$$

and the Donnan potential ($\Delta\psi$) equals the Nernst potential

$$\Delta\psi = \frac{RT}{zF} \ln \frac{C_2^+}{C_1^+} \quad (7.9)$$

B. Donnan Potential and Osmotic Pressure

The calculations in this subsection extend the development described above. Ion binding by the charged species and complex electrostatic interactions are not taken into account. The development is similar to that given by Robinson (129). In the capillary lumen the total plasma concentration of plasma proteins is ~1 mM and the valency is assumed to be −17. A simplified plasma composition includes cations (Na^+; 155 mM) and anions (Cl^-; 138 mM). Furthermore, as a first approximation, the protein concentration in the interstitial space is assumed to be zero. According to Equation 7.5, for $C_{P,2} = 0$ the concentration of cations and anions in the tissue fluid is equal. Substitution into Equation 7.7 yields

$$C_2^+ = C_2^- = 146.25 \text{ mM} \quad (7.10a)$$

and the Donnan potential across the capillary wall is predicted to be

$$\Delta\psi = 26.5 \ln(146.2/155) = -1.5 \text{ mV} \quad (7.10b)$$

The negative sign indicates the lumen is negative relative to the tissue. Measurements of electrical potential across the capillary wall have indicated values ≤2 mV (26). The distribution of ions leads to an excess of solute on the luminal side. The excess ion concentration in the lumen (C_{ex}) in mM is given as

$$C_{ex} = 155 + 138 - 2 \times 146.25 = 0.5 \text{ mM} \quad (7.11)$$

The total ideal colloid osmotic pressure from 1 mM protein is therefore predicted to be

hypothesis that slow labeling is caused by a highly restricted diffusive process at the vesicle entrance. On the other hand the results are as expected if only a fraction of the luminal vesicles are available for labeling at $t < 40$ s after exposure to the tracer. Possibly a channel linking the vesicle lumen to capillary lumen is patent for only a very small fraction of the time a vesicle resides at the luminal surface. These processes require detailed experimental study because vesicle filling may represent the rate-limiting step in the transport of macromolecules.

C. Movement of Vesicles Within Cytoplasm

In the simplest model (Fig. 8.3) a uniform population of vesicles is assumed to bud off from the luminal surface and make a complete transit across the cell (123). If V_v represents the volume of vesicular contents moving across the cell per unit of time

$$V_v = \pi(4/3)r_v^3 N_v \quad (8.5)$$

where N_v is the number of vesicles completing a single crossing per unit of time. Assuming that movement of vesicles is symmetrical, $V_{v,1\rightarrow2} = V_{v,2\rightarrow1}$, and vesicular flux ($J_s$) is

$$J_s = V_v\phi_v(C_1 - C_2) \quad (8.6)$$

where C_1 is the luminal concentration and C_2 is the abluminal concentration (123). The term $V_v\phi_v$ has the units of a permeability–surface area product

$$(PS)_v = V_v\phi_v = \phi N_v(4/3)r_v^3 \quad (8.7)$$

Models of various degrees of sophistication have been developed that describe the coefficient N_v (Eqs. 8.5 and 8.7) in terms of the kinetics of vesicular attachment and detachment at the luminal and abluminal surfaces and Brownian diffusion of free vesicles within the cytoplasm of the endothelial cell (6, 56, 130, 134, 158). The models also assume that a vesicle, once free in the cytoplasm, moves like a "ferry boat" or "shuttle" to the other side without further exchange of contents with other vesicles. The experiments shown in Figure 8.1 allow some of the assumption in the vesicle-shuttle model to be evaluated. The figure shows the labeling of cytoplasmic and abluminal vesicles with ferritin from experiments on single capillaries of frog mesentery in addition to the results for the luminal vesicles. In the steady state the fraction of cytoplasmic vesicles labeled with ferritin (N_L/N_T) in the cytoplasm should be equal to the mean of the values of N_L/N_T in luminal and abluminal vesicles if exchange is symmetrical. The data in Figure 8.1 are in agreement with this prediction. On the other hand a striking inconsistency with the predictions of the shuttle model was found when the number of molecules per vesicle was examined. The steady-state number of molecules per vesicle was found to be significantly less in cytoplasmic vesicles than the number per vesicle measured for luminal vesicles. This observation shows that, contrary to the assumptions underlying all theoretical models of vesicular transport to date, vesicles do exchange content during passage across the endothelial cell.

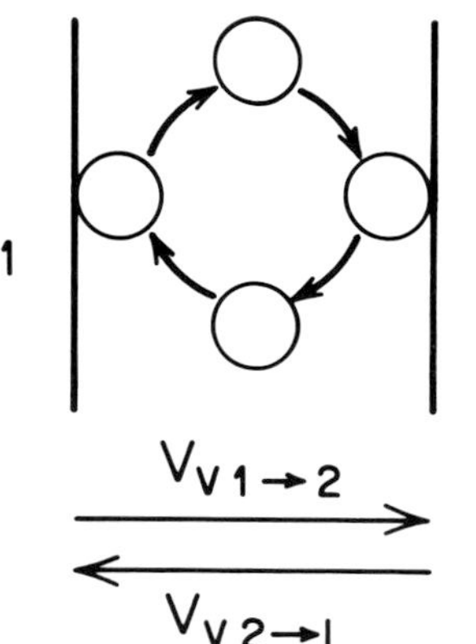

FIG. 8.3. Shuttle mechanism of vesicle transport. Vesicles are assumed to bud off from luminal surface and make complete transit to abluminal surface. In symmetrical system, volume of vesicle contents crossing cell per unit time is equal in each direction.

Clough and Michel (20) proposed the mechanism shown in Figure 8.4 to account for macromolecular transport by vesicles—slowly labeling vesicles at the luminal surface undergo transient fusion and separation with adjacent vesicles. In this way the principal transport mechanism for macromolecules carried by vesicles is exchange between adjacent vesicles rather than translocation of individual vesicles. Additional evidence for the fusion of vesicles is presented by Simionescu et al. (137) and by Bundgaard et al. (15). No quantitative models including transient fusion and separation have been developed, althought the kinetics of transport between a series of exchanging compartments is described by a relation similar to the diffusion equations.

D. Measurement of Transcapillary Exchange—Vesicle Transport Versus Ultrafiltration

Symmetrical vesicular exchange cannot produce a net volume flow. Renkin (120) assumed that the bulk of transcapillary volume flow (J_v) occurs through a pathway impermeable to macromolecules. For steady-state ultrafiltration of macromolecules through a membrane consisting of a vesicular pathway in parallel with a water pathway, the solute concentration on the tissue side of the capillary wall (C_2) is given by the relation $C_2 = J_{s,v}/J_{v,p}$. Therefore from Equation 8.6

$$\frac{C_2}{C_1} = \frac{V_v\phi_v}{V_v\phi_v + J_{v,p}} = C_L/C_P \quad (8.8)$$

Usually C_1 is set equal to the plasma concentration (C_P), and C_2 is assumed to be equal to the lymph concentration (C_L). From Equation 8.7

$$\frac{C_L}{C_P} = \frac{(PS)_v}{(PS)_v + J_L} \quad (8.9)$$

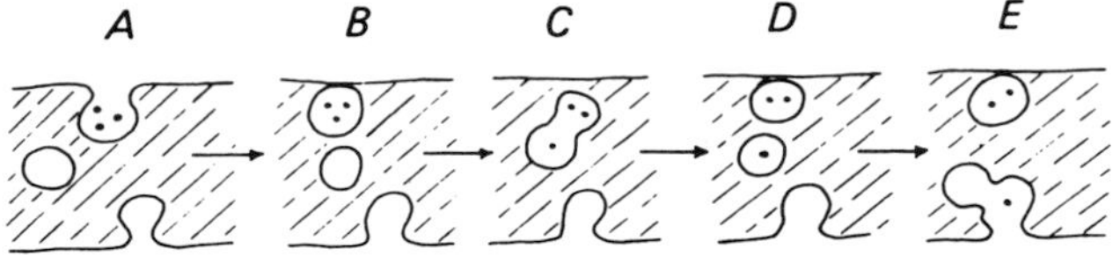

FIG. 8.4. Hypothesis to account for entry of ferritin into cytoplasmic and abluminal vesicles of endothelial cells. Two mechanisms are proposed: *1*) small number of rapidly labeling vesicles that have access to luminal surface via channels formed by relatively stable fusion of adjacent vesicles (*left*) and *2*) slowly labeling vesicles that undergo transient fusion and separation with their neighbors allowing intermixing of vesicular contents (*right*). [From Clough and Michel (20).]

where J_L is the lymph flow, which must equal the net rate of transcapillary volume flow in a homogenous capillary bed at steady state. Equation 8.9 also describes any alternative diffusive mechanism of vesicular transport. Because Equation 8.9 does not account for solute flux caused by convective transport, the values of $(PS)_v$, calculated from measured plasma-to-lymph concentration ratios and lymph flows, overestimate large-molecule permeabilities when solvent drag of macromolecules occurs. Perl (113) modified Equation 8.6 to account for both vesicular and convective-diffusion transport with the Kedem-Katchalsky flux equation

$$J_s = (PS)_v(C_P - C_L) + (PS)_p(C_P - C_L) + [J_{v,p}(1 - \sigma_{f,p})(C_L + C_P)/2] \tag{8.10}$$

With the ultrafiltration theory developed in V. PORE THEORY (p. 327) the total solute flux is more accurately described by

$$J_s = (PS)_v(C_P - C_L) + (PS)_p(C_P - C_L) \cdot \{Pe/[\exp(Pe) - 1]\} + J_{v,p}(1 - \sigma_{f,p})C_P \tag{8.11}$$

Equations 8.10 and 8.11 describe an inhomogeneous membrane consisting of a vesicle pathway and a pore pathway through which proteins are transported. (The pore pathway is designated by the subscript lp.) For steady-state filtration $C_L = J_s/J_L$, where J_L may be greater than $J_{v,p}$. Therefore from Equation 8.11 and the steady-state ultrafiltration condition

$$\frac{C_L}{C_P} = \frac{(PS)_v + (PS)_{lp}\{Pe/[\exp(Pe) - 1]\}_{lp} + J_{v,lp}(1 - \sigma_{f,lp})}{(PS)_v + (PS)_{lp}\{Pe/[\exp(Pe) - 1]\}_{lp} + J_L} \tag{8.12}$$

where Pe_{lp} is the large-pore Péclet number, $J_{v,lp} \cdot (1 - \sigma_{lp})/(PS)_{lp}$. Equation 8.12 has not been applied to the analysis of macromolecular transport. The conditions required to simplify Equation 8.12 to forms more usually applied are specified next.

1. Volume flow is all through large pores and the Péclet number in large pores is small ($J_L = J_{v,lp}$ and $Pe < 1$)

$$\frac{C_L}{C_P} = \frac{(PS)_T + [J_{v,lp}(\overline{1 - \sigma_f})_{lp}/2]}{(PS)_T + [J_{v,lp}(\overline{1 + \sigma_f})_{lp}/2]} \tag{8.13}$$

where $(PS)_T = (PS)_v + (PS)_{lp}$.

2. Flow is not all through large pores and the Péclet number in large pores is small ($J_L \neq J_{v,lp}$; $Pe < 1$)

$$\frac{C_L}{C_P} = \frac{(PS)_T + [J_L(\overline{1 - \sigma_f})/2]}{(PS)_T + [J_L(\overline{1 + \sigma_f})/2]} \tag{8.14}$$

where $\overline{1 - \sigma_f} = (J_{v,lp}/J_L)(1 - \sigma_f)_{lp}$. The value of $J_{v,lp}/J_L$ is not constant as J_L changes (see Table 5.5*C*).

3. Flow is all through large pores and the Péclet number in large pores is large ($J_L = J_{v,lp}$; $Pe > 5$)

$$\frac{C_L}{C_P} = \frac{(PS)_v + J_v(1 - \sigma_f)_{lp}}{(PS)_v + J_v} \tag{8.15}$$

Note that $(PS)_{lp}$ no longer appears in the equation because $Pe/[\exp(Pe) - 1]_{lp}$ is effectively zero for $Pe > 5$.

4. Flow is not all through large pores and the Péclet number in large pores is large ($J_L \neq J_{v,lp}$; $Pe > 5$)

$$\frac{C_L}{C_P} = \frac{(PS)_v + J_L(\overline{1 - \sigma_f})}{(PS)_v + J_L} \tag{8.16}$$

which may be rearranged into the form of the Pappenheimer ultrafiltration equation described in V. PORE THEORY (p. 327)

$$\frac{C_L}{C_P} = \frac{\dfrac{(PS)_v}{J_L} + (\overline{1 - \sigma_f})}{\dfrac{(PS)_v}{J_L} + 1} \tag{8.17}$$

Here also, $\overline{1 - \sigma_f} = (J_{v,lp}/J_L)(1 - \sigma_f)_{lp}$. The ratio $J_{v,lp}/J_L$ approaches limiting values at high lymph flows (see Eq. 5.92).

Equation 8.17 shows that, even under conditions in which the Péclet number in the porous pathway is so large that diffusion is overwhelmed by convective flow, the ratio C_L/C_P does not necessarily equal $\overline{1 - \sigma_f}$ but depends on the value of $(PS)_v/J_L$. Application of Equation 8.17 with $(PS)_v/J_L > 0$ to experimental data is more difficult than application of the limiting case in which $(PS)_v/J_L$ is zero [see V. PORE THEORY (p. 327); Table 5.5]. Nevertheless systematic use of Equation 8.17 is required if the relative importance of vesicular and large-pore pathways is to be properly studied.

Preliminary observations suggest the direction for further studies with Equation 8.17. Clearly the rate of change of C_L/C_P as lymph flow increases is a critical parameter for distinguishing between vesicular transport and solvent drag. For example, if C_L/C_P is exactly constant as lymph flow increases, $(PS)_v$ must be zero. However, quite small changes in C_L/C_P may imply significant contributions of vesicular transport at elevated lymph flows. Specifically, if $(PS)_v/J_L$ for fibrinogen equals 0.02 at a lymph flow of 2×10^{-4} ml/s, C_L/C_P in Figure 5.9 will fall from 0.08 to 0.06 as lymph flow increases from 2 to 8×10^{-4} ml/s. If $(PS)_v/J_L$ for fibrinogen is 0.02 at a lymph flow of 2×10^{-4} ml/s, then $\overline{1 - \sigma_f}$ calculated from Equation 8.17 is 0.06 instead of 0.08 and $(PS)_v$ for fibrinogen is 0.04×10^{-4} cm^3/s. The calculated estimate of diffusive flux across the capillary wall via vesicles will be increased.

E. *Tissue-to-Blood Transport of Macromolecules*

If ultrafiltration through a large-pore pathway is the only pathway for large-molecule transport across the capillary wall, net transport of macromolecules from tissue to blood is highly unlikely—backdiffusion through large pores is always opposed by blood-to-tissue fluid flow even during periods of net reabsorption. Several experiments clearly demonstrate tissue-to-blood transport (66, 115). Further study of tissue-to-blood transport of macromolecules may provide new insights into vesicule-pathway mechanisms.

F. *Effect of Hydrostatic Pressure on Vesicular Transport*

Renkin (123) proposed a modification of the model described by Equation 8.6, which describes asymmetric vesicle exchange. The model describes a net volume flow across the vesicle pathway—a pore pathway is no longer required to explain coupling between macromolecule flux and volume flow. A model in which 10% of the volume flow is accounted for by vesicles is consistent with the data described by Figure 5.9.

G. *Transport of Small Lipid-Soluble Solutes Via Cell Membrane Pathways*

The pathways for lipid-soluble solutes across the capillary wall have permeability properties similar to those described for cell membranes. With test substances of closely related chemical structure, Renkin

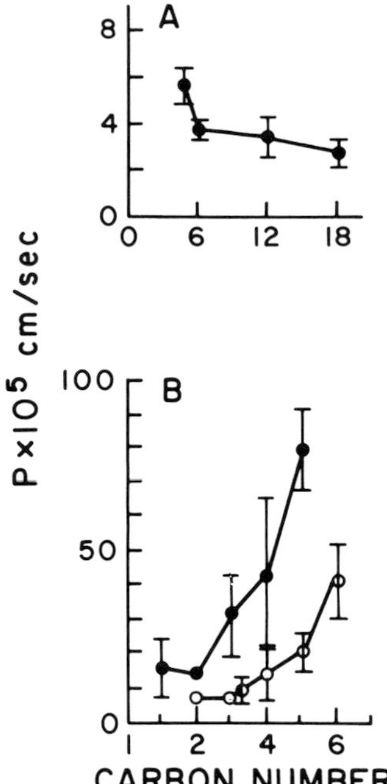

FIG. 8.5. Comparison of permeability coefficients of hydrophilic and lipophilic solutes in dog lung. *A*: ●, carbohydrates (e.g., xylose, glucose, sucrose, and raffinose). *B*: ○, terminal diols from C_2 through C_6; ●, amides from C_1 through C_5; ◑, 1,2-propanediol. [*A* from Chinard (19); *B* modified from Perl et al. (114).]

(117, 118) demonstrated that the dissipation rate of transcapillary concentration gradients of small lipid-soluble solutes was more directly related to their lipid solubility than to their molecular weight. These results were interpreted in terms of a pathway for lipophilic solute across the endothelial cells in parallel with pathways for hydrophilic solutes. The pathway involves diffusion across two plasma membranes in series and diffusion through the cell cytoplasm. An extensive investigation of homologous series of compounds has been made by Chinard (18). Figure 8.5 compares the permeability coefficients in the dog lung of hydrophilic carbohydrates (Fig. 8.5*A*) with 6–18 carbon atoms with the permeability coefficients of normal amides and normal alkane diols (Fig. 8.5*B*). For carbohydrates the permeability falls with increasing molecular weight; for amides the permeability first drops, then rises rapidly with increasing molecular weight. The results for amides with 3 or more carbon atoms are in accord with their increasing olive oil–water partition coefficient. The fall in permeability from formamide (mol wt, 59; K_{oil}, 0.0012) to acetamide (mol wt, 59; K_{oil}, 0.0025) indicates that the more lipid-insoluble solutes share both a lipid and an aqueous pathway.

Curry (31) demonstrated that the partitioning of small lipid-soluble solutes, which are also soluble in water, between aqueous and lipid pathways depends not only on the solubility in the lipid pathway but also on the diffusion capacity (PS) of the aqueous pathway.

In the continuous capillaries of the frog mesentery at 25°C, the flux of antipyrine is divided almost equally between lipophilic and hydrophilic pathways. At the same temperature almost all the antipyrine flux across mammalian skeletal muscle and lung capillaries occurs via the lipophilic pathway. For the purpose of this discussion the most significant difference between the capillary walls of frog mesentery and skeletal muscle is the magnitude of the permeability of the aqueous pathway, not the permeability of the lipid pathways. In fact, estimates of the magnitude of the permeability of the lipid pathway in frog mesenteric and mammalian lung capillaries are quite similar.

Although properties of the lipophilic pathway across the capillary wall are similar to the properties of pathways across cell membranes, the precise nature of the pathway remains poorly understood. Chinard (18) made a direct comparison between the permeability coefficients of the capillary wall in the dog lung and the permeability coefficients of the same solutes across the plasma membranes of a mixture of endothelial and epithelial cells gathered from the lung. Surprisingly the permeability coefficients measured from isolated cells are an order of magnitude larger than the permeability coefficients measured from blood-to-tissue transport in the intact lung. An even larger discrepancy is found when the permeability of the epithelial membranes is compared with cell membrane permeabilities. The results suggest that structures other than diffusion barriers across cell membranes limit transcapillary exchange. Scow et al. (133) suggested that lateral diffusion in the plasma membranes of endothelial cells may provide a mechanism for transcapillary exchange of lipid-soluble solutes. According to this hypothesis the diffusion distances for lipid-soluble solutes are longer than the 50–100 Å associated with translational diffusion across cell membranes. Membrane pathways around the cell or those formed by the fusion of vesicles to form continuous membrane pathways across the cell may be over 1,000 Å long.

H. Analysis of Measured Permeability Coefficients for Small Lipid-Soluble Solutes

Figure 8.6 shows the permeability to normal amides and normal alkane diols measured in lung capillaries plotted against their olive oil–water partition coefficients. The results conform to the hypothesis that the permeability coefficient of the lipophilic portion of a membrane (P_{lipid}) of thickness Δx can be expressed in terms of a spatially averaged partition coefficient (ϕ_{m-w}) and a spatially averaged diffusion coefficient (D_m) (37)

$$P_{lipid} = \phi_{m-w} \frac{D_m}{\Delta x} \tag{8.18}$$

If the partition coefficient for solutes in the lipids of the endothelial cell membrane were equal to the olive oil–water partition coefficient, the slope of the relation in Figure 8.6 would be 1.0. In fact the slope of the relation is close to 0.5, which indicates that the lipids in the endothelial cell membrane are less lipophilic than olive oil; the same conclusion was reached by Curry (31). A better estimate of ϕ_{m-w} is required to examine the diffusive mechanisms.

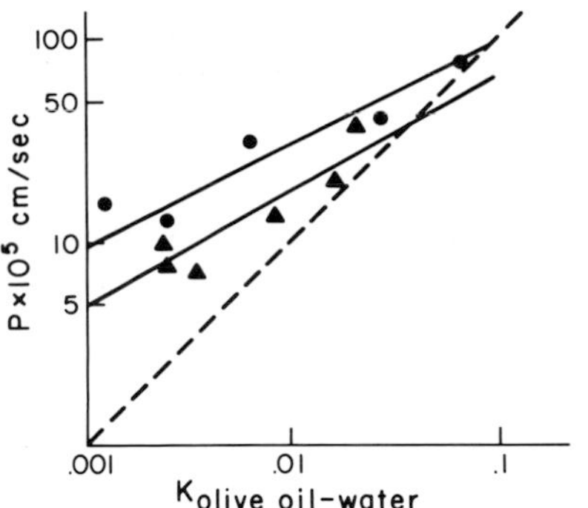

FIG. 8.6. Permeability coefficients of normal amides (●) and normal alkane diols (▲) plotted against their olive oil–water partition coefficients. Both scales are logarithmic. *Broken line* has slope of 1. Slope less than unity indicates that lipids of endothelial cell are less lipophilic than olive oil.

TABLE 8.2. *Partition and Diffusion Coefficients of Lipophilic Solutes in Capillary Wall*

Solute	$P \times 10^5$ cm/s	ϕ	$D_m/\Delta x \times 10^5$ cm/s
Antipyrine	22	0.18	1.22
Aminopyrine	38	0.38	1.00

Direct measurements of the partition coefficients in cell membranes are rare. Curry (31) estimated the partition coefficients of antipyrine and aminopyrine in the endothelial cell membranes of frog mesentery by using data from erythrocyte membranes. The values of $D_m/\Delta x$ calculated from the measured permeability coefficients at 20°C are given in Table 8.2. Although the values for partition coefficient are highly speculative, the order-of-magnitude analysis demonstrates the feasibility of the model for lateral diffusion.

Suppose the lipid pathway is transcellular. Then $D_m/\Delta x$ in Table 8.2 is determined by two cell membranes in series. If the membranes are assumed to be 100-Å thick, the apparent membrane diffusion coefficient for translation across the membrane is on the order of 10^{-9} cm²/s. This value is three orders of magnitude smaller than the lateral diffusion coefficients of solutes with molecular weights similar to antipyrine (e.g., pyrene) in cell membranes (52). An alternative mechanism that accounts for the values of $D_m/\Delta x$ is lateral diffusion of the molecules via a pathway several hundred angstroms in length. These pathways may occupy $<1\%$ of the total surface. Both transcellular and circumcellular pathways are probably available in endothelial cells. Factors determining

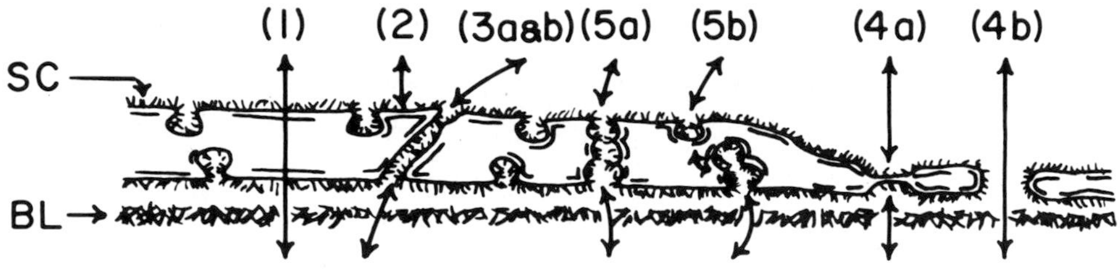

FIG. 9.1. Transport pathways in capillary endothelium. *1*) Endothelial cell pathway; *2*) lateral membrane diffusion pathway; *3*) intercellular junctions; *4*) endothelial cell fenestrae; *5*) endothelial cell vesicles. BL, basal lamina; SC, cell surface coat. [Modified from Renkin (121), by permission of the New York Academy of Sciences.]

the relative importance of each pathway as a function of the physical and chemical properties of the solute remain to be determined.

IX. MULTIPLE PATHWAYS FOR TRANSCAPILLARY EXCHANGE

The thermodynamic and mechanical models developed in the previous sections are tools for investigating the role of the vascular endothelium as a transport barrier and regulator of transcapillary exchange. The endothelium is now recognized to be a complex structure that offers several pathways for exchange (Fig. 9.1) (125). These pathways include transport *1*) through the endothelial cells by crossing two plasma membranes and the cell cytoplasm; *2*) within the cell membranes by lateral diffusion in the lipid phase through intercellular junctions or vesicular channels; *3*) through interendothelial cell junctions in the aqueous extracellular phase either *a*) via small pores or a fibrous meshwork impermeable to plasma proteins or *b*) via large pores or a less-dense area in a fiber meshwork permeable to plasma proteins; *4*) through endothelial cell fenestrae, e.g., through *a*) specialized openings across the cells or *b*) areas at which the two cell membranes are fused and modified, bypassing the aqueous cytoplasmic phase; and *5*) by endothelial cell vesicles that *a*) move back and forth between cell surfaces (transcytosis) or *b*) communicate transiently with one another to exchange their contents or establish temporary open channels.

In series with all these pathways is the basal lamina, a layer of fine collagenous fibers that may also be a barrier to permeation of large molecules. Moreover the endothelial cell surfaces are covered by a feltwork of delicate glycoprotein strands that extends into the junctions and also lines the vesicles. This feltwork may also contribute to the permeability barrier. The principal conclusions drawn from the analyses in this chapter require partitioning of fluxes for lipid-soluble solutes, water, and macromolecules between pathways with extracellular characteristics and other pathways with cellular characteristics (Table 9.1).

TABLE 9.1. *Partition of Fluxes Between Transcapillary Pathways*

Species	Pathways	Analyses
Water	1, 3a, 3b, 4a, 4b	Figures 5.10, 5.14, 5.15, 5.16, 5.17, 6.1, 6.3, 8.4; Table 5.5
Lipophilic solutes	1, 2, 3, 4	Figures 8.4, 8.5; Table 8.2
Hydrophilic solutes	3a, 3b, 4a, 4b	Figures 5.4, 5.5, 5.14, 5.16, 5.17, 6.1, 6.3
Macromolecules	3a, 3b, 4a, 4b, 5a, 5b	Figures 5.5, 5.9, 5.10, 5.17, 6.1, 6.3, 8.1, 8.2, 8.3, 8.4

For description of pathways see IX. MULTIPLE PATHWAYS FOR TRANSCAPILLARY EXCHANGE, this page.

The analytical tools required to analyze multiple pathways across the capillary membrane are more complex than those needed to study homogeneous pathways. The tools are available and are becoming increasingly precise. The real challenge in capillary permeability studies is the design and implementation of precise experimental studies that will provide clearer answers to the numerous questions raised in this chapter.

I am grateful to Drs. E. M. Renkin, C. C. Michel, V. H. Huxley, D. Levitt, and R. H. Adamson for their helpful criticisms and to Phoebe Ling for typing the manuscript.

The work was supported in part by National Heart, Lung, and Blood Institute Grant HLB 18010. The author is an Established Investigator of the American Heart Association.

REFERENCES

1. ADAMSON, R. H., AND F. E. CURRY. Water flow through a fiber matrix of hyaluronic acid (Abstract). *Microvasc. Res.* 23: 239, 1982.
2. ANDERSON, J. L. Configurational effect of the reflection coefficient on rigid solutes in capillary pores. *J. Theor. Biol.* 90: 405–426, 1981.
3. ANDERSON, J. L. Concentration effects on distribution of macromolecules in large pores. *Proc. NY Acad. Sci.* 404: 52–53, 1982.
4. ANDERSON, J. L., AND D. M. MALONE. Mechanism of osmotic flow in porous membranes. *Biophys. J.* 14: 957–982, 1974.
5. ANDERSON, J. L., AND J. A. QUINN. Restricted transport in small pores. A model for steric exclusion and hindered particle motion. *Biophys. J.* 14: 130–150, 1974.
6. ARMINSKI, L., S. WEINBAUM, AND R. PFEFFER. Time dependent theory for vesicular transport across vascular endothelium. *J. Theor. Biol.* 85: 13–43, 1980.
7. BEAN, C. P. The physics of porous membranes—neutral pores.

In: *Membranes*, edited by G. Eisenman. New York: Dekker, 1972, vol. 1, p. 1–54.
8. BECK, R. E., AND J. S. SCHULTZ. Hindrance of solute diffusion within membranes as measured with microporous membranes of known pore geometry. *Biochim. Biophys. Acta* 255: 273–303, 1972.
9. BRACE, R. A., D. N. GRANGER, AND A. E. TAYLOR. Analysis of lymphatic protein flux data. II. Effects of capillary heteroporosity on estimates of reflection coefficient and PS products. *Microvasc. Res.* 14: 215–226, 1977.
10. BRACE, R. A., D. N. GRANGER, AND A. E. TAYLOR. Analysis of lymphatic protein flux data. III. Use of the nonlinear flux equation to estimate PS. *Microvasc. Res.* 16: 297–303, 1978.
11. BRENNER, B. M., C. BAYLIS, AND W. M. DEEN. Transport of molecules across renal glomerular capillaries. *Physiol. Rev.* 56: 502–534, 1978.
12. BRENNER, H., AND L. J. GAYDOS. The constrained Brownian movement of spherical particles in cylindrical pores of comparable radius. Models of the diffusive and convective transport of solute molecules in membranes and porous media. *J. Colloid Interface Sci.* 58: 312–356, 1977.
13. BRESLER, E. H., AND L. J. GROOME. On equations for combined convective and diffusive transport of neutral solute across porous membranes. *Am. J. Physiol.* 241 (*Renal Fluid Electrolyte Physiol.* 10): F469–F476, 1981.
14. BRESLER, E. H., E. A. MASON, AND R. P. WENDT. Appraisal of equations for neutral solute flux across porous sieving membranes. *Biophys. Chem.* 4: 229–236, 1976.
15. BUNDGAARD, M., J. FRØKJAER-JENSEN, AND C. CRONE. Endothelial plasmalemmal vesicles as elements in a system of branching invaginations from the cell surface. *Proc. Natl. Acad. Sci. USA* 76: 6439–6442, 1979.
16. CARMAN, P. C. Fluid flow through granular beds. *Trans. Inst. Chem. Eng. London* 15: 150–166, 1937.
17. CASLEY-SMITH, J. R., AND J. C. CHIN. The passage of cytoplasmic vesicles across endothelial and mesothelial cells. *J. Microsc.* 93: 167–189, 1971.
18. CHINARD, F. P. The alveolar-capillary barrier: some data and speculation. *Microvasc. Res.* 19: 1–17, 1980.
19. CHINARD, F. P., W. PERL, AND A. B. RITTER. Interaction of aqueous and lipid pathways in the pulmonary endothelium. In: *Microcirculation*, edited by J. Grayson and W. Zingg. New York: Plenum, 1976, vol. 2, p. 71–74.
20. CLOUGH, G., AND C. C. MICHEL. The role of vesicles in the transport of ferritin through frog endothelium. *J. Physiol. London* 315: 127–142, 1981.
21. CLOUGH, G., C. C. MICHEL, M. E. PHILLIPS, AND M. R. TURNER. Cationised ferritin reduces the permeability of frog capillaries: native ferritin does not (Abstract). *J. Physiol. London* 320: 41P–42P, 1981.
22. CRANK, J. *The Mathematics of Diffusion.* Oxford, UK: Clarendon, 1975, p. 203–253.
23. CRANK, J., AND G. S. PARK. *Diffusion in Polymers.* New York: Academic, chapt. 1, 1968, p. 1–39.
24. CRONE, C., AND O. CHRISTENSEN. Transcapillary transport of small solutes and water. In: *Cardiovascular Physiology III*, edited by A. C. Guyton and D. B. Young. Baltimore, MD: University Park, 1979, vol. 18, p. 149–218. (Int. Rev. Physiol. Ser.)
25. CRONE, C., AND O. CHRISTENSEN. Electrical resistance of a capillary endothelium. *J. Gen. Physiol.* 77: 349–371, 1981.
26. CRONE, C., J. FRØKJÆR-JENSEN, J. J. FRIEDMAN, AND O. CHRISTENSEN. The permeability of single capillaries to potassium ions. *J. Gen. Physiol.* 71: 195–220, 1978.
27. CRONE, C., AND N. A. LASSEN (editors). *Capillary Permeability.* Copenhagen: Munksgaard, 1970. (Alfred Benzon Symp. 2.)
28. CURRY, F. E. A hydrodynamic description of the osmotic reflection coefficient with application to the pore theory of transcapillary exchange. *Microvasc. Res.* 8: 236–252, 1974.
29. CURRY, F. E. Permeability coefficients of the capillary wall to low molecular weight hydrophilic solutes measured in single perfused capillaries of frog mesentery. *Microvasc. Res.* 17: 290–308, 1979.
30. CURRY, F. E. Is the transport of hydrophilic substances across the capillary wall determined by a network of fibrous molecules? *Physiologist* 23(1): 90–93, 1980.
31. CURRY, F. E. Antipyrine and aminopyrine permeability of individually perfused frog capillaries. *Am. J. Physiol.* 240 (*Heart Circ. Physiol.* 9): H597–H605, 1981.
32. CURRY, F. E., AND V. H. HUXLEY. Comparison of the capillary membrane properties determining fluid exchange in single capillaries and whole organs. *Int. J. Microcirc. Clin. Exp.* 1: 381–391, 1982.
33. CURRY, F. E., V. H. HUXLEY, AND R. H. ADAMSON. Permeability of single capillaries to intermediate sized colored solutes. *Am. J. Physiol.* 245 (*Heart Circ. Physiol.* 14): H495–H505, 1983.
34. CURRY, F. E., AND C. C. MICHEL. A fiber matrix model of capillary permeability. *Microvasc. Res.* 20: 96–99, 1980.
35. CURRY, F. E., J. C. MASON, AND C. C. MICHEL. Osmotic reflexion coefficients of capillary walls to low molecular weight hydrophilic solutes measured in single perfused capillaries of frog mesentery. *J. Physiol. London* 261: 319–336, 1976.
36. DEEN, W. M., B. SATVAT, AND J. M. JAMIESON. Theoretical model for glomerular filtration of charged solutes. *Am. J. Physiol.* 238 (*Renal Fluid Electrolyte Physiol.* 7): F126–F139, 1980.
37. DIAMOND, J. M., AND Y. KATZ. Interpretation of nonelectrolyte partition coefficients between dimyristoyl lecithin and water. *J. Membr. Biol.* 17: 121–154, 1974.
38. DIANA, J. N., S. C. LONG, AND H. YAO. Effect of histamine on the equivalent pore radius in capillaries of isolated dog hindlimb. *Microvasc. Res.* 4: 413–437, 1972.
39. DRAKE, R., AND E. DAVIS. Letter to the editors. *Microvasc. Res.* 15: 259, 1978.
40. DURBIN, R. P. Osmotic flow of water across cellulose membranes. *J. Gen. Physiol.* 44: 315–326, 1960.
41. EFFROS, R. M. Osmotic extraction of hypotonic fluid from the lungs. *J. Clin. Invest.* 54: 935–947, 1974.
42. EINSTEIN, A. The elementary theory of the Brownian motion. *Z. Elektrochem.* 14: 235–239, 1908.
42a. EINSTEIN, A. *Investigations on the Theory of the Brownian Movement.* New York: Dover, 1956.
43. EMERSLEBEN, O. The Darcy filter formula. *Phys. Z.* 26: 601–610, 1925.
44. FAIRMAN, R. P., J. E. MILLEN, AND F. L. GLAUSER. The role of electric charge interaction on normal pulmonary microvascular permeability (Abstract). *Federation Proc.* 41: 1247, 1982.
45. FAXEN, H. About T. Bohlin's paper: on the drag on rigid spheres moving in a viscous liquid inside cylindrical tubes. *Kolloid Z.* 167: 146, 1959.
46. FERRY, J. D. Statistical evaluation of sieve constants in ultrafiltration. *J. Gen. Physiol.* 20: 95–104, 1936.
47. FINKELSTEIN, A., AND A. MAURO. Physical principles and formalisms of electrical excitability. In: *Handbook of Physiology. The Nervous System*, edited by J. M. Brookhart and V. B. Mountcastle. Bethesda, MD: Am. Physiol. Soc., 1977, sect. 1, vol. I, pt. 1, chapt. 6, p. 161–213.
48. FLOREY, H. W. Inflammation. In: *General Pathology*, edited by H. W. Florey. Oxford, UK: Oxford Univ. Press, 1970, p. 40–123.
49. FRØKJÆR-JENSEN, J., AND F. E. CURRY. Hydraulic conductivity and sucrose reflection coefficients of individually perfused capillaries in frog muscle (Abstract). *Federation Proc.* 41: 1253, 1982.
50. FURTH, R. The diffusiometer and its application to the study of the molecular constitution of liquids. *J. Sci. Instrum.* 22: 61–65, 1945.
52. GALLA, H. J., W. HARTMAN, U. THEILEN, AND E. SACKMANN. On two-dimensional passive random walk in lipid bilayers and fluid pathways in biomembranes. *J. Membr. Biol.* 48: 215–236, 1979.

53. GARBY, L., AND S. AREEKUL. Reflection coefficients of neutral and sulphate-substituted dextran molecules in the capillaries of the isolated rabbit ear. In: *Capillary Permeability*, edited by C. Crone and N. A. Lassen. Copenhagen: Munksgaard, 1970, p. 560–562. (Alfred Benzon Symp. 2.)
54. GARLICK, D. G., AND E. M. RENKIN. Transport of large molecules from plasma to interstitial fluid and lymph in dogs. *Am. J. Physiol.* 219: 1595–1605, 1970.
55. GIDDINGS, J. C., E. KUCERA, C. P. RUSSELL, AND M. N. MYERS. Statistical theory for the equilibrium distribution of rigid molecules in inert porous networks. Exclusion chromatography. *J. Phys. Chem.* 72: 4397–4408, 1968.
56. GREEN, H. S., AND J. R. CASLEY-SMITH. Calculations on the passage of small vesicles across endothelial cells by Brownian motion. *J. Theor. Biol.* 35: 103–111, 1972.
57. HABERMAN, W. C., AND R. M. SAYRE. Motion of rigid and fluid spheres in stationary and moving liquids in side cylindrical tubes. David Taylor Model Basin report no. 1143, October, 1958. Washington, DC: US Navy Dept., 1958, p. 1–65.
58. HAMMEL, H. T. Forum on osmosis. I. Osmosis: diminished solvent activity or enhanced solvent tension. *Am. J. Physiol.* 237 (*Regulatory Integrative Comp. Physiol.* 6): R95–R107, 1979.
59. HAPPEL, J., AND H. BRENNER. *Low Reynolds Number Hydrodynamics.* Leyden, Netherlands: Noordhoff, 1973, p. 318.
60. HELFFERICH, F. G. Ion exchanger membranes. In: *Ion Exchange.* New York: McGraw-Hill, 1962, chapt. 8, p. 339–420.
61. HILDEBRAND, J. H. Forum on osmosis. II. A criticism of "solvent tension" in osmosis. *Am. J. Physiol.* 237 (*Regulatory Integrative Comp. Physiol.* 6): R108–R109, 1979.
62. HILDEBRAND, J. H., AND R. L. SCOTT. *Regular Solutions.* Englewood Cliffs, NJ: Prentice-Hall, 1962, chapt. 3, p. 26–40.
63. IBERALL, A. S. Permeability of glass wool and other highly porous media. *J. Res. Natl. Bur. Stand.* 45: 398–406, 1950.
64. IBERALL, A. S., AND A. M. SCHINDLER. A kinetic theory, near-continuum model for membrane transport. *Ann. Biomed. Eng.* 1: 489–497, 1973.
65. JACOBS, M. H. Diffusion processes. *Ergeb. Biol.* 12: 1–160, 1935. Reprinted as *Diffusion Processes.* Berlin: Springer-Verlag, 1967, p. 102–114.
66. JOHANSSON, B. R. Capillary permeability to interstitial microinjections of macromolecules and influence of capillary hydrostatic pressure on endothelial ultrastructure. *Acta Physiol. Scand. Suppl.* 463: 45–50, 1979.
67. KARNOVSKY, M. J. The ultrastructural basis of capillary permeability studied with peroxidase as a tracer. *J. Cell Biol.* 35: 213–236, 1967.
68. KATCHALSKY, A., AND P. F. CURRAN. *Nonequilibrium Thermodynamics in Biophysics.* Cambridge, MA: Harvard Univ. Press, 1965.
69. KEDEM, O., AND A. KATCHALSKY. Thermodynamic analysis of the permeability of biological membranes to non-electrolytes. *Biochim. Biophys. Acta* 27: 229–245, 1958.
70. KEDEM, O., AND A. KATCHALSKY. A physical interpretation of the phenomenological coefficients of membrane permeability. *J. Gen. Physiol.* 45: 143–179, 1961.
71. KEDEM, O., AND A. KATCHALSKY. Permeability of composite membranes. *Trans. Faraday Soc.* 59: 1931–1953, 1963.
72. KEIZER, J. Dissipation and fluctuation in nonequilibrium thermodynamics. *J. Chem. Phys.* 64: 1679–1687, 1976.
73. KEIZER, J. Thermodynamics at nonequilibrium steady states. *J. Chem. Phys.* 69: 2609–2620, 1978.
74. KLEIN, E., F. F. HOLLAND, AND K. EBERLE. Comparison of experimental and calculated permeability and rejection coefficients for hemodialysis membranes. *J. Membr. Sci.* 5: 173–188, 1979.
75. LANDIS, E. M., AND J. R. PAPPENHEIMER. Exchange of substances through the capillary walls. In: *Handbook of Physiology. Circulation*, edited by W. F. Hamilton. Washington, DC: Am. Physiol. Soc., 1963, sect. 2, vol. II, chapt. 29, p. 961–1034.
76. LANKEN, P. N., P. M. SAMPSON, J. H. HANSEN-FLASCHEN, M. MAGNO, A. P. FISHMAN, AND G. C. PIETRA. Effect of charge on the movement of macromolecules from plasma to lung lymph (Abstract). *Federation Proc.* 441: 1247, 1982.
77. LASSEN, N. A., AND J. TRAP-JENSEN. Estimation of the fraction of the interendothelial slit which must be open in order to account for the observed transcapillary exchange of small hydrophilic molecules in skeletal muscle in man. In: *Capillary Permeability*, edited by C. Crone and N. A. Lassen. Copenhagen: Munksgaard, 1970, p. 647–653. (Alfred Benzon Symp. 2.)
78. LEVICK, J. R. Capillary Permeability. Oxford, UK: Oxford University, 1972. Dissertation.
79. LEVICK, J. R., AND C. C. MICHEL. The effect of bovine albumin on the permeability of frog mesenteric capillaries. *Q. J. Exp. Physiol.* 58: 87–97, 1973.
80. LEVITT, D. G. Kinetics of diffusion and convection in 3.2 Å pores. Exact solution by computer simulation. *Biophys. J.* 13: 186–206, 1973.
81. LEVITT, D. G. General continuum analysis of transport through pores. I. Proof of Onsager's reciprocity postulate for uniform pore. *Biophys. J.* 15: 533–551, 1975.
82. LIFSON, N. Revised equations for the osmotic transient method. In: *Capillary Permeability*, edited by C. Crone and N. A. Lassen. Copenhagen: Munksgaard, 1970, p. 302–305. (Alfred Benzon Symp. 2.)
83. LIGHTFOOT, E. N., J. B. BASSINGTHWAIGHTE, AND E. F. GRABOWSKI. Hydrodynamic models for diffusion in microporous membranes. *Ann. Biomed. Eng.* 4: 78–90, 1976.
84. LOUDON, M. F., C. C. MICHEL, AND I. F. WHITE. The labeling of vesicles in frog endothelial cells with ferritin. *J. Physiol. London* 296: 97–112, 1979.
85. LUFT, J. H. Fine structure of capillary and endocapillary layer as revealed by ruthenium red. *Federation Proc.* 25: 1773–1783, 1966.
86. MANNING, G. S. Binary diffusion and bulk flow through a potential energy profile: a kinetic basis for the thermodynamic equations of flow through membranes. *J. Chem. Phys.* 49: 2668–2675, 1968.
87. MASON, J. C., F. E. CURRY, AND C. C. MICHEL. The effects of proteins upon the filtration coefficients of individually perfused frog mesenteric capillaries. *Microvasc. Res.* 13: 185–202, 1977.
88. MAURO, A. Forum on osmosis. III. Comments on Hammel and Scholander's solvent tension theory and its application to the phenomenon of osmotic flow. *Am. J. Physiol.* 237 (*Regulatory Integrative Comp. Physiol.* 6): R110–R113, 1979.
89. MAURO, A. The role of negative pressure in osmotic equilibrium and osmotic flow. In: *Water Transport Across Epithelia: Barriers, Gradients, and Mechanisms*, edited by H. H. Ussing, N. Bindslev, N. A. Lassen, and D. Sten-Knudsen. Copenhagen: Munksgaard, 1981, p. 107–110. (Alfred Benzon Symp. 15.)
90. MICHEL, C. C. Flows across the capillary wall. In: *Cardiovascular Fluid Dynamics*, edited by D. H. Bergel. London: Academic, 1972, vol. 2, p. 241–298.
91. MICHEL, C. C. The measurement of permeability in single capillaries. *Arch. Int. Physiol. Biochim.* 86: 657–667, 1978.
92. MICHEL, C. C. The investigation of capillary permeability in single vessels. *Acta Physiol. Scand. Suppl.* 463: 67–74, 1979.
93. MICHEL, C. C. Filtration coefficients and osmotic reflexion coefficients of the walls of single frog mesenteric capillaries. *J. Physiol. London* 309: 341–355, 1980.
94. MICHEL, C. C., AND M. R. TURNER. The effect of molecular charge on the permeability of frog mesenteric capillaries to myoglobin (Abstract). *J. Physiol. London* 316: 51P–52P, 1981.
95. MOELWYN-HUGHES, E. A. The dissolved state. In: *Physical Chemistry.* Oxford, UK: Pergamon, 1961, p. 772–800.
96. MUNCH, W. D., L. P. ZESTAR, AND J. L. ANDERSON. Rejection of polyelectrolytes from microporous membranes. *J. Membr. Sci.* 5: 77–102, 1979.
97. OGSTON, A. G. Methods of describing unidimensional diffusion in binary liquid systems. *Trans. Faraday Soc.* 50: 1303–1311, 1954.

98. OGSTON, A. G. The spaces in a uniform random suspension of fibres. *Trans. Faraday Soc.* 54: 1745–1757, 1958.
99. OGSTON, A. G., AND C. C. MICHEL. General descriptions of passive transport of neutral solute and solvent through membranes. *Prog. Biophys. Mol. Biol.* 34: 197–217, 1978.
100. OGSTON, A. G., B. N. PRESTON, AND J. D. WELLS. On the transport of compact particles through solutions of chain-polymers. *Proc. R. Soc. London Ser. A* 333: 297–316, 1973.
101. OGSTON, A. G., AND E. F. WOODS. The sedimentation of some fractions of a degraded dextran. *Trans. Faraday Soc.* 50: 635–643, 1954.
102. ONSAGER, L. Reciprocal relations in irreversible processes. *Phys. Rev.* 38: 2255–2279, 1931.
103. PAINE, P. L., AND P. SCHERR. Drag coefficients for the movement of rigid spheres through liquid-filled cylindrical pores. *Biophys. J.* 15: 1087–1091, 1975.
104. PALADE, G. E. Blood capillaries of the heart and other organs. *Circulation* 24: 368–384, 1961.
105. PALADE, G. E., AND R. R. BURNS. Structural modulations of plasmalemmal vesicles. *J. Cell Biol.* 37: 633–649, 1968.
106. PALADE, G. E., M. SIMIONESCU, AND N. SIMIONESCU. Structural aspects of the permeability of the microvascular endothelium. *Acta Physiol. Scand. Suppl.* 463: 11–32, 1979.
107. PAPPENHEIMER, J. R. Passage of molecules through capillary walls. *Physiol. Rev.* 33: 387–423, 1953.
108. PAPPENHEIMER, J. R. Osmotic reflection coefficients in capillary membranes. In: *Capillary Permeability*, edited by C. Crone and N. A. Lassen. Copenhagen: Munksgaard, 1970, p. 278–286. (Alfred Benzon Symp. 2.)
109. PAPPENHEIMER, J. R., E. M. RENKIN, AND L. M. BORRERO. Filtration, diffusion and molecular sieving through peripheral capillary membranes. A contribution to the pore theory of capillary permeability. *Am. J. Physiol.* 167: 13–46, 1951.
110. PATLAK, C. S., D. A. GOLDSTEIN, AND J. F. HOFFMAN. The flow of solute and solvent across a two-membrane system. *J. Theor. Biol.* 5: 426–442, 1963.
111. PERL, W. Modified filtration-permeability model of transcapillary transport—a solution to the Pappenheimer pore puzzle. *Microvasc. Res.* 3: 233–251, 1971.
112. PERL, W. A friction coefficient, series-parallel channel model for transcapillary flux of nonelectrolytes and water. *Microvasc. Res.* 6: 169–193, 1973.
113. PERL, W. Convection and permeation of albumin between plasma and interstitium. *Microvasc. Res.* 10: 83–94, 1975.
114. PERL, W., F. SILVERMAN, A. C. DELEA, AND F. P. CHINARD. Permeability of dog lung endothelium to sodium, diols, amides, and water. *Am. J. Physiol.* 230: 1708–1721, 1976.
115. PERRY, M., AND D. GARLICK. Transcapillary efflux of gammaglobulin in rabbit skeletal muscle. *Microvasc. Res.* 9: 119–126, 1975.
116. PRIGOGINE, I. Classical thermodynamics of mixtures. In: *The Molecular Theory of Solutions*. New York: Interscience, 1957, chapt. 1, p. 6–13.
117. RENKIN, E. M. Capillary permeability to lipid-soluble molecules. *Am. J. Physiol.* 168: 538–545, 1952.
118. RENKIN, E. M. Capillary and cellular permeability to some compounds related to antipyrine. *Am. J. Physiol.* 173: 125–130, 1953.
119. RENKIN, E. M. Filtration, diffusion and molecular sieving through porous cellulose membranes. *J. Gen. Physiol.* 38: 225–248, 1954.
120. RENKIN, E. M. Transport of large molecules across capillary walls. (Eighth Bowditch Lecture.) *Physiologist* 7: 13–28, 1964.
121. RENKIN, E. M. Multiple pathways of capillary permeability. *Circ. Res.* 41: 735–743, 1977.
122. RENKIN, E. M. Relation of capillary morphology to transport of fluid and large molecules; a review. *Acta Physiol. Scand. Suppl.* 463: 81–91, 1979.
123. RENKIN, E. M. Transport of proteins by diffusion, bulk flow and vesicular mechanisms. *Physiologist* 23(1): 57–61, 1980.
124. RENKIN, E. M., AND F. E. CURRY. Transport of water and solutes across capillary endothelium. In: *Membrane Transport in Biology*, edited by G. Giebisch, D. C. Tosteson, and H. H. Ussing. Berlin: Springer-Verlag, 1978, vol. 4, p. 1–45.
125. RENKIN, E. M., AND F. E. CURRY. Endothelial permeability: pathways and modulations. *Proc. NY Acad. Sci.* 401: 248–259, 1982.
126. RENKIN, E. M., W. L. JOYNER, C. H. SLOOP, AND P. D. WATSON. Influence of venous pressure on plasma-lymph transport in the dog's paw: convective and dissipative mechanisms. *Microvasc. Res.* 14: 191–204, 1977.
127. RENKIN, E. M., AND J. R. PAPPENHEIMER. Wasserdurchlässigkeit und Permeabilität der Capillarwände. *Ergeb. Physiol.* 49: 59–126, 1957.
128. RENKIN, E. M., P. D. WATSON, C. H. SLOOP, W. L. JOYNER, AND F. E. CURRY. Transport pathways for fluid and large molecules in microvascular endothelium of the dog's paw. *Microvasc. Res.* 14: 205–214, 1977.
129. ROBINSON, J. R. *Prelude to Physiology*. Oxford, UK: Blackwell, 1975, p. 37–44.
130. RUBIN, B. T. A theoretical model of the pinocytotic vesicular transport process in endothelial cells. *J. Theor. Biol.* 64: 619–647, 1977.
131. SCHULTZ, J. S., R. VALENTINE, AND C. Y. CHOI. Reflection coefficients of homopore membranes: effect of molecular size and configuration. *J. Gen. Physiol.* 73: 40–60, 1979.
132. SCHULTZ, S. G. *Basic Principles of Membrane Transport*. Cambridge, UK: Cambridge Univ. Press, 1980.
133. SCOW, R. O., E. J. BLANCHETTE-MACKIE, AND L. C. SMITH. Role of capillary endothelium in the clearance of chylomicrons. A model for lipid transport from blood by lateral diffusion in cell membranes. *Circ. Res.* 39: 149–162, 1976.
134. SHEA, S. M., M. J. KARNOVSKY, AND W. H. BOSSERT. Vesicular transport across endothelium: simulation of a diffusion model. *J. Theor. Biol.* 24: 30–42, 1969.
135. SHIRAHAMA, T., AND A. S. COHEN. The role of mucopolysaccharides in vesicle architecture and endothelial transport. *J. Cell Biol.* 52: 198–206, 1972.
136. SIMIONESCU, N. Transcytosis and the traffic of membranes in the endothelial cell. In: *International Cell Biology 1980–1981*, edited by H. G. Schweiger. Berlin: Springer-Verlag, 1981, p. 657–672.
137. SIMIONESCU, N., M. SIMIONESCU, AND G. E. PALADE. Permeability of muscle capillaries to small hemepeptides. Evidence for the existence of patent transendothelial channels. *J. Cell Biol.* 64: 586–607, 1975.
138. SMIT, J. A. M., J. C. EIJSERMANS, AND A. J. STAVERMAN. Friction and partition in membranes. *J. Phys. Chem.* 79: 2168–2175, 1975.
139. SMIT, J. A. M., AND A. J. STAVERMAN. Comments on "Onsager's reciprocal relations: an examination of its application to a simple process." *J. Phys. Chem.* 74: 966–967, 1970.
140. SMITH, F. G., III, AND W. M. DEEN. Electrostatic double-layer interactions for spherical colloids in cylindrical pores. *J. Colloid Interface Sci.* 78: 444–465, 1980.
141. SOODAK, H., AND A. S. IBERALL. Forum on osmosis. IV. More on osmosis and diffusion. *Am. J. Physiol.* 237 (*Regulatory Integrative Comp. Physiol.* 6): R114–R122, 1979.
142. SPIEGLER, K. S. Transport process in ionic membranes. *Trans. Faraday Soc.* 54: 1408–1428, 1958.
143. SPIEGLER, K. S., AND O. KEDEM. Thermodynamics of hyperfiltration (reverse osmosis): criteria for efficient membranes. *Desalination* 1: 311–326, 1966.
144. STAVERMAN, A. J. The theory of measurement of osmotic pressure. *Rec. Trav. Chim. Pays-Bas.* 70: 344–352, 1951.
145. STEN-KNUDSEN, O. Passive transport processes. In: *Membrane Transport in Biology*, edited by G. Giebisch, D. C. Tosteson, and H. H. Ussing. Berlin: Springer-Verlag, 1978, vol. 1, p. 5–113.
146. SULLIVAN, R. R., AND K. L. HERTEL. The permeability method for determining specific surface of fibers and powders. *Adv. Colloid Sci.* 1: 37–80, 1942.

147. TAYLOR, A. E., D. N. GRANGER, AND R. A. BRACE. Analysis of lymphatic protein flux data. I. Estimation of the reflection coefficient and permeability surface area product for total protein. *Microvasc. Res.* 13: 297–313, 1977.
148. TOSTESON, D. C. Comments in closing discussion. In: *Capillary Permeability*, edited by C. Crone and N. A. Lassen. Copenhagen: Munksgaard, 1970, p. 658. (Alfred Benzon Symp. 2.)
149. TRAP-JENSEN, J., AND N. A. LASSEN. Restricted diffusion in skeletal muscle capillaries in man. *Am. J. Physiol.* 220: 371–376, 1971.
150. TRUESDELL, C. Mechanical basis of diffusion. *J. Chem. Phys.* 37: 2336–2344, 1962.
151. TRUESDELL, C. *Rational Thermodynamics.* New York: McGraw-Hill, 1969, p. 148–149.
152. VAN BRUGGEN, J. T., J. D. BOYETT, A. L. VAN BUEREN, AND W. R. GALEY. Solute flux coupling in a homopore membrane. *J. Gen. Physiol.* 63: 639–656, 1974.
153. VERNIORY, A., R. DUBOIS, P. DECOODT, J. P. GASSEE, AND P. P. LAMBERT. Measurement of the permeability of biological membranes. Application to the glomerular wall. *J. Gen. Physiol.* 62: 489–507, 1973.
154. VILKER, V. L., C. K. COLTON, AND K. A. SMITH. The osmotic pressure of concentrated protein solutions: effect of concentration and pH in saline solutions of bovine serum albumin. *J. Colloid Interface Sci.* 79: 548–566, 1981.
155. WAGNER, R. C., AND J. R. CASLEY-SMITH. Endothelial vesicles. *Microvasc. Res.* 21: 267–298, 1981.
156. WANGENSTEEN, O. D., E. LYSAKER, AND P. SAVARYN. Pulmonary capillary filtration and reflection coefficients in adult rabbit. *Microvasc. Res.* 14: 81–97, 1977.
157. WEAST, R. C. Viscosity of water 9°C to 100°C. In: *Handbook of Chemistry and Physics* (49th ed.), edited by R. C. Weast. Cleveland, OH: CRC, 1968, p. F36.
158. WEINBAUM, S., AND C. G. CARO. A macromolecular transport model for the arterial wall and endothelium based on ultrastructural specialization observed in electromicroscopic studies. *J. Fluid Mech.* 74: 611–640, 1976.
159. WENDT, R. P., E. KLEIN, E. H. BRESLER, F. F. HOLLAND, R. M. SERIND, AND H. VILLA. Sieving properties of hemodialysis membranes. *J. Membr. Sci.* 5: 23–49, 1979.
160. WILLIAMS, M. C., AND S. L. WISSIG. The permeability of muscle capillaries to horseradish peroxidase. *J. Cell Biol.* 66: 531–555, 1975.

CHAPTER 9

Fluid movements through capillary walls

C. CHARLES MICHEL | *University Laboratory of Physiology, Oxford, United Kingdom*

CHAPTER CONTENTS

Formulation of Starling's Hypothesis
Filtration theory
Reabsorption of tissue fluid into blood
Quantitative Support for Starling's Hypothesis
Measurements of pressure and filtration rates in single capillaries
Fluid movements, protein osmotic pressure, and mean capillary pressure in intact and perfused tissues
General and Theoretical Considerations of Starling's Hypothesis
General implications
Coupling of fluid filtration to solute permeability
Osmotic pressure of protein solutions
Mixtures of macromolecules
Measurements of Transcapillary Fluid Movement
Single capillaries
Measurements of hydraulic conductivity in single mammalian and avian capillaries
Measurements of hydraulic conductivity in single microperfused frog capillaries
Measurements of filtration coefficients in organs and tissues
Fluid Balance in Organs and Tissues
Techniques for measuring Starling forces
Capillary pressure
Interstitial fluid pressure
Plasma colloid osmotic pressure (oncotic pressure)
Colloid osmotic pressure of interstitial fluid (tissue oncotic pressure)
Fluid balance and interstitial fluid pressure in tissues at low venous pressures
Adjustments of filtration rate after changes in venous pressure
Lung
Limbs
Intestine
Steady-state reabsorption of fluid into vascular system
Is capillary pressure regulated?
Properties of Channels Conducting Fluid Through Capillary Walls
Filtration rates and filtration coefficients in single vessels
Evidence for an exclusive water channel
Effects of macromolecules on hydraulic conductivity
Deductions concerning nature of fluid-conducting pathways

TOWARD THE END of the last century, Starling (230) proposed that fluid flow through capillary walls was passive. He suggested that the energy for transcapillary fluid flow lay in the differences in hydrostatic and osmotic pressures between the circulating plasma and the tissues. Since then both qualitative and quantitative investigations have supported Starling's hypothesis, though the estimates of fluid movements have sometimes been uncertain and the identification of the appropriate forces has often been indirect and incomplete. This chapter is concerned with the story's development, with the methods involved in measuring and describing fluid movements between the plasma and the tissues, and with the properties of the channels that conduct fluid through the capillary walls.

FORMULATION OF STARLING'S HYPOTHESIS

Filtration Theory

The idea that the tissue fluids are formed by filtration of the blood through capillary walls was first formulated in a modern sense by Ludwig (150). Others before him may appear to have suggested the principle, but not until the middle of the nineteenth century was it generally agreed that capillaries had walls (130, 199), and only then was it necessary to propose a mechanism for fluid movement through this barrier between the blood and tissues. Ludwig's view was based on experiments done in his laboratory by Noll (177). These studies appeared to show that the chief factor determining the flow of lymph was the capillary blood pressure.

The extent to which Ludwig's idea was accepted, understood, and developed is reflected in Cohnheim's *Lectures on General Pathology* (27). Cohnheim had worked in Ludwig's laboratory in 1869; though a pupil of Virchow's and a pathologist, he was very much a physiologist in outlook. Cohnheim clearly believed that tissue fluids and lymph were formed by the filtration of plasma through capillary walls. He noted (27, p. 156) that lymph flow from a limb was normally very low while the limb was at rest but that lymph flow became rapid as soon as the principal veins were occluded. As the lymph flow increased, its protein content diminished; this was consistent with the view that the capillary wall passively filtered the proteins. Experiments by Runeberg [quoted by Cohnheim (27, p. 514)] investigating the filtration of albumin solutions through membranes made from rabbit intestine showed that increases in the filtration rate caused decreases in the content of albumin in the filtrate. Runeberg's experiments also confirmed the "well known physical fact that solutions of albumin filter more readily through membranes, the less concentrated that they are" (27, p. 453). Cohnheim (27, p. 453) had observed that the injection of a dilute salt solution into the femoral artery of a dog sometimes gave rise to edema, but he noted that there was no edema in the limbs when the albumin content of the circulating plasma was reduced to one-half its normal value. The failure of the limbs of a dog to show edema or an increased lymph flow after the infusion of large volumes of 0.6% NaCl solution into the circulation dissuaded Cohnheim from concluding that the filtration of fluid through capillary walls was determined by both the protein content of the plasma and the capillary pressure. This was in spite of his observation that such infusions produced marked edema and increased lymph flow in the abdominal organs and secretory glands. He concluded that hypoalbuminemia per se was not the primary cause of edema but that edema would develop more rapidly during hypoalbuminemia as a result of mild inflammation or increased capillary pressure. Cohnheim believed that the different effects of large intravascular infusions on the tissues of the viscera and limbs could be accounted for by differences in the permeability of their blood vessels (27, p. 463).

Toward the latter part of the nineteenth century, views on the formation of tissue fluid and lymph were dominated by the teaching of Heidenhain (100). Heidenhain assembled three lines of evidence that led him to believe that Ludwig's filtration theory was incorrect. *1*) A series of experiments that showed that the flow of lymph from the thoracic duct did not vary predictably with changes in arterial pressure. *2*) The flow of thoracic duct lymph was increased by the intravenous injection or infusion of substances that Heidenhain called lymphogogues; these substances stimulated lymph flow out of all proportion to (or even in spite of) their effects on the arterial blood pressure. *3*) Some time after certain substances (e.g., glucose or peptone) had been infused into the blood, they would be present in the lymph at a concentration greater than that found in a simultaneous sample of plasma. On the strength of this evidence, Heidenhain rejected Ludwig's filtration hypothesis. Lymph, he suggested, was a secretion of the capillary endothelial cells into the tissue spaces.

In 1892 Starling came to work with Heidenhain in Breslau. He returned to London a few months later and during the next 2 years carried out experiments that clarified Heidenhain's observations and virtually settled the question of lymph formation in favor of filtration (6). In collaboration with Bayliss (9) he demonstrated that changes in arterial pressure did not reflect changes in capillary pressure. This led to a reinterpretation of several of Heidenhain's experiments. For example, Heidenhain had observed that ligation of the inferior vena cava proximal to the hepatic vein gave rise to a large increase in lymph flow despite a fall in arterial pressure. He interpreted this as being contrary to the Ludwig hypothesis. Starling now demonstrated that although arterial pressure fell after occlusion of the inferior vena cava, venous (and hence capillary) pressure in the abdominal viscera rose very considerably. The increased flow of lymph could thus be readily accounted for in terms of increased filtration. In addition, some of Heidenhain's lymphogogues were shown to raise capillary pressure, whereas others appeared to increase capillary permeability. Finally, Starling (231) pointed out the fallacy of comparing simultaneous concentrations of a substance in the blood and the lymph when the concentration in the blood is falling.

Thus Heidenhain's evidence for the active secretion of lymph now appeared consistent with the formation of lymph by filtration. A delightful account of Heidenhain's theory and Starling's experiments on this subject can be found in Barcroft's Bayliss-Starling Memorial Lecture (6).

Reabsorption of Tissue Fluid Into Blood

Satisfied that tissue fluid was formed by filtration through capillary walls, Starling turned to the question of whether it could be absorbed directly into the blood. Cohnheim (27, p. 437) had argued that fluid was absorbed from the tissues directly into the blood after hemorrhage, and Starling considered the arguments for this in his classic paper on capillary fluid balance (230). Hemorrhage involves the loss of red blood cells (RBCs) and plasma. Shortly after hemorrhage there is a fall in hematocrit accompanied by a fall in the protein concentration of the plasma. Starling (like Cohnheim) interpreted the fall in hematocrit as a movement of fluid into the blood that partially or completely restored the plasma volume but consequently diluted the cells. Because lymph flow is reduced after hemorrhage, Starling concluded that the fluid must have been absorbed directly into the blood vessels from the tissues.

Starling then reported the results of an experiment on the removal of artificial edema. He separately perfused the hindlimbs of a dog with the animal's own blood. He injected a large volume of 1% NaCl solution into the tissues of the right leg and used the left leg as a control. As the perfusion continued, the NaCl solution passed from the tissues of the right leg into the blood. The plasma protein concentration of the venous blood leaving the right leg decreased in proportion to the volume of tissue fluid absorbed. The plasma protein concentration of the venous blood leaving the left leg was unchanged.

Having established that fluid could be absorbed directly into the blood, Starling sought the mechanism involved. He examined the possible role of tissue fluid pressure in a series of experiments but concluded that this was not of major importance to fluid absorption. He then drew attention to the difference in protein concentration between the plasma and the tissue fluids and suggested that this might be responsible for a small difference in osmotic pressure. To investigate this Starling built an osmometer and estimated that the protein osmotic pressure of serum was between 30 and 41 mmHg. As he concluded (230):

> The importance of these measurements lies in the fact that, although the osmotic pressure of the proteids of the plasma is so insignificant, it is of an order of magnitude comparable to that of the capillary pressures; and whereas capillary pressure determines transudation, the osmotic pressure of the proteids of the serum determines absorption.

In support of his hypothesis, Starling demonstrated that crystalloid solutions are absorbed rapidly from the tissues, whereas serum is only slowly removed from the peritoneal cavity and is hardly removed at all from the tissues of a limb.

Starling suggested that fluid might be filtered from the arterial end of an average capillary where the hydrostatic pressure might exceed the protein osmotic pressure; at the venous end, however, hydrostatic pressure might be less than the protein osmotic pressure, and fluid could be reabsorbed into the circulation. He also saw the implications of his hypothesis in determining total blood volume. Filtration of fluid out of the circulation would continue to concentrate the proteins of the plasma and dilute those of the tissue fluids until the average difference in protein osmotic pressure across the capillary walls balanced the average difference in hydrostatic pressure. Starling realized that once such a state was reached a further increase in the filtration rate would be checked as it diluted the extravascular protein and concentrated the protein in the vascular system.

Thus by the end of the nineteenth century, the forces responsible for fluid movement through capillary walls had been identified and their importance demonstrated in a series of admittedly qualitative experiments. Quantitative experiments were necessary to investigate Starling's hypothesis further, but because of the technical difficulties involved these were delayed until well into the twentieth century.

QUANTITATIVE SUPPORT FOR STARLING'S HYPOTHESIS

Measurements of Pressure and Filtration Rates in Single Capillaries

Some 30 years after Starling's paper (230) was published, Landis (123) described the measurement of pressure and fluid filtration in single capillaries of the frog mesentery. Capillary hydrostatic pressure was determined directly by micropuncture with a glass micropipette held in a Chamber's micromanipulator. Fluid movements through the capillary wall were estimated while the vessel was temporarily occluded by a fine glass needle. Landis had observed that RBCs in such an occluded segment of capillary sometimes moved toward the occlusion site and sometimes moved away from it (Fig. 1). He deduced that these movements of the RBCs reflected movements of fluid through the capillary wall into and out of the column of fluid between the RBCs and the site of occlusion. He found that the rate of filtration or absorption attenuated with time; in addition the proteins within the fluid column were concentrated and diluted and the surface area of the column was changed. By measuring the initial rate of RBC movement, Landis was able to determine capillary filtration before the plasma protein concentration had changed. Landis measured transcapillary fluid movement and capillary pressure (P_c) in a large number of capillaries in the frog mesentery; expressing fluid movement as flow per unit area of capillary wall, he obtained a linear correlation between fluid movement and capillary pressure (Fig. 2). When transcapillary fluid movement was zero, capillary pressure lay in the region of 7–14 cmH_2O.

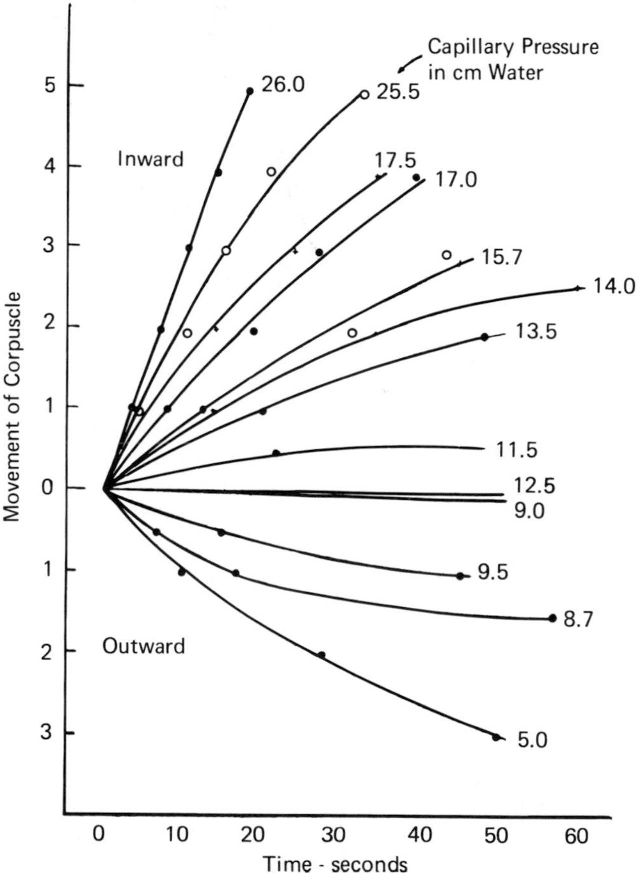

FIG. 1. Movement of red blood cells in occluded capillaries in frog mesentery. Ordinate represents changes of position of cell relative to site of occlusion. Each *curve* represents movements of single cell in capillary at given capillary pressure. Inward movements (toward occlusion site) indicate filtration of fluid from capillary; outward movements indicate fluid reabsorption. [From Landis (123).]

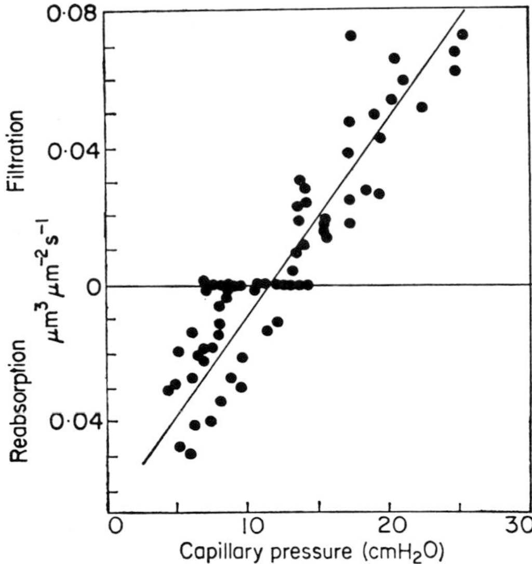

FIG. 2. Relationship between capillary pressure and initial rate of filtration or reabsorption of fluid after occlusion of frog mesentery capillaries. Each *point* represents measurement for a single capillary; thus regression line through *points* is average value for this relationship. Slope of relationship is average hydraulic conductivity of walls of mesenteric capillaries; pressure where neither filtration nor reabsorption occurs is effective osmotic pressure across capillary walls. [From Landis (123).]

TABLE 1. *Direct Measurements of Capillary Pressure*

	Avg Capillary Pressure, cmH_2O		Plasma Colloid Osmotic Pressure, cmH_2O	Ref.
	Arteriolar	Venular		
Frog				
Mesentery	14.4	10.1		122
Muscle	15.0	9.5	7–14	127
Skin	14.5	10.1		127
Rat mesentery	30.0	17.0	20–28	125
Guinea pig mesentery	38.5	17.0	23–28	125
Human nailfold skin	43.5	16.5	28.0–38.0	126
	27.2*			

* Pressure at midpoint of capillary loop.

This corresponded to the range of protein osmotic pressures determined by White (245) for the plasma of frogs from the same species. If the sum of the hydrostatic and protein osmotic pressures of the pericapillary fluid is close to zero in the frog mesentery, Landis's findings are direct evidence in support of Starling's hypothesis.

Landis went on to measure capillary pressures in the skin and muscle of the frog (127), the mesenteries of rats and guinea pigs (125), and in the nailfold skin of humans (126). His average values of capillary pressure for each species agreed closely with estimates of the protein osmotic pressure of the plasma (Table 1).

Fluid Movements, Protein Osmotic Pressure, and Mean Capillary Pressure in Intact and Perfused Tissues

An early attempt to test the application of Starling's hypothesis to the intact tissues of humans was made by Landis and Gibbon (131). They estimated net fluid filtration into the forearm while the venous pressure was raised by a sphygmomanometer cuff. The volume of a section of the forearm was measured at the beginning and end of the period of venous congestion with a pressure plethysmograph. Because the pressure plethysmograph measured arm volume in the presence of an external pressure of 240 mmHg or more, the changes in volume that it recorded (reduced arm volume) were independent of changes in vascular volume. The filtration rate into a unit volume of forearm was calculated from the change in reduced arm volume over a known period of raised venous pressure. The filtration rate increased linearly with venous pressure with a slope of 0.0033 $ml \cdot min^{-1} \cdot 100\ ml^{-1}$ tissue $\cdot\ cmH_2O^{-1}$ rise in venous pressure.

Krogh et al. (121) compared the filtration rate measured at given venous pressures with their subjects in a recumbent position and then again in the same subjects after a 30-min period of quiet standing on a tilt table. Quiet standing increased the concentration of circulating plasma proteins, thereby raising osmotic pressure (Π_P) by 3.3–8.7 cmH_2O. In these experiments, they found that a rise in Π_P was accompanied by a fall in filtration rate at constant venous pressure. This reduction of filtration rate, divided by the increment of Π_P yielded values between 0.0027 and 0.0045 $ml \cdot min^{-1} \cdot 100\ ml^{-1}$ forearm tissue $\cdot\ mmHg^{-1}$. Thus the dependence of filtration rate on Π_P was quantitatively similar (though with opposite sign) to the dependence of filtration rate on venous pressure—a finding that could be regarded as strong evidence for believing that Starling's hypothesis applied to the capillaries of the human forearm.

The most impressive evidence for the applicability of Starling's hypothesis in a mammalian capillary bed came from the work of Pappenheimer and Soto-Rivera (186). They studied the isolated hindlimbs of cats and dogs and estimated fluid movements into and out of the tissues by continuously weighing their preparations. They argued that net filtration from the blood to the tissues would register as a gain in limb weight and reabsorption of fluid as a weight loss. Under isogravimetric conditions net fluid movement was zero and a method was devised of calculating the mean capillary pressure ($\overline{P}_c$) from the arterial pressure (P_a) and the venous pressure (P_v) in this state. The total resistance to blood flow through the limb was divided into a precapillary element (R_{pre}) and a postcapillary element (R_{post}). Under isogravimetric conditions, blood outflow from the veins equals blood inflow through the arteries. Thus if $\dot{Q}_{iso}$ is the isogravimetric blood flow

$$\dot{Q}_{iso} = \frac{1}{R_{pre}}(P_a - \overline{P}_c) = \frac{1}{R_{post}}(\overline{P}_c - P_v) \quad (1)$$

Pappenheimer and Soto-Rivera (186) found that R_{post} was independent of P_v and that variations of $\dot{Q}_{iso}$ and P_v under isogravimetric conditions ($\overline{P}_c$ constant) yielded the linear relation predicted from the rearrangement of Equation 1

$$P_v = \overline{P}_c - R_{post}\dot{Q}_{iso} \quad (2)$$

Thus in any isogravimetric state $\overline{P}_c$ and R_{post} could be calculated from a series of values of P_v and $\dot{Q}_{iso}$. Pappenheimer and Soto-Rivera were able to vary the isogravimetric P_c by varying the protein concentration of the perfusate. When isogravimetric P_c was compared with the protein osmotic pressure of the perfusate a close correspondence was found (Fig. 3). (The small discrepancy was consistent with the reasonable view that the pericapillary fluid contained protein at a low concentration.) By varying Π_P, and thus the isogravimetric P_c, Pappenheimer and Soto-Rivera (186) were able to establish the causal relationship between transcapillary fluid movement and the hydrostatic and protein osmotic pressures of the capillary blood that Starling had predicted (230).

Knowing the value of R_{post}, they were also able to calculate the changes of P_c after step changes in P_v. Under these circumstances the limb ceased to be isogravimetric, and the movement of water between the blood and the tissues could be followed from the changes in weight of the limb. The relationship between change of limb weight and change of P_c was linear (Fig. 4) with a slope of 0.01 $g \cdot min^{-1} \cdot 100\ g^{-1} \cdot cmH_2O^{-1}$. This value was the same for filtration and reabsorption.

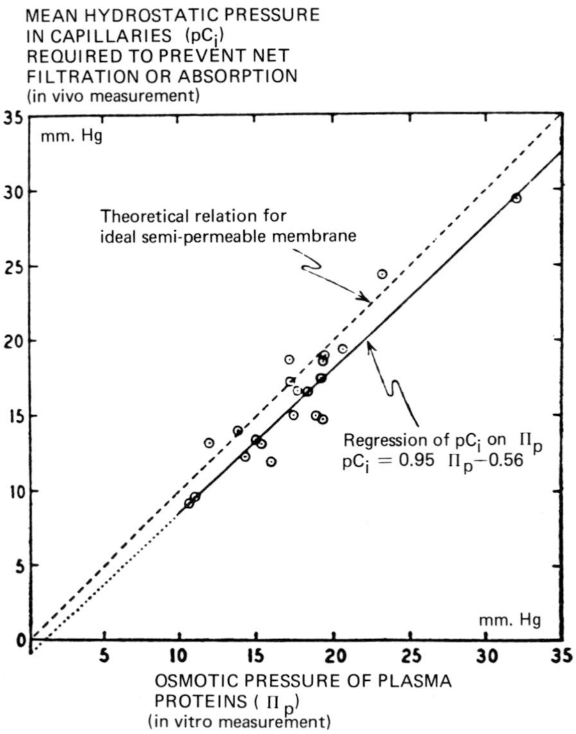

FIG. 3. Relationship between isogravimetric capillary pressure in isolated perfused cat and dog hindlimbs and colloid osmotic pressure of perfusate. [From Pappenheimer and Soto-Rivera (186).]

GENERAL AND THEORETICAL CONSIDERATIONS OF STARLING'S HYPOTHESIS

General Implications

Starling's hypothesis can be written as an equation. Thus

$$J_v/A = L_p[(P_c - \Pi_c) - (P_i - \Pi_i)] \quad (3)$$

or

$$J_v/A = L_p(\Delta P - \Delta\Pi) \quad (4)$$

where J_v/A is the volume flow per unit area of capillary wall (A); P_c and P_i are the hydrostatic pressures in the capillary and pericapillary fluid, respectively; Π_c and Π_i are the protein osmotic pressures of the capillary plasma and pericapillary fluid, respectively; L_p is the hydraulic conductivity of the capillary wall or its filtration coefficient; $\Delta P = (P_c - P_i)$; and $\Delta\Pi = (\Pi_c - \Pi_i)$.

Although supported by experimental evidence, Equations 3 and 4 are only approximations. When multiplied by the partial molal volume for water, the bracketed term in Equation 4 represents the difference in chemical potential (free energy per mole) between the water of the plasma and the water of the pericapillary fluid, provided that all solutes other than the proteins are at equal concentrations on the two sides of the membrane. For the total difference in osmotic pressure to be expressed across a membrane, the mem-

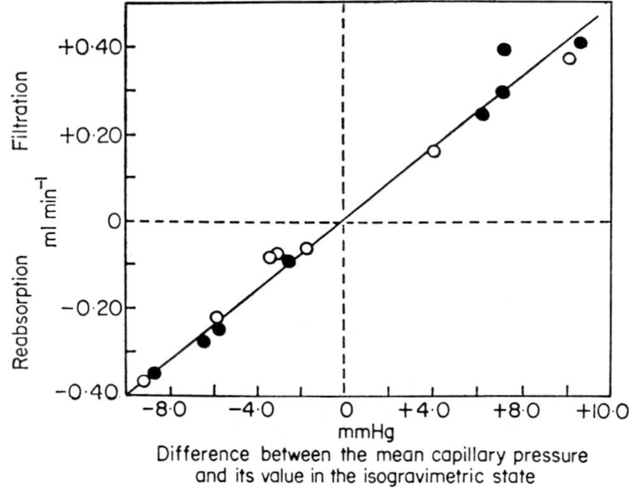

FIG. 4. Relationship between net fluid movement in cat's perfused hindlimb and difference between mean capillary pressure and isogravimetric capillary pressure. Slope of regression line is capillary filtration coefficient and equals 0.014 $ml \cdot min^{-1} \cdot 100\ g^{-1} \cdot mmHg^{-1}$. [From Pappenheimer and Soto-Rivera (186).]

brane has to be impermeable to the solute responsible for the osmotic pressure (responsible for reducing free energy per mole of water). Because capillary walls are not completely impermeable to plasma proteins, it is necessary to qualify the osmotic pressure terms in Equations 3 and 4 with the osmotic reflection coefficient (σ)

$$J_v/A = L_p[(P_c - \sigma\Pi_c) - (P_i - \sigma\Pi_i)] \quad (5)$$

$$J_v/A = L_p(\Delta P - \sigma\Delta\Pi) \quad (6)$$

As discussed in the chapter by Curry in this *Handbook*, σ is a measure of the relative ease with which a given solute and solvent can pass through a membrane. For an ideal aqueous solution it can be defined either as the fraction of the total osmotic pressure that can be exerted across the membrane (233), or as the fraction of solute that is separated from its solution when the latter is filtered through the membrane in the absence of a concentration difference across the membrane (10, 116, 192, 233) or at an infinitely high filtration rate. The equivalence of these definitions can be appreciated intuitively from a consideration of ultrafiltration. The fraction of solute separated from a solution as it is being filtered through a membrane (in the absence of diffusion) represents the fraction of the osmotic pressure of the solution that opposes filtration. Thus, if the membrane is perfectly semipermeable ($\sigma = 1$), all the solute is separated from solution during ultrafiltration and the full osmotic pressure of the solution opposes filtration. If the membrane cannot separate solute from solution ($\sigma = 0$), the solution's osmotic pressure will offer no resistance to filtration. This equivalence of the definitions of σ in terms of effective osmotic pressure and ultrafiltration rests on the equality of ratios of concentration and the corresponding ratios of osmotic pressure. This equality is present only for dilute solutions of ideal solutes; it should not be assumed to apply to solutions of macromolecules, including the plasma proteins at the concentrations at which they are present in plasma.

So far the plasma and the pericapillary fluid have been regarded as solutions made up of a single solute (plasma protein) and water. Of course this is far from the truth, and a more correct formulation of Equation 6 is

$$J_v/A = L_p(\Delta P - \sum_j \sigma_j\Delta\Pi_j) \quad (7)$$

where the term $\sum_j \sigma_j\Delta\Pi_j$ represents the total effective osmotic pressure, with σ_j and $\Delta\Pi_j$ being the reflection coefficient and osmotic pressure difference for the jth solute. Note that the summation of osmotic differences, although straightforward for dilute solutions of ideal solutes, is more complicated when the relationships between osmotic pressure and concentration are markedly nonlinear (as indeed they are for solutions of macromolecules such as the plasma proteins).

Equation 7 is an acceptable general description of fluid movement through capillary walls. Starling (230) argued that the composition of the plasma and the interstitial fluid (ISF) differed only in its plasma protein content and thus $\Delta\Pi = 0$ for all solutes except plasma proteins. This is usually true, because most capillary walls are very permeable to ions and low-molecular-weight solutes (see the chapters by Curry and by Crone and Levitt in this *Handbook*) and small differences in their concentration can be rapidly dissipated by diffusion. The contribution of these diffusible solutes is further diminished by their relatively low reflection coefficients at most capillary walls (σ to NaCl for most capillaries appears to be in the range of 0.05–0.01). However, these arguments about low-molecular-weight solutes do not apply to the capillaries of the central nervous system, which are less permeable to sucrose than most other capillaries are to serum albumin (see the chapter by Fenstermacher and Rapoport in this *Handbook*). Indeed changes in the concentrations of low-molecular-weight solutes may be expected to dominate fluid movements into and out of the brain (54). For other capillaries, however, in natural (as opposed to experimental) circumstances the term $\sum_j \sigma_j\Delta\Pi_j$ in Equation 7 is accounted for by the plasma proteins; because at most capillary walls σ for serum albumin is > 0.8 (in the absence of inflammation or other stimuli), Equation 7 approximates Equation 6, as the observations of Landis (123) and Pappenheimer and Soto-Rivera (186) showed.

If Equation 6 or 7 is used to describe fluid balance in a real capillary, two types of question arise. The first concerns the extent to which the forces ΔP and $\Delta\Pi$ may be modified by transcapillary fluid movement. A period of filtration might be expected to raise P_i. The extent to which it does so depends on the compliance of the pericapillary space, the hydraulic conductivity and compliance of the interstitium, and the link between the hydration of the interstitium and the lymph flow. At this stage it is worth emphasizing that the properties of the pericapillary space, not those of the entire interstitium, immediately determine transcapillary fluid movement. Properties of the pericapillary space (such as its compliance) may differ from those of the interstitium as a whole and thus contribute to the apparent discrepancies between estimates of interstitial compliance made with different techniques (5, 49, 86). Filtration may not only raise P_i but, as Starling appreciated, it may also lower Π_i. Where the capillary wall is permeable to protein, the filtration rate is coupled to the flux of protein. This coupling occurs because the pericapillary protein concentration is a determinant of fluid flux and its own steady-state value is determined by the ratio of protein efflux from the capillary to the filtration rate. The exact nature of the coupling depends on the mechanisms responsible for protein flux through the capillary wall; by making reasonable assumptions, however, this is described in general terms in the next section. The osmotic pressure of protein solutions is also briefly considered.

The second type of question concerns the coefficients L_p and σ, and the area of capillary wall available for exchange. The filtration coefficient in capillary beds cannot be measured, but a coefficient, referred to here as the capillary filtration coefficient (CFC), (59) can be estimated. The CFC approximates the product L_pA, and from values of CFC estimated under different conditions it appears that A can vary considerably and have a profound influence on the extent to which filtration occurs in some capillary beds. Changes in CFC and changes in the extravascular forces are often investigated in the same series of experiments, and they are discussed together in this chapter. The interpretation of L_p and σ in terms of the nature of the fluid-conducting channels in the capillary wall and the flow within them represents a different set of problems and is considered in later sections of this chapter (see PROPERTIES OF CHANNELS CONDUCTING FLUID THROUGH CAPILLARY WALLS, p. 398).

Coupling of Fluid Filtration to Solute Permeability

For simplicity let us consider that the plasma and pericapillary fluid consist of solutions of a single ideal solute (plasma protein) for which there is a simple linear relation between concentration and osmotic pressure. Thus fluid filtration is described by

$$J_v/A = L_p(\Delta P - \sigma RT\Delta C) = L_p[\Delta P - \sigma RT(C_P - C_i)] \quad (8)$$

where C_P and C_i are the concentrations of solute in the plasma and in the pericapillary space, respectively. If the flux of solute through unit area of the capillary wall is J_s/A, then in the steady state

$$C_i = J_s/J_v \quad (9)$$

Equation 9 can be substituted into Equation 8, and a quadratic expression for J_v written in terms of L_p, σ, ΔP, Π_P, and J_s. To proceed further one must make some assumption about the mechanism of solute transport. If solute transport is passive and occurs by diffusion and convection through the same channels that carry the water, it can be described by the expression

$$J_s = J_v \frac{(1 - \sigma)(C_i - C_P e^{\beta})}{(1 - e^{\beta})} \quad (10)$$

where $\beta = J_v(1 - \sigma)/P_D$ and P_D is the diffusional permeability coefficient of the membrane to the solute [(17, 190, 192); see also the chapter by Curry in this *Handbook*].

Combining Equations 9 and 10 yields

$$C_i = C_P \frac{(1 - \sigma)}{(1 - \sigma e^{-\beta})} \quad (11)$$

$$\Delta C = (C_P - C_i) = C_P\sigma \frac{(1 - e^{-\beta})}{(1 - \sigma e^{-\beta})} \quad (12)$$

This expression for ΔC may now be substituted in Equation 8. Because J_v appears in the resulting equation both as itself and in the exponential term, an explicit description of J_v is not obtained, but ΔP can be described as a function of J_v

$$\Delta P = \frac{J_v/A}{L_p} + \sigma^2\Pi_P \frac{(1 - e^{-\beta})}{(1 - \sigma e^{-\beta})} \quad (13)$$

Equation 13 is portrayed graphically in Figure 5. Superimposed on the nonlinear steady-state relationship is a pair of lines with a slope L_p representing transient changes of J_v with ΔP at constant values of $\Delta\Pi$. Reducing ΔP from 30 cmH_2O to 20 cmH_2O initially reverses fluid movement with a filtration rate per unit area of 3×10^{-7} cm/s, becoming an absorption rate of 2.2×10^{-7} cm/s. If ΔP is held at 20 cmH_2O, absorption dwindles to zero, and a new steady state is set up with a filtration rate of 0.4×10^{-7} cm/s. Restoring the pressure at this stage to 30 cmH_2O initially raises filtration per unit area to 5.4×10^{-7} cm/s, but it finally returns to 3×10^{-7} cm/s. From this it is clear that absorption can only be a transient phenomenon when solute (protein) permeability is finite.

As β increases Equation 13 approximates to:

$$J_v/A = L_p(\Delta P - \sigma^2\Pi_P) \quad (14)$$

This result, which is equivalent to the statement that at infinite J_v/A, $\sigma = 1 - C_i/C_P$, suggests that some estimates of σ for large molecules (e.g., ref. 164) may prove to be estimates of σ^2.

The assumptions made in deriving Equation 13 (e.g., linear relation between C and Π) do not materially affect the conclusions drawn from it. The curve depicting the steady-state relationship between J_v/A and ΔP can be derived numerically with more complicated models.

Equations 11–13 can be used to evaluate the assumption that the ions and other low-molecular-weight solutes of the plasma make a negligible contribution to the osmotic pressure term ($\sum_j \sigma_j\Delta\Pi_j$ in Eq. 7). For NaCl, taking $\sigma = 0.3$ as the highest reported value (193) and a low P_D value of 2.5×10^{-5} cm/s (see the chapter by Crone and Levitt in this *Handbook*) suggests that at J_v/A values of 10^{-6} cm/s the sieving of NaCl might oppose filtration with an osmotic pressure of 6 cmH_2O. It is uncertain, however, whether such a high value of σ for NaCl ever coexists with such high filtration rates.

Osmotic Pressure of Protein Solutions

It is well known that the van't Hoff relationship

$$\Pi = RTc \quad (15)$$

(where R is the universal gas constant and T is the

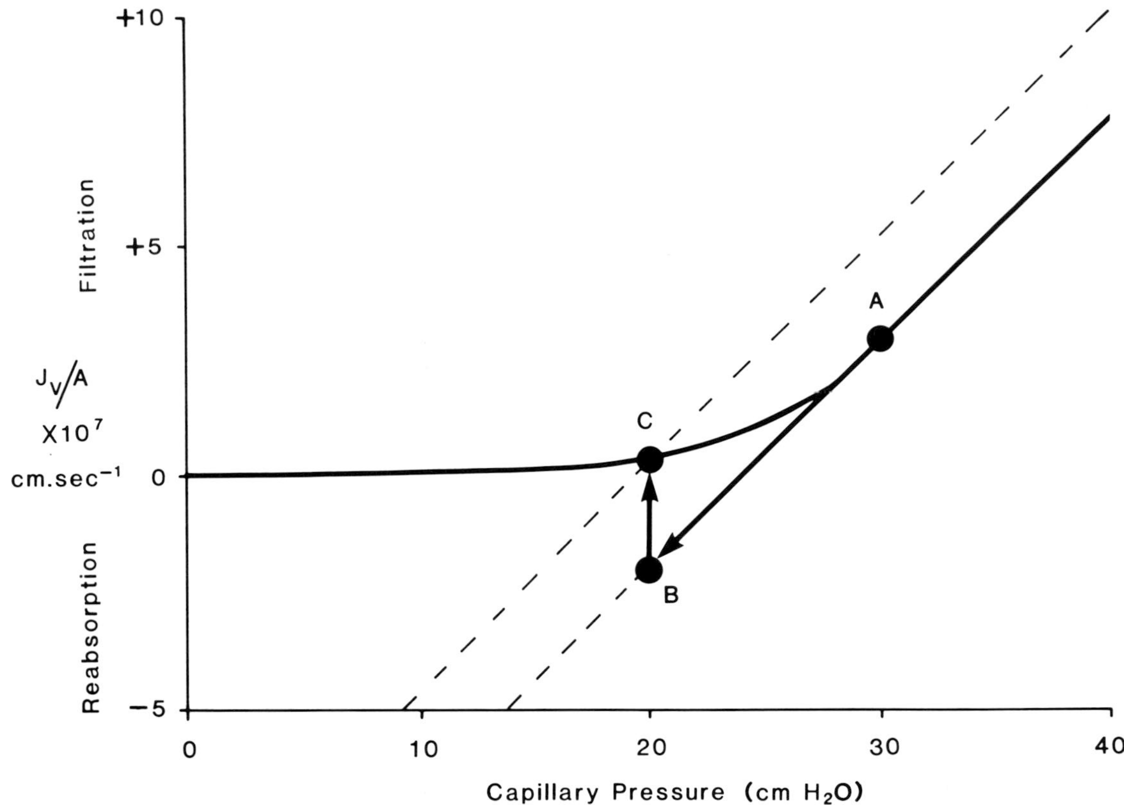

FIG. 5. Theoretical relationships between filtration rate per unit area of capillary wall (J_v/A) and transmural capillary pressure (ΔP). *Solid curve* represents steady-state relationship predicted by Eq. 13, for a vessel where hydraulic conductivity (L_p) = 5×10^{-8} cm·s^{-1}·cmH$_2$O^{-1}, the osmotic reflection coefficient (σ) = 0.9, the diffusional permeability (P_D) = 10^{-8} cm/s, and the protein osmotic pressure (Π_P) = 30 cmH$_2$O. *Dashed lines* are drawn with slope L_p; *arrows* from A to B and B to C indicate transient changes in J_v/A after rapid reduction in ΔP from 30 to 20 cmH$_2$O.

absolute temperature) does not describe the relationship between Π and c (molar concentration) for solutions of macromolecules. In a previous *Handbook*, Landis and Pappenheimer (132) summarized much of the available data for the relationship between Π and c for serum albumin solutions (Eq. 16) and for plasma (Eq. 17)

$$\Pi(\text{albumin}) = 2.8c + 0.18c^2 + 0.012c^3 \qquad (16)$$

$$\Pi(\text{plasma}) = 2.1c + 0.16c^2 + 0.009c^3 \qquad (17)$$

where the concentrations (c) are expressed in grams per 100 ml and Π is in millimeters of mercury. These expressions have been widely used, but one should expect that the equation for plasma might vary slightly with variations of the albumin-to-globulin ratio.

Navar and Navar (171) reported a modified version of Equation 17 for dog plasma

$$\Pi(\text{dog plasma}) = 1.4c + 0.22c^2 + 0.005c^3 \qquad (18)$$

This expression has also been widely used.

The theory of the osmotic pressure of macromolecular solutions has been investigated from the viewpoint of the entropy of mixing (57, 213), and considerable understanding of the factors contributing to their nonideal behavior has been gained. Tombs and Peacocke (237) give a comprehensive review of this work in the first half of their monograph, and Dick (42) provides an excellent introductory account. Even for an ideal solute, however, the van't Hoff relation is an approximation applicable only at low concentration. Indeed the theoretical relationship between Π and c for such a solute is of the form

$$\Pi = RTc_s\left(\frac{1}{M_r} + \frac{c_s V_w}{2M_r} + \ldots\right) \qquad (19)$$

where M_r is the molecular weight of the solute and V_w is the partial molal volume of water. When c_s (in g/cm^3) is small, the second and higher terms in the parentheses are negligible.

For nonideal solutions an expression analogous to Equation 19 may be written

$$\Pi = RTc_s\left(\frac{1}{M_r} + Bc_s + Cc_s^2 + \ldots\right) \qquad (20)$$

The terms B and C are not negligible here. They are called the second and third virial coefficients because of the analogy between the chemical potential and the potential of average force between solute molecules in dilute solution and pressure and the potential of average force between molecules in a gas. Equations of this general form may be used to describe solutions where the solute is a neutral macromolecule and even where the solute is a charged macromolecule (providing that salt at a higher concentration than the macromolecule is also present in the system).

The second virial coefficient is determined by three separate components (20, 213, 214, 237). The first is the so-called Donnan term, which arises from the net charge on the macromolecule and leads to an asymmetrical distribution of salt ions (as well as the macromolecule) across the osmometer membrane. It becomes negligible only when the total salt concentration is relatively large or where there is no binding of ions to the macromolecule. If the macromolecule binds only H^+, then this component becomes zero at the isoelectric pH; if other ions are bound as well (as is the case for serum albumin) this term may reach a minimum at a pH well removed from the isoelectric point.

The second component of B is the entire coefficient, if the macromolecule is uncharged. It represents the variation of the activity coefficient of the macromolecule with its own concentration and is related to the molecule's effective size and shape in solution. It is sometimes described as the excluded-volume effect.

The third component of B represents the interaction between macromolecules and the salt and the nonideality of the salt itself. Although this component is small for most proteins, it is by no means negligible for serum albumin that binds Cl^-.

The third virial coefficient is usually small but plays a significant part in concentrated solutions of charged macromolecules (172).

MIXTURES OF MACROMOLECULES. The nonlinear relationships between Π and c for solutions of macromolecules complicate the calculation of total osmotic pressure for mixtures of macromolecules. Thus if two solutions of macromolecules are combined, the increment change in osmotic pressure may be greater than the sum of the osmotic pressures of the two components alone but at the same concentration. One neutral macromolecule excludes a second from those regions of solution in its own vicinity, thus reducing the volume of solution available to the second and raising both its activity and osmotic pressure.

Effects of this kind are seen between all macromolecules that do not attract or bind to one another. Interactions between proteins and connective tissue polysaccharides (like hyaluronic acid) are of particular interest (135, 178) and may be important in understanding the osmotic pressures generated within the ISF (82, 83, 248, 261).

MEASUREMENTS OF TRANSCAPILLARY FLUID MOVEMENT

Single Capillaries

In his classic measurements of capillary pressure and fluid filtration in single capillaries of the frog mesentery, Landis (123) not only obtained direct evidence for Starling's hypothesis but also made the first estimate of the hydraulic conductivity of the capillary wall. This is given by the slope of the regression line relating fluid movement to capillary pressure in Figure 2. Landis was well aware of the importance of estimating L_p and proceeded to investigate the effects on it of hypoxia (124), pH and tissue injury (123), and temperature (18). His value for L_p was an average and not the specific value of an individual capillary. Its determination depended on having a wide range of capillary pressures within the capillary bed.

Since the late 1960s a series of attempts have been made to measure the L_p of single vessels. The measurements have all been based on different variations of the Landis microocclusion technique (138, 141, 167, 227, 260). Some interesting theoretical analyses of filtration from occluded microvessels (14, 15, 138, 167) have been published, and their methods, results, and theories have been comprehensively reviewed by Gore and McDonagh (75).

The microocclusion method has been developed in two different ways. The methods initiated by Zweifach and his colleagues have been applied to mammalian capillaries. They all employ the animal's own RBCs as flow markers, and L_p is calculated from changes of filtration rate with changes in protein osmotic pressure. The methods initiated by Michel and his colleagues (35, 141, 167) involve the microperfusion of capillaries, and L_p is determined from changes of filtration rate with changes in capillary hydrostatic pressure. So far microperfusion techniques have been applied only to vessels in the frog mesentery, but they have been used in a number of different experimental designs to investigate the permeability of these vessels (33–35, 141, 156, 164, 167).

MEASUREMENTS OF HYDRAULIC CONDUCTIVITY IN SINGLE MAMMALIAN AND AVIAN CAPILLARIES. In an early study, Zweifach and Intaglietta (260) measured the filtration rate per unit area of capillary wall in a single vessel of the rabbit omentum before and after injecting 25% albumin into the animal's circulation. From the changes in filtration rate and plasma osmotic pressure, they calculated the hydraulic conductivity of the capillary wall; in doing this they assumed that capillary hydrostatic pressure did not change and that the capillary walls had a reflection coefficient of one for plasma proteins. Instead of changing the osmotic pressure of the plasma, Smaje et al. (227) changed the osmotic pressure of the pericapillary fluid by immersing tissues in albumin solutions of different concentrations. Measurements of L_p were obtained in this way for vessels in the rat cremaster muscle. An elegant development of the technique arose from a consideration of the changes in protein concentration occurring in a single capillary during occlusion. Smaje et al. (226) pointed out that after occlusion the filtration rate fell with time because the protein osmotic pressure rose as the intravascular protein became more concentrated. If all the plasma protein was retained in a column of concentrating plasma between two marker RBCs, and if the initial concentration of protein was known, all subsequent values could be calculated from the changes in fluid volume until equilibrium was reached. These changes in protein concentration could be converted into changes of osmotic pressure, and the relation between filtration rate and protein osmotic pressure could then be used to determine L_p.

This method was further refined by Lee et al. (138); they used an analytical model to obtain values of L_p and $\Delta P + \Pi_i$ from the curve of changing RBC interval (fluid column length) and time. Even more efficient methods of curve fitting and analysis have since been developed (216).

All these methods assume that for plasma proteins $\sigma = 1$. Although this assumption is not unreasonable, it has two major disadvantages. *1*) Because the method estimates $L_p\sigma$, it cannot be used to investigate a change of permeability where L_p might increase and σ decrease. *2*) It may compromise the interpretation of equilibrium volume. It is assumed (61, 138, 226) that at equilibrium Π_c in the occluded capillary is equal to $(\Delta P + \Pi_i)$; if $\sigma < 1$, however, $\Pi_c = (\Delta P/\sigma + \Pi_i)$. If P_c is measured directly and subtracted from the equilibrium value of Π_c (with the hope of estimating $P_i + \Pi_i$), even with σ as high as 0.8–0.9, large errors may be involved (61).

A further assumption is that the capillary is a rigid cylinder and the RBC movements represent filtration and not changes of capillary volume. Estimates of capillary compliance by Smaje et al. (225) indicate that this is a reasonable assumption in most circumstances, but very high filtration rates [and thus high L_p values (76)] should be considered suspect until the compliance element has been eliminated as a possible artifact.

A summary of measurements of L_p obtained in single mammalian and avian capillaries is given in Table 2. Note that these values are all considerably greater than estimates of L_p made from measurements of total filtration rates in whole organs and tissues together with histological estimates of capillary surface area. However, so far L_p has not been estimated in single vessels of capillary beds where the filtration properties were independently investigated by macroscopic techniques. Therefore it is doubtful that such comparisons are valid.

All these studies have revealed large variations among values of L_p in different capillaries of the same vascular bed. Usually vessels at the venous end of the microcirculation have higher L_p values than vessels at the arterial end (247, 260); in addition, Gore et al. (76) have reported large arteriovenous gradients of L_p within the same vessel. These observations are entirely consistent with the well-known observation of an arteriovenous gradient of vascular permeability to dyes and colored molecules (130, 166, 170, 211).

TABLE 2. *Measurements of Hydraulic Conductivity of Walls of Single Mammalian and Avian Capillaries*

	Hydraulic Conductivity, $\times 10^7$ cm·s^{-1}·cmH$_2$O^{-1}	n	Ref.
Rabbit omentum			
Arterial end	2 – 8	12	260
	25 ± 13	6	227
	30.6 ± 15	10	138
Venous end	16 – 25	13	260
	46 ± 33	5	227
	44 ± 11	7	138
Rat cremaster muscle	1.0 ± 0.2	10	227
Rat intestinal muscle			
Arterial end	16 ± 1.5	66	72
Venous end	66 ± 3.7	66	72
Mean	41.9 ± 6.1	132	72
Guinea pig mesentery			
Control	17 ± 7	13	25
Scorbutic	24 ± 13	8	25
Avian skeletal muscle			
Postural	160 ± 133	8	152
Locomotor	59 ± 88	8	152
Cat mesentery			
Capillaries	13.2 ± 7.3	29	61
	6.1 ± 1.6	9	225
Venules	19.9 ± 11.0	21	61
	16.3 ± 2.9	7	225

Values are ranges or means ± SD; n is sample size.

MEASUREMENTS OF HYDRAULIC CONDUCTIVITY IN SINGLE MICROPERFUSED FROG CAPILLARIES. Three microperfusion techniques have been described for estimating L_p in single capillaries of the frog mesentery (141, 167). The first two involve the use of RBCs as flow markers, and these techniques may be used as alternative methods of calculating L_p from the same set of experimental observations (167). For both techniques a single capillary in the frog mesentery is cannulated with a micropipette and perfused with Ringer's solution containing a low concentration of human RBCs. After a perfusion period the capillary is occluded with a glass microneedle at a point some distance downstream from the cannulation site. Movements of a marker RBC within the occluded segment of capillary are recorded on videotape and are interpreted to reflect fluid movements through the capillary wall between the cell and the occlusion site. Because the flow velocity along the capillary is very low, the pressure within the capillary is almost equal to the pressure applied to the micropipette (difference <0.5 cmH$_2$O).

The first method of calculating L_p involves making a series of estimates of the initial filtration rate per unit area of capillary wall when a series of different pressures are applied to the capillary via the micropipette. Then L_p is determined from the regression line relating J_v/A to P_c, as in Figure 6. Providing the micropipette is sealed into the capillary and the micropipette tip is large enough to allow RBCs to move freely between the micropipette and the capillary, the method yields reproducible values of L_p and the effective osmotic difference ($\sigma\Delta\Pi$) across the capillary walls. It is used routinely as the method of first choice in the author's laboratory.

A second method was devised to overcome initial concern over the possibility of a compliance artifact affecting the calculation of the filtration rate immediately after occlusion. Michel et al. (167) showed that the volume of fluid in an occluded capillary changed exponentially as it approached equilibrium. A simple theory predicted that the exponential constant depended on L_p, ΔP, and r, the capillary radius. With ΔP assumed to be equal to P_c, L_p was calculated and was found to agree reasonably well with values of L_p determined from changes in J_v/A and P_c in the same vessel (155, 167). The fears that a compliance artifact complicated the estimates of initial filtration rate were allayed by comparison of the two methods and estimates of the time course of the compliance effect in frog mesenteric capillaries (155). Several studies showed that once P_c exceeded 5–10 cmH_2O, the compliance effect was small (141, 167) and short lived (155).

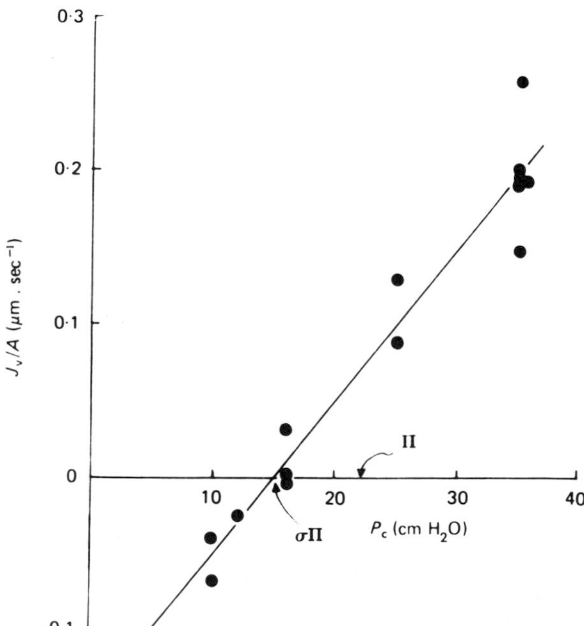

FIG. 6. Relationship between filtration rate per unit area of capillary wall (J_v/A) and capillary pressure (P_c) in a single frog mesenteric capillary perfused with Ringer's solution containing bovine serum albumin. Negative values of J_v/A indicate fluid absorption into capillary. Slope of regression line through *points* is hydraulic conductivity for capillary wall; intersection of regression line with the pressure axis shows effective osmotic pressure of perfusate at capillary wall ($\sigma\Delta\Pi$). Osmotic pressure of perfusate in membrane osmometer is also indicated (Π). [From Michel (164).]

The L_p of frog mesenteric capillaries was also investigated by a densitometric method (141). Wiederhielm (247) had previously used changes in the optical density of an intravascular dye to measure filtration rates in single frog mesenteric capillaries. Levick and Michel (141) used methods like those of Michel et al. (167) but estimated J_v/A from changes in optical density rather than RBC movements. Although they made relatively few measurements of L_p, Levick and Michel (141) were able to show that L_p could be determined densitometrically with simple apparatus and that the resulting values were within the range found for frog mesenteric capillaries by the RBC technique.

Table 3 summarizes all the measurements of L_p made on single frog mesenteric capillaries. It is gratifying to see that the mean value of all the recent determinations agrees closely with the value originally reported by Landis (123).

As in the studies on single mammalian vessels, there is considerable variation in the L_p values for different capillaries in the microcirculation of the frog mesentery. Strong reasons exist for believing that this represents a real variation in the permeability of different vessels and is not merely a consequence of methodological error. Thus a histogram of values of L_p shows a similar skewed distribution to a histogram of values of K^+ permeability for frog mesenteric capillaries [Fig. 7; (31)] despite the great differences in technique (and susceptibility to error) involved in these two estimates of permeability. Furthermore the average L_p of vessels at the venous end of the capillary bed is at least twice as large as that of vessels at the arterial end (164). This finding is not only consistent with the qualitative

TABLE 3. *Measurements of Hydraulic Conductivity for Frog Mesenteric Capillaries*

Hydraulic Conductivity, $\times 10^3$ $\mu m \cdot s^{-1} \cdot cmH_2O^{-1}$	n	Ref.
5.6[a]		123
2.0[b]	44	167
5.0[c]	79	167
2.23 ± 0.12[d]	22	35
8.9[e]	8	141
9.0[c]	57	156
6.58 ± 0.622[d]	38	164
4.83 ± 0.95[d,e]	8	164
11.33 ± 0.69[d,f]	10	164
2.62 ± 2.38[d]	16	33
5.31[g]		

[a] Mean estimate based on regression line relating determinations of J_v/A and P_c made on 72 different capillaries; it is therefore an average value for the mesenteric capillary bed and not for single vessels. [b] Median value, method 1. [c] Median value, method 2. [d] Mean ± SE. [e] Arterial and midcapillaries. [f] Venous capillaries. [g] Overall mean.

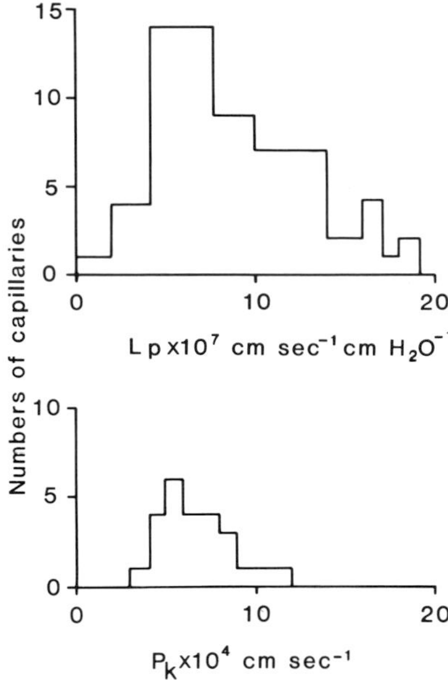

FIG. 7. Histograms showing distribution of values for hydraulic conductivity (L_p, *top*) and K^+ permeability (P_k, *bottom*) in single capillaries in frog mesentery. [Data for L_p from Michel et al. (167); data for K^+ permeability from Crone et al. (31).]

picture of an arteriovenous gradient of permeability to dyes and colored molecules in these vessels (130, 166, 211), but it is also in accordance with values of relative L_p (242) and recent measurements of the electrical conductivity of these capillary walls (30).

Measurements of Filtration Coefficients in Organs and Tissues

Attempts to estimate the average hydraulic conductivities of capillary walls in whole organs and tissues are beset with many difficulties, not the least of which is estimating the total number of capillaries (and thus the total area of capillary wall) through which fluid movements occur. A few workers (e.g., refs. 185, 215) have attempted to estimate the number of capillaries per unit volume of the tissue on which their physiological estimates of fluid filtration were made. Most physiological investigations have not been supplemented by histological data of this kind. Because the potential variation of capillary surface area with differences in perfusion in any one tissue is so great (quite apart from differences in species), no corrections are made for it in this chapter. Filtration coefficients determined in capillary beds are referred to here as CFC.

The estimation of CFC requires measurements of transvascular fluid movement with changes in capillary pressure. Transvascular fluid movement has most often been estimated from changes in the volume or weight of an organ or tissue. There are two difficulties of interpretation here: *1*) after a change in vascular pressure there is a change in vascular volume that has to be subtracted from the total volume to estimate the change of extravascular volume, and *2*) after a change in filtration rate the extravascular hydrostatic and osmotic pressures may change (see *Coupling of Fluid Filtration to Solute Permeability*, p. 381). Thus the problem is to be able to dissect the contribution of changes in vascular volume from the record of changing weight or volume of the tissue, so that the earliest changes in extravascular volume may be estimated when it is hoped that the extravascular forces are still close to their control values.

Krogh et al. (121) and Landis and Gibbon (131) both recognized these problems. It led them to abandon the use of the ordinary plethysmograph for measuring fluid filtration into the human forearm and to introduce the pressure plethysmograph for this purpose. Figure 8 shows that the initial increase in total volume of the arm is eliminated from the record of reduced arm volume. It also shows how the rate of increase of reduced arm volume diminishes with time after a rise in venous pressure.

A more recent attempt to separate changes in vascular volume from changes in the total volume (or weight) of a tissue is illustrated by the experiment of Lunde and Waaler (151). They attempted to estimate fluid filtration into the lung (Fig. 9) and monitored changes in vascular volume by measuring the radioactivity emitted from ^{51}Cr-labeled RBCs present in circulating blood. [This technique appears to have been introduced by Åblad and Mellander (1).]

In many investigations, however, filtration rates are taken directly from changes of total tissue volume or weight in the absence of independent estimates of changes in vascular volume. In these studies the initial rapid change in volume after a change of vascular pressure is interpreted as the change of vascular volume and the slow secondary change is taken as transcapillary filtration or reabsorption. In studies on the small intestine Johnson and Hanson (111) plotted tissue weight semilogarithmically against time to accentuate the difference between the two phases; others have not followed this practice, however, and have interpreted their records of tissue weight or volume by drawing tangents to the curves at arbitrary times. Unfortunately it is not always clear exactly when the rapid phase ends, particularly if the slow phase of volume change is attenuating moderately quickly (as happens in the lungs). Thus estimates of filtration rate based on the interpretation of weight or volume records without independent assessment of changes in vascular volume regularly give rise to controversy (44, 159, 210, 218, 219, 241). They are acceptable only when it can be demonstrated that filtration rate remains constant for a considerable period of time after venous pressure has been changed (45, 185, 218).

Fluid shifts between the plasma and the tissues have been calculated from changes in plasma protein concentration and hematocrit (4, 43, 94, 220, 244). Thus

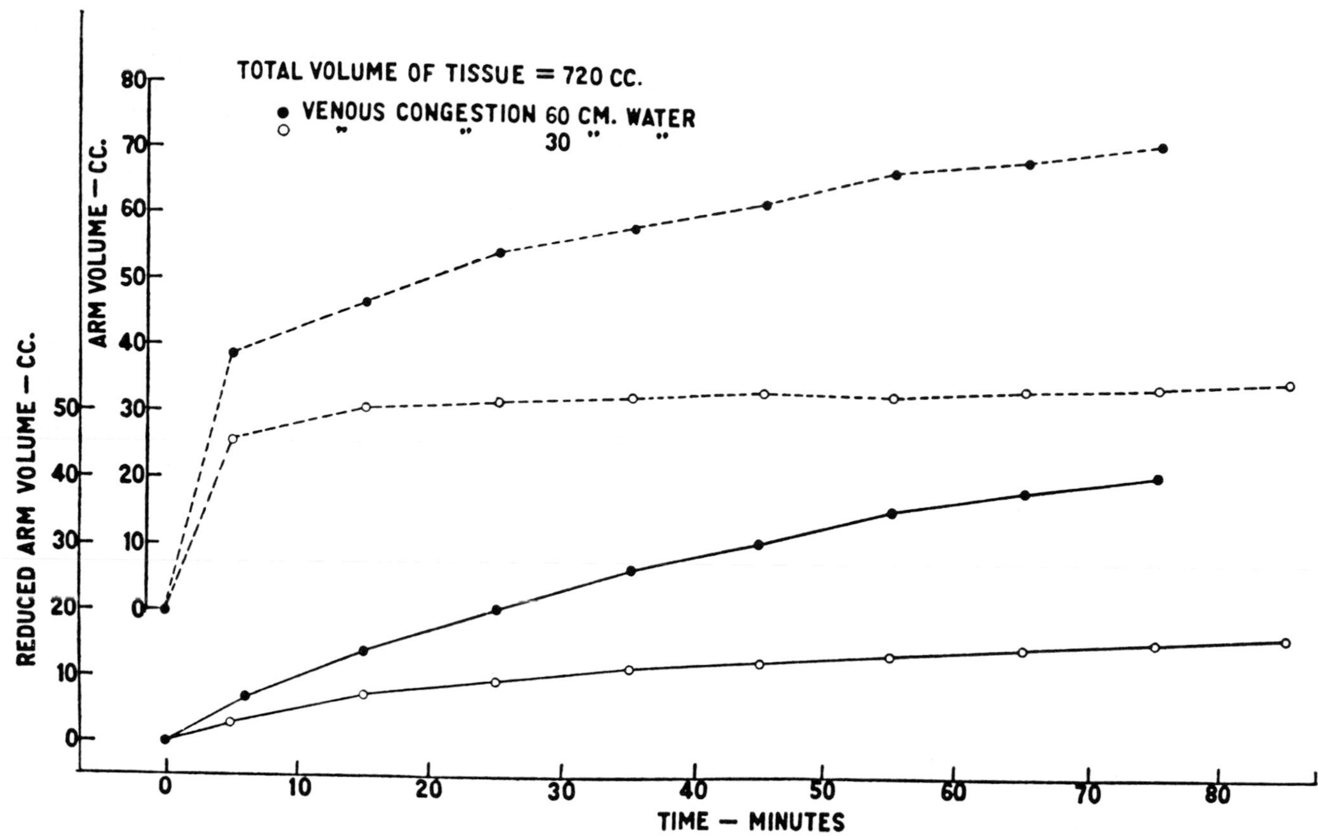

FIG. 8. Changes in volume of section of human forearm and changes in reduced volume of same forearm (measured with pressure plethysmograph at 34°C–35°C) after step increases of venous pressure from 0 to 30 cmH_2O and 0 to 60 cmH_2O. [From Landis and Gibbon (131), by copyright permission of The American Society for Clinical Investigation.]

in an investigation of transvascular fluid movements in the small intestine, Hanson and Johnson (94) calculated the extraction of fluid from the circulating blood after a rise of venous pressure from the arteriovenous difference in plasma protein concentration. This calculated fluid extraction correlated closely with the fluid filtration rate estimated from the secondary (slow) phase of weight change of the preparation. Friedmann (62) has described a method for continuously recording the protein osmotic pressure of venous blood. He applied it in studies of filtration into skeletal muscle (63), but the method appears to also have considerable potential for investigating fluid and protein exchange in other vascular beds. When, however, changes of hematocrit and plasma protein concentration are used to calculate total shifts of fluid between blood and interstitial fluid in the whole organism (220, 221), the conclusions should be viewed with caution. The whole-body hematocrit may be as much as 10% less than the hematocrit of blood in the large vessels (84), and changes in hematocrit may reflect changes in the distribution of blood between the small and large vessels rather than changes in total volume.

Effros devised a more sophisticated method of using transient changes in the concentration and dilution of the blood to estimate transvascular fluid movements (48). A bolus of hypertonic solution is injected into the arterial blood, and the transient changes in the concentration and dilution of effluent venous blood are recorded. If the solute responsible for the hypertonicity of the bolus is unable to cross capillary walls, then CFC can be estimated. This method has been used to determine the CFC of human cerebral capillaries (191). A more detailed description of it is given in the chapter by Crone and Levitt in this *Handbook*. Syrota and his colleagues (235) developed a sophisticated analysis of the osmotic bolus technique.

In a steady state the net filtration of fluid into a tissue equals the net loss of fluid from it in the lymph. Thus lymph flow can be used to estimate net filtration under steady-state conditions. Some workers (51, 98, 189) have used measurements of the Starling forces and total lymph flow to estimate CFC for an organ or tissues. The values of CFC obtained in this way are always less than those found for the same tissues by other techniques. The main problems with these measurements appear to be the uncertainty of the volume of tissue that the lymph drains and the uncertainty of whether the values of the variables used are true steady-state values appropriate for lymph formation.

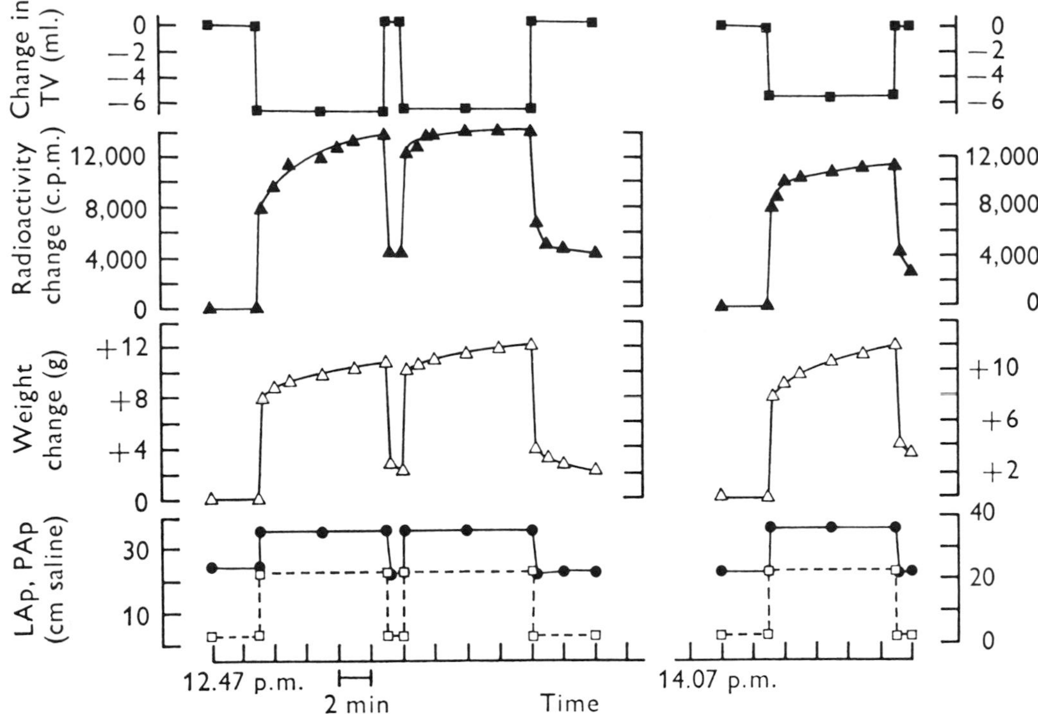

FIG. 9. Changes in tidal volume (TV), radioactivity emitted from ^{51}Cr-labeled red cells, weight, and pulmonary arterial pressure (PAp) after step increases and decreases of left atrial pressure (LAp) in an isolated perfused rabbit lung. Changes in emitted radioactivity indicate changes in blood volume of lung that must be subtracted from weight changes before weight changes are used to calculate transvascular fluid shifts. [From Lunde and Waaler (151).]

However, lymph flow is often neglected in estimates of CFC where fluid filtration is assessed from changes in tissue volume, and possibly a serious underestimate could result from this omission.

In estimating the mean capillary pressure of a capillary bed most workers have acknowledged the relationship derived by Pappenheimer and Soto-Rivera (186)

$$P_c = \frac{P_a + P_v\ (R_{pre}/R_{post})}{1 + R_{pre}/R_{post}} \tag{21}$$

In some cases arbitrary values of R_{pre}/R_{post} have been substituted into Equation 21 to estimate P_c under isogravimetric or isovolumetric conditions (58, 158). In other cases large variations of R_{pre}/R_{post} with changes of either P_a or P_v have led to alternative methods of estimating P_c. Thus Johnson (110), working on the isolated perfused intestine and having adjusted P_a and P_v to establish an isogravimetric state, stopped the arterial inflow and adjusted P_v to maintain the preparation at constant weight. In the absence of flow the isogravimetric P_v and the isogravimetric P_c should be equal. This modification of the isogravimetric technique was used by Johnson and his colleagues (110, 113) and adapted by Taylor and his collaborators, who used it to estimate P_c in limb capillaries (22), lung capillaries, and in the capillaries of the small intestine (169). For pulmonary capillaries, empirical formulas have been devised for calculating P_c from P_a and P_v (65, 232).

The value of P_c that should be used to determine CFC is the value averaged over all exchange vessels in proportion to their contribution to the product of L_p and the total membrane area A_m for the entire capillary bed. In a perfectly uniform microvascular bed, the isogravimetric method should estimate this average P_c. If, however, there is nonuniformity of R_{pre}/R_{post} (and/or L_p), the classic isogravimetric method or the calculation of P_c from Equation 21 may be in error. This is because with equal flows to regions of high and low R_{pre}/R_{post}, the high values of R_{pre}/R_{post} dominate the mean. The Johnson development of the measurement of isogravimetric P_c appears to be free from this error because P_c is estimated from P_v when flow is zero. It is probably the most appropriate technique for determining P_c for CFC measurements, though the errors of the original technique appear to have been very small when it was first used.

Table 4 summarizes some average values for CFC in various organs and tissues. These values are usually interpreted to be the sum of the products of L_pA_m for all the exchange vessels in the microvascular bed. When divided by values that are estimates of capillary surface area they should yield values for the mean L_p. There is always considerable uncertainty about the appropriate value for capillary surface area, and this is discussed in relation to solute permeability measurements in the chapter by Crone and Levitt in this *Handbook*.

FLUID BALANCE IN ORGANS AND TISSUES

Although Starling's hypothesis is universally accepted as correct, there is still much to learn about the exact values of the Starling forces and the ways in which their variation in vivo determines the balance of fluid between the blood and the interstitium. Writing half a century ago, Landis (128) emphasized that of all the factors determining fluid movements through the capillary wall, capillary pressure was the most variable. This variability of P_c is particularly true in large animals such as humans. The absolute values of pressure in the human circulation are greatly affected by gravity, and thus changes in the position of a capillary bed with respect to the heart may cause large changes of P_c within the bed. Under physiological conditions, P_c is influenced more by changes in P_v than by changes in P_a; consequently studies on tissue fluid balance are considered here for conditions where P_v has been maintained close to zero and a steady state may exist, and for conditions where P_v has been acutely raised and a new steady state is being established. The special problem of the continuous reabsorption of fluid in renal and intestinal capillaries and the question of whether P_c is directly regulated are also considered. Furthermore because many of the recent investigations were stimulated by the development of new techniques for estimating Starling forces, a brief description of them is also given.

TABLE 4. *Capillary Filtration Coefficients of Capillary Beds in Various Tissues*

	CFC, ml·min^{-1}·100 g^{-1} wet wt·mmHg^{-1}	Ref.
Human		
Forearm	0.0057*	121, 131
Foot		
Supine	0.0075	159
Erect	0.0019	159
Lower leg, supine	0.0012	218
Lowered 50 cm	0.0012	218
Cat		
Hindlimb	0.0105	185, 186
Isolated calf	0.01 – 0.015	26, 59, 159
Small intestine	0.10 – 0.15	58, 59
	0.09 ± 0.06†	207
P_v = 0 mmHg	0.56	169
P_v = 30 mmHg	0.086	169
Dog		
Hindlimb	0.014	41, 186
Hindpaw	0.028	22
Small intestine	0.11 ± 0.005†	207
P_v = 10 mmHg	0.38	113
P_v = 20 mmHg	0.11	113
Lung		
Tissue analysis	0.065	89
Isolated perfused	0.07	65
	0.106	193
Intact lobe	0.11	45
Rat		
Hindlimb, perfused	0.033	205
	0.015	209
	0.037‡	209
Rabbit		
Heart	0.35	240
Lung, isolated	0.18	173
	0.95	241
Sheep, lung	0.010	51
	0.011	189

* Value based on assumption that a 1-mmHg rise in venous pressure causes a 0.8-mmHg rise in capillary pressure. † Average ± SE. ‡ Maximum vasodilation.

Techniques for Measuring Starling Forces

CAPILLARY PRESSURE. The isogravimetric technique (186) and its development by Johnson (110) remain the principal indirect methods for measuring P_c (these methods are discussed in *Measurements of Filtration Coefficients in Organs and Tissues*, p. 386). During the past 12 years there have been an increasing number of direct measurements of P_c. Although the classic Landis method is still occasionally used, the servo-null technique of Wiederhielm (246, 251) has made the direct measurement of P_c easier and more reliable, particularly in vessels of small diameter and where P_c is rapidly changing. In the Landis technique (122), a micropipette filled with a reference fluid is viewed under a microscope and inserted into a vessel. The reference fluid is either colored with dye or contains flow markers (such as suspended RBCs) so that its flow through the tip can be observed. Pressure is applied to the pipette via a water manometer system and is adjusted manually until the flow stops; the pressure in the manometer is then taken to equal the pressure inside the vessels.

In the servo-null technique (246, 251), the micropipette is filled with concentrated NaCl (3 M) and movements of this fluid through the micropipette tip are detected by measuring the electrical resistance between the interior of the pipette and the surrounding tissues. When the concentrated salt solution flows out of the pipette, it lowers the electrical resistance in the region of the tip; when fluid moves into the tip, the salt solution is diluted and resistance increases. When resistance is constant, there is no net flow through the tip and the pressure within the pipette balances that outside the tip. By continuously monitoring the tip resistance and adjusting the pressure applied to the reference fluid via a small electrical pump, the zero flow condition can be maintained, and a continuous reading of the pressure of the reference fluid can be obtained from a transducer in series with the pipette and the pump. This method has been carefully developed, and its response time is short enough to accurately record pressure pulsations in arteries and capillaries (154, 241). The method has been modified slightly and made commercially available by Intaglietta et al. (108).

INTERSTITIAL FLUID PRESSURE. Much of the current interest in the Starling forces and tissue fluid balance was stimulated by Guyton's (85) introduction of the capsule technique for measuring ISF pressure. Direct measurement of P_{ISF} had previously been attempted by measuring the pressure of a fluid brought into contact with tissues through a fine needle. Although this technique is still used, blockage of the needle tip and the detection and prevention of very low flows are major problems. Guyton saw that these difficulties of the needle method could be overcome if a relatively large pool of fluid, in equilibrium with the surrounding ISF, could be formed within the tissues. He thought that such a pool might be formed in the cavity of a chronically implanted perforated capsule. In 1963 he reported the first measurement of interstitial fluid pressure with this technique. Once the capsules had healed into the subcutaneous tissues of dogs, the fluid pressures within their cavities were 4–7 mmHg subatmospheric. The subatmospheric pressure of capsular fluid has been confirmed repeatedly, but the interpretation of these pressures remains controversial (5, 87, 88, 95, 248–250). The wick method, originally developed by Scholander et al. (217), also yielded subatmospheric pressures for subcutaneous tissues. In this technique a reference fluid makes contact with the tissues between the fibers of a cotton wick. The wick is enclosed in a needle so that it can be introduced into tissues; once in position the tip of the needle may be withdrawn from the end of the wick. The wick technique has the advantage that it can be used in a particular subject without long-term premeditation. Wick pressures recorded from mammalian subcutaneous tissues are usually in the range of −1.0 mmHg to −2.0 mmHg (53, 133, 197, 228, 229).

Much of the controversy surrounding the nature of the pressures recorded by the wick and capsule techniques arises from disagreements of terminology and whether the pressures recorded represent the hydrostatic pressure of the interstitial space or an osmotic (or swelling) pressure caused by the glycosaminoglycan molecules trapped within the interstitial matrix. Whatever the solution of this question proves to be, the subatmospheric pressures recorded by the capsule and wick techniques show that water in the interstitial space is at a lower chemical potential than water in a solution of similar ionic composition at atmospheric pressure. For transcapillary fluid movements, the importance of this problem lies in the extent to which this reduction of the chemical potential of water in the interstitium contributes to the overall difference in chemical potential across the walls of vascular and lymphatic capillaries.

PLASMA COLLOID OSMOTIC PRESSURE (ONCOTIC PRESSURE). Although many workers use formulas such as Equations 16 and 17 to calculate the protein osmotic pressure of solutions from their protein concentration, direct measurement of protein osmotic pressure is preferable and can be made quickly and easily with the Hansen osmometer (93). The response time of the Hansen osmometer has been greatly improved by the development of artificial ultrafiltration membranes that combine a relatively small pore size with a high hydraulic conductivity (198).

COLLOID OSMOTIC PRESSURE OF INTERSTITIAL FLUID (TISSUE ONCOTIC PRESSURE). In a previous section (see *Coupling of Fluid Filtration to Solute Permeability*, p. 381) it was argued that the oncotic pressure of the pericapillary fluid could play a crucial role in transcapillary fluid balance. So far, however, pericapillary fluid has not been directly sampled, and thus its composition and potential energy can only be deduced from other measurements. Interstitial fluid from nonedematous tissues has been sampled directly (28, 92, 212), but many investigators assume that the protein concentration of the ISF is the same as that in the lymph draining the tissues. This assumption requires some scrutiny. Because lymph protein content changes as lymph flows through lymph nodes (11), postnodal lymph protein concentration may differ considerably from that of the ISF. In a careful review of the available data, Renkin (202) concluded that the differences in protein concentration between ISF and prenodal lymph were small, and recent direct measurements support his view (212). When the protein concentration of the lymph is used to calculate Π_{ISF}, however, additional caution is required. It has been argued (5, 82, 83, 187, 261) that the interstitial matrix excludes plasma proteins from some regions of the interstitial space, so that the activity coefficients of the proteins, and thus their contributions to the total osmotic pressure of the ISF, are increased above those of proteins at equal concentrations in solutions lacking a matrix. If such exclusion of plasma protein does occur within the interstitium, then the equal protein concentrations in the ISF and in lymph means that Π_{ISF} is greater than the lymph oncotic pressure. Alternatively, if protein osmotic pressures of lymph and ISF are equal, then the protein concentration in the lymph must exceed that of the ISF. Such inequalities may be small (~1 cmH_2O), but many investigators have concerned themselves over such small differences in recent years in their attempts to examine what Diana and Fleming (39) called the "fine tuning of the Starling forces."

Fluid Balance and P_c in Tissues at Low Venous Pressures

Several recent studies have estimated all the Starling forces on the same preparation. Usually it has been found that the isogravimetric (or isovolumetric)

P_c agrees closely with the value calculated by difference from the other Starling forces.

Chen, Granger, and Taylor (22) estimated P_c under isovolumetric conditions in the hindpaw of the dog. The P_{ISF} was determined with a Guyton capsule implanted some 4–6 wk before the experiment, Π_{ISF} was estimated from the lymph protein concentration, and Π_p and lymph flow were also measured. At low venous pressure, P_c was 12.8 mmHg and the forces favoring net fluid filtration exceeded those favoring reabsorption by 0.5 mmHg. In a similar study, Brace and Guyton (16) estimated P_{ISF} (with a capsule), Π_p, and Π_{ISF} (from lymph) first in the intact forelimb of a dog and then in the same limb after it had been isolated. Isogravimetric P_c in the isolated limb was 15.6 mmHg, which exceeded that calculated from $\Pi_p - \Pi_{ISF} + P_{ISF}$ by 0.3 mmHg. In the intact forelimb P_c could not be measured, but from the other variables the authors deduced its value to lie between 10 and 11 mmHg.

In the isolated dog intestine preparation, Johnson and Hanson (111, 112) found that isogravimetric P_c was lower than plasma oncotic pressure by 7 mmHg. In a later study on the same preparation, Johnson and Richardson (114) combined these data with measurements of P_{ISF} (needle method) and Π_{ISF} (from lymph) and concluded that the forces favoring filtration exceeded those favoring reabsorption by 3–6 mmHg. Net filtration does occur in this preparation under isogravimetric conditions and is seen as lymph flow, but the tissues have a high CFC and the lymph flows observed by Johnson and Richardson (114) were too low to account for the apparent difference in Starling forces. A much smaller imbalance of forces in the cat intestine was observed by Mortillaro and Taylor (169), and Taylor (236) has recently attempted to reconcile the findings of Johnson and Richardson (114) with those of his own group.

All these studies indicate that when tissues are in a steady state of fluid balance and venous pressure is low, $P_c < \Pi_c$. The small net filtration necessary for lymphatic flow appears to be determined by the extravascular forces (Π_i and P_i). This picture is entirely consistent with the model previously considered (see *Coupling of Fluid Filtration to Solute Permeability*, p. 381), where at low P_c, net filtration is maintained in the steady state by protein leakage into the pericapillary space.

Direct measurements of P_c, however, appear to be equal to or greater than Π_c (Table 5). Indeed the approximate agreement between direct measurements of P_c reported by Landis (122, 123, 125, 126) and the plasma oncotic pressure was regarded originally as strong evidence in support of the Starling hypothesis. Recent direct measurements suggest that P_c is usually slightly greater than Π_c even when it is measured at the venous end of capillaries (108, 142, 259). There seems to be little evidence for the textbook diagram that depicts a linear arteriovenous gradient of P_c neatly straddling Π_c, so that filtration of fluid from the arterial end of the capillary is balanced by reabsorption of fluid from the venous end.

TABLE 5. *Recent Direct Estimates of Capillary Pressure*

	P_c, cmH_2O	Π_p, cmH_2O	Ref.
Cat mesentery	43.1		259
	40.8		70
Rat intestine			
Muscle	32.4	27.2	74
Mucosa	18.8		74
Human skin			
Nailfold of finger and toe	43		142
Arterial limb	49	34	142
Venous limb	34		142
Nailfold of finger			
Arteriolar limb	15–75		154
Venular limb	15–53		154
Nailfold	39.4	36.7	96

P_c, capillary pressure; Π_p, protein osmotic pressure.

In attempting to account for the discrepancy between direct and indirect estimates of P_c, it should first be said that when fluid balance has been investigated in single vessels, it has been found that there is always net filtration when $P_c > \Pi_c$ (61, 167, 227). One is therefore forced to conclude that when direct measurements of P_c have been reported, either the entire vascular bed was not in fluid balance or that the single vessels were not representative of the total population of exchange vessels. At present there is no evidence to refute either conclusion, and there are reasons to believe that in some situations both may be true. Levick and Michel (142) and Tooke (238) observed that P_c in human skin varies directly with skin temperature. It is therefore possible that there is net fluid filtration into the tissues of warm skin and reabsorption of tissue fluid into the blood from cold skin. This would be consistent with the common experience of swelling and shrinking of the fingers in warm and cold weather. There are also good reasons for believing that direct measurements of P_c may not represent the functional average pressure in the exchange vessels. Thus a large fraction of the functional fluid exchange area of the vascular bed may lie downstream from the capillaries (247) where P_c has been measured. It is also possible that direct measurements of P_c are not representative because they are conducted on vessels in which there is flow. Perhaps an important contribution to net reabsorption of tissue fluid may be made in vessels where blood flow is temporarily arrested. Chambers and Zweifach (21) discussed this idea in relation to vasomotion over 35 years ago, and it was recently taken up and developed by Intaglietta (106, 107) and Endrich (107) using data for P_c and flow in single vessels of the cat tenuissimus muscle.

Gore and Bohlen presented an interesting analysis

of microvascular pressures in the mammalian small intestine in a series of papers (71, 73, 74). They measured P_c in the smooth muscle and mucosa of the small intestine of the rat. Whereas $\overline{P}_c = 23.8$ mmHg in smooth muscle, in mucosal capillaries $\overline{P}_c = 13.8$ mmHg. Using the distribution of silica particles (avg diam 10 μm) as an indication of the distribution of blood flow between mucosa and smooth muscle, Gore and Bohlen (74) calculated an average P_c value for the whole intestine of 16.8 mmHg. This is only slightly greater than the reported average values of isogravimetric P_c for this preparation of 13–15 mmHg (110, 111). The effects of heterogeneity of P_c on the functional $\overline{P}_c$ were discussed earlier (see *Measurements of Filtration Coefficients in Organs and Tissues*, p. 386). Note that even the simple treatment of heterogeneity of P_c used by Gore and Bohlen (74) is remarkably successful in bringing together direct and indirect estimates of P_c on one vascular bed.

Adjustments of Filtration Rate After Changes in Venous Pressure

In many tissues the increased filtration of fluid that accompanies a rise in venous pressure diminishes with time even though the venous pressure remains raised. There appear to be three general reasons for this attenuation of filtration: *1)* an adjustment of the Starling forces to new steady-state values, *2)* an increase in lymph flow, and *3)* changes in the microvasculature that increase R_{pre}/R_{post} and appear to diminish CFC. Because these factors delay or prevent the onset of edema (121), they have been described as safety factors (88, 175, 236). Their relative importance varies among different vascular beds; to illustrate this the changes occurring in the lungs, the limbs, and the intestine are considered next.

LUNG. From a consideration of the coupling of fluid and protein fluxes through the capillary wall, it was argued (see *Coupling of Fluid Filtration to Solute Permeability*, p. 381) that the steady-state relationships between fluid filtration per unit area and transcapillary pressure (ΔP) are markedly nonlinear (see Fig. 5). With normal low permeability to protein, the curve divides into two regions: a low-pressure range where steady-state J_v/A changes little with ΔP and a high-pressure range where the relationship closely approximates L_p. If the reflection coefficient of the capillary wall to protein is close to unity, the division between high- and low-pressure regions is determined by Π_c.

The steady-state relationship between net filtration and P_c for the capillaries of the lungs closely resembles the theoretical curve of Figure 5. Although the coupling of fluid and protein fluxes is important for pulmonary fluid balance, other factors are involved, and the transition from low- to high-pressure regions of the relationship is more exaggerated than the curve in Figure 5. The mean P_c in the lungs of all mammals is much lower than its value in capillary beds of the systemic circulation. Taking an average value for P_c of 10 cmH_2O and an average Π_c of 30 cmH_2O places the starting point for fluid balance in the lungs well in the low-pressure region of the J_v/A versus ΔP curve (see Fig. 5). This is another way of saying that steady-state fluid filtration into the lungs is determined more by extravascular forces than by changes of P_c.

Guyton and Lindsey (89) were the first researchers to build up a picture of the rate of fluid accumulation in the lungs with changes in left atrial pressure. They found that increments of left atrial pressure had little effect on the fluid content of dog lung tissue until the left atrial pressure exceeded 25 mmHg. At higher pressures the rate of fluid accumulation increased directly with left atrial pressure (Fig. 10). The pressure above which fluid accumulation in the lung becomes sensitive to left atrial pressure was called the critical pressure. Because the pulmonary artery pressure is normally in the range of 12–20 mmHg (37), the pulmonary P_c should normally be well below the critical pressure. The critical pressure was similar to the plasma oncotic pressure, and the critical P_c could be reduced by reducing Π_c (64, 89). Drake et al. (45) recently found that the critical P_c varies linearly with Π_c, and if two very deviant points are omitted from their data, the relationship between critical P_c and Π_c has a slope of one and an intercept that differs insignificantly from zero. Levine et al. (143) independently demonstrated a nonlinear relationship between fluid accumulation and left atrial pressure. These authors, however, preferred to interpret the data as a continuous curve rather than two essentially linear relations with an inflection point at the critical P_c.

Working below the critical P_c in isolated perfused rabbit lungs, Lunde and Waaler (151) showed that an increment of left atrial pressure increased vascular volume and also gave rise to the transient filtration of a small volume of fluid. This filtration was rapidly checked, and only continued when P_c was raised above the critical value. Later workers have confirmed this picture and some (173) have attempted to calculate the CFC for the lung on the basis of these transient increases of J_v. The values reported (174) agree closely with those calculated from data of J_v and P_c above the critical value.

Guyton and his colleagues (90, 160) have argued that below the critical P_c, filtration is checked by a rise in P_i. Lunde and Waaler (151) suggested that filtration of small volumes of fluid into the pericapillary space diluted the protein concentration sufficiently for the resulting increase in $\Pi_c - \Pi_i$ to be great enough to halt further filtration. There is evidence now that both factors are important and that lymph flow plays a vital role in the intact lung.

For a rise of P_i to check filtration, the compliance

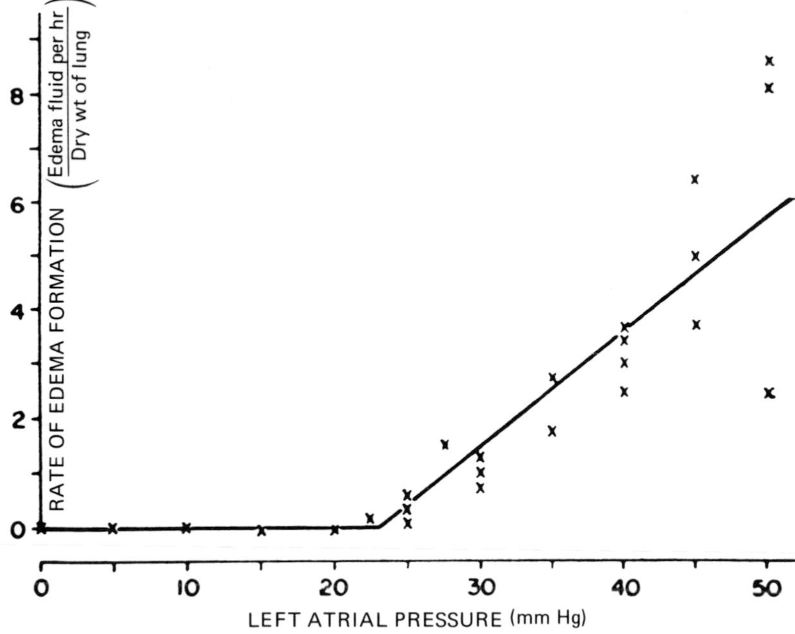

FIG. 10. Changes in fluid content of dog's lungs subjected to prolonged elevations of left atrial pressure. No increase in fluid content was detected until pressure was >25 mmHg, i.e., osmotic pressure of plasma proteins. [From Guyton and Lindsey (89), by permission of the American Heart Association, Inc.]

of the pulmonary interstitium must be low at low pulmonary P_c and high at levels above the critical P_c. This is apparently true in canine lungs (68, 69, 188). Parker et al. (188) have suggested that starting at normal values of P_i and pulmonary interstitial volume, P_i may increase by up to 6 mmHg to offset filtration resulting from increments of P_c.

Although the steady-state fluid balance of the lung may be simulated in theory by the appropriate coupling of fluid and protein fluxes through the capillary walls (151), the importance of this coupling has only recently been appreciated. Parker et al. (187) have observed that as pulmonary P_c is increased, the pulmonary extravascular volume available for albumin increased to a greater extent than the ISF volume. They interpreted this to mean that at normal or low interstitial volumes, albumin is excluded from regions of the pulmonary interstitial space by macromolecules such as hyaluronic acid and collagen. As interstitial volume increases, the concentration of all interstitial macromolecules falls, and thus the volume available for albumin rises more rapidly than the total volume. In such a system the chemical activity of albumin, and thus its effect on Π_i, falls more rapidly than its concentration; this phenomenon has been called exclusion amplification. Exclusion amplification has been explored theoretically (178) and experimentally (135) in systems of hyaluronic acid and albumin, and its possible role in the interstitium has been discussed by Laurent (134), Wiederhielm (248, 250), and Granger (82, 83).

The lymph flow is of greatest importance in maintaining fluid balance in the intact lung. Over the past 10 years many studies have been carried out in Staub's laboratory on pulmonary lymph flow in chronically prepared sheep. A clear relationship between lymph flow and intrapulmonary vascular pressure was established in this preparation (51). Drake et al. (45) recently found that in the intact lung of an anesthetized dog, lymph flow increases progressively with P_c until it reaches a maximum value at a P_c that approximates to the critical value.

Below the critical P_c, fluid accumulation in the lungs is minimized by adjustments of lymph flow and by changes of P_i and Π_i. The critical P_c depends on Π_c and appears to approximate to it (45). It is apparently also related to a change in pulmonary interstitial compliance and to the attainment of maximum lymph flow. Lymph flow and interstitial compliance are probably determined by the hydration of the lung; because pulmonary hydration ultimately depends on Π_c and P_c, the interaction of all the Starling forces is involved. Because the critical P_c is usually greater than the pulmonary arterial pressure, with normal pulmonary hemodynamics and normal Π_c, a human being or animal should be well protected against pulmonary edema.

Fishman and his colleagues (55, 143, 196) expressed an alternative interpretation of the nonlinear filtration characteristics of the lung. They suggested that increases in pulmonary P_c stretch the pores through which fluid and protein traverse the capillary wall, thereby accounting for high rates of fluid (and protein) accumulation at high P_c. Although some ultrastructural evidence supports this view (55, 196), the physiological evidence (45, 174) is inconsistent with it. Apparently CFC does not increase with P_c (45, 174), and although CFC can be increased in perfused lungs by changing from steady to pulsatile perfusion pressures, this appears to represent an increase in perfused capillary surface rather than an increase in permeability (99).

LIMBS. When the limbs are at heart level, P_c within them appears to approximate Π_c. Because in awake humans the extremities are usually below the heart, in these regions of the limbs P_c is usually greater than Π_c. Thus as Landis and Gibbon (131) pointed out:

> If capillary blood pressure and the colloid osmotic pressure of the blood were the sole factors involved in fluid balance it would be difficult to explain how it is possible for the human being to avoid dependent edema whenever the erect posture is assumed.

Evidence for an additional factor was first described over 50 years ago by Drury and Jones (47). They observed that after venous congestion of a limb the rate of increase of tissue volume diminished with time. Waterfield (242) reported similar progressive reduction in the rate of swelling of the human feet during quiet standing, and the phenomenon was well described by Krogh et al. (121) and Landis and Gibbon (131) in their studies on the human forearm using a pressure plethysmograph. Data from Landis and Gibbon (131) are shown in Figure 11, and it can be seen that for moderate increases in venous pressure, the rate of swelling of the tissue is reduced to zero within 10–20 min.

Landis and Gibbon (131) interpreted this progressive reduction of filtration in terms of a rising tissue pressure. Landis and Pappenheimer (132) estimated

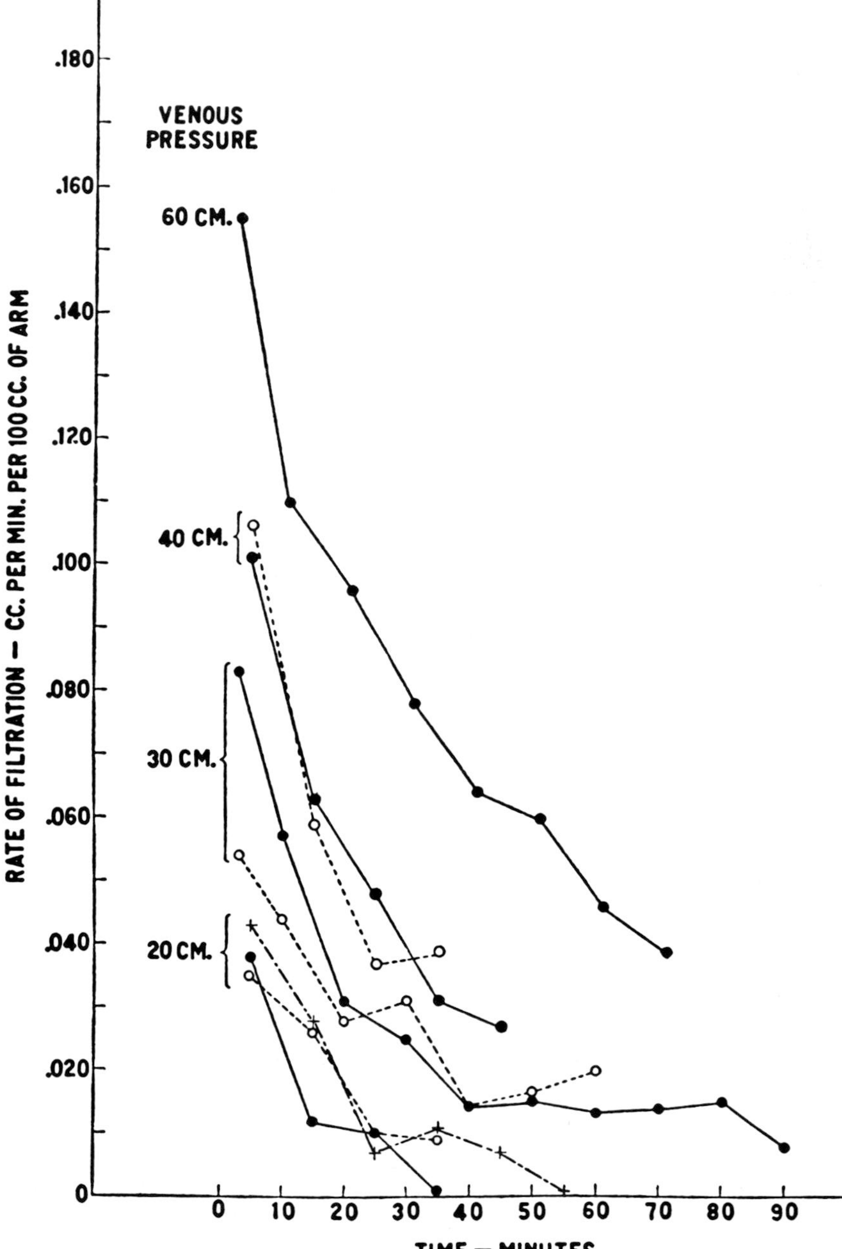

FIG. 11. Changes in rate of filtration into human forearm after elevation of venous pressure for long periods of time. [From Landis and Gibbon (131), by copyright permission of The American Society for Clinical Investigation.]

the rise in P_i necessary to account for the reduction of filtration in these experiments and concluded that with a venous pressure of 60 cmH_2O, P_i would have to rise to 30 cmH_2O in 1 h, suggesting a compliance of the interstitium of 0.2 $ml \cdot cmH_2O^{-1} \cdot 100\ g^{-1}$ of tissue. Only Chen et al. (22) found evidence for the development of such high values of P_{ISF} with increased venous pressure. Recording P_{ISF} from a porous capsule implanted in the hindpaw of a dog, Chen et al. (22) observed an increase in P_{ISF} from −5.44 cmH_2O to 16.32 cmH_2O as P_c was raised from 13.6 cmH_2O to 54.4 cmH_2O. Such high values of P_{ISF} appear to be rare in the limbs in the absence of gross edema. In his original study of the compliance of the interstitial space of the dog hindlimb, Guyton (86) reported values of 0.3 $ml \cdot cmH_2O^{-1} \cdot 100\ g^{-1}$ at low ISF volumes, but as ISF volume increased so did compliance; once P_i became equal to the atmospheric pressure, interstitial compliance lay in the range of 1–2 $ml \cdot cmH_2O^{-1} \cdot 100\ g^{-1}$, increasing only when the tissues became visibly edematous. Indirect estimates of interstitial compliance in cat skeletal muscle by Eliassen et al. (49) gave values of 1–2 $ml \cdot cmH_2O^{-1} \cdot 100\ g^{-1}$ over a wide range of tissue volumes. Furthermore, Fadnes and Noddeland (52), using the wick method in healthy subjects tilted to 45° for 1 h, failed to detect changes in P_i in the subcutaneous tissues of the human ankle. Although a rise of P_i may be important in preventing edema in the dog paw (and possibly also beneath the deep fascia of human hands and feet), there is little evidence to suggest that changes of P_{ISF} maintain fluid balance in other tissues of the limbs.

In 1964 Mellander et al. (159) suggested that local vascular responses in the lower extremities of humans protected the tissues from edema during standing. They reported that CFC in the foot of a standing subject is approximately one-sixth its value for the same foot when the subject lies down (159). They suggested that the reduction of CFC on standing was a reduction of the filtration area brought about by the closure of precapillary sphincters. In parallel experiments on the isolated calf preparation of the cat, Mellander et al. (159) noted a similar decrease in CFC and an increase in vascular resistance when the calf was lowered and venous pressure raised. They deduced that the increased resistance was largely a precapillary phenomenon. More recently, direct measurements of P_c in the nailfold capillaries of human feet by Levick and Michel (142) confirmed that there is a large increase in precapillary resistance on standing. In the supine position R_{pre}/R_{post} was 2:1 or 3:1, but on standing it was increased 10-fold. Taking values of CFC from Mellander et al. (159) and their own values for P_c, Levick and Michel (142) calculated that during quiet standing the feet should swell at a rate of 30 ml/h, a value comparable to that reported by Waterfield (242). They questioned, however, the interpretation of the reduction of CFC being achieved by a closure of precapillary sphincters alone. In the presence of such high venous pressures, vessels closed off at the arterial end should fill retrogradely and still contribute to filtration when venous pressure is raised. They noted that they themselves had observed in the toe nailfold no reduction in the number of capillaries filled with blood as the subject moved from a supine to a standing position.

The latter point has been taken up by Sejrsen et al. (218, 219), who carefully examined the changes in vascular volume in human legs during venous congestion. When a cuff is used to apply a step rise in venous pressure of 40 mmHg to the lower limb of a supine subject, the vascular volume distal to the cuff may increase for up to 5 min before a new steady value is attained. If the foot is lowered 50 cm, the increase in vascular volume after a step rise in venous pressure is complete much more quickly. When Sejrsen et al. (218) estimated CFC in supine subjects by slowly lowering the calf of the leg from 5 to 25 cm below the heart (and allowing for changes in vascular volume), they obtained an average value of 0.0012 $ml \cdot min^{-1} \cdot 100\ g^{-1} \cdot mmHg^{-1}$. This is similar to the value reported by Mellander et al. (159) for standing subjects. Since Mellander et al. estimated CFC from changes in total tissue volume occurring between 1.5 and 4 min after the increase in venous pressure, Sejrsen et al. (218) argue that Mellander et al. (159) overestimated CFC in their supine subjects because a change in vascular volume was included in the change of tissue volume used to calculate filtration rate. In the standing subject the vascular volume changes in the lower leg are completed much sooner after an additional rise in venous pressure, and the plethysmographic estimation of tissue fluid filtration is less susceptible to the vascular volume artifact. Sejrsen et al. (218) concluded that dependent edema of the feet and lower legs is prevented by the low CFC of these tissues (and to a lesser extent by the increase in local vascular resistance that occurs on standing, reducing the rise of P_c).

An alternative interpretation that retains the hypothesis of Mellander et al. (159) was suggested independently by both E. M. Renkin and S. Mellander (personal communications). They suggested that on standing, closure of the precapillary sphincters stops flow in five-sixths of the capillary bed and that fluid rapidly filters from these vessels to establish a new Starling equilibrium. A rough calculation suggests that with a CFC of 0.01 $ml \cdot min^{-1} \cdot 100\ g^{-1} \cdot mmHg^{-1}$ (159) capillaries closed off by their precapillary sphincters may concentrate their plasma protein rapidly enough to be within 1% of a new equilibrium value within 2 min. These capillaries would therefore not be included in the estimation of CFC if filtration rates were not measured during the first 2 min after the rise of venous pressure. In this way the reduction of CFC on standing is the result of the closure of precapillary sphincters as Mellander et al. proposed. If this hypothesis is correct, the plasma protein concentration must be more than doubled in the closed-off vessels for a Starling equilibrium to be achieved with a P_c of ~100 mmHg. If the capillaries represent 20% of the total blood volume, then after a period of standing the plasma protein concentration in the veins of the leg should be raised by just less than 20%. In fact, Youmans et al. (256) measured increases in total plasma protein concentration of 27% in the venous plasma after subjects had stood for 1 h, and recently this has been confirmed by Noddeland et al. (176).

Apparently changes of P_c in the limbs are buffered from changes of venous pressure by local alterations of precapillary-to-postcapillary resistance. These microvascular changes may involve the arrest of flow through large areas of the capillary bed; this appears to reduce CFC because once fluid has equilibrated between the tissues and the stagnant plasma of these vessels, no more fluid is lost. Alternatively [if Sejrsen et al. (218, 219) are correct] the capillaries of potentially dependent regions of the limbs (such as the lower parts of legs and feet) may have a much lower L_p than capillaries in other regions. Thus relative rates of filtration may change considerably during the day, but the volumes of fluid filtered are usually small.

The mechanism of the local microvascular adjustments is not clear. Mellander et al. (159) argued that it was a myogenic phenomenon. Henriksen (101–103) and Henriksen and Sejrsen (104) suggested that the increased vascular resistance accompanying the lowering of the extremities in humans (or a rise in venous pressure there) depends on the presence of functioning sympathetic nerves (though not on their central connections). They suggested that an axon reflex is involved in this increased vascular resistance (103, 104).

Lymph flow from the extremities varies considerably with venous pressure (179, 204, 255), activity (179, 255), and skin temperature (179, 255). In sheep the lymphatics of the legs are intrinsically contractile (255). Renkin (202) has argued that the changes in protein concentration that reportedly occur as lymph flows through the nodes (11) may be largely (if not entirely) the result of the absorption of fluid into the node and not the movement of protein into the lymph. It has recently been suggested that contractile lymphatics may also be present in the legs (180). If this proves to be so, it would be surprising if intrinsic contractions of the lymphatics play a major role in the fluid balance of a limb, in view of the effectiveness of limb immobilization in preventing the spread of infection via the lymphatics (7).

INTESTINE. Adjustments of the microcirculation, of the Starling forces, and of lymph flow are all involved in fluid balance between the blood and tissues of the intestine.

As in the limbs, a rise in venous pressure is accompanied by an apparent fall of CFC (58, 113, 169). Thus Johnson and Hanson (113) observed a fall of CFC from 0.38 $ml \cdot min^{-1} \cdot 100\ g^{-1} \cdot mmHg^{-1}$ to 0.112 $ml \cdot min^{-1} \cdot 100\ g^{-1} \cdot mmHg^{-1}$ as P_c was raised from 10 to 20 mmHg, whereas Mortillaro and Taylor (169) reported a fall from 0.56 to 0.083 $ml \cdot min^{-1} \cdot 100\ g^{-1} \cdot mmHg^{-1}$ as venous pressure was raised from 0 to 30 mmHg. Like the reductions of CFC noted in the limbs, the change was believed to be the result of closure of the precapillary sphincters, a proposal supported by more recent experiments of Granger et al. (80). All workers observed a large increase in R_{pre}/R_{post} with an increase in venous pressure.

Adjustments of the Starling forces have also been demonstrated to follow rises in the venous pressure of the intestine. As venous pressure rises Π_c increases (94) and Π_i falls [as judged by the lymph protein concentration (114, 169)]. Johnson and Richardson (114) noted that the lymph-to-plasma concentration ratio for total protein fell from 0.77 to 0.107 as venous pressure rose from 0 to 25 mmHg. Similar changes have been reported by Granger et al. (79). Estimates of P_i for the intestine suggest it is normally slightly positive, in the range of 1–2 mmHg (78, 169); however, with small increments of ISF volume, ISF compliance rises from 0.4 to 4.0 ml/mmHg.

An increase in intestinal venous pressure may also lead to a profound increase in lymph flow. At a venous pressure of zero, lymph flow is small (0.04–0.08 $ml \cdot min^{-1} \cdot 100\ g^{-1}$) but increases 20-fold when venous pressure is raised to 30 mmHg (169). Granger et al. (77) have related lymph flow to the hydration of the interstitial matrix, and their data suggest that lymph flow rises steeply and linearly with ISF volumes exceeding 25 ml/100 g.

Steady-State Reabsorption of Fluid Into Vascular System

It was argued previously that where a capillary is finitely permeable to plasma proteins, steady-state reabsorption of fluid cannot be maintained by the Starling mechanism alone (see *Coupling of Fluid Filtration to Solute Permeability*, p. 381). Ultimately protein accumulates outside the capillary and diminishes the gradient of osmotic pressure, on which fluid absorption depends, until it is less than the opposing gradient of hydrostatic pressure. This conclusion may appear to be inconsistent with the fact that continuous reabsorption of fluid into the blood occurs in the capillaries of the intestinal mucosa and renal tubules. In both cases, however, the vessels absorb a protein-free secretion produced by the neighboring epithelium, and presumably the diversion of a fraction of this secretion into the lymphatics prevents the concentration of plasma proteins in the pericapillary spaces from rising.

Recent studies on fluid absorption from the small intestine are consistent with this picture. Fluid absorption from the intestinal lumen into the blood appears to depend on the correct adjustment of the

Starling forces at the capillary wall. If the Starling forces are set to favor filtration, absorption of fluid into the blood will cease; if the mucosal interstitium is sufficiently expanded, however, fluid is filtered from the plasma into the intestinal lumen, a condition that is referred to as "filtration secretion" (91, 169, 254). In the cat ileum preparation, lymph flow increases during fluid absorption (77, 78); once absorption rates exceed 0.15 $ml \cdot min^{-1} \cdot 100\ g^{-1}$, the relationship is linear, with lymph flow accounting for ~20% of the fluid absorbed. Granger et al. (78) argue that the rise in lymph flow and the associated fall in lymph protein concentration reflect a greater fall of Π_{ISF} than Π_L owing to 'exclusion amplification' in the interstitial space. Increased reabsorption of fluid by the epithelium expands the intestinal interstitium, and Granger et al. (77) believe that this interstitial hydration ultimately determines intestinal lymph flow; they have shown that lymph flow increases linearly with interstitial volume. In the rat there is also a linear relationship between the volume absorption rate and intestinal lymph flow (136, 137). Micropuncture studies by Lee (136) reveal a linear relationship between the pressure within the lymphatics at the base of a villus and the lymph flow; Lee (137) also suggests that pressure within the lymphatics is probably equivalent to P_i.

From these studies it appears that net fluid absorption from the intestinal lumen to the blood is accompanied by a proportional flow of lymph. If the earlier arguments are correct, the diversion of some of the protein-free secretion into the lymph is essential for maintaining low values of Π_i and therefore the continuous absorption of fluid directly into the blood. The story is not completely clear, however. Granger et al. (78) pointed out that for any given ISF volume, lymph flow is lower during volume absorption than it is during capillary filtration. Furthermore when lymph flow is increased above control values, either by raising P_c or by the reabsorption of fluid from the intestinal lumen, the fall in protein concentration and osmotic pressure of the intestinal lymph is always less during fluid absorption at any given lymph flow. This means that protein flux through the capillary walls into the lymph is increased during fluid absorption (81), a conclusion reached from different evidence by Barrowman (8), who noted that the increase is particularly obvious during absorption of fats.

If the continuous absorption of fluid into the capillaries of the intestinal mucosa seems to be more complicated than first imagined, it nevertheless appears to conform to the general principles deduced from Starling's hypothesis. The same cannot be said so confidently about the reabsorption of fluid into the peritubular capillaries and vasa recta of the kidney. Although it is generally agreed that the Starling forces are responsible for fluid absorption into the renal vasculature, the accumulation of plasma protein within the renal interstitium and its clearance by the renal lymphatics are poorly understood. The geometric complexity of the renal microcirculation, the envelopment of the kidney in a rigid capsule, and the apparent absence of lymphatics in the medulla deter one from generalizing on the possible relationships between the total reabsorption of fluid and renal lymph flow. Renal lymph flow is comparable to urine flow and thus represents <1% of the fluid reabsorbed from the tubules back into the blood. The renal lymph protein concentration appears to lie between 20% and 40% of the plasma concentration (13, 97, 153), and thus capillary permeability to protein apparently is very low indeed. Bell et al. (12) also reached this conclusion using quite different evidence.

Is Capillary Pressure Regulated?

The hypothesis that P_c is regulated arises from two different types of observation. Zweifach (258, 259) made a large number of direct measurements of P_c in the omentum and mesentery and found that P_c remained constant in a certain number of capillaries despite wide variations in arterial pressure.

Johnson and Hanson (111) used the isogravimetric technique to examine the effects of varying arterial pressure on P_c in the isolated dog intestine. They found that on some occasions a fall in arterial pressure did not alter the isogravimetric state; some mechanism apparently maintained P_c. This observation was consistent with reports from Folkow, Mellander, and their colleagues (58, 60, 146, 158) and was examined more closely by Järhult and Mellander (109) in the lower leg muscles of the cat. Step decreases of local arterial pressure from 170 to 30 mmHg led to little or no change of tissue volume or of the calculated value of P_c, and CFC was found to vary inversely with arterial pressure.

Gore (70) has criticized the view that P_c is regulated. Alone and in conjunction with Bohlen (73), Gore studied flow and P_c in the microcirculation of the cat mesentery. As arterial pressure was lowered, the pattern of flow through different vessels altered and P_c remained constant in some vessels. Although this confirmed Zweifach's observations (258, 259), Gore argued that it is flow and not P_c that is regulated. He suggested that it is as a consequence of flow regulation that P_c remains almost constant in some vessels, despite large fluctuations in arterial pressure.

Gore's view makes good sense when one is considering only the response to changes in arterial pressure, but when venous pressure is raised at constant arterial pressure, R_{pre}/R_{post} has been shown to increase in the isolated perfused intestine (58, 111), isolated perfused cat muscle (159), and human hands and feet (103, 142). In these cases the local response cannot be construed as a mechanism for regulating blood flow. Indeed blood flow is reduced by the rise in venous pressure and further reduced by the increased resistance. The increase of R_{pre}/R_{post} could be seen as a mechanism for regulating P_c, however, or at least for minimizing the effects of increments of venous pressure on P_c. The contribution of increased R_{pre}/R_{post} in minimizing the rise of P_c in the human foot during quiet standing is small but not trivial. For movements of the hands below the level of the heart (and in other dependent regions), changes of R_{pre}/R_{post} may be relatively more important in minimizing changes of P_c.

PROPERTIES OF CHANNELS CONDUCTING FLUID THROUGH CAPILLARY WALLS

Ever since capillary blood vessels were recognized to have walls, the simplest model of capillary permeability was an impermeable membrane penetrated by water-filled pores. The ability of most capillary walls to filter serum proteins but allow rapid equilibration of small hydrophilic solutes suggested that the pores had diameters comparable to the dimensions of the serum albumin molecule. Although Krogh (119) attempted to estimate the size of the pores from the passage of dyes, starch, and ink particles through capillary walls in the frog hindlimb, and Landis (123) considered that fluid flow through the pores might obey Poiseuille's law, the theory was only qualitative until 1951. Pappenheimer and his colleagues (185) then expressed the pore theory in a rigorous quantitative manner, and in this way it has continually been modified and developed (see the chapter by Curry in this *Handbook*, and refs. 2, 10, 32, 36, 144, 145, and 148).

In 1953, just as the pore theory came of age, Palade (181) made the first electron micrographs of capillary walls. Although the size of the postulated pores was well within the resolution of the electron microscope, they were not identified. Indeed not until Karnovsky (115) showed that horseradish peroxidase (used as a protein tracer in electron microscopy) appeared to penetrate the junctions between endothelial cells in mouse heart capillaries did morphological evidence exist for a channel equivalent to the Pappenheimer pore or slit. The importance of the intercellular junction as a channel in normal continuous capillaries was upheld by some (252, 253) and disputed by others (222). Simionescu, Simionescu, and Palade (223) provided evidence that channels passing through endothelial cells are formed by the fusion of vesicles, and they suggest that these structures are the morphological equivalent of the Pappenheimer pores in true continuous capillaries [though intercellular junctions may make a contribution in venules (182, 224)]. In fenestrated capillaries the fenestrations are almost certainly regions of high L_p, but physiological experiments suggest that they are able to retain serum proteins even though the delicate diaphragms covering them may not always be seen by electron microscopists (105).

Although the morphological identification of channels through the endothelium remains controversial (see the chapter by Simionescu and Simionescu in this *Handbook*), physiological measurements have continued to yield information about the properties of the fluid-conducting pathways. The remainder of this chapter is concerned with the biophysical properties of these channels and with their interpretation in terms of a quantitative model of capillary permeability.

Filtration Rates and Filtration Coefficients in Single Vessels

In recent years studies on frog single mesenteric capillaries have confirmed and extended traditional views of fluid movement through the capillary wall (e.g., ref. 165). Because these vessels are morphologically very similar to continuous mammalian capillaries (19, 23, 149, 157), it is reasonable to suggest that the fluid-conducting channels are also similar.

Figure 12 shows the results of an experiment where a single vessel was perfused first with Ringer's solution containing 8.0 g serum albumin/100 ml and then with Ringer's solution containing 2.0 g serum albumin/100 ml. Three deductions about the fluid-conducting channels can be made from these data. *1*) The linearity of the relationship between J_v/A and P_c indicates that conducting properties of the channels are not affected by a wide range of values of P_c, i.e., the pores are not stretched at high P_c. *2*) Whether fluid is moving into the vessel during reabsorption or out of the vessel during filtration, L_p has the same value. Thus there is no rectification of fluid movement in the channels. *3*) Changing the serum albumin concentration of the perfusate changes the position but not the slope of the relationship between J_v/A and P_c. If this shift is represented as a difference in P_c at constant J_v/A, it

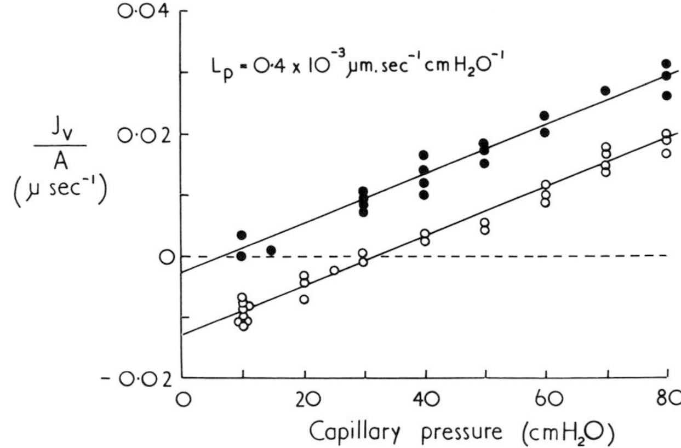

FIG. 12. Relationship between the filtration and reabsorption of fluid per unit area of capillary wall (J_v/A) and capillary pressure in single frog mesenteric capillary. Capillary was perfused first with Ringer's solution containing ~8.0 g of bovine serum albumin/100 ml (○), and then with Ringer's solution containing 2.5 g bovine serum albumin/100 ml (●). [From Michel (165).]

is equal to 75% of the difference in Π_c between the two perfusates. Because there was probably some serum albumin in the pericapillary space when these measurements were made, σ for albumin at this capillary wall was probably >0.75. Thus serum albumin was largely excluded from the fluid-conducting channels.

Insight into the nature of fluid flow within the channels comes from measurements of L_p in the same vessel at two different temperatures. This experiment was performed by Curry (34) and Michel (164). Both found that slow changes of tissue temperature in frog mesenteric capillaries over the range of 2°C–27°C gave rise to changes in L_p that were inversely proportional to the changes in the viscosity (η) of water with temperature. Their data are summarized in Figure 13, which shows that the product of $L_p\eta$ is not altered significantly by changes in temperature. In 1953 Pappenheimer (183) reported the same result from experiments he conducted with Renkin and Eversole on the isolated perfused limb (see also ref. 183a). They concluded that fluid flow through capillary walls is viscous, implying that the channels conducting fluid are wide enough to accommodate several water molecules side by side (165). Such water-filled channels should be available to small hydrophilic solutes, which, on entering them, would increase the local viscosity; this prediction receives some support from the observations of Vargas and Johnson (240).

Evidence that water shares some of its channels with small hydrophilic molecules comes from an examination of the variations in permeability among different vessels in the frog mesentery. It was noted earlier that there is a similar variation of L_p and of K^+ permeability between different frog mesenteric vessels. Curry (33) measured L_p and permeability to sucrose and NaCl in the same vessel and found a good correlation between L_p and solute permeability (Fig. 14). If the relationship between solute permeability and L_p is as linear as it appears to be in Figure 14, and if flow through the fluid-conducting channels is viscous, the local variations in permeability and L_p appear to be the result of variations in the number of channels or pores per unit area of capillary wall rather than variations in their size. Michel (164) reached this conclusion more directly by measuring L_p and σ for albumin and myoglobin in capillaries from different sites in the frog mesentery. Taking care to avoid vessels that showed signs of inflammation, Michel (164) found variations of L_p over an order of magnitude without any accompanying trend in values of σ for albumin (Fig. 15). In this study (164) he confirmed

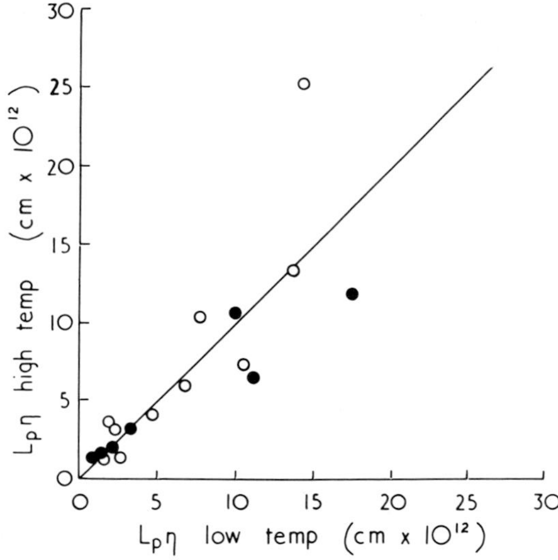

FIG. 13. Product of hydraulic conductivity and viscosity of water ($L_p\eta$) at high temperature plotted against its value for same capillary at low temperature. *Line* through *points* is line of identity indicating that variations of L_p with temperature resulted from variations of η. ●, Data of Michel (164); ○, data of Curry (34). [From Michel (165).]

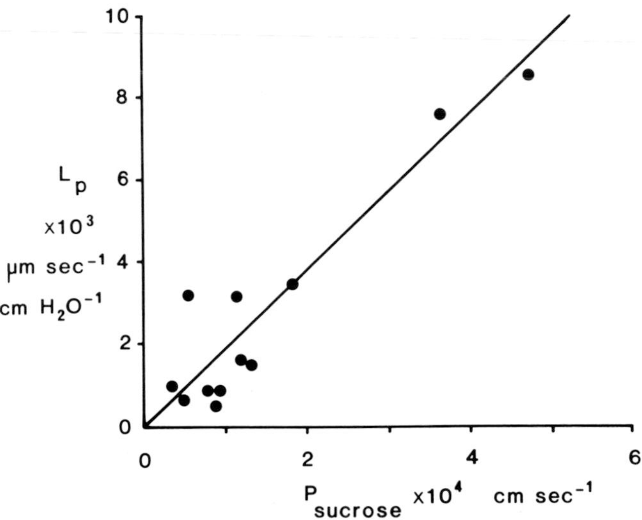

FIG. 14. Relationship between variations in hydraulic conductivity (L_p) and variations in permeability to sucrose ($P_{sucrose}$) in single capillaries of frog mesentery. [Data from Curry (33).]

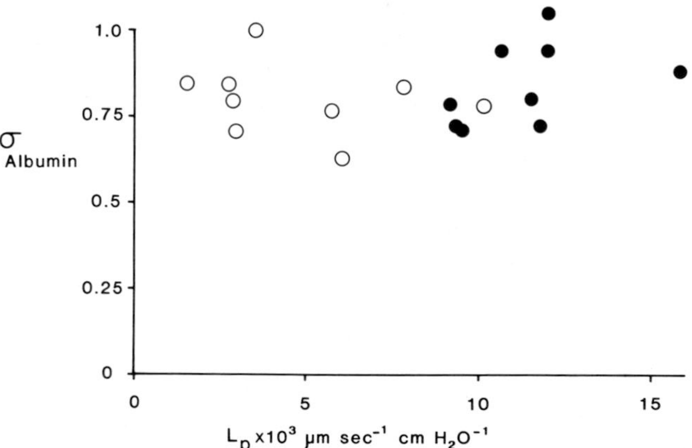

FIG. 15. Relationship between variations in osmotic reflection coefficient (σ) for bovine serum albumin and variations in hydraulic conductivity (L_p) in single frog mesentery capillaries. Each *point* represents a different vessel. ○, Arterial and midcapillaries; ●, venous capillaries. [From Michel (164).]

that L_p is, on the average, two or more times greater at the venous end of the capillary bed than it is at the arterial end (247, 260). Apparently, however, the well-known arteriovenous gradient of permeability (211) is not due to the presence of large leaks or pores at the venous end of the capillary bed (130, 170) but is instead the result of the greater frequency of channels or small pores responsible for normal permeability (139). In addition, Crone and Christensen (30) recently reported a gradient of electrical conductivity for the walls of frog mesenteric vessels similar to the gradient of L_p.

Thus it seems that most of the fluid-conducting channels responsible for L_p are shared by water and small hydrophilic solutes. There is evidence, however, that a small fraction of the channels are available exclusively to water.

Evidence for an Exclusive Water Channel

From measurements of the diffusion of Na^+ and tritium out of capillaries in the dog heart, Yudilevich and Alvarez (257) concluded that the area of capillary wall through which water could exchange must be at least twice the area available to Na^+. They suggested that the additional area available to water might be through the plasmalemmal membranes of the endothelial cells, membranes that they believed might have a low permeability to Na^+. They appreciated that their conclusion was relevant to the interpretation of the reflection coefficient of the capillary wall for small molecules; this point was taken up by Pappenheimer (184) and then developed by Lifson (147) and Tosteson (239) in terms of the parallel-pathway model (67, 117).

Support for an aqueous diffusion pathway in addition to that available to hydrophilic molecules was provided by Stray-Pedersen and Steen (233a) in studies on the rete mirabile of the eel, but the contribution of this exclusive pathway to net fluid movement remained unclear. Although several studies have demonstrated that perfusion of the lungs with a hypertonic solution extracts water from the tissues (48, 193), it is not clear whether the water entered the vascular system itself or merely entered the extracellular fluid by a route unavailable to small solutes.

Less equivocal evidence for an exclusive water channel was provided by Curry, Mason, and Michel (35) working on frog single mesenteric capillaries. In these experiments the mesentery was washed with Ringer's solution made hypertonic by the addition of a known concentration of a small hydrophilic solute. A single capillary in the mesentery was perfused with Ringer's solution of normal osmolarity; when a steady state was established, transient osmotic flows of fluid through the wall of the perfused capillary were estimated during brief microocclusions. Because the tissues of the mesentery were soaked in a relatively large volume of hypertonic solution for many minutes prior to microocclusion, the flow of water out of the perfused capillary was not complicated by major shifts in fluid between the intracellular and extracellular compartments of the tissue. Thus the osmotic flow could be interpreted to result from the transcapillary osmotic pressure difference and could be used to calculate σ for the test solute at the capillary wall. For NaCl, urea, sucrose, and cyanocobalamin, Curry et al. (35) found that σ was ~0.1. Their data, supplemented by more recent data, are shown in Figure 16, where the values of σ for the different solutes are plotted against their molecular size. If one extrapolates the line to the value for a solute of the same size as a water molecule, one obtains a value of 0.08. In a channel shared by water and hydrophilic molecules, where selectivity is determined by molecular size, σ for a molecule the size of water should be zero. From this reasoning, Curry et al. (35) concluded that there were channels in the capillary wall available exclusively to water and unavailable to small solute molecules. The L_p of this pathway has been estimated to lie between 0.1×10^{-3} $\mu m \cdot s^{-1} \cdot cmH_2O^{-1}$ and 0.3×10^{-3} $\mu m \cdot s^{-1} \cdot cmH_2O^{-1}$ (33, 35, 164), and it appears to contribute <10% to the overall L_p of the average frog mesenteric capillary.

Although the exclusive water channel has been regarded as a transcellular route for water (29, 35, 203), Michel (165) pointed out that if this is so, endothelial cell membranes must be among the most permeable of cell membranes to water. Curry et al. (35) suggested that the exclusive water channel might represent the tight regions of the intercellular junctions, and in this context the renal proximal tubular epithelium of the rat appears to combine a relatively high L_p of 2.8×10^{-3} $\mu m \cdot s^{-1} \cdot cmH_2O^{-1}$ with a high value of σ for NaCl (3).

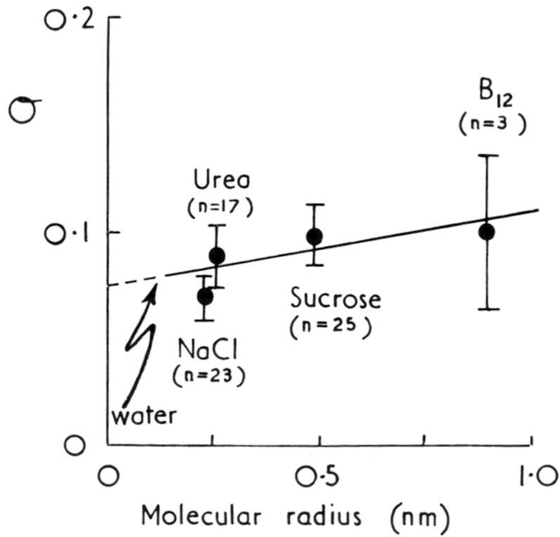

FIG. 16. Relationship between osmotic reflection coefficient (σ) and molecular radius of small hydrophilic molecules at walls of single frog mesenteric capillaries. [From Michel (165).]

Effects of Macromolecules on Hydraulic Conductivity

In addition to being responsible for the effective osmotic pressure across capillary walls, plasma proteins also appear to have a major effect on capillary permeability. Drinker (46) first provided evidence for such an effect on permeability. Following up work by Ellinger and Heymann (50) and Krogh and Harrop (120), Drinker showed that the effective osmotic pressure of a perfusate containing gum acacia was greatly increased across the capillary walls of the perfused hindfoot of the frog by the addition of low concentrations of serum. The increment of effective osmotic pressure greatly exceeded the increment of total osmotic pressure resulting from the added plasma protein, and Drinker concluded that the proteins were adsorbed onto the capillary wall, thereby reducing its permeability. Danielli (38) confirmed and considerably extended these findings, and the idea that capillary permeability was determined by a layer of adsorbed plasma protein was incorporated into the intercellular-cement theory of Chambers and Zweifach (21). Electron microscopy of the capillary wall did not provide much support for the intercellular-cement theory (56), and interest in the possible role of adsorbed protein modifying permeability was temporarily put aside.

Physiological evidence, however, continued to accumulate. Kinter and Pappenheimer (118) showed that low concentrations of serum proteins more than doubled the effective osmotic pressures of dextran perfusates in the isolated cat hindlimb. Furthermore the CFC values of cat or rat hindlimbs were more than doubled when they were perfused with protein-free solutions (118, 201), an effect that could be reversed by the addition of more than 0.2% plasma protein to the perfusate. These observations were recently confirmed in three different laboratories (40, 208, 243).

Extensive investigations of the effects of proteins on permeability have been carried out on single capillaries (140, 156, 168). Mason, Curry, and Michel (156) showed that the L_p of single frog mesenteric capillaries was 4–5 times greater when vessels were perfused with protein-free solutions than when the same vessels were perfused with frog plasma or bovine serum albumin. Bovine serum albumin at concentrations as low as 0.1 g/100 ml was able to prevent the increase in L_p accompanying perfusion with Ringer's solution. The effect appeared to be unrelated to an interaction with Ca^{2+} (156) and was not accompanied by conspicuous changes in capillary ultrastructure (157).

The suggestion that dextrans and Ficoll 70 (a polymer of sucrose and epichlorohydrin, M_r 70,000) might be as effective as plasma proteins in preventing the increase in L_p of capillaries perfused with Ringer's solution (66) appears to have been clarified in a series of recent reports (40, 168a, 168b, 195). In frog single mesenteric capillaries, addition of Ficoll 70 at a concentration of 4.0 g/100 ml to a Ringer's perfusate reduces L_p to ~50% of its value for the same vessel perfused with Ringer's solution alone. Although the addition of bovine serum albumin at a concentration as low as 0.1 g/100 ml will halve the L_p yet again (and more than double the effective osmotic pressure of the perfusate), Ficoll 70 alone, at a concentration of 4.0 g/100 ml, does reduce L_p. In contrast with bovine serum albumin, which exerts a maximum effect on L_p at perfusate concentrations of 0.1 g/100 ml, Ficoll 70 has to be present in the perfusate at a concentration >1.0 g/100 ml before it has any effect on L_p. At higher perfusate concentrations of Ficoll 70, L_p falls with the reciprocal of the concentration of Ficoll 70 (provided no albumin or serum is present), and extrapolation of the relationship suggests that at an infinite concentration of Ficoll 70, L_p is reduced to approximately the level that would exist in the same vessel in the presence of 0.1% serum albumin (168a). Diana and his colleagues (40) reported a reciprocal relationship between CFC of the isolated perfused hindlimb preparation and the dextran concentration in a protein-free perfusate. In addition, L_p appears to vary reciprocally with protein concentration in single vessels perfused with Ringer's solutions containing myoglobin and hemoglobin (195).

Because serum albumin and perhaps certain other plasma proteins exert maximum effects on L_p at low concentrations, it is reasonable to suggest that these molecules bind reversibly to sites on the capillary wall. Once the sites are saturated, permeability is reduced to the extent that unbound molecules of serum albumin are almost entirely excluded from the fluid-conducting channels. According to this hypothesis, molecules such as Ficoll 70, dextran, hemoglobin, and myoglobin do not bind to the capillary wall; in the absence of serum albumin, they can reduce L_p by entering the porous regions, increasing its local viscosity or plugging the channels to an extent determined by their molecular size and concentration.

Recent work from my laboratory is consistent with this view of the effects on L_p of macromolecules that bind and do not bind to the capillary wall. Electron micrographs suggest that native ferritin does not bind to the surface layers of endothelial cells, and when perfused through frog single mesenteric capillaries, native ferritin has a small concentration-dependent effect on L_p. Cationized ferritin, by contrast, does bind to the surface coat of endothelial cells, and at perfusate concentrations of 0.1 g/100 ml and greater, it reduces L_p to <50% of its value for the same vessel perfused with Ringer's solution alone (24, 239a). The effects of cationized ferritin on L_p are not increased by raising the perfusate concentration above 0.1 g/100 ml, and electron micrographs suggest that cationized ferritin reaches a maximum concentration in the surface layer of endothelial cells at this concentration.

These experiments with cationized and native ferritin are interesting in at least two respects: not only do they show the different effects on L_p of molecules that bind to the capillary wall and molecules that do not, but they also indicate that the binding of molecules to the surface coat of endothelial cells is sufficient to reduce L_p and to increase the selectivity of the capillary wall as a molecular filter. Thus capillary permeability may be determined as much by the properties and composition of the endothelial surface coat as by the dimensions of the channels that penetrate the endothelium.

As yet no one has proved that serum albumin reduces permeability in the same way as cationized ferritin, but the effects of plasma proteins on permeability are great. Under normal circumstances the circulating plasma protein concentrations are sufficient for these molecules to have maximum effects on permeability. Because these effects largely determine the selectivity of the capillary wall to macromolecules and account for 60%–80% of its L_p, the interaction of plasma proteins with the capillary wall must be built into any comprehensive model of the structures responsible for capillary permeability.

Deductions Concerning Nature of Fluid-Conducting Pathways

From the evidence just presented it is possible to build a quantitative picture of the fluid-conducting channels.

The constancy of L_p over a wide range of P_c and its independence of the direction of fluid flow through the capillary wall suggest that the fluid-conducting channels are relatively stable structures. Furthermore there appear to be two types of channel: one exclusively available to water, the other shared by water and hydrophilic solutes. If the total hydraulic conductivity of the capillary wall is $\bar{L}_p$ and if it receives contributions $L_{p,e}$ and $L_{p,p}$ from the exclusive water channels and the shared channels, respectively, then

$$\bar{L}_p = L_{p,e} + L_{p,p} \tag{22}$$

In frog mesenteric capillaries $L_{p,p}/\bar{L}_p$ is nearly always >0.9, and this is consistent with the finding that $\bar{L}_p$ varies linearly with permeability to small hydrophilic solutes and inversely with viscosity. If A_p is the fraction of the surface area of capillary wall permeable to both water and hydrophilic solutes, and Δx is the length of the channels (thickness of porous regions)

$$L_{p,p} = \frac{A_p}{\Delta x} \cdot \frac{K}{\eta} \tag{23}$$

where K is a constant. Pappenheimer (183) pointed out that expressions such as Equation 23 are equivalent to those derived from Darcy's law that hydraulic engineers use to describe flow through porous media. Pappenheimer and his colleagues (185) and Renkin (200) interpreted K in terms of Poiseuille flow through regular cylindrical pores or rectangular slits, but other interpretations are possible (36, 194).

Engineers use the Carman-Kozeny equation to describe flow through media packed with obstacles of approximately regular shape and size (e.g., grains of sand). This expression represents the dimensions of the channels around and between the obstacles in terms of the mean hydraulic radius, where $\bar{r}_H$ is defined as the fraction of water in the total volume of the porous regions of the medium (ϵ) divided by the surface area (S) on all the obstacles in unit volume wetted by the water: i.e., $\bar{r}_H = \epsilon/S$. Thus in terms of the Carman-Kozeny equation the hydraulic conductivity can be represented as

$$L_{p,p} = \frac{A_p}{\Delta x} \cdot \frac{1}{k_o}\frac{\epsilon}{\eta} \cdot \bar{r}_H^2 = \frac{A_p}{\Delta x} \cdot \frac{1}{k_o} \cdot \frac{\epsilon^3}{\eta S^2} \tag{24}$$

where k_o is a constant determined by the geometry of the channels between the obstacles and thus by the shape of obstacles. With cylindrical or spherical obstacles, k_o has an empirical value of 4.5 (234).

Because native ferritin appears to be excluded from the luminal surface and luminal vesicles of the endothelium (23, 149), Michel (161–164) suggested that the molecular selectivity of the capillary wall was determined by a network of fibrous molecules that cover the endothelial cells and fill the channels running between and through them. According to this model the number and the size of the channels through the endothelium determine A_p, the area of porous regions per unit area of capillary wall, but the filtering properties of channels are determined by the tightness of the network or matrix. Thus the differences in L_p and permeability to small hydrophilic solutes among individual vessels in the frog mesentery represent variation in A_p, whereas the constancy of σ for albumin represents the constant filtering properties of the network. Curry and Michel (36) considered the network as a random arrangement of cylindrical fibrous molecules and wrote expressions for L_p, σ, and solute permeability. Thus from the Carman-Kozeny equation the expression for $L_{p,p}$ is

$$L_{p,p} = \frac{A_p}{\Delta x} \cdot \frac{r_f^2}{18\eta} \cdot \frac{\epsilon^3}{(1-\epsilon)^2} \tag{25}$$

where r_f is the radius of the fibrous molecules of the network.

Although Curry and Michel (36) used their expressions to successfully account for permeability data on single vessels, their model does not directly identify that component of the permeability determined by the interaction of the plasma proteins with the capillary wall. If the plasma proteins are believed to be adsorbed onto the surface coat of endothelial cells in the same way as cationized ferritin is adsorbed, then filtration occurs through a network of fibrous chains and globular molecules. Regarding the glycoprotein chains as cylinders and the globular proteins as spheres, the

Carman-Kozeny equation for the L_p of the porous regions becomes

$$L_{p,p} = \frac{A_p}{\Delta x} \cdot \frac{2}{9\eta} \frac{(1\text{-}V_f - V_s)^3}{\left(\dfrac{2V_f}{r_f} + \dfrac{3V_s}{r_s}\right)^2} \qquad (26)$$

where V_f and V_s are the volumes of fibrous and spherical molecules, respectively, per unit volume of the porous regions, and r_f and r_s are the radii of the fibrous and spherical molecules (239a). Taking $r_f = 0.6$ nm and assuming that $V_f = 0.02$, Equation 26 accounts for the effects of cationized ferritin on L_p. To account for the maximum effect of serum albumin on L_p, Equation 26 requires that serum albumin occupy between 5% and 10% of the volume of the porous regions in the capillary wall.

This protein-matrix theory has potential subtleties. Attention has been drawn to the importance of the ordering of obstacles in a matrix in determining its ability to exclude macromolecules (165). If the obstacles are spaced regularly, they exclude macromolecules from the matrix much more effectively than if they are randomly arranged. If the matrix changes from a regular to a more random arrangement (e.g., an abnormal protein might cause clumping of the matrix component), then permeability to macromolecules may increase without much change in either L_p or permeability to small molecules. Although speculative, the matrix theory, like the pore theory, makes quantitative predictions; because it is more closely related to known structures in the capillary wall than is the pore theory, however, the protein-matrix model should be more easily improved or disproved by further experimentation.

REFERENCES

1. ÅBLAD, B., AND S. MELLANDER. Comparative effects of hydralazine, sodium nitrite and acetylcholine on resistance and capacitance blood vessels and capillary filtration in skeletal muscle in the cat. *Acta Physiol. Scand.* 58: 319–329, 1963.
2. ANDERSON, J. L., AND D. M. MALONE. Mechanism of osmotic flow in porous membranes. *Biophys. J.* 14: 957–982, 1974.
3. ANDREOLI, T. E., AND J. A. SCHAFER. External solution osmotic disequilibrium: the driving force for proximal tubular volume absorption. In: *Water Transport Across Epithelia: Barriers, Gradients, and Mechanisms*, edited by H. H. Ussing, N. B. Bindslev, N. A. Lassen, and O. Sten-Knudsen. Copenhagen: Munksgaard, 1981, p. 332–345. (Alfred Benzon Symp. 15.)
4. ARTURSON, G., AND I. KJELLMER. Capillary permeability in skeletal muscle during rest and activity. *Acta Physiol. Scand.* 62: 41–45, 1964.
5. AUKLAND, K., AND G. NICOLAYSEN. Interstitial fluid volume: local regulatory mechanisms. *Physiol. Rev.* 61: 556–643, 1981.
6. BARCROFT, H. Review lecture. Bayliss-Starling Memorial Lecture 1976. Lymph formation by secretion or filtration? *J. Physiol. London* 260: 1–20, 1976.
7. BARNES, J. M., AND J. TRUETA. Absorption of bacteria, toxins and snake venoms from the tissues. Importance of the lymphatic circulation. *Lancet* 1: 623–626, 1941.
8. BARROWMAN, J. A. *Physiology of the Gastro-intestinal Lymphatic System.* Cambridge, UK: Cambridge Univ. Press, 1978, p. 176–180. (Physiol. Soc. Monog. 33.)
9. BAYLISS, W. M., AND E. H. STARLING. Observations on venous pressures and their relationships to capillary pressures. *J. Physiol. London* 16: 159–202, 1894.
10. BEAN, C. P. The physics of porous membranes—neutral pores. In: *Membranes*, edited by G. Eisenman. New York: Dekker, 1972, vol. 1, p. 1–54.
11. BEH, K. J., D. L. WATSON, AND A. K. LASCELLES. Concentrations of immunoglobulins and albumin in lymph collected from various regions of the body of the sheep. *Aust. J. Exp. Biol. Med. Sci.* 52: 81–86, 1974.
12. BELL, D. R., G. G. PINTER, AND P. D. WILSON. Albumin permeability of the peritubular capillaries in the rat renal cortex. *J. Physiol. London* 279: 621–640, 1978.
13. BELL, R. D., R. J. SINCLAIR, AND W. L. PARRY. Influence of renal fluid dynamics on renal lymph pressure, flow and composition. *Lymphology* 3: 143–148, 1974.
14. BLAKE, T. R., AND J. F. GROSS. Fluid exchange from a microoccluded capillary with axial variation of filtration parameters. *Biorheology* 13: 357–366, 1976.
15. BLAKE, T. R., AND G. P. SCHNEYER. On the occluded capillary. *Microvasc. Res.* 7: 362–375, 1974.
16. BRACE, R. A., AND A. C. GUYTON. Interaction of transcapillary Starling forces in the isolated dog forelimb. *Am. J. Physiol.* 233 (*Heart Circ. Physiol.* 2): H136–H140, 1977.
17. BRESLER, E. H., E. A. MASON, AND R. P. WENDT. Appraisal of equations for neutral solute flux across porous sieving membranes. *Biophys. Chem.* 24: 229–236, 1976.
18. BROWN, E., AND E. M. LANDIS. Effect of local cooling on fluid movement, effective osmotic pressure and capillary permeability in the frog's mesentery. *Am. J. Physiol.* 149: 302–315, 1947.
19. BUNDGAARD, M., AND J. FRØKJAER-JENSEN. Functional aspects of the ultrastructure of terminal blood vessels: a quantitative study on consecutive segments of the frog mesenteric microvasculature. *Microvasc. Res.* 23: 1–30, 1982.
20. CASSASSA, E. F., AND H. EISENBERG. On the definition of components in solutions containing charged macromolecular species. *J. Phys. Chem.* 64: 753–756, 1960.
21. CHAMBERS, R., AND B. W. ZWEIFACH. Intercellular cement and capillary permeability. *Physiol. Rev.* 27: 436–463, 1947.
22. CHEN, H. I., H. J. GRANGER, AND A. E. TAYLOR. Interaction of capillary, interstitial and lymphatic forces in the canine hind paw. *Circ. Res.* 39: 245–254, 1976.
23. CLOUGH, G., AND C. C. MICHEL. The role of vesicles in the transport of ferritin through frog endothelium. *J. Physiol. London* 315: 127–142, 1981.
24. CLOUGH, G., C. C. MICHEL, M. E. PHILLIPS, AND M. R. TURNER. Cationized ferritin reduces the permeability of frog capillaries: native ferritin does not (Abstract). *J. Physiol. London* 320: 41P–42P, 1981.
25. CLOUGH, G., AND L. H. SMAJE. Changes in capillary permeability in scurvy (Abstract). *Biorheology* 14: 203, 1977.
26. COBBOLD, A., B. FOLKOW, I. KJELLMER, AND S. MELLANDER. Nervous and local chemical control of pre-capillary sphincters in skeletal muscle as measured by changes in filtration coefficient. *Acta Physiol. Scand.* 57: 180–192, 1963.
27. COHNHEIM, J. The pathology of the circulation [transl. from German]. In: *Lectures on General Pathology: A Handbook for Practitioners and Students*, edited by A. B. McKee. London: New Sydenham Soc., 1889.
28. CREESE, R., J. L. D'SILVA, AND D. M. SHAW. Interfibre fluid from guinea-pig muscle. *J. Physiol. London* 162: 44–53, 1962.
29. CRONE, C., AND O. CHRISTENSEN. Transcapillary transport

of small solutes and water. In: *Cardiovascular Physiology III*, edited by A. C. Guyton and D. B. Young. Baltimore, MD: University Park, 1979, vol. 18, p. 149–213. (Int. Rev. Physiol. Ser.)

30. CRONE, C., AND O. CHRISTENSEN. Electrical resistance of a capillary endothelium. *J. Gen. Physiol.* 77: 349–371, 1981.
31. CRONE, C., J. FRØKJOER-JENSEN, J. J. FRIEDMAN, AND O. CHRISTENSEN. The permeability of single capillaries to potassium ions. *J. Gen. Physiol.* 71: 195–220, 1978.
32. CURRY, F. E. A hydrodynamic description of the osmotic reflection coefficient with application to the pore theory of transcapillary exchange. *Microvasc. Res.* 8: 236–252, 1974.
33. CURRY, F. E. Permeability coefficients of the capillary wall to low molecular weight hydrophilic solutes measured in single perfused capillaries of frog mesentery. *Microvasc. Res.* 17: 290–308, 1979.
34. CURRY, F. E. Effect of temperature on hydraulic conductivity of single capillaries. *Am. J. Physiol.* 240 (*Heart. Circ. Physiol.* 9): H29–H32, 1981.
35. CURRY, F. E., J. C. MASON, AND C. C. MICHEL. Osmotic reflexion coefficients of capillary walls to low molecular weight hydrophilic solutes measured in single perfused capillaries of the frog mesentery. *J. Physiol. London* 261: 319–336, 1976.
36. CURRY, F. E., AND C. C. MICHEL. A fibre matrix model of capillary permeability. *Microvasc. Res.* 20: 96–99, 1980.
37. DALY, I. DE B., AND C. HEBB. *Pulmonary and Bronchial Vascular Systems.* London: Arnold, 1966, p. 130–133.
38. DANIELLI, J. F. Capillary permeability and oedema in the perfused frog. *J. Physiol. London* 98: 109–129, 1940.
39. DIANA, J. N., AND B. P. FLEMING. Some current problems in microvascular research. *Microvasc. Res.* 18: 144–152, 1979.
40. DIANA, J. N., B. J. KEITH, AND B. P. FLEMING. Influence of macromolecules on capillary filtration coefficients in isolated dog hindlimbs (Abstract). *Microvasc. Res.* 20: 106–107, 1980.
41. DIANA, J. N., S. C. LONG, AND H. YAO. Effect of histamine on equivalent pore radius in capillaries of isolated dog hindlimb. *Microvasc. Res.* 4: 413–437, 1972.
42. DICK, D. A. T. *Cell Water.* London: Butterworths, 1966, p. 15–43.
43. DILL, D. B., AND D. L. COSTILL. Calculation of percentage changes in volumes of blood, plasma, and red cells in dehydration. *J. Appl. Physiol.* 37: 247–248, 1974.
44. DRAKE, R. E., A. MORRISS, AND J. GABEL. Effect of vascular distension on filtration characteristics studied using gravimetric techniques. *Microvasc. Res.* 16: 453–455, 1978.
45. DRAKE, R. E., J. H. SMITH, AND J. C. GABEL. Estimation of the filtration coefficient in intact dog lungs. *Am. J. Physiol.* 238 (*Heart Circ. Physiol.* 7): H430–H438, 1980.
46. DRINKER, C. K. The permeability and diameter of the capillaries in the web of the brown frog (*Rana temporaria*) when perfused with solutions containing pituitary extract and horse serum. *J. Physiol. London* 63: 249–269, 1927.
47. DRURY, A. N., AND N. W. JONES. Observations upon the rate at which oedema forms when the veins of the human limb are congested. *Heart* 14: 55–70, 1927.
48. EFFROS, R. M. Osmotic extraction of hypotonic fluid from the lung. *J. Clin. Invest.* 54: 935–947, 1974.
49. ELIASSEN, E., B. FOLKOW, S. M. HILTON, B. ÖBERG, AND B. RIPPE. Pressure-volume characteristics of the interstitial fluid space in the skeletal muscle of the cat. *Acta Physiol. Scand.* 90: 583–593, 1974.
50. ELLINGER, A., AND P. HEYMANN. Die treibenden Kräfte für den Flüssigkeitsstrom im Organismus. *Arch. Exp. Pathol. Pharmakol.* 90: 336–392, 1921.
51. ERDMANN, A. J., III, T. R. VAUGHAN, JR., K. L. BRIGHAM, W. C. WOOLVERTON, AND N. C. STAUB. Effect of increased vascular pressure on lung fluid balance in unanesthetized sheep. *Circ. Res.* 37: 271–284, 1975.
52. FADNES, H. O., AND H. NODDELAND. Cited by K. Aukland. In: *Tissue Fluid Pressure and Composition*, edited by A. R. Hargens. Baltimore, MD: Williams & Wilkins, 1981, p. 92.
53. FADNES, H. O., R. K. REED, AND K. AUKLAND. Interstitial fluid pressure in rats measured with a modified wick technique. *Microvasc. Res.* 14: 27–36, 1977.
54. FENSTERMACHER, J. D., AND J. A. JOHNSON. Filtration and reflection coefficients of the rabbit-blood brain barrier. *Am. J. Physiol.* 211: 341–346, 1966.
55. FISHMAN, A. P., AND G. G. PIETRA. Permeability of pulmonary vascular endothelium. In: *Lung Liquids*, edited by R. Porter and M. O'Connor. New York: Elsevier, 1976, p. 28–39. (Ciba Found. Symp. 38.)
56. FLOREY, H. W., J. C. F. POOLE, AND G. A. MEEK. Endothelial cells and cement lines. *J. Pathol. Bacteriol.* 77: 625–636, 1959.
57. FLORY, P. J. *Principles of Polymer Chemistry.* Ithaca, NY: Cornell Univ. Press, 1953.
58. FOLKOW, B., O. LUNDGREN, AND I. WALLENTIN. Studies on the relationship between flow resistance, capillary filtration coefficient and regional blood volume in the intestine of the cat. *Acta Physiol. Scand.* 57: 270–283, 1963.
59. FOLKOW, B., AND S. MELLANDER. Measurements of capillary filtration coefficient and its use in studies of the control of capillary exchange. In: *Capillary Permeability*, edited by C. Crone and N. A. Lassen. Copenhagen: Munksgaard, 1970, p. 614–623. (Alfred Benzon Symp. 2.)
60. FOLKOW, B., AND B. ÖBERG. Autoregulation and basal tone in consecutive vascular sections of skeletal muscle in reserpine treated cats. *Acta Physiol. Scand.* 53: 105–113, 1961.
61. FRAZER, P. A., L. H. SMAJE, AND A. VERRINDER. Microvascular pressures and filtration coefficients in the cat mesentery. *J. Physiol. London* 283: 439–456, 1978.
62. FRIEDMAN, J. J. A modified colloidal osmotic transducer for the determination of transcapillary fluid movement. *Microvasc. Res.* 5: 222–227, 1973.
63. FRIEDMAN, J. J. The influence of sympathetic adrenergic nerve stimulation on pre- and post-capillary resistance. *Microvasc. Res.* 6: 297–304, 1973.
64. GAAR, K. A., JR., A. E. TAYLOR, L. J. OWENS, AND A. C. GUYTON. Effect of capillary pressure and plasma proteins on the development of pulmonary edema. *Am. J. Physiol.* 213: 79–82, 1967.
65. GAAR, K. A., JR., A. E. TAYLOR, L. J. OWENS, AND A. C. GUYTON. Pulmonary capillary pressure and filtration coefficient in the isolated perfused lung. *Am. J. Physiol.* 213: 910–914, 1967.
66. GAMBLE, J. The effects of bovine albumin on the vascular permeability of the perfused rat mesentery (Abstract). *J. Physiol. London* 285: 15P–16P, 1978.
67. GARBY, L., AND S. AREEKUL. A method for estimation of the "leak" to "pore" number ratio in capillary membranes. In: *Capillary Permeability*, edited by C. Crone and N. A. Lassen. Copenhagen: Munksgaard, 1970, p. 306–309. (Alfred Benzon Symp. 2.)
68. GOLDBERG, H. S. Effect of lung volume history on rate of edema formation in isolated canine lobe. *J. Appl. Physiol.: Respirat. Environ. Exercise Physiol.* 45: 880–884, 1978.
69. GOLDBERG, H. S., W. MITZNER, AND G. BATRA. Effect of transpulmonary and vascular pressures on rate of pulmonary edema formation. *J. Appl. Physiol.: Respirat. Environ. Exercise Physiol.* 43: 14–19, 1977.
70. GORE, R. W. Pressures in cat mesenteric arterioles and capillaries during changes in systemic arterial blood pressure. *Circ. Res.* 34: 581–591, 1974.
71. GORE, R. W. Intestinal capillary pressures deduced from microscopic and isogravimetric studies. *Bibl. Anat.* 15: 168–171, 1977.
72. GORE, R. W. Fluid exchange across single capillaries in rat intestinal muscle. *Am. J. Physiol.* 242 (*Heart Circ. Physiol.* 11): H268–H287, 1982.
73. GORE, R. W., AND H. G. BOHLEN. Pressure regulation in the microcirculation. *Federation Proc.* 34: 2031–2037, 1975.
74. GORE, R. W., AND H. G. BOHLEN. Microvascular pressures in rat intestinal muscle and mucosal villi. *Am. J. Physiol.* 233 (*Heart Circ. Physiol.* 2): H685–H693, 1977.
75. GORE, R. W., AND P. F. MCDONAGH. Fluid exchange across

single capillaries. *Annu. Rev. Physiol.* 42: 337–357, 1980.

76. Gore, R. W., W. E. Schoknecht, and H. G. Bohlen. Filtration coefficients of single capillaries in rat intestinal muscle. In: *Microcirculation*, edited by J. Grayson and W. Zingg. New York: Plenum, 1976, vol. 1, p. 331–332.
77. Granger, D. N., N. A. Mortillaro, P. R. Kvietys, G. Rutili, J. C. Parker, and A. E. Taylor. Role of the interstitial matrix during intestinal volume absorption. *Am. J. Physiol.* 238 (*Gastrointest. Liver Physiol.* 1): G183–G189, 1980.
78. Granger, D. N., N. A. Mortillaro, P. R. Kvietys, and A. E. Taylor. Regulation of interstitial fluid volume in the small bowel. In: *Tissue Fluid Pressure and Composition*, edited by A. R. Hargens. Baltimore, MD: Williams & Wilkins, 1981, p. 173–183.
79. Granger, D. N., R. E. Parker, R. A. Brace, and A. E. Taylor. Analysis of permeability characteristics of intestinal capillaries. *Circ. Res.* 44: 335–344, 1979.
80. Granger, D. N., P. D. I. Richardson, and A. E. Taylor. Volumetric assessment of the capillary filtration coefficient in the cat small intestine. *Pfluegers Arch.* 381: 25–33, 1979.
81. Granger, D. N., and A. E. Taylor. Effects of solute-coupled transport on lymph flow and oncotic pressures in the cat ileum. *Am. J. Physiol.* 235 (*Endocrinol. Metab. Gastrointest. Physiol.* 4): E429–E439, 1978.
82. Granger, H. J. Role of interstitial matrix and lymphatic pump in the regulation of transcapillary fluid balance. *Microvasc. Res.* 18: 209–228, 1979.
83. Granger, H. J. Physicochemical properties of the extracellular matrix. In: *Tissue Fluid Pressure and Composition*, edited by A. R. Hargens. Baltimore, MD: Williams & Wilkins, 1981, p. 43–61.
84. Gregersen, M. I., and S. Chien. Blood volume. In: *Medical Physiology* (12th ed.), edited by V. B. Mountcastle. St. Louis, MO: Mosby, 1968, p. 244–261.
85. Guyton, A. C. A concept of negative interstitial pressure based on pressures in implanted perforated capsules. *Circ. Res.* 12: 399–414, 1963.
86. Guyton, A. C. Interstitial fluid pressure. II. Pressure-volume curves of interstitial space. *Circ. Res.* 16: 452–460, 1965.
87. Guyton, A. C., B. J. Barber, and D. S. Moffatt. Theory of interstitial pressure. In: *Tissue Fluid Pressure and Composition*, edited by A. R. Hargens. Baltimore, MD: Williams & Wilkins, 1981, p. 11–19.
88. Guyton, A. C., H. J. Granger, and A. E. Taylor. Interstitial fluid pressure. *Physiol. Rev.* 51: 527–563, 1971.
89. Guyton, A. C., and A. W. Lindsey. Effects of elevated left atrial pressure and decreased plasma protein concentration on the development of pulmonary edema. *Circ. Res.* 7: 649–657, 1959.
90. Guyton, A. C., A. E. Taylor, R. E. Drake, and J. C. Parker. Dynamics of subatmospheric pressure in the pulmonary interstitial fluids. In: *Lung Liquids*, edited by R. Porter and M. O'Connor. New York: Elsevier, 1976, p. 77–96. (Ciba Found. Symp. 38.)
91. Hakim, A. A., and N. Lifson. Effects of pressure on water and solute transport by dog intestinal mucosa in vitro. *Am. J. Physiol.* 216: 276–284, 1969.
92. Haljamaë, H. Sampling of nanoliter volumes of mammalian subcutaneous tissue fluid and ultra-micro flame photometric analysis of the K^+ and Na^+ concentrations. *Acta Physiol. Scand.* 78: 1–10, 1970.
93. Hansen, A. T. A self recording electronic osmometer for quick measurements of colloid osmotic pressure in small samples. *Acta Physiol. Scand.* 53: 197–213, 1961.
94. Hanson, K. M., and P. C. Johnson. Evidence for local arteriovenous reflex in intestine. *J. Appl. Physiol.* 17: 509–513, 1962.
95. Hargens, A. R. (editor). *Tissue Fluid Pressure and Composition.* Baltimore, MD: Williams & Wilkins, 1981.
96. Hargens, A. R., J. B. Cologne, F. J. Menninger, J. S. Hogan, B. J. Tucker, and R. M. Peters. Normal transcapillary pressures in human skeletal muscle and subcutaneous tissues. *Microvasc. Res.* 22: 177–189, 1981.
97. Hargens, A. R., B. J. Tucker, and R. C. Blantz. Renal lymph protein in the rat. *Am. J. Physiol.* 233: (*Renal Fluid Electrolyte Physiol.* 2): F269–F273, 1977.
98. Hargens, A. R., and B. W. Zweifach. Transport between blood and peripheral lymph in the intestine. *Microvas. Res.* 11: 89–101, 1976.
99. Hauge, A., and G. Nicolaysen. The importance of flow pulsatility for the rate of transvascular fluid filtration in rabbit lungs. *J. Physiol. London* 290: 569–579, 1979.
100. Heidenhain, von R. Versuche und Fragen zur Lehre der Lymphbildung. *Pfluegers Arch. Gesamte Physiol. Menschen Tiere* 49: 209–301, 1891.
101. Henriksen, O. Effect of chronic sympathetic denervation upon local regulation of blood flow in human subcutaneous tissue. *Acta Physiol. Scand.* 97: 377–384, 1976.
102. Henriksen, O. Local nervous mechanism in regulation of blood flow in human subcutaneous tissue. *Acta Physiol. Scand.* 97: 385–391, 1976.
103. Henriksen, O. Local sympathetic reflex mechanism in regulation of blood flow in human subcutaneous adipose tissue. *Acta Physiol. Scand. Suppl.* 450: 7–48, 1977.
104. Henriksen, O., and P. Sejrsen. Local reflex in microcirculation in human skeletal muscle. *Acta Physiol. Scand.* 99: 19–26, 1977.
105. Hurley, J. V. *Acute Inflammation.* London: Churchill Livingstone, 1972, p. 21–32.
106. Intaglietta, M. Vasomotor activity, time dependent fluid exchange and tissue pressure. *Microvasc. Res.* 21: 153–164, 1981.
107. Intaglietta, M., and B. A. Endrich. Experimental and quantitative analysis of microcirculatory water exchange. *Acta Physiol. Scand. Suppl.* 463: 59–66, 1979.
108. Intaglietta, M., R. F. Pawula, and W. R. Tompkins. Pressure measurements in the mammalian microvasculature. *Microvasc. Res.* 2: 212–220, 1970.
109. Järhult, J., and S. Mellander. Autoregulation of capillary hydrostatic pressure in skeletal muscle during regional arterial hypo- and hypertension. *Acta Physiol. Scand.* 91: 32–41, 1974.
110. Johnson, P. C. Effect of venous pressure on mean capillary pressure and venous resistance of the intestine. *Circ. Res.* 16: 294–300, 1965.
111. Johnson, P. C., and K. M. Hanson. Effect of arterial pressure on arterial and venous resistance of intestine. *J. Appl. Physiol.* 17: 503–508, 1962.
112. Johnson, P. C., and K. M. Hanson. Relation between venous pressure and blood volume in the intestine. *Am. J. Physiol.* 204: 31–34, 1963.
113. Johnson, P., and K. M. Hanson. Capillary filtration in the small intestine of the dog. *Circ. Res.* 19: 766–773, 1966.
114. Johnson, P. C., and D. R. Richardson. The influence of venous pressure on filtration forces in the intestine. *Microvasc. Res.* 7: 296–306, 1974.
115. Karnovsky, M. J. The ultrastructural basis of capillary permeability studied with peroxidase as a tracer. *J. Cell Biol.* 35: 213–236, 1967.
116. Kedem, O., and A. Katchalsky. Thermodynamic analysis of the permeability of biological membranes to non-electrolytes. *Biochim. Biophys. Acta* 27: 229–246, 1958.
117. Kedem, O., and A. Katchalsky. Permeability of composite membranes. Part 2. Parallel elements. *Trans. Faraday Soc.* 59: 1931–1940, 1963.
118. Kinter, W. B., and J. R. Pappenheimer. Cited by Landis and Pappenheimer (132).
119. Krogh, A. *The Anatomy and Physiology of Capillaries.* New Haven, CT: Yale Univ. Press, 1929, p. 326.
120. Krogh, A., and G. A. Harrop. On the substance responsible for capillary forces. *J. Physiol. London* 54: cxxv, 1921.
121. Krogh, A., E. M. Landis, and A. H. Turner. The movement of fluid through the human capillary wall in relation to venous

pressure and to the colloid osmotic pressure of the blood. *J. Clin. Invest.* 11: 63–95, 1932.

122. LANDIS, E. M. The capillary pressure in frog mesentery as determined by micro-injection methods. *Am. J. Physiol.* 75: 548–570, 1926.
123. LANDIS, E. M. Micro-injection studies of capillary permeability. II. The relation between capillary pressure and the rate at which fluid passes through the walls of single capillaries. *Am. J. Physiol.* 82: 217–238, 1927.
124. LANDIS, E. M. Micro-injection studies of capillary permeability. III. The effect of lack of oxygen on the permeability of the capillary wall to fluid and to the plasma proteins. *Am. J. Physiol.* 83: 528–542, 1928.
125. LANDIS, E. M. The capillary blood pressure in mammalian mesentery as determined by the micro-injection method. *Am. J. Physiol.* 93: 353–362, 1930.
126. LANDIS, E. M. Micro-injection studies of capillary blood pressure in human skin. *Heart* 15: 209–228, 1930.
127. LANDIS, E. M. Capillary pressure and hyperemia in muscle and skin of the frog. *Am. J. Physiol.* 98: 704–716, 1931.
128. LANDIS, E. M. Capillary pressure and capillary permeability. *Physiol. Rev.* 14: 404–481, 1934.
129. LANDIS, E. M. The capillary circulation. In: *Circulation of the Blood: Men and Ideas*, edited by A. P. Fishman and D. W. Richards. New York: Oxford Univ. Press, 1964, p. 355–406.
130. LANDIS, E. M. Heteroporosity of the capillary wall as indicated by cinematographic analysis of the passage of dye. *Ann. NY Acad. Sci.* 116: 765–773, 1964.
131. LANDIS, E. M., AND J. H. GIBBON, JR. The effects of temperature and of tissue pressure on the movement of fluid through the human capillary wall. *J. Clin. Invest.* 12: 105–138, 1933.
132. LANDIS, E. M., AND J. R. PAPPENHEIMER. Exchange of substances through the capillary walls. In: *Handbook of Physiology. Circulation*, edited by W. F. Hamilton and P. Dow. Washington, DC: Am. Physiol. Soc., 1963, sect. 2, vol. II, chapt. 29, p. 961–1034.
133. LADEGAARD-PEDERSEN, H. J. Measurement of the interstitial pressure in the subcutaneous tissues in dogs. *Circ. Res.* 26: 765–770, 1970.
134. LAURENT, T. C. The structure and function of the intercellular polysaccharides in connective tissue. In: *Capillary Permeability*, edited by C. Crone and N. A. Lassen. Copenhagen: Munksgaard, 1970, p. 261–277. (Alfred Benzon Symp. 2.)
135. LAURENT, T. C., AND A. G. OGSTON. The interaction between polysaccharides and other macromolecules. IV. The osmotic pressure of mixtures of serum albumin and hyaluronic acid. *Biochem. J.* 89: 249–253, 1963.
136. LEE, J. S. Lymph capillary pressure of rat intestinal villi during fluid absorption. *Am. J. Physiol.* 237 (*Endocrinol. Metab. Gastrointest. Physiol.* 6): E301–E307, 1979.
137. LEE, J. S. Lymph pressure in intestinal villi and lymph flow during fluid secretion. In: *Tissue Fluid Pressure and Composition*, edited by A. R. Hargens. Baltimore, MD: Williams & Wilkins, 1981, p. 165–172.
138. LEE, J. S., L. H. SMAJE, AND B. W. ZWEIFACH. Fluid movement in occluded single capillaries of rabbit omentum. *Circ. Res.* 28: 358–370, 1971.
139. LEVICK, J. R., AND C. C. MICHEL. The permeability of individually perfused frog mesenteric capillaries to T1824 and T1824-albumin as evidence for a large pore system. *Q. J. Exp. Physiol.* 58: 67–85, 1973.
140. LEVICK, J. R., AND C. C. MICHEL. The effect of bovine albumin on the permeability of frog mesenteric capillaries. *Q. J. Exp. Physiol.* 58: 87–97, 1973.
141. LEVICK, J. R., AND C. C. MICHEL. A densitometric method for determining the filtration coefficients of single capillaries in the frog mesentery. *Microvasc. Res.* 13: 141–151, 1977.
142. LEVICK, J. R., AND C. C. MICHEL. The effects of position and skin temperature on the capillary pressures in the fingers and toes. *J. Physiol. London* 274: 97–109, 1978.
143. LEVINE, O. R., R. B. MELLINS, R. M. SENIOR, AND A. P. FISHMAN. The application of Starling's Law of capillary exchange to the lung. *J. Clin. Invest.* 46: 934–944, 1967.
144. LEVITT, D. G. General continuum analysis of transport through pores. I. Proof of Onsager's reciprocity postulates for uniform pores. *Biophys. J.* 15: 533–551, 1975.
145. LEVITT, D. G. General continuum analysis of transport through pores. II. Nonuniform pores. *Biophys. J.* 553–563, 1975.
146. LEWIS, D. H., AND S. MELLANDER. Competitive effects of sympathetic control and tissue metabolites on resistance and capacitance vessels and capillary filtration in skeletal muscle. *Acta Physiol. Scand.* 56: 162–188, 1962.
147. LIFSON, N. Revised equations for the osmotic transient method. In: *Capillary Permeability*, edited by C. Crone and N. A. Lassen. Copenhagen: Munksgaard, 1970, p. 302–304. (Alfred Benzon Symp. 2.)
148. LIGHTFOOT, E. N., J. B. BASSINGTHWAIGHTE, AND E. F. GRABOWSKI. Hydrodynamic models for diffusion in microporous membranes. *Ann. Biomed. Eng.* 4: 78–90, 1976.
149. LOUDON, M. F., C. C. MICHEL, AND I. F. WHITE. The labelling of vesicles in frog endothelial cells with ferritin. *J. Physiol. London* 296: 97–112, 1979.
150. LUDWIG, C. F. W. *Lehrbuch der Physiologie des Menschen.* Leipzig, Germany: Winter, 1858–1861, vol. 2, p. 562.
151. LUNDE, P. K. M., AND B. A. WAALER. Transvascular fluid balance in the lung. *J. Physiol. London* 205: 1–18, 1969.
152. McDONAGH, P. F., AND R. W. GORE. Comparison of hydraulic conductivities in single capillaries of red versus white skeletal muscle (Abstract). *Microvasc. Res.* 15: 269, 1978.
153. MADDOX, D. A., C. M. BENNETT, W. M. DEEN, R. J. GLASSOCK, D. KNUTSON, AND B. M. BRENNER. Control of proximal tubule fluid reabsorption in experimental glomerulonephritis. *J. Clin. Invest.* 55: 1315–1325, 1975.
154. MAHLER, F., M. H. MUHEIM, M. INTAGLIETTA, A. BOLLINGER, AND M. ANLIKER. Blood pressure fluctuations in human nailfold capillaries. *Am. J. Physiol.* 236 (*Heart Circ. Physiol.* 5): H888–H893, 1979.
155. MASON, J. C. Studies on the Permeability of Single Capillaries. Oxford, UK: Oxford Univ. Press, 1976, Ph.D. Thesis.
156. MASON, J. C., F. E. CURRY, AND C. C. MICHEL. The effects of proteins upon the filtration coefficient of individually perfused frog mesenteric capillaries. *Microvasc. Res.* 13: 185–202, 1977.
157. MASON, J. C., F. E. CURRY, I. F. WHITE, AND C. C. MICHEL. The ultrastructure of frog mesenteric capillaries of known filtration coefficient. *Q. J. Exp. Physiol.* 64: 217–224, 1979.
158. MELLANDER, S. Comparative studies on the adrenergic neuro humoral control of resistance and capacitance blood vessels in the cat. *Acta Physiol. Scand.* 50, Suppl. 176: 1–86, 1960.
159. MELLANDER, S., B. ÖBERG, AND H. ODELRAM. Vascular adjustments to increased transmural pressure in cat and man with special reference to shifts in capillary fluid transfer. *Acta Physiol. Scand.* 61: 34–48, 1964.
160. MEYER, B. J., A. MEYER, AND A. C. GUYTON. Interstitial fluid pressure. V. Negative pressure in the lungs. *Circ. Res.* 22: 263–271, 1968.
161. MICHEL, C. C. Flow through capillary walls. In: *Cardiovascular and Pulmonary Dynamics*, edited by M.-Y. Jaffrin. Paris: INSERM, 1978, p. 209–220.
162. MICHEL, C. C. The measurement of permeability in single capillaries. *Arch. Int. Physiol. Biochim.* 86: 657–667, 1978.
163. MICHEL, C. C. The investigation of capillary permeability in single vessels. *Acta Physiol. Scand. Suppl.* 463: 67–74, 1979.
164. MICHEL, C. C. Filtration coefficients and osmotic reflexion coefficients of the walls of single frog mesenteric capillaries. *J. Physiol. London* 309: 341–355, 1980.
165. MICHEL, C. C. The flow of water through the capillary wall. In: *Water Transport Across Epithelia: Barriers, Gradients, and Mechanisms*, edited by H. H. Ussing, N. Bindslev, N. A. Lassen, and O. Sten-Knudsen. Copenhagen: Munksgaard, 1981, p. 268–279. (Alfred Benzon Symp. 15.)

166. MICHEL, C. C., AND J. R. LEVICK. Variations in permeability along individually perfused capillaries of the frog mesentery. *Q. J. Exp. Physiol.* 62: 1–10, 1977.
167. MICHEL, C. C., J. C. MASON, F. E. CURRY, J. E. TOOKE, AND P. HUNTER. A development of the Landis technique for measuring the filtration coefficient of individual capillaries in the frog mesentery. *Q. J. Exp. Physiol.* 59: 283–309, 1974.
168. MICHEL, C. C., AND M. E. PHILLIPS. The effects of Ficoll 70 and bovine serum albumin on the permeability properties of individually perfused frog mesenteric capillaries (Abstract). *J. Physiol. London* 291: 39P, 1979.
168a. MICHEL, C. C., AND M. E. PHILLIPS. The effects of Ficoll 70 on the filtration coefficient of single frog mesenteric capillaries (Abstract). *J. Physiol. London* 315: 12P–13P, 1981.
169. MORTILLARO, N. A., AND A. E. TAYLOR. Interaction of capillary and tissue forces in the cat small intestine. *Circ. Res.* 39: 348–358, 1976.
170. NAKAMURA, Y., AND H. WAYLAND. Macromolecular transport in the cat mesentery. *Microvasc. Res.* 9: 1–21, 1975.
171. NAVAR, P. D., AND L. G. NAVAR. Relationship between colloid osmotic pressure and plasma protein concentration in the dog. *Am. J. Physiol.* 233 (*Heart Circ. Physiol.* 2): H295–H298, 1977.
172. NICHOL, L. W., A. G. OGSTON, AND B. N. PRESTON. The equilibrium sedimentation of hyaluronic acid and of two synthetic polymers. *Biochem. J.* 102: 407–416, 1967.
173. NICOLAYSEN, G. Increase in capillary filtration rate resulting from reduction in the intravascular calcium ion concentration. *Acta Physiol. Scand.* 81: 517–527, 1971.
174. NICOLAYSEN, G., B. A. WAALER, AND P. AARSETH. On the existence of stretchable pores in the exchange vessels of the isolated rabbit lung preparation. *Lymphology* 12: 201–207, 1979.
175. NICOLL, P. A., AND A. E. TAYLOR. Lymph formation and flow. *Annu. Rev. Physiol.* 39: 73–95, 1977.
176. NODDELAND, H., K. AUKLAND, AND G. NICOLAYSEN. Plasma colloid osmotic pressure in venous blood from the human foot in orthostasis. *Acta Physiol. Scand.* 113: 447–454, 1981.
177. NOLL, F. Ueber den Lymphstrom in den Lymphgefässen und die wesentlichsten anatomischen Bestandtheile der Lymphdrüsen. *Z. Rat. Med.* 9: 52–93, 1850.
178. OGSTON, A. G. Some thermodynamic relationships in ternary systems, with special reference to the properties of systems containing hyaluronic acid and protein. *Arch. Biochem. Biophys. Suppl.* 1: 39–51, 1962.
179. OLSZEWSKI, W. L., AND A. ENGESET. Intrinsic contractility of prenodal lymph vessels and lymph flow in human leg. *Am. J. Physiol.* 239 (*Heart Circ. Physiol.* 8): H775–H783, 1980.
180. OLSZEWSKI, W., A. ENGESET, P. M. JAEGER, J. SOKOLOWSKI, AND L. THEODORSEN. Flow and composition of leg lymph in normal men during venous stasis, muscular activity and local hyperthermia. *Acta Physiol. Scand.* 99: 149–155, 1977.
181. PALADE, G. E. Fine structure of blood capillaries. *J. Appl. Phys.* 24: 1423, 1953.
182. PALADE, G. E., M. SIMIONESCU, AND N. SIMIONESCU. Structural aspects of the permeability of the microvascular endothelium. *Acta Physiol. Scand. Suppl.* 463: 11–32, 1979.
183. PAPPENHEIMER, J. R. Passage of molecules through capillary walls. *Physiol. Rev.* 33: 387–423, 1953.
183a. PAPPENHEIMER, J. R. Ultrafiltration and diffusion through biological membranes. In: *The National Institutes of Health Annual Lectures, 1954.* Washington, DC: U.S.P.H. Publ. 467, 1956, p. 2–25.
184. PAPPENHEIMER, J. R. Osmotic reflection coefficients in capillary membranes. In: *Capillary Permeability*, edited by C. Crone and N. A. Lassen. Copenhagen: Munksgaard, 1970, p. 278–286. (Alfred Benzon Symp. 2.)
185. PAPPENHEIMER, J. R., E. M. RENKIN, AND L. M. BORRERO. Filtration, diffusion and molecular sieving through peripheral capillary membranes. A contribution to the pore theory of capillary permeability. *Am. J. Physiol.* 167: 13–46, 1951.
186. PAPPENHEIMER, J. R., AND A. SOTO-RIVERA. Effective osmotic pressure of the plasma proteins and other quantities associated with the capillary circulation in the hind-limbs of cats and dogs. *Am. J. Physiol.* 152: 471–491, 1948.
187. PARKER, J. C., H. J. FALGOUT, F. A. GRIMBERT, AND A. E. TAYLOR. The effect of increased vascular pressure on albumin excluded volume and lymph flow in the dog lung. *Circ. Res.* 47: 866–875, 1980.
188. PARKER, J. C., A. C. GUYTON, AND A. E. TAYLOR. Pulmonary interstitial and capillary pressures estimated from intra-alveolar fluid pressures. *J. Appl. Physiol.: Respirat. Environ. Exercise Physiol.* 44: 267–276, 1978.
189. PARKER, J. C., R. E. PARKER, D. N. GRANGER, AND A. E. TAYLOR. Vascular permeability and transvascular fluid and protein transport in the dog lung. *Circ. Res.* 48: 549–560, 1981.
190. PATLAK, C. S., D. A. GOLDSTEIN, AND J. F. HOFFMAN. The flow of solute and solvent across a two-membrane system. *J. Theor. Biol.* 5: 426–442, 1963.
191. PAULSON, O. B., M. M. HERTZ, T. G. BOLWIG, AND N. A. LASSEN. Filtration and diffusion of water across the blood-brain barrier in man. *Microvasc. Res.* 13: 113–124, 1977.
192. PERL, W. A friction coefficient, series parallel channel model for transcapillary flux of nonelectrolytes and water. *Microvasc. Res.* 6: 169–193, 1973.
193. PERL, W., P. CHOWDHURY, AND F. P. CHINARD. Reflection coefficients of dog lung endothelium to small hydrophilic solutes. *Am. J. Physiol.* 228: 797–809, 1975.
194. PHILIP, J. R. Theory of flow and transport processes in pores and porous media. In: *Circulatory and Respiratory Mass Transport*, edited by G. E. W. Wolstenholme and J. Knight. London: Churchill, 1969, p. 22–44. (Ciba Found. Symp.)
195. PHILLIPS, M. E., AND M. R. TURNER. The effects of haemoglobin and myoglobin on the filtration coefficient of single frog mesenteric capillaries (Abstract). *J. Physiol. London* 320: 39P, 1981.
196. PIETRA, G. G., J. P. SZIDON, M. M. LEVANTHAL, AND A. P. FISHMAN. Hemoglobin as a tracer in hemodynamic pulmonary edema. *Science* 166: 1643–1646, 1969.
197. PRATHER, J. W., D. N. BOWES, D. A. WARRELL, AND B. W. ZWEIFACH. Comparison of capsule and wick techniques for measurement of interstitial fluid pressure. *J. Appl. Physiol.* 31: 942–945, 1971.
198. PRATHER, J. W., K. A. GAAR, JR., AND A. C. GUYTON. Direct continuous recording of plasma colloid osmotic pressure of whole blood. *J. Appl. Physiol.* 24: 602–605, 1968.
199. RATHER, L. J. *Addison and the White Corpuscles: An Aspect of Nineteenth-Century Biology.* London: Wellcome Inst. Hist. Med., 1972, p. 59–65.
200. RENKIN, E. M. Filtration, diffusion and molecular sieving through porous, cellulose membranes. *J. Gen. Physiol.* 38: 225–243, 1954.
201. RENKIN, E. M. Exchange of substances through capillary walls. In: *Circulatory and Respiratory Mass Transport*, edited by G. E. W. Wolstenholme and J. Knight. London: Churchill, 1968, p. 50–66. (Ciba Found. Symp.)
202. RENKIN, E. M. Lymph as a measure of the composition of interstitial fluid. In: *Pulmonary Edema*, edited by A. P. Fishman and E. M. Renkin. Bethesda, MD: Am. Physiol. Soc., 1979, p. 145–159.
203. RENKIN, E. M., AND F. E. CURRY. Transport of water and solutes across capillary endothelium. In: *Membrane Transport in Biology*, edited by G. Giebisch, D. C. Tosteson, and H. H. Ussing. Heidelberg: Springer-Verlag, 1978, vol. 4, p. 1–45.
204. RENKIN, E. M., W. L. JOYNER, C. H. SLOOP, AND P. D. WATSON. The influence of venous pressure on plasma lymph transport in the dog's paw. Convective and dissipative mechanisms. *Microvasc. Res.* 14: 191–204, 1977.
205. RENKIN, E. M., AND B. D. ZAUN. Effects of adrenal hormones on capillary permeability in perfused rat tissues. *Am. J. Physiol.* 180: 498–502, 1955.
206. RICHARDSON, D. R., AND B. W. ZWEIFACH. Pressure relationships in the macro- and microcirculation of the mesentery.

Microvasc. Res. 2: 474–488, 1970.

207. RICHARDSON, P. D. I., D. N. GRANGER, AND A. E. TAYLOR. Capillary filtration coefficient: the technique and its application to the small intestine. *Cardiovasc. Res.* 13: 547–561, 1979.
208. RIPPE, B., AND B. FOLKOW. Capillary permeability to albumin in normotensive and spontaneously hypertensive rats. *Acta Physiol. Scand.* 101: 72–83, 1977.
209. RIPPE, B., A. KAMIYA, AND B. FOLKOW. Simultaneous measurements of capillary diffusion and filtration exchange during shifts in filtration-absorption and at graded alterations in the capillary permeability surface area product (PS). *Acta Physiol. Scand.* 104: 318–336, 1978.
210. RITTER, A. B., AND F. P. CHINARD. Calculation of osmotic reflection coefficients from constant infusion experiments on isolated perfused lungs. *Microvasc. Res.* 19: 234–238, 1980.
211. ROUS, P., H. P. GILDING, AND F. SMITH. A gradient of vascular permeability. *J. Exp. Med.* 51: 807–830, 1930.
212. RUTILI, G., AND K. E. ARFORS. Collections of interstitial fluid: a comparison between wick and micropuncture techniques. *Microvasc. Res.* 15: 107–110, 1978.
213. SCATCHARD, G. Physical chemistry of protein solutions. I. Derivation of the equations for the osmotic pressure. *J. Am. Chem. Soc.* 68: 2315–2319, 1946.
214. SCATCHARD, G., A. C. BATCHELDER, AND A. BROWN. Preparation and properties of serum and plasma proteins. VI. Osmotic equilibria in solutions of serum albumin and sodium chloride. *J. Am. Chem. Soc.* 68: 2320–2329, 1946.
215. SCHAFER, D. E., AND J. A. JOHNSON. Permeability of mammalian heart capillaries to sucrose and inulin. *Am. J. Physiol.* 206: 985–991, 1964.
216. SCHOKNECHT, W. E., AND R. W. GORE. An efficient algorithm for the computation of capillary filtration coefficients (Abstract). *Bull. Am. Phys. Soc.* 20: 824, 1975.
217. SCHOLANDER, P. F., A. R. HARGENS, AND S. L. MILLER. Negative pressure in the interstitial fluid of animals. *Science* 161: 321–328, 1968.
218. SEJRSEN, P., O. HENRIKSEN, AND W. P. PAASKE. Effect of orthostatic blood pressure changes upon capillary filtration-absorption rate in the human calf. *Acta Physiol. Scand.* 111: 287–291, 1981.
219. SEJRSEN, P., O. HENRIKSEN, W. P. PAASKE, AND S. T. NIELSEN. Duration of increase in vascular volume during venous stasis. *Acta Physiol. Scand.* 111: 293–298, 1981.
220. SENAY, L. C. Changes in plasma volume and protein content during exposures of working men to various temperatures before and after acclimatization to heat: separation of the roles of cutaneous and skeletal muscle circulation. *J. Physiol. London* 224: 61–81, 1972.
221. SENAY, L. C. Body fluids and temperature responses of heat-exposed women before and after ovulation with and without rehydration. *J. Physiol. London* 232: 209–219, 1973.
222. SIMIONESCU, N., M. SIMIONESCU, AND G. E. PALADE. Permeability of muscle capillaries to exogenous myoglobin. *J. Cell Biol.* 57: 424–452, 1973.
223. SIMIONESCU, N., M. SIMIONESCU, AND G. E. PALADE. Permeability of muscle capillaries to small heme-peptides. Evidence for the existence of patent transendothelial channels. *J. Cell Biol.* 64: 586–607, 1975.
224. SIMIONESCU, N., M. SIMIONESCU, AND G. E. PALADE. Open junctions in the endothelium of the post capillary venules of the diaphragm. *J. Cell Biol.* 79: 27–46, 1978.
225. SMAJE, L. H., P. A. FRAZER, AND G. CLOUGH. The distensibility of single capillaries and venules in the cat mesentery. *Microvasc. Res.* 20: 358–376, 1980.
226. SMAJE, L. H., J. S. LEE, AND B. W. ZWEIFACH. A new approach to the indirect measurement of capillary pressure and filtration coefficient. Basel, Switzerland: Karger, 1971, p. 254–258. (Eur. Conf. Microcirc., 6th, Aalborg, 1970.)
227. SMAJE, L. H., B. W. ZWEIFACH, AND M. INTAGLIETTA. Micropressures and capillary filtration coefficients in single vessels of the cremaster muscle of the rat. *Microvasc. Res.* 2: 96–110, 1970.
228. SNASHALL, P. D., AND F. A. BOOTHER. Interstitial gel swelling pressure in human subcutaneous tissue measured with a cotton wick. *Clin. Sci. Mol. Med.* 46: 241–251, 1974.
229. SNASHALL, P. D., J. LUCAS, A. GUZ, AND M. A. FLOYER. Measurement of interstitial fluid pressure by means of a cotton wick in man and animals: an analysis of the origin of the pressure. *Clin. Sci.* 41: 35–52, 1971.
230. STARLING, E. H. On the absorption of fluids from connective tissue spaces. *J. Physiol. London* 19: 312–326, 1896.
231. STARLING, E. H. The production and absorption of lymph. In: *Textbook of Physiology*, edited by E. A. Schafer. London: Pentland, 1898, vol. 1, p. 285–311.
232. STAUB, N. C. The forces regulating fluid filtration in the lung. *Microvasc. Res.* 15: 45–56, 1978.
233. STAVERMAN, A. J. The theory of measurement of osmotic pressure. *Rec. Trav. Chim. Pays-Bas Belg.* 70: 344–352, 1951.
233a. STRAY-PEDERSEN, S., AND J. B. STEEN. The capillary permeability of the *rete mirabile* of the eel, *Anguilla vulgaris. Acta Physiol. Scand.* 94: 401–422, 1975.
234. SULLIVAN, R. R., AND K. L. HERTEL. The permeability method for determining specific surface of fibers and powders. *Adv. Colloid Sci.* 1: 37–80, 1942.
235. SYROTA, A., B. BUI-XUAN, C. GENAIN, D. THEVEN, J. M. VALLOIS, AND J. J. POCIDALO. Thermodynamic coefficients in capillary membrane of dog lung for small hydrophilic molecule transport evaluated by an osmotic bolus method. In: *Cardiovascular and Pulmonary Dynamics*, edited by M.-Y. Jaffrin. Paris: INSERM, 1978, vol. 71, p. 291–298.
236. TAYLOR, A. E. Capillary fluid filtration: Starling forces and lymph flow. *Circ. Res.* 49: 557–575, 1981.
237. TOMBS, M. P., AND A. R. PEACOCKE. *The Osmotic Pressure of Biological Macromolecules.* Oxford, UK: Oxford Univ. Press, 1974, p. 1–65.
238. TOOKE, J. R. A capillary pressure disturbance in young diabetics. *Diabetes* 29: 815–819, 1980.
239. TOSTESON, D. I. Closing discussion. In: *Capillary Permeability*, edited by C. Crone and N. A. Lassen. Copenhagen: Munksgaard, 1970, p. 302–304. (Alfred Benzon Symp. 2.)
239a. TURNER, M. R., G. CLOUGH, AND C. C. MICHEL. The effects of cationised ferritin and native ferritin upon filtration coefficients of single frog capillaries. Evidence that proteins in the endothelial cell coat influence permeability. *Microvasc. Res.* 25: 205–222, 1983.
240. VARGAS, F., AND J. A. JOHNSON. Permeability of rabbit heart capillaries to nonelectrolytes. *Am. J. Physiol.* 213: 87–93, 1967.
241. WANGENSTEEN, O. D., E. LYSAKER, AND P. SAVARYN. Pulmonary capillary filtration and reflection coefficients in the adult rabbit. *Microvasc. Res.* 19: 239–241, 1977.
242. WATERFIELD, R. L. The effect of posture on the volume of the leg. *J. Physiol. London* 72: 121–131, 1931.
243. WATSON, P. D. The effect of protein and dextran on capillary filtration coefficient in isolated cat hindlimb (Abstract). *Microvasc. Res.* 21: 261–262, 1981.
244. WELCH, K., K. SADLER, AND G. GOLD. Volume flow across choroidal ependyma of the rabbit. *Am. J. Physiol.* 210: 232–236, 1966.
245. WHITE, H. L. On glomerular filtration. *Am. J. Physiol.* 68: 523–529, 1924.
246. WIEDERHIELM, C. A. Servo micropipet pressure recording technic. In: *Methods in Medical Research*, edited by R. F. Rushmer. Chicago, IL: Year Book, 1975, p. 199–201.
247. WIEDERHIELM, C. A. Analysis of small vessel function. In: *Physical Bases of Circulatory Transport: Regulation and Exchange*, edited by E. B. Reeve and A. C. Guyton. Philadelphia, PA: Saunders, 1967, p. 313–326.
248. WIEDERHIELM, C. A. The interstitial space. In: *Biomechanics: Its Foundations and Objectives*, edited by Y. C. Fung, N. Perrone, and M. Anliker. Englewood Cliffs, NJ: Prentice-Hall, 1972, p. 273–286.
249. WIEDERHIELM, C. A. Dynamics of capillary fluid exchange: a

non-linear computer simulation. *Microvasc. Res.* 18: 48–82, 1979.

250. WIEDERHIELM, C. A. The tissue pressure controversy, a semantic dilemma. In: *Tissue Fluid Pressure and Composition*, edited by A. R. Hargens. Baltimore, MD: Williams & Wilkins, 1981, p. 21–33.
251. WIEDERHIELM, C. A., J. W. WOODBURY, S. KIRK, AND R. F. RUSHMER. Pulsatile pressures in the microcirculation of frog's mesentery. *Am. J. Physiol.* 207: 173–176, 1964.
252. WISSIG, S. L. Identification of the small pore in muscle capillaries. *Acta Physiol. Scand. Suppl.* 463: 33–44, 1979.
253. WISSIG, S. L., AND M. C. WILLIAMS. The permeability of muscle capillaries to microperoxidase. *J. Cell Biol.* 76: 341–359, 1978.
254. YABLONSKI, M. E., AND N. LIFSON. Mechanism of production of intestinal secretion by elevated venous pressure. *J. Clin. Invest.* 57: 904–915, 1976.
255. YOFFEY, J. M., AND F. C. COURTICE. *Lymphatics, Lymph and the Lymphomyeloid Complex*. New York: Academic, 1970, p. 171–175.
256. YOUMANS, J. B., H. S. WELLS, D. DONLEY, AND D. G. MILLER. The effect of posture (standing) on the serum protein concentration and colloid osmotic pressure of blood from the foot in relation to the formation of edema. *J. Clin. Invest.* 13: 447–459, 1934.
257. YUDILEVICH, D. L., AND O. A. ALVAREZ. Water, sodium, and thiourea transcapillary diffusion in the dog heart. *Am. J. Physiol.* 213: 308–314, 1967.
258. ZWEIFACH, B. W. Local regulation of capillary pressure. *Circ. Res.* 28/29, Suppl. 1: I129–I134, 1971.
259. ZWEIFACH, B. W. Quantitative studies of microcirculatory structure and function. I. Analysis of pressure distributions in the terminal bed in cat mesentery. *Circ. Res.* 34: 843–857, 1974.
260. ZWEIFACH, B. W., AND M. INTAGLIETTA. Mechanics of fluid movement across single capillaries in the rabbit. *Microvasc. Res.* 1: 83–101, 1968.
261. ZWEIFACH, B. W., AND A. SILBERBERG. The interstitial-lymphatic flow system. In: *Cardiovascular Physiology III*, edited by A. C. Guyton and D. B. Young. Baltimore, MD: University Park, 1979, vol. 18, p. 215–260. (Int. Rev. Physiol. Ser.)

CHAPTER 10

Capillary permeability to small solutes

CHRISTIAN CRONE | *Department of Physiology, The Panum Institute, University of Copenhagen, Copenhagen, Denmark*

DAVID G. LEVITT | *Department of Physiology, University of Minnesota, Minneapolis, Minnesota*

CHAPTER CONTENTS

Principal Considerations in Determination of Capillary Permeability
Methods
Whole-Organ Studies
  Diffusion methods
    Blood-clearance techniques
    Tissue-uptake techniques
  Osmotic methods
    Tissue transients
    Blood transients
Rate-Limiting Processes in Blood-Tissue Exchange
  Lipophilic solutes
  Water permeability
Transport Rates In Vivo—Capillary Diffusion Capacities
Capillary Surface Area
Data From Whole-Organ Experiments
  Diffusion permeabilities
  Permeability ratios
  Reflection coefficients
Single-Capillary Studies
  Single-injection technique
  Sac method
  Interstitial-diffusion method
  Results
  Electrical resistance of capillary walls
  Dye-diffusion studies
  Gradient of permeability
  Interstitial diffusion
Facilitated Transport in Endothelium
Active Transport in Endothelium
Interpretation of Permeability Studies
  Background
  Equivalent model of hydrophilic channel
    Diffusion
    Fractional slit surface area
    Electrical resistance
    Filtration coefficient
    Osmotic reflection coefficient
  Other approaches to equivalent slit widths
    Diffusion restriction
    Reflection coefficient
    Combination of diffusion and filtration data
    Sieving data
Conclusions

THE CAPILLARY WALL is interposed between the major compartments of the extracellular space (plasma and interstitial fluid) and allows material in the stirred plasma compartment to reach the stationary interstitial phase and vice versa. The function of the microcirculation is to reduce the distance for the exchange of materials to a length at which diffusion is sufficiently rapid. The distance that dissolved substances must travel from the blood to the cells is variable, but in most tissues the longest diffusion distance is 20–50 μm. A solute with a diffusion coefficient (D) of 10^{-5} cm^2/s would take ~1 s to go this distance, $\bar{t} = x^2/2D$, where t is time and x is distance; this is about the same order of magnitude as the time the blood spends in the capillary. Although ~99.9% of the capillary surface area is covered by the plasma membranes of endothelial cells, the remaining fraction of the surface area allows very effective solute transport. Typically 10%–50% of small hydrophilic solutes traverse the capillary membrane in a single transit (diffusion-limited transport).

Lipophilic and hydrophilic solutes must be differentiated because the barriers encountered by these two classes of substances in the capillary wall are very different. Most hydrophilic solutes are mainly restricted to the paracellular pathway, whereas lipophilic solutes (notably gases and nonpolar organic molecules but also water) use the cellular pathway. These last substances are usually completely extracted in a single capillary passage (flow-limited transport).

Early research showed that transcapillary escape of hydrophilic solutes is very fast (103, 134); half times in plasma for small substances are on the order of a few minutes. The intense research that followed these early observations has provided a theoretical framework that allows the interpretation of experimental results in terms of permeability coefficients (P), osmotic reflection coefficients (σ), and filtration coefficients (L_p). Knowledge of these three principal parameters allows one to rationalize the mechanics of permeation through a physical analogy of the capillary membrane. A model at this level correlated transport and membrane structure. This interpretation of transport became the center of interest and caused a lively debate about whether this model, the so-called pore hypothesis, best describes structure and function (69, 158, 175, 191, 244, 258, 280, 364).

The pore theory attempts to interpret diffusion, filtration, and osmotic events in terms of permeation through rigid water-filled pores. Poiseuillean flow in the pores and diffusion restriction caused by interaction between solutes and the pore wall played a principal role in the early formulation of the pore theory (245, 247, 284). Other mechanisms of pore permeation have recently been proposed (79, 81, 213).

Experiments on capillary permeability are often done with foreign solutes of known size used as rigid probes to characterize pore size; however, the information obtained can be applied to the transport of naturally occurring solutes such as glucose, amino acids, vitamins, hormones, and transmitters. Thus the results are of practical as well as of theoretical interest. Information about the transcapillary passage of lipids (e.g., fatty acids, sterols, lipid-soluble vitamins) is still rather scanty (289a, 327a); the issue is complicated by various degrees of protein binding. Lipid-soluble molecules diffuse through endothelial cells, which ensures very fast transfer (273a).

PRINCIPAL CONSIDERATIONS IN DETERMINATION OF CAPILLARY PERMEABILITY

In the study of capillary permeability the evaluation of results depends greatly on the experimental technique used. Each method has its limitations and requires several explicit assumptions in order to derive permeability values from the primary data. Before discussing methodologies the theoretical foundations of capillary permeability are briefly surveyed.

In principle, material can cross the capillary wall by *1*) simple diffusion, *2*) filtration and solvent drag, *3*) facilitated diffusion, *4*) active transport, and *5*) vesicular transport. The emphasis in this chapter is on diffusional transport, which is the dominant mechanism (171, 245). Solute transport is, however, somewhat dependent on simultaneously occurring volume transport (filtration or osmosis), as expressed by

$$J_s = PS\overline{\Delta C} + (1 - \sigma)J_v\overline{C}_s \tag{1}$$

where J_s is the net flux of solute, S is the capillary surface area, $\overline{\Delta C}$ is the average concentration difference across the capillary wall, σ is the osmotic reflection coefficient, J_v is the volume flux, and $\overline{C}_s$ is the mean test solute concentration in the capillary membrane.

For most solutes (except macromolecules) the convective term is negligible, and Equation 1 reduces to $J_s = PS\overline{\Delta C}$, which provides the experimental definition of capillary permeability

$$P = \frac{J_s}{S\overline{\Delta C}} \tag{2}$$

To determine P it is necessary to measure J_s across the capillary membrane, $\overline{\Delta C}$, and S. The principal problem in transcapillary transport is that the capillary membrane "sees" different concentrations in the arterial end and the venous end because of the combination of blood flow and diffusion. Therefore $\overline{\Delta C}$ across the membrane is not well defined, and flow is a very important determinant in capillary diffusion experiments (Fig. 1).

There are two experimental approaches to the measurement of $\overline{\Delta C}$. *1*) The osmotic equivalent is determined according to van't Hoff's law, $\overline{\Delta C} = \Delta\Pi/\sigma RT$, where $\Delta\Pi$ is the average osmotic pressure difference caused by the added test substance, R is the gas constant, and T is absolute temperature. This equation was the main basis of early osmotic-transient experiments (248). *2*) Experiments are performed under conditions of unidirectional flux of test solute and negligible concentration on the *trans* side of the capillary wall. Under these experimental conditions the average intracapillary concentration can be equated with the average concentration difference that drives the flux. This view provides a basis for the indicator-diffusion technique (59), which requires the use of

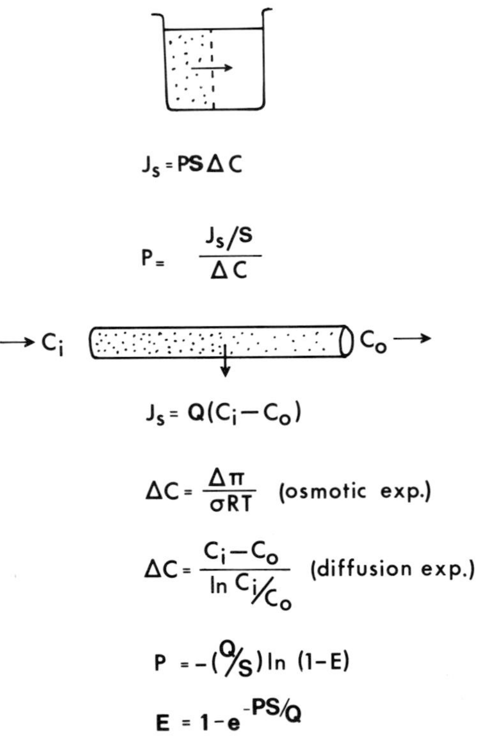

$J_s = PS\Delta C$
$P = \frac{J_s/S}{\Delta C}$
C_i
C_o
$J_s = Q(C_i - C_o)$
$\Delta C = \frac{\Delta\pi}{\sigma RT}$ (osmotic exp.)
$\Delta C = \frac{C_i - C_o}{\ln C_i/C_o}$ (diffusion exp.)
$P = -(Q/S)\ln(1-E)$
$E = 1 - e^{-PS/Q}$

FIG. 1. Formalism of membrane permeability in 2 situations. *Top*: membrane exposed to same concentration over entire surface. *Bottom*: membrane exposed to falling concentration in lengthwise direction (capillary). *P*, membrane permeability; Q, solvent flow; *S*, membrane area; E, unidirectional fractional solute extraction; J_s, net solute flux; C_i, input concentration; C_o, output concentration; $\Delta\Pi$, average osmotic pressure difference; *R*, gas constant; *T*, absolute temperature; ΔC, concentration difference.

labeled or foreign compounds to measure unidirectional fluxes.

The parameter directly measured by the osmotic-transient method and the indicator-diffusion method is the permeability–surface area product (or, equivalently, the capillary diffusion capacity). Independent measurement of the capillary surface area is necessary to determine permeability.

The first mathematical model of transcapillary transport (22), which analyzed pulmonary gas transport, clearly defined the problem of determining the average concentration (or tension) difference across the capillary. Bohr's analysis (22) showed how to combine flow, diffusion, and surface area. M. Krogh (170), on the suggestion of Bohr, used CO as a tracer gas because its tension in the blood, relative to that in the alveoli, is insignificant and thus can be disregarded—an approximation similar to that used in indicator-diffusion theory (59). A. Krogh (166) reduced the complexity of gas diffusion in tissues to events in a single-capillary–tissue unit (Krogh tissue cylinder) and thus paved the way for analysis of whole-organ experiments based on single-capillary models.

Few fields in physiology have experienced development of such an impressive variety of experimental methods as is the case in studies of capillary permeability. Many of the techniques involve a rather sophisticated analysis and assumptions that are important for the evaluation of results. Because no comprehensive account of the scenario of experimental approaches has been given earlier, this chapter focuses on methodologies.

METHODS

There are two reasons for determining the capillary permeability of a solute. In a given tissue with a known blood flow there is the practical problem of determining the rate of extravascular buildup or removal of a drug or metabolite. The data accumulated over the last 30 years for various classes of solutes and types of capillaries (summarized in DATA FROM WHOLE-ORGAN EXPERIMENTS, p. 437) are probably sufficient to provide qualitative results for most tissues. These studies also provide information that allows the solutes to be used as experimental probes of the mechanism of transcapillary exchange. Most of the work in recent years has been directed to this second purpose.

To determine capillary permeability on the basis of organ measurements, several assumptions are made about individual capillary-tissue regions and the interactions between neighboring regions. Often these assumptions cannot be evaluated directly. This discussion focuses on the assumptions required by each method and emphasizes those methods or conditions that are nearly independent of specific model assumptions.

In principle, analysis of single-capillary measurements is based on a more complete physical characterization of the capillary-tissue unit. It should be possible to interpret these measurements in terms of the known physical constants without the need for many assumptions. In practice, however, some simplifying assumptions are also necessary for these experiments. At present single-capillary and whole-organ measurements should be regarded as complementary approaches to the study of transcapillary transport; each method has its own strengths and weaknesses. The information sought with each approach is not necessarily the same.

Whole-organ experiments provide information about the behavior of a large population of capillaries. This information can only be applied to the single-capillary level by means of many assumptions. However, single-capillary experiments are only representative of an individual unit; it is not immediately evident that the behavior of the capillary bed in an organ can be deduced from such measurements. Single-capillary approaches are useful for studying the detailed mechanisms of membrane permeation because they describe a well-defined capillary membrane section, which can be subjected to structural analysis after the experiment. These methods are also the only techniques that can study the longitudinal gradient of capillary permeability. Whole-organ experiments study all the permeable segments of the microvasculature, including venules and arterioles, as a single unit. Thus these two approaches supplement each other, and both are needed to describe exchange phenomena. The situation is reminiscent of that in kidney physiology, where clearance techniques and micropuncture techniques each serve particular purposes.

In view of the large amount of information presented in this chapter, a few hints may be helpful for the reader who wants to avoid being overwhelmed. The person who is mainly interested in the results and implications of studies on capillary permeability is advised to proceed directly to the section entitled DATA FROM WHOLE-ORGAN EXPERIMENTS (p. 437) and should specifically consult Tables 5, 6, and 12–15, which contain most of the available quantitative data. The reader who is especially interested in interpreting permeability in terms of capillary wall structure (routes of transport) should proceed to the section entitled INTERPRETATION OF PERMEABILITY STUDIES (p. 449). The detailed description and analysis of experimental approaches that follows may be of particular interest as background knowledge for those considering undertaking experiments themselves or interested in the historical developments in this field.

WHOLE-ORGAN STUDIES

Most approaches can be grouped under diffusion

methods or osmotic methods. These general approaches, which are based on the introduction of a test solute into the blood perfusing the organ, can be used with two principal modifications: *1*) the study of changes in blood or perfusate composition during passage through the organ and *2*) the study of changes occurring in the tissue. Furthermore either a single-injection technique (bolus technique) or a constant-infusion technique (integral technique) can be used. Thus whole-organ techniques can be systematized as shown in Table 1. Table 2 lists diffusion coefficients for some typical solutes used in many experiments on capillary permeability.

Diffusion Methods

BLOOD-CLEARANCE TECHNIQUES. *Constant-infusion technique.* Capillary permeability can be measured directly by infusion of trace amounts of a solute at a constant concentration through the arterial supply of an organ and observation of concentration changes of that solute in the venous outflow. The test solute concentration (C_s) in the vein will decrease by the amount that is lost from the capillary, which depends on capillary permeability. Gradually solute will accumulate in the tissue and the venous outflow concentration will rise. Early in the experiment it can be assumed that the tissue concentration (C_t) is negligible relative to the capillary concentration (C_c), and an equation can be derived for the venous concentration (C_v) independent of specific organ details. Because this equation is probably the most important expression in the field of capillary permeability (59, 276), its derivation is given here. The solute is supplied in trace amounts, and it is assumed that the transcapillary flux is unidirectional early in the experiment; i.e., the accumulation of tracer in the tissue is neglected. If C_t is close to zero, a differential equation for C_c can be derived by applying mass balance to a small element in the capillary (Fig. 2)

$$-Q\,\frac{dC}{dx} = PSC/l \tag{3}$$

where l is capillary length and Q is flow. Integrating from $x = 0$ to x

$$C(x)/C_a = e^{-(PS/Q)(x/l)} \tag{4}$$

The venous concentration at distance $x = l$ is C_v and thus

$$C_v/C_a = e^{-PS/Q} \tag{5}$$

or

$$\ln(C_v/C_a) = -PS/Q \tag{5a}$$

It is convenient to introduce the unidirectional extraction (E), which can be determined with tracer solutes. (This is quite different from a steady-state or net extraction, and the reader should always understand whether in a given experiment E signifies unidirectional or net extraction.)

$$E = (C_a - C_v)/C_a \tag{6}$$

which gives

$$PS/Q = -\ln(1 - E) \tag{6a}$$

or

$$P = -(Q/S)\ln(1 - E) \tag{7}$$

The major problem with this approach is that for low-molecular-weight solutes the assumption of negligible tissue concentration is valid only for the first few capillary transit times (1–10 s); because of arterial dispersion of the tracer, a constant C_a cannot be established in vivo.

The most important use of the constant-infusion technique has been for the uptake of ^{42}K and ^{86}Rb,

TABLE 1. *Classification of Approaches to Whole-Organ Permeability Studies*

	Technique	Ref.
Diffusion methods		
Blood clearance	Single injection	47, 58
	Constant infusion	276
Tissue uptake	Single injection	232
	Constant infusion	298
Osmotic methods		
Blood transients	Single injection	94
	Constant infusion	247
Tissue transients	Single injection	
	Constant infusion	346

TABLE 2. *Diffusion Coefficients (D) of Hydrophilic Solutes and Water*

	Molecular Radius, Å	Ref.	*D* at 25°C, 10^{-5} cm²/s	Ref.	*D* at 37°C, 10^{-5} cm²/s	Ref.
Inulin	10–25	220, 221	0.16	37	0.23	37
[Carboxyl-^{14}C]inulin					0.30	176
Hydroxy[methyl-^{14}C]inulin					0.25	176
Sucrose	5.2	304	0.52	53	0.70	176
Glucose or mannitol	4.4	16	0.67	197	0.91	176
Na^+	1.8	21	1.4	300	1.8	281
K^+	2.2	21	1.95	288		
THO	1.4	288	2.44	350	3.2	350

Stokes-Einstein radius: $r = RT/6\pi\eta N_A D$, where N_A is Avogadro's number and η is viscosity. $D_2/D_1 = T_2\eta_1/T_1\eta_2$.

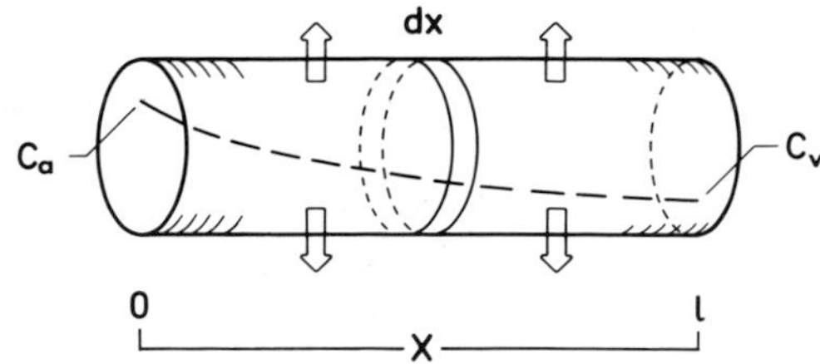

FIG. 2. Relation between capillary blood flow, surface area, and diffusion transport. C_a, arterial concentration; C_v, venous concentration; dx, capillary segment; l, capillary length. Analysis leads to Eqs. 6a and 7.

which (assuming that cellular exchange is rapid) have very large extravascular distribution volumes; and therefore the extravascular concentrations of these substances should remain low for some time (276). The constant-infusion technique is not widely used to assess capillary permeability but rather to measure changes in capillary surface area during perfusion variations induced by sympathetic stimulation or pharmacological vasodilation (285).

Single-injection (indicator-diffusion) technique. In vivo measurements of extraction during a single capillary transit were made possible by the quantitative adaptation by Crone (56, 57, 59) and Martín and Yudilevich (204) of the double-indicator principle described by Chinard and co-workers (46, 47). Prior to the development of this quantitative method, permeabilities from indicator-diffusion experiments were simply given as fractional losses of test solutes (47, 108, 109). Doubts are sometimes expressed about the validity of the indicator-diffusion approach as a means of assessing capillary permeability (44, 374).

In this technique a bolus containing the test (diffusible) solute and a reference (impermeable) solute is injected into the artery and measured in discrete samples at the venous outflow (Figs. 3 and 4). If the concentrations of test (C_s) and reference (C_R) solutes are equal in the injected bolus (or are properly scaled), then for each segment that passes through the organ the venous concentration of the reference solute should be equal to the arterial concentration of the diffusible solute for that segment (allowing for intravascular dispersion). Thus the ratio of C_s to C_R in the vein is described by Equations 5 and 6

$$E = 1 - C_s/C_R = 1 - e^{-PS/Q}$$

This method of measuring capillary permeability requires an arterial cannula for delivery of the bolus, a venous cannula to obtain a sample of the outflow from the organ, and a device for rapid fractional collection of blood samples. It can be performed in vivo with minimal perturbation of normal function. It can also be repeated sequentially on the same organ at relatively short intervals (~1 min). A simultaneous measurement of the flow is necessary to determine P from E (Eq. 7). This measurement can be obtained by applying the standard Stewart-Hamilton dye-dilution

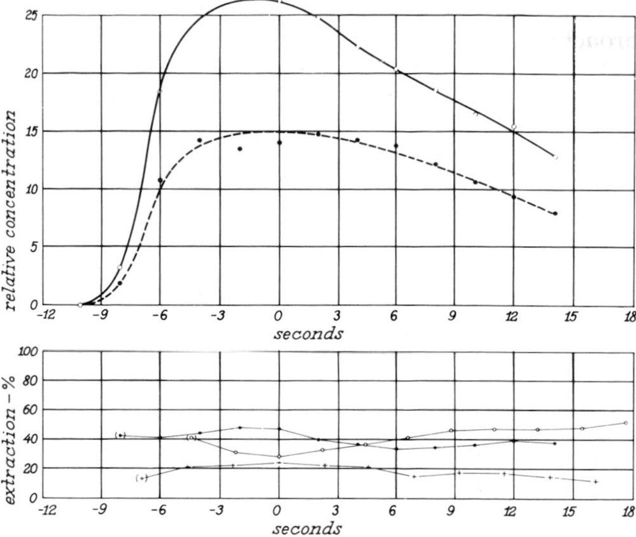

FIG. 3. Relative concentration curves and percent extractions for dog hindlimb. *Top:* ○, Evan's blue–albumin; ●, sucrose. *Bottom:* sucrose extraction values from 3 experiments. Average permeability (P) = 0.74×10^{-5} cm/s. [From Crone (58).]

procedure to the reference indicator (135). Because many fractional blood samples are collected, the method requires a high blood flow; however, it has been used in experiments on rats (144, 223, 287).

The central assumption of this method is that the tissue concentration of the test solute is close to zero. The tissue concentration of the test solute gradually rises, and the contribution of this backflux to the venous concentration may become significant. One solution to this problem is to extrapolate Equation 7 to time zero, when the assumption is valid (204).

This approach is satisfactory if the tissue is homogeneous. For a heterogeneous tissue, however, this procedure provides a measure of the pathways with the shortest transit time—pathways that would be expected to have the smallest value of E. Inserting E into an equation containing the average whole-organ flow may give false results; E should be matched with the flow in the subregion with the fastest transit time. Heterogeneity seems to be present in the heart (289) and the brain (145). To obtain a more representative average of organ capillary permeability, E can be averaged up to the time of peak reference concentration either by taking the arithmetic mean (59) or by determining the area extraction (Fig. 5). The maximum value of E can also be used as a possible solution to this problem (133). The various methods for determining extraction are discussed by Crone (63) and by Bassingthwaighte (13). The single-injection and constant-infusion techniques are compared by Yudilevich et al. (372).

There are two cases in which the indicator-diffusion technique can be interpreted simply and unambiguously. In the first case extraction remains relatively constant for some time and then begins to decrease as

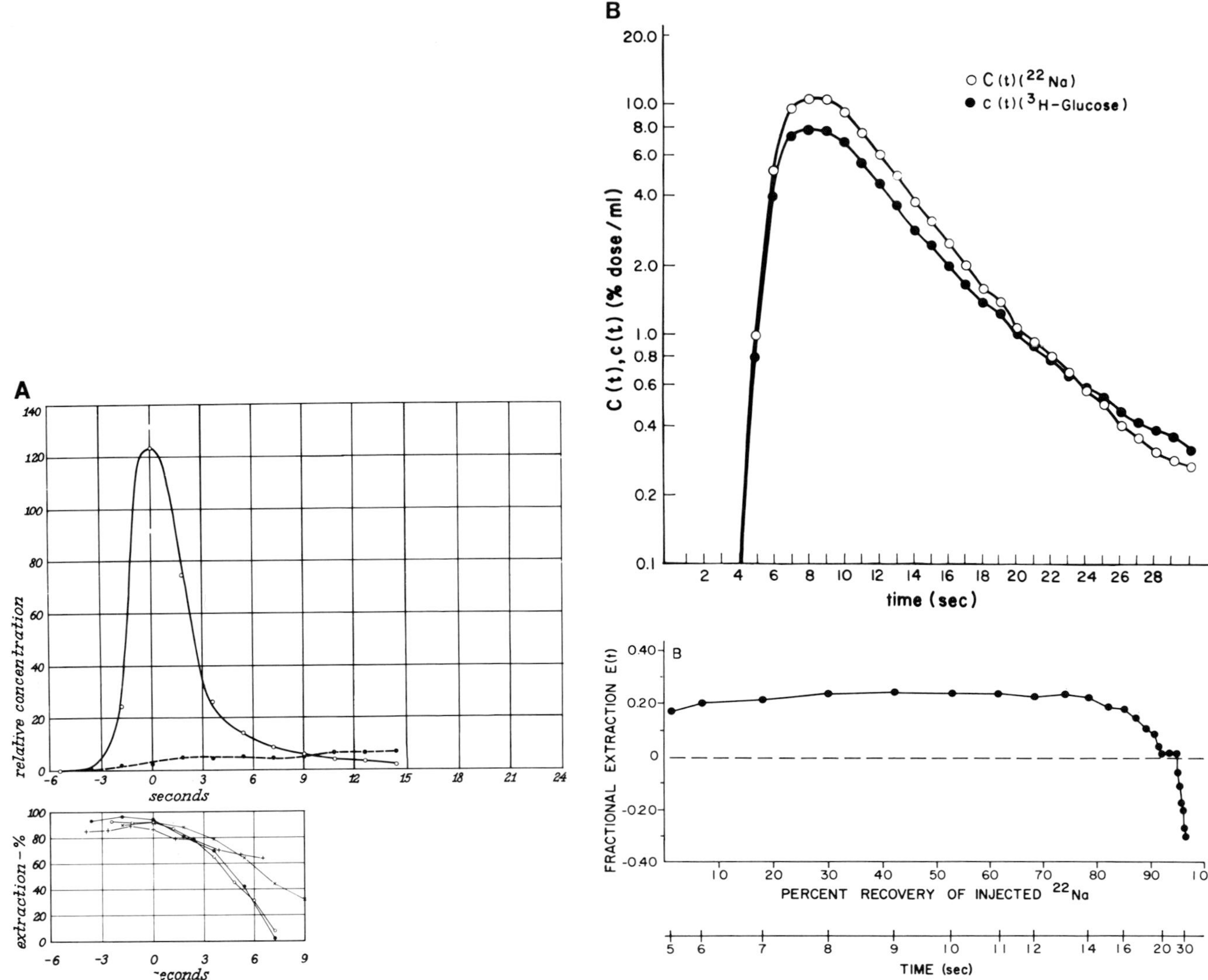

FIG. 4. Solute extraction in dog brain. *A*, *top*: ○, Evan's blue-albumin; ●, butanol. *A*, *bottom*: butanol extraction values from 4 experiments. Average permeability (P) = 10^{-4} cm/s. *B*, *top*: typical dilution curves obtained after simultaneous arterial injection of ^{22}Na and [^{3}H]glucose. C(t) and c(t) are isotope concentrations in venous blood relative to their concentrations in injectate. *B*, *bottom*: plot of fractional extraction of glucose versus total area under ^{22}Na curve in *B*, *top*. Notice constancy of glucose extraction signifying homogeneity and almost unidirectional uptake with minimal backdiffusion. [*A* from Crone (60); *B* from Betz et al. (17).]

backflux increases (Figs. 6 and 7). A constant extraction can result from a coincidental cancellation of the effects of heterogeneity and backflux; however, this seems unlikely, and it should be safe to assume that the organ is relatively homogeneous. Under these conditions the early (constant) E value can be used to determine capillary permeability (Eq. 7). In the second case it is known that backflux is negligible. Early E values can then be regarded as true measures of the capillary permeability of the components of a heterogeneous organ; an average organ permeability can be obtained from an average of the early part of the curve (i.e., up to the peak of C_R) and the whole-organ flow. The time at which backflux becomes important is a function of the value of PS/Q and the ratio of the extravascular volume of distribution (V_t) to the capillary volume (V_c). As PS/Q decreases or V_t/V_c increases, the time at which backflux becomes important increases and the second condition is satisfied. This condition is usually met in the brain and in skeletal muscles because of the low capillary permeability of most hydrophilic solutes (59). Backflux corrections have been analyzed by Perl et al. (262), and an interesting analysis of the indicator-diffusion technique in the presence of organ heterogeneity has recently been given by Bass and Robinson (9a).

Organ models involving partial differential equations. If the simplifying conditions are not satisfied, a

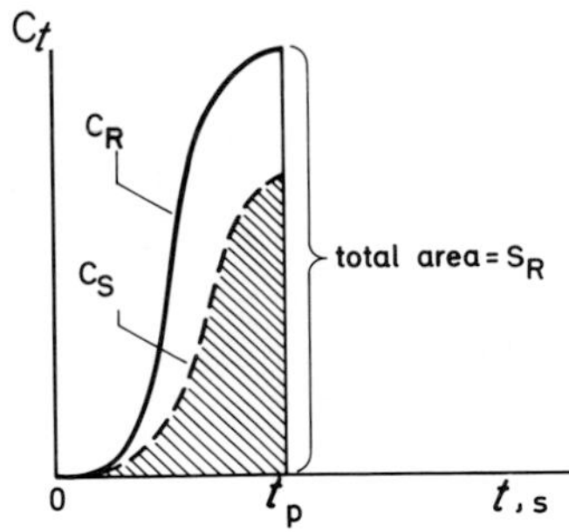

FIG. 5. Average extraction (E) calculated from integrated areas under curves for test solute (C_s) and reference solute (C_R). E = (S_R − S_s)/S_R, where S_s and S_R are the areas under curves for test and reference solutes, respectively. To avoid backdiffusion problems, areas are calculated from appearance to peak of C_R. t, Time; t_p, peak time; C_t, concentration at time t.

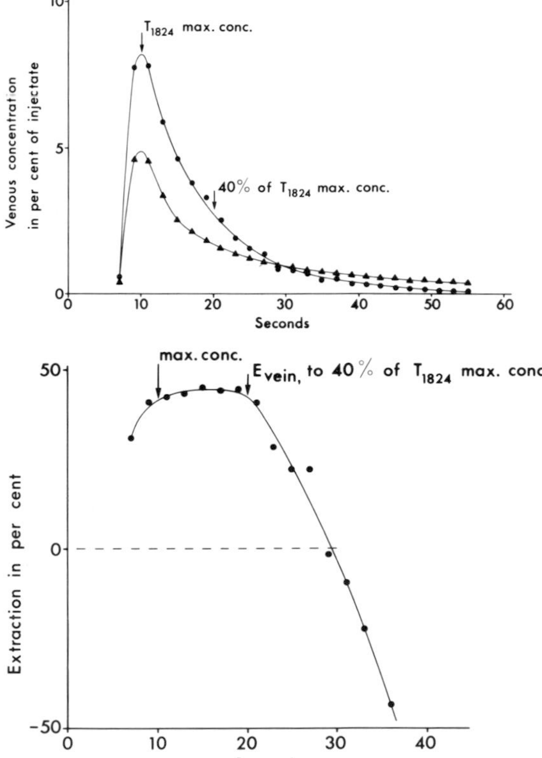

FIG. 6. *Top*: venous outflow curves after bolus injection of Evan's blue–albumin (T_{1824}) and ^{51}Cr-labeled edetic acid (EDTA) in cat skeletal muscle. Values given in percent of injectate concentration. *Bottom*: extractions calculated from values for Evan's blue–albumin and ^{51}Cr-EDTA in each sample. [From Sejrsen (306).]

complete solution for a specific organ model must be obtained (10, 13, 128, 181, 186, 289, 295, 373). A complete analysis of the venous concentration as a function of time requires a detailed model of the organ including such factors as axial and radial tissue diffusion and exchange between neighboring capillaries. A mathematical solution (characterized by a set of parameters that includes the mean and standard deviation of the distributions of flow and surface area of each capillary) is obtained for the venous outflow of an organ model. The parameters are then adjusted to fit the venous outflow curves. This is especially necessary for the lung, where backflux is a severe problem because of the relatively small extravascular space. Rowlett and Harris (295) examined in detail a number of different organ models that can be used to interpret lung studies. This has also been done for the vasoconstricted heart to provide a quantitative description of the relatively great heterogeneity that is observed (128, 133, 289).

The use of organ models provides at best only a rough approximation of true capillary permeability (or its distribution in a heterogeneous organ). The model contains many more adjustable parameters than can possibly be determined experimentally. For example, the outflow from each capillary region is determined by the product of the venous concentration (which depends on PS/Q and V_t/V_c for that region) and flow. The distribution for each capillary region of S (which depends on capillary length) and Q must be known and correlated in order to determine the capillary permeability (which is usually assumed to be the same for all capillaries). The distribution of the pre- and postcapillary vessel transit times must also be known and correlated, if possible, with the distribution of l and Q values. Finally, the capillary model currently used is highly oversimplified. For example, it neglects interactions between neighboring capillaries, which can be important in some cases (139, 187). Because of the many adjustable parameters, a number of different models can probably fit the experimental data. It is not yet possible to independently check the parameters determined by organ modeling.

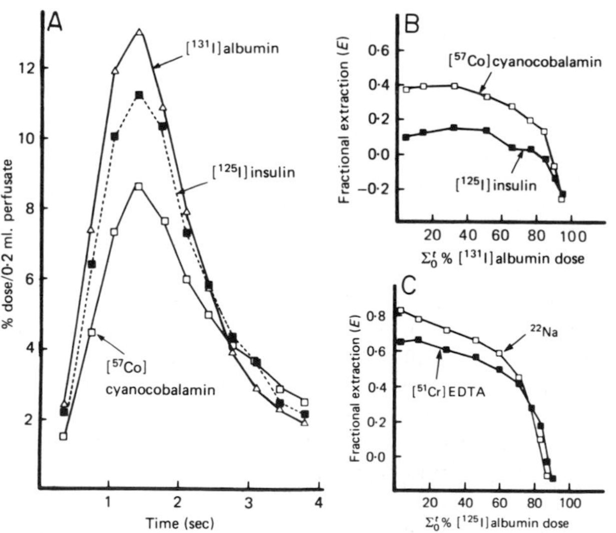

FIG. 7. *A*: venous outflow curves after bolus injection of labeled albumin, insulin, and vitamin B_{12} (cyanocobalamin). Concentrations are normalized with respect to concentrations in injectate. *B*: fractional extractions of vitamin B_{12} and insulin. *C*: ^{22}Na and ^{51}Cr-EDTA. Plateau and return of extravascular material are seen. Experiments on cat submandibular gland. [From Mann et al. (203).]

Limitations of indicator-diffusion technique. The indicator-diffusion technique reaches maximum relative accuracy at an E value of ~0.2–0.5 ($PS/Q \simeq 0.5$; Table 3) and decreases as E approaches either 0 or 1. For example, if E is actually 1, factors such as shunting, backflux, and exchange between arteries and veins and between neighboring tissue regions will limit the value of E to a maximum of ~0.9 ($PS/Q = 2.3$). In such cases the method can only be used to place a lower bound on P; it cannot accurately distinguish between substances with higher P values. The presence of backdiffusion indicates that the experiments are conducted under partially or wholly flow-limited conditions and better data will be obtained if flow is increased. Because increased flow may be accompanied by recruitment of capillaries, resulting in an increased capillary surface area, it is difficult to define experimental conditions rigorously. It is also experimentally difficult to distinguish between solutes with E values less than ~0.05 ($PS/Q = 0.05$) because analytical inaccuracies become important in small extractions. The early part of the dilution curve is always badly defined because of the low concentrations.

It has been pointed out that slight suction in the sampling catheter may lead to inflow from other tissues (144). This is of particular importance in the brain, where extracerebral contamination (from muscle and scalp) ruins experiments because of the great differences in capillary permeability (83). Experiments on the brain should not be carried out without a macromolecular reference substance because contamination can only be disclosed in this way.

Taylor diffusion. A completely different problem with the indicator-diffusion method is related to the assumption that the concentration of the reference solute is equal to the concentration of the test solute if the permeability of the test solute is zero; i.e., the intravascular behavior of the two solutes is identical. Because the test solute is usually smaller and has a higher diffusion coefficient than the reference solute, the test solute will be less dispersed by parabolic flow (Taylor's effect) than the reference solute [Fig. 8; (177)]. The magnitude of this effect is small, producing differences in E values of only a few percent. For the brain, however, where the permeability of many solutes is very small, this error can be important and is probably the reason why early determinations of solute permeability in brain vessels gave values that were too high (61).

TABLE 3. *Corresponding Values of PS/Q and E*

PS/Q	E
0.1	0.1
0.3	0.25
0.5	0.4
1.0	0.6
5.0	0.99

PS, permeability–surface area product; Q, flow; E, extraction.

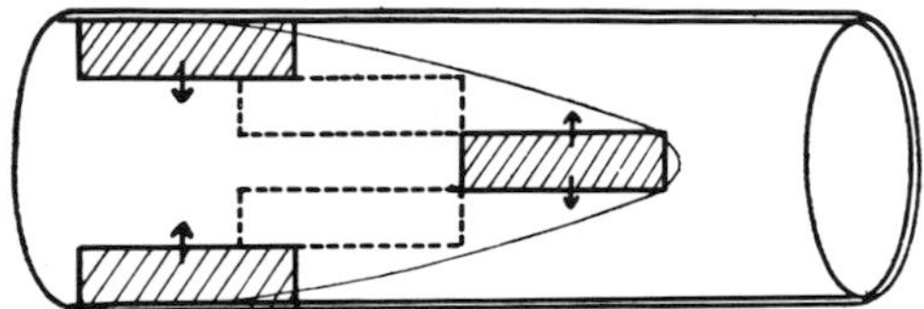

FIG. 8. Interlaminar diffusion. For central (fastest) stream, diffusion makes transit slower. For stream nearest wall (slowest), diffusion makes transit faster. [From Lassen and Crone (177).]

There are two ways to correct for this error. Because the dispersion effect simply sharpens the peak of the test solute, the error is avoided if E is averaged over most of the peak (177, 179). For the low-permeability solutes for which this error is important, backflux is negligible even when most of the peak is used. In the brain the most direct approach to this problem is to use a low-molecular-weight reference solute (such as mannitol) with a diffusion coefficient close to that of the test solute (145, 372); but a macromolecular tracer may also be necessary for the reasons mentioned.

Red cell penetration. Red blood cells are often permeable to the test solute and impermeable to the reference solute, which leads to a second and more serious source of error. It may cause several effects that complicate the interpretation of results from a blood-perfused organ studied with the indicator-diffusion method. As the tracer in the injected bolus flows through the organ, its concentration is altered because of its movement into the red cells. This is a problem when the half time for red cell exchange is on the same order of magnitude as the organ transit time (292). Although an approximate correction for this effect is possible with mathematical modeling (29, 127, 259), the best solution is to avoid if possible diffusible solutes with a significant red cell permeability (e.g., urea, ethylene glycol, ^{36}Cl). This cannot always be done, however, and in experiments on glucose permeation into the human brain, correction for red cell penetration is necessary (145). Roselli (292) examined in detail the effect of preequilibration of tracer and blood in the injectate.

In summary the indicator-diffusion technique, under conditions where its results can be interpreted unambiguously (relatively constant early extraction or small PS/Q), provides a simple and accurate method of measuring capillary permeability and is probably the method of choice. To the extent that these conditions are not met, the permeability values determined by this method become less accurate. In the two cases where muscle capillary data from whole-organ and from single-capillary studies were compared, the results correlated satisfactorily (111, 236). Except for the early results obtained with the osmotic-transient technique (248), indicator-diffusion data correlate well with results obtained from several other whole-organ methods (see Tables 12–14). Many of the theoretical problems encountered with this methodology are, of course, shared with other diffusion approaches (7, 9, 10); however, it is very valuable in clinical use because it requires few interventions (28, 145, 337).

The indicator-diffusion technique can be used to measure the uptake of test solutes in parenchymal cells during a single passage through the organ (39). This modification uses an extracellular reference solute that ideally passes through the capillaries freely; the loss of test solute relative to the loss of extracellular reference solute reflects cellular uptake. The permeability as defined in Equation 7 then describes the permeability of the cell membranes (371a). This technique has allowed determination of the kinetics of nonlinear cell membrane passage of many substrates.

TISSUE-UPTAKE TECHNIQUES. In these methods, test solute is added to the arterial blood and the concentration of solute in the tissue is then measured. A variation of this approach involves indirectly measuring the tissue concentration by external counting of a γ-emitting test solute. These methods are most important in studies of organs or intraorgan regions (e.g., skin, fat) that are not drained by a single, easily cannulated vein (as required by the indicator-diffusion method). An advantage of the method is that its accuracy does not decrease for low-permeability solutes. Thus it is the method of choice for solutes with permeabilities so low ($E < 5\%$) that the indicator-diffusion method is inaccurate. Most measurements of protein permeability, for example, are obtained with this method or with a modification of it such as the use of lymph concentration as a measure of tissue concentration (see the chapter by Taylor and Granger in this *Handbook*).

Constant-infusion technique. A major disadvantage of the direct tissue-analysis method is that only one value for a given time point can be determined per experiment; therefore many experiments must be performed to determine the time course and capillary permeability. This problem has stimulated the development of modifications that provide an estimate of capillary permeability from just one measurement (116, 230). The problem is avoided, however, in the external counting methods where the tissue concentration is measured as a function of time in one experiment (133, 305, 306). Johnson and Wilson (155) have described the most useful model for relating extravascular concentration to capillary permeability. The model is based on the assumption that the extravascular volume of distribution (V_t) is well mixed and that the system is homogeneous, so that a single rate constant can be defined (Fig. 9). For a step-input arterial concentration the extravascular concentration (C_t) is equal to

$$C_t = C_a(1 - e^{-kt}) \qquad (8)$$

where

$$k = Q/V_t(1 - e^{-PS/Q}) \qquad (9)$$

$$P = 0.69V_t/S(t_{1/2}) \qquad (10)$$

Thus tissue concentration rises exponentially with the rate constant k. When permeability is small ($PS/Q \ll 1$), k reduces to

$$k - PS/V_t \qquad (11)$$

and permeability determination does not depend on blood flow; i.e., the rate of tissue uptake is diffusion limited.

When PS/Q is large, k approximates to

$$k = Q/V_t \qquad (11a)$$

and Equation 8 reduces to

$$C_t = C_a(1 - e^{-Qt/V_t}) \qquad (12)$$

which describes the flow-limited condition (163).

By measuring tissue concentrations at different times after the step input, k can be determined. The value of V_t is determined from the equilibrium volume of distribution corrected for the vascular volume. This is essentially the procedure used by Schafer and Johnson (298) for sucrose and inulin in the rabbit heart, by Wittmers et al. (367) for inulin in various tissues of the rabbit, and by Amtorp (2) for nonelectrolytes in the brain.

The procedure has been modified in two ways so that permeability can be estimated from a single time point without needing a step-input arterial concentration. Both modifications require sampling the tissue while the extravascular concentration is still small relative to the blood concentration. With this time limit and an arbitrarily varying arterial concentration ($C_{a,t}$), Equation 8 reduces to

$$C_t = k \int_0^t C_{a,t} dt \qquad (13)$$

An important advantage of working within this early time limit is that the validity of Equation 13 does not depend on assumptions such as the extravascular space being well mixed. In the brain a test solute is injected intravenously, a sample of carotid artery blood is withdrawn at a constant rate, and the average

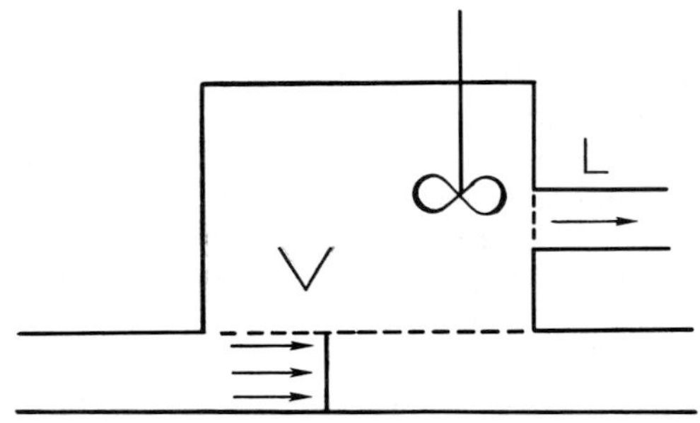

FIG. 9. Representation of model for capillary exchange. V, extravascular distribution volume; L, lymph drainage; *arrows*, fluid velocity. [From Johnson (151).]

concentration in the sample up to time t is measured (122, 230, 269). The extravascular concentration is determined by subtracting the vascular component (determined by intravascular tracer) from the total tissue solute concentration. This subtraction procedure somewhat limits the validity of Equation 13 because, for experimental accuracy, the time must be long enough for the extravascular concentration to become a significant fraction of the total. Thus the tissue concentration is not negligible relative to the blood and the permeability value obtained from Equation 2 is underestimated (230). If $PS/Q \ll 1$ then Equation 11 is valid and permeability is independent of blood flow. In studies of simultaneous uptake of butanol it was found that for highly permeable solutes (such as glucose in the brain) k in Equation 8 depends on regional blood flow (122).

If successive experiments are executed with increasing duration, the amount of test solute in the tissue increases linearly for a while (proving the basic assumption of unidirectional flux). Extrapolation of this line to time zero gives the vascular content of solute, which must be subtracted from the tissue content (Fig. 10).

Single-injection technique. Oldendorf and co-workers (26, 232, 233) have developed a very simple experimental procedure that eliminates the necessity of vascular subtraction and upstream withdrawal of arterial blood. A bolus of the test solute and a highly diffusible reference tracer [heavy water (THO) or an alcohol] is given in a sudden close-arterial injection. The tissue is then sampled after allowing enough time for the test solute in the vasculature to wash out but not long enough for the washout from the tissue to be significant (in the rat brain 15 s was originally considered optimal). If it is assumed that THO is limited by blood flow so that for this short time it is all trapped in the organ, the concentration of THO in the tissue ($C_{t,R}$) is equal to

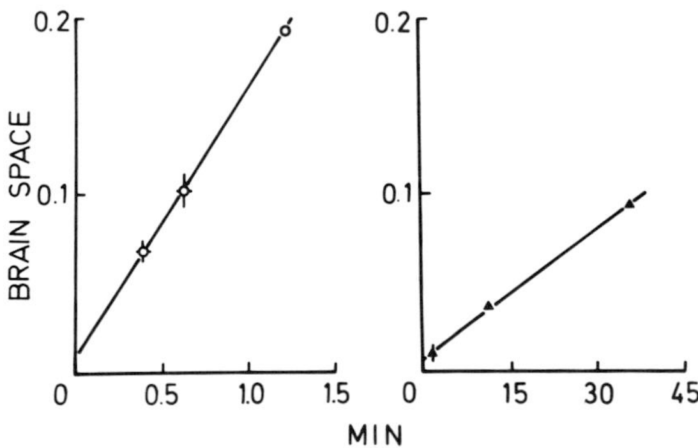

FIG. 10. Unidirectional brain uptake of D-glucose (*left*) and D-mannitol (*right*). Slopes of lines define transfer rate (clearance). *Points*: exposure times of 20, 40, and 70 s for D-glucose; 20 s and 10 and 35 min for D-mannitol. Abscissa, time of decapitation. Ordinate, ratio of counts in brain and plasma [apparent volume of distribution of isotope in brain (ml/g)]. [From Gjedde (117).]

$$C_{t,R} = (Q/V_t) \int_0^t C_{a,t} dt \quad (14)$$

where $C_{a,t}$ is the arterial concentration of THO scaled to equal the arterial concentration of test solute. The integrals in Equations 13 and 14 are then equal and

$$C_t/C_{t,R} = kV_t/Q = PS/Q \quad (15)$$

The last equality is only valid when $PS/Q < 0.1$ or $-\ln(1 - E) \simeq E$. If PS/Q is not small the general expression for k (Eq. 9) must be used (123). This procedure provides a measurement of capillary permeability if the flow to the tissue region is known (26). The ratio in Equation 15 is usually used alone as a relative measure of permeability, the uptake index (UI) (232).

Because brain uptake of THO is subject to some diffusion limitation (23), the relation between the uptake index and the unidirectional extraction is more accurately described by (26)

$$UI = \frac{1 - e^{-PS/Q}}{1 - e^{-P_{t,R}S/Q}} \quad (16)$$

where the denominator is the extraction of THO. Thus only if the denominator $\simeq 1$ is the uptake index equal to the extraction. For THO the uptake index overestimates the true extraction. This has led to the use of more permeable reference indicators (e.g., butanol or nicotine). Another problem with the single-injection tissue-uptake technique is the assumption of complete tracer retention in the brain when the vessels are cleared. This does not always hold true. For a complete description of the backflux of tracers from the tissue, additional exponential terms for efflux must be added to Equation 16.

Perhaps the best solution to this problem is the use of labeled microspheres as reference solutes (194). Microspheres provide a more accurate estimate of flow and because they are permanently trapped, the problem of subsequent washout from the tissue is eliminated. The technique is not without problems, however, particularly if used in close injection (as in the Oldendorf method) rather than intracardiac injection because securing uniform distribution of spheres across the vascular cross section is difficult (121).

Because intra-arterial injection changes inflow pressure and completely displaces residual blood (with effects on viscosity), flow conditions during the experiment are ill defined. Vascular clearing by the test bolus, however, is a unique advantage in the study of facilitated capillary transport of solutes with competitors in plasma (e.g., amino acids) because the concentration of solute in the test bolus can be adjusted according to experimental requirements. The great methodological advantage is simplicity; the technique is perfectly designed for rapid scanning of capillary permeability to a great number of substances. Figure 11 shows the overriding importance of the lipid/water

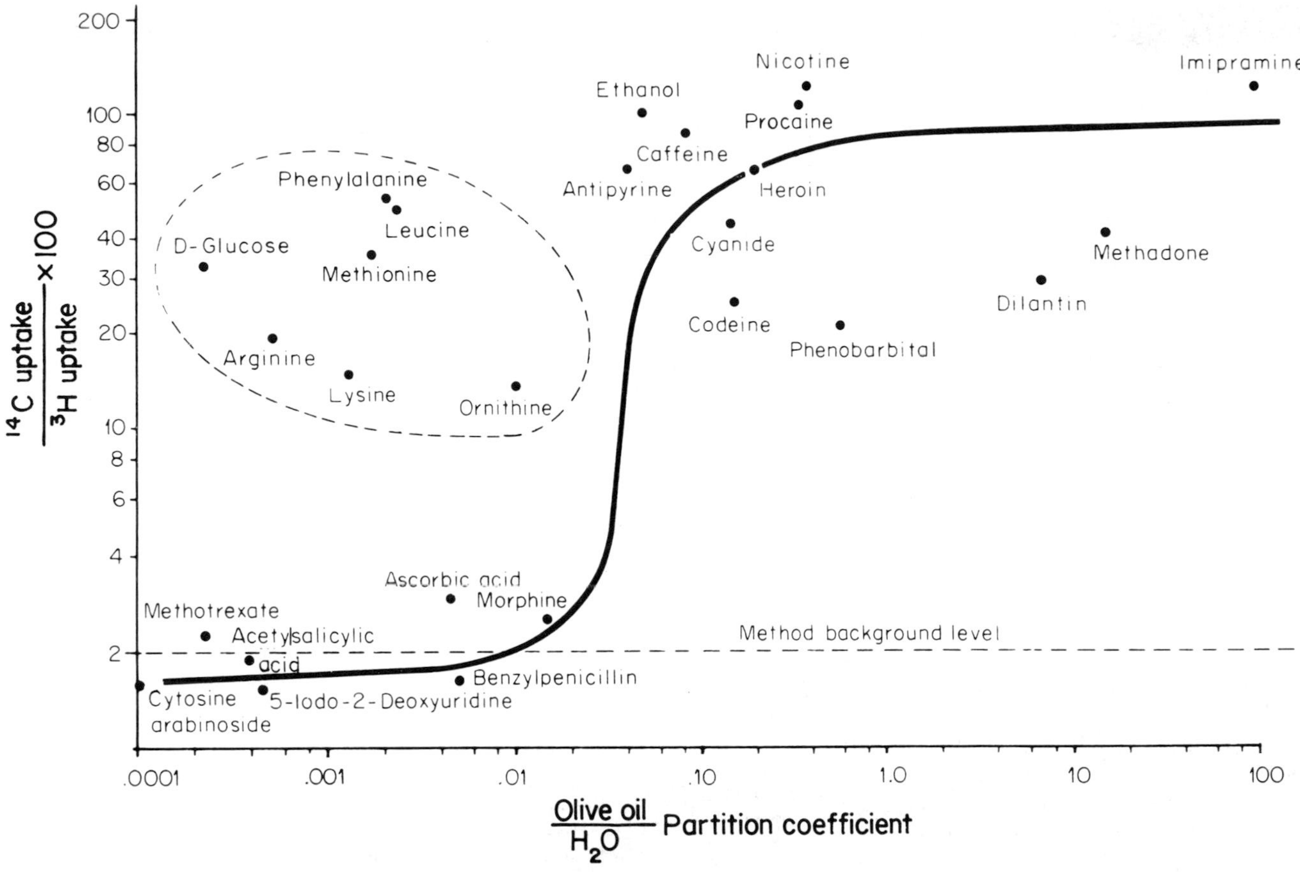

FIG. 11. Brain uptake (relative to uptake of THO) vs. lipid/water partition coefficient during course of single brain passage after intracarotid arterial injection. Drugs with partition coefficient > ~0.03 show nearly complete extraction. Encircled substances on *left*, which have minimal lipid affinity yet show appreciable uptake, are substances with special facilitating transport mechanisms in brain endothelium. [From Oldendorf (234).]

partition coefficient for solute uptake in the brain as demonstrated by the Oldendorf technique. The method has been used extensively in mapping transcapillary transport of amino acids in the brain. These amino acids are classified according to their diffusion facilitation and interaction and have a wide range of transport rates and transport kinetic constants (251). Many amino acids display mutual inhibition.

The use of tissue-analysis methods has been extended to the liver in recent years (250), and there is no reason why they cannot be used in studies of other organs. They are experimentally simple and provide an estimate of capillary permeability that does not require a detailed understanding of organ kinetics. The major disadvantage is that they require the death of the animal for tissue analysis.

A recent development has made it possible to do repeated experiments with tissue-analysis techniques. An ion-sensitive microelectrode is used to determine tissue uptake in response to injection of a test solute into the blood (Figs. 12 and 13). The input plasma integral is determined by withdrawal of arterial blood or, in the brain where extraction is minimal, by venous

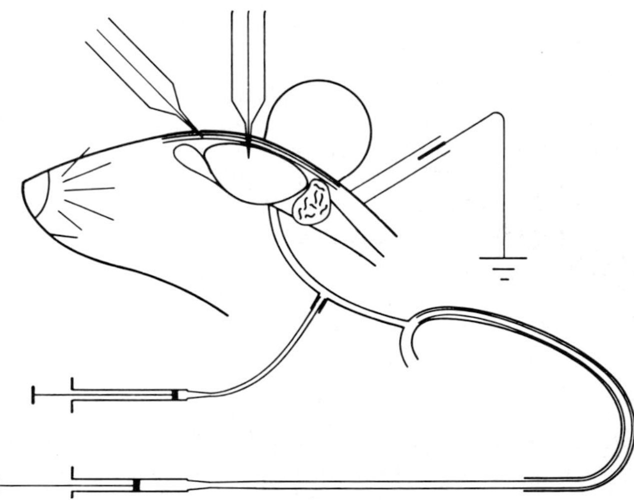

FIG. 12. Experimental setup for tissue-uptake determination with ion-sensitive microelectrodes. Injections of high-K^+ solutions are given either in carotid artery or in aortic arch of rat. Two K^+-sensitive microelectrodes are positioned in brain interstitial fluid and in sagittal sinus. [From Hansen et al. (136).]

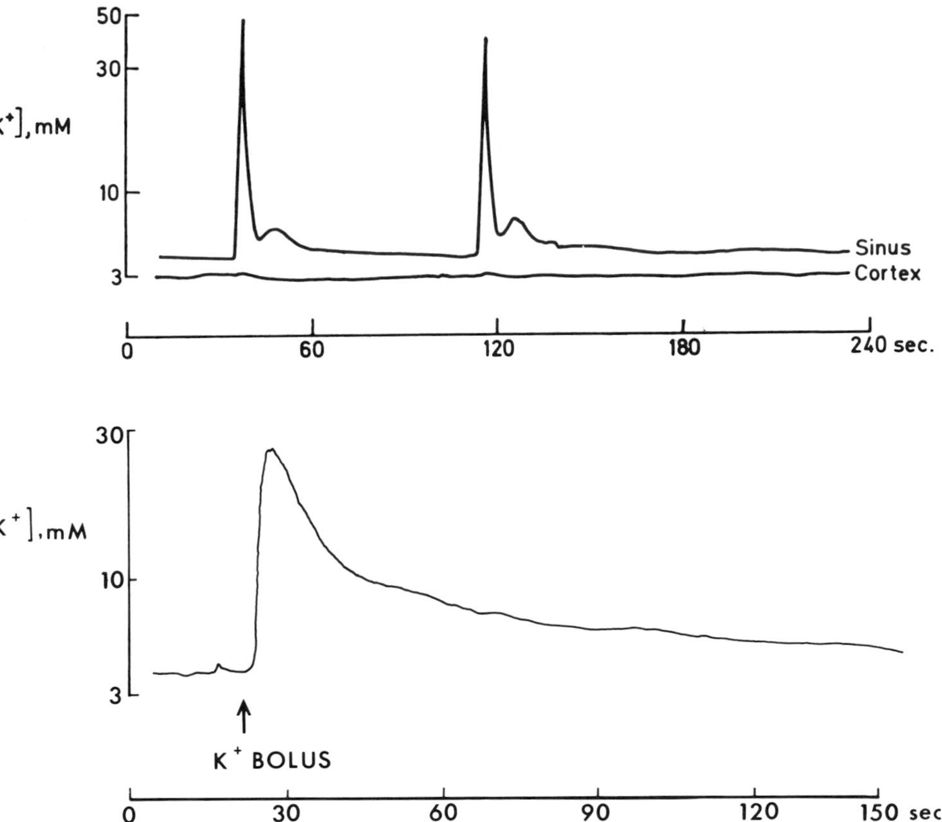

FIG. 13. *Top*: time course of K^+ concentration in sagittal sinus (*upper curve*) and in cortex (*lower curve*) in response to single injection of high-K^+ solution into carotid artery. Electrode in brain does not sense any concentration change, although variation in sinus shows bolus passed through brain vasculature. *Bottom*: time course of K^+ concentration in interstitial fluid of rat mesentery in response to injection into aorta. Much greater response in mesentery reflects high capillary permeability. [From Hansen et al. (136).]

sampling from the sagittal sinus. This technique is used infrequently (136) but is generally applicable for solutes that can be monitored with ion-sensitive microelectrodes. The method should also be useful in determining whether there is in fact an exponential rise in the tissue concentration of test solute in response to a step change in plasma concentration.

Residue detection. With the residue-detection technique, a γ-emitting test solute is administered in a close-arterial bolus injection and the amount of tracer remaining in the organ is monitored by external counting. After allowing time for the labeled solute to be washed out of the vascular space (~30 s), organ radioactivity is assumed to represent the labeled-solute concentration in the extravascular space. Thus the external count is proportional to the tissue concentration and decays ideally with a single-exponential rate as described by Equation 8. Capillary permeability can be determined from the decay time constant (Eq. 9). Permeability is usually assumed to be small, and thus Equation 11 can be used in place of Equation 9, and it is not necessary to measure flow. Permeability can also be determined from Equation 6, which requires information about tracer extraction and plasma flow. Extraction can be determined from the ratio of extrapolated residue activity (at peak time) and peak radioactivity as suggested by Sejrsen (305) (Fig. 14). If the permeability value is not large, flow can be determined from the mean transit time of the intravascular portion (throughput). Assuming true monoexponential washout of residue, rapid throughput can be found by the peeling-off technique, and the mean transit time is calculated from the reconstructed concentration-time curve (305, 306) based on Zierler's equations for blood flow measurement by external counting of radioisotopes (375). This principle was extensively used by Paaske (237–240) in experiments on skin, subcutaneous tissue, and skeletal muscle. The washout curve is only monoexponential for a limited time, however, and only the first part of the time-residue curve can be used for extrapolation. Thus the problem of correctly matching flow and extraction arises. Because the experiments require truly diffusion-limited conditions, the washout of tracer from the tissue should be independent of flow; however, this is often difficult to ascertain. Residue-detection techniques were compared with permeability determinations from outflow studies on heart and muscle, and good correlation was found (133, 306).

The deviation of the residue curve from a monoexponential time course probably reflects tissue heterogeneity. In experiments on Ringer-perfused muscle, the time-residue curve was constructed from successive collections of the total outflow of tracer (73). The fractional efflux (excreted amount per residue per minute) fell constantly with time but rose briefly when flow was transiently stopped (Fig. 15), as though redistribution had occurred within tissue regions. This

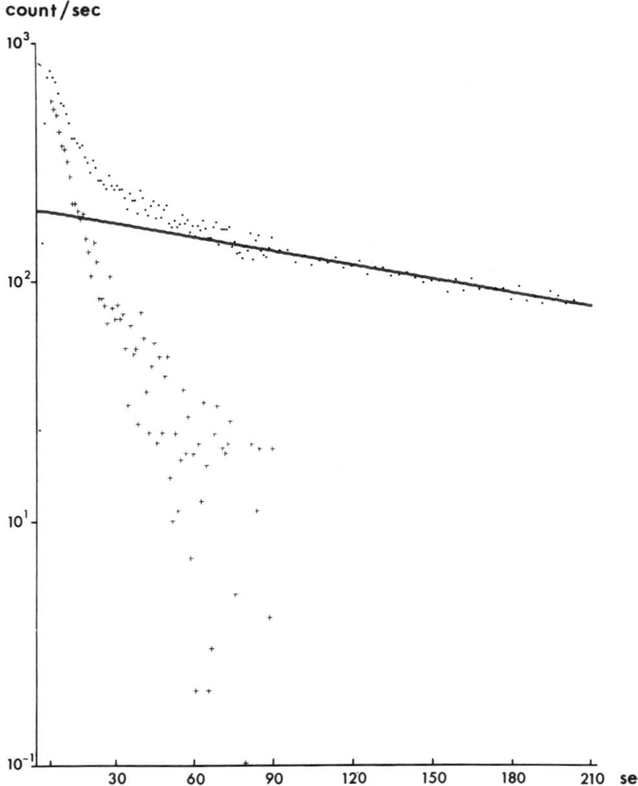

FIG. 14. Residue detection in adipose tissue after intra-arterial bolus injection of [^{57}Co]vitamin B_{12}. Monoexponential regression line is calculated in interval from 150 to 300 s. ●, Recorded count values corrected for background activity; +, intravascular transit curve obtained by subtraction of regression line from original count values. $P = 0.5 \times 10^{-5}$ cm/s. [From Paaske (239).]

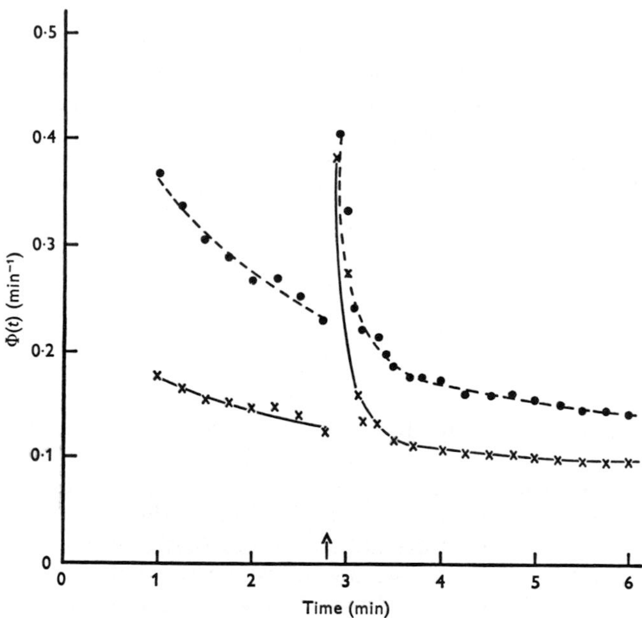

FIG. 15. Time course of fractional escape rate, $\Phi(t)$ for sucrose (●) and inulin (×) with interruption of flow for 1 min (*arrow*). Isolated cat gastrocnemius muscle perfused with nonrecirculating albumin-Ringer's solution. [From Crone and Garlick (73).]

observation stresses one of the well-known ambiguities in the whole-organ approach to capillary permeability (i.e., heterogeneity of tissue clearance).

The effect of heterogeneity on tissue concentration and throughput curves for deuterium (D_2O), including effects of stopping flow, has been extensively studied (73, 131, 195, 290, 334, 335).

The importance of the heterogeneity problem is demonstrated by in vivo studies of microcirculatory beds. Figure 16 shows an example from the frog mesentery where the various lengths of microvessels are clearly seen.

Osmotic Methods

TISSUE TRANSIENTS. *Single-injection technique.* The single-injection technique is aimed primarily at determining the osmotic reflection coefficients of the capillary membrane to various solutes. A relationship exists between the time course of an osmotic transient and the rate of solute passage across the capillary, and therefore permeability values can also be determined with osmotic methods. As shown in Table 1, osmotic tissue transients can in principle be studied in response to single (bolus) injections. However, this methodological principle has not yet been tested. One possible approach is rapid measurement of increases in tissue osmolality in response to the passage of a hypertonic plasma bolus. This can theoretically be done with a microprobe that is sensitive to osmolality (e.g., a glass microelectrode with a semipermeable membrane in the tip). The interstitium, however, is interposed between two water-permeable membranes (capillary membrane and cell membrane) and thus the transient change in osmotic pressure in the interstitium is determined from the relative solute and water permeabilities of the two membranes weighted with their respective surface areas; the transients may only be measurable within the tissue cells.

Constant-infusion technique. Osmotic-transient method for determination of reflection coefficients and diffusional permeabilities. In this procedure, a

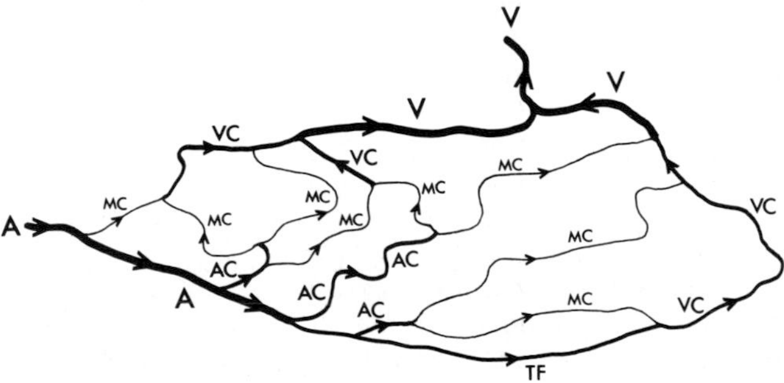

FIG. 16. Drawing of vessels in frog mesenteric microvasculature from microscopic view during in vivo perfusion. A, artery; AC, arterial capillaries; MC, midcapillaries; VC, venous capillaries; V, veins; TF, throughfare channel. [From Bundgaard and Frøkjær-Jensen (34).]

solute is suddenly added to the arterial input of an organ and the resultant osmotic volume flow across the capillary as a function of time is measured by the change in organ weight. Vargas and Johnson (345) developed this method [which is essentially a variation of the isogravimetric measurements used by Pappenheimer et al. (247)] to measure the reflection coefficients of solutes. It remains the only available experimental method for determining reflection coefficients of small solutes in the whole organ. They also showed that the time course of the osmotic transient can be used to determine the permeability of solutes (346). Recently this method and its assumptions have been carefully reevaluated in a series of papers (20, 152, 153, 342–344). These studies have provided us with a good understanding of the strengths and weaknesses of the method and of the degree of confidence that can be placed in the results obtained with it.

The method is first presented in terms of the original model (345). The assumptions of the model are explicitly stated and numbered. A recent analysis of these assumptions and modifications of the model is then discussed.

If it is assumed that *1)* the organ capillaries are homogeneous with a total hydraulic permeability (K_f), then the total volume flux across the capillaries is described by

$$J_v = K_f[(P_c - P_t) - RT\Sigma\sigma_i(C_c - C_t)_i] \quad (17)$$

where P_c and P_t are the hydrostatic pressures in the capillary and tissue, respectively; σ_i is the osmotic reflection coefficient of the *i*th solute; and C_c and C_t are the capillary and tissue concentrations, respectively, of the *i*th solute. The organ is perfused long enough to establish a steady-state volume flux, and then the change in volume flux (ΔJ_v) is measured after the sudden addition of a test solute to the perfusion solution. If it is assumed that *2)* P_c and P_t and *3)* C_c and C_t for the solutes present during the steady state (resident solutes) are unaffected by this sudden change and that *4)* the extravascular volume of distribution of the test solute is well mixed and can be described at any given time *t* by a single value of tissue concentration, then the change in volume flux is described by

$$\Delta J_v(t) = -RTK_f\sigma_s(C_c - C_t)_s \quad (18)$$

The tissue concentration of the test solute starts at zero and then rises as the solute moves from the capillary to the tissue. The rate of this rise depends on capillary permeability. By extrapolating ΔJ_v to $t = 0$ (when $C_t = 0$), an expression for σ_s can be obtained

$$\sigma_s = -\Delta J_v(0)/(RTK_f\bar{C}_0) \quad (19)$$

where $\bar{C}_0$ is the average capillary concentration of the test solute at $t = 0$. Vargas and Johnson (345) assumed *5)* the flow was fast enough that $\bar{C}_0 \simeq C_a$ in all capillaries and used the following expression to determine σ_s, experimentally

$$\sigma_s = -\Delta J_v(0)/(RTK_fC_a) \quad (20)$$

Finally, organ (i.e., heart) weight was continuously measured and it was assumed that *6)* the rate of change of organ weight was equal to ΔJ_v. Assumption *4* is not required for the determination of σ_s (Eq. 19) if it is possible to make a fairly accurate extrapolation to $t = 0$ (when $C_t = 0$).

The determination of σ, which is relatively independent of the organ model and its assumptions, requires only the measurement of $\Delta J_v(0)$ (Fig. 17). In contrast, capillary permeability is determined from the time course of ΔJ_v and depends much more on a detailed description of the organ. Johnson and Wilson (155), using a model based on all the above except assumption *5* and with the additional assumption that *7)* the solvent drag across the capillary is negligible, determined the capillary and extravascular concentrations of solute as functions of time and showed that for *t* greater than about two capillary passage times

$$C_c(x)/C_a = 1 - (1 - e^{-PS/Q(x/l)})e^{-kt} \quad (21)$$

and

$$C_t/C_a = 1 - e^{-kt} \qquad k = (Q/V_t)(1 - e^{-PS/Q}) \quad (22)$$

where *x* denotes the position in the capillary and *l* is capillary length. The expression then for ΔJ_v as a function of time is

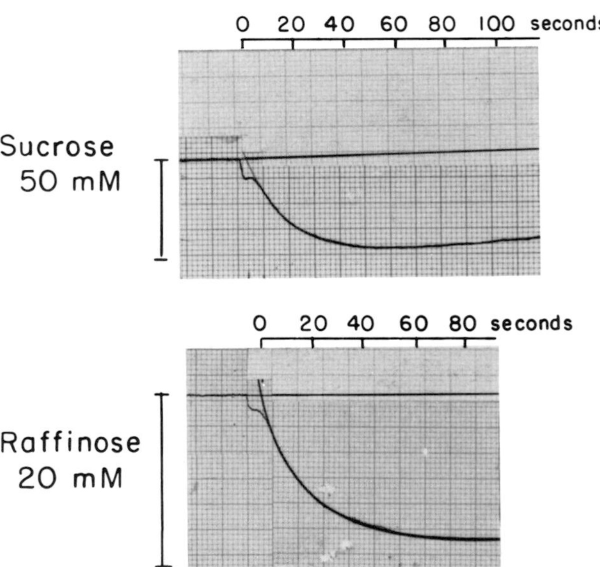

FIG. 17. Recordings of osmotic transients obtained for sucrose (*top*) and raffinose (*bottom*). Magnitude of 1 g is indicated by *vertical bar* at *left* of each recording. Initial irregularities are switching artifacts. [From Vargas and Johnson (345).]

$$\Delta J_v(t) = -\sigma RTK_f\left[l^{-1}\int_0^l C_c(x)dx - C_t\right]$$
$$= C_a\sigma RTK_f\left[\left(\frac{1 - e^{-PS/Q}}{PS/Q}\right)(e^{-kt})\right] \quad (23)$$

The time constant k for the solute can be determined from a plot of log ΔJ_v versus t. The value of P can then be determined from k (Eq. 9 or 22) and the known values of Q, S, and V_t. With this procedure, Vargas and Johnson (346) calculated P and σ in the rabbit heart for a series of nonelectrolytes (Tables 12–15).

Although the assumptions in the method were discussed in detail in the original paper, the quantitative importance of the assumptions has only been established by a recent series of papers from Johnson and his colleagues (20, 152, 153). They have analyzed the theoretical osmotic transient for a detailed model that incorporates lymph flow, the exchange of water across the cells, the elastic properties of the extravascular space, changes in extravascular pressure and in NaCl concentration, solvent drag, gradients along the capillary, and dispersion of the solute front between the input and the capillary. They first designed a model organ based on lymph flow, tissue elasticity, permeability, reflection coefficient, and other parameters in the rabbit heart. Then the experimental value of σ was determined by extrapolating the theoretical ΔJ_v value back to $t = 0$ (Eq. 19); the experimental value of PS was determined from the semilogarithmic plot of ΔJ_v versus t. (Eq. 23). By comparing the experimental values with the assigned model values, they were able to test the validity of the assumptions.

Johnson and Bloom (152) found a significant error in the determination of PS—the experimental values were about twice the model value for inulin and about half the model value for NaCl. Inulin and NaCl represent opposite extremes of solute characteristics, and thus the factors responsible for the errors are different for the two solutes. The explanation of these errors in measurement of PS is illustrated by the model calculations shown in Figures 18 and 19. The effects of change in cellular and extracellular volume on change in total organ volume (weight) are demonstrated for inulin (Fig. 18*A*) and NaCl (Fig. 18*B*) osmotic transients. Figures 19*A* (inulin) and 19*B* (NaCl) show the changes in driving forces for volume flow across the capillary.

Inulin has relatively high σ and low PS values and therefore produces a large and long-lasting volume flux across the capillary. This volume flux comes primarily from the extracellular space with little change in cellular volume (Fig. 18*A*). Because of the elasticity of the tissue, this large volume change causes a significant fall in tissue pressure, which results in a larger ΔP (Fig. 19*A*). The change in tissue pressure, which was neglected in the original model (assumption 2), contributes significantly to the decrease in J_v during the transient and is largely responsible for the error in PS. The decrease in tissue pressure has been directly measured by small needles inserted into the perfused heart (343). Thus, to obtain an accurate PS value for a solute like inulin, it is necessary either to include an estimate of tissue elasticity in a more detailed model or to directly measure tissue pressure. The contribution of the resident solute (Fig. 19*A*) to volume flux during an inulin transient is negligible (152) in contrast to the results of a theoretical study by Grabowski and Bassingthwaighte (130).

A very different factor is responsible for the underestimate of PS for NaCl. Because NaCl has very low σ and large PS values, high concentrations of the solute must be used to obtain a measurable osmotic transient. This leads to large shifts of water across the

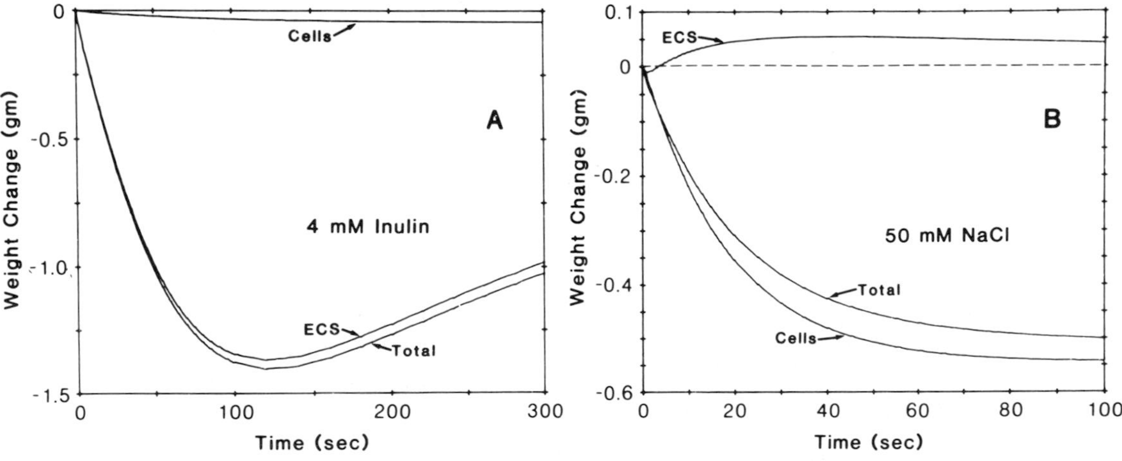

FIG. 18. Results of osmotic-transient experiment for theoretical model of organ similar to rabbit heart. Changes in weight (or volume) of cells, extracellular space (ECS), and total organ during osmotic transient with inulin (*A*) or NaCl (*B*). [Modified from Bloom and Johnson (20).]

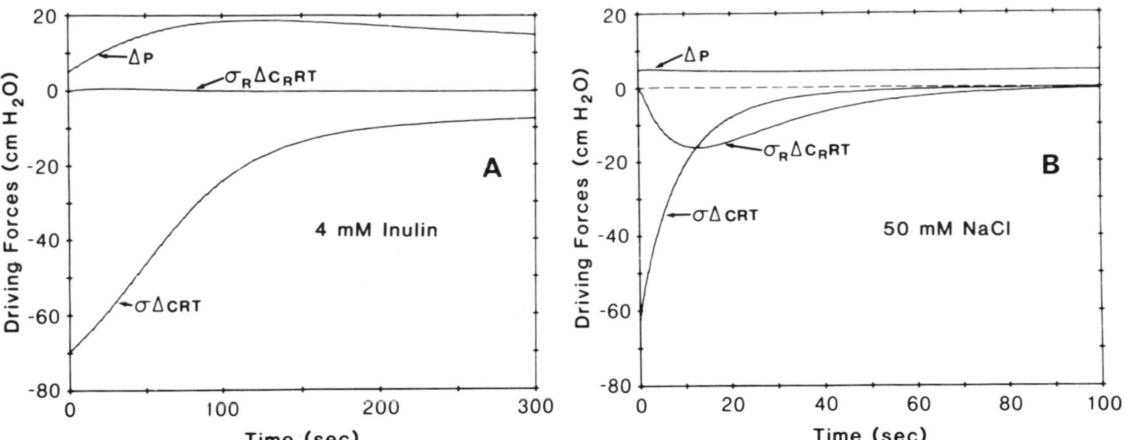

FIG. 19. Driving forces for fluid movement during transient. $\sigma \Delta CRT$, effective osmotic force of test solute inulin (*A*) or NaCl (*B*); $\sigma_R \Delta C_R RT$, effective osmotic force of resident solute (NaCl) present before transient started; ΔP, hydrostatic pressure difference. Positive ΔP (even at $t = 0$) results from lymph flow prior to transient. [Modified from Bloom and Johnson (20).]

heart muscle cell membrane. In fact nearly all organ weight loss is caused by changes in cellular volume (Fig. 18*B*), whereas the change in extracellular volume and therefore tissue pressure (Fig. 19*B*) is very small. This volume shift causes a significant decrease in the resident NaCl concentration. This decrease, which was neglected in the original model (assumption *3*), significantly alters the volume flux and produces the error in *PS* values. Theoretical analysis (152) shows that the error results from using the wrong value for V_t in Equation 22. Because of the rapid movement of water across the cell membrane, the heart behaves as if the entire extravascular space (cellular and extracellular) is available for dilution of NaCl. If this total volume is used in Equation 22, the model and experimental values for *PS* are in good agreement. The appropriate value for V_t ranges from the true interstitial volume for solutes like inulin (high σ, low *PS*) to the total extravascular volume for solutes like NaCl (low σ, high *PS*). The detailed model (including additional organ parameters) must be used to determine the correct V_t value of intermediate solutes.

Vargas et al. (344) recently measured *PS* for Cr-labeled ethylenediaminetetraacetic acid (EDTA), a strongly absorbing dye) with the osmotic-transient method and simultaneously with direct measurement of the change in dye concentration in the venous effluent (Eq. 22). No significant difference was found between the *PS* values obtained with the two methods. Based on the preceding theoretical discussion, this agreement may exist because Cr-EDTA is intermediate between NaCl and inulin and because the errors caused by changes in tissue pressure and in resident-solute concentration are probably small and tend to cancel each other.

Determination of the reflection coefficient by the osmotic-transient method only requires knowledge of the values of ΔJ_v and the average capillary concentration of the test solute at $t = 0$ (Eq. 19). Johnson et al. (153) calculated an experimental reflection coefficient by extrapolating the transients for their detailed organ model back to $t = 0$ and used Equation 20 (which assumes that $\overline{C}_0 \simeq C_a$) to determine σ. Vargas et al. (344) recently suggested that a better estimate is obtained when $\overline{C}_0$ is determined from

$$\overline{C}_0/C_a = (1 - e^{-(PS/Q)})/(PS/Q) \qquad (24)$$

When Equation 24 is used with the data provided by Johnson et al. (153), the experimental reflection coefficient differs by less than 2% from the model value as long as the solute permeability is not too large ($PS/Q < 1.5$).

This analysis indicates that it should be possible to obtain accurate estimates of the reflection coefficient with Equation 24 for $\overline{C}_0$ in Equation 19; however, this requires that *PS* be known. It can be assumed that for solutes with low permeability values, $PS/Q \ll 1$, so that $\overline{C}_0 \simeq C_a$. For $PS/Q = 0.1$, for example, $\overline{C}_0/C_a = 0.95$, and σ is underestimated by only 5% if C_a is used in Equation 19. For more highly permeable solutes it is necessary to use either high flows (so that *PS*/Q stays small) or some estimate of *PS*. In the original study by Vargas and Johnson (345) the *PS*/Q value for urea was ~0.35 and σ was underestimated by ~16%.

Vargas and Blackshear (342, 343) have experimentally examined other possible sources of error in the determination of the reflection coefficient for sucrose. By measuring the venous concentration change of an impermeable dye (blue dextran), they verified the assumption that the rate of change in heart weight during an osmotic transient is equal to transcapillary flow. By varying the NaCl concentration of the perfusion medium, they investigated the influence of the resident-solute concentration on the measurement of the reflection coefficient and concluded that there were no detectable effects.

The hydraulic permeability or filtration coefficient (K_f) (needed in Eq. 19) is an important source of uncertainty in the measurement of the reflection coefficient. The direct approach uses hydraulic permeability from a hydrostatic-pressure transient. One complication in an experiment of this type is that a change in hydrostatic pressure produces a change in vascular volume that must be subtracted from the change in total organ weight to obtain the transcapillary volume flux. This problem is especially severe in the lung where the vascular volume change may account for 90% of the change in total organ weight. Also, if there is a heterogeneous distribution of cleft sizes or a hydraulic permeability gradient from the capillary to the small veins, this pressure K_f may introduce a different weighting of the distribution than that of the appropriate osmotic K_f. An alternative approach uses the osmotic transient for albumin (or some other large molecule) as a standard to which smaller solutes are compared (i.e., arbitrarily assign albumin a σ value of 1). This procedure avoids the problems encountered with the pressure K_f; however, only a relative reflection coefficient can thus be determined. In the brain and heart the absolute value of σ for albumin is ~1 (Table 15), and therefore this is not an important problem. In the lung, however, the reported values of σ for albumin range from ~0.2 to ~0.8. This variation is probably caused in part by the difficulty of correcting for the vascular volume change, and at present only the relative reflection coefficients are reliable for the lung (cf. Table 15).

The osmotic-transient method is the only experimental method available for the measurement of the reflection coefficient of an organ. Thus it is fortunate that recent theoretical and experimental analyses indicate that this method should provide a good estimate of the true organ reflection coefficient.

BLOOD TRANSIENTS. *Single-injection technique.* Effros (94) realized that the transient elevation of the osmotic concentration of plasma flowing from an organ in response to an intra-arterially injected hyperosmotic bolus of urea, NaCl, or sucrose contains information about the reflection coefficient of the capillary membrane. The flow of fluid drawn from the organ into the blood by osmosis (J_v) is given by

$$J_v = \sigma K_f(\overline{C} - C_0) \qquad (25)$$

where $\overline{C}$ is the average excess osmolality along the capillaries and C_0 is the resident osmolality of the blood and tissues. The fluid withdrawn from the organ dilutes the blood; the degree of blood dilution multiplied by the venous organ blood flow (Q_v) gives J_v. The blood dilution is found from hemoglobin and Evan's blue–albumin determinations, and C_a and C_v are related by

$$C_v/C_a = \frac{Q_v - J_v}{Q_v} \qquad (26)$$

Outflow osmolality relative to inflow osmolality is reduced in proportion to the amount of fluid extracted from the lungs, and therefore arterial inflow osmolality can be determined. Assuming exponential decline of excess osmolality during capillary passage, average capillary osmolality is $\overline{C} = (C_a - C_v)/(\ln C_a - \ln C_v)$. Thus σK_f can be found experimentally, for example, by averaging the first three or four collected samples (Fig. 20). Blood dilution rapidly vanishes, followed by the return of fluid to the organ and a small transient elevation of blood osmolality; thus the curve is biphasic. In experiments on lung capillaries 2%–4% of the pulmonary water content was removed before net return began after a few seconds. The extracted fluid flow amounted transiently to 5%–10% of the total pulmonary blood flow.

To calculate the reflection coefficient, the organ filtration coefficient must be known. Effros (94) did not determine this value, and therefore only relative values for reflection coefficients are given. Only small differences were found for sucrose, NaCl, and urea.

Because the method involves a calculated average transcapillary osmotic concentration difference, any flow limitation leads to an overestimate of the driving force and an underestimate of the reflection coefficient.

Effros (94) suggested that the fluid removed from the lungs, which was strongly hypotonic (Fig. 20*B*), represents an osmotic flow from the cellular compartment with no significant flux through the interendothelial clefts (Fig. 21). Wangensteen et al. (352) recently verified these results and concluded that the reflection coefficients of the clefts for NaCl, urea, and sucrose are close to zero.

The osmotic-bolus technique has been used in human studies to determine the filtration coefficient of brain capillaries (255).

Constant-infusion technique. In the strict sense, this approach has not been used. However, the experiments by Pappenheimer et al. (247) logically belong under this heading, although the isogravimetric technique they used is actually a hybrid of several approaches. Their studies were done on an isolated perfused hindlimb. The addition of an extra solute to the perfusate caused fluid withdrawal, as reflected in the reduction of limb weight. If venous pressure (and therefore intracapillary pressure) is increased, net fluid movement can be prevented (isogravimetry). The increase in hydrostatic pressure (ΔP) is assumed to be equivalent to the osmotic force ($\Delta \Pi$) and thus an average transcapillary concentration difference can be calculated with van't Hoff's law: $\Delta \Pi = RT\Delta C$ (assuming $\sigma = 1$). If J_s is simultaneously calculated as $Q(C_a - C_v)$, the flux equation can be solved and *PS* determined from (cf. Eq. 2)

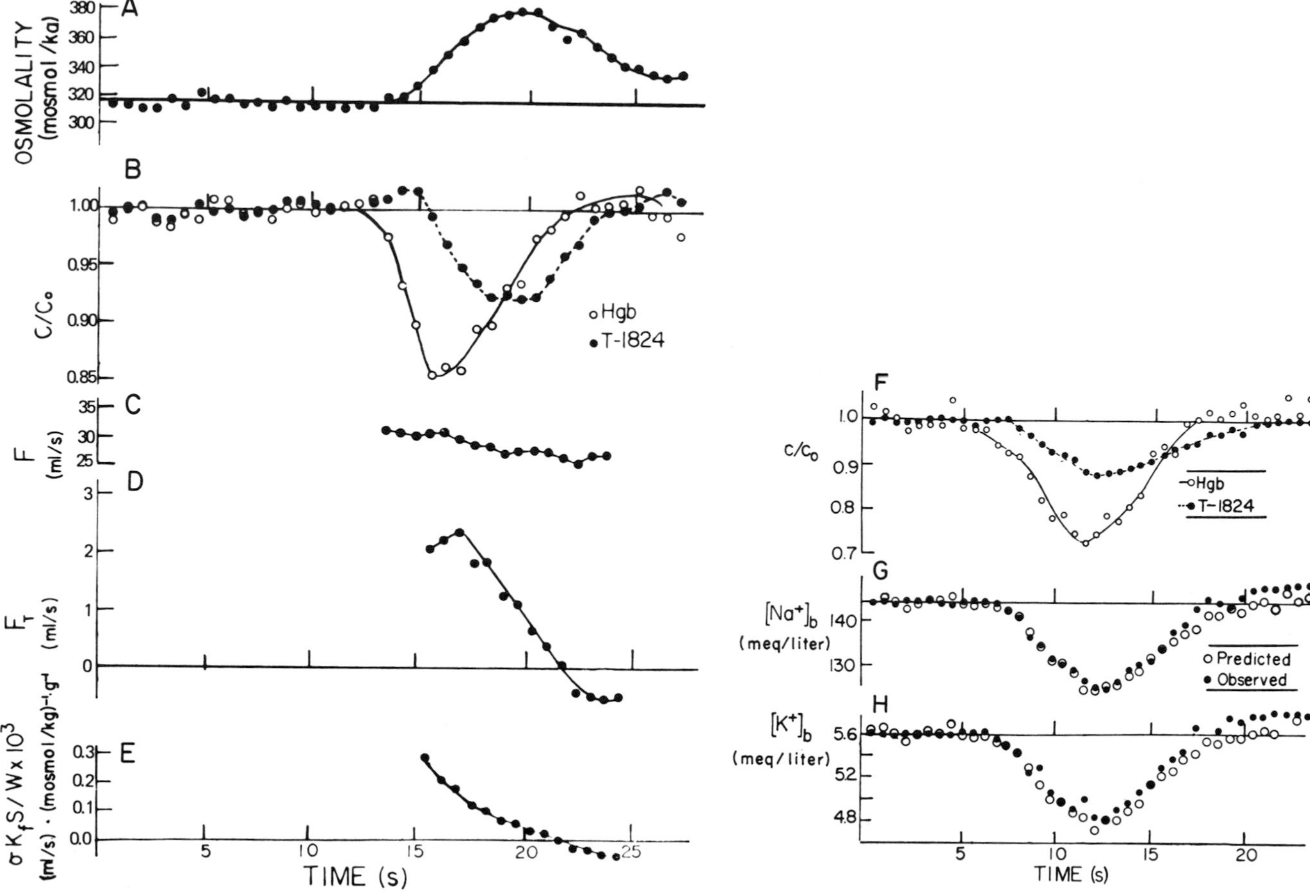

FIG. 20. Responses of lung to injection of hypertonic sucrose solution. *A*: plasma osmolality (determined by freezing-point depression). *B*: fractional changes in whole-blood concentration of hemoglobin (Hgb) and Evan's blue–albumin. Note earlier and more pronounced decline of hemoglobin levels, attributed to impairment of red cell passage through lungs. *C*: F, instantaneous pulmonary blood flow. *D*: F_T, calculated transcapillary fluid flow. Negative values of F_T indicate return of fluid to tissue. *E*: calculated values of net fluid movement per unit of excess osmolality. *F*: whole-blood concentrations of Na^+ and K^+ predicted from concomitant hemoglobin and Evan's blue–albumin concentrations (assuming extracted fluid does not contain either ion). *G* and *H*: predicted concentrations compared with observed concentrations. [From Effros (94).]

$$PS = \frac{Q(C_a - C_v)RT}{\Delta P} \tag{27}$$

Many studies have shown that, because capillary membranes in muscle are permeable to low-molecular-weight hydrophilic solutes, the reflection coefficient is less than one (66, 132, 151, 160, 193, 243, 257, 258, 281, 339). The results do not give *PS* but *PS*/σ because σ was omitted in the calculations. Theoretically the results overestimate permeabilities by various degrees depending on the reflection coefficient (67, 257). The effect of heteroporosity has been analyzed (254); it is suggested that there is volume circulation under isogravimetric conditions in a heteroporous membrane.

Several proposals have been suggested for correction of the original data. Renkin and Curry (281) recently suggested revised values that had been decreased by a factor of 10 for small solutes (less for bigger solutes). These revised values correlate well with those obtained with other methods. Thus there is satisfactory correspondence between permeabilities for small solutes obtained with a host of techniques (see Table 5).

Pappenheimer et al. (247) also determined the half times of osmotic transients as transcapillary diffusion progressed toward equilibrium. Half times of ~10 min were found for solutes such as glucose or sucrose. If the system is treated as a two-compartment system, i.e., the perfusate (V_1) and the extravascular distribution space (V_2), then in analogy with Flexner et al. (103)

$$\frac{C_t - C_{eq}}{C_0 - C_{eq}} = e^{-kt} \tag{28}$$

where $k = PS\,[(V_1 + V_2)/(V_1V_2)]$; C_t is the concentration of inflow at time *t*; C_0 is the concentration at the start of the experiment; and C_{eq} is the concentration of solute at equilibrium in the blood and tissue. The

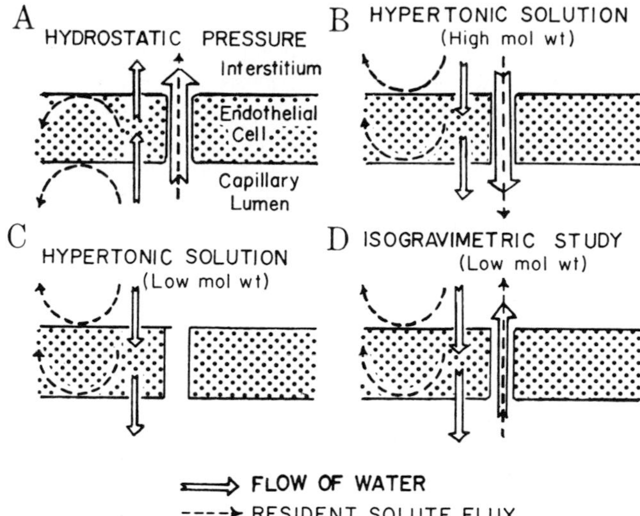

FIG. 21. Parallel-path model of fluid and resident solute movements through pulmonary capillary cells and junctions in response to rise in capillary hydrostatic pressure (*A*), increase in vascular concentration of high-molecular-weight substance (*B*), increase in vascular concentration of low-molecular-weight substance (*C*), and simultaneous isogravimetric increase in serum osmolality (with low-molecular-weight substance) and capillary hydrostatic pressure (*D*). [From Effros (94).]

sizes of the compartment were $V_1 = 150$ ml and $V_2 = 30$ ml. Thus $PS/D \sim 0.016 \times 10^5$ cm/100 g tissue, which is 10–20 times smaller than the values obtained with van't Hoff's equation and close to the newly revised values. Pappenheimer et al. (247) were aware of this large discrepancy but rejected compartmental analysis by arguing that the capillary mean concentration is significantly lower than arterial inflow concentration, and therefore the analysis is inapplicable. The small arteriovenous concentration difference in most experiments, however, speaks against this as a serious problem. Renkin (275) later used compartmental analysis to determine urea and antipyrine permeability in perfused cat hindlimbs.

Kedem and Katchalsky (160) noticed that the earliest osmotic pressure difference was only 5%–30% of the expected value; thus a full osmotic effect was never exerted (Fig. 22) because of low reflection coefficients. If this directly obtained reflection coefficient is used, the permeability for small solutes is diminished by a factor of ~20 (for inulin, ~3). It is still undecided, even with the revised figures, whether or not selective diffusion restriction occurs among small hydrophilic solutes in muscle capillaries as suggested in the original papers (245, 247).

RATE-LIMITING PROCESSES IN BLOOD-TISSUE EXCHANGE

At least three different factors determine the time course of solute exchange between blood and tissue: *1*) blood flow, *2*) capillary permeability, and *3*) rate of diffusion in the extravascular space. To measure capillary permeability the experimental conditions must be arranged so that capillary exchange is the rate-limiting process. For solutes that have a high permeability (e.g., Na^+), however, this is usually not possible and the process becomes flow dependent. The interaction between blood flow and capillary permeability is illustrated by the tissue-uptake technique where the time constant (k) for the rise in tissue concentration is described by Equations 8 and 9: $k = (Q/V_t)[1 - \exp(-PS/Q)]$. Clearly k depends on both P and Q. If permeability is very small ($PS/Q \ll 1$; i.e., permeability limited), Equation 11 applies: $k = PS/V_t$. Permeability is usually assumed to be small so that it can be determined from Equation 11.

If permeability is very large ($PS/Q \gg 1$; i.e., flow limited), then k becomes independent of P (Eq. 11a): $k = Q/V_t$. This is illustrated in Figure 23, which shows that for highly permeable solutes only the early part of the capillary membrane is effective for exchange. Under such conditions permeability may be seriously underestimated. As a general procedure the flow-limited time constant (Eq. 11a) should be compared with the time constant of the experimental process being studied. If they are similar it should be realized that the process may actually be flow limited.

There are at least two tissue models that yield flow-

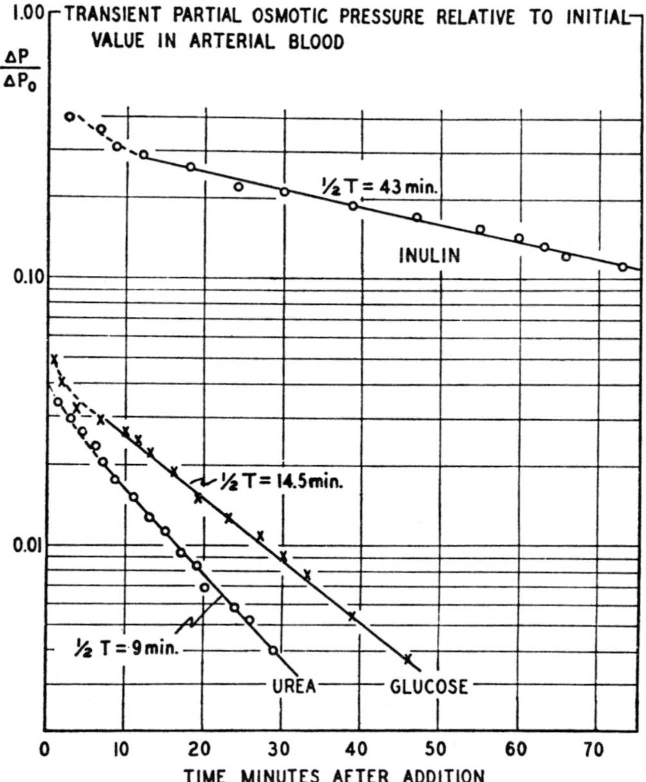

FIG. 22. Osmotic transients in hindlimb muscles of cat. [From Pappenheimer et al. (247).]

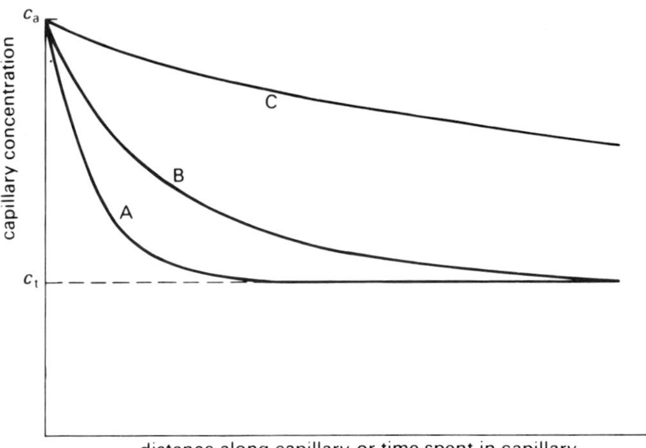

FIG. 23. Intracapillary concentration of diffusible solute falls during single-capillary transit. If concentration falls to insignificant values before outlet, solute transport is limited by flow; augmentation of blood flow rate makes a larger part of the capillary available for transcapillary transport—thus an increase in blood flow itself leads to an increase in capillary diffusion capacity. [From Michel (210).]

limited kinetics (188). One is the well-mixed extravascular space model where the time constant for tissue concentration is described by Equation 11a. This expression was originally used by Kety (163) to measure regional blood flow from the tissue uptake of inert gases. Another model, used by Goresky (126), describes the uptake in liver sinusoids. This model (297) is based on the assumption that radial diffusion in the tissue is very fast, whereas axial diffusion is zero. Both models are flow limited in the sense that the rate constant describing the process is directly proportional to blood flow and independent of capillary permeability.

The most direct test of flow dependence involves inducing variations in the blood flow; the changes in the experimental parameter of interest are then observed. By definition, if the process is flow limited the time course should be directly proportional to flow. For example, for D_2O exchange in heart and skeletal muscle (334, 369) and in liver (154), venous outflow curves for a wide range of blood flows become superimposed on each other if they are plotted as a function of cumulative flow (Qt). This test has its limitations because capillary surface area may increase as flow increases. Thus the time constant (Eq. 11) may also increase with flow even if the process is permeability limited. This apparently occurs to some extent in skeletal muscle, heart, adipose tissue, and brain (1, 93, 196, 279, 283). It can be very difficult to determine the relative importance of different factors (see the chapter by Renkin in this *Handbook*), but it is important to be aware of the problem.

The rate of extravascular diffusion (the third factor that can influence blood-tissue exchange) does not enter into Equation 11 because the equation reasonably assumes that the interstitial space is well-mixed; i.e., diffusion is infinitely fast. Extravascular diffusion usually becomes important only when capillary density is very low, resulting in large extravascular diffusion distances. The relative importance of these three factors is illustrated in the study by Wittmers et al. (367). They compared the time constant of the uptake of inulin in various tissues of the rabbit with the time constant expected when exchange is limited by permeability, flow, or extravascular diffusion ($k = 2SD_I/x_{max}V_t$, where D_I is the interstitial diffusion coefficient and x_{max} is the maximum tissue diffusion distance). For most tissues the observed time constant was significantly smaller than expected for a flow-limited or tissue diffusion–limited process. This implies that tissue uptake of inulin was permeability limited; thus a valid measure of capillary permeability can be obtained. In the small intestine, however, the time constant was about the same as expected for a flow-limited process; therefore capillary permeability could not be determined. Except for the ear the resistance to inulin presented by tissue diffusion was negligible.

For solutes with high capillary permeability values (such as Na^+ or similar small solutes), it is difficult to measure capillary permeability with the tissue-uptake technique because the rate constant becomes flow dependent. Theoretically the indicator-diffusion technique should be more accurate for these solutes because extraction provides a direct measure of PS/Q; it should even be possible to measure very large permeability values. Experimentally, however, this method also becomes inaccurate for high permeability solutes because factors such as backflux, heterogeneity, shunting, and exchange between neighboring capillaries limit the maximum value of extraction to ~0.8–0.9, even when permeability is infinite and the extraction value should be 1.0. Thus the reliability of the method decreases as extraction increases; when the extraction value reaches 0.8 ($PS/Q \simeq 1.6$), the true permeability may actually be many times larger (260, 262).

Lipophilic Solutes

Accurate values for the permeability of many small lipophilic solutes are not available because transcapillary transport of these solutes is flow limited, and thus only lower limits can be given. Transcapillary transport of lipid-soluble substances occurs across the entire capillary surface area by passage through endothelial cells and water-filled channels. Knowledge from studies of cell permeability is generally directly applicable to passage through endothelial cells (49, 86). It is the tendency for solutes to leave the water phase that is decisive for their ability to pass cell membranes. Therefore endothelial cell permeability increases with the diminishing ability of molecules to form hydrogen bonds with water. This is amply borne out in many studies of homologous series of diols, amides, and aliphatic alcohols (45, 61, 262, 268), which have shown that the oil/water partition coefficient reliably predicts capillary permeability. Chinard (45) found permeabilities as high as 30–100 × 10^{-5} cm/s for lipophilic solutes in lung capillaries (Fig. 24). The passage through the cell moiety of the capillary wall has a much greater temperature dependence than the passage through the hydrophilic pathway, which may be explained either by lateral diffusion in the cell membrane or by diffusion across the cell membrane (80).

The very high capillary permeability of lipophilic solutes has been exploited in the many techniques of blood-flow measurement with highly diffusible indicators (12, 163).

Water Permeability

For many years water permeability (studied with D_2O or THO) was considered to be wholly flow limited (73, 104, 146, 370). However, it has recently been claimed that at very high flow rates there are signs of diffusion limitation of water (23, 95).

Diffusional water permeability in capillaries is high of course because water permeates very quickly across cell membranes (despite its hydrophilic nature), as shown by studies of red cell permeability to water. The same high permeability is found in endothelial cells; water uses the entire capillary surface area, which augments permeability and allows rates that are ~10–100 times faster than the rates of solutes that only diffuse through the interendothelial cleft (95, 262, 290, 324). Measurement of water exchange rates is experimentally difficult because permeation is largely

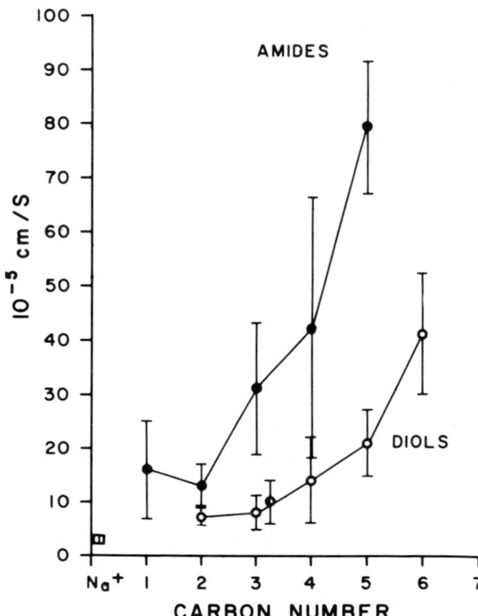

FIG. 24. Permeabilities in pulmonary capillaries of homologous series of amides and diols with increasing chain lengths. ○, Terminal diols from C_2 through C_6; ●, amides from C_1 through C_5. Lung capillary surface area is 500 cm^2/g wet wt. [From Perl et al. (260).]

flow limited. It is doubtful whether correct values for water permeability in capillaries can be obtained without corrections for backdiffusion. The most effective corrections are given by Perl et al. (262), who also found the highest water permeabilities so far reported. Crone and Christensen (69) have reported on water permeability, and Table 4 shows values for diffusional water permeability in various capillaries.

TRANSPORT RATES IN VIVO—CAPILLARY DIFFUSION CAPACITIES

As mentioned in the introduction to METHODS (p. 413), experiments on capillary permeability provide information about the time course of extravascular concentration changes in response to changes in plasma concentration. This may be of interest in pharmacology and certain experimental situations. Knowledge of capillary permeability may also be useful in considerations of the effective transcapillary concentration difference required to allow a given net flux across the capillaries in an organ.

As an example, transcapillary glucose transport in skeletal muscle capillaries is analyzed here. If the net flux of glucose across capillaries (consumption) in the steady state is known, the effective concentration difference across the capillary membrane can be calculated from Equation 2, $\overline{\Delta C} = J_{net}/PS$. The net uptake in resting muscle is 1.4 μmol·100 g^{-1}·min^{-1} (62) and PS is 5 ml·100 g^{-1}·min^{-1} (see Table 5). Thus

$$\overline{\Delta C} = \frac{1.4\ \mu\text{mol}\cdot 100\ \text{g}^{-1}\cdot\text{min}^{-1}}{5\ \text{ml}\cdot 100\ \text{g}^{-1}\cdot\text{min}^{-1}} = 0.3\ \text{mM}$$

This concentration difference should be compared with an average intracapillary glucose concentration of 5 mM.

Under heavy exercise, glucose consumption in muscle may rise to 60 μmol·100 g^{-1}·min^{-1} (43). If, under these conditions, capillary surface area increases by a factor of 4, PS becomes 20 ml·100 g^{-1}·min^{-1}. Thus

$$\overline{\Delta C} = \frac{60\ \mu\text{mol}\cdot 100\ \text{g}^{-1}\cdot\text{min}^{-1}}{20\ \text{ml}\cdot 100\ \text{g}^{-1}\cdot\text{min}^{-1}} = 3.0\ \text{mM}$$

This shows that the transcapillary concentration dif-

TABLE 4. *Diffusional Water Permeability in Various Organs*

	Permeability, 10^{-5} cm/s	Ref.
Brain	20	95
Heart	60	290
Lung	150	262
Rete mirabile	33	324
Frog mesentery	>80	69
Human red cell*	530	243

* Value for human red cell has been included because of possible similarities between endothelial cell permeability (P) and red cell P. Values for capillary P to water refer to passage across two plasma membranes plus P in interendothelial clefts.

ference of nutrients may become quite large compared with the average intracapillary concentration. The low interstitial glucose concentration is compensated for by a decrease by half in intercapillary diffusion distance. These considerations can be checked by determining the interstitial glucose concentration under heavy exercise (e.g., with a glucose-sensitive microelectrode).

Glucose consumption in rat brain is 100 μmol·100 $g^{-1}\cdot min^{-1}$ (317). For a plasma glucose concentration of 8 mM, PS = 18 ml·100 $g^{-1}\cdot min^{-1}$ (see Fig. 39). Thus

$$\overline{\Delta C} = \frac{100\ \mu mol \cdot 100\ g^{-1} \cdot min^{-1}}{18\ ml \cdot 100\ g^{-1} \cdot min^{-1}} = 5.5\ mM$$

This calculation shows that the interstitial glucose concentration in the brain is quite low. [The application of the permeability–surface area product concept for the brain capillary is not straightforward, as explained in FACILITATED TRANSPORT IN ENDOTHELIUM (p. 446), because PS in the brain is concentration dependent and different in the two directions across the capillary.]

The permeability–surface area product is obtained from permeability studies. This product is useful for calculating the time course of tissue saturation and desaturation based on Equations 8–10. The half time for extravascular buildup (or emptying) is

$$t_{1/2} = \frac{V_t}{PS} \ln 2 = \frac{V_t}{PS} 0.69 = \frac{0.69}{k} \tag{29}$$

This expression is only applicable under truly diffusion-limited circumstances where the half time is independent of blood flow.

Many solutes have permeabilities that, under prevailing flow and surface area conditions, place the solute in the intermediate zone where transport is dependent on both flow and capillary diffusion capacity. Therefore the permeability–surface area product (or capillary diffusion capacity) should only be used when the value is known to be independent of flow. The neutral term *clearance* should be used for uncertain states.

The increase in capillary diffusion capacity that often accompanies increasing flow (Figs. 25–27) reflects several possible mechanisms: diminishing flow limitation, diminishing heterogeneity, or recruitment of capillary surface area. The unequivocal test that might demonstrate which mechanism is operating involves examining PS-versus-Q curves to observe whether there is a shift from one curve to another (see Fig. 40). However, there are an infinite number of such curves if recruitment occurs. The formula $PS = -Q \ln(1 - E)$ is based on consideration of a single capillary, but in reality innumerable capillaries (with different parameters) participate and the analysis is very complicated. Recruitment does not necessarily mean that additional capillaries are opened and perfused anew. The flow in some capillaries may simply be slower than in others. Under increasing flow conditions the linear flow velocity generally increases and the capillaries become more efficient at exchange. The

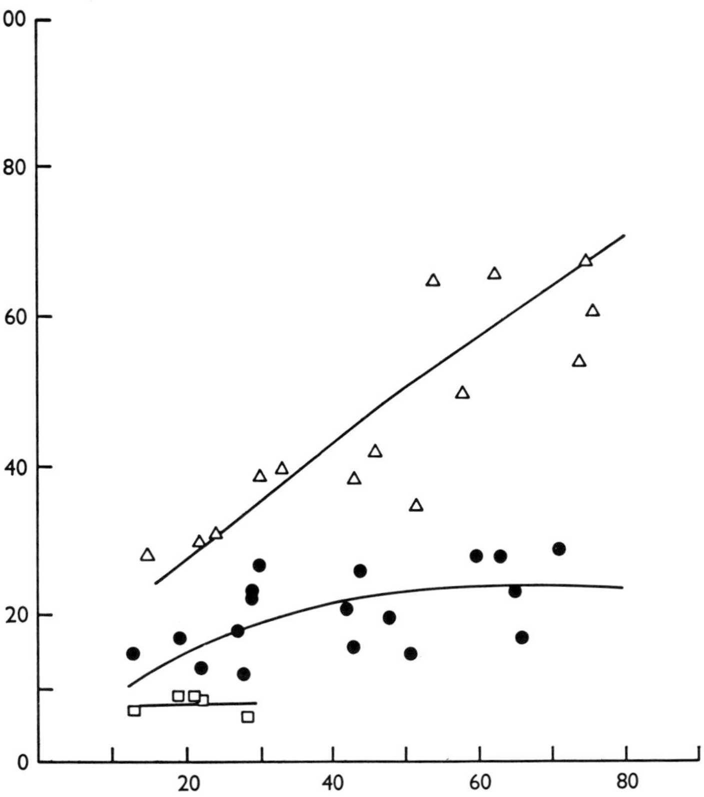

FIG. 25. Relationship between permeability–surface area product and blood flow for experiments on dog heart in which tracers were simultaneously injected. Inulin (□) and sucrose (●) reached relatively constant values, but ^{36}Cl (△) continued to increase. Abscissa, blood flow (ml·min^{-1}·100 g^{-1}); ordinate, capillary diffusion capacity (ml·min^{-1}·100 g^{-1}). [From Alvarez and Yudilevich (1).]

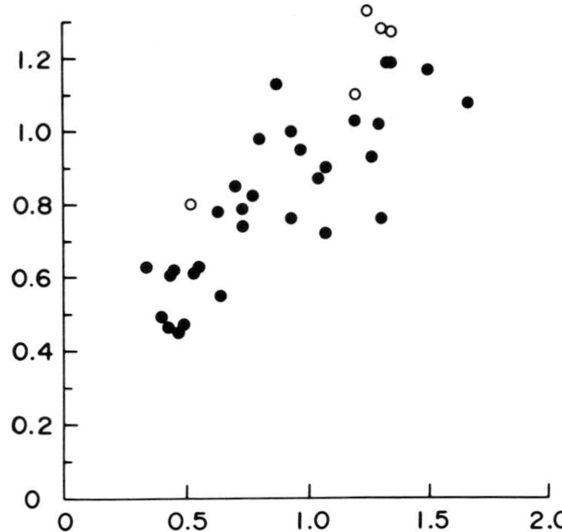

FIG. 26. Effect of plasma flow on capillary permeability–surface area product for $^{42}K^+$ in isolated blood-perfused canine hearts. Abscissa, plasma flow ($ml \cdot min^{-1} \cdot g^{-1}$); ordinate, capillary diffusion capacity ($ml \cdot min^{-1} \cdot g^{-1}$). [From Tancredi et al. (330).]

decreasing flow limitation in slowly perfused vessels is seen as augmentation of effective capillary surface area (291). Thus no distinct criterion exists to explain increased values of *PS* with increased flow. It is interesting that late in his life Krogh, who first proposed capillary intermittence (168), wrote about this phenomenon: "these results make good the contention that the distances between open capillaries are closely related to the metabolic requirements, but of the shifting of open capillaries from one position to another in the resting muscle I was never able to obtain convincing proof" (170). This unsolved, perhaps unsolvable, problem stresses that the physiological use of anatomical determinations of capillary surface area based on microscopic studies is ambiguous because the effective capillary surface area may be different from the anatomical capillary surface area.

Tables 5–7 contain values for the capillary diffusion capacities of hydrophilic solutes commonly used in experiments on capillary permeability. Because they include solutes with molecular weights ranging from 20 to 5,000, blood-to-tissue transport rates for many substances that occur naturally can be assessed in various organs. The unidirectional transport rate is $\overline{C}_c PS$.

The tables also give values for 95% equilibration times in the extracellular space in response to a step change in plasma (from Eq. 29). Skeletal muscle exchanges much more slowly than heart partly because of a lower flow rate and partly because of less capillary surface area. Brain capillaries obviously behave quite differently than those of other organs, and as is well known it is almost impossible to attain equilibrium between plasma and brain tissue because of the extreme tightness of brain endothelium.

Permeabilities for fenestrated capillaries found in the kidney, salivary glands, endocrine glands, and intestines are incompletely known. The experiments that have been done show that permeability is distinctly higher in organs with fenestrated capillaries (203, 335b; cf. Table 5). These high permeabilities presumably reflect the fact that fenestrae act as passageways for hydrophilic solutes and by their very size increase the fractional pore area.

CAPILLARY SURFACE AREA

To convert capillary diffusion capacities to permeabilities it is necessary to know the capillary surface area in different organs. Exact knowledge of the func-

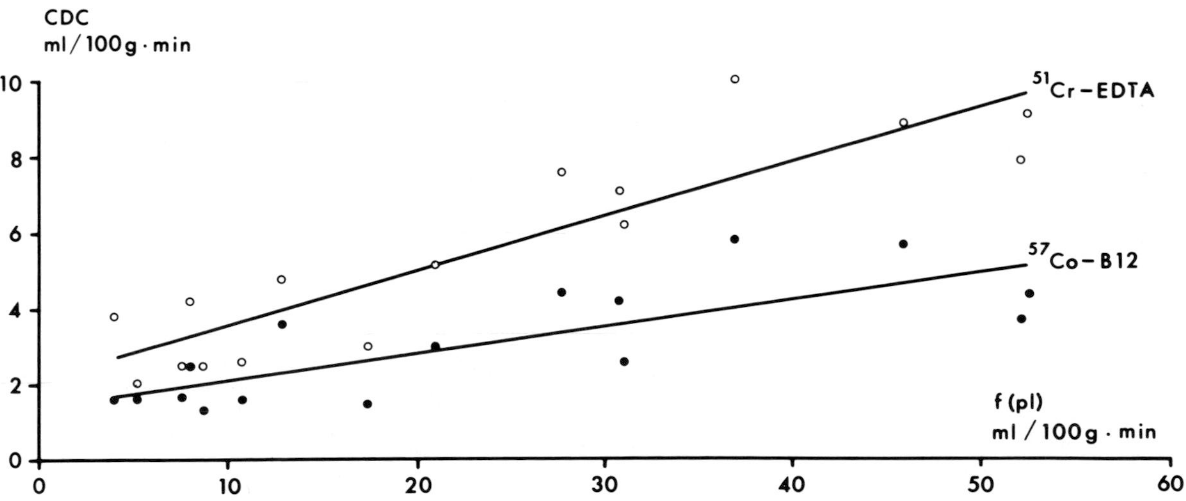

FIG. 27. Capillary diffusion capacity of ^{51}Cr-EDTA (○) and [^{57}Co]vitamin B_{12} (●) determined simultaneously with plasma flow range of 4–52.4 $ml \cdot min^{-1} \cdot 100\ g^{-1}$. Experiments on cat skeletal muscle. Ratio of diffusion capacities of test solutes remained constant throughout whole range of flows. Diffusion coefficient in water at 37°C of ^{51}Cr-EDTA is $0.7 \times 10^{-5}\ cm^2/s$ and of [^{57}Co]vitamin B_{12} is $0.4 \times 10^{-5}\ cm^2/s$. [From Paaske (240).]

TABLE 5. *Transcapillary Exchange Rates in Various Organs*

	Sodium			D-Glucose, Mannitol, or Fructose			Sucrose or Cr-EDTA			Inulin		
	PS	$t_{0.95}$	Ref.	*PS*	$t_{0.95}$	Ref.	*PS*	$t_{0.95}$	Ref.	*PS*	$t_{0.95}$	Ref.
Heart	120	0.63	93	31	2.4	1	24	2.5	1	7.8	9.6	1
	114	0.65	1				21.6	2.8	138	10.8	4.3	180
	102	0.72	133				37.2	1.6	180	19.2	3.1	367
	312	0.23	202				52.2	1.2	373			
	78	0.97	373				32.4	1.9	140			
Skeletal muscle	37	2.0	322	5.5	13.6	336	3.0	19.2	58	0.59	76	281
	15	5.0	336	4.6	16.3	58	7.2	8.6	286	0.84	53	242
	14.3	5.2	281				5.4	11.1	240	1.08	41	58
	7.2	10.0	372				4.5	13.3	281	1.62	28	367
							3.0	19.2	336			
Subcutaneous tissue							3.0	20	196			
							2.0	30	241			
Skin							3.7	16	238			
Lung				45	1.7	327a				22.8	3.3	367
										90	1.1	264
Salivary gland							800	0.09	203	176	0.4	203
Pancreas							110	0.6	136a			
Intestinal capillaries										23	2.5	264a
Peritubular capillaries										1,200	0.1	335a

PS, permeability–surface area product ($ml \cdot min^{-1} \cdot 100\ g^{-1}$); $t_{0.95}$, 95% equilibration time (min).

TABLE 6. *Transcapillary Exchange Rates in Brain*

	PS	$t_{0.95}$, h	Ref.
Inulin	0.0014	277	230
Sucrose	0.020	37	2
	0.040	19	230
	0.075	10	118
Sodium	0.23	3.3	315a
	0.16	4.6	84
	0.13	5.8	185
Mannitol	0.14	5.3	2
	0.24	3.1	118
	0.21	3.6	310
Chloride	0.19	3.9	315a

PS, permeability–surface area product ($ml \cdot min^{-1} \cdot 100\ g^{-1}$); $t_{0.95}$, 95% equilibration time (h).

TABLE 7. *Average Turnover Times*

	Sucrose	Inulin	Sodium	Mannitol
Heart	1.7	5.7	0.64	2.4
Skeletal muscle	14.5	41	5.7	15.0
Brain	22	277	5.2	4

Turnover times are calculated as $t_{0.95} = -(\ln 0.05)/(PS/V_t)$ where *PS* is the permeability–surface area product; V_t (ml/100 g) is tissue volume; and $t_{0.95}$ is 95% equilibration time (given in min for heart and skeletal muscle and in h for brain). The speed with which extracellular space is exchanged with plasma is expressed as $t_{0.95}$. It was assumed that for the brain V_t = 15, for the heart and lung V_t = 25, and for skeletal muscle V_t = 15.

tional capillary surface area under given experimental conditions is difficult to obtain; however, attempts have been made to measure intercapillary spacing in vivo with photographic techniques (143, 148, 256). The majority of these studies have been made on tissue sections, but it is difficult to know to what extent all visible capillary cross sections are actually perfused.

The anatomical data give an indication of the variations in capillary surface area between tissues. Krogh (168) observed that tissues with a high rate of respiration generally have a higher capillary density than more quiescent tissues. Capillary surface areas range from a low of 50–60 cm^2/g to 800–1,200 cm^2/g (Table 8). The values for capillary surface area in the lung are uncertain because the proper reference parameter is difficult to define. Because the lung is primarily a vascular organ with a high blood content, a definition of capillary surface area relative to wet weight is somewhat meaningless. The best reference parameter is the weight of the experimental animal. Weibel (357, 358) has provided very accurate values for the relation between lung capillary surface area and body weight for a number of animals including humans, which make it possible to assess lung capillary surface area quite accurately in a given experiment. Regrettably, however, very few of the many studies of pulmonary capillary diffusion capacities for small solutes include this information. Thus data on solute permeability in lung capillaries are rather uncertain and even the order of magnitude of the permeability value is questionable.

Capillary surface area in skeletal muscle is also difficult to assess accurately because of the recruitment problem. Several studies indicate that the active capillary surface area in muscle can vary by a factor of four (from ~60 to 250 cm^2/g) depending on the metabolic state (240, 279). Other studies indicate a 10-fold variation (147). An increase in the number of functioning capillaries by a factor of four reduces the intercapillary distance by half. Because diffusion time is proportional to the square of the distance, even a small reduction in intercapillary distance is an efficient way of meeting higher metabolic requirements.

TABLE 8. *Capillary Surface Areas in Various Tissues*

	Species	Area, cm^2/g wet wt	Ref.
Heart	Dog	500	15
	Rat	575	338
Brain cortex	Rat	130	208a
		140	6
	Cat	150	256
Kidney			
Glomeruli	Human	52	348
Peritubular capillaries	Human	1,200	266
	Dog	350	58
		820	282
Lung	Rabbit	3,500	263
	Dog	3,000	357
Skeletal muscle			
Tenuissimus	Cat	90	98
		130	301
Spinotrapezius	Rat	62	301
Gastrocnemius	Dog	220	41
	Rabbit	62	263
Hindlimb	Cat	70	247
Extensor hallucis proprius	Rat	160	225
Cremaster	Rat	240	314

The mechanism of capillary recruitment has recently been studied by Honig et al. (148a), and the heterogeneity of the microcirculation has been studied with India ink perfusions of skeletal muscle (282a).

Methods of determining capillary surface areas are not discussed in detail in this chapter. With the light microscope the information is mainly based on counting capillaries in cross sections of tissues. Modern stereological techniques have made important contributions, and the electron microscope has been used to obtain better information (301, 357). When the capillary surface area is calculated from the number of capillaries per square millimeter of tissue (N/S) the following formula applies (15)

$$S = \frac{2\pi r N}{\rho S} \tag{30}$$

where $2r$ is the average intercapillary distance and ρ is the density of the tissue (1.06 for muscle, 0.9 for brain). The correction for tissue density is used to convert figures obtained as surface area per volume of tissue to surface area per gram of tissue.

Microscopic studies provide information about the intercapillary distance from which the radius of the equivalent Krogh cylinder is obtained. Thews (332) gives the following formula for calculation of the Krogh cylinder radius (r_K) from capillary length per unit volume of tissue

$$r_K = \sqrt{\frac{2}{3\sqrt{3}\, l}} \tag{31}$$

or

$$r_K = \sqrt{\frac{2S}{3\sqrt{3}\, N}} \tag{32}$$

from a model where the tissue consists of closely packed hexagonal columns (Fig. 28).

Capillary density is of course primarily a function of the metabolic rate. Because oxygen consumption per gram of tissue is higher in small animals than in large, there is a tendency for capillary density to increase in small mammals (Table 9).

Capillaries in most tissues are rather unevenly organized (in contrast to skeletal muscle), and therefore the concept of a capillary with a surrounding cylinder of tissue is only a rough approximation in many cases, although it has proved to be a valuable concept (273). Table 10 gives values for half intercapillary distances (equivalent to r_K) in various mammalian organs. The intercapillary distance also depends on the size of the parenchymal cells. In frog tissues the distances are about twice as long (265, 332) as those found in mammals. Figure 29 illustrates some of these points.

A useful compilation of capillary densities in skeletal muscle has been made by Plyley and Groom (265). From these figures the number of capillaries per muscle fiber is calculated to be ~1. Capillary length varies from tissue to tissue, and connections that divide a

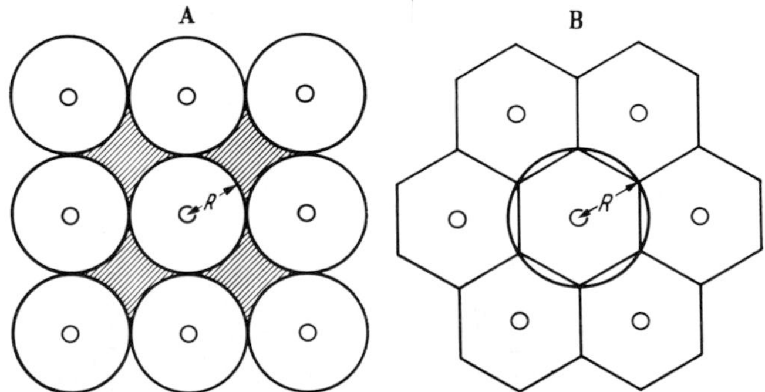

FIG. 28. Tissue volume supplied by single capillary calculated from incorrect assumption that half intercapillary distance equals radius of tissue cylinder (*A*) and better assumption of array of closely packed hexagonal tissue columns (*B*). In *B*, correct radius equals circumcircle. [From Thews (332).]

TABLE 9. *Capillary Density in Muscles of Some Mammalian Species*

	Density, counts/mm²		
	Gastrocnemius		Masseter
	White	Red	
Dog	*	780	830
Rabbit	270	420	1,050
Guinea pig	490	1,090	1,700
Rat	370	1,250	1,220
Mouse	630	1,850	2,270

* White fibers not present in dog gastrocnemius. [Data from Schmidt-Nielsen and Pennycuik (302).]

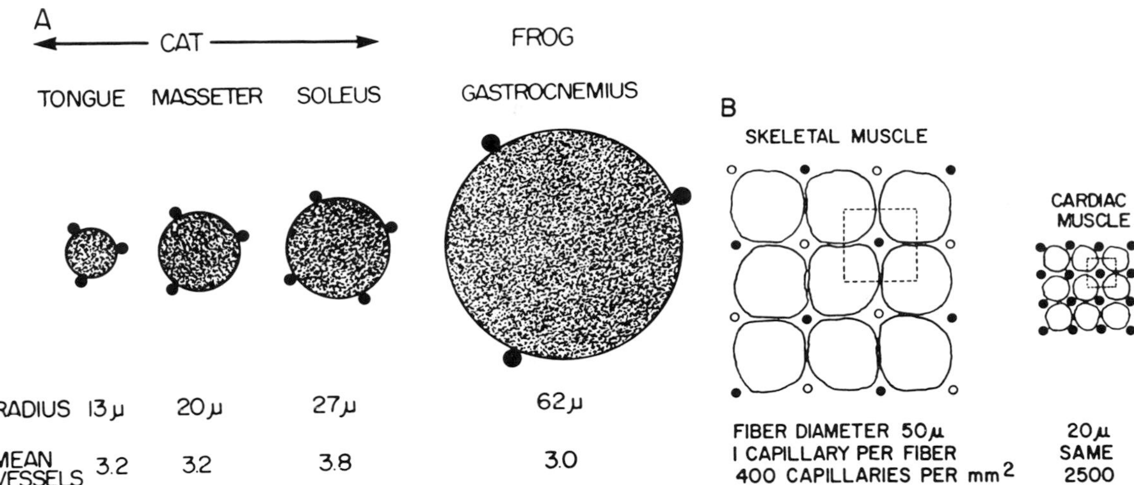

FIG. 29. *A*: mean number of vessels surrounding fibers in muscles of cat and frog. Number remains relatively constant in spite of 23-fold range of fiber cross-sectional area. *B*: relative capillary densities in skeletal and cardiac muscle. [*A* from Plyley and Groom (265); *B* from Renkin (278).]

TABLE 10. *Half Intercapillary Distances (Krogh Cylinder Radius) in Various Tissues*

	Species	Radius, μm	Technique	Ref.
Gastrocnemius	Dog	14	H	41
Masseter	Guinea pig	11	H	166
Cremaster	Rat	17	H	314
Heart	Dog	9	H	15
	Rat	10	IV	205
		10	H	163a
Area postrema	Cat	11	H	192
Brain cortex	Cat	12	IV	256
		17	H	91
Brain white matter		26	H	91

H, histological method; IV, in vivo method.

TABLE 11. *Average Capillary Lengths and Linear Flow Velocities in Various Organs*

	Length, μm	Ref.	Average Velocity, μm/s	Ref.
Skeletal muscle	1,000	98	500	98
	530	225		
	1,000	147	250	147
			400	38
Cremaster	600	314	700	314
Heart	1,100	18		
	500–1,000	15		
Brain			1,500	256
Lung	600–800	319	900	319
Skin			650	99
Mesentery			1,200	114

long capillary into small segments are often seen between neighboring capillaries (314). Capillaries are particularly long in muscle, mesentery, and renal medulla tissues; they are shorter in the brain and heart (Table 11).

A capillary length of 1,000 μm with a diameter of 6 μm gives a surface area of ~20,000 μm^2. Transit times are quite variable, ranging from 0.5 to 4 s (38, 147), and change in an unpredictable manner with overall organ flow. There is no satisfactory information about reduction of capillary transit times at high flows, but the range of transit times is reduced (289). The red cell velocities shown in Table 11 represent average values, but there is always a large distribution of velocities in individual capillaries (156).

The total capillary surface area in an individual can be roughly estimated. In the human lung, for example, the total capillary surface area is ~70 m^2 (357), in the human glomeruli it is ~50 m^2 (348), and in the human heart it is ~15 m^2. Assuming that the average capillary surface area is 100 cm^2/g tissue, an adult human has a total capillary surface area of ~700 m^2 (a smaller figure than given in most text books). If the total capillary blood volume for an adult human is ~350 ml, the depth of capillary blood spread out on this surface area is 5 μm.

Variations of permeability values are not only caused by different experimental techniques in various laboratories but also by the different estimates of capillary surface area used for conversion to permeabilities. This point must be borne in mind and it should be stressed that capillary permeability values obtained in whole-organ experiments at best give relatively crude information. The inherent inhomogeneity of the microcirculation, which is so conspicuous when the vessels are observed in vivo, adds to the general uncertainty concerning precise values of capillary permeability to small solutes. Undoubtedly there is a discrepancy between the idealized mathematical models and the real complexities of the microcirculation. This uncertainty may never be fully overcome in whole-organ experiments.

DATA FROM WHOLE-ORGAN EXPERIMENTS

Diffusion Permeabilities

Selected data from the different methods are summarized in Tables 12–14. They include results from various organs for typical hydrophilic test solutes such as NaCl, sucrose, and inulin, which differ sufficiently in molecular size to show differences in permeability.

Although there is much scatter in the data from experiments with the same solute on the same organ, the average supposedly comes close to a true permeability value. The average values clearly show that brain endothelium belongs in a special category of tissues with extremely low solute permeabilities. For other organs the permeability coefficients are about 10^{-5} cm/s; heart capillaries apparently have a slightly higher permeability than skeletal muscle capillaries, whereas the permeability of lung capillaries tends to be lower. However, much depends on the assumed capillary surface area in the different organs because permeability is calculated from the permeability–surface area product.

The average figure of $\sim 10^{-5}$ cm/s shows that a capillary membrane is ~1,000 times more permeable than a cell membrane, which may have permeability values of $\sim 10^{-8}$ cm/s. In the brain the presence of a facilitating diffusion mechanism for D-glucose (and other important solutes) selectively increases the transcapillary transport rate by a factor of 100 at normal plasma concentrations so that D-glucose is transported as quickly as in capillaries of other organs.

It must be stressed that, besides the uncertainty connected with the capillary surface area, another problem arises from the uncertainty about the degree of capillary heterogeneity. For example, an experimen-

TABLE 12. *Capillary Permeabilities to Na^+ or K^+*

	Permeability, 10^{-5} cm/s	Method	Ref.
Skeletal muscle	2.9	ID	371
	3.2	ID	92
	5.5	ID	336
	8.7	CL	322
Mean	5.1		
Heart	2.5	ID	373
	3.1	ID	133
	3.5	ID	330
	3.8	ID	1
	10.0	ID	202
Mean	4.6		
Lung	2.8	ID	368
	2.9*	ID	262
Mean	2.9		
Brain	0.056	TU	85
	0.028	ID	136
	0.047	TU	315a
Mean	0.044		

ID, indicator-diffusion technique; CL, tissue-clearance technique; TU, tissue-uptake technique. * If corrected for backdiffusion, Na^+ permeability increases to 10.2×10^{-5} cm/s (45).

TABLE 13. *Capillary Permeability to Sucrose (or Cr-EDTA)*

	Permeability, 10^{-5} cm/s	Method	Ref.
Skeletal muscle	0.54	ID	337
	0.74	ID	58
	1.16	ID	306
	1.35	ID	286
	1.50	RD	240
	1.90	CA	275
	2.30	VO	115
Mean	1.4		
Heart	0.80	ID	1
	1.08	RD	140
	1.20	ID	14
	1.24	ID	180
	1.74	ID	373
	2.40	OT	130
	3.30	ID	289
	4.40	ID	202
	5.00	OT	344
	5.90	OT	346
	11.00	TU	298
Mean	3.5		
Lung	0.47	ID	29
	0.77	ID	11
	1.03	ID	29
	1.10	ID	264
	1.10	TU	353
	2.40	ID	228
	3.00	TU	229
	3.50	ID	45
Mean	1.7		
Brain	0.0028	TU	230
	0.013	TU	118
	0.014	TU	2
Mean	0.01		

ID, indicator-diffusion technique; RD, residue-detection technique; CA, compartmental analysis; VO, venous-outflow technique; OT, osmotic-transient technique; TU, tissue-uptake technique.

TABLE 14. *Capillary Permeability to Inulin*

	Permeability, 10^{-5} cm/s	Method	Ref.
Skeletal muscle	0.12	TU	367
	0.14	ID	337
	0.20	VO	242
	0.26	ID	59
	0.29	FER	115
Mean	0.2		
Heart	0.27	ID	1
	0.36	ID	180
	0.40	TU	298
	0.51	TU	367
	0.54	TU	346
	0.58	OT	14
Mean	0.4		
Lung	0.40	TU	367
	0.45	ID	264
Mean	0.4		
Brain	0.001	TU	2
	0.0001	TU	230
Mean	0.0005		

TU, tissue-uptake technique; ID, indicator-diffusion technique; VO, venous-outflow technique; FER, fractional escape rate; OT, osmotic-transient technique.

tally observed extraction value of 0.8 could result from a combination of flow limitation (E = 1) in 80% of the capillaries and a complete shunt (E = 0) in 20% of the capillaries. The permeability determined from the overall extraction of 0.8 will seriously underestimate the permeability of 80% of the capillaries. As mentioned earlier, fenestrated capillaries have much higher permeabilities. In the choroidal microvessels in the eye a sodium permeability as high as 180×10^{-5} cm/s was determined with an average extraction of 0.66 (337a).

For this and other reasons it is impossible to decide whether the relatively small differences in permeabilities in skeletal muscle, heart, and lung are significant. Permeability values for sucrose (or the equivalent Cr-EDTA) in skin and adipose capillaries are not different from those in skeletal muscle (240, 241), and it is very possible that the permeabilities of continuous capillaries in various organs are similar (237, 263).

Although the values for capillary permeabilities in most organs with continuous capillaries are rather similar, the solute exchange efficiency of the capillary beds can be rather different because of differences in capillary surface area and flow rate. Thus it is important to know what information about capillary permeability is needed in any particular case.

Permeability Ratios

Because pores with dimensions comparable to those of the diffusing solutes hamper large molecules more than small ones (diffusion restriction), permeabilities for graded sizes of test molecules should not vary in proportion to free-diffusion coefficients. According to pore theory, diffusion restriction is clearly seen when the diffusing molecule is one-tenth the size of the pore (16, 69, 274, 284). When the ratio between molecular radius and pore radius is 0.5, diffusion velocity is decreased by 90% if the pore or cleft had the same narrow dimensions throughout its length.

Thus deviations of permeability ratios from ratios of free-diffusion coefficients indicate diffusion restriction and indirectly provide information about cleft width. This criterion has been used in many studies. If the indicator-diffusion technique is used, permeability ratios are given by

$$\frac{P_1}{P_2} = \frac{\ln(1 - \mathrm{E}_1)}{\ln(1 - \mathrm{E}_2)} \tag{33}$$

The advantage of this equation is that flow and surface area cancel out if two test solutes are studied at the same time. This equation was first used by Crone (59) with sucrose and inulin as test solutes. The permeability ratio was found to correspond to the ratio of free-diffusion coefficients in skeletal muscle. Schafer and Johnson (298) argued that if one solute tends to be more flow limited than the other the ratio will approach the ratio of free-diffusion coefficients, and thus the criterion is rather weak. The most extensive study of permeability ratios has been carried out by Paaske (239, 240), who studied pairs of indicators (Cr-EDTA and vitamin B_{12} with ratios of free-diffusion coefficients of 1.8) over a very large range of flows [from 4 to 52 $\mathrm{ml \cdot 100\ g^{-1} \cdot min^{-1}}$ in skeletal muscle; (see Fig. 27)]. Permeability ratios corresponded to ratios of free-diffusion coefficients throughout the range of flows. In the heart these ratios were also similar (1, 93, 130). In the rete mirabile of the eel similar conclusions were drawn (271, 324).

If permeability ratios for sucrose and inulin are calculated from the average values in Tables 12–14, some degree of diffusion restriction is indicated. The divergent opinions on this point may relate to the fact that permeability is largely affected by the long, wide portions of the interendothelial cleft if the narrowest part is small relative to the total cleft depth (see INTERPRETATION OF PERMEABILITY STUDIES, p. 449). This may well be the situation if there are very short regions of close apposition of junctions down the length of the pore (158, 365).

Reflection Coefficients

The results from studies of the reflection coefficients of various solutes are summarized in Table 15. Data for the frog mesentery are from single-capillary experiments, whereas the rest of the results are from studying whole organs with the osmotic-transient method. In agreement with the permeability data, reflection coefficients for the brain show that the blood-brain barrier is essentially impermeable to solutes the size of mannitol or larger ($\sigma = 1$). This is probably caused by a very tight junction between endothelial cells.

Three sets of data are shown for the rabbit heart, including the original data from Vargas and Johnson (345) and more recent results (130, 343). Vargas and Blackshear (343) used a filtration coefficient determined from a pressure change in the calculation of the reflection coefficient (Eq. 23); the other investigators assumed that $\sigma = 1$ for albumin. To compare the different studies the results must be multiplied by the inverse of the observed reflection coefficient for albumin (0.8).

Two important conclusions can be inferred from a qualitative analysis of the heart data.

1. An estimate of the maximum fraction of the hydraulic water flow that goes through the endothelial cells (as opposed to through an extracellular route) can be obtained from the reflection coefficient for NaCl. To survive, endothelial cells must have a very low Na^+ permeability and σ must equal 1 for NaCl. The observed reflection coefficient is described by

$$\sigma = [\sigma_c(K_{f,c}/K_f)] + [\sigma_t(K_{f,t}/K_f)] \tag{34}$$

where $K_{f,c}$, $K_{f,t}$, σ_c, and σ_t are the cellular and extracellular (experimentally observed) hydraulic permeability coefficients and reflection coefficients, respec-

TABLE 15. *Reflection Coefficients in Capillary Endothelium of Various Organs*

	Species	Perfusate	Temp, °C	Concn, mosM	NaCl	Urea	Sucrose	Raffinose	Inulin	Albumin	Ref.
Brain	Rabbit	Blood	37	40		0.44	0.98	1.0	1.0	1.0	101
Heart	Rabbit	Ringer			0.07	0.09	0.19	0.22	0.39	0.80	342
			22	20–50		0.10	0.30	0.38	0.69		345
			22	5–150	0.08		0.14	0.19	0.46		130
Skeletal muscle	Dog	Blood	37			0.06	0.11	0.14	0.54		88
			37	20–100		0.06	0.13	0.25	0.68	0.91	87
				3–60	0.02	0.04	0.06	0.13	0.38		281*
				3–60	0.11	0.11	0.13	0.14	0.28	0.98	281†
Lung	Rat	Ringer	37		0.05	0.05	0.08		0.39	0.87	285a
	Rabbit (newborn)		22	4–400	0.04		0.04	0.06	0.07	0.11	207
	Rabbit (adult)		22	5–55	0.05		0.05	0.06	0.14	0.40	352
	Dog	Blood	24			0.02	0.04				331
			36	10–50	0.30	0.30	0.39	0.35			261
Adipose tissue	Rabbit	Blood	37	30	0.02		0.03	0.03		0.91	5
Mesentery	Frog	Ringer	14–16	8–200	0.07	0.07	0.12			0.82	81

Albumin was added to Ringer perfusates except for the studies of Wangensteen et al. (352) and Vargas and Johnson (345). * Corrected from Pappenheimer et al. (247). † Calculated values based on specific model.

tively. Because $K_{f,c}$ is maximum when $\sigma_t = 0$, the observed σ (0.07) for NaCl implies that no more than 7% of the bulk water goes through the cells and at least 93% must take an extracellular route. Actually σ_t is probably close to 0.07 for NaCl so that the cellular pathway contribution is actually less than 7%.

2. The extracellular water pathway clearly distinguishes between the different solutes. Because the reflection coefficient increases with increasing solute size, the pathway must be small enough to significantly restrict the movement of the solute (e.g., sucrose).

The data for skeletal muscle from Diana et al. (87, 88) were obtained by direct measurement of the reflection coefficient with the osmotic-transient method. The data of Renkin and Curry (281), however, are less direct and require more assumptions. Their results are similar to those for the heart, which suggests that the bulk water flow is going through clefts of a similar size. Because the diffusive flux should be going through the same pores, the permeability of a solute like raffinose should be restricted relative to NaCl; however, this prediction has not been wholly confirmed experimentally. The discrepancy between permeability and reflection coefficient data may be explained by the different sensitivities of the two parameters to the detailed pore geometry.

For the lung the results of three different laboratories are listed in Table 15. The results of Wangensteen et al. (352) and Taylor and Gaar (331) are in general agreement; however, the values obtained by Perl et al. (261) are ~10 times larger. The source of this discrepancy is probably in the determination of K_f, which is needed to calculate the reflection coefficient (Eq. 19). The discrepancy presents a difficult experimental problem. If only relative data are considered, the results of the three laboratories are similar. The lack of discrimination and small reflection coefficients for solutes no larger than sucrose were thought to indicate the existence of two routes of water transport—one through the cell membrane with $\sigma = 1$ for all solutes and one through relatively large aqueous channels with $\sigma \simeq 0$ for small solutes (NaCl, sucrose, and raffinose), $\sigma \simeq 0.1$ for inulin, and $\sigma \simeq 0.3$ for albumin (352). Small solutes rapidly cross the capillary and, as verified by morphometric methods (351), produce osmotic volume changes in tissue cells (endothelial and epithelial) with no significant change in interstitial volume. These cellular volume changes are responsible for the osmotic transient observed with small solutes. The width of the interendothelial clefts was estimated to be 100 Å from the reflection coefficients for inulin and albumin. The small reflection coefficients for these macromolecules does not seem consistent with measurements of lymph/plasma albumin ratios determined at high rates of lymph flow (97, 252); the true reflection coefficient for albumin in the lung must be regarded at present as an unsettled question.

The reflection coefficient data for the frog mesentery have been interpreted in terms of a model similar to that discussed for the lung (82). Again there are two routes of water transport—one through the cell membrane with $\sigma = 1$ and one through relatively large pores with $\sigma \simeq 0$ for small solutes. With this assumption the results are reasonably consistent with an estimated cleft width of ~80 Å. The reflection coefficient for sucrose in single capillaries in frog skeletal muscle was 0.12 (112a). It is of considerable interest that the reflection coefficients of mesentery and muscle are similar despite the fact that the solute permeability is 10 times larger in mesentery than in muscle.

SINGLE-CAPILLARY STUDIES

Over fifty years ago Landis (173) showed that single capillaries could be submitted to experimentation. With the microocclusion technique he provided the first quantitative data on the filtration permeability of the capillary wall. Through the work of Wiederhielm (359–361) and Michel and co-workers (82, 211, 216), single-capillary studies were reintroduced and the power of the technique greatly expanded (see the chapter by Michel in this *Handbook*).

Quantitative evaluation of diffusion permeability at the single-capillary level is a recent acquisition that began with studies on the escape of dyes from capillaries (173, 174, 209, 217, 218, 293).

The introduction of electrophysiological methods by Crone and co-workers (67, 70–72, 74) and by Frøkjær-Jensen (111) allowed quantification of the diffusional permeability of single capillaries. Concurrently it was shown that a modification of the microocclusion technique also provides data for diffusional permeability (78, 212). Importantly the microocclusion technique allows uncharged solutes to be studied.

The great advantage of single-capillary studies is that the surface area through which diffusion takes place is known and the transcapillary concentration difference can be determined.

Single-Injection Technique

After Walker (349) introduced the ion-sensitive microelectrode, the way was paved for determination of ion permeability of single capillaries. Crone and Friedman (71) first carried out bolus-injection experiments on single capillaries in the frog mesentery. A bolus of isotonic Ringer's fluid containing K^+ partly substituted for Na^+ was injected into a small arteriole or an arterial capillary. The bolus subsequently traveled through a nearby capillary. The K^+ concentration was monitored by two electrodes in the capillary separated by 400–800 μm (Fig. 30). The extraction of excess K^+ was calculated from the difference between the areas under the concentration curves monitored by the two electrodes. The capillary flow rate during the bolus passage was determined from the difference in appearance time (Δt) of the bolus front at the two electrodes, because $Q = \pi r_c^2 l/\Delta t$, where r_c is the radius of the capillary and l is the length of the interelectrode capillary segment. Inserting these figures in the equation $P = -(Q/S)\ln(1 - E)$ gives

$$P = -\frac{r_c \ln(1 - E)}{2\Delta t} \tag{35}$$

which assumes a small or negligible extravascular concentration of the test ion during the rising phase of the K^+ bolus. To ensure this, the outside of the preparation was constantly flushed with ordinary Ringer's solution to remove excess K^+. Potassium permeability values of 70×10^{-5} cm/s were found, which are ~10 times higher than the values obtained in whole-organ experiments on muscle and heart. Single-capillary experiments on muscle tissue (111, 236) showed that the permeability to small ions is ~5–10 times smaller than in the mesentery. Two modifications of the microelectrode technique were developed and are described here.

Sac Method

A capillary segment containing a high-K^+ Ringer's fluid is closed between two glass microneedles. Two ion-sensitive microelectrodes are used; one is placed within the closed segment, and the other is placed just outside the capillary wall. The decrease with time of excess K^+ within the segment ($C_{c,t}$) is observed. The concentration on the outside of the capillary wall ($C_{out,t}$) is determined with another electrode.

The rate of loss of mass per unit length is

$$\pi r^2 \frac{dC_{c,t}}{dt} = -2\pi r P(C_{c,t} - C_{out,t}) \tag{36}$$

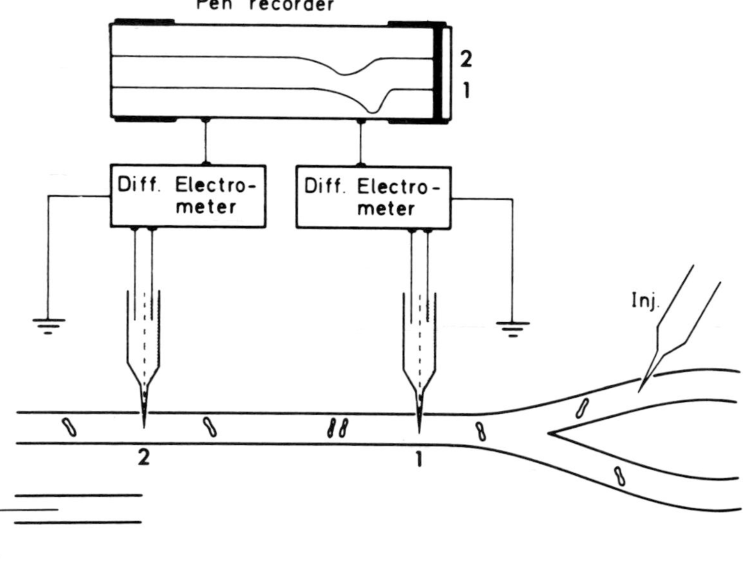

FIG. 30. Bolus-injection method applied to single capillary. Bolus of K^+ is injected into capillary; concentration of K^+ within capillary is monitored downstream by two K^+-sensitive microelectrodes. Response of electrodes is fed into a differential electrometer and recorded on double-pen recorder. [From Crone et al. (72).]

or

$$\frac{dC_{c,t}}{dt} = -\Delta C_t \frac{2P}{r} \tag{37}$$

where $\Delta C_t = C_{c,t} - C_{out,t}$. Capillary permeability is then given by

$$P = -\left(\frac{dC_c/dt}{\Delta C_t}\right)\left(\frac{r}{2}\right) \tag{38}$$

In practice the differential quotient in this expression can be replaced by a difference quotient, or it can be determined from graphical analysis. Capillary permeability can be determined at any time during the discharge of the sac (Fig. 31). The most accurate determination is at $t = 0$, when the concentration difference across the wall is greatest. No specific assumptions concerning the time course of C_c and C_{out} are necessary because both values are determined experimentally.

Interstitial-Diffusion Method

Another approach to studying ion permeability of single capillaries is based on the time course of tissue buildup outside a capillary perfused with a high-K^+ Ringer's solution (e.g., in the frog mesentery). With a mathematical model of the combined capillary-interstitial-superfusate geometry, capillary permeability and interstitial diffusion velocity were experimentally determined (72). This approach is only possible because of the rather low permeability of mesothelial membranes covering the mesenteric capillaries (112). The low permeability of the mesothelial membranes has been disregarded in many experiments on frog mesentery; however, this is not always permissible. Figure 32 illustrates the electrophysiological technique that has been used to determine the ion permeability of the mesenteric mesothelium in vivo. Average values for K^+ permeability of 2–6 × 10^{-5} cm/s were found—

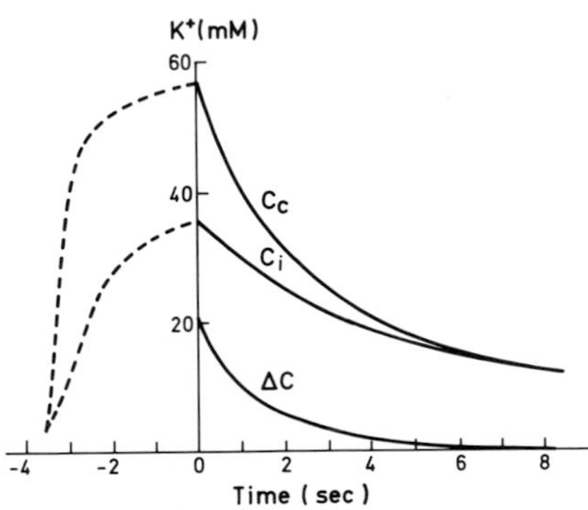

FIG. 31. Efflux of K^+ from closed capillary segment. Graph shows rise and fall of K^+ concentration within (C_c) and just outside (C_i) capillary during brief infusion of isotonic 60-mM K^+-Ringer's solution and subsequent discharge through capillary wall. *Lower curve* (ΔC) shows time course of transcapillary K^+ concentration gradient. [From Crone et al. (72).]

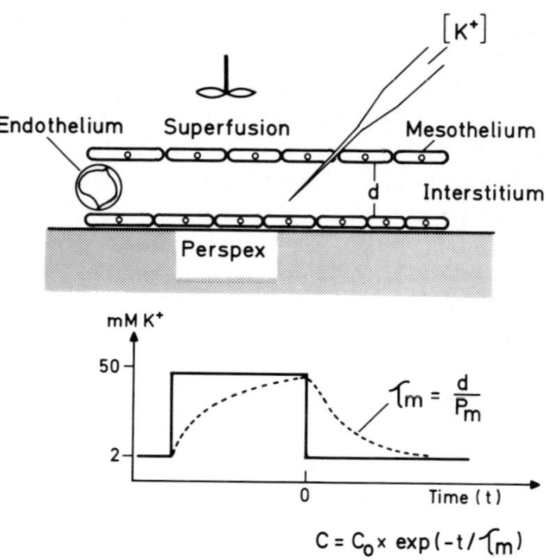

FIG. 32. *Top*: cross section of frog mesentery. Interstitium is covered toward abdominal cavity by single layer of cells forming mesothelium. Concentration of K^+ in interstitium is measured by K^+-sensitive microelectrodes. *Bottom*: superfusion solution (*solid line*) is changed in square-wave pulse and response in interstitial concentration (*dashed line*) is followed. Mesothelial permeability (P_m) is derived from exponential time course of interstitial K^+ concentration. [From Frøkjær-Jensen and Christensen (112).]

one-tenth the permeability of the capillaries in the mesentery (112).

Results

The histogram of K^+ permeabilities in the frog mesenteric capillaries is skewed upward (72, 78). Michel et al. (216) also observed this skewedness in determinations of filtration coefficients. It probably reflects a tendency for permeability to increase with time after exposure and may be a warning that some of the results may overestimate actual permeabilities in undisturbed vessels. An increased leakiness was demonstrated after exposure of postcapillary venules in the hamster cheek pouch (327) and salivary glands (329).

Measurements of K^+ permeability in single muscle vessels have been performed by Frøkjær-Jensen (111) with the bolus-injection technique. He found K^+ permeability to be substantially lower than in the mesentery, i.e., from 5 to 15 × 10^{-5} cm/s. Permeability increased with time and the lowest figures were probably the most reliable for in vivo conditions, which brings the determinations for single vessels close to values found in whole-organ experiments [see Table 12; (133, 309)].

Curry (78) modified the microocclusion technique to provide information about the solute permeability of single frog mesenteric vessels. The concentration difference of a test solute across the capillary wall was determined at various perfusion flows when excess solute was added to the outside of the mesentery. The average concentration difference was calculated from its osmotic effect reflected in the increment of filtration. Assuming the concentration difference across the wall decreases exponentially from the tip of the perfusion cannula, an expression containing P can be derived that permits calculation of permeability from experiments performed at different capillary perfusion rates. These experiments gave a permeability value of 44×10^{-5} cm/s for NaCl, in keeping with the K^+ permeability found with ion-sensitive microelectrodes.

Single vasa recta in the kidney of the rat have been studied with perfusion techniques (222). Urea permeability was found to be 47×10^{-5} cm/s, in agreement with the idea that fenestrated capillaries have extremely high permeabilities. Inulin permeability of peritubular capillaries determined from whole-organ experiments was calculated to be 69×10^{-5} cm/s (335b).

A variation of single-capillary studies is represented by the perfusion studies of the eel rete mirabile (224, 271, 323, 324). This preparation, used by Krogh (166) and Steen (320), has the advantage of being a pure capillary preparation. It is supplied by one artery and drained by one vein, between which about 50,000 capillaries are interposed in parallel in a very regular pattern. The capillaries are predominantly undisturbed because they are not directly touched. Another advantage is that the capillaries can be perfused through the arterial and venous vessels; collection of either perfusate occurs near the swim bladder, which is removed (Fig. 33). The perfusion can be performed either in parallel or countercurrent. For parallel perfusions

$$P = \frac{Q}{2S} \ln\left(\frac{\Delta C_1}{\Delta C_2}\right) \tag{39}$$

where ΔC_1 is the arteriovenous concentration difference of the test substances in the input perfusates, and ΔC_2 is the arteriovenous concentration difference of the test substances in the output perfusates.

The permeability in the rete increased when the protein concentration was reduced to 20% of normal or when the albumin concentration was below 0.33 g/100 ml (224). Rasio et al. (271) used the same preparation but extended the range of molecular weights studied. They did not find evidence of selective diffusion restriction of molecules up to the size of albumin.

Electrical Resistance of Capillary Walls

The study of capillary permeability at the single-capillary level also includes measurement of the electrical resistance of the capillary wall (67, 70, 236). This approach consists of injecting current into an exposed capillary and mapping the electrical potential field inside and outside the capillary in response to current flow. The theory is derived from that used to characterize the passive permeability of the nerve axon membrane.

The potential profile within the capillary is determined by the capillary wall resistance and by the resistance of plasma (blood) within the capillary. If the capillary is surrounded by fluid, external resistance may be ignored and the potential profile within the capillary is exponential with a length constant λ

$$\lambda = \sqrt{r_m/r_i} \tag{40}$$

where r_m is the membrane resistance per centimeter length ($\Omega \cdot$cm) and r_i is the internal resistance per centimeter length (Ω/cm). Because the specific resistance (ρ_i) of the inner medium (plasma or blood) is known, r_i can be calculated as $\rho_i/\pi a^2$, where a is the radius of the capillary. From $r_m = R_m/2\pi a$ the specific resistance of the capillary wall (R_m) can be calculated.

Current is injected through a conventional glass micropipette (tip diam 0.5–1 μm) filled with 2 M KCl, and the potential is measured with another microelectrode. The length constant is determined by successive impalements of the capillary at various distances from the current source (Fig. 34).

The formal basis of the length-constant concept is the field equation

$$\frac{d^2V}{r_i dx^2} = \frac{V_x}{r_m} \tag{41}$$

Letting $\sqrt{r_m/r_i} = \lambda$, the field equation is $d^2V/dx^2 = (1/\lambda^2)V$ with the solution

$$V_x = V_0 e^{-x/\lambda} \tag{42}$$

for current injected at $x = 0$. The capillary wall resistance is calculated from

$$R_m = r_i \lambda^2 2\pi a \tag{43}$$

When the method was first used (70), a more com-

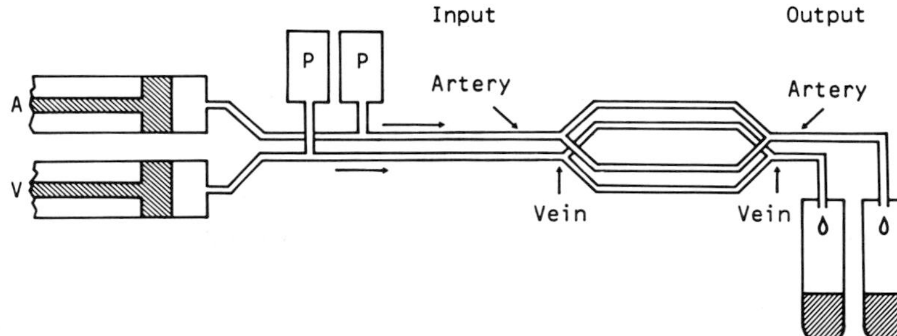

FIG. 33. Technique for investigation of capillary permeability in rete of swim bladder. Perfusates are delivered to rete from arterial (A) and venous (V) syringes via input artery and effluent vein, respectively. Arterial syringe contains test substances. Input pressures are measured by pressure transducers (P) connected to input tubes by T couplings. Outflow from rete is collected from output artery and vein in 2 preweighed test tubes. [From Myhre and Steen (224).]

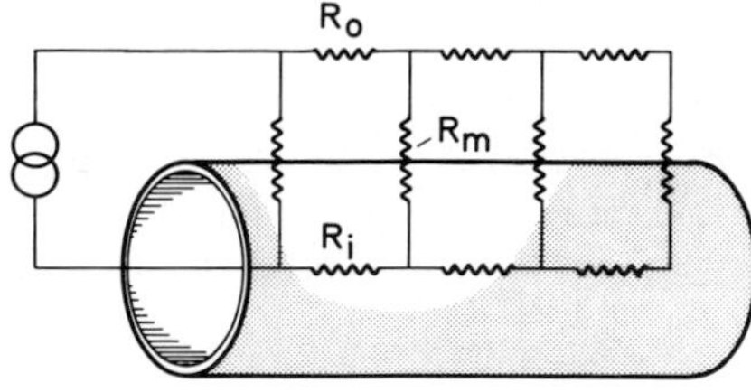

FIG. 34. Electrical resistances in capillary plasma (R_i), capillary endothelium (R_m), and interstitial fluid (R_o). Battery symbolizes current-injection unit, which delivers a square-wave pulse. Potential attentuation is determined with conventional glass microelectrodes inserted into capillary at various distances from current source.

plicated mathematical description was necessary because of the special geometric conditions in frog mesentery—the capillaries lie between two mesothelial membranes with resistances higher than that of the endothelium (Fig. 35).

The average resistance of frog-mesenteric capillary is 1.9 $\Omega \cdot cm^2$ (70). The arterial capillaries have a slightly higher resistance (3.0 $\Omega \cdot cm^2$) than the middle and venous capillaries (0.95 $\Omega \cdot cm^2$).

The method has been applied to brain capillaries (74) and muscle capillaries (236) in the frog where electrical resistance is 1,900 $\Omega \cdot cm^2$ and 25 $\Omega \cdot cm^2$, respectively. An involved mathematical analysis was necessary to interpret the measurements in muscle capillaries because of the distributed resistances in the extravascular space.

The length constant depends on the dimension of the vessel and in itself has only limited significance. The length constant in frog mesenteric capillaries is 60–100 μm and in brain capillaries is 1,000 μm.

The relation between membrane conductance and ion permeability is given by (321)

$$g_j = z_j C_j P_j \frac{F^2}{RT} \tag{44}$$

where g_j is the partial conductance of a given ionic species, z_j is the valency, and F is Faraday's number (96,500 coul/mol). Assuming for the sake of argument that a mesenteric capillary exclusively contains isotonic KCl, a wall conductance of 0.54 $\Omega^{-1} \cdot cm^{-2}$ is calculated. This corresponds closely to the experimentally determined resistance values, indicating that Na^+ and K^+ have similar mobilities and that there is no selective diffusion hindrance to the transcapillary movement of any of the small ions.

A K^+ permeability of $<2.7 \times 10^{-7}$ cm/s was calculated for brain capillaries (85, 136). This permeability is 1,000 times smaller than that in the mesentery in correspondence with the difference in electrical resistance (70, 74).

Determination of capillary permeability with microelectrodes (particularly the easier approach with current injection) opens the way to studies of fast changes in capillary permeability, which has not been explored much so far.

Table 16 summarizes permeabilities and electrical resistances in various endothelia and epithelia. Endothelia and epithelia both show great variation in their electrical resistance and ion permeability. Because passive permeability in both endothelia and epithelia is probably dominated by the nature of the intercellular cleft, it may be profitable to compare permeability values and structural details in the two kinds of planar, multicellular sheets (65, 191, 214). Brain capillary endothelium may be classified as a tight epithelium [Fig. 36; (68)]. This is in accordance with the findings that vasopressin increases water permeability in the brain (267) and that hypertonic solutions augment solute permeability (333).

Dye-Diffusion Studies

Studies of transcapillary dye diffusion have a special place among single-capillary techniques because they give topographical information about permeation. They can also be used for quantitative evaluation of solute permeability (212). Dyes naturally came into use at a time when radioactively labeled compounds were unknown, but they have survived the appearance of tracer substances because of the spatial resolution unattainable with other methods. In early studies dyes were mainly used to answer a qualitative question: does a solute permeate or not? Thus the concept of a

TABLE 16. *Electrical Resistance and K^+ or Na^+ Permeability of Endothelial and Epithelial Tissues*

	Resistance, $\Omega \cdot cm^2$	Ref.	Permeability, 10^{-5} cm/s	Ref.
Frog skin	3,600	341		
Brain endothelium	1,900	74	0.03	136
Toad urinary bladder	1,500	48		
Rabbit collection tubule	860	142		
Necturus gallbladder	300	113		
Necturus proximal tubule	70	24	0.3	24
Frog muscle endothelium	20–30	236	5–15	111
Rat proximal kidney tubule	5	141	2.3	299
Frog mesenteric endothelium	1–3	70	70	72

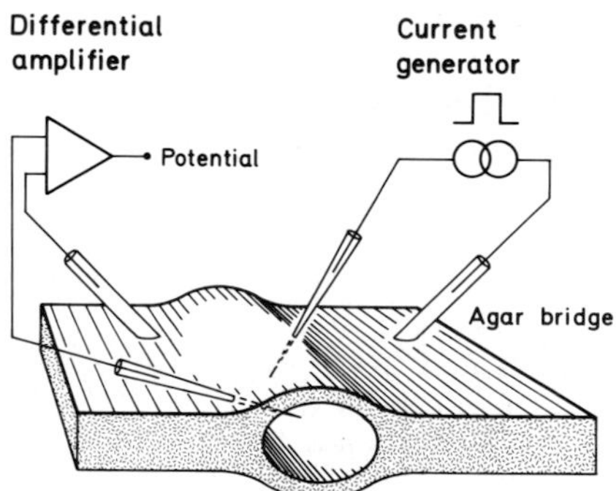

FIG. 35. Representation of experimental setup. Square-wave current pulses are injected into capillary via glass microelectrode. Electrical potential is measured with second glass microelectrode connected to high-impedance electrometer via Ag-AgCl wire. [From Crone and Christensen (70).]

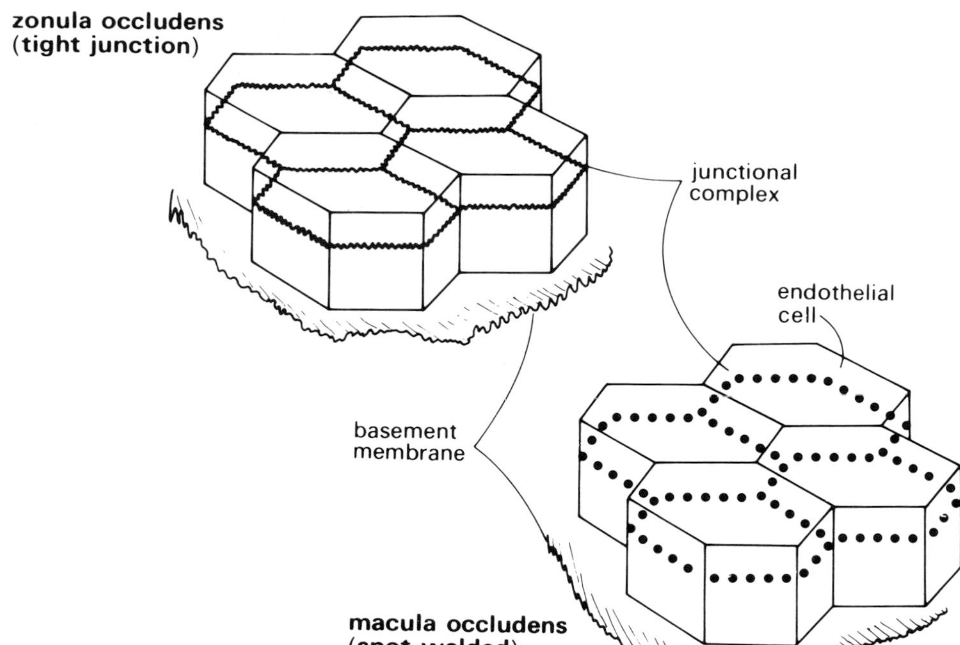

FIG. 36. Representation of arrangement of junctional complex between endothelial cells demonstrating analogy between endothelia and epithelia. Diagram illustrates how interendothelial permeability is controlled by junctional structure. [From Caro et al. (40).]

blood-brain barrier arose from studies of trypan blue diffusion into tissues after intravenous injection. The technique provides information about lesions of brain microvessels (30, 150). Dye studies also give evidence of very low permeability in testicular capillaries (164).

In the 1930s, dye-diffusion studies were used to demonstrate a permeability gradient along the microvasculature as evidenced by an earlier and more intense extravascular coloration around the venous end of capillaries and collecting venules (294, 315, 316). Landis (173) used dyes to investigate whether increased intracapillary pressure leads to more rapid solute escape reflecting a stretched-pore phenomenon; however, he did not find evidence of such a phenomenon. Many years later the same negative conclusion was drawn from experiments showing independence of single-capillary filtration coefficients from intracapillary pressure (82), which is a very significant argument against the concept of stretched pores.

A new development in dye-diffusion studies began with the use of fluorescent dyes (3, 366). Image-intensification techniques and intravital videodensitometry, aided by computer analysis allowing pictorial representation of whole tissue fields as contour maps, have made numerical analysis of interstitial diffusion possible (105, 106, 227, 355, 356, 362). In the pioneering studies by Wiederhielm et al. (362), patent blue V was used rather than a fluorescent dye.

The interpretation of observations from dye-diffusion studies requires definite knowledge about the homogeneity of the dye solution, molecular size, pH of the dye, and degree of protein binding, but these factors are rarely known or not reported in most papers. In addition dyes may damage the vessels because, before the advent of fluorescent techniques, rather high concentrations were needed to get sufficient absorbance.

Wiederhielm (360) and Levick and Michel (184) made special use of protein-bound dyes and determined filtration coefficients in single capillaries by increases in capillary optical density during net filtration. Dye techniques have also been used to show that albumin reduces capillary permeability (183).

Gradient of Permeability

The extensive studies by Rous and associates (293) showed that the opportunity for dyes to pass from the blood to the tissues increases progressively along the microvessels. This was seen in frog muscle, skin, and mesentery, as well as in mammalian tissues (139a, 294, 316). The highest permeability was found where capillaries merge to form collecting venules. Even arterioles were permeable to some dyes (e.g., patent blue V). Observations of more slowly diffusing dyes showed an early coloration outside the capillaries and venules. In bird muscle (e.g., chicken and pigeon) the permeability gradient was not seen, but this could be caused by a countercurrent arrangement of the very short microvessels (316). In studies of frog mesentery Landis (173) found that trypan red comes out more intensely in the arterial portion; however, this observation was not corroborated by Rous and Smith (294), who found the venular portion to be more permeable. They advocated speed in experiments on exposed tissues in order to avoid secondary phenomena affecting permeability. Landis did not inject dye until the mesentery was superfused with Ringer's solution for an hour or two.

The permeability gradient was thought to result from structural differentiation along the capillary. After repeated measurements Landis (174) argued that the presence of large pores in the venular end explains what had been interpreted as a permeability gradient. Michel and Levick (215) disputed this viewpoint and suggested that variations in capillary permeability may occur in undamaged tissues without loss of molecular selectivity (e.g., by variations in area for diffusion).

The matter remains unsettled at this time; however, vessels fixed in situ in the frog abdomen (and therefore not exposed) were shown in a few instances to have large apertures in the venules (34), which could be examples of naturally occurring large pores with diameters of 2,000–5,000 Å. The idea of a permeability gradient in the true sense must logically refer to *1*) an increasing number of pores or channels toward the venular end, *2*) junctions that are looser, or *3*) real transendothelial channels such as have been demonstrated in the venous end of frog mesenteric capillaries (33, 34) and in muscle capillaries (312).

It is probably important to distinguish between a physiological permeability gradient and one that develops under special conditions. In small venules, endothelial cells have been shown to retract under the influence of histamine so that large openings are formed between cells (199, 200). With bovine serum albumin tagged with the fluorochrome fluorescein isothyanate (172), histamine applied in low doses to the exposed rat mesentery created intense fluorescence (hot spots) around some but not all venules and small veins (105) a few minutes after administration. Fluorescence was never observed around arteries, arterioles, or capillaries. The mesentery was treated with utmost care to avoid spontaneous dye leakage. The very high filtration coefficients found in the venular portion of mammalian mesenteric microvessels (107) may relate to the formation of gaps. Serial sectioning of small lengths of affected venules at 500-Å intervals and subsequent electron-microscopic analysis and reconstruction provided a three-dimensional image of the presence of large gaps between endothelial cells or in some cases through the endothelial cell itself. The gap size appeared to be several thousand angstroms. Inflammatory events rapidly lead to the same characteristic pattern of escape of fluorescent macromolecules in the venous portion (326). Unfortunately artifactual holes sometimes form in the capillary wall during experiments on exposed tissue. Perhaps fluorescent macromolecules should be routinely injected into the circulation during experiments on single capillaries so that the use of vessels with overt damage can be avoided. Another possibility is to use blockers of prostaglandin metabolism such as indomethacin or histamine H_2-receptor blockers (111, 327).

Interstitial Diffusion

Dye-diffusion experiments, besides giving information about regional differences in capillary permeability, have invited studies of solute transport in interstitial tissues. Modern instrumentation allows dynamic studies of the spread of tagged solutes after they leave the capillaries (106). Such studies are done on various mesenteric preparations, which in formal analysis are treated as two-dimensional slabs. Analysis of successive contour maps led to estimates of diffusion coefficients for macromolecules of increasing size that, when expressed relative to free-diffusion coefficients, show clear restrictive effects. These effects become more pronounced as molecular size increases (Fig. 37). Fox and Wayland (106) found that with fluorescein isothyanate–labeled dextrans (mol wt 3,400–41,200) and fluorochrome-labeled serum albumin the relative diffusion coefficient (D'/D) ranged from 0.26 (for dextran, mol wt 3,400) to 0.073 (for serum albumin). The apparent diffusion coefficient for serum albumin was approximately half the apparent diffusion coefficient for dextrans with the same free-diffusion coefficient, which might be explained by the significantly more negative charge on the protein molecules interacting with a negatively charged matrix. In uncharged plastic membranes with pore diameters between 300 and 500 Å, however, proteins were found to have a larger reflection coefficient than dextrans with the same mean molecular size; this might be explained by differences in molecular rigidity (303).

The general reduction of interstitial diffusion velocity has not been satisfactorily explained, but a number

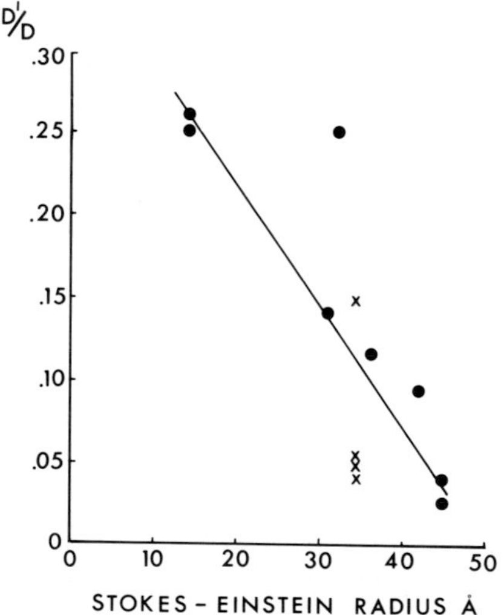

FIG. 37. Reduction of diffusion coefficient in rat mesentery interstitium. Ratio of restricted-diffusion and free-diffusion coefficients (D'/D) may be extrapolated to zero around a Stokes-Einstein radius of 50 Å. Extrapolation to solute with radius of 3 Å (Na^+ or K^+) gives reduction of diffusion velocity to one-third in accordance with Crone et al. (72). [From Watson (354).]

of factors may interact including tortuosity, exclusion, microviscosity, and frictional drag. The particular interest of these considerations of capillary wall solute permeability is the possibility that capillary permeability, rather than being determined by pore size, is a function of the ground matrix filling the pores (81, 213). According to this concept, selective restriction is caused by fibers in the matrix; the size of the pore only acts by defining the area accessible to permeating molecules. This means that diffusion is already slowed at the inner surface of the endothelium (glycocalyx) and subsequently in the pore matrix and basement membrane with the effect continuing in the interstitium. Extrapolation of the values in Figure 37 to small solutes such as Na^+ or K^+ leads to interstitial diffusion coefficients of ~25%–30% of the free-diffusion coefficients. This is exactly the value determined by Crone et al. (72) in the frog mesentery.

The diffusion velocity of low-molecular-weight solutes in interstitial tissue has been determined in vitro in heart muscle experiments where tracers are deposited at one side of a tissue slab in an Ussing-type diffusing chamber. Their appearance on the other side was followed as a function of time (296, 325). Concentration profiles in the cerebral tissue from the ventricular surface were also analyzed (253). The same reduction to ~25% of the free-diffusion coefficient was found in these studies.

Watson (354) has suggested, on the basis of data from Fox and Wayland (106), that measurements of capillary permeability that show diffusion restriction rather reflect the restriction properties of the interstitium; consequently ordinary experiments on capillary permeability actually measure the diffusion resistance of the interstitial matrix. Similarly Intaglietta and de Plomb (149) proposed that filtration rates are determined by the hydraulic conductance of interstitial tissue. The presence of a capillary membrane obviously cannot be disregarded simply because endothelial cells drastically reduce the area available for diffusion of hydrophilic solutes. In fact single-capillary studies (72) with ion-sensitive microelectrodes on both sides of the capillary wall showed a 40%–60% jump in concentration of test solutes across the capillary wall in the mesentery. The same conclusion was borne out by measurements of the electrical resistance of capillary walls (70) where the relative potential decrease was ~50%. In frog cerebral capillaries the relative potential decrease across the capillary wall was >95% (94) when current was injected into a capillary. On the other hand it is evident that the time for saturation or desaturation of an organ with a test solute depends on diffusion rates in the interstitial tissue and that the capillary wall may not be the only rate-limiting parameter.

FACILITATED TRANSPORT IN ENDOTHELIUM

For many years it was debated whether the hindrance to diffusion between blood and brain tissue was caused by the endothelium or by the surrounding glial cells. A very simple experiment shows that it must be the endothelium that constitutes the blood-brain barrier. If two solutes with different free-diffusion coefficients are injected into an organ intra-arterially and collected in the effluent after one capillary passage, the solute with the higher diffusion coefficient will be present in lower amounts because more will have left the capillaries during the passage through the organ. If the two solutes are D-[^{14}C]-glucose and ^{42}K, less ^{42}K will appear in the effluent and the ratio of D-[^{14}C]glucose to ^{42}K will be >1. This is a mere reflection of the higher ^{42}K diffusion rate in hydrophilic pores and was found in experiments on skeletal muscle (Fig. 38). In the brain, however, exactly the opposite happens; more D-[^{14}C]glucose was retained and the ratio was <1. It was argued that this might be caused by fast metabolic removal of D-[^{14}C]glucose from the brain creating a large sink. When the experiment was repeated with 3-*O*-methylglucose (which is not metabolized), however, exactly the same results were reported (Fig. 38). The only reasonable explanation of this simple experiment is that special transport mechanisms for D-[^{14}C]glucose are present in the brain endothelium; a passive porous filter cannot explain the findings.

Thus studies of brain capillaries provided the first information that mediated transendothelial transport occurs in capillaries. According to the pore theory, transcapillary transport is a passive, dissipative process proportional to existing gradients; understanding unidirectional transport of D-[^{14}C]glucose in brain capillaries as a nonlinear function of plasma concentration (56, 57, 61) reveals an interaction between the diffusing species and the membrane not envisaged in the pore theory. The demonstration of saturability (56), competitive interaction (233, 308), stereospecificity (75), and counterflow (17) indicates that D-[^{14}C]glucose interacts with a specific protein in the membrane ("transporter"). It was suggested earlier that the transport of D-[^{14}C]glucose in brain capillaries involves passage through the endothelial cells (61).

It is not known whether the ability to facilitate transendothelial transport is caused by induction from neighboring glial cells or whether the mechanism is intimately connected with the presence of tight junctions between the endothelial cells (272). Facilitated transport of glucose through endothelial cells has not been demonstrated in other endothelia (64, 270). Facilitated transport of vascoactive hormones into endothelial cells occurs in lung capillaries (41a, 116, 196a, 296a, 327a).

Solutes that pass into the brain interact with a cellular endothelial membrane, which facilitates passage, as in the liver where blood is directly exposed to the cell membranes of hepatocytes. The equations describing solute exchange in the two organs are very similar, but no definite attempt has been made to unify the mathematical interpretations. Detailed models of the conditions in both the liver (8, 10, 161,

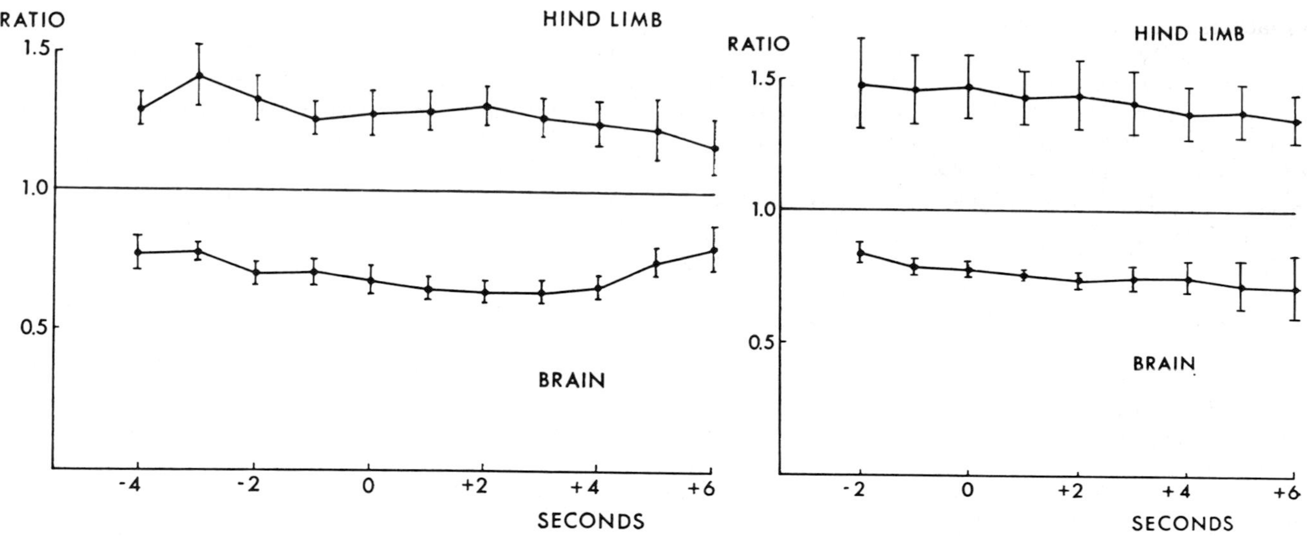

FIG. 38. *Left*: venous outflow concentration ratios of D-[^{14}C]glucose and ^{42}K in experiments on brain and hindlimb. *Right*: venous outflow concentation ratios of 3-*O*-[^{14}C]methylglucose and ^{42}K in experiments on brain and hindlimb. Abscissa: time; peak of dilution curve is arbitrarily called zero time. Ordinate: concentration ratios; *vertical bar* = ±1 SE. [From Crone and Thompson (75).]

162) and the brain (4, 76, 117, 118, 198, 250) have been made. Concepts from general enzymology are used in both organ models, and the exchange unit is treated as a cylinder with a Michaelis-Menten mechanism in the wall.

Analysis of facilitated transport processes across capillaries is based on the formalism for symmetrical transport proposed by Lefevre (182) and Wilbrandt and Rosenberg (363). The situation in endothelium is somewhat complicated because the transported solute passes through two consecutive endothelial membranes (248). Net transport (J_1) across the luminal membrane of the endothelial cell is given by

$$J_1 = \frac{T_{max}C_P}{C_P + K_m} - \frac{T_{max}C_{endo}}{C_{endo} + K_m} \tag{45}$$

where C_{endo} is the concentration in the cytoplasm of the endothelial cell; C_P is the concentration in the plasma; and T_{max} and K_m are the maximal transport capacity and half-saturation constant, respectively. For net transport across the abluminal membrane (J_2), a similar expression holds

$$J_2 = \frac{T_{max}C_{endo}}{K_m + C_{endo}} - \frac{T_{max}C_I}{K_m + C_I} \tag{45a}$$

where C_I is the concentration in the interstitial fluid. In the steady state and for identical membranes, $J_1 = J_2 = (J_1 + J_2)/2 = J_{net}$, where J_{net} is the net transport from blood to brain.

This formalism was developed by Pappenheimer and Setchell (248) to characterize glucose transport in brain capillaries. They determined net fluxes at various glucose concentrations in plasma (taking the interstitial glucose concentration to be equal to the cerebrospinal fluid concentration). From Equations 45 and 45a it follows that

$$J_{net} = \frac{T_{max}C_P}{C_P + K_m} - \frac{T_{max}C_I}{C_I + K_m} \tag{45b}$$

where T_{max} is the maximal transport capacity of the capillary ($\sim J_{max}/2$).

Most investigators have used tracer methods to characterize facilitated diffusion. Here Equation 45b takes the form

$$J^* = \frac{T_{max}C_1^*}{C_1 + K_m + C_1^*} - \frac{T_{max}C_2^*}{C_2 + K_m + C_2^*} \tag{46}$$

where J^* is the net flux of radioactive glucose and C_1^* and C_2^* are the tracer concentrations on either side of the capillary wall, which is treated as a single membrane.

A tracer experiment is based on the assumption that the tracer concentration on the *trans* side of the membrane is negligible ($C_2^* \ll C_1^*$). Furthermore, because C_1^* is vanishingly small relative to C_1, Equation 46 reduces to

$$J^* = \frac{T_{max}C_1^*}{C_1 + K_m} \tag{47}$$

which is the equation that most experiments, including the indicator-diffusion and Oldendorf techniques, are based on. The significant experimental parameter is the unidirectional tracer extraction, which is given by (118, 198)

$$E^* \simeq 1 - e^{-[T_{max}/(C_1 + K_m)]/Q} \tag{48}$$

Equation 48 shows that the extraction is concentration dependent, decreasing with increasing concentration. The kinetic constants can be determined from measurements of the unidirectional tracer extraction at various glucose levels. Equation 47 is analogous to the equation for unidirectional extraction in single-injection experiments (see Eq. 7). Thus

$$PS \simeq \frac{T_{max}}{C_1 + K_m} \qquad (49)$$

In principle the equation $-Q \ln(1 - E^*) = T_{max}/(C_1 + K_m)$ permits the determination of the two Michaelis-Menten constants if tracer extractions E_1^* and E_2^* are determined at two different plasma glucose concentrations. Determination of the average intracapillary concentration ($C_1 \simeq (C_a + C_v)/2$) requires a simultaneous measurement of the arteriovenous glucose difference.

Initially it may be surprising that the tracer concentration decreases exponentially in a system obeying Michaelis-Menten kinetics (cf. Eq. 48). However, because the intracapillary concentration of unlabeled glucose is practically constant (because of the small arteriovenous difference for glucose), the tracer "senses" a transport mechanism with a constant occupation fraction. Thus the access of the tracer molecules to this mechanism is proportional to the local tracer concentration; i.e., the decrease is exponential. Because of this the concentration profiles of labeled and unlabeled solutes in the capillary are different (except in the theoretical case of zero brain glucose concentration). This fact, which has been overlooked in many studies, makes experiments where unlabeled-glucose concentration changes during the experiments somewhat ambiguous (118, 198). The special features of glucose transport into brain are shown in Figure 39, and kinetic constants are given in Table 17.

Extraction can be calculated from the loss of tracer from the blood during a single passage or from tissue uptake after very short exposure times (20 s). The tissue sampling technique requires correction for tracer glucose remaining within vessels.

The nature of the facilitating transport system in brain endothelium is unknown, but it apparently has many features in common with facilitated transport in red cell membranes (226). Glucose transport in both membranes is insensitive to insulin (17, 60, 124).

The net effect of the facilitating mechanism for glucose transport is to increase permeability by a factor of 100 at normal glucose concentrations. The permeability–surface area product for glucose in the rat brain is ~20 ml·100 g^{-1}·min^{-1} at concentrations between 5 and 10 mM (118). Thus a capillary surface area of 150 cm^2/g gives a permeability value of 2.5×10^{-5} cm/s. Comparing this value to permeabilities for Na^+ and sucrose (see Tables 12 and 13) shows how insignificant passive diffusion in the brain is relative to mediated transport in the brain.

Evidence suggests that the transport system is labile with respect to its kinetics in response to lasting alterations of plasma concentrations. This interesting phenomenon reflects the presence of induction mechanisms similar to those present in epithelia (54, 55, 119, 120, 208a).

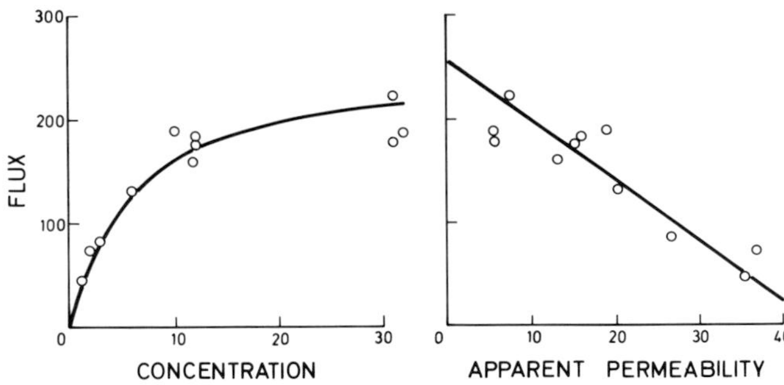

FIG. 39. *Left*: unidirectional blood-brain glucose flux vs. arterial-plasma concentration in rats anesthetized with halothane. Abscissa, mM; ordinate, μmol·min^{-1}·100 g^{-1}. *Right*: transformation of values from *left* shows unidirectional blood-brain glucose flux vs. apparent permeability of blood-brain barrier to glucose. Apparent permeability equals flux divided by concentration. Permeability decreases with increasing flux. *Right* shows similarity to Eadie-Hofstee plot of enzymatic reactions and Scatchard plot of ligand binding to receptors. Abscissa, ml·min^{-1}·100 g^{-1}; ordinate, μmol·min^{-1}·100 mg^{-1}. [Adapted from Gjedde (118).]

TABLE 17. *Kinetic Constants for Glucose Transport From Blood to Brain in Dog*

	K_m, mM	T_{max}, μmol·100 g^{-1}·min^{-1}
Control	8.26	175
Pentobarbital	8.60	183
Insulin	8.06	152

T_{max}, maximum transport capacity of capillaries; K_m, Michaelis-Menten constant for transport system. [From Betz et al. (17).]

There is no unequivocal evidence that nonelectrolytes can be transported against concentration gradients. Glucose movement is generally believed to be passive ("equilibrating") across brain endothelium. The description of glucose transport in the brain is further complicated by the fact that new capillary surface may be recruited (358a). Figure 40 illustrates the several curves that describe the relation between unidirectional glucose flux and flow—a situation analogous to variations in capillary diffusion capacity at different degrees of recruitment.

ACTIVE TRANSPORT IN ENDOTHELIUM

In view of the generally very leaky nature of endothelium it is unlikely that active transport plays a role in transcapillary solute movement, in contrast to the importance of active transport in epithelia. This of course reflects the fundamental fact that capillaries are usually passive filters. There is one possible exception to this rule: the ionic composition of brain interstitial fluid is regulated (25, 27). There seems to be a K^+ homeostasis; K^+ is pumped out of brain interstitial fluid in response to artificial elevations of the interstitial concentration. The process must be an active one. Studies with isolated brain capillary preparations (125, 157) claim to show energy-requiring K^+ trans-

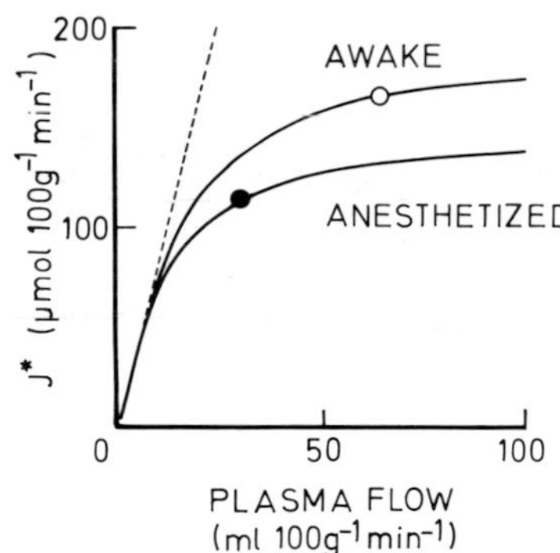

FIG. 40. Unidirectional glucose flux as function of plasma flow for awake and anesthetized rats at normoglycemia (8.5 mM). J*, net flux. [From Gjedde (118). © 1983. Munksgaard Int. Publ., Ltd., Copenhagen, Denmark.]

port (123), and ATPase has been found at the abluminal membrane of the capillary endothelium (102). If cerebral capillaries behave as a tight epithelium, several active transport processes will probably be identified in this special endothelium. It is of immediate interest to disclose the presence of an inward-directed Na^+ pump (96). The demonstration that cerebral endothelial cells contain a greater number of mitochondria than muscle endothelium (235) is also of great interest for considerations about active transport processes in endothelium.

These aspects of active transendothelial transport should be distinguished from active ion transport across the endothelial plasma membrane, which adjusts the ionic composition of the endothelial cytoplasm. Very little is known about the regulation of the endothelial cell interior apart from the studies of ion selectivity of the endothelial cell membrane (229a).

INTERPRETATION OF PERMEABILITY STUDIES

Background

Plasma solutes are brought to the capillaries by convection in bigger vessels whose walls are relatively impermeable. However, there will be some finite permeability in every part of the circulatory system because all vessels are covered with endothelial cells similar to those in the capillary segment. Two facts explain the functional impermeability of large vessels. The surface/volume ratio is very unfavorable and conductance of the vessel wall as a whole is poor. However, as the vessels divide, the walls become thinner and the surface area increases; thus the possibility of transvascular solute transport improves and exchange does begin before the capillary region is reached.

Duling and co-workers (90) addressed the problem of solute loss from the circulation before the capillary level. They showed that lipophilic gases permeate through arterioles. The inert gas xenon is also exchanged between neighboring vessels (307). Heat exchange is well known between large vessels because of its extraordinarily high conductance in blood and vessel walls.

These aspects of transvascular exchange are mentioned to emphasize that there is not an absolute distinction between capillaries and other vascular sections but rather degrees of difference. The unique role of capillaries is to create an extraordinarily favorable surface:volume ratio and to be situated very close to all tissue cells. However, the design of the whole system is imperfect in the sense that there is no absolute distinction between permeable and impermeable portions. Venules must always be included in any consideration of capillary permeability because the solute permeability and surface area of venules equals that of capillaries. The relative contributions of the two consecutive systems cannot be analyzed because relatively little information is available about capillary-venule surface relations; however, estimates of microvascular surface area may generally be too low because they do not include venules. Wiederhielm (361) mentions that venular surface area is greater than capillary surface area (thus the Starling forces responsible for fluid reabsorption need only be very small). A striking example is found in the kidney where peritubular capillaries are thought to have a surface area 20 times as large as that of the filtering glomerular capillaries [see Table 3; (282)].

Because of these nonidealities of the circulatory system, different solutes are not exposed to the same surface area, functionally speaking. For example, urea may diffuse out of arterioles whereas inulin may only permeate through true capillaries. Thus when permeability ratios of two test solutes are compared they may not refer to the same surface areas as is often tacitly assumed.

The very great differences in permeability of hydrophilic and lipophilic solutes are well known. For the interpretation of permeability data this difference is basic because the two classes of solutes are transferred across quite different surface areas. Hydrophilic solutes diffuse through a minute fraction of the surface whereas lipophilic solutes use practically the entire surface. This is in accord with the general principles of passive cell membrane passage characterized by Collander (49–51). He demonstrated the overriding importance of lipid solubility for passive passage through cell membranes. The passage rate of a small hydrophilic molecule such as mannitol ($D \sim 10^{-5}$ cm^2/s) through a cell membrane typically gives a permeability coefficient of 10^{-8} cm/s, which directly shows that transcapillary transport of such molecules is not through endothelial cells. If the same molecule diffuses through a hypothetical layer of water 1 μm deep, the permeability coefficient will be 10^{-1} cm/s. Capillary nonelectrolyte permeability is $\sim 10^{-5}$ cm/s (see Tables 12–14). Assuming free diffusion in the intercellular pathway, a molecule the size of mannitol requires a fractional hydrophilic surface area of $10^{-5}/10^{-1}$ or 0.01%. Larger molecules encounter greater diffusion hindrance because of frictional and entrance effects, and the virtual surface area available for free diffusion is increasingly reduced with molecular size and approaches zero for macromolecules.

In the following discussion the hydrophilic pathway is treated as a slit with plane parallel walls. The hydrophilic pathway is classically called a pore, and the distinction between pores and slits may not be sharp. However, because the only serious candidate for the hydrophilic pathway is the intercellular (junctional) pathway, the pore should be considered as a slitlike structure. The endothelial cells are not physically impermeable but in fact are permeable to water. The solute permeability of the endothelial cell proper is largely unknown, but if the brain endothelium reflects endothelial cell permeability, a good estimate would be 1,000 times lower than the permeability of the interendothelial pathway despite the vastly larger surface area (per cm^2).

On the basis of this general picture of the capillary membrane several questions may be asked. *1*) Does a fractional slit area of 0.01% comply with morphological measurements? *2*) What information do permeation studies (diffusion, filtration, and reflection coefficient measurements) give about slit dimensions and geometry? Or, alternatively, can a cleft model be construed that behaves like the interendothelial junction? *3*) What are the degrees of freedom in cleft modeling? Are many different models compatible with results from the macroapproach to capillary permeability?

Because detailed modeling is only meaningful if based on very reliable quantitative data, it may be found that the available data are too ill defined to provide very precise pore definition. The following discussion addresses this question and attempts to evaluate the present position of the classic pore hypothesis.

Equivalent Model of Hydrophilic Channel

To interpret the available data for diffusion, filtration, and reflection coefficients, a model must be chosen and analyzed to the extent that it can be fitted to observations. In their first attempt to formulate a quantitative model, Pappenheimer et al. (247) chose a membrane perforated by cylindrical pores (although they also analyzed the rectangular slit model) and proposed equivalent pore diameters of 70–90 Å for the muscle capillary membrane. This model has been widely used and represents the main paradigm employed in interpretations of transport data. In an extensive review of endothelial morphology, Majno and Joris (201) strongly expressed the insurmountable problems of interpreting whole-organ data in terms of specific models of endothelial pathways, not only because of the morphological heterogeneity of consecutive segments of the capillary wall but also because of heterogeneity over short distances as seen, for example, in the presence of a small number of fenestrae in typical continuous capillaries (34, 52, 165). This gives single-capillary studies a definite advantage in cleft modeling.

Because most single-capillary studies have been carried out on frog mesenteric capillary, this discussion attempts to analyze this capillary in more detail based on a very simple model of the interendothelial cleft. The simplest model, shown in Figure 41 with other

TABLE 18. *Morphological and Functional Data for Frog Mesenteric Capillaries*

		Ref.
K^+ permeability	70×10^{-5} cm/s	72
Filtration coefficient	54×10^{-8} cm·s^{-1}·cmH$_2$O^{-1}	216
Electrical resistance	1–3 Ω·cm^2	70
Interendothelial slit length	2,000 cm/cm^2	35
Interendothelial slit depth	0.7×10^{-4} cm/s	34
K^+ diffusion coefficient (20°C)	1.8×10^{-5} cm^2/s	288
Reflection coefficients		
NaCl	0.07	81
Myoglobin	0.21	219
Albumin	0.81	213

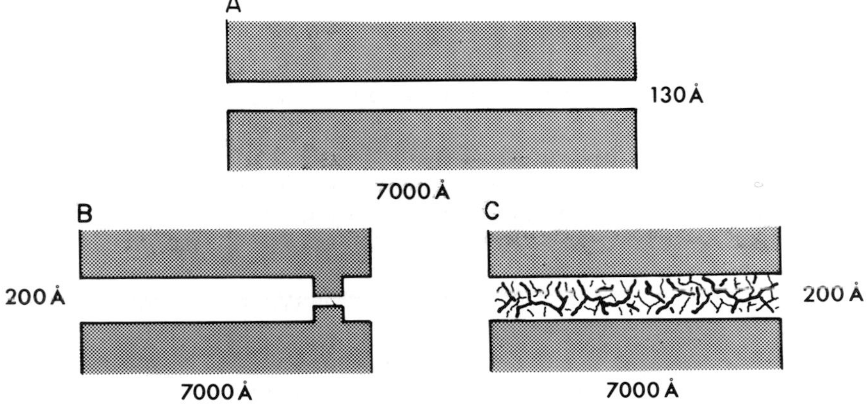

FIG. 41. Three alternative cleft models. *A*: original Pappenheimer-Renkin model proposed slits with parallel plates (245). *B*: constricted-cleft model assumes obligatory passage through 2 consecutive segments. Short segment is narrowed to 50 Å, whereas long segment is 200 Å wide. Regions of tight junctions may constitute circumferential belts around endothelial cells, or they may be discontinuous. *C*: fiber-matrix model places important diffusion and filtration hindrances within pore in form of matrix. [From Crone and Christensen (70).]

slit models, is that of a cleft with plane parallel walls. The plane parallel model is analyzed first followed by the model with slits of various dimensions in its wide and tight portions. The analysis is based on the values shown in Table 18.

DIFFUSION. In this first simple analysis, pore restriction effects on solutes as small as K^+ are neglected. Diffusional permeability is defined as

$$P = \frac{Dlw}{\Delta x} \tag{50}$$

where the values of P and D are known, l is the total slit length per square centimeter, Δx is the slit depth, and w (the slit width) is unknown. This equation is solved for w with the known values of K^+ permeability

$$P_{K^+} = \frac{(1.8 \times 10^{-5}) \times 2{,}000 \times w}{0.7 \times 10^{-4}} = 70 \times 10^{-5} \text{ cm/s}$$

so that

$$w = 130 \times 10^{-8} \text{ cm}$$

This value is used in the following calculations as a test of the cleft hypothesis. The calculation assumes that the entire interendothelial junction is open. This may or may not be true, but according to the sketch in Figure 42, the organization of ridges and grooves visible in a freeze-fracture replica will allow molecular diffusion around these structures.

Palade et al. (244) stressed that molecules smaller than 20 Å may pass the so-called tight portions, which are only morphologically tight to electron-dense tracers larger than 20 Å. Simionescu et al. (313) showed that junctions in the venular end of mesenteric capillaries contain only one macula densa. This suggests that the junction is virtually open but does not mean, for example, that 10%–20% of the slit length could not be closed, which would not change the essence of the argument.

FRACTIONAL SLIT SURFACE AREA. Because the slit length per square centimeter of surface area and width are known, the fractional surface area can be calculated

$$w \times l = (130 \times 10^{-8}) \times 2{,}000 = 2.6 \times 10^{-3} \text{ cm}^2/\text{cm}^2$$

Thus the hydrophilic pathway occupies ~0.25% of the surface. The fractional pore area in the mesenteric capillary is larger than the 0.01% calculated in an earlier example, reflecting the fact that solute permeability in the mesentery is ~10 times larger than in muscle capillaries. Perry and Garlick (264) calculated a fractional cleft area in rabbit lung of 0.005%.

The term *pore area per unit path length* is sometimes used (88, 245, 281). The slit area per diffusion path length for the mesenteric capillary (per cm²) is $(2.6 \times 10^{-3})/(0.7 \times 10^{-4}) = 37 \text{ cm}^{-1}$. Renkin and Curry (281) revised the early transient osmotic data and gave 2 cm^{-1} for NaCl in the muscle capillary. This indicates

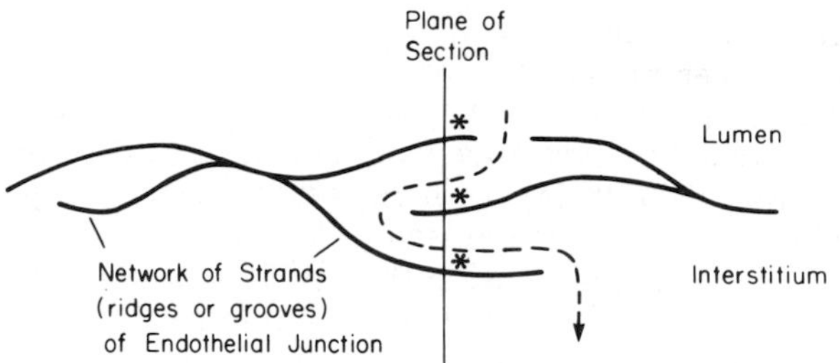

FIG. 42. Diagram of freeze-fracture image of endothelial junction in muscle capillary. *Curved lines* illustrate network formed by lines of contact between apposed plasma membranes of adjacent endothelial cells. *Dashed line* traces pathway through region of discontinuity in network. *Straight line* represents plane of vertical thin section through region of discontinuity. In thin section, endothelial cleft is bridged by 3 sites of membrane contact marked with *asterisks.* Tortuous pathway through junction would not be detected. [From Wissig and Williams (365).]

that only a small fraction of the junction in muscle capillaries is open to small solutes as calculated by Lassen and Trap-Jensen (178) and supported by experiments on single muscle capillaries (111, 236). Michel (213) calculated a value of 80 cm^{-1} from filtration data for the frog mesenteric capillary.

ELECTRICAL RESISTANCE. In this simple slit model the electrical resistance of 1 cm² capillary wall is calculated from the specific resistance (ρ_o) of frog Ringer's fluid, which is 90 Ω·cm, and the above slit dimensions. The resistance is inversely proportional to area and proportional to slit depth. Thus

$$R_m = \frac{\rho_o \times \Delta x}{w \times l} = \frac{90 \times (0.7 \times 10^{-4})}{2{,}000 \times (130 \times 10^{-8})} = 2.7\ \Omega \cdot \text{cm}^2$$

which agrees with the experimentally obtained value of 1–3 Ω·cm² (70).

FILTRATION COEFFICIENT. Bjerrum and Manegold (19) derived an expression for filtration through a slit with plane parallel walls in which

$$L_p = \frac{(w/2)^2 wl}{3\eta \Delta x} \tag{51}$$

where L_p is the hydraulic conductance. Insertion of the relevant values gives

$$L_p = \frac{[(65)^2 \times 10^{-16}](130 \times 10^{-8})(2{,}000)}{3(0.7 \times 10^{-4})(1.0 \times 10^{-5})}$$

$$= 50 \times 10^{-8} \text{ cm} \cdot \text{s}^{-1} \cdot \text{cmH}_2\text{O}^{-1}$$

[The viscosity is assumed to be that of water (0.01 poise at 20°C), which is equivalent to 1.0×10^{-5} cm·s^{-1}·cmH$_2$O^{-1}.] This value agrees with the experimentally determined value (213).

OSMOTIC REFLECTION COEFFICIENT. Curry (77) has tabulated the reflection coefficients for small solutes in a plane parallel model (Table 19) as a function of the ratio of molecular diameter to slit diameter. With

TABLE 19. *Reflection Coefficients (σ) in a Plane Parallel Model*

Molecular Diameter/ Slit Diameter	σ
0.0	0.0
0.1	0.02
0.2	0.05
0.3	0.11
0.4	0.21
0.5	0.31
0.6	0.44
0.7	0.58
0.8	0.72
0.9	0.88
1.0	1.00

From Curry (77).

TABLE 20. *Morphometric Data About Interendothelial Pathways*

	Species	Cleft Length, cm/cm²	Cleft Depth, cm × 10⁻⁴	Ref.
Skeletal muscle	Rabbit	1,700	0.9	263
	Dog	2,000	0.9	41
Diaphragm	Rat	2,000		311
Mesentery	Frog	2,000	0.7	34
Lung (adult)	Rabbit	2,200	1.4	263
Lung (fetal)	Rabbit	2,900	1.2	263

a molecular diameter of 70 Å for albumin, a slit width of ~85 Å explains a reflection coefficient of 0.81. Thus reflection coefficient data for this macromolecule are not well correlated; however, the value is not wholly inconsistent with the estimated average slit width of 130 Å. For smaller molecules the correlation is better, and thus the experimental value for albumin is critical. A small constriction in the cleft would eliminate the discrepancy as explained below.

This analysis of permeability, based on a very simple slit model, demonstrates the need for better morphometric data to allow testing of equivalent models. Basic information such as the length and depth of interendothelial clefts is only available for a few tissues (Table 20). Even though more data may become available, there is the additional difficulty of variation in slit length (per cm²) and cleft depth in consecutive microvessels [arterioles, capillaries, and venules; (Fig. 43)]. This kind of heterogeneity will always place a limit on the correlation of functional and morphological data.

From rough estimates of the interendothelial cleft length in skeletal muscle (159), it was found that 3%–18% of the interendothelial slit must be open to explain experimental diffusion and filtration data (178). Casley-Smith et al. (41) calculated a value of 4.8% for the fraction of open-to-total junctional length in skeletal muscle. This numerical treatment of the mesenteric capillary is based on the simplest slit model; however, others have used more detailed models of slit geometry (41, 129, 178, 257, 258, 263) including a narrow portion along the cleft (see Fig. 41). Morphometric analysis has shown that the narrow segment occupies ~2%–5% of the entire slit depth. The width of the wide part of the slit is 150–250 Å (311), whereas that of the narrow portion is ~50 Å. Measurements can be even more refined, and Perry (263) has provided the most detailed quantitative evaluation of slit topography in lung and muscle.

At present it is uncertain whether it is profitable to go much further in cleft modeling because shrinkage and preparation artifacts can affect the very fine measurements in a critical way (also, the resolving power of electron microscopes is ~5 Å). Bruns and Palade (31) strongly stressed that there is a limit to what ultramicroscopical information can provide and warned against too literal an interpretation of EM data. This point was also stressed by Bundgaard (32) in his critical review on morphological pore identification.

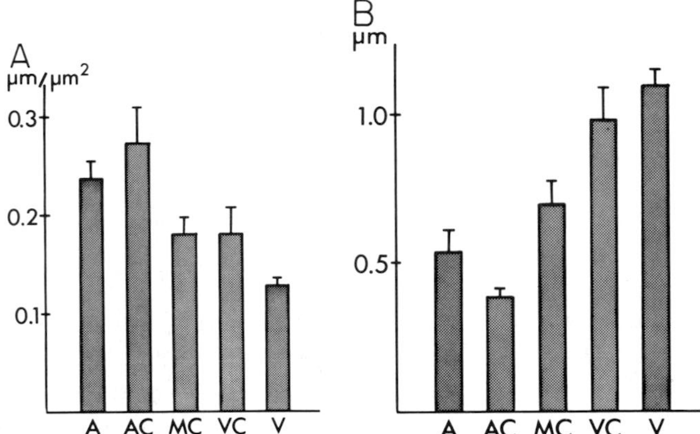

FIG. 43. *A*: variations of interendothelial cleft length (per μm²) in frog mesenteric microcirculation. Diagram shows heterogeneity at microscopic level; there is no unique geometrical equivalent to real pore dimensions. *B*: variation of cleft depth in various segments of frog mesenteric microvasculature determined from electron micrographs with morphometric methods. A, arteriole; AC, arterial capillary; MC, midcapillary; VC, venous capillary; V, venule. [From Bundgaard and Frøkjær-Jensen (34).]

In slit modeling, a short narrow pathway along the slit (see Fig. 34) does not significantly affect diffusion permeability. The permeability of a short narrow segment (400 Å long by 40 Å wide) for a solute like K^+ is 3.6×10^{-3} cm/s, i.e., ~500 times higher than in the 7,000-Å long wide portion of the pore. This indicates that its presence is not noticeable in diffusion experiments. The same applies to electrical resistance, which is linearly related to pore dimensions. The filtration coefficient is reduced to one-half of that in a plain 130-Å rectangular slit, which is still considered a relatively weak change.

The parameter most strongly affected by a tight zone in the cleft is the reflection coefficient. Because reflection coefficients are smaller than can be explained by a 130–200 Å pore, it is reasonable to speculate about slits with narrow portions, which correspond very well to morphological observations (158, 159). Perry (263) and Casley-Smith et al. (41) were successful in attempting to reconstruct diffusion and filtration permeabilities from actual geometrical measurements of clefts with a long wide and a short narrow portion. It seems reasonable to accept this representation of the hydrophilic pathway in endothelia (Fig. 44). Variations between capillaries in various organs are probably caused mainly by differences in open junctional length (per unit surface area) and depth; the effective junction width is probably similar for most tissues (263). This conclusion explains the fact that diffusion and filtration permeabilities covary over a large range of values, whereas reflection coefficients stay constant (see Table 15). This is not the case, however, if variation is caused by changes in slit width because this would result in a stronger influence on filtration.

The permeability data in Tables 12–14 do not indicate major permeability differences between continuous capillaries (with the exception of the brain and the mesentery). The differences between the average and the extremes can unrestrainedly be explained by

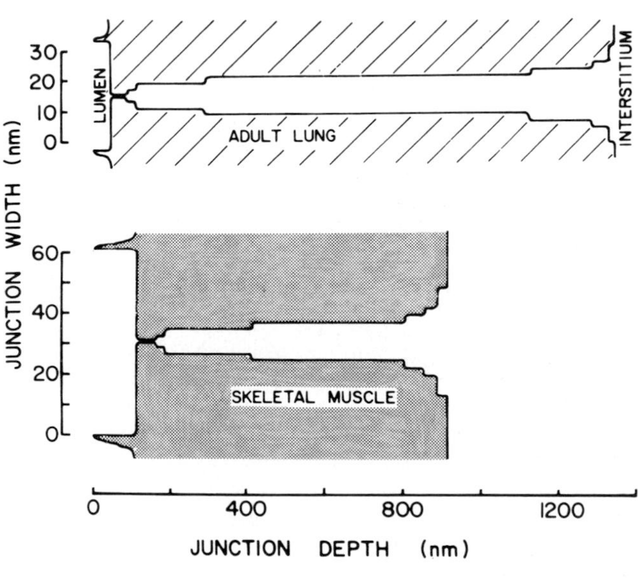

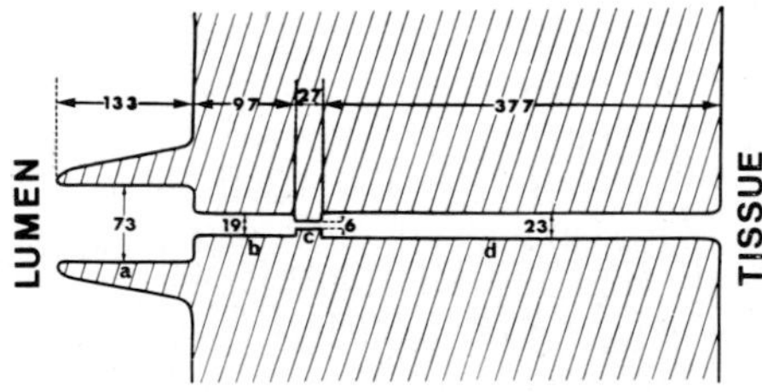

FIG. 44. *Top*: representation of mean dimensions of interendothelial junctions in adult lung and skeletal muscle capillaries. *Bottom*: representation of paracellular pathway (junction) in skeletal muscle capillary. [*Top* from Perry (263); *bottom* from Casley-Smith et al. (41).]

the degree to which the junctions are closed. Only a small fraction of the junction in a mesenteric capillary is closed, whereas in the brain the junctions are almost completely closed. Between these extremes lie tissues such as skeletal muscle, heart, lung, fat, and skin with more or less similar permeabilities and perhaps ~10% effectively open junctions. Apparently intracapillary pressure plays a role in determining the degree of openness. Permeability tends to be higher in low-pressure microvascular beds or sections than in high-pressure vessels (with the exception of specialized capillaries).

In contrast to the plentitude of data from mammalian organs, there is a striking lack of information from other species (i.e., fishes and birds), and there is a need for comparative studies. Very high values were found in a study of protein permeability in elasmobranch capillaries (137).

Other Approaches to Equivalent Slit Widths

In the numerical analysis of the mesenteric capillary, an equivalent slit width was calculated that satisfied most experimental data; however, the procedure employed is only one of several possible methods, many of which have been summarized by Renkin and Curry (281). Equivalent slit dimensions can be systematically assessed by *1*) determination of diffusion restriction for molecules of different sizes, *2*) determination of reflection coefficients, *3*) combination of diffusion and filtration data, or *4*) sieving data (requiring collection of lymph). The procedures are briefly summarized below.

DIFFUSION RESTRICTION. Permeability can be expressed in terms of a virtual pore area

$$P = \frac{DS'_p}{\Delta x S} \tag{52}$$

where S'_p is the virtual pore area, which becomes smaller as molecular size increases, and S is the total capillary surface area. The equation is equivalent to

$$P = \frac{D' S_p}{\Delta x S} \tag{53}$$

where D' signifies a restricted diffusion coefficient, S_p is the true pore (cleft) area, and S_p/S is a dimensionless factor that gives the fractional pore area for solutes that diffuse freely in the clefts. According to Faxen (100; cf. also ref. 281)

$$\frac{D'}{D} = (1 - \alpha)(1 - 1.004\alpha + 0.418\alpha^3 - 0.169\alpha^5) \tag{54}$$

where α is the ratio of solute diameter to slit width.

Thus if permeability for a graded series of hydrophilic molecules is determined, α can be found by curve fitting, and w is obtained. These determinations require data for at least two solutes of different sizes.

If the diffusion pathway has variable dimensions with perhaps very short narrow portions, the diffusion restriction criterion is not very strong because, as explained above, the short narrow segment does not noticeably influence diffusion. This may explain the many conflicting conclusions drawn from determinations of diffusion restriction. Considering the most likely slit construction, this approach probably will not contribute much to our knowledge of morphology.

Another criticism is that even if the diffusion experiments cover a large range of blood flows, some flow limitation may occur at the highest flow. This implies underestimation of the permeabiliy of the smallest solutes and thus disguises diffusion restriction.

REFLECTION COEFFICIENT. Based on hydrodynamic theories of solute and water permeation through plane parallel infinite slits, formal relations between the reflection coefficient and the ratio of molecular diameter to slit width have been worked out (77, 281)

$$1 - \sigma = \left(1 - \frac{3}{2}\,\alpha^2 + \frac{1}{2}\,\alpha^3\right)\left(1 - \frac{1}{3}\,\alpha^2\right) \quad (55)$$

Again, determination of reflection coefficients for a graded series of hydrophilic solutes and subsequent fitting procedures should give the slit width from the best fit of α. The reflection coefficient of regular cylindrical pores has been analyzed by Levitt (189, 190) with continuum theory. For a cylindrical pore

$$\sigma = \frac{16}{3}\,\alpha^2 + \frac{20}{3}\,\alpha^3 \quad (56)$$

One problem with this approach is that the experiments determine the reflection coefficient for the entire membrane, not just for the slit. The relation between these factors is described by Equation 34. The contribution of the endothelial cells to the total reflection coefficient is relatively small and is discussed in *Osmotic Methods*, p. 423.

Curry et al. (81) have made a careful study of the relative contributions of the cell membrane and the slit to the total experimental reflection coefficient for single-capillary measurements. They found that slit reflection coefficients for four solutes of different size (vitamin B_{12}, sucrose, urea, and NaCl) are very low, between 0.00 and 0.05. Recent experiments give values for myoglobin and albumin of 0.21 and 0.81, respectively (213, 219).

Michel (213, 214) and Curry (79) proposed that these data are explained by a matrix-type model that ignores possible interactions with the cleft wall. Although this cannot be ruled out at present, the correlation between kinetic calculations (especially for the single capillary) and morphological slit dimensions is strong (although indirect) evidence that slits are the rate-limiting barrier of the capillary wall for hydrophilic substances.

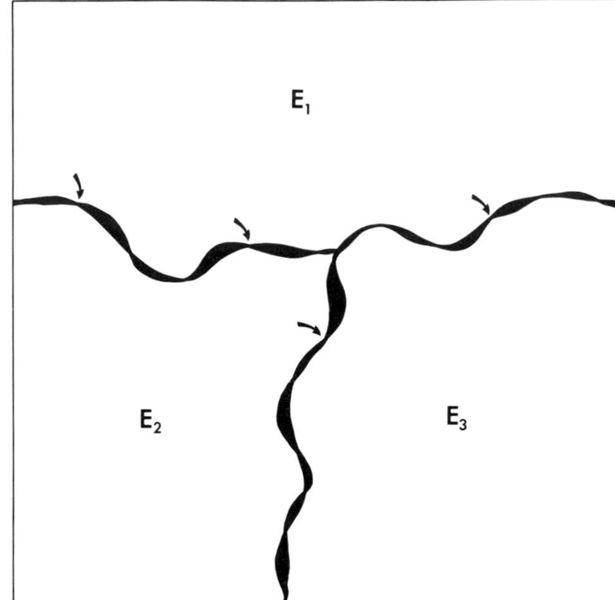

FIG. 45. Interendothelial junctional zones viewed from inner surface of capillary showing variations of spacing including regions of complete closure (*arrows*). E_1, E_2, and E_3 indicate cell membranes of contiguous endothelial cells.

The morphology of the capillary wall, including cells and slits, explains why small solutes of various sizes may have the same overall reflection coefficient up to a certain molecular diameter. The slit reflection coefficient for small solutes is zero, and osmotic withdrawal of fluid from the extravascular space is caused by transendothelial fluid movement (cf. Fig. 21). As the reflection coefficient begins to increase, the effects of solute-slit interactions are seen and the true slit reflection coefficient (σ_{slit}) can be calculated from (352)

$$\sigma_{slit} = \sigma - \sigma_{ss} \quad (57)$$

where σ_{ss} is the reflection coefficient for small solutes. Wangensteen et al. (352) calculated the membrane reflection coefficients for inulin and albumin in the lung. However, the values must include a correction factor for σ_{ss} to determine the actual slit coefficients, which are 0.09 and 0.35 for inulin and albumin, respectively. The values indicate quite large slit dimensions. Wangensteen et al. (352) gave pore radii of 100 Å, corresponding to slit widths of 130 Å. Normand et al. (229) reported equivalent radii of 150 Å. Although

FIG. 46. Transmission electron micrograph of junctions in endothelium of mesenteric capillary (*A*) and cerebral capillary (*B*) in frog (*Rana temporaria*). *A*: cleft is obliterated by single apposition between adjacent plasma membranes. *B*: junctional arrangement, which includes 8–10 membrane appositions, occupies entire outline of cleft. *L*, lumen. *Bar*, 0.2 μm. (By courtesy of Bundgaard.)

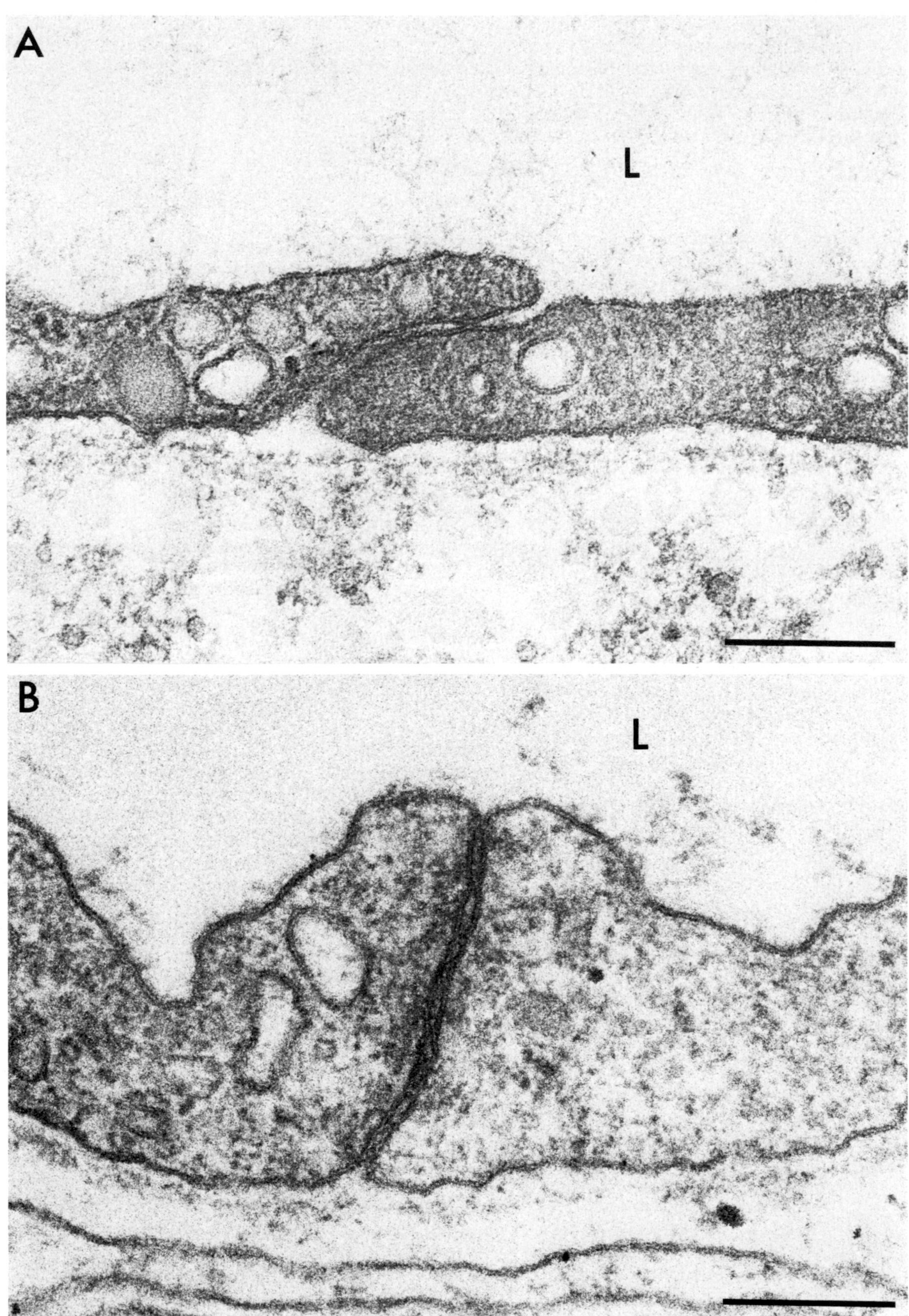
A
L
B
L

the reflection coefficient may define the narrowest part of a cleft, it must be emphasized that this value alone is not sufficient to define the cleft dimensions because the wide part of the cleft is more decisive in diffusion permeability. Thus a combination of data is necessary for slit modeling.

COMBINATION OF DIFFUSION AND FILTRATION DATA. If diffusion and filtration only occur through the junctional slits, the slit width can be found from the permeability and filtration coefficients. Because the filtration coefficient includes pressure-dependent filtration through endothelial cells, correction must be made for the fraction of flow not passing through the slits (10% at most). Under these conditions the following equations can be applied

$$P_{\text{slit}} = D\text{w}l/\Delta x$$

and

$$L_{\text{p,slit}} = \frac{(\text{w}/2)^2\ \text{w}l}{3\eta\Delta x}$$

where P_{slit} and $L_{\text{p,slit}}$ refer to the permeability and hydraulic conductance, respectively, of slit passages only. Combination of the equations gives

$$\text{w} = \frac{12\eta D L_{\text{p,slit}}}{P_{\text{slit}}} \tag{58}$$

Because only single-capillary experiments permit a distinction between slit filtration and total capillary membrane filtration, this approach has only been used for the mesenteric capillary where it gives an equivalent slit width of 130 Å (72). However, a slit with a short narrow portion of 50 Å and a long wide portion of 200 Å is equally compatible with the measured values.

SIEVING DATA. Sieving requires lymph or urine collection and allows evaluation of the hydrophilic channel. The equivalent slit size in the glomerular capillaries is based on sieving data from experiments with various macromolecules (89, 347). Sieving experiments are secondary for small-solute transport because of very small sieving effects. Even for a molecule as large as inulin the lymph/plasma ratio is ~1 (277).

Although the pore theory of solute permeation through capillaries must be correct in the sense that hydrophilic solutes pass through water-filled channels that are in all likelihood the paracellular pathways, its quantitative extrapolations are somewhat uncertain. Strangely this uncertainty about dimensions is shared with the paracellular pathway in epithelia (341).

In the original version of the pore theory (247), the hydrophilic pathways were treated as regular cylindrical pores. Although this is not consonant with known ultrastructure, which rather suggests slitlike pathways, it is of course possible to use the concept and to arrive at pore densities ranging from 1 μm^{-2} in muscle to 10 μm^{-2} in mesentery (72). Passive permeability of brain capillaries would comply with a pore density of 0.01 μm^{-2}.

CONCLUSIONS

In this overview of small-solute transport the capillary membrane is treated as a purely passive filter, except for the special conditions in the brain. Because the membrane is so completely dominated by passive processes, it is possibly the simplest biological membrane—a proposition reflected by the fact that passive permeability of capillaries is now understood with reasonable confidence and that the inherent limitations in obtaining even more accurate values are beginning to appear.

Methodology in capillary permeability at the whole-organ level is well described and systematized and the limitations of the methods are largely known. Further methodological advancement will probably occur at the single-capillary level where new developments are taking place.

Transcapillary transport has many problems in common with passive transport across the epithelial paracellular pathway. In the further elucidation of this pathway, both sides should gain from the interchange of ideas and observations.

We have stated that the interendothelial pathway in capillary endothelium (junction, cleft, slit, pore, or crack) represents the morphological equivalent of the small-pore system (Fig. 45). A watertight proof that the junctional region is the hydrophilic channel has not yet been provided, but much circumstantial evidence suggests that this pathway is the main candidate. It is hardly possible to explain permeability of sucrose and inulin in any other way, and it is certainly not possible to explain the reflection coefficients of sucrose (as low as 0.1; see Table 15). Direct evidence is provided by Ohori (231) and Takada (328), who demonstrated precipitation of electrolyte salts in the junction. Figure 46 illustrates two extremes of the interendothelial junction as seen in transmission electron microscopy—the virtually open cleft in the mesentery and the practically impermeable interendothelial junction in the brain with many membrane fusions. Junction morphology generally correlates very well with the permeability characteristics of capillaries in the two tissues.

Another possibility is represented by the transendothelial channel (312). We find compelling evidence for this theory lacking, and many quantitative aspects of small-solute transport are not easily explained within this framework (32, 33). Also it has proven difficult to demonstrate transendothelial channels in three-dimensional reconstructions of endothelial vesicular structures (32a, 110). It is worth keeping in mind, however, that under special conditions a system of transcellular endothelial channels may become operative (e.g., under the influence of specific chemical agents, in inflammatory conditions). The role of endothelial vesicles in transport is now being debated and new ideas concerning these structures are under way, according to which the vesicles are not free to move but are part of infoldings of the plasma membrane (36, 36a, 110).

Regarding the normal physiological state, the view expressed by Chambers and Zweifach (42) and earlier by Starling (318) is probably correct. Starling wrote

> The endothelial wall of the capillaries presents a structure which would suggest the possibility of a leakage or filtration. The separate flat cells of which it is composed abut on the adjacent cells, but are not directly continuous with these, a slender crack being left containing either lymph or cement substance, probably the former, which stains black with nitrate of silver.
>
> It is very difficult to determine whether the cells themselves permit the passage of the fluid constituents of the blood, as we have seen to be the case in the intestine; but that the cracks between the cells will allow of the passage of fluid is suggested by the fact that under abnormal conditions white and red corpuscles may pass out by these channels.

This view, which we find much support for, is consistent with the main idea of the pore theory (245). In our opinion this theory still stands as the main paradigm in transcapillary solute transport.

REFERENCES

1. Alvarez, O. A., and D. L. Yudilevich. Heart capillary permeability to lipid-insoluble molecules. *J. Physiol. London* 202: 45–58, 1969.
2. Amtorp, O. Estimation of capillary permeability of inulin, sucrose and mannitol in rat brain cortex. *Acta Physiol. Scand.* 110: 337–342, 1980.
3. Arfors, K. E., and H. Hint. Studies of the microcirculation using fluorescent dextran. *Microvasc. Res.* 3: 440, 1971.
4. Bachelard, H. S., P. M. Daniel, E. R. Love, and O. E. Pratt. The transport of glucose into the brain of the rat in vivo. *Proc. R. Soc. London Ser. B* 183: 71–82, 1973.
5. Ballard, K., and W. Perl. Osmotic reflection coefficients of canine subcutaneous adipose tissue endothelium. *Microvasc. Res.* 16: 224–236, 1978.
6. Bär, T. The vascular system of the cerebral cortex. In: *Advances in Anatomy, Embryology and Cell Biology*, edited by A. Brodal, W. Hild, J. van Limborgh, R. Ortmann, T. H. Schiebler, G. Tondury, and E. Wolff. Berlin: Springer-Verlag, 1980, vol. 59.
7. Bass, L. Flow dependence of first-order uptake of substances by heterogeneous perfused organs. *J. Theor. Biol.* 86: 365–376, 1980.
8. Bass, L., S. Keiding, K. Winkler, and N. Tygstrup. Enzymatic elimination of substrates flowing through the intact liver. *J. Theor. Biol.* 61: 393–409, 1976.
9. Bass, L., and P. Robinson. How small is the functional variability of liver sinusoids? *J. Theor. Biol.* 81: 761–769, 1979.

9a. Bass, L., and P. Robinson. Capillary permeability of heterogeneous organs: a parsimonious interpretation of indicator diffusion data. *Clin. Exp. Pharmacol. Physiol.* 9: 363–388, 1982.

10. Bass, L., P. Robinson, and A. J. Bracken. Hepatic elimination of flowing substrates: the distributed model. *J. Theor. Biol.* 72: 161–184, 1978.
11. Basset, G., Y. Fulla, F. Moreau, and J. Turiaf. Lung capillaries permeability to small molecules. *Bibl. Anat.* 13: 17–20, 1975. (Eur. Conf. Microcirc., Le Touquet, 8th, 1974.)
12. Bassingthwaighte, J. B. Blood flow and diffusion through mammalian organs. *Science* 167: 1347–1353, 1970.
13. Bassingthwaighte, J. B. A concurrent flow model for extraction during transcapillary passage. *Circ. Res.* 35: 483–503, 1974.
14. Bassingthwaighte, J. B., T. Yipintsoi, and E. F. Grabowski. Myocardial capillary permeability: hydrophilic solutes penetrate 100 Å intercellular clefts. *Bibl. Anat.* 13: 24–27, 1975.
15. Bassingthwaighte, J. B., T. Yipintsoi, and R. B. Harvey. Microvasculature of the dog left ventricular myocardium. *Microvasc. Res.* 7: 229–249, 1974.
16. Beck, R. E., and J. S. Schultz. Hindrance of solute diffusion within membranes as measured with microporous membranes of known pore geometry. *Biochim. Biophys. Acta* 255: 273–303, 1972.
17. Betz, A. L., D. D. Gilboe, D. L. Yudilevich, and L. Drewes. Kinetics of unidirectional glucose transport into the isolated dog brain. *Am. J. Physiol.* 225: 586–592, 1973.
18. Bing, R. J., K. Helberg, and H. Wayland. Microcirculation of the heart. *Adv. Exp. Med. Biol.* 22: 253–266, 1972.
19. Bjerrum, N., and E. Manegold. Über Kollodium-Membranen. II. Der Zusammenhang zwischen Membranstruktur und Wasserdurchlässigkeit. *Kolloid Z.* 43: 5–14, 1927.
20. Bloom, G., and J. A. Johnson. A model for osmotically induced weight transients in the isolated rabbit heart. *Microvasc. Res.* 22: 67–79, 1981.
21. Bockris, J. O., and A. K. Reddy. *Modern Electrochemistry.* New York: Plenum, 1970, vol. 1, p. 622.
22. Bohr, C. Über die spezifische Tätigkeit der Lungen bei der respiratorischen Gasaufnahme und ihr Verhalten zu der durch die Alveolarwand stattfindenden Gasdiffusion. *Skand. Arch. Physiol.* 22: 240–260, 1909.
23. Bolwig, T. G., and N. A. Lassen. The diffusion permeability to water of the rat blood-brain barrier. *Acta Physiol. Scand.* 93: 415–422, 1975.
24. Boulpaep, E. L. Permeability changes of the proximal tubule of *Necturus* during saline loading. *Am. J. Physiol.* 222: 517–531, 1972.
25. Bradbury, M. W. B. *The Concept of a Blood-Brain Barrier.* New York: Wiley, 1979, 465 p.
26. Bradbury, M. W. B., C. S. Patlak, and W. H. Oldendorf. Analysis of brain uptake and loss of radiotracers after intracarotid injection. *Am. J. Physiol.* 229: 1110–1115, 1975.
27. Bradbury, M. W. B., and B. Stulcova. Efflux mechanism contributing to the stability of the potassium concentration in cerebrospinal fluid. *J. Physiol. London* 208: 415–430, 1970.
28. Brigham, K. L., S. L. Faulkner, R. D. Fisher, and H. Bender. Lung water and urea indicator dilution studies in cardiac surgery patients. Comparisons of measurements in aortocoronary bypass and mitral valve replacement. *Circulation* 53: 369–376, 1976.
29. Brigham, K. L., H. Sundell, T. R. Harris, Z. Catterton, I. Hovar, and M. Stahlman. Lung water and vascular permeability in sheep. Newborns compared with adults. *Circ. Res.* 42: 851–855, 1978.
30. Broman, T. *The Permeability of Cerebrospinal Vessels in Normal and Pathological Conditions.* Copenhagen: Munksgaard, 1949.
31. Bruns, R. R., and G. E. Palade. Studies on blood capillaries.

II. Transport of ferritin molecules across the wall of muscle capillaries. *J. Cell Biol.* 37: 277–299, 1968.

32. BUNDGAARD, M. Transport pathways in capillaries—in search of pores. *Annu. Rev. Physiol.* 42: 325–336, 1980.
33. BUNDGAARD, M., C. CRONE, AND J. FRØKJÆR-JENSEN. Extreme rarity of transendothelial channels in the frog mesenteric capillary (Abstract). *J. Physiol. London* 291: 38P, 1979.
34. BUNDGAARD, M., AND J. FRØKJÆR-JENSEN. Functional aspects of the ultrastructure of terminal blood vessels: A quantitative study on consecutive segments of the frog mesenteric microvasculature. *Microvasc. Res.* 23: 1–30, 1982.
35. BUNDGAARD, M., J. FRØKJÆR-JENSEN, AND C. CRONE. Determination of the interendothelial cleft length (Abstract). *Acta Physiol. Scand.* 105: 3A–4A, 1979.
36. BUNDGAARD, M., J. FRØKJÆR-JENSEN, AND C. CRONE. Endothelial plasmalemmal vesicles as elements in a system of branching invaginations from the cell surface. *Proc. Natl. Acad. Sci. USA* 76: 6439–6442, 1979.

36a. BUNDGAARD, M., P. HAGMAN, AND C. CRONE. The three-dimensional organization of plasmalemmal vesicular profiles in the endothelium of rat heart capillaries. *Microvasc. Res.* 25: 358–368, 1983.

37. BUNIM, J. J., W. W. SMITH, AND H. W. SMITH. The diffusion coefficient of inulin and other substances of interest in renal physiology. *J. Biol. Chem.* 118: 667–677, 1937.
38. BURTON, K. S., AND P. C. JOHNSON. Reactive hyperemia in individual capillaries of skeletal muscle. *Am. J. Physiol.* 223: 517–524, 1972.
39. BUSTAMANTE, J. C., G. E. MANN, AND D. L. YUDILEVICH. Specificity of neutral amino acid uptake at the basolateral side of the epithelium in the cat salivary gland in situ. *J. Physiol. London* 313: 65–79, 1981.
40. CARO, C. G., T. J. PEDLEY, R. C. SCHROTER, AND W. A. SEED. *The Mechanics of the Circulation.* New York: Oxford Univ. Press, 1978, 527 p.
41. CASLEY-SMITH, J. R., H. S. GREEN, J. L. HARRIS, AND P. J. WADEY. The quantitative morphology of skeletal muscle capillaries in relation to permeability. *Microvasc. Res.* 10: 43–64, 1975.

41a. CATRAVAS, J. D., AND C. N. GILLIS. Pulmonary clearance of 5-hydroxytryptamine and norepinephrine *in vivo*: effects of pretreatment with imipramine or cocaine. *J. Pharm. Exper. Therap.* 213: 120–127, 1980.

42. CHAMBERS, R. W., AND B. W. ZWEIFACH. Intercellular cement and capillary permeability. *Physiol. Rev.* 27: 436–463, 1947.
43. CHAPLER, C. K., AND W. N. STAINSBY. Carbohydrate metabolism in contracting dog skeletal muscle in situ. *Am. J. Physiol.* 215: 995–1004, 1968.
44. CHINARD, F. P. Kidney, water, and electrolytes. *Annu. Rev. Physiol.* 26: 187–226, 1964.
45. CHINARD, F. P. The alveolar-capillary barrier: some data and speculations. *Microvasc. Res.* 19: 1–17, 1980.
46. CHINARD, F. P., AND T. ENNS. Transcapillary pulmonary exchange of water in the dog. *Am. J. Physiol.* 178: 197–202, 1954.
47. CHINARD, F. P., G. J. VOSBURGH, AND T. ENNS. Transcapillary exchange of water and of other substances in certain organs of the dog. *Am. J. Physiol.* 183: 221–234, 1955.
48. CIVAN, M. M., AND H. S. FRAZIER. The site of the stimulatory action of vasopressin on sodium transport in toad bladder. *J. Gen. Physiol.* 51: 589–605, 1968.
49. COLLANDER, R. The permeability of plant protoplasts to non-electrolytes. *Trans. Faraday Soc.* 33: 985–990, 1937.
50. COLLANDER, R. The permeability of plant protoplasts to small molecules. *Physiol. Plant.* 2: 300–311, 1949.
51. COLLANDER, R. The permeability of *Nitella* cells to non-electrolytes. *Physiol. Plant.* 7: 420–445, 1954.
52. COLLIN, H. B. Ultrastructure of fenestrated blood capillaries in extra-ocular muscles. *Exp. Eye Res.* 8: 16–20, 1969.
53. CRAIG, L. C. Differential dialysis. *Science* 144: 1093–1099, 1964.
54. CREMER, J. E., L. D. BRAUN, AND W. H. OLDENDORF. Changes during development in transport processes of the blood-brain barrier. *Biochim. Biophys. Acta* 448: 633–637, 1976.
55. CREMER, J. E., V. J. CUNNINGHAM, W. M. PARDRIDGE, L. D. BRAUN, AND W. H. OLDENDORF. Kinetics of blood-brain barrier transport of pyruvate, lactate and glucose in suckling, weanling and adult rats. *J. Neurochem.* 33: 439–445, 1979.
56. CRONE, C. The diffusion of some organic non-electrolytes from blood to brain tissue. *Acta Physiol. Scand.* 50, Suppl. 175: 33–34, 1960.
57. CRONE, C. The Diffusion of Some Organic Non-electrolytes from Blood to Brain Tissue. Copenhagen: Munksgaard, 1961, p. 1–180. PhD thesis. (In Danish; summary in English.)
58. CRONE, C. Does "restricted diffusion" occur in muscle capillaries? *Proc. Soc. Exp. Biol. Med.* 112: 453–455, 1963.
59. CRONE, C. The permeability of capillaries in various organs as determined by use of the "indicator diffusion" method. *Acta Physiol. Scand.* 58: 292–305, 1963.
60. CRONE, C. Facilitated transfer of glucose from blood into brain tissue. *J. Physiol. London* 181: 103–113, 1965.
61. CRONE, C. The permeability of brain capillaries to non-electrolytes. *Acta Physiol. Scand.* 64: 407–417, 1965.
62. CRONE, C. Glucose uptake in potassium-depolarized mammalian muscle. *Acta Physiol. Scand.* 68: 105–117, 1966.
63. CRONE, C. Capillary permeability—techniques and problems. In: *Capillary Permeability*, edited by C. Crone and N. A. Lassen. Copenhagen: Munksgaard, 1970, p. 15–31. (Alfred Benzon Symp. 2.)
64. CRONE, C. Transcapillary transport of D- and L-glucose in isolated skeletal muscle. *Acta Physiol. Scand.* 87: 138–144, 1973.
65. CRONE, C. Endothelia and epithelia. In: *Microcirculation. Transport Mechanisms; Disease States*, edited by J. Grayson and W. Zingg. New York: Plenum, 1976, vol. 2, p. 7–10.
66. CRONE, C. The electrical resistance of a capillary wall: a new approach to capillary permeability (Abstract). *J. Physiol. London* 301: 70P, 1979.
67. CRONE, C. Permeability of single capillaries compared with results from whole-organ studies. *Acta Physiol. Scand. Suppl.* 463: 75–80, 1979.
68. CRONE, C. Tight and leaky endothelia. In: *Water Transport Across Epithelia Barriers, Gradients, and Mechanisms*, edited by H. H. Ussing, N. Bindslev, N. A. Lassen, and O. Sten-Knudsen. Copenhagen: Munksgaard, 1981, p. 258–267. (Alfred Benzon Symp. 15.)
69. CRONE, C., AND O. CHRISTENSEN. Transcapillary transport of small solutes and water. In: *Cardiovascular Physiology III*, edited by A. C. Guyton and D. B. Young. Baltimore, MD: University Park, 1979, vol. 18, p. 149–213.
70. CRONE, C., AND O. CHRISTENSEN. The electrical resistance of a capillary endothelium. *J. Gen. Physiol.* 77: 349–371, 1981.
71. CRONE, C., AND J. J. FRIEDMAN. A method for determining potassium permeability of a single capillary (Abstract). *Acta Physiol. Scand.* 96: 13A–14A, 1976.
72. CRONE, C., J. FRØKJÆR-JENSEN, J. J. FRIEDMAN, AND O. CHRISTENSEN. The permeability of single capillaries to potassium ions. *J. Gen. Physiol.* 71: 195–220, 1978.
73. CRONE, C., AND D. GARLICK. The penetration of inulin, sucrose, mannitol, and tritiated water from the interstitial space in muscle into the vascular system. *J. Physiol. London* 210: 387–404, 1970.
74. CRONE, C., AND S. P. OLESEN. Electrical resistance of brain microvascular endothelium. *Brain Res.* 241: 49–55, 1981.
75. CRONE, C., AND A. M. THOMPSON. Comparative studies of capillary permeability in brain and muscle. *Acta Physiol. Scand.* 87: 252–260, 1973.
76. CUNNINGHAM, V. J., AND G. S. SARNA. Estimation of the kinetic parameters of unidirectional transport across the blood-brain barrier. *J. Neurochem.* 33: 433–437, 1979.
77. CURRY, F. E. A hydrodynamic description of the osmotic

reflection coefficient with application to the pore theory of transcapillary exchange. *Microvasc. Res.* 8: 236–252, 1974.
78. CURRY, F. E. Permeability coefficients of the capillary wall to low molecular weight hydrophilic solutes measured in single perfused capillaries of frog mesentery. *Microvasc. Res.* 17: 290–308, 1979.
79. CURRY, F. E. Is the transport of hydrophilic substances across the capillary wall determined by a network of fibrous molecules? *Physiologist* 23(1): 90–93, 1980.
80. CURRY, F. E. Antipyrine and aminopyrine permeability of individually perfused frog capillaries. *Am. J. Physiol.* 240 (*Heart Circ. Physiol.* 9): H597–H605, 1981.
81. CURRY, F. E., J. C. MASON, AND C. C. MICHEL. Osmotic reflection coefficients of capillary walls to low molecular weight hydrophilic solutes measured in single perfused capillaries of the frog mesentery. *J. Physiol. London* 261: 319–336, 1976.
82. CURRY, F. E., AND C. C. MICHEL. A fiber matrix model of capillary permeability. *Microvasc. Res.* 20: 96–99, 1980.
83. D'ALECY, L. G., C. J. ROSE, S. A. SELLERS, AND J. P. MANFREDI. Cerebral sodium extraction in the dog: a test for extracerebral contamination. *Am. J. Physiol.* 238 (*Heart Circ. Physiol.* 7): H868–H875, 1980.
84. DAVSON, H., AND C. P. LUCK. The effect of acetazolamide on the chemical composition of the aqueous humour and cerebrospinal fluid of some mammalian species and on the rate of turnover of ^{24}Na in these fluids. *J. Physiol. London* 137: 279–293, 1957.
85. DAVSON, H., AND K. WELCH. The permeation of several materials into the fluids of the rabbit's brain. *J. Physiol. London* 218: 337–351, 1971.
86. DIAMOND, J. M., AND E. M. WRIGHT. Biological membranes: the physical basis of ion and nonelectrolyte selectivity. *Annu. Rev. Physiol.* 31: 581–646, 1969.
87. DIANA, J. N., AND M. H. LAUGHLIN. Effect of ischemia on capillary pressure and equivalent pore radius of the isolated dog hindlimb. *Circ. Res.* 35: 77–101, 1974.
88. DIANA, J. N., S. C. LONG, AND H. YAO. Effect of histamine on equivalent pore radius in capillaries of isolated dog hindlimb. *Microvasc. Res.* 4: 413–437, 1972.
89. DU BOIS, R., AND E. STOUPEL. Permeability of artificial membranes to a pluridisperse solution of ^{125}I-polyvinyl-pyrrolidone. *Biophys. J.* 16: 1427–1445, 1976.
90. DULING, B. R., AND R. M. BERNE. Longitudinal gradients in periarteriolar oxygen tension. *Circ. Res.* 27: 669–678, 1970.
91. DUNNING, H. S., AND H. G. WOLFF. The relative vascularity of the trigeminal ganglion and nerve, cerebral cortex and white matter. *Trans. Am. Neurol. Assoc.* 62: 150–154, 1936.
92. DURAN, W. N. Effects of muscle contraction and of adenosine on capillary transport and microvascular flow in dog skeletal muscle. *Circ. Res.* 41: 642–647, 1977.
93. DURAN, W. N., AND D. L. YUDILEVICH. Estimate of capillary permeability coefficients of canine heart to sodium and glucose. *Microvasc. Res.* 15: 195–205, 1978.
94. EFFROS, R. M. Osmotic extraction of hypotonic fluid from the lungs. *J. Clin. Invest.* 54: 935–947, 1974.
95. EICHLING, J. O., M. E. RAICHLE, R. L. GRUBB, JR., AND M. M. TER-POGOSSIAN. Evidence of the limitations of water as a freely diffusible tracer in brain of the rhesus monkey. *Circ. Res.* 35: 358–364, 1974.
96. EISENBERG, H. M., AND R. L. SUDDITH. Cerebral vessels have the capacity to transport sodium and potassium. *Science* 206: 1083–1085, 1979.
97. ERDMANN, J. A., T. R. VAUGHAN, K. L. BRIGHAM, W. C. WOOLVERTON, AND N. C. STAUB. Effect of increased vascular pressure on lung fluid balance in unanesthetized sheep. *Circ. Res.* 37: 271–284, 1975.
98. ERIKSSON, E., AND R. MYRHAGE. Microvascular dimensions and blood flow in skeletal muscle. *Acta Physiol. Scand.* 86: 211–222, 1972.
99. FAGRELL, B., A. FRONEK, AND M. INTAGLIETTA. A microscope-television system for studying flow velocity in human skin capillaries. *Am. J. Physiol.* 233 (*Heart Circ. Physiol.* 2): H318–H321, 1977.
100. FAXEN, H. Der Widerstand gegen Bewegung einer starren Kugel in einer zähen Flüssigkeit, die zwischen zwei paralellen ebenen Wänden eingeschlossen ist. *Ann. Phys. Leipzig* 68: 89–119, 1922.
101. FENSTERMACHER, J. D., AND J. A. JOHNSON. Filtration and reflection coefficients of the rabbit blood-brain barrier. *Am. J. Physiol.* 211: 341–346, 1966.
102. FIRTH, J. A. Cytochemical localization of the K^+ regulating interface between blood and brain. *Experientia* 33: 1093–1094, 1977.
103. FLEXNER, L. B., D. B. COWIE, AND G. J. VOSBURGH. Studies on capillary permeability with tracer substances. *Cold Spring Harbor Symp. Quant. Biol.* 13: 88–98, 1948.
104. FLEXNER, L. B., A. GELLHORN, AND M. MERRELL. Studies on rates of exchange of substances between the blood and extravascular fluid. *J. Biol. Chem.* 144: 35–40, 1942.
105. FOX, J., F. GALEY, AND H. WAYLAND. Action of histamine on the mesenteric microvasculature. *Microvasc. Res.* 19: 108–127, 1980.
106. FOX, J. R., AND H. WAYLAND. Interstitial diffusion of macromolecules in the rat mesentery. *Microvasc. Res.* 18: 255–276, 1979.
107. FRASER, P. A., L. H. SMAJE, AND A. VERRINDER. Microvascular pressures and filtration coefficients in the cat mesentery. *J. Physiol. London* 283: 439–456, 1978.
108. FREIS, E. D., T. F. HIGGINS, AND H. J. MOROWITZ. Transcapillary exchange rates of deuterium oxide and thiocyanate in the forearm of man. *J. Appl. Physiol.* 5: 526–532, 1952–1953.
109. FREIS, E. D., H. W. SCHNAPER, J. C. ROSE, AND L. S. LILIENFIELD. Renal transcapillary, net exchange in the dog. *Circ. Res.* 6: 432–437, 1958.
110. FRØKJÆR-JENSEN, J. Three-dimensional organization of plasmalemmal vesicles in endothelial cells. An analysis by serial sectioning of frog mesenteric capillaries. *J. Ultrastruct. Res.* 73: 9–20, 1980.
111. FRØKJÆR-JENSEN, J. Permeability of simple muscle capillaries to potassium ions. *Microvasc. Res.* 24: 168–183, 1982.
112. FRØKJÆR-JENSEN, J., AND O. CHRISTENSEN. Potassium permeability of the mesothelium of the frog mesentery. *Acta Physiol. Scand.* 105: 228–238, 1979.
112a. FRØKJÆR-JENSEN, J., AND F. E. CURRY. Hydraulic conductivity and sucrose osmotic reflection coefficients of individually perfused capillaries in frog muscle (Abstract). *Federation Proc.* 41: 1253, 1982.
113. FRÖMTER, E. The route of passive ion movement through the epithelium of *Necturus* gallbladder. *J. Membr. Biol.* 8: 259–301, 1972.
114. GAEHTGENS, P., H. J. MEISELMAN, AND H. WAYLAND. Erythrocyte flow velocities in mesenteric microvessels of the cat. *Microvasc. Res.* 2: 151–162, 1970.
115. GARLICK, D. G. Factors affecting the transport of extracellular molecules in skeletal muscle. In: *Capillary Permeability*, edited by C. Crone and N. A. Lassen. Copenhagen: Munksgaard, 1970, p. 228–238. (Alfred Benzon Symp. 2.)
116. GILLIS, C. N., L. H. CRONAU, S. MANDEL, AND G. L. HAMMOND. *J. Appl. Physiol.: Respirat. Environ. Exercise Physiol.* 46: 1178–1183, 1979.
117. GJEDDE, A. High and low affinity transport of D-glucose from blood to brain. *J. Neurochem.* 36: 1463–1471, 1981.
118. GJEDDE, A. Modulation of substrate transport to the brain. *Acta Neurol. Scand.* 67: 3–25, 1983.
119. GJEDDE, A., AND C. CRONE. Induction processes in blood-brain transfer of ketone bodies during starvation. *Am. J. Physiol.* 229: 1165–1169, 1975.
120. GJEDDE, A., AND C. CRONE. Blood-brain glucose transfer is repressed in chronic hyperglycemia. *Science* 214: 456–457, 1981.
121. GJEDDE, A., S. M. DE LA MONTE, AND J. J. CARONNA. Cerebral

K. Eurenius, G. C. McMillan, C. B. Nelson, C. J. Schwartz, and S. Wessler. New York: Plenum, 1978, p. 169–225.

202. MANN, G. E. Alterations of myocardial capillary permeability by albumin in the isolated, perfused rabbit heart. *J. Physiol. London* 319: 311–323, 1981.

203. MANN, G. E., L. H. SMAJE, AND D. L. YUDILEVICH. Permeability of the fenestrated capillaries in the cat submandibular gland to lipid-insoluble molecules. *J. Physiol. London* 297: 335–354, 1979.

204. MARTÍN, P., AND D. YUDILEVICH. A theory for the quantification of transcapillary exchange by tracer-dilution curves. *Am. J. Physiol.* 207: 162–168, 1964.

205. MARTINI, J., AND C. R. HONIG. Direct measurement of intercapillary distance in beating rat heart in situ under various conditions of O_2 supply. *Microvasc. Res.* 1: 244–256, 1969.

206. MASON, J. C., F. E. CURRY, AND C. C. MICHEL. The effects of proteins upon the filtration coefficient of individually perfused frog mesenteric capillaries. *Microvasc. Res.* 13: 185–202, 1977.

207. MATALON, S. V., AND O. D. WANGENSTEEN. Pulmonary capillary filtration and reflection coefficients in the newborn rabbit. *Microvasc. Res.* 14: 99–110, 1977.

208. MCCALL, A. L., W. R. MILLINGTON, AND R. J. WURTMAN. Metabolic fuel and amino acid transport into the brain in experimental diabetes mellitus. *Proc. Natl. Acad. Sci. USA* 79: 5406–5410, 1982.

208a. METZGER, H., S. HEUBER-METZGER, A. STEINACKER, AND J. STRUBER. Staining PO_2 measurement sites in the rat brain cortex and quantitative morphometry of the surrounding capillaries. *Pfluegers Arch.* 388: 21–27, 1980.

209. MICHEL, C. C. Direct observations of sites of permeability for ions and small molecules in mesothelium and endothelium. In: *Capillary Permeability*, edited by C. Crone and N. A. Lassen. Copenhagen: Munksgaard, 1970, p. 628–642. (Alfred Benzon Symp. 2.)

210. MICHEL, C. C. Flows across the capillary wall. In: *Cardiovascular Fluid Dynamics*, edited by D. H. Bergel. London: Academic, 1972, vol. 2, p. 241–298.

211. MICHEL, C. C. Differences in permeability at different sites of the capillary bed of frog mesentery. *Bibl. Anat.* 15: 460–462, 1977. (Eur. Conf. Microcirc., 9th, Antwerp, 1976.)

212. MICHEL, C. C. The measurement of permeability in single capillaries. *Arch. Int. Physiol. Biochim.* 86: 657–667, 1978.

213. MICHEL, C. C. Filtration coefficients and osmotic reflection coefficients of the walls of single frog mesenteric capillaries. *J. Physiol. London* 309: 341–355, 1980.

214. MICHEL, C. C. The flow of water through the capillary wall. In: *Water Transport Across Epithelia: Barriers, Gradients, and Mechanisms*, edited by H. H. Ussing, N. Bindslev, N. A. Lassen, and O. Sten-Knudsen. Copenhagen: Munksgaard, 1981, p. 268–279. (Alfred Benzon Symp. 15.)

215. MICHEL, C. C., AND J. R. LEVICK. Variations in permeability along individually perfused capillaries of the frog mesentery. *Q. J. Exp. Physiol.* 62: 1–10, 1977.

216. MICHEL, C. C., J. C. MASON, F. E. CURRY, AND J. E. TOOKE. A development of the Landis technique for measuring the filtration coefficient of individual capillaries in the frog mesentery. *Q. J. Exp. Physiol.* 59: 283–309, 1974.

217. MICHEL, C. C., G. R. SNOW, AND J. A. TASKER. A method for measuring the permeability of individually perfused capillaries of the frog mesentery to coloured molecules (Abstract). *J. Physiol. London* 234: 25P–26P, 1973.

218. MICHEL, C. C., AND J. A. TASKER. Permeability patterns of frog mesenteric capillaries to coloured molecules (Abstract). *J. Physiol. London* 258: 112P–113P, 1976.

219. MICHEL, C. C., AND M. R. TURNER. The effect of molecular charge on the permeability of frog mesenteric capillaries to myoglobin (Abstract). *J. Physiol. London* 316: 61P, 1981.

220. MIDDLETON, E. Passage of inulin and *p*-aminohippuric acid through artificial membranes: implications for measurement of renal function. *J. Membr. Biol.* 20: 347–363, 1975.

221. MIDDLETON, E. The molecular configuration of inulin: implications for ultrafiltration theory and glomerular permeability. *J. Membr. Biol.* 34: 93–101, 1977.

222. MORGAN, T., AND R. W. BERLINER. Permeability of the loop of Henle, vasa recta, and collecting duct to water, urea, and sodium. *Am. J. Physiol.* 215: 108–115, 1968.

223. MURRAY, J. E., AND A. PLIOPLYS. An indicator-dilution technique for study of blood-to-brain solute passage in the rat. *J. Appl. Physiol.* 33: 681–683, 1972.

224. MYHRE, K., AND J. B. STEEN. The effect of plasma proteins on the capillary permeability in the rete mirabile of the eel (*Anguilla vulgaris L.*). *Acta Physiol. Scand.* 99: 98–104, 1977.

225. MYRHAGE, R., AND O. HUDLICKÁ. The microvascular bed and capillary surface area in rat extensor hallucis proprius muscle (EHP). *Microvasc. Res.* 11: 315–323, 1976.

226. NAFTALIN, R. J., AND G. D. HOLMAN. Transport of sugars in human red cells. In: *Membrane Transport in Red Cells*, edited by J. C. Ellory and V. L. Lew. London: Academic, 1977, p. 257–300.

227. NAKAMURA, Y., AND H. WAYLAND. Macromolecular transport in the cat mesentery. *Microvasc. Res.* 9: 1–21, 1975.

228. NEUFELD, G. R., J. J. WILLIAMS, D. J. GRAVES, L. R. SOMA, AND B. E. MARSHALL. Pulmonary capillary permeability in man and a canine model of chemical pulmonary edema. *Microvasc. Res.* 10: 192–207, 1975.

229. NORMAND, I. C. S., R. E. OLVER, E. O. R. REYNOLDS, AND L. B. STRANG. Permeability of lung capillaries and alveoli to nonelectrolytes in the foetal lamb. *J. Physiol. London* 219: 303–330, 1971.

229a. NORTHOVER, B. J. The membrane potential of vascular endothelial cells. *Adv. Microcirc.* 9: 136–160, 1980.

230. OHNO, K., K. D. PETTIGREW, AND S. I. RAPOPORT. Lower limits of cerebrovascular permeability to nonelectrolytes in the conscious rat. *Am. J. Physiol.* 235 (*Heart Circ. Physiol.* 4): H299–H307, 1978.

231. OHORI, R. Morphological demonstration in electron micrographs of the passage of some electrolyte solutions between capillary endothelial cells. *Nagoya Med. J.* 9: 15–25, 1963.

232. OLDENDORF, W. H. Measurement of brain uptake of radiolabeled substances using a tritiated water internal standard. *Brain Res.* 24: 372–376, 1970.

233. OLDENDORF, W. H. Brain uptake of radiolabeled amino acids, amines, and hexoses after arterial injection. *Am. J. Physiol.* 221: 1629–1639, 1971.

234. OLDENDORF, W. H. Lipid solubility and drug penetration of the blood-brain barrier. *Proc. Soc. Exp. Biol. Med.* 147: 813–816, 1974.

235. OLDENDORF, W. H., AND W. J. BROWN. Greater number of capillary endothelial cell mitochondria in brain than in muscle. *Proc. Soc. Exp. Biol. Med.* 149: 736–738, 1975.

236. OLESEN, S. P., AND C. CRONE. Electrical resistance of muscle capillary endothelium. *Biophys. J.* 42: 31–41, 1983.

237. PAASKE, W. P. Capillary permeability in cutaneous tissue. *Acta Physiol. Scand.* 98: 492–499, 1976.

238. PAASKE, W. P. Absence of restricted diffusion in cutaneous capillaries. *Acta Physiol. Scand.* 100: 332–339, 1977.

239. PAASKE, W. P. Absence of restricted diffusion in adipose tissue capillaries. *Acta Physiol. Scand.* 100: 430–436, 1977.

240. PAASKE, W. P. Capillary permeability in skeletal muscle. *Acta Physiol. Scand.* 101: 1–14, 1977.

241. PAASKE, W. P., AND S. L. NIELSEN. Capillary permeability in adipose tissue. *Acta Physiol. Scand.* 98: 116–122, 1976.

242. PAASKE, W. P., AND P. SEJRSEN. Transcapillary exchange of 14-C-inulin by free diffusion in channels of fused vesicles. *Acta Physiol. Scand.* 100: 437–445, 1977.

243. PAGANELLI, C. V., AND A. K. SOLOMON. The rate of exchange of tritiated water across the human red cell membrane. *J. Gen. Physiol.* 41: 259–277, 1957.

244. PALADE, G. E., M. SIMIONESCU, AND N. SIMIONESCU. Structural aspects of the permeability of the microvascular endothelium. *Acta Physiol. Scand. Suppl.* 463: 11–32, 1979.

245. PAPPENHEIMER, J. R. Passage of molecules through capillary walls. *Physiol. Rev.* 33: 387–423, 1953.
246. PAPPENHEIMER, J. R. Osmotic reflection coefficients in capillary membranes. In: *Capillary Permeability*, edited by C. Crone and N. A. Lassen. Copenhagen: Munksgaard, 1970, p. 278–286. (Alfred Benzon Symp. 2.)
247. PAPPENHEIMER, J. R., E. M. RENKIN, AND L. M. BORRERO. Filtration, diffusion and molecular sieving through peripheral capillary membranes. A contribution to the pore theory of capillary permeability. *Am. J. Physiol.* 167: 13–46, 1951.
248. PAPPENHEIMER, J. R., AND B. P. SETCHELL. Cerebral glucose transport and oxygen consumption in sheep and rabbits. *J. Physiol. London* 233: 529–551, 1973.
249. PARDRIDGE, W. M., AND L. S. JEFFERSON. Liver uptake of amino acids and carbohydrates during a single circulatory passage. *Am. J. Physiol.* 228: 1155–1161, 1975.
250. PARDRIDGE, W. M., AND W. H. OLDENDORF. Kinetics of blood-brain barrier transport of hexoses. *Biochim. Biophys. Acta* 382: 377–392, 1975.
251. PARDRIDGE, W. M., AND W. H. OLDENDORF. Transport of metabolic substrates through the blood-brain barrier. *J. Neurochem.* 28: 5–12, 1977.
252. PARKER, J. C., H. J. FALGOUT, F. A. GRIMBERT, AND A. E. TAYLOR. The effect of increased vascular pressure on albumin-excluded volume and lymph flow in the dog lung. *Circ. Res* 47: 866–875, 1980.
253. PATLAK, C. S., AND J. D. FENSTERMACHER. Measurements of dog blood-brain transfer constants by ventriculocisternal perfusion. *Am. J. Physiol.* 229: 877–884, 1975.
254. PATLAK, C. S., AND S. I. RAPOPORT. Theoretical analysis of net tracer flux due to volume circulation in a membrane with pores of different sizes. *J. Gen. Physiol.* 57: 113–124, 1971.
255. PAULSON, O. B., M. M. HERTZ, T. G. BOLWIG, AND N. A. LASSEN. Filtration and diffusion of water across the blood-brain barrier in man. *Microvasc. Res.* 13: 113–124, 1977.
256. PAWLIK, G., A. RACKL, AND R. J. BING. Quantitative capillary topography and blood flow in the cerebral cortex of cats: an in vivo microscopic study. *Brain Res.* 208: 35–58, 1981.
257. PERL, W. Modified filtration-permeability model of transcapillary transport: a solution of the Pappenheimer pores puzzle? *Microvasc. Res.* 3: 233–251, 1971.
258. PERL, W. A friction coefficient, series-parallel channel model for transcapillary flux of non-electrolytes and water. *Microvasc. Res.* 6: 169–193, 1973.
259. PERL, W. Red cell permeability effect on the mean transit time of an indicator transported through an organ by red cells and plasma. *Circ. Res.* 36: 352–357, 1975.
260. PERL, W. Analytical approaches to tracer exchange. In: *Microcirculation. Transport Mechanisms; Disease States*, edited by J. Grayson and W. Zingg. New York: Plenum, 1976, vol. 2, p. 17–28.
261. PERL, W., P. CHOWDHURY, AND F. P. CHINARD. Reflection coefficients of dog lung endothelium to small hydrophilic solutes. *Am. J. Physiol.* 228: 797–809, 1975.
262. PERL, W., F. SILVERMAN, A. C. DELEA, AND F. P. CHINARD. Permeability of dog lung endothelium to sodium, diols, amides, and water. *Am. J. Physiol.* 230: 1708–1721, 1976.
263. PERRY, M. A. Capillary filtration and permeability coefficients calculated from measurements of interendothelial cell junctions in rabbit lung and skeletal muscle. *Microvasc. Res.* 19: 142–157, 1980.
264. PERRY, M. A., AND D. G. GARLICK. Permeability and pore radii of pulmonary capillaries in rabbits of different ages. *Clin. Exp. Pharmacol. Physiol.* 5: 361–377, 1978.
264a. PERRY, M. A., AND D. N. GRANGER. Permeability of intestinal capillaries to small molecules. *Am. J. Physiol.* 241 (*Gastrointest. Liver Physiol. 4*): G24–G30, 1981.
265. PLYLEY, M. J., AND A. C. GROOM. Geometrical distribution of capillaries in mammalian striated muscle. *Am. J. Physiol.* 228: 1376–1383, 1975.
266. PÜTTER, A. Aktive Oberflache und Organfunktion. *Z. Allg. Physiol.* 12: 125–214, 1911.
267. RAICHLE, M. E., J. O. EICHLING, M. G. STRAATMAN, M. J. WELCH, K. B. LARSON, AND M. M. TER-POGOSSIAN. Blood-brain barrier permeability of ^{11}C-labeled alcohols and ^{15}O-labeled water. *Am. J. Physiol.* 230: 543–552, 1976.
268. RAICHLE, M. E., AND R. L. GRUBB, JR. Regulation of brain water permeability of centrally released vasopressin. *Brain Res.* 143: 191–194, 1978.
269. RAPOPORT, S. I., K. OHNO, W. R. FREDERICKS, AND K. D. PETTIGREW. Regional cerebrovascular permeability to (^{14}C) sucrose after osmotic opening of the blood-brain barrier. *Brain Res.* 150: 653–657, 1978.
270. RASIO, E. A. Passage of glucose through the cell membrane of capillary endothelium. *Am. J. Physiol.* 228: 1103–1107, 1975.
271. RASIO, E. A., M. BENDAYAN, AND C. A. GORESKY. Diffusion permeability of an isolated rete mirabile. *Circ. Res.* 41: 791–798, 1977.
272. REESE, T. S., AND M. J. KARNOVSKY. Fine structural localization of a blood-brain barrier to exogenous peroxidase. *J. Cell Biol.* 34: 207–217, 1967.
273. RENEAU, D. D., JR., D. F. BRULEY, AND M. H. KNISELY. A mathematical simulation of oxygen release, diffusion, and consumption in the capillaries and tissue of the human brain. In: *Chemical Engineering in Medicine and Biology*, edited by D. Hershey. New York: Plenum, 1967, p. 135–241.
273a. RENKIN, E. M. Capillary permeability to lipid-soluble molecules. *Am. J. Physiol.* 168: 538–545, 1952.
274. RENKIN, E. M. Filtration, diffusion and molecular sieving through porous cellulose membranes. *J. Gen. Physiol.* 38: 225–243, 1954.
275. RENKIN, E. M. Effects of blood flow on diffusion kinetics in isolated, perfused hindlegs of cats. *Am. J. Physiol.* 183: 125–136, 1955.
276. RENKIN, E. M. Transport of potassium-42 from blood to tissue in isolated mammalian skeletal muscles. *Am. J. Physiol.* 197: 1205–1210, 1959.
277. RENKIN, E. M. Transport of large molecules across capillary walls. *Physiologist* 7: 13–28, 1964.
278. RENKIN, E. M. Blood flow and transcapillary exchange in skeletal and cardiac muscle. In: *Int. Symp. on Coronary Circulation and Energetics of the Myocardium, Milan, 1966.* Basel: Karger, 1967, p. 18–30.
279. RENKIN, E. M. Exchange of substances through capillary walls. In: *Circulatory and Respiratory Mass Transport*, edited by G. E. W. Wolstenholme and J. Knight. London: Churchill, 1969, p. 50–66. (Ciba Found. Symp.)
280. RENKIN, E. M. Transport pathways through capillary endothelium. *Microvasc. Res.* 15: 123–135, 1978.
281. RENKIN, E. M., AND F. E. CURRY. Transport of water and solutes across capillary endothelium. In: *Transport Across Biological Membranes: Transport Organs*, edited by G. Giebisch and D. C. Tosteson. Berlin: Springer-Verlag, 1978, vol. 4, p. 1–45.
282. RENKIN, E. M., AND J. P. GILMORE. Glomerular filtration. In: *Handbook of Physiology. Renal Physiology*, edited by J. Orloff and R. W. Berliner. Washington, DC: Am. Physiol. Soc., 1973, sect. 8, chapt. 9, p. 185–248.
282a. RENKIN, E. M., S. D. GRAY, AND L. R. DODD. Filling of microcirculation in skeletal muscles during timed India ink perfusions. *Am. J. Physiol.* 241 (*Heart Circ. Physiol.* 10): H174–H186, 1981.
283. RENKIN, E. M., O. HUDLICKÁ, AND R. M. SHEEHAN. Influence of metabolic vasodilatation on blood-tissue diffusion in skeletal muscle. *Am. J. Physiol.* 211: 87–98, 1966.
284. RENKIN, E. M., AND J. R. PAPPENHEIMER. Wasserdurchlässigkeit und Permeabilität der Capillarwände. *Ergeb. Physiol. Biol. Chem. Exp. Pharmakol.* 49: 59–126, 1957.
285. RENKIN, E. M., AND S. ROSELL. The influence of sympathetic adrenergic vasoconstrictor nerves on transport of diffusible solutes from blood to tissues in skeletal muscle. *Acta Physiol. Scand.* 54: 223–240, 1962.

285a. RIPPE, B., AND B. HARALDSSON. Capillary permeability in rat hindquarters as estimated by measurements of osmotic reflection coefficients (Abstract). *Acta Physiol. Scand. Suppl.* 508: 60, 1982.
286. RIPPE, B., A. KAMIYA, AND B. FOLKOW. Simultaneous measurements of capillary diffusion and filtration exchange during shifts in filtration-absorption and at graded alterations in the capillary surface area product (PS). *Acta Physiol. Scand.* 104: 318–336,1978.
287. RIPPE, B., AND L. STAGE. An "on-line" colorimetric method for repeated, rapid determinations of capillary diffusion capacity. *Acta Physiol. Scand.* 102: 108–115, 1978.
288. ROBINSON, R. A., AND R. H. STOKES. *Electrolyte Solutions.* London: Butterworths, 1959.
289. ROSE, C. P., AND C. A. GORESKY. Vasomotor control of capillary transit time heterogeneity on the canine coronary circulation. *Circ. Res.* 39: 541–554, 1976.
289a. ROSE, C. P., AND C. A. GORESKY. Constraints on the uptake of labeled palmitate by the heart. The barriers at the capillary and sarcolemma surface and the control of intracellular sequestration. *Circ. Res.* 41: 534–545, 1977.
290. ROSE, C. P., C. A. GORESKY, AND G. G. BACH. The capillary and sarcolemmal barriers in the heart: an exploration of labeled water permeability. *Circ. Res.* 41: 515–533, 1977.
291. ROSE, C. P., C. A. GORESKY, P. BELANGER, AND M.-J. CHEN. Effect of vasodilation and flow rate on capillary permeability surface product and interstitial space size in the coronary circulation. A frequency domain technique for modeling multiple dilution data with Laguerre functions. *Circ. Res.* 47: 312–329, 1980.
292. ROSELLI, R. J. Effect of red cell permeability on transcapillary tracer transport. The case of negligible back diffusion. *Bull. Math. Biophys.* 42: 765–795, 1980.
293. ROUS, P., H. P. GILDING, AND F. SMITH. The gradient of vascular permeability. *J. Exp. Med.* 51: 807–830, 1930.
294. ROUS, P., AND F. SMITH. The gradient along the capillaries and venules of frog skin. *J. Exp. Med.* 53: 219–242, 1931.
295. ROWLETT, R. D., AND T. R. HARRIS. A comparative study of organ models and numerical techniques for the evaluation of capillary permeability from multiple-indicator data. *Math. Biosci.* 29: 273–298, 1976.
296. SAFFORD, R. E., E. A. BASSINGTHWAIGHTE, AND J. B. BASSINGTHWAIGHTE. Diffusion of water in cat ventricular myocardium. *J. Gen. Physiol.* 72: 513–538, 1978.
296a. SAID S. I. Metabolic functions of the pulmonary circulation. *Circ. Res.* 50: 325–333, 1982.
297. SANGREN, W. C., AND C. W. SHEPPARD. A mathematical derivation of the exchange of a labeled substance between a liquid flowing in a vessel and an external compartment. *Bull. Math. Biophys.* 15: 387–394, 1953.
298. SCHAFER, D. E., AND J. A. JOHNSON. Permeability of mammalian heart capillaries to sucrose and inulin. *Am. J. Physiol.* 206: 985–991, 1964.
299. SCHAFER, J. A., S. L. TROUTMAN, AND T. E. ANDREOLI. Volume reabsorption, transepithelial potential differences, and ionic permeability properties in mammalian superficial proximal straight tubules. *J. Gen. Physiol.* 64: 582–607, 1974.
300. SCHANTZ, E. J., AND M. A. LAUFFER. Diffusion measurements in agar gel. *Biochemistry* 1: 658–663, 1962.
301. SCHMID-SCHÖNBEIN, G., B. ZWEIFACH, AND S. KOVALCHECK. The application of stereological principles to morphometry of the microcirculation in different tissues. *Microvasc. Res.* 14: 303–317, 1977.
302. SCHMIDT-NIELSEN, K., AND P. PENNYCUIK. Capillary density in mammals in relation to body size and oxygen consumption. *Am. J. Physiol.* 200: 746–750, 1961.
303. SCHULTZ, J. S., R. VALENTINE, AND C. Y. CHOI. Reflection coefficients of homopore membranes: effect of molecular size and configuration. *J. Gen. Physiol.* 73: 49–60, 1979.
304. SCHULTZ, S. G., AND A. K. SOLOMON. Determination of the effective hydrodynamic radii of small molecules by viscometry. *J. Gen. Physiol.* 44: 1189–1199, 1961.
305. SEJRSEN, P. Single injection, external registration method for measurement of capillary extraction. In: *Capillary Permeability*, edited by C. Crone and N. A. Lassen. Copenhagen: Munksgaard, 1970, p. 256–260. (Alfred Benzon Symp. 2.)
306. SEJRSEN, P. Capillary permeability measured by bolus injection, residue and venous detection. *Acta Physiol. Scand.* 105: 73–92, 1979.
307. SEJRSEN, P., AND K. H. TONNESEN. Shunting by diffusion on inert gas in skeletal muscle. *Acta Physiol. Scand.* 86: 82–91, 1972.
308. SEPÚLVEDA, F. V., AND D. L. YUDILEVICH. The specificity of glucose and amino acid carriers in the capillaries of the dog brain (Abstract). *J. Physiol. London* 250: 21P–23P, 1975.
309. SHEEHAN, R. M., AND E. M. RENKIN. Capillary, interstitial and cell membrane barriers to blood-tissue transport of potassium and rubidium in mammalian skeletal muscle. *Circ. Res.* 30: 588–607, 1972.
310. SIEMKOWICZ, E. Brain uptake of mannitol and sucrose after cerebral ischemia. Effect of hyperglycemia. *Acta Physiol. Scand.* 112: 359–363, 1981.
311. SIMIONESCU, M., N. SIMIONESCU, AND G. E. PALADE. Morphometric data on the endothelium of blood capillaries. *J. Cell Biol.* 60: 128–152, 1974.
312. SIMIONESCU, M., N. SIMIONESCU, AND G. E. PALADE. Segmental differentiations of cell junctions in the vascular endothelium. The microvasculature. *J. Cell Biol.* 67: 863–885, 1975.
313. SIMIONESCU, N., M. SIMIONESCU, AND G. E. PALADE. Permeability of muscle capillaries to small heme-peptides. Evidence for the existence of patent transendothelial channels. *J. Cell Biol.* 64: 586–607, 1975.
314. SMAJE, L., B. W. ZWEIFACH, AND M. INTAGLIETTA. Micropressures and capillary filtration coefficients in single vessels of the cremaster muscle of the rat. *Microvasc. Res.* 2: 96–110, 1970.
315. SMITH, F., AND M. DICK. The influence of the plasma colloids on the gradient of capillary permeability. *J. Exp. Med.* 56: 371–389, 1932.
316. SMITH, F., AND P. ROUS. The gradient of vascular permeability. IV. The permeability of the cutaneous venules and its functional significance. *J. Exp. Med.* 54: 499–514, 1931.
316a. SMITH, Q. R., C. E. JOHANSON, AND D. M. WOODBURY. Uptake of ^{36}Cl and ^{22}Na by the brain-cerebrospinal fluid system: comparison of the permeability of the blood-brain and blood-cerebrospinal fluid barrier. *J. Neurochem.* 37: 117–124, 1981.
317. SOKOLOFF, L., M. REIVICH, C. KENNEDY, M. H. DESROSIERS, C. S. PATLAK, K. D. PETTIGREW, O. SAKURADA, AND M. SHINOHARA. The [^{14}C]deoxyglucose method for the measurement of local cerebral glucose utilization: theory, procedure, and normal values in the conscious and anesthetized albino rat. *J. Neurochem.* 28: 897–916, 1977.
318. STARLING, E. H. *The Fluids of the Body.* London: Constable, 1909, 186 p.
319. STAUB, N. C., AND E. L. SCHULTZ. Pulmonary capillary length in dog, cat and rabbit. *Respir. Physiol.* 5: 371–378, 1968.
320. STEEN, J. B. The rete mirabile and a note on its diffusion characteristics. In: *Capillary Permeability*, edited by C. Crone and N. A. Lassen. Copenhagen: Munksgaard, 1970, p. 394–397. (Alfred Benzon Symp. 2.)
321. STEN-KNUDSEN, O. Passive transport processes. In: *Membrane Transport in Biology. Concepts and Models*, edited by G. Giebisch, D. C. Tosteson, and H. H. Ussing. Berlin: Springer-Verlag, 1978, vol. 1, p. 5–113.
322. STRANDELL, T., AND J. T. SHEPHERD. The effect in humans of exercise on relationship between simultaneously measured ^{131}Xe and ^{24}Na clearances. *Scand. J. Clin. Lab. Invest.* 21: 99–107, 1968.
323. STRAY-PEDERSEN, S. The effect of Ca^{++}, Mg^{++} and H^+ on the capillary permability of the rete mirabile of the eel, *Anguilla vulgaris L. Acta Physiol. Scand.* 94: 423–441, 1975.

324. STRAY-PEDERSEN, S., AND J. B. STEEN. The capillary permeability of the rete mirabile of the eel, *Anguilla vulgaris L. Acta Physiol. Scand.* 94: 401–422, 1975.
325. SUENSON, M., D. R. RICHMOND, AND J. B. BASSINGTHWAIGHTE. Diffusion of sucrose, sodium, and water in ventricular myocardium. *Am. J. Physiol.* 227: 1116–1123, 1974.
326. SVENSJÖ, E. Characterization of leakage of macromolecules in postcapillary venules. An intravital and electron microscopy study in the hamster cheek pouch. *Acta Univ. Ups.* 34: 1–42, 1978.
327. SVENSJÖ, E., K.-E. ARFORS, G. ARTURSON, AND G. RUTILI. The hamster cheek pouch preparation as a model for studies of macromolecular permeability of the microvasculature. *Ups. J. Med. Sci.* 83: 71–79, 1978.
327a. SYROTA, A., M. GIRAULT, J.-J. POCIDALO, AND D. L. YUDILEVICH. Endothelial uptake of amino acids, sugars, lipids, and prostaglandins in rat lung. *Am. J. Physiol.* 243: (*Cell Physiol.* 12): C20–C26, 1982.
328. TAKADA, M. Electron microscopic observations on the passage of electrolyte solutions and trypan blue fluid through the walls of venules and capillaries of the venous side. *Nagoya Med. J.* 9: 113–124, 1963.
329. TAKADA, M., AND K. MORI. Spontaneous separation of the endothelial cell junctions of the venules in the large salivary glands of the intact mouse. *Microvasc. Res.* 3: 204–206, 1971.
330. TANCREDI, R. G., T. YIPINTSOI, AND J. B. BASSINGTHWAIGHTE. Capillary and cell wall permeability to potassium in isolated dog hearts. *Am. J. Physiol.* 229: 537–544, 1975.
331. TAYLOR, A. E., AND K. A. GAAR, JR. Estimation of equivalent pore radii of pulmonary capillary and alveolar membranes. *Am. J. Physiol.* 218: 1133–1140, 1970.
332. THEWS, G. Die Sauerstoffdiffusion in Gehirn. Ein Beitrag zur Frage der Sauerstoffversorgung der Organe. *Pfluegers Arch. Gesamte Physiol. Menschen Tiere* 271: 197–226, 1960.
333. THOMPSON, A. M. Hyperosmotic effects on brain uptake of non-electrolytes. In: *Capillary Permeability*, edited by C. Crone and N. A. Lassen. Copenhagen: Munksgaard, 1970, p. 459–467. (Alfred Benzon Symp. 2.)
334. THOMPSON, A. M., H. M. CAVERT, AND N. LIFSON. Kinetics of distribution of D_2O and antipyrine in isolated perfused rat liver. *Am. J. Physiol.* 192: 531–537, 1958.
335. THOMPSON, A. M., H. M. CAVERT, N. LIFSON, AND R. L. EVANS. Regional tissue uptake of D_2O in perfused organs: rat liver, dog heart and gastrocnemius. *Am. J. Physiol.* 197: 897–902, 1959.
335a. TÖRNQUIST, P. Capillary permeability in cat choroid, studied with the single injection technique. *Acta Physiol. Scand.* 106: 425–430, 1979.
335b. TRAINOR, C., AND M. SILVERMAN. Transcapillary exchange of molecular weight markers in the postglomerular circulation: application of a barrier-limited model. *Am. J. Physiol.* 242 (*Renal Fluid Electrolyte Physiol.* 11): F436–F446, 1982.
336. TRAP-JENSEN, J., AND N. A. LASSEN. Capillary permeability for smaller hydrophilic tracers in exercising skeletal muscle in normal man and in patients with long-term diabetes mellitus. In: *Capillary Permeability*, edited by C. Crone and N. A. Lassen. Copenhagen: Munksgaard, 1970, p. 135–152. (Alfred Benzon Symp. 2.)
337. TRAP-JENSEN, J., AND N. A. LASSEN. Restricted diffusion in skeletal muscle capillaries in man. *Am. J. Physiol.* 220: 371–376, 1971.
338. TUREK, Z., M. GRANDTNER, AND F. KREUZER. Cardiac hypertrophy, capillary and muscle fiber density, muscle fiber diameter, capillary radius and diffusion distance in the myocardium of growing rats adapted to a simulated altitude of 3500 m. *Pfluegers Arch.* 335: 19–28, 1972.
339. USSING, H. H. Transport through biological membranes. *Annu. Rev. Physiol.* 15: 1–14, 1953.
340. USSING, H. H., N. BINDSLEV, N. A. LASSEN, AND O. STEN-KUNDSEN (editors). *Water Transport Across Epithelia: Barriers, Gradients, and Mechanisms.* Copenhagen: Munksgaard, 1981. (Alfred Benzon Symp. 15.)
341. USSING, H. H., AND E. E. WINDHAGER. Nature of shunt path and active sodium transport path through frog skin epithelium. *Acta Physiol. Scand.* 61: 484–504, 1964.
342. VARGAS, F. F., AND G. L. BLACKSHEAR. Transcapillary osmotic flows in the in vitro perfused heart. *Am. J. Physiol.* 240 (*Heart Circ. Physiol.* 9): H448–H456, 1981.
343. VARGAS, F. F., AND G. L. BLACKSHEAR. Secondary driving forces affecting transcapillary osmotic flows in perfused heart. *Am. J. Physiol.* 240 (*Heart Circ. Physiol.* 9): H457–H464, 1981.
344. VARGAS, F. F., G. L. BLACKSHEAR, AND R. J. MAJERLE. Permeability and model testing of heart capillaries by osmotic and optical methods. *Am. J. Physiol.* 239 (*Heart Circ. Physiol.* 8): H464–H468, 1980.
345. VARGAS, F., AND J. A. JOHNSON. An estimate of reflection coefficients for rabbit heart capillaries. *J. Gen. Physiol.* 47: 667–677, 1964.
346. VARGAS, F., AND J. A. JOHNSON. Permeability of rabbit heart capillaries to nonelectrolytes. *Am. J. Physiol.* 213: 87–93, 1967.
347. VERNIORY, A., R. DU BOIS, P. DECOODT, J. P. GASSEE, AND P. P. LAMBERT. Measurement of the permeability of biological membranes. Application to the glomerular wall. *J. Gen. Physiol.* 62: 489–507, 1973.
348. VIMTRUP, B. On the number, shape, structure and surface area of the glomeruli in the kidneys of man and mammals. *Am. J. Anat.* 41: 123–151, 1928.
349. WALKER, J. L. Ion specific liquid ion exchanger microelectrodes. *Anal. Chem.* 43: 89A–93A, 1971.
350. WANG, J. H., C. V. ROBINSON, AND I. S. EDELMAN. Self-diffusion and structure of liquid water. III. Measurement of the self-diffusion of liquid water with H_2, H_3, and ^{18}O as tracers. *J. Am. Chem. Soc.* 75: 466–469, 1953.
351. WANGENSTEEN, D., H. BACHOFEN, AND E. R. WEIBEL. Lung tissue volume changes induced by hypertonic NaCl: morphometric evaluation. *J. Appl. Physiol.: Respirat. Environ. Exercise Physiol.* 51: 1443–1450, 1981.
352. WANGENSTEEN, O. D., E. LYSAKER, AND P. SAVARYN. Pulmonary capillary filtration and reflection coefficients in the adult rabbit. *Microvasc. Res.* 14: 81–97, 1977.
353. WANGENSTEEN, O. D., L. E. WITTMERS, JR., AND J. A. JOHNSON. Permeability of the mammalian blood-gas barrier and its components. *Am. J. Physiol.* 216: 719–727, 1969.
354. WATSON, P. D. The interstitial matrix as a barrier in blood-to-lymph solute movement. *Physiologist* 23(1): 86–89, 1980.
355. WAYLAND, H., J. R. FOX, AND M. D. ELMORE. Quantitative fluorescent tracer studies in vivo. *Bibl. Anat.* 13: 61–64, 1975. (Eur. Conf. Microcirc., 8th Le Touquet-Paris-Plage, 1974.)
356. WAYLAND, H., AND W. G. FRASHER, JR. Intravital microscopy on the basis of telescopic principles: design and application of an intravital microscope for microvascular neurophysiological studies. In: *Modern Techniques in Physiological Sciences*, edited by J. F. Gross, R. Kaufmann, and E. Wetterer. New York: Academic, 1973, p. 126–162.
357. WEIBEL, E. R. Morphological basis of alveolar-capillary gas exchange. *Physiol. Rev.* 53: 419–495, 1973.
358. WEIBEL, E. R. Oxygen demand and the size of respiratory structures in mammals. In: *Lung Biology in Health and Disease. Evolution of Respiratory Processes: A Comparative Approach,* edited by S. C. Wood and C. Lenfant. New York: Dekker, 1979, vol. 13, p. 289–346.
358a. WEISS, H. R., E. BUCHWEITZ, T. J. MURTHA, AND M. AULETTA. Quantitative regional determination of morphometric indices of the total and perfused capillary network in the rat brain. *Circ. Res.* 51: 494–503, 1982.
359. WIEDERHIELM, C. A. Transcapillary and interstitial transport phenomena in the mesentery. *Federation Proc.* 25: 1789–1798, 1966.
360. WIEDERHIELM, C. A. Analysis of small vessel function. In: *Physical Bases of Circulatory Transport: Regulation and Exchange*, edited by E. B. Reeve and A. C. Guyton. Philadelphia, PA: Saunders, 1967, p. 313–326.

361. WIEDERHIELM, C. A. Dynamics of transcapillary fluid exchanges. *J. Gen. Physiol.* 52: 29s–63s, 1968.
362. WIEDERHIELM, C. A., M. L. SHAW, T. H. KEHL, AND J. R. FOX. A digital system for studying interstitial transport of dye molecules. *Microvasc. Res.* 5: 243–250, 1973.
363. WILBRANDT, W., AND T. ROSENBERG. The concept of carrier transport and its corollaries in pharmacology. *Pharmacol. Rev.* 13: 109–183, 1961.
364. WISSIG, S. L. Identification of the small pore in muscle capillaries. *Acta Physiol. Scand. Suppl.* 463: 33–44, 1979.
365. WISSIG, S. L., AND M. C. WILLIAMS. Permeability of muscle capillaries to microperoxidase. *J. Cell Biol.* 76: 341–359, 1978.
366. WITTE, S. Investigations of transvascular plasma passage with fluorescent microscopic technique. *Bibl. Anat.* 7: 218–222, 1965. (Eur. Conf. Microcirc., 3rd, Jerusalem, 1964.)
367. WITTMERS, L. E., M. BARTLETT, AND J. A. JOHNSON. Estimation of the capillary permeability coefficients of inulin in various tissues of the rabbit. *Microvasc. Res.* 11: 67–78, 1976.
368. YIPINTSOI, T. Single-passage extraction and permeability estimation of sodium in normal dog lungs. *Circ. Res.* 39: 523–531, 1976.
369. YIPINTSOI, T., AND J. B. BASSINGTHWAIGHTE. Circulatory transport of iodoantipyrine and water in the isolated dog heart. *Circ. Res.* 27: 461–477, 1970.
370. YUDILEVICH, D. L., AND O. A. ALVAREZ. Water, sodium, and thiourea transcapillary diffusion in the dog heart. *Am. J. Physiol.* 213: 308–314, 1967.
371. YUDILEVICH, D. L., AND N. DEROSE. Blood-brain transfer of glucose and other molecules measured by rapid indicator dilution. *Am. J. Physiol.* 220: 841–846, 1971.
371a. YUDILEVICH, D. L., AND G. E. MANN. Unidirectional uptake of substrates at the blood side of epithelia: stomach, salivary gland, pancreas. *Federation Proc.* 41: 3045–3053, 1982.
372. YUDILEVICH, D. L., E. M. RENKIN, O. A. ALVAREZ, AND I. BRAVO. Fractional extraction and transcapillary exchange during continuous and instantaneous tracer administration. *Circ. Res.* 23: 325–336, 1968.
373. ZIEGLER, W. H., AND C. A. GORESKY. Transcapillary exchange in the working left ventricle of the dog. *Circ. Res.* 29: 181–207, 1971.
374. ZIERLER, K. L. Theory of use of indicators to measure blood flow and extracellular volume and calculation of transcapillary movement of tracers. *Circ. Res.* 12: 464–472, 1963.
375. ZIERLER, K. L. Equations for measuring blood flow by external monitoring of radioisotopes. *Circ. Res.* 16: 309–321, 1965.

CHAPTER 11

Exchange of macromolecules across the microcirculation

AUBREY E. TAYLOR | D. NEIL GRANGER | *Department of Physiology, College of Medicine, University of South Alabama, Mobile, Alabama*

CHAPTER CONTENTS

Techniques and Theoretical Background
- Theoretical considerations
- Experimental approaches
  - Osmotic transients
  - Plasma disappearance curves for radioactive macromolecules
  - Microscopic visualization of macromolecule leakage
  - Lymph studies
  - Pore estimates

Regional Differences in Capillary Permeability
- Continuous capillary beds
  - Subcutaneous tissue
  - Lung
  - Skeletal muscle
  - Adipose tissue
  - Myocardium
  - Nervous system
  - Intravital microscopy studies
- Fenestrated capillary beds
  - Kidney
  - Gastrointestinal organs
- Discontinuous capillaries
  - Liver
- Whole-body capillary permeability

Mechanisms of Transcapillary Solute Transport

Transport Pathways
- Continuous capillaries
- Fenestrated capillaries
- Discontinuous capillaries

Summary

THE MECHANISMS by which large molecules cross capillary walls and gain access to the interstitium have intrigued physiologists for the past century. From the earliest observations it was apparent that the lymphatics draining different organs contain varying concentrations of plasma proteins. By the late 1950s it was established that most proteins present in plasma cross capillary walls, diffuse through the tissues, and return to the plasma via the lymphatic system. Grotte (147) and Mayerson (225) presented convincing evidence indicating that the concentration of a macromolecule in lymph is a function of its molecular size. In addition the early studies demonstrated that capillaries are heteroporous—i.e., both small and large pores are necessary to describe the movement of large molecules across capillary walls. Thus as a result of Grotte and Mayerson's studies, the stage was set for the development of techniques and mathematical approaches for describing the transport of large molecules across capillary walls.

Mayerson's chapter in the previous *Handbook* section on circulation (224) presented qualitative estimates of capillary selectivity with lymph as the basic experimental tool. In the same volume Landis and Pappenheimer's chapter (203) discussed capillary permeability in a more quantitative fashion; however, their analyses were primarily limited to permeability data for small molecules. At that time the mathematical approach used to assess membrane permeability had only recently been developed by Kedem and Katchalsky (192, 193).

The *Handbook* articles of Mayerson and Landis and Pappenheimer, as well as the application of irreversible thermodynamics to biological membranes, provided the stimulus for several hundred papers dealing with large-molecule permeability. In this treatise the information presented over the past 15 years pertaining to the permeability of mammalian capillaries to macromolecules is summarized. This chapter is divided into sections dealing individually with the theory and techniques used to assess macromolecule permeability, regional differences in capillary permeability, mechanisms of macromolecule exchange, and pathways for macromolecule exchange.

TECHNIQUES AND THEORETICAL BACKGROUND

Capillary permeability to macromolecules has been evaluated by several methods: *1*) measuring the disappearance of radioactive solutes from the plasma; *2*) monitoring the rate of macromolecule accumulation in or disappearance from a tissue; *3*) comparing the concentration (or composition) of native proteins or radioactive macromolecules in lymph to that in plasma; *4*) visualizing (microscopically) the leakage of fluorescein or dye-labeled macromolecules from the vasculature; and *5*) applying the concept of osmotic transients (95, 203, 224).

Each of these approaches has provided important and useful information regarding the permeability properties of capillaries in several different tissues. Each technique possesses unique advantages and limitations. The major objective of this section is to describe the theory on which each approach is based and how information obtained from the method can be used to predict the permeability characteristics of the capillary wall.

Theoretical Considerations

Several equations have been developed to describe the process of molecular exchange across membranes. With the introduction of irreversible thermodynamics into biology in the late 1950s, Kedem and Katchalsky (192, 193) proposed a set of simple and logical equations describing solvent flow J_v and solute flow J_s across porous barriers

$$J_v = L_pS(\Delta P - \sigma \Delta \Pi) \quad (1)$$

and

$$J_s = J_v\,(1 - \sigma)\overline{C}_s + PS\Delta C \quad (2)$$

where L_pS is the hydraulic conductance (and is the product of hydraulic conductivity L_p and the surface area S); ΔP is the hydrostatic pressure gradient, σ the reflection coefficient, $\Delta \Pi$ the osmotic pressure gradient, PS the permeability coefficient–surface area product, ΔC the solute concentration gradient ($C_P - C_L$), and $\overline{C}_s$ is the average molar concentration of solute within the porous structure of the membrane.

The importance of Equations 1 and 2 is that a membrane-solvent-solute system can be described in terms of flows and forces that are explicitly defined, i.e., ΔP, $\Delta \Pi$, ΔC, J_v, and J_s. The flows are related to both hydrostatic and osmotic forces acting across the membrane rather than only hydrostatic (Poiseuille's equation) or diffusional forces (Fick's law of diffusion). In addition the Kedem-Katchalsky formulations define a particular membrane-solvent-solute system in terms of three parameters: the hydraulic conductance, the permeability coefficient, and the reflection coefficient. Although Pappenheimer and co-workers (260) used permeability coefficients and volume conductances to describe the permeability characteristics of the capillary wall, they assumed a value of unity for the reflection coefficient of all macromolecular solutes. This important parameter, which is related to membrane selectivity, was defined by Staverman (352) in 1951. The reflection coefficient equals zero if the membrane is freely permeable to the molecule and equals one if the solute is totally reflected by or impermeable to the membrane. Thus, for the first time in membrane theory, equations were written that described the membrane's ability to restrict the passage of different-sized molecules and obviated the assumption that solutes are either freely permeable or impermeable.

In 1963 Patlak et al. (277) used basic physics to derive an equation describing solute flux across a membrane but also incorporated the selectivity factor σ_d into the analysis. The result is referred to as the exact or nonlinear flux equation and is described as

$$J_s = J_v\,(1 - \sigma_d)\left[\frac{(C_P - C_L)e^{-x}}{1 - e^{-x}}\right] \quad (3)$$

where C_P and C_L are the concentrations of the solute in the plasma and tissues, respectively, and x is the Péclet number [$x = (1 - \sigma_d)J_v/PS$].

Although both the Kedem-Katchalsky and Patlak equations have been available to investigators for approximately 20 years, most have preferred to use the former to describe solute flux across biological membranes. Why has the Kedem-Katchalsky equation been so attractive to workers in the field? First, the equation is linear and does not contain the complexity of the exponential function in the Patlak equation. Second, the Kedem-Katchalsky equation conveniently separates diffusive ($PS\Delta C$) and convective [$J_v(1 - \sigma)\overline{C}_s$] solute fluxes, whereas the Patlak equation in its original form is not easily separated into diffusive and convective components. In addition the Kedem-Katchalsky equations make no assumption regarding the geometric structure of the capillary membrane, i.e., the equation is phenomenological. The expressions and terms in the Kedem-Katchalsky equations are also readily applied to data acquired in biological and artificial systems. The Patlak equation has subsequently been rearranged by Bresler (59) and by Sha'afi et al. (337), yielding Equations 4 and 5, respectively

$$J_s = J_v(1 - \sigma_d)C_P + \left[\frac{J_v(1 - \sigma_d)\ \Delta C}{e^x - 1}\right] \quad (4)$$

$$J_s = J_v(1 - \sigma_d)\left(\frac{C_P + C_L}{2}\right) + \left[\frac{J_v(1 - \sigma_d)(e^x + 1)\ \Delta C}{2(e^x - 1)}\right] \quad (5)$$

These forms more readily allow for separation of diffusive and convective fluxes.

Experimental Approaches

OSMOTIC TRANSIENTS. Starling (347) was the first to recognize that the hemodilution occurring after intravascular injection of a hypertonic salt solution is some function of solute size. He noted a relatively greater hemodilution with Na_2SO_4 than with NaCl solutions of equivalent osmolarity. Pappenheimer et al. (260) extended this observation and measured osmotic transients in hindlimb capillaries for several small lipid-insoluble substances. Renkin (300) later demonstrated that lipid-soluble substances produce no observable osmotic transients in the isolated hindlimb. The results of these investigations led to the conclusion that the passive permeation characteristics of muscle capillaries primarily depend on the ratio of the molecular radius to the membrane pore size and on the lipid solubility of the molecule.

The osmotic-transient approach has been applied to organs in which the weight or volume of the tissue can be continuously monitored. A solution of known concentration (usually hyperosmotic) is injected into the arterial supply of an organ that is neither losing nor gaining weight (isogravimetric). Equation 1 would predict the following relationship between solvent flux (here, the rate of weight loss by the tissue) and the osmotic pressure gradient of the solute

$$-J_v = -L_p S \sigma_d \Delta\Pi$$

or

$$\sigma_d = \frac{J_v}{L_p S \Delta\Pi} \tag{6}$$

If L_pS and $\Delta\Pi$ are known, the osmotic reflection coefficient can be estimated from Equation 6 when J_v is predicted by extrapolating the rate of weight loss to time 0 (111, 380). Although Pappenheimer's approach used the same basic theory, it did not incorporate σ into the osmotic-transient analysis. Pappenheimer's equation is

$$\frac{A_s}{\Delta x} = \frac{\dot{Q}(C_a - C_v)RT}{D_s \Delta P} \tag{7}$$

where $A_s/\Delta x$ is the area available to solute for free diffusion A_s divided by the path length Δx; $\dot{Q}$ is the rate of blood flow; C_a and C_v are the concentrations of the test molecule in arterial and venous blood, respectively; RT is the product of the universal gas constant and absolute temperature; and D_s is the coefficient of free diffusion of the solute. The hydrostatic pressure gradient is altered to exactly balance the effective osmotic pressure of the solute.

Pappenheimer's approach differs from the osmotic-transient method (based on irreversible thermodynamics) in that capillary pressure is elevated to maintain an isogravimetric condition in the face of the osmotic tendency to decrease organ weight. In addition the outflow concentrations of the test solutes were measured in Pappenheimer's study to estimate the area available to the solute. The Pappenheimer approach provided the first estimate of the size of small-pore systems in continuous capillaries.

Although the osmotic-transient approach has been widely employed to study capillary permeability, it has several physiological problems that may limit its usefulness. These include *1*) an unstirred extravascular space, *2*) capillary heteroporosity, *3*) tissue heterogeneity, *4*) overestimation of $\Delta\Pi$ acting across the capillary, *5*) overestimation of L_p, *6*) local vascular resistance and blood volume changes, and *7*) osmotically induced changes in capillary permeability (133).

PLASMA DISAPPEARANCE CURVES FOR RADIOACTIVE MACROMOLECULES. With the advent of radioactive tracers several groups of investigators placed radioactive albumin (or other macromolecules such as dextrans) into the circulation and followed the plasma concentration as a function of time. Estimates of capillary permeability have been derived from the rate of decrease of tracer concentration in plasma during the first hour after injection [transcapillary exchange rate (266)]. The plasma disappearance curve of a given macromolecule is influenced by factors other than capillary permeability, i.e., its extravascular volume of distribution and concentration, and the capillary surface area available for exchange. The first hour of the whole-body plasma disappearance curve is also heavily weighted toward the more rapidly exchanging capillary beds in the liver, intestine, and lungs. In spite of both the theoretical and physiological problems associated with the use of plasma disappearance curves to assess capillary permeability, they do constitute one of the few techniques available for evaluating macromolecule permeability in humans. Many of the theoretical problems associated with this approach can be eliminated by measuring the volume of distribution of the macromolecules from small biopsies and by using lymph to determine the interstitial concentration. The data obtained with this approach are qualitative and may lead to serious errors when one attempts to define the mechanisms of macromolecule transport (204).

MICROSCOPIC VISUALIZATION OF MACROMOLECULE LEAKAGE. Since its introduction into capillary physiology by Landis in 1927 (202, 203), the in vivo microscopic technique for observing macromolecule extravasation has proven to be an important tool for delineating the location of leaks (i.e., large pores) along the length of the capillary. Through the use of dyes (or fluorescent compounds) with an affinity for binding macromolecules, this technique allows one to correlate macromolecule extravasation to vessel structure. Furthermore by varying the size of the dye-labeled macromolecule, one can correlate the degree or rate of extravasation to solute size. An inherent limitation of this approach is that the results acquired are generally qualitative in nature, and in addition the reliability of the method's conclusions depends to a large extent on the assumption that the dye is totally bound to the macromolecule, with negligible free (unbound) dye (202, 209). Recent modifications of the technique may allow for more quantitative estimates of capillary permeability (240).

LYMPH STUDIES. It has long been assumed that the composition of lymph is identical to that of interstitial fluid under steady-state conditions (326, 409). Numerous investigators have provided indirect data to support or refute this assumption. Direct comparisons of interstitial fluid samples with lymph collected simultaneously from the same tissue generally support the contention that the concentrations of macromolecules in lymph and interstitial fluid are identical. Interstitial fluid sampled by micropipette appears to be closest in composition to prenodal lymph (327). Indirect sources of interstitial fluid, i.e., capsule and wick samples, frequently exhibit a higher protein content than lymph due to inflammation (22, 155, 212, 297, 360). However, when steps are taken to minimize the influence of inflammation, the difference in protein content between capsular fluid and lymph is small (297, 304, 366, 367).

Several researchers have addressed the possibility that the composition of lymph may be modified after it has entered the collecting lymphatic (304). The bulk of these data indicates that exchange of solutes and water between lymphatic vessels and interstitial spaces is probably very small. However, there is considerable evidence suggesting that the composition of lymph is modified within lymph nodes (90, 291, 304), and thus the concentration of macromolecules in postnodal lymph may not be representative of interstitial fluid. The available data, therefore, suggest that lymph can provide an estimate of interstitial fluid composition under steady-state conditions given that the source of lymph is a prenodal lymphatic. Lymph acquired under non-steady-state conditions and/or from a postnodal lymphatic is of questionable value when assumed to represent interstitial fluid.

From the time of Starling (348) it was known that the concentration of proteins in lymph varies from tissue to tissue. Although Starling realized that the tissue-to-tissue variability of lymph protein content most likely represents regional differences in capillary permeability, the technique of using lymph macromolecule concentration as an estimate of capillary permeability was not introduced until the mid-1900s by Grotte (147) and Mayerson (225). Their studies provided the impetus for the development of newer approaches for assessing capillary selectivity. Figures 1 and 2 show the lymphatic data obtained by Grotte and Mayerson for various dextrans. The curves obtained by Grotte (Fig. 1) indicate that macromolecules gain access to lymph in accordance with solute size. Mayerson's data (Fig. 2) clearly indicate differences in equilibration times of macromolecules in the lymph of different tissues. Faster equilibration time could be attributed to either greater capillary surface areas for exchange, larger leak sites, or variation between different tissue compartment sizes and turnover rates.

Since Grotte and Mayerson's studies a great deal of effort has been expended in trying to interpret the behavior of lymphatic protein fluxes relative to capillary wall porosity. The lymphatic protein-flux technique requires the measurement of lymph flow and the lymph and plasma solute concentrations in a particular tissue. Additional information is gained by analyzing the relative concentrations of macromolecules of various sizes in lymph and plasma. By studying the lymphatic fluxes (equal to the product of lymph flow and lymph protein concentration) at defined steady states, different models for solute exchange can be developed.

Renkin (302) pioneered one of the first methods for analyzing lymphatic protein fluxes in terms of the permeability–surface area product. If σ is assumed to be one in Equation 2, J_s is described as

$$J_s = PS\Delta C$$

which when rewritten yields

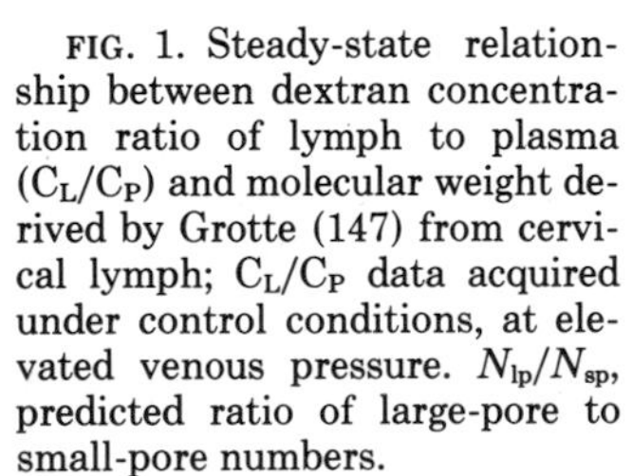

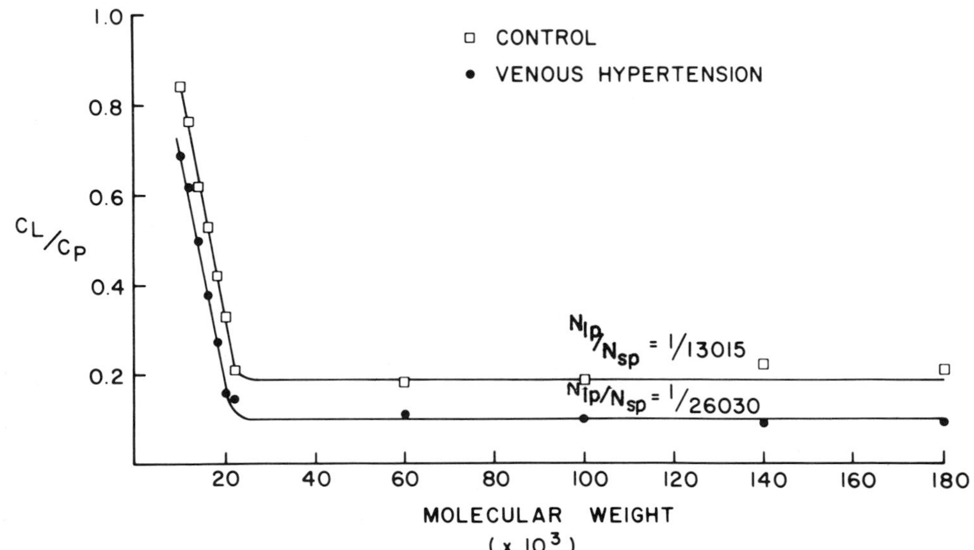

FIG. 1. Steady-state relationship between dextran concentration ratio of lymph to plasma (C_L/C_P) and molecular weight derived by Grotte (147) from cervical lymph; C_L/C_P data acquired under control conditions, at elevated venous pressure. N_{lp}/N_{sp}, predicted ratio of large-pore to small-pore numbers.

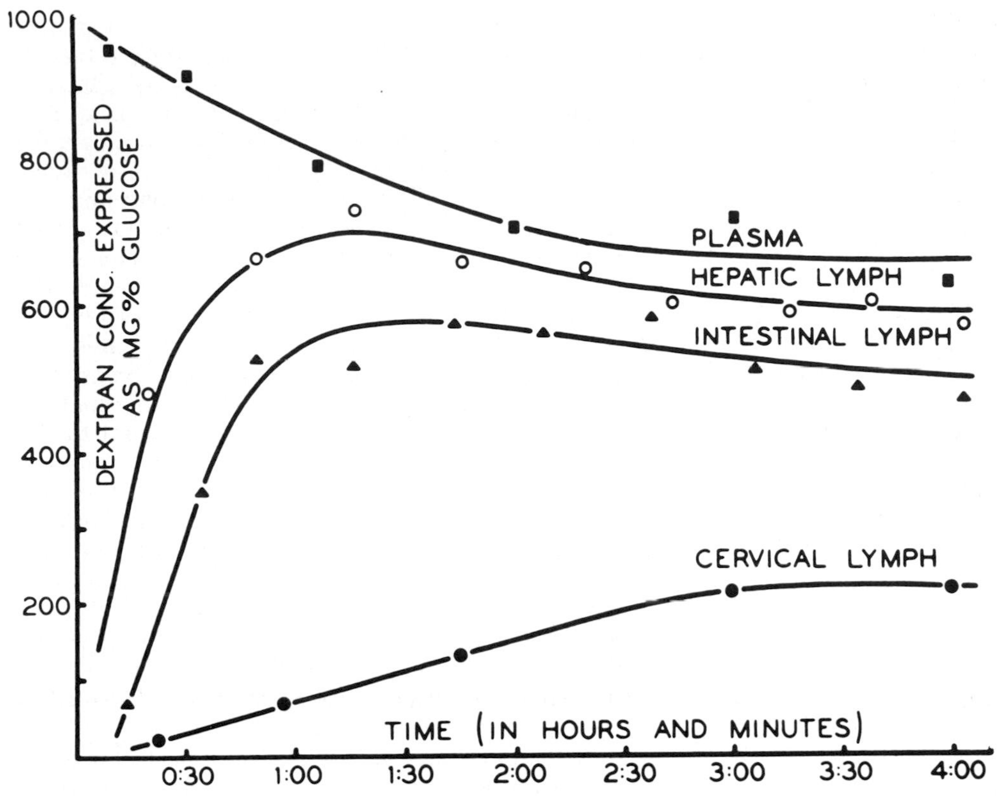

FIG. 2. Plot of dextran (35,000 mol wt) concentration in plasma, hepatic lymph, intestinal lymph, and cervical lymph in dog. [From Mayerson et al. (225).]

$$PS = \frac{J_v C_L}{C_P - C_L} \tag{8}$$

Equation 8 has been used by Carter, Joyner, and Renkin (78), Garlick and Renkin (126), and others (60, 64, 65) to describe capillary permeability to macromolecules. It is generally believed that both diffusive and convective processes are involved in the movement of macromolecules across capillary walls. However, Renkin's calculation of *PS* ignores convection, and its use leads to an overestimation of *PS*.

In recent years investigators have attempted to describe lymphatic protein fluxes in terms of both diffusion and convection by predicting values for σ and *PS* with Equations 2 and 3. Figure 3 is a plot of the solute concentration ratio of lymph to plasma C_L/C_P, as a function of J_v (here, lymph flow) predicted by the Kedem-Katchalsky (192) equation [assuming $\overline{C}_s$ = either C_P or $(C_L + C_P)/2$] and the Patlak (277) equation. The equations (143) used to generate the curves are

$$\frac{C_L}{C_P} = \frac{1 - \sigma_d}{1 - \sigma_d e^{-x}} \tag{9}$$

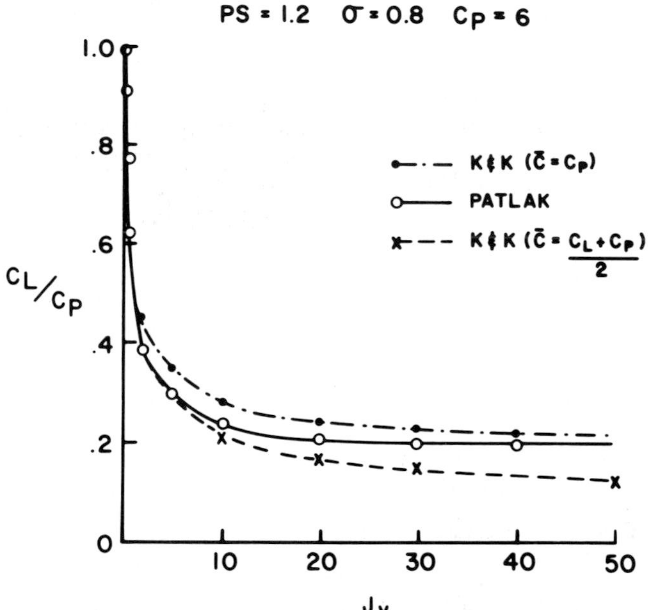

FIG. 3. Predicted relationship between C_L/C_P and lymph flow with Eqs. 9 (Patlak) and 10 and 11 (Kedem-Katchalsky).

For $\overline{C}_s = (C_L + C_P)/2$

$$\frac{C_L}{C_P} = \frac{\{[(1 - \sigma)/2] + (PS/J_v)\}}{\{[(1 + \sigma)/2] + (PS/J_v)\}} \tag{10}$$

For $\overline{C}_s = C_P$

$$\frac{C_L}{C_P} = \frac{[(1 - \sigma) + (PS/J_v)]}{[1 + (PS/J_v)]} \tag{11}$$

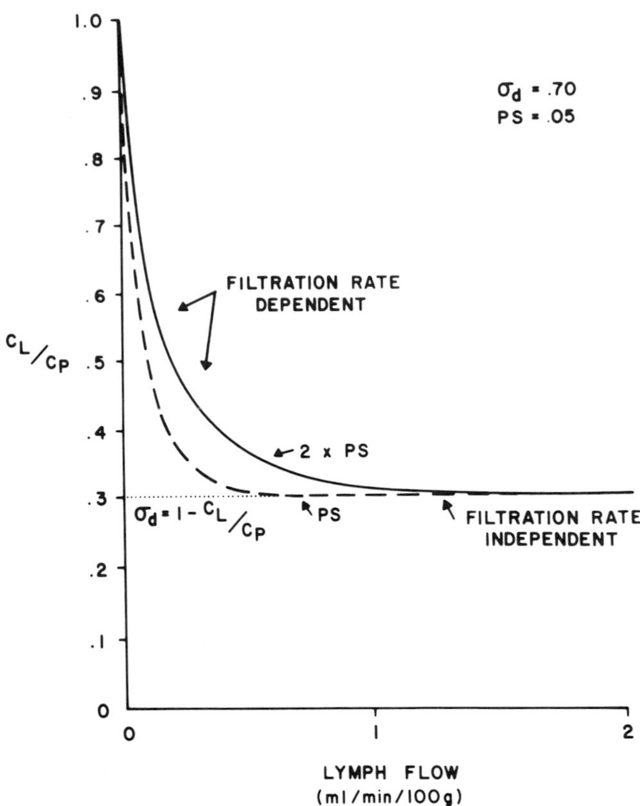

FIG. 4. Relationship predicted by Eq. 9 between C_L/C_P and lymph flow at two capillary surface areas. Theoretically, osmotic reflection coefficient can be estimated by $\sigma_d = 1 - (C_L/C_P)$ when C_L/C_P is filtration rate independent (143).

Note two important predictions from the three equations. Equation 10 (which incorporates the arithmetic mean for $\overline{C}_s$) predicts that C_L/C_P approaches a value of $(1 - \sigma_d)/(1 + \sigma_d)$ at high J_v. In contrast C_L/C_P in Equations 9 and 11 (which incorporate $\overline{C}_s = C_P$) approaches $1 - \sigma$ at high J_v. Since C_L/C_P at high J_v values must approach $1 - \sigma_d$, Equation 10 cannot be used to describe solute fluxes at high filtration rates unless $1 - \sigma$ in Equation 10 is replaced by $(1 - 2C_L)/(C_P + C_L)$.

The relationships between C_L/C_P and lymph flow (capillary filtration rate) predicted by Equations 9 and 11 have been reproduced experimentally in the intestine (143) and other tissues (262, 264, 318). Figure 4 illustrates that when lymph flow is increased from its normal value (by elevating venous pressure), C_L/C_P decreases (filtration rate dependent) until sufficiently high lymph flows are acquired and C_L/C_P becomes uninfluenced by further increases in lymph flow (filtration rate independent). This relationship is true even if capillary surface area is increased; however, the lymph flow required for C_L/C_P to become filtration rate independent is also increased. From Equations 9 and 11 it is apparent that σ_d can be estimated by using the value for C_L/C_P that is filtration rate independent. Thus there is both theoretical and experimental evidence to support the contention that σ_d can be estimated by C_L/C_P at high capillary filtration rates (58, 143, 395).

Why C_L/C_P becomes filtration rate independent at high lymph flows can be readily explained by analyzing the Patlak relationship in Equations 4 and 5. Assuming the second term in this equation represents the diffusion term and selecting values of 1.0 and 0.9 for PS and σ, respectively, the diffusion component $J_v(1 - \sigma_d)/(e^x - 1)$ was calculated at different values for J_v in Figure 5. The Péclet number in the nonlinear flux equation is the parameter that determines at which lymph flow C_L/C_P becomes filtration rate independent. Note that the diffusion component decreases dramatically as J_v is increased, such that for $x > 5$, diffusion becomes negligible and C_L/C_P approximates $1 - \sigma_d$. This behavior of diffusional fluxes can also be deduced from the Kedem-Katchalsky equation with either expression for the solute concentration profile. (See APPENDIX A.)

Equation 5 is a representation of the Patlak equation in the form of the Kedem-Katchalsky equation using the arithmetic mean mode. Although this equation predicts that C_L/C_P approaches $1 - \sigma_d$ at high J_v, it predicts another interesting phenomenon, i.e., that PS appears to increase with J_v. Can this happen physically? When the Kedem-Katchalsky equation (incorporating the arithmetic mean for $\overline{C}_s$) is used to calculate σ_d and PS from lymphatic protein flux, σ_d and PS do increase with J_v (52, 53, 368). However, some of the problems associated with applying Equation 10 to lymph data may be due to different pressures acting along the length of the capillary wall (52, 53).

In recent years three approaches based on the linear flux equation have been developed to estimate PS and

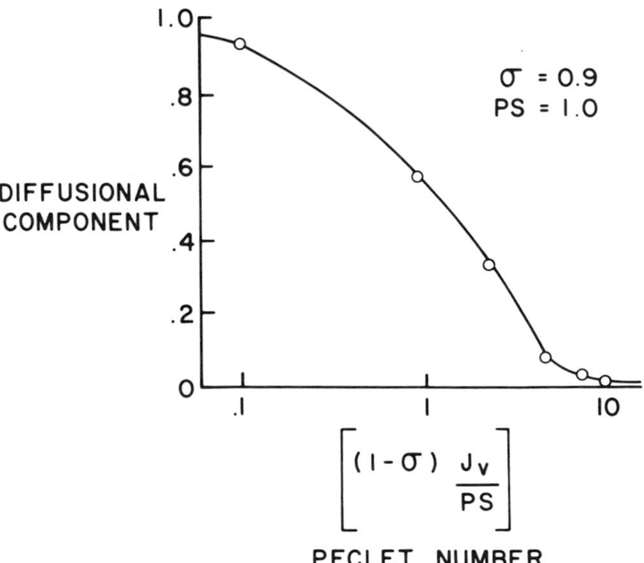

FIG. 5. Relationship between diffusional component of Eq. 9 and Péclet number, $(1 - \sigma_d)J_v/PS$.

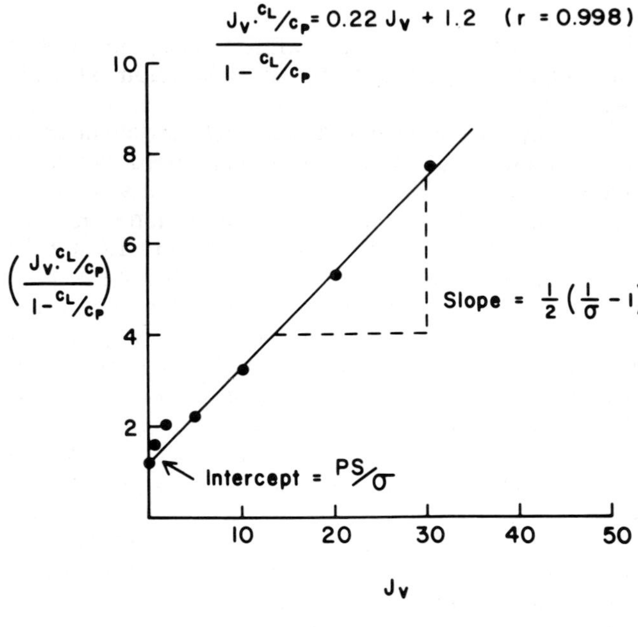

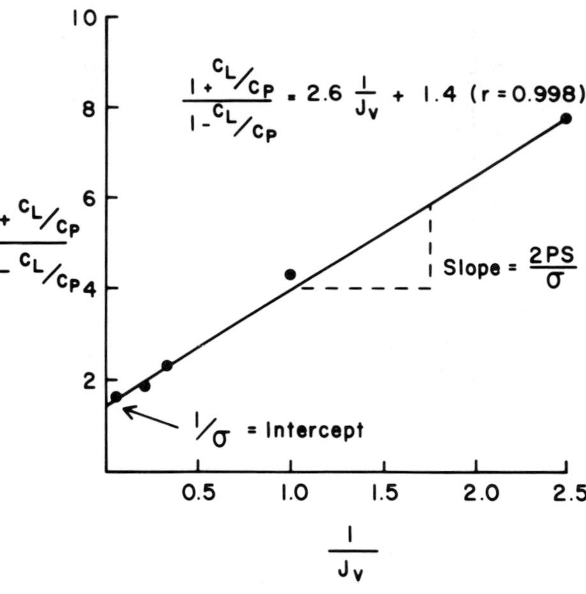

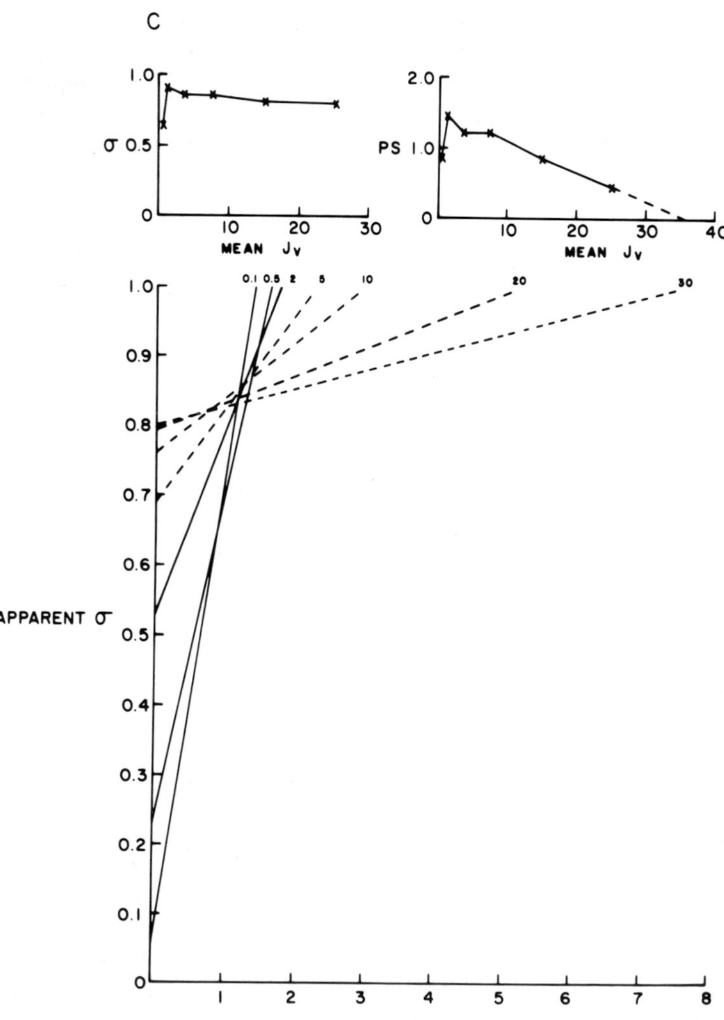

FIG. 6. *A*: Renkin et al.'s (312) analysis for estimating σ and *PS* from data of lymphatic protein flux at various filtration rates by using Eq. 12. Equation of the line and correlation coefficient (r) also given. *B*: Perl's (278) analysis for estimating σ and *PS* from data of lymphatic protein flux based on Eq. 13. *C*: cross-point analysis (368) for estimating σ and *PS* from data on lymphatic protein flux based on Eq. 10. (From M. Perry, unpublished observations.)

σ_d from data of lymphatic protein flux. All approaches utilize several lymph flux states to graphically obtain σ_d and PS. The graphical analyses are based on the following forms of Equation 10

$$\frac{J_v(C_L/C_P)}{1 - (C_L/C_P)} = \frac{[(1/\sigma) - 1]J_v}{2} + \frac{PS}{\sigma} \quad (12)$$

and

$$\frac{1 + (C_L/C_P)}{1 - (C_L/C_P)} = \frac{2PS}{\sigma}\left(\frac{1}{J_v} + \frac{1}{\sigma}\right) \quad (13)$$

For the Renkin analysis [Fig. 6*A*; (312)] the intercept gives PS/σ and the term ½ $(1/\sigma - 1)$ yields the slope. When the data generated are fit by least-squares analyses (51), the slopes and intercepts are 0.69 and 0.83, respectively. When the data are plotted by the Perl equation [Fig. 6*B*; (278)] σ and PS are 0.71 and 0.92, respectively. However, one low J_v value was excluded from the Perl analysis. If this point is included, then $\sigma = 0.59$ and $PS = 0.59$. Therefore it is evident from Figures 6*A* and 6*B* that both analyses underestimate the true values for σ and PS.

Another method used to estimate σ and PS is to obtain two flux states and solve the resulting equations for two unknowns (52, 53, 82, 83, 368). When this analysis was applied to lymph flux data, however, it was observed that both σ and PS increased with increased lymph flow. Figure 6*C* shows such an analysis for flux data where the values for C_P and C_L were obtained at several lymph flows. Note that the curves do not intersect at a common point, indicating that σ and PS are not constant. Furthermore this analysis demonstrates that PS approaches zero as σ approaches its true value.

In these analyses we have assumed that the flux occurring across a membrane can be described by the nonlinear flux equation. This needs some justification. First, few would argue that the Patlak equation is physically incorrect; it is the best equation available for describing solute fluxes across a membrane (58). Second, in any sieving experiment the value for C_L/C_P must approach $1 - \sigma$ at high volume flows (143, 223, 395, 396); this does not occur with the Kedem-Katchalsky equation, which incorporates the arithmetic mean (see Fig. 3). Third, the flux equation must approach PS at zero volume flow; this is true for both the Patlak and Kedem-Katchalsky equations. With these criteria it appears that the nonlinear flux equation correctly predicts the physical events that should occur across any sieving barrier and that Equation 10 does not accurately describe σ and PS (see APPENDIX A).

PORE ESTIMATES. The earliest predictions of the number and size of pores in the microcirculation were made by estimates of small-molecule selectivity (111, 260, 301), i.e., A_s/A_w (area available to solute relative

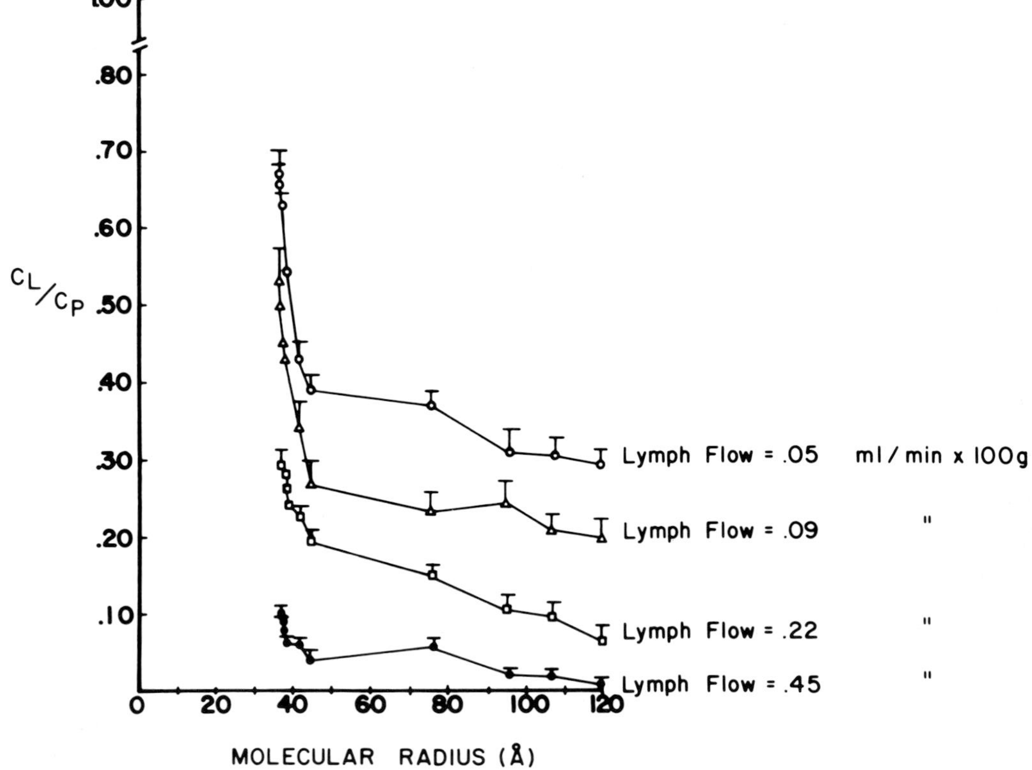

FIG. 7. Steady-state relationship between C_L/C_P and molecular radius at different lymph flows in cat ileum (143).

to area available to water). Large-molecule permeability could then be deduced by extrapolating A_s/A_w to larger molecular radii. In contrast Grotte (147) used actual C_L/C_P values of dextran molecules to estimate the size and relative number of pores in the capillary wall. Figure 7 is a replot of data obtained from the small intestine (143). The C_L/C_P ratios for endogenous proteins of various sizes were acquired at four different lymph flows. Grotte's estimates of the ratio of large pores (N_{lp}) to small pores (N_{sp}) can be expressed

$$\frac{N_{lp}}{N_{sp}} = \frac{r_{lp}^2}{r_{sp}^2[1/(C_L/C_P)] \cdot (\text{large-pore intercept})} \tag{14}$$

where r_{lp} is the radius of the large pores (assumed to be 200 Å), r_{sp} is the radius of the small pores (assumed to be 50 Å), and $[1/(C_L/C_P)] \cdot$(large-pore intercept) is the extrapolated C_L/C_P ratio for the largest molecules. When this analysis is used for the data in Figure 7, N_{lp}/N_{sp} decreases from 1:730 to 1:1,024 to 1:2,125 to 1:6,400 as lymph flow increases. This indicates a change in the relative proportion of solute flux occurring through the small and large pores.

Renkin et al. (313) recently presented a pore analysis based on the relationship between the total membrane reflection coefficient σ_d and volume conductance L_{PT} to the reflection coefficient σ_i and volume conductance $(L_{PT})_i$ of each set of pores

$$\sigma_d = \frac{\Sigma[(\sigma_d)_i \cdot (L_{PT})_i]}{L_{PT}} \tag{15}$$

Figure 8 is a plot of $1 - \sigma_d$ versus solute radius that was generated by assuming that a membrane has three populations of pores: 10,000 with 8-Å radii, 500 with 50-Å radii, and 1 with a radius of 200 Å. The conductance of each set of pores was calculated by Poiseuille's equation. The reflection coefficient for each solute was calculated for each set of pores with the equation relating σ to solute radii (a) and pore radii (r) developed by Drake and Davis (108) from Levitt's (210) earlier analysis (see APPENDIX B). A comprehensive review of the various formulas used to model restriction to diffusion and hydrodynamic interactions in pores and slits is provided in the chapter by Curry in this *Handbook*. Thus

$$\sigma = \tfrac{16}{3}(a/r)^2 - \tfrac{20}{3}(a/r)^3 + \tfrac{7}{3}(a/r)^4 \tag{16}$$

The resulting data were then fit by using different plots of Equation 16. First, the best fit for the larger solutes is obtained. A 200-Å pore fits the large solutes extremely well. The 200-Å curve is then subtracted from the points falling above the line. This produces the lower squares, which are best fit by a pore curve of 50 Å. From this plot one can also estimate the percentage of the total conductance for each set of pores. For the 200-Å pores the line of identity intercepts the $1 - \sigma_d$ axis at 0.35 and the small-pore line of identity intercepts at 0.60. From Figure 8 the following hydrodynamic relationships yield the ratio of large-pore to small-pore areas (A_{lp}/A_{sp}) and the ratio of large-pore to small-pore numbers (N_{lp}/N_{sp})

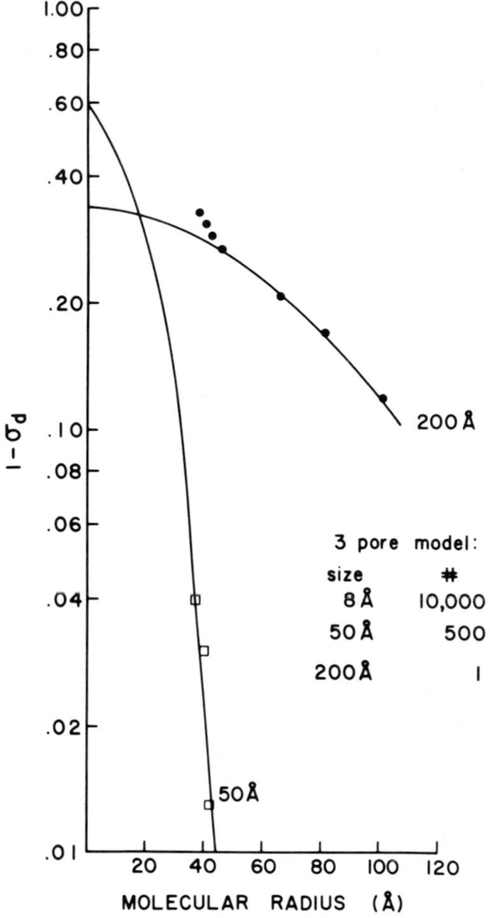

FIG. 8. Demonstration of pore-stripping analysis (313) for determining pore sizes. Data generated with a three-pore model comprising pores of 8, 50, and 200 Å. [Adapted from Renkin et al. (313).]

$$\frac{A_{lp}}{A_{sp}} = \frac{r_{sp}^2}{r_{lp}^2} \cdot \left(\frac{\text{large-pore intercept}}{\text{small-pore intercept}}\right) \tag{17}$$

$$\frac{N_{lp}}{N_{sp}} = \left(\frac{A_{lp}}{A_{sp}}\right)\left(\frac{r_{sp}^2}{r_{lp}^2}\right) \tag{18}$$

From the intercepts and pore radii in Figure 8, A_{lp}/A_{sp} was calculated to be 1:27 and N_{lp}/N_{sp} to be 1:438. Therefore the pore-stripping approach fits the model-data extremely well and the slight error involved in the computation presumably results from the difficulty in fitting the vertical curves generated for small pores.

A plot of $1 - \sigma_d$ versus radius requires that σ_d be known. If σ is estimated by Equation 10, then the pore sizes and the numbers are in error. Since the contribution of solute movement through large and small pores is affected by the total fluid movement across the membrane, it is imperative that an estimate of pore size and distribution be made only when the

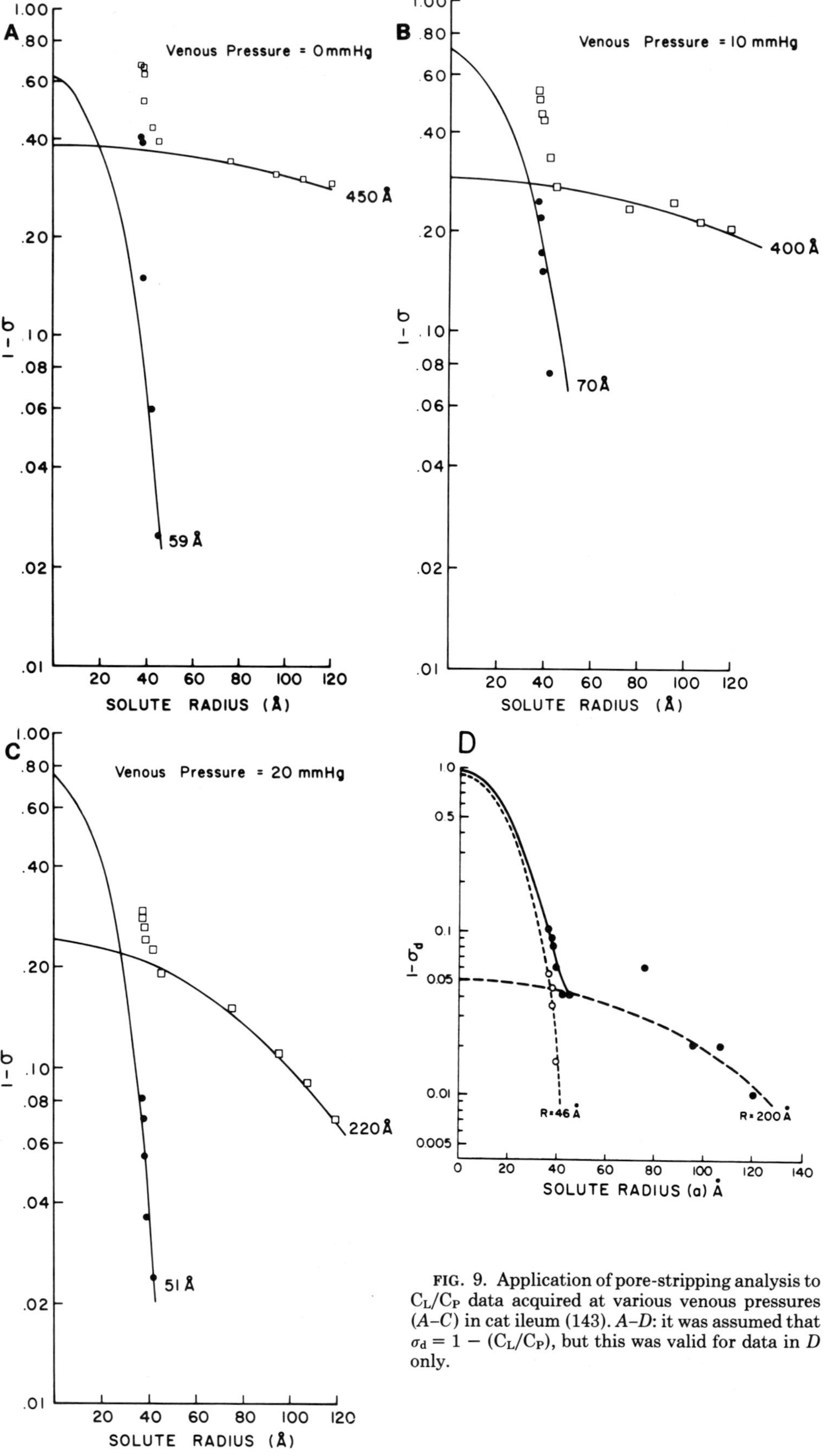

FIG. 9. Application of pore-stripping analysis to C_L/C_P data acquired at various venous pressures (*A–C*) in cat ileum (143). *A–D*: it was assumed that $\sigma_d = 1 - (C_L/C_P)$, but this was valid for data in *D* only.

solute concentration in lymph becomes filtration rate independent. Figure 9*A–D* depicts estimated values for $1 - \sigma$ as a function of molecular radius at different lymph flows corresponding to venous pressures of 0, 10, 20, and 30 mmHg in the cat ileum (143). From Figure 9 it is evident that the size and number of pores predicted by the pore-stripping analysis is heavily influenced by the lymph flow at which the sieving data are acquired. Although different pore sizes and numbers are predicted for the various conditions, only the data in *D* can be appropriately applied to this analysis, since filtration rate independence was attained for all solutes only in this instance.

In this chapter the pore-stripping analysis of Renkin et al. (313) has been applied to the data in the literature. In spite of its limitations this pore analysis is simple, straightforward, and surprisingly consistent from organ to organ.

REGIONAL DIFFERENCES IN CAPILLARY PERMEABILITY

Continuous Capillary Beds

Capillaries with continuous endothelia and an uninterrupted basement membrane are the most widely distributed in mammalian tissues. The ultrastructural appearance of these capillaries has generally led physiologists to assume that they offer more restriction to solute movement than other capillary types, and their permeability characteristics have thus received far more attention. In this section a summary is provided of the available information regarding macromolecule permeability of the following tissues possessing continuous capillaries: subcutaneous tissue, lung, skeletal muscle, myocardium, nervous tissue, and adipose tissue. Since most of this information was derived from lymphatic protein analyses, particular emphasis is placed on lymph data.

SUBCUTANEOUS TISSUE. The dynamics of macromolecule transport across continuous capillaries of subcutaneous tissue has been extensively analyzed. In general most of the information regarding capillary permeability in subcutis was derived either from forepaw or hindpaw preparations. This tissue is unique in that it offers a considerable amount of data on interstitial fluid and lymph protein concentrations. In fact this is the only tissue where the general assumption that protein composition in lymph equals that in the interstitium has been validated. The protein content of simultaneously acquired lymph and interstitial fluid samples has been determined in subcutaneous tissue of rabbits by using micropuncture techniques (327). These studies indicate that the protein concentration of the interstitium and the initial and collecting lymphatics are not significantly different from each other. Results derived by more indirect approaches generally agree with these observations (304, 366).

Table 1 summarizes the available data on the solute concentration ratio of lymph or interstitial fluid to plasma in subcutaneous tissue of several mammalian species. Although there is some variability in C_L/C_P for total proteins between species and among different laboratories, it is clear that the normal values for C_L/C_P in subcutis are significantly lower than those observed in other tissues. In spite of the relatively low C_L/C_P values, there is evidence for selective restriction

TABLE 1. *Solute Concentration Ratios of Lymph to Plasma in Subcutaneous Tissue*

	Stokes-Einstein Radius, Å	C_L/C_P	Ref.
*Human**			
Albumin	37	0.63†	289
IgG	56	0.51†	289
Dog‡			
Total proteins		0.28	181
α-Globulin	30	0.39	78
Albumin	37	0.23–0.38	34, 78, 126, 390
Transferrin	43	0.44	78
Haptoglobin	46	0.27	78
IgG	56	0.17–0.28	34, 78
Dextran 110	72	0.13	78
Fibrinogen	100	0.05–0.16	34, 78, 390
Dextran	21.5	0.40	126
	23.3	0.56	
	30	0.47	
	32	0.21	
	49	0.08	
	61.5	0.10	
	71.5	0.07	
	82.5	0.04	
	104	0.07	
	130	0.05	
Dextran	20	1.00	17
	26.4	0.50	
	35	0.23	
	38	0.15	
	50	0.06	
	54	0.05	
	60	0.03	
*Rabbit**			
Total proteins		0.32–0.38†	91, 155
Albumin	37	0.36†	155
Total globulins		0.24†	155
Acid phosphatase	100,000§	0.28	91
β-Glucuronidase	200,000§	0.08	27
FITC-dextran	10.1	1.0 †	327
	16.3	0.98†	
	20.5	0.78†	
	26.4	0.56†	
	31.5	0.36†	
	43	0.16†	
	56	0.11†	
	85	0.12†	
*Rat**			
Total proteins		0.49–0.56†	22, 114
Albumin	37	0.62†	22

FITC, fluorescein isocyanate. * Data from wick fluid. † Ratio of concentrations in interstitial fluid to plasma. ‡ Data from hindpaw lymph. § Molecular weight.

of macromolecules at the capillary wall on the basis of solute size. Figure 10 illustrates the relationship between C_L/C_P (or ratio of interstitial fluid to plasma) for long-chain polymer molecules and solute radius in the paw of dog and rabbit (17, 126, 327). The data show no clear delineation between species and no distinction in the ratios derived from lymph or interstitial fluid. As a whole the data show a rapid decline in C_L/C_P for solute radii below 40 Å. Above 40 Å, C_L/C_P remains virtually constant up to a solute radius of 130 Å. The steep fall in C_L/C_P below a 40-Å radius suggests that the small-pore size approximates this dimension. The constant residual permeability up to a 130-Å radius can be attributed to either large pores (>130 Å) or vesicular exchange.

Garlick and Renkin (126, 310) predicted, from the relationship between the permeability–surface area product (calculated by assuming that convective transport is negligible) and the effective molecular radius, that macromolecular transport across capillaries in the dog paw could be explained by both small pores 40 Å in radius and by vesicular exchange. Whereas the experimental data for molecules greater than 40 Å were equally consistent with those for large pores with 800-Å radii, the existence of large pores of this magnitude was dismissed because a "grossly disproportionate fraction of ultrafiltration" (126, 310) would have to occur through these pores.

Rutili and Hagander (329) have recently described a model that explains the sieving of dextran molecules of various sizes at a normal filtration rate in rabbit subcutaneous tissue. According to their pore model, the sieving data were consistent with two populations of pores in the capillary membrane—one with 48.5-Å radii and the other with radii >800 Å. Although this model is essentially identical to that dismissed by Garlick and Renkin (126) in favor of vesicular exchange, there is one difference between these pore models: the basic assumption regarding the mechanism of macromolecular transport, i.e., diffusion or convection. Garlick and Renkin's analysis was based on the premise that the concentration gradient within a pore is linear and independent of filtration rate—a condition biased toward diffusive transport (and vesicular exchange). Alternatively Rutili and Hagander (329) assumed that macromolecule transport through large pores is entirely convective, thereby negating the role of bidirectional vesicular transport.

Figure 11 illustrates the relationship between C_L/C_P for albumin and lymph flow in the dog paw. Although C_L/C_P varies inversely with lymph flow, it appears that sufficiently high filtration rates were not achieved in order for C_L/C_P (for albumin and larger molecules) to become filtration rate independent (126, 183, 310). This precludes a precise estimation of σ_d by using $1 - (C_L/C_P)$. It is possible, however, to determine a minimal value for σ_d from maximal washdown values

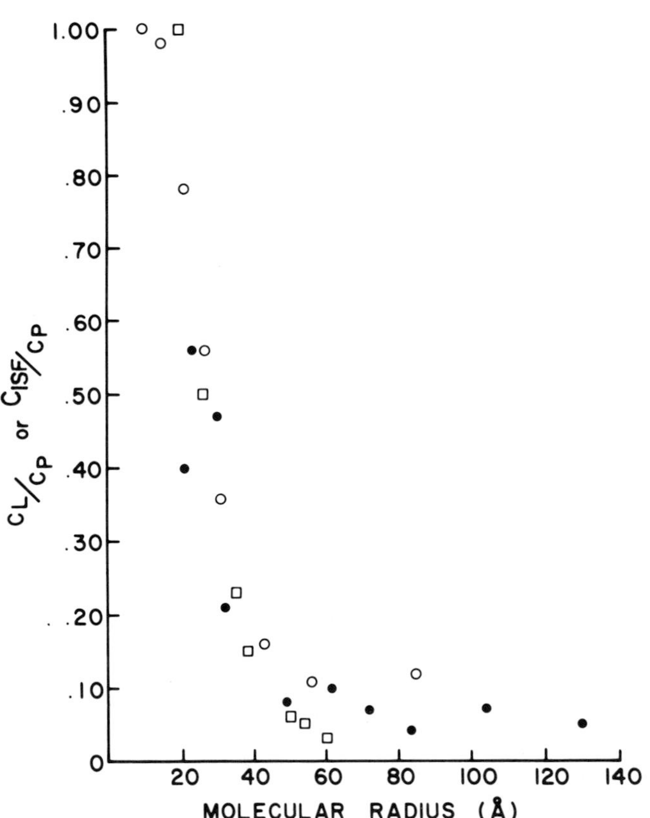

FIG. 10. Steady-state relationship between C_L/C_P or ratio of concentrations in interstitial fluid to plasma (C_{ISF}/C_P) and molecular radius in subcutaneous tissue (17, 126, 327). ● and □, From dog paw lymph; ○, from rabbit interstitial fluid.

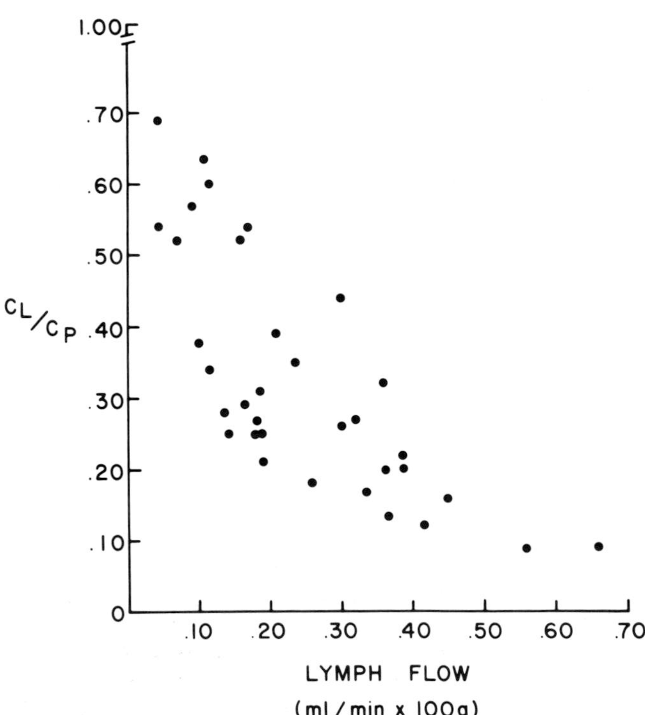

FIG. 11. Relationship between C_L/C_P for albumin and lymph flow in dog paw (126, 183, 310).

of C_L/C_P. From Figure 11 and from the work of Rutili, Granger, Taylor, and co-workers (328), it is evident that σ_d for albumin is at least 0.90. Using C_L/C_P values acquired at high venous pressures, one would predict minimal σ_d values for total plasma proteins of 0.93 and 0.87 in dog (84, 328) and rat (115) subcutaneous tissues, respectively. The inability to achieve a C_L/C_P value for subcutaneous tissue that is filtration rate independent may reflect either a disproportionately large capillary surface area relative to filtration rate or a tendency for subcutis capillaries to leak when venous pressure is elevated. The latter possibility is supported by observations of high permeabilities and diminished sieving at high lymph flows (183) and venous pressures (312) in some studies.

Studies have also been undertaken to evaluate the relative roles of convection and diffusion in macromolecular transport across capillaries in the dog paw (312, 313). From values of lymph flow and C_L/C_P, reflection coefficients and permeability–surface area products were calculated from Equations 10 and 11 (see TECHNIQUES AND THEORETICAL BACKGROUND, p. 467, for description of the Renkin method). With this approach σ values were obtained that ranged from 0.82 for albumin to 0.95 for dextran 110 (with radius of 71.5 Å). Little difference in σ was observed for solutes with effective radii between 35.5 and 56 Å. At control capillary filtration rates, convection accounted for 30% of the total flux of albumin into lymph. The relative contribution of convection to the total flux increased as the size of the molecule or lymph flow increased.

From the relation of σ to molecular size Renkin and his co-workers (313) were able to estimate the dimensions and relative hydraulic conductivity of transport pathways in capillaries of the dog paw. Figure 12 illustrates the relationship between $1 - \sigma$ and solute radius. The best fit of the data was derived by using pores of 280-Å radius. Unlike all other tissues analyzed with this approach the data for the paw do not predict a small-pore size comparable with that estimated from the relationship between C_L/C_P and solute radius (Fig. 10). The inability to predict a small-pore size from the paw data suggests either that the dimensions of the small pores in this tissue differ considerably from those of other tissues (i.e., they are less than 35 Å) or that the σ values acquired are significantly different from σ_d. The latter possibility seems likely, since the relationship between C_L/C_P for albumin and lymph flow (Fig. 11) suggests that σ_d for albumin is at least 0.90 whereas the calculated σ value for albumin is 0.82. Although the use of σ (calculated from the Kedem-Katchalsky equation) may be appropriate in estimating convective and diffusive fluxes, this parameter cannot be used to estimate pore sizes unless it is equal to σ_d. The difficulties in interpreting sieving data relative to pore size are discussed in TECHNIQUES AND THEORETICAL BACKGROUND, p. 467. Recent studies by Perry, Granger, Taylor, and co-workers (283a) substantiate the contention that a small-pore population can be demonstrated in the paw when values of σ_d that are filtration rate independent are used. From the analysis of the relation between $1 - \sigma$ and molecular size (Fig. 12) Renkin et al. (313) also concluded that 81.5% of the volume flow across capillaries must be assigned to small pores or the endothelial cell membrane—pathways impermeable to molecules the size of albumin. Cytoplasmic vesicles were proposed as the structural equivalent of the 280-Å pore predicted by this analysis (307). The vesicles were considered to account for at least 75% of the total diffusive transport across the capillary membrane.

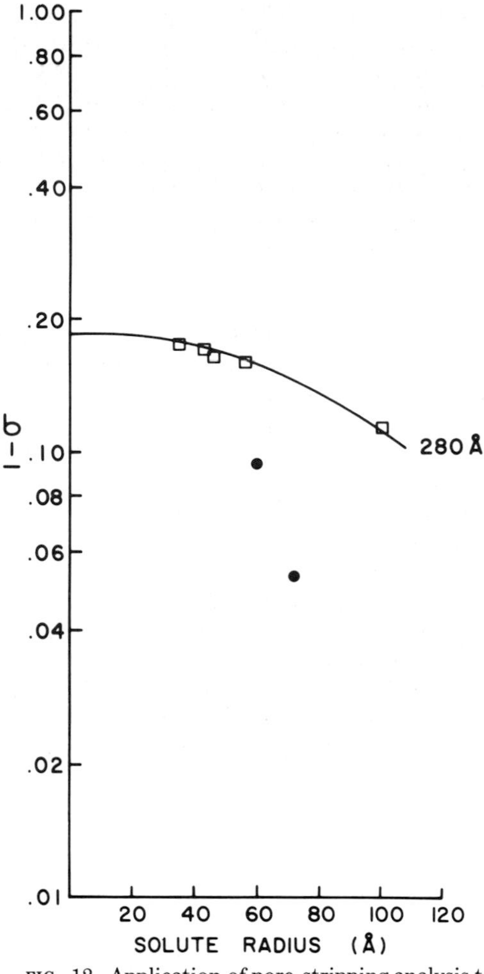

FIG. 12. Application of pore-stripping analysis to data for reflection coefficients for various solutes in dog paw. [Adapted from Renkin et al. (313).]

Many pharmacological and pathological conditions have been shown to alter the permeability and/or protein flux across the capillaries of the paw. Injections of histamine or bradykinin into dog paw increase lymph flow and C_L/C_P for macromolecules (78, 182, 305). Vasodilators (e.g., acetylcholine, papaverine), serotonin, and prostaglandins increase paw lymph flow yet do not alter or decrease C_L/C_P (78, 181, 182). The increased protein flux produced by the vasodilators and serotonin was considered to result from an increased exchange-vessel surface area and augmentation of fluid filtration (78, 181). Histamine and bradykinin, on the other hand, diminished the selectivity of the blood-lymph barrier with respect to solute size (see Fig. 13*A*). The changes in permeability produced by histamine and bradykinin were attributed entirely to an alteration of the pathway for large-molecule transport (308). Based on the responses of lymph flow and C_L/C_P to elevation of venous pressure during histamine treatment (lymph protein transport was unaffected by elevating venous pressure), it was concluded that this substance (and bradykinin) exerts its effect primarily via a pressure-insensitive mechanism, i.e., vesicular transport. However, a doubling of the internal radius of the vesicles (from 250 to 500 Å) and a 20-fold increase in their volume turnover were required to explain the macromolecular transport characteristics in the presence of histamine or bradykinin (308). Recent studies suggest that the effects of intra-arterial histamine on lymph protein transport are not sustained and that when this is taken into account, elevated venous pressure does enhance protein transport (145). Thus the mechanism by which histamine enhances transcapillary protein leakage remains controversial.

Studies on paw lymph have proven to be particularly useful for delineating the pathophysiological alterations produced at a burn wound. After thermal injury (scalding the paw for 10 s in water at 100°C) interstitial fluid volume, lymph flow, and C_L/C_P increase in the paw (17, 124). The changes in solute selectivity produced 1 h after scalding are depicted in Figure 13*B*. The reduction in selectivity produced by scalding persists up to 1 wk after the injury. Morphological correlations of the increased microvascular permeability demonstrate that fluorescein-labeled dextran (145,000 mol wt) extravasates primarily at the postcapillary venule after thermal injury of the hamster cheek pouch (17). Furthermore the number of endothelial vesicles remains constant and their diameters do not increase (in fact, the reverse occurs) after thermal injury. Histamine, prostaglandins, and other chemical mediators of inflammation are released in significant quantities after thermal injury (15, 16). Chemical mediation of the effects of thermal injury on capillary permeability is indicated by the apparent rise in lymph flow and microvascular permeability in nonburned tissue (17).

An experimental preparation that closely resembles the paw in composition (i.e., composed of skin and connective tissue) is the isolated rabbit ear. From this preparation Areekul (8–10) has acquired considerable data on macromolecule transport across continuous capillaries. The relationship between isogravimetric capillary pressure and plasma oncotic pressure predicts a value of 0.94 for the capillaries' osmotic reflection coefficient to total plasma proteins. The osmotic reflection coefficient for various dextran fractions increased with molecular radius such that σ_d for a 26-Å fraction was 0.45, while σ_d was 0.75 for 71.5-Å fractions. Removal of plasma proteins from the perfusate significantly reduced σ_d for each fraction. Addition of albumin (0.5 g/100 ml) to the perfusate returned the values for σ_d acquired with whole-plasma perfusate close to those for the control plasma perfusate. Dextran molecules substituted with sulfate groups (negatively charged) exhibited higher osmotic reflection coefficients than the corresponding neutral molecule, suggesting that permeation sites of these molecules are negatively charged.

LUNG. Lung lymph contains plasma proteins in concentrations that are approximately 75% of those in

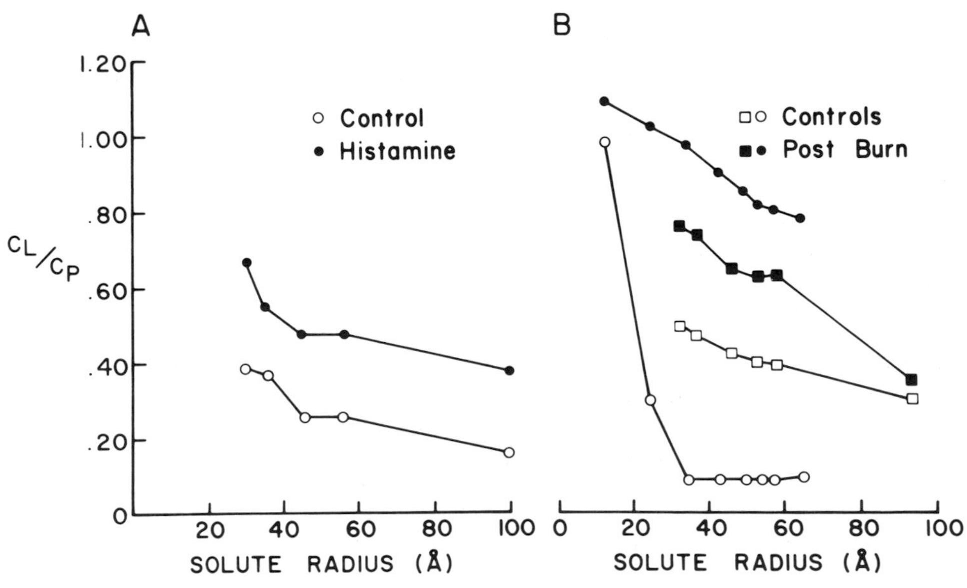

FIG. 13. Relationship between C_L/C_P for proteins and solute radius in dog paw after intravenous administration of histamine (*A*) and 1 h after scalding (*B*) [*A* adapted from Carter et al. (78); *B* adapted from Arturson (17) and Ganrot et al. (125).]

plasma. Considerable controversy presently exists as to which portion of the lung's microcirculation (alveolar, prealveolar, postalveolar, or bronchial) leaks the protein that finally exits the lung via the lymph. The alveolar vessels are of the continuous type.

Investigators have presented microscopic evidence that horseradish peroxidase (40,000 mol wt) does not escape across the capillary walls in the region of the alveoli (285), but it is readily measurable in lymph (235). Freeze-fracture studies (176, 333) also indicate that the endothelium is tight in the alveolar region. E. E. Schneeberger (unpublished observations) has recently completed a freeze-fracture study in which the postalveolar capillaries appear to have less organization in their junctional processes. This observation is consistent with a greater macromolecule permeability at these sites. The ultrastructural evidence, therefore, suggests that the major source of protein in lymph is probably not the alveolar vessels. The available physiological information concerning the leakage sites in the postalveolar (or venular) end of the pulmonary capillaries is scant; however, these studies do suggest that the major protein leak sites in the pulmonary circulation reside in postalveolar blood vessels (45, 174). Since this has been postulated in some capillary beds, it is probably safe to assume that the venular end of the microcirculation also leaks in the lung. The available data suggest that although lung lymph contains large amounts of protein, the exact site of leakage from the pulmonary circulation remains uncertain.

Three methods for studying protein transport in lung tissues have been employed: *1*) lymph protein fluxes, *2*) tissue accumulation of a tracer such as radioiodinated albumin, or *3*) external counting procedures at the chest wall to determine the leakage of radioactive proteins or macromolecules into the tissues. Because of the difficulties involved with interpreting the latter two methods in a quantitative fashion, the remainder of this section focuses on macromolecule data obtained by analysis of lymph protein fluxes. However, it must be emphasized that lung lymph cannot be readily collected in humans and so investigators must rely on monitoring of external tissue radioactivity to obtain such information about pulmonary capillary permeability (131, 290).

The use of lung lymph to assess vascular permeability has been opposed by several research groups. One major objection is that the most frequently cannulated lung lymphatics are postnodal. It is now well accepted that postnodal lymph differs from prenodal lymph with respect to protein content (190, 291). Most large collecting lymphatics contain lymph originating from different extrapulmonary tissues. Most notably the right thoracic duct often contains chylomicrons from the small intestine, which indicates how this lymphatic—commonly thought to drain the lung—contains fluid from distant sources (373). The lung also has a bronchial and pulmonary circulation that can contribute to the protein content of lymph (286, 362). Some investigators believe that lymph obtained from lung sources originates mainly from the highly permeable fenestrated capillaries of the bronchial circulation (286). However, it is now known that fenestrated capillaries are not necessarily leaky (see GASTROINTESTINAL ORGANS, p. 495) so this effect may not be of any great significance—particularly when one considers that the surface area of the bronchial circulation is extremely small. Many workers in the field contend that the protein content of interstitial fluid is modified as it traverses the interstitium and circulates within the lymphatic. Studies have indicated that the latter possibility does not appear to be a serious problem in pulmonary lymphatics (242, 386), but the former is an important concern because the lung interstitium is compartmentalized (alveolar, extraalveolar, perivascular, and peribronchial) (362, 392). This compartmentation could cause problems when one attempts to relate lymph to interstitial fluid, particularly under non-steady-state conditions (149, 263).

Several investigators have used the right duct–cannulation procedure for collecting lung lymph. However, the right duct in dogs is known to contain lymph derived from many sources—the heart, the chest wall, and the abdominal thoracic duct (229, 230, 385, 389, 409). Therefore any interpretation of protein fluxes with right duct lymphatics must be done with a great deal of caution, since lymph flow and composition can be influenced by nonpulmonary sources. A new method for cannulating lung lymphatics in the sheep has become very popular (349, 350). The technique consists of cannulating the caudal mediastinal lymph node. With this experimental model, lymph can be obtained from closed-chest, unanesthetized animals—clearly an improvement over the classic right duct–cannulation procedures. Recent studies (107) indicate that the lymph collected in this experimental model may at times contain extrapulmonary lymph.

Another method for collecting lung lymph involves cannulating a small prenodal lymphatic at the lung hilus (107, 261, 262). This procedure has been successful in both isolated and intact dog lung. It obviates several problems inherent in other procedures: *1*) the lymph does not pass through nodes, *2*) the possibility of extrapulmonary lymph contamination is reduced (certainly in the isolated lung), and *3*) the isolated lung studies are minimally influenced by leakage of proteins from the bronchial circulation.

Table 2 and Figure 14 show the lung C_L/C_P data for several endogenous proteins and povidone (polyvinylpyrrolidone, PVP). The capillaries in lung demonstrate selectivity, since in all cases C_L/C_P decreases with molecular size. The data in Figure 14 suggest that the differences between lymph collected in various animals are minimal. As molecular radius in-

TABLE 2. *Solute Concentration Ratios of Lymph to Plasma in Lung*

	Stokes-Einstein Radius, Å	C_L/C_P	Ref.
Sheep, adult			
Total protein		0.57–0.80	39, 43, 44, 49, 63, 64, 104, 113
Albumin	37	0.75–0.92	39, 43, 44, 50, 63, 64, 113
Globulins		0.45–0.61	
Fibrinogen	108	0.25	227
Low-density lipoprotein	120	0.25	227
Fractions			
I	35.5	0.77–0.80	
II	42.0	0.72–0.76	
III	45.0	0.67–0.72	
IV	48.0	0.69–0.74	63, 64
V	62.0	0.62–0.63	
VI	72.0	0.62–0.60	
VII	82.0	0.40–0.46	
VIII	96.0	0.42–0.40	
I	110	0.24	
II	54	0.45	50
III	37	0.68	
PVP			
A	110	0.20	
B	89	0.25	
C	75	0.29	
D	58	0.43	
E	46	0.54	
F	38	0.63	50
G	34	0.68	
H	31	0.70	
I	25	0.80	
J	21	0.88	
K	17	1.0	
Sheep, mature fetus			
Fractions			
I	110	0.28	
II	54	0.51	50
III	37	0.77	
Albumin	37	0.76	2

	Stokes-Einstein Radius, Å	C_L/C_P	Ref.
Sheep, immature fetus			
Fractions			
I	110	0.29	
II	54	0.52	50
III	37	0.84	
Sheep, newborn			
Fractions			
I	110	0.21	
II	54	0.50	50
III	37	0.85	
Total protein		0.61	113
Albumin	37	0.77	113
Dog, right thoracic duct			
Adult			
Total protein		0.65–0.69	48, 370
Albumin	37.5	0.68–0.83	6, 48, 245, 246, 370, 411
Globulins		0.43–0.57	6, 245–247, 411
IgG	56	0.81	48
IgM	121	0.28	48
α_1-Antitrypsin	32.8	0.70	
Haptoglobin	46.0	0.63	370
α_2-Macroglobulin	93.5	0.44	
Puppy			
Total protein		0.60	
Albumin	37	0.75	48
IgG	56	0.43	
IgM	121	0.25	
Dog, lung lymphatic*			
Total protein		0.66	107, 262
Fractions			
I	37	0.85	
II	40	0.68	
III	44	0.61	262
IV	53	0.56	
V	100	0.31	
VI	120	0.29	

PVP, povidone (polyvinylpyrrolidone). * Represents prenodal lymph; all others are postnodal.

creases from 37 to 110 Å, C_L/C_P decreases from ~0.70 to 0.25. In addition these data demonstrate that the C_L/C_P decreases to ~0.4 at a molecular radius of 60 Å and thereafter decreases at a much slower rate as the radius of the molecule increases. This relationship is similar to that observed in most other tissues. However, the C_L/C_P data shown in Figure 14 and Table 2 were measured at normal lymph flows.

Figure 15 demonstrates the effect of increased lymph flow on the relationship between C_L/C_P and molecular radius (262). It is evident that C_L/C_P decreases irrespective of solute size when lymph flow is increased. Figure 16 illustrates the relationship between C_L/C_P for total proteins and lymph flow in the sheep lung (264). As observed in other tissues, C_L/C_P decreases as lung lymph flow is increased until high lymph flows are achieved, at which time C_L/C_P becomes filtration rate independent. From this relationship one would predict that $\sigma_d = 0.75$ for total proteins in sheep lung. Similar relationships have also been reported on dog lung for total protein ($\sigma_d = 0.66$) and for several endogenous protein fractions of known molecular radius (262).

Figure 17 is a plot of $1 - \sigma$ as a function of molecular radius from data obtained in dog lung (262). These lung data can be described with two sets of pores: a small-pore system with pores of 80-Å radius, which accounts for 81% of the hydraulic conductance, and a large-pore system with pores of 200-Å radius, providing 16% of the hydraulic conductance. No more than

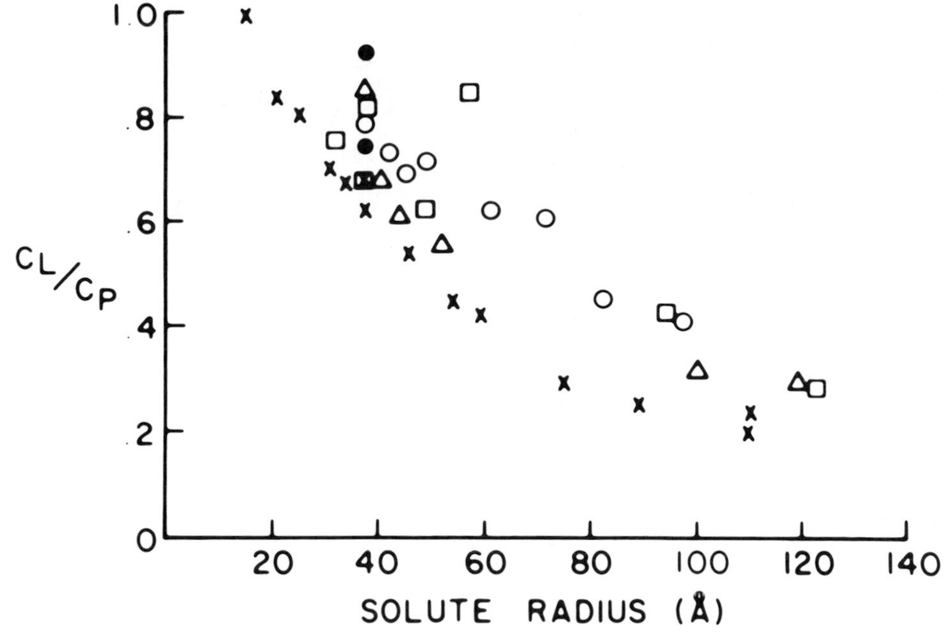

FIG. 14. Relationship between C_L/C_P for proteins and PVP (×) and solute radius in lungs of sheep and dog. ○, ×, and □, sheep data; △, dog data. [Data from Boyd et al. (50), Brigham and Owen (63, 64), Parker, Parker, Granger, and Taylor (262), and Taylor et al. (370).]

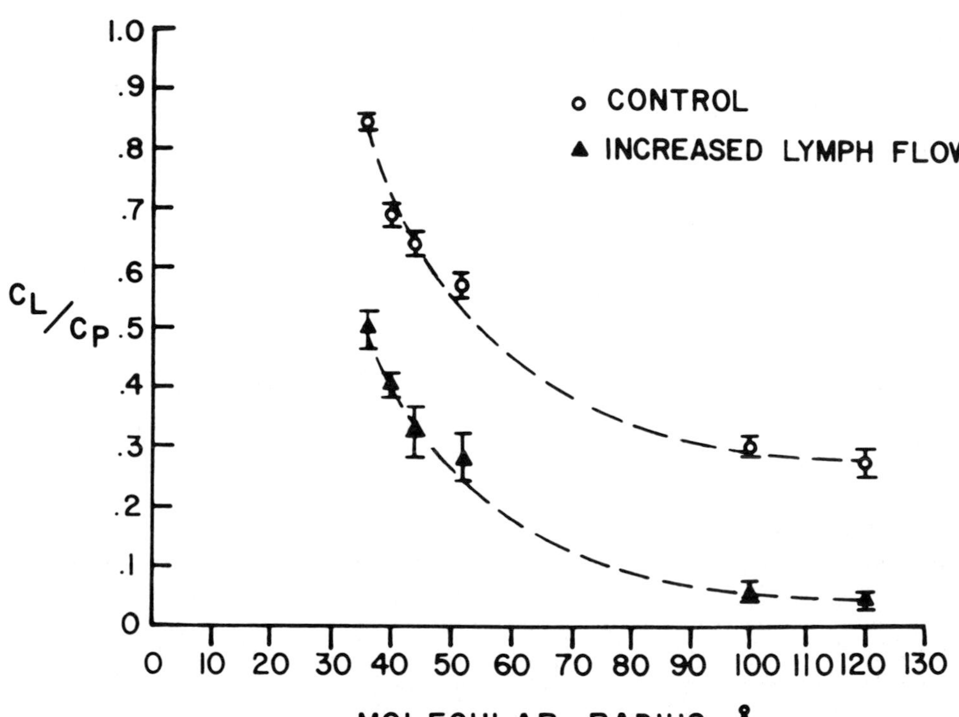

FIG. 15. Relationship between C_L/C_P for endogenous plasma proteins and molecular radius at different lymph flows. [Adapted from Parker, Parker, Granger, and Taylor (262).]

3% of the hydraulic conductance can be accounted for by pores smaller than 80 Å. Furthermore this analysis predicts values for A_{lp}/A_{sp} and N_{lp}/N_{sp} of 1:31 and 1:195, respectively. The PVP data shown in Figure 14 are also consistent with a small-pore population of about 80 Å and a large-pore system of 200-Å radius.

McNamee and Staub (227) recently analyzed several proteins in sheep lung lymph (albumin, globulin, β-lipoprotein, and fibrinogen). Although several "equivalent" three-pore models were constructed from their data, a two-pore model consisting of "pores" with radii of 60 and 228 Å (through which 73% and 27% of the filtration occurs, respectively) also describes the experimental results. Other models based on lung lymph data have been developed with populations of pores with radii of 20, 125, and 1,000 Å (41, 42, 62). The use of a large number of 20-Å pores necessitates the incorporation of an intermediate-sized pore in order to predict the observed protein fluxes. In reality the 20-Å pores simply dilute the capillary filtrate and

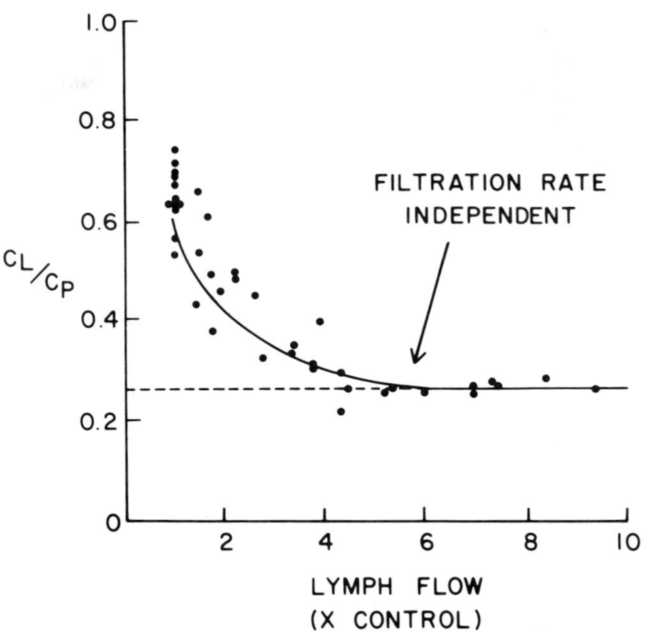

FIG. 16. Relationship between C_L/C_P for total proteins and lymph flow in sheep lungs. Assuming $\sigma_d = 1 - (C_L/C_P)$ when C_L/C_P is filtration rate independent, σ_d for total proteins is 0.75. [Adapted from Parker et al. (264).]

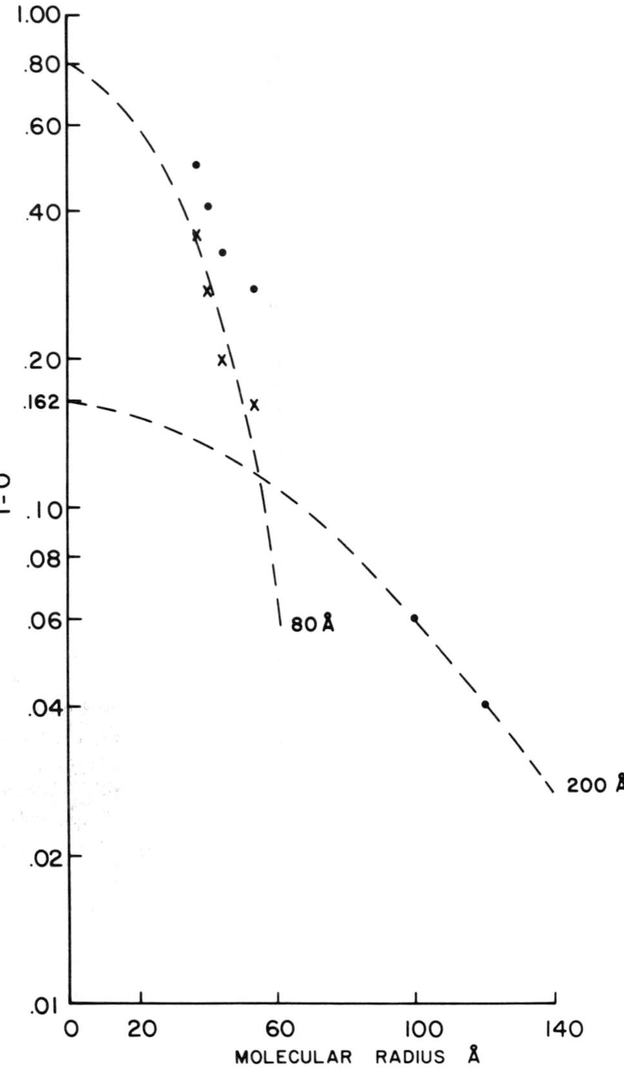

FIG. 17. Pore-stripping analysis for data of lymphatic protein flux in dog lung. [Adapted from Parker, Parker, Granger, and Taylor (262).]

do not alter the predicted pore size. As emphasized in *Theoretical Considerations,* p. 468, it is imperative that C_L/C_P be obtained at a state that is filtration independent in order to predict the true pore sizes of the membrane. In fact the three-pore models are no different from Boyd et al.'s (50) original two-pore model (120 Å plus a few large leaks) except that a large number of small pores allows the filtrate to be easily diluted. Yet all proteins are diluted to the same extent, so the same pore sizes result even though the σ_d for each molecule is larger in the three-pore model.

It appears from these data that either lung capillaries are more leaky than previously thought, based on physiological studies (148), or that increasing pressure in the pulmonary circulation causes opening of large leak sites. Since alveolar fluid contains high concentrations of plasma proteins (40%–50% of plasma) in hydrostatic edema (386, 387), Pietra et al. (285) and Shirley et al. (339) have proposed the concept of "stretched pores" to explain the phenomenon. However, a very simple model demonstrates that pore stretching is unlikely in the lung. If the radii of the smaller pores were stretched, the filtration coefficient would increase dramatically because of the large number of smaller pores. An increase of this magnitude in the pulmonary filtration coefficient has not been observed even in leaky lungs, which indicates that a few large holes may open to provide the high protein fluxes observed in edematous states.

Recent studies by Parker et al. (263) indicate that a steady-state C_L/C_P may not be achieved after elevation of left atrial pressure in most lung lymph studies. These investigators elevated left atrial pressure over several days and sampled lymph in the sheep. The value for C_L/C_P was much lower on successive days in spite of the fact that the left atrial pressures were fairly constant over this time. These findings suggest that sufficient time is not allowed for C_L/C_P to reach a steady state in most acute lung studies or that a chronically elevated left atrial pressure reduces pulmonary capillary permeability.

During the last 10 years lymph has been extensively used to estimate changes in pulmonary capillary permeability. Permeability estimates are generally based on the changes in C_L/C_P and lymph flow occurring after various interventions. If C_L/C_P remains unaltered or is increased and if lymph flow also increases, then this was believed to indicate an increased capillary permeability (351). This approach has been useful in investigating the effects of numerous substances on lung vascular permeability: histamine (61, 64), *Pseudomonas* (65, 70), serotonin (63), increased cerebrospinal fluid pressure (96, 218, 231, 284, 378), emboli (26, 219, 330), aspirin (49), clotting factors (39), endotoxin (64, 245), shock (6, 166, 247, 373, 411), and burns (104). In these studies C_L/C_P either increased, decreased slightly, or remained unaltered, while lymph flow increased. These changes were generally interpreted as representing an increased vascular permeability. However, when they are studied in greater detail, many of these conditions appear to increase capillary surface area (or increase the number of pores of all sizes per unit surface area) rather than alter capillary permeability (369).

Ideally the following procedure should be used to assess pulmonary capillary permeability from lymph data. First, control steady-state lymph flows and protein content should be measured at normal vascular pressures. Then, left atrial pressure should be elevated (~10–15 mmHg) and lymph flow and lymph proteins allowed to attain new steady states. Left atrial pressure should then be returned to control levels and the particular test imposed (e.g., histamine infusion). Left atrial pressure should again be elevated to the pretest level and the lymph protein concentration and lymph flow be allowed to attain a new steady state. By plotting C_L/C_P as a function of lymph flow it is relatively easy to qualitatively assess permeability changes because each animal serves as its own control. Figure 18 depicts the possible response of C_L/C_P versus lymph flow obtained with this experimental design. Line 1 represents the response of C_L/C_P and lymph flow to an increase in left atrial pressure only. If a substance is introduced into the system (and left atrial pressure is again elevated by the same increment—ideally to the same capillary pressure) and line 2 is the resulting relationship, then there can be little doubt that capillary permeability has risen. Line 3 could represent either an increased capillary permeability or an increased capillary surface area (since this lymph flow change could adequately be explained by capillary recruitment). Although line 4 may also be interpreted to represent either an increased capillary permeability or surface area, the latter possibility is rather unlikely because this would require a large change in capillary surface area. Thus it is obvious that any relationship between lines 1 and 2 is difficult to interpret with respect to capillary permeability, since changes in capillary surface area cannot be excluded. This analysis allows one to determine whether capillary permeability and surface area have remained unaltered by a particular perturbation because one would expect line 1 to be reproduced under such conditions.

Since studies of altered capillary permeability have not been performed in lungs when C_L/C_P is filtration rate independent, an analysis of changes in pore dimension is not possible without constructing very complex mathematical models. Studies in which all protein fractions are determined at a state of filtration rate independence are necessary to determine how various physiological and pharmacological compounds affect pulmonary capillary porosity. [For an example of how this approach can provide useful information, see data in ref. 329a obtained in the dog lung after damage from α-naphthylthiourea (ANTU).] Such an experimental protocol should be employed in the lung if quantitative information is to be generated in altered permeability states.

Estimates of permeability of pulmonary capillaries to albumin have also been acquired with the osmotic-transient approach. In saline-perfused rabbit lungs, σ_d for albumin was estimated to be 0.40 (388). Similar studies in plasma-perfused dog lungs indicate that σ_d = 0.60–0.72 for albumin (279, 365). The latter values for σ_d are consistent with an equivalent pore radius of 65–75 Å.

SKELETAL MUSCLE. Although skeletal muscle comprises the largest percentage of the total body mass, surprisingly little information is available regarding

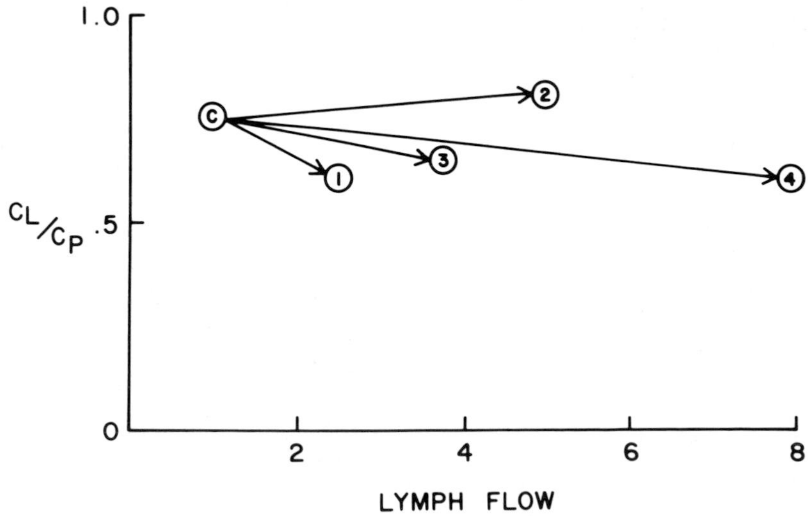

FIG. 18. Possible responses of C_L/C_P and lymph flow to venous pressure elevation alone (*line 1*) or in conjunction with some other intervention (*lines 2, 3, 4*). C, control values for C_L/C_P and lymph flow.

the permeability characteristics of capillaries in this tissue. Most of the available information was derived from studies of lymphatic protein flux. An inherent difficulty with interpreting the lymph data in this tissue is the frequent failure to acquire lymph that is uncontaminated by sources outside of muscle. Table 3 indicates that lymph presumed to be derived from muscle contains all the proteins present in plasma. The value for C_L/C_P decreases from 0.72 to 0.07 as the molecular radius increases from 37 Å (albumin) to 120 Å (IgM). Similar relationships between C_L/C_P and solute radius are observed with both PVP and dextran fractions (147). It is obvious from Table 3 that the C_L/C_P data have not been derived from a pure skeletal muscle preparation. The data from the human foot may reflect this problem, since there appears to be little or no selectivity between albumin and α-macroglobulin (299). Both the PVP studies and Grotte's classic dextran experiments do demonstrate selectivity (147). The PVP data were collected by Youlten (410) from a superfused rat cremaster muscle, and therefore the protein concentrations were much more dilute than lymph collected from such a preparation. Figure 19 represents a plot of all C_L/C_P data as a function of molecular radius for "skeletal muscle."

The PVP data are plotted in Figure 20 as a function of molecular radius. When pore-stripping analysis is applied to this set of data, small- and large-pore systems with radii of 67 and 220 Å are obtained. The ratios A_{lp}/A_{sp} and N_{lp}/N_{sp} are 1:361 and 1:3610, respectively. The value for pore number is about one-tenth the value calculated by Grotte (147) by using graded dextrans. The curves in Figure 20 cannot be used to actually calculate the relative hydraulic conductances of the two sets of pores because of superfusate dilution. However, it is relatively safe to assume that most of the hydraulic conductance can be attributed to the smaller pores, since the intercept is 36 times that of the corresponding large-pore system. Although C_L/C_P is quite low for the large molecules in

TABLE 3. *Solute Concentration Ratios of Lymph to Plasma in Skeletal Muscle*

	Stokes-Einstein Radius, Å	C_L/C_P	Ref.
Human leg			
Resting			
Total protein		0.55	255
Albumin	37	0.72	255
Exercise			
Total protein		0.25	254, 255
Albumin	37	0.27–0.33	254, 255
IgG	53.4	0.17	
IgA	56.8	0.16	254
IgM	121.0	0.07	
Human foot			
Total protein		0.25	
Prealbumin	32.5	0.36	
Albumin	37.0	0.29	
Unidentified		0.21	
First postalbumin		0.21	
Second and third postalbumin		0.28	
Fourth postalbumin		0.29	299
Transferrin	36.7	0.24	
Posttransferrin		0.26	
Slow globulins		0.23	
Haptoglobins	0.21	0.23	
Globulins		0.20	
α_2-Macroglobulin	93.5	0.20	
Dog forepaw			
Total protein		0.33–0.43	5, 146, 151, 296
Dog leg			
Albumin	37	0.28	
α_1-Antitrypsin	32.8	0.27	125
Haptoglobin	46.0	0.19	
α_2-Macroglobulin	93.5	0.17	

	Stokes-Einstein Radius, Å	C_L/C_P	Ref.
Dextran	<15	1.0	
	20	0.9	
	25	0.6	147
	30	0.43	
	35	0.25	
	≥50	0.18	
Cat calf muscles			
Albumin	37	0.1	7
Cat hindlimb			
Total protein		0.54	211
Lactate dehydrogenase	42	0.65	211
Rat hindlimb			
Total protein		0.52	
Albumin	37	0.37	23
Globulins		0.76	
Rat cremaster muscle			
PVP	<15	1.0	
	15–16	0.75	
	16–18	0.275	
	18–20	0.180	
	20–25	0.108	
	25–31	0.046	410
	31–40	0.019	
	37	0.010	
	40–51	0.009	
	51–66	0.005	
	66–90	0.002	
	>90	0.001	
Rabbit hindlimb			
Albumin	37	0.40–0.94	5, 76, 93
Low-density lipoproteins			
1	200	0.33	
2	400	0.18	93
3	700	0.07	
Globulins		0.50	93, 282

PVP, povidone (polyvinylpyrrolidone). Many of these data were not collected from skeletal muscle but rather represent samples from a mixed vascular bed of skin, muscle, and bone. For cremaster muscle, data may not represent a filtration-independent C_L/C_P, since a superfusion fluid was used to sample the tissues.

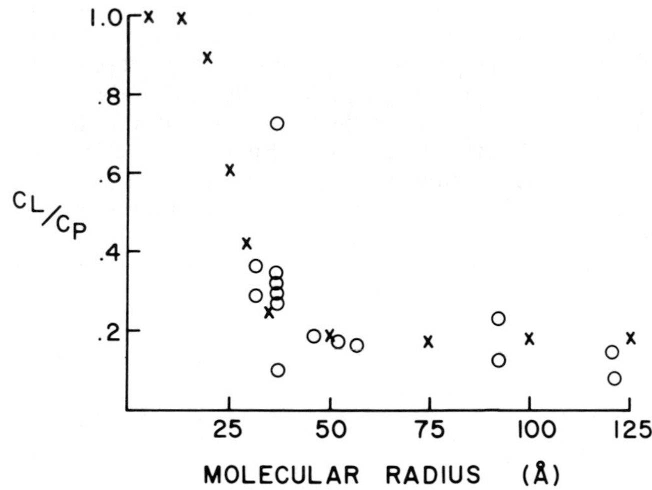

FIG. 19. Relationship between C_L/C_P for dextrans (○) and PVP fractions (X) and molecular radius in skeletal muscle. [Data from Courtice and Sabine (93), Ganrot et al. (125), Grotte (147), Olszewski and Engeset (254), and Youlten (410).]

Figure 20, the data were derived from a system that was probably not filtration independent, and the small- and large-pore systems may be smaller than predicted.

Table 3 incorporates a set of data that clearly indicates the behavior of C_L/C_P in skeletal muscle at enhanced capillary filtration rates. Human leg lymph was collected in both resting and exercise states (254, 255). Note that C_L/C_P for albumin decreased from 0.72 in the resting state to 0.25 during exercise. Although this washdown of lymph proteins may be attributed to the fact that lymph is derived from two different sources, a more likely explanation is that capillary filtration rate increases in working muscle and C_L/C_P approaches filtration rate independence.

The lymphatic protein-flux technique has provided considerable information regarding the effects of various pharmacological and pathological interventions on the permeability of muscle capillaries to macromolecules. Numerous studies indicate that histamine significantly increases lymphatic protein flux in dog forelimb and hindlimb preparations (25, 120, 145, 146, 151, 217, 221, 222, 226, 308). Although some investigators contend that histamine primarily affects capillary surface area (105), the dramatic rise in both lymph flow and C_L/C_P during histamine infusions clearly indicates an increase in macromolecule permeability (145). Of particular interest are observations that the histamine-induced protein efflux is prevented by β-adrenergic stimulation (146, 222). Local intra-arterial infusion of bradykinin also increases forelimb lymphatic protein flux. The bradykinin-induced increase in protein efflux is prevented by vasopressin and serotonin, an effect that appears to be independent of blood flow, vascular pressures, or perfused surface area (5, 146, 150, 197, 216, 296, 358). Ischemia lasting 2 h does not appear to affect the permeability

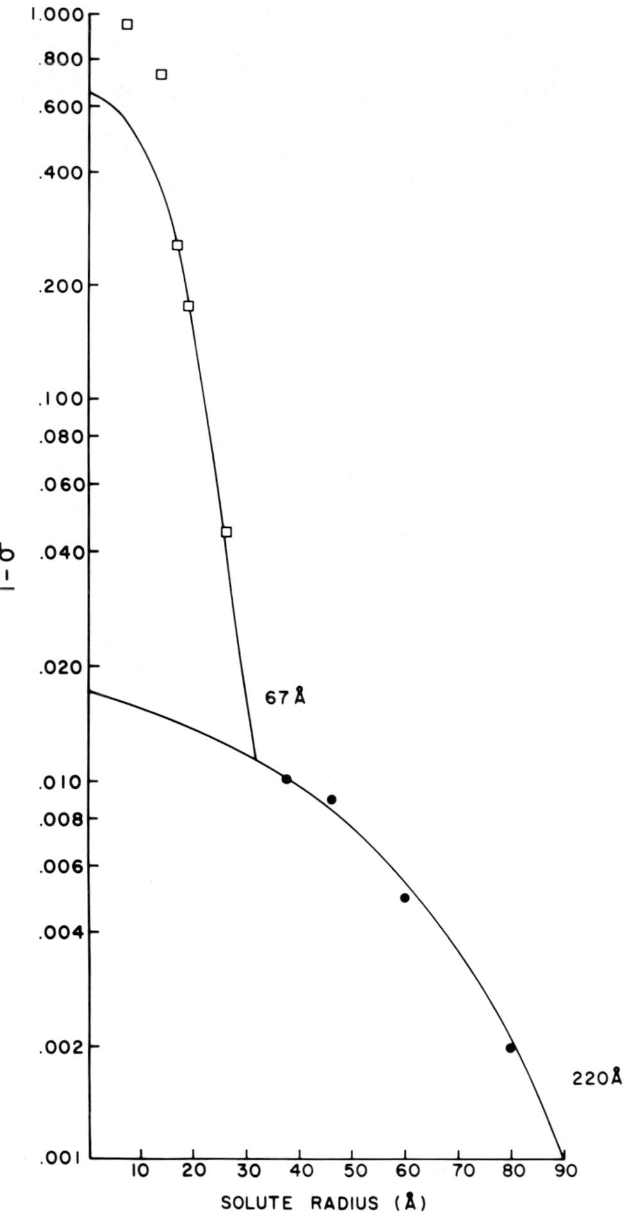

FIG. 20. Pore-stripping analysis for PVP sieving data in cremaster muscle. [Adapted from Youlten (410).]

of muscle capillaries to plasma proteins (226). Thermal injury (394), diabetes mellitus (3), increased venous pressure (122, 196), hypertension (32), and vibration stress (196) have also been shown to increase macromolecule permeability in skeletal muscle preparations.

Estimates of capillary permeability of skeletal muscle to macromolecules have also been acquired by the osmotic-transient approach and the initial clearance of radiolabeled albumin in isogravimetric preparations. The data acquired with the osmotic-transient approach suggest that the osmotic reflection coefficient for molecules the size of albumin is essentially one (105, 260). Application of the data for radiolabeled albumin clearance to the Kedem-Katchalsky formulations predicts $\sigma_d = 0.93$ for this solute (321). Since albumin clearance decreases during cooling of skeletal muscle in accordance with values predicted for fluid viscosity changes, it has been suggested that vesicular exchange does not contribute significantly to the transcapillary flux of albumin in this tissue (321).

ADIPOSE TISSUE. Estimates of macromolecule permeability of capillaries in adipose tissue are limited. Ballard and Perl (27) determined osmotic reflection coefficients of capillaries for various solutes in isolated, perfused canine adipose tissue by the osmotic-transient method. An osmotic reflection coefficient of 0.91 was acquired for the linear polymer Ficoll 70. According to current hydrodynamic formulations, this σ_d value is consistent with an equivalent pore radius of ~80 Å. Permeability estimates for other macromolecules are presently unavailable.

MYOCARDIUM. Relatively little attention has been given to the transport of macromolecules across the capillaries of the myocardium, in spite of the fact that this tissue has provided much of what is known about small-solute permeability in continuous capillaries (4, 160, 379, 380, 408). Most of the available information on permeability of myocardial capillaries to macromolecules is based on lymph protein studies. Under normal experimental conditions C_L/C_P for total proteins ranges between 0.58 and 0.90 in dog heart (118, 161, 199, 375, 376). Figure 21 depicts the relationship between C_L/C_P and molecular radius (for various dextran fractions and endogenous proteins) in dog myocardium at normal lymph flows (11, 12, 18, 199). The data indicate selective restriction of solutes at the capillary wall on the basis of molecular size. Arturson et al. (18, 21) have described the dextran C_L/C_P data for dog heart with small pores of radii 35–60 Å and an additional set of larger pores of radii 120–160 Å; they found N_{lp}/N_{sp} = 1:10,000. More reliable estimates of pore size require that C_L/C_P data be acquired at high capillary filtration rates so that pore-stripping analysis can be performed.

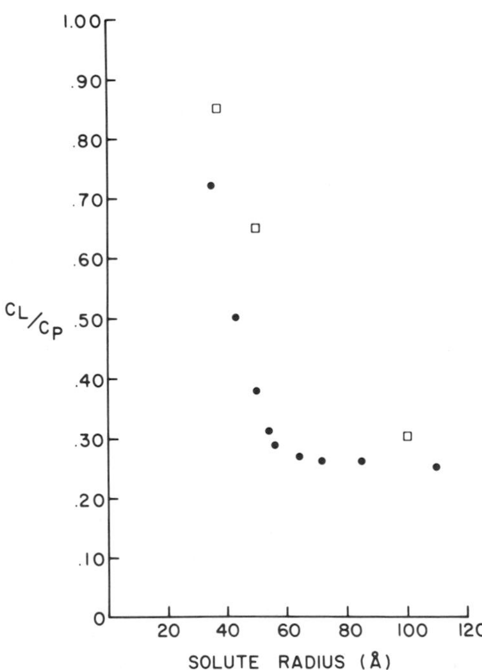

FIG. 21. Relationship between C_L/C_P for dextrans (●) and proteins (□) from dog myocardium. [Data from Arturson et al. (21) and Karnovsky (191).]

Elevation of coronary venous pressure results in a rise in myocardial lymph flow and a reduction in C_L/C_P for dextrans and plasma proteins (18, 21, 199, 375). The reduction in C_L/C_P is relatively small for a given increase in lymph flow as compared with that in other tissues. The inability to significantly reduce C_L/C_P at high lymph flows is similar to the situation in the lung and may result from the disproportionately large exchange-vessel surface area relative to capillary filtration rate. An alternative explanation is that capillary permeability rises when venous pressure is elevated via the stretched-pore effect. Arturson et al.'s (18, 21) observations support this possibility: the C_L/C_P for high-molecular-weight dextrans (>65,000) almost doubles at elevated coronary venous pressure in spite of a fivefold increase in lymph flow.

The major theme of most studies on cardiac lymph flow and protein composition concerns the effect of acute myocardial ischemia on capillary permeability (118, 161, 220, 361, 376). Experimental myocardial infarction in dogs generally produces a rise in lymph flow and C_L/C_P and a decrease in the lymph concentration ratio of albumin to globulin (118, 376). Calculated permeability–surface area products for total proteins also rise after ischemia even in experiments where lymph flow is reduced (161). There are no data available regarding changes in selectivity of myocardial capillaries to macromolecules of various size after an infarct. One of the inherent limitations of such a study and of the aforementioned C_L/C_P data is that cytoplasmic enzymes (such as lactate dehydrogenase, serum glutamic oxalacetic transaminase, and creatine kinase) enter the lymph via the interstitium in significant quantities after an infarct (118, 220, 361).

Estimates of myocardial capillary permeability to albumin have also been acquired with the osmotic-transient method (40). Independent determinations of osmotic conductance for bovine albumin and hydraulic conductance of capillaries in the rabbit heart perfused with Ringer's solution yield a σ_d value of 0.75 for albumin. According to current hydrodynamic formulations, this value is consistent with an equivalent pore radius of 65 Å. Recently a σ_d value of 0.86 for albumin was obtained in the same heart model (G. Blackshear, unpublished observations).

NERVOUS SYSTEM. It is well known that the blood-brain barrier is extremely impermeable to macromolecules. Horseradish peroxidase, a protein that crosses the capillary walls in skeletal muscle within minutes, is confined within the lumen of capillaries in the parenchyma of the brain. The main barriers preventing the penetration of proteins through the walls of cerebral blood vessels are the tight junctions (zonulae occludens) between the vascular endothelial cells. Furthermore cerebrovascular endothelial cells exhibit little or no pinocytotic activity to suggest transcellular macromolecule exchange (68, 189, 292, 298). Although the blood-brain barrier is not penetrated by macromolecules under normal experimental conditions, transcapillary leakage does occur under various experimentally induced pathological conditions. These include intra-arterial administration of metabolic poisons (68, 179) and hyperosmotic solutions (69, 293), thermal injury (31, 103), arterial hypertension (153, 154, 156, 249), air or fat embolization (68), hypovolemia (167), and traumatic injury (68). Total occlusion of the arterial blood supply to the brain for 1–48 h does not appear to alter the integrity of the blood-brain barrier; however, macromolecule extravasation is observed after reperfusion (168, 169, 252). Free radicals are believed to cause the damage to the blood-brain barrier at reperfusion (77). It is generally considered that the route of protein leakage under pathological conditions is between endothelial cells or across severely damaged cells rather than by enhanced pinocytotic transport (68, 292).

Certain regions of the brain, such as the choroid plexus, median eminence, and area postrema, are considered to lie outside the blood-brain barrier. The capillaries in these regions are fenestrated and the endothelia are connected by gap junctions. Pinocytotic transport also occurs within the endothelia of these capillaries (70). Protein tracers such as horseradish peroxidase readily diffuse out of the choroid plexus and gain access to the cerebrospinal fluid (CSF) (292). However, prior to entering the CSF, macromolecules must cross the choroidal epithelial membrane. Ultrastructural evidence suggests that the epithelial layer (not the capillaries) is the rate-limiting barrier for movement of macromolecules (67) from blood to CSF. Proteins are therefore believed to find their way into CSF via leaks within the epithelia membrane and by vesicular transport.

Cerebrospinal fluid undergoes several modifications on its way from the ventricles to the arachnoid villi. Nevertheless one can expect the relative concentration of macromolecules in CSF to provide an indication of whether the endothelial-epithelial barrier in the choroid plexus selectively restricts solutes on the basis of size. Although the total protein concentration in CSF normally ranges between 15 and 65 mg/100 ml (335), a significant inverse relationship exists between the steady-state concentration ratio of CSF to plasma and the hydrodynamic radius of plasma proteins (117). Table 4 summarizes the available information on CSF-to-plasma ratios for various endogenous proteins in humans (117). The proteins in CSF are derived solely from blood except for prealbumin and transferrin, which are synthesized by the central nervous system (335).

TABLE 4. *Endogenous Human Protein Concentration Ratios of CSF to Serum*

	Hydrodynamic Radius, Å	C_{CSF}, mg/liter	C_{CSF}/C_{serum}, $\times 10^4$
Prealbumin	32.5	17.3	0.62–0.72
α_1-Antitrypsin	32.8	17.3	0.0439
α_1-Antichymotrypsin	34.2		0.0463
Hemopexin	35.0		0.0380
Albumin	35.8	155	0.0422
α_2-HS-glycoprotein	36.0	1.7	0.0355
Transferrin	36.7	14.4	0.0704
Acid α_1-glycoprotein	38.5	3.6	0.0541
Profibrinolysin	42.7	0.25	0.0161
Ceruloplasmin	46.8	0.97	0.0265
IgG	53.4	12.3	0.0125
IgA	56.8	1.3	0.0074
α_2-Macroglobulin	93.5	2.0	0.0090
Fibrinogen	108.5	0.65	0.0022
IgM	121.0	0.60	0.0086
β-Lipoprotein	124.0	0.59	0.0016

CSF, cerebrospinal fluid. [Data from Felgenhauer (117).]

Felgenhauer (117) compared the sieving coefficients of CSF to those derived from other tissues. He concluded that plasma proteins enter the CSF through pores 200 Å in radius. Furthermore he proposed that the basement membrane of the fenestrated capillaries in the choroid plexus is the site at which these pores reside. Rapoport and Pettigrew (294) recently criticized Felgenhauer's hypothesis for its disregard of the ultrastructural evidence that the epithelial cell layer is the restrictive barrier for movement of proteins from blood to CSF. Using Felgenhauer's data, they developed a model that allows a more quantitative interpretation of CSF-to-plasma ratios in terms of current theories of restricted diffusion and ultrafiltration through aqueous channels. Basic assumptions inherent in the model are that the blood-CSF barrier consists of two membranes (capillary and epithelial layer) in series and that the epithelial layer is the rate-limiting restrictive barrier. The model predictions suggest that the protein concentration ratio of CSF to blood can be explained by a mechanism consisting of two pathways—a set of 117-Å pores and pinocytotic vesicles.

To compare the sieving coefficient data for CSF with that for lymph in other tissues, the protein ratios of CSF to plasma were subjected to pore-stripping analysis. Figure 22 illustrates the relationship between these ratios and the solute radius. From this analysis the radii of small and large pores at the blood-CSF barrier were predicted to be 70 and 180 Å, respectively. This analysis also predicts values for A_{lp}/A_{sp} and N_{lp}/N_{sp} of 1:52 and 1:345, respectively. The most

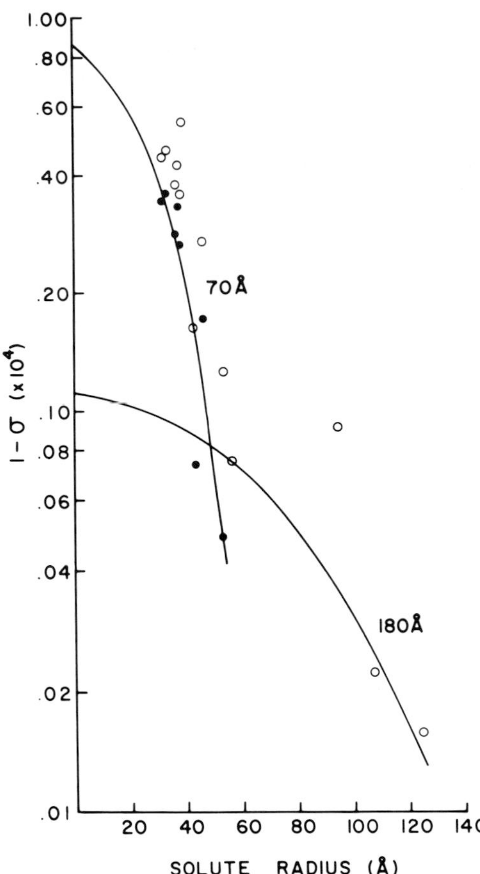

FIG. 22. Pore-stripping analysis based on CSF-to-blood ratios of various solutes for choroid plexus in humans. Note that percentage of total conductance for each set of pores is × 10^4. [Data from Felgenhauer (117).]

striking feature of this analysis is the similarity in pore sizes predicted for the blood-CSF barrier and other tissues (e.g., lung and skeletal muscle). While similarity in pore sizes does not prove a priori that the capillary membrane is the limiting barrier for protein leakage into the CSF, it does indicate that it may be more important than the ultrastructural data suggested.

Vascular permeability in the peripheral nervous system has been studied in several species with fluorescein-labeled albumin and γ-globulins, and horseradish peroxidase. Unlike in the blood-brain barrier, there is significant leakage of proteins across capillaries supplying the peripheral nerves and ganglia. This presumably results from the fact that the capillaries perfusing some of these structures are of the fenestrated type. However, there appear to be phylogenetic variations with respect to vascular permeability in the endoneural vessels (250, 251, 253, 393).

INTRAVITAL MICROSCOPY STUDIES. Because of the inherent limitations in whole-organ studies of capillary permeability, there has been a renewed interest during the past decade to develop methods for investigating macromolecular transport across individual microvessels. Vital microscopic techniques have been used to study capillary permeability in a wide variety of transparent tissues, particularly mesentery and hamster cheek pouch. The use of protein- or dextran-bound, light-absorbing dyes and fluorescent compounds allows for direct visualization of macromolecule extravasation and correlation to vessel structure. In addition modifications of Landis and Pappenheimer's (203) original occlusion method have allowed osmotic reflection coefficients for various macromolecules to be estimated in single perfused capillaries.

Much attention has been given to the concept of Rous et al. (324) and others (177, 202, 324) that the large-pore system is located exclusively at the venous end of the capillary and that there is a "gradient of permeability along the capillaries" (177, 324). Landis (202) originally observed localized regions of high permeability to Evans blue–albumin at the venous end of individually perfused capillaries of the frog mesentery. Levick and Michel (209) repeated Landis's studies and found no observable extravasation of Evans blue–albumin across the true capillaries, yet a measurable permeability to free Evans blue was noted. These authors concluded that Landis's experimental procedure did not ensure complete conjugation of Evans blue and albumin and that he was actually observing the movement of unconjugated dye. Studies by other investigators, however, tend to support the contention that the large pores (or a high concentration of small pores) are mostly localized at the venous capillaries or venules. Hauck (162, 163) and Hauck and Schróer (164), working with warm-blooded animals, reported that fluorescent dyes not bound to plasma proteins leak along the entire length of mesenteric capillaries, while extravascular penetration of protein-bound fluorescent dyes was restricted to the venous side of the capillary bed. The more recent studies by Nakamura and Wayland (240) and others (14, 357) are in agreement with Hauck's results. Of particular interest are the observations that *1)* the leakage of fluorescein isocyanate (FITC)–dextran becomes somewhat restricted to the venular segment of the capillary when the effective molecular radius of the tracer exceeds 30 Å, and *2)* even FITC-dextrans with molecular weights as large as 393,000 are seen in the perivascular space of the microvessels (240).

Although the existence of large pores on the venular end of capillaries under normal physiological conditions remains controversial, there is substantial evidence to indicate that large interendothelial gaps (large pores) formed at the venular level account for the vascular leakage of tracer macromolecules in response to various pharmacological interventions. Intravital microscopic observations of the extravasation of Evans blue–albumin and vascular labeling with colloidal carbon particles suggest that estrogens, progesterone, histamine, serotonin, bradykinin, angiotensin, and other vasoactive substances increase vascular permeability of microvessels in the mesentery of warm-blooded animals and in the hamster cheek pouch (54, 74, 127, 187, 213, 244, 334). The microvessels in the mesentery of cold-blooded animals (frogs) are not responsive to most substances studied—except urethan and compound 48/80 (309). A recurring theme in virtually all studies is that vascular leakage of macromolecules most frequently occurs at the venular end of the capillary. While these studies provide definitive data regarding the location along the vasculature where leakage occurs, i.e., the venules, the resolution afforded by Evans blue–albumin extravasation and colloidal carbon labeling does not allow differentiation to be made between large gap formation and increased numbers of small pores. Although vesicular labeling with colloidal carbon particles is generally considered to occur only in abnormal states, there is some evidence that the particles are taken up by normal microvessels and ultimately interfere with normal microvascular function (54).

Intravital microscopic studies employing fluorescein-labeled macromolecules in conjunction with electron microscopy have provided data of a more definitive nature regarding interendothelial gap formation in venules. Intravital microscopic observations of the extravasation of intravenously injected fluorescein-labeled dextrans (or albumin) in the hamster cheek pouch (13, 37, 172, 184, 214, 355, 356, 359) and rat mesentery (121) indicate that chemical mediators of inflammation (bradykinin, histamine, and prostaglandins) reversibly enhance macromolecular leakage at the level of the postcapillary venule (see Fig. 23). Electron-microscope sections of vessels exhibiting extravasation of fluorescent tracers in vivo reveal gaps between endothelial cells ranging in size from 0.1 to 1.0 μm (121, 172). The minimum diameter of the postcapillary venules where gaps occur is 8.6 μm and the maximum diameter is 14.0 μm (356). The fact that β-stimulants inhibit the permeability effects of the inflammatory mediators, without influencing their vasodilator action (and intravascular pressure effects), suggests that the contraction and subsequent separation of endothelial cells are receptor mediated (14, 359). The physiological implications of these studies is that endothelial cells of the postcapillary venules may behave as a functional unit that can selectively respond to changes in the composition of its external environment (14). Whether the preparations per se inherently predispose the venules to these responses remains to be determined. Clearly steps taken to minimize trauma and the release of vasoactive agents reduce the frequency of macromolecule leakage at the venules (357).

There is also information of a more quantitative nature on the permeability of mesenteric capillaries to macromolecules. Michel (232, 233) recently estimated the osmotic reflection coefficient for albumin and myoglobin in single frog mesenteric capillaries. He found σ_d for myoglobin to be 0.35 and σ_d for serum albumin to be 0.82. According to current hydrodynamic theories, these σ_d values are consistent with cylindrical pores of 55–60 Å. In some capillaries both L_p and σ_d for albumin were measured. Although there was an approximate tenfold variability in L_p, σ_d remained remarkably constant between capillaries, suggesting that pore number is more variable than pore size among different capillaries.

Fenestrated Capillary Beds

Capillaries with fenestrated endothelia and a continuous basement membrane are usually found in organs whose functions demand high rates of fluid exchange, i.e., kidney, small intestine, and salivary glands. The structural and physiological aspects of macromolecule permeability of the fenestrated capillaries in kidney and intestine have been analyzed in a more quantitative fashion than capillaries in all other tissues. Furthermore these organs have provided much of the theoretical and experimental framework for the current concepts of transcapillary solute exchange. This section presents a summary of the available information regarding permeability in the following organs possessing fenestrated capillaries: kidney (glo-

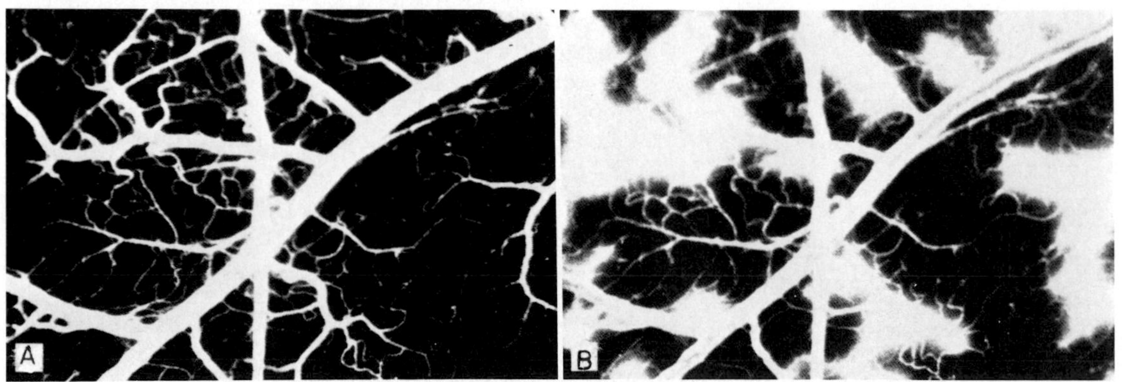

FIG. 23. Micrographs of hamster cheek pouch vasculature prior to (*A*) and after (*B*) application of bradykinin. Note extravasation of fluorescein isocyanate–dextran after bradykinin application. [From Arfors et al. (14).]

merular and peritubular), small intestine, stomach, and colon.

KIDNEY. *Glomerular capillaries.* The capillaries of the renal glomerulus are structurally unique. They differ from other capillaries in several respects, the most important of which are the considerably thicker basement membranes and the presence of an epithelial layer consisting of interdigitating foot processes. One or both of these layers and the endothelium (by virtue of its surrounding negative charge density) are generally considered to be the limiting restrictive barriers to the movement of macromolecules from blood to the Bowman's space. A detailed description of the structural basis of glomerular permeability is provided in several recent reviews (116, 191, 205, 316, 381).

Physiological estimates of glomerular capillary permselectivity have been derived largely from studies of differential solute clearance in which the urinary excretion of some test macromolecule (e.g., dextran, PVP) is compared with that of a reference solute, such as inulin. If both the test and reference solutes are neither secreted nor reabsorbed, the fractional clearance is equivalent to the concentration of the macromolecule (test solute) in Bowman's space relative to that in plasma water; this is the sieving coefficient (55, 56, 100). Figure 24 illustrates the effect of molecular size on the fractional clearance of neutral dextrans in the rat kidney under control conditions and after plasma volume expansion (83). The results indicate that the clearance of dextrans of molecular radius less than 20 Å is identical to that of inulin. For larger dextrans there is a progressive decrease in fractional clearance, approaching zero for dextran radii greater than 42 Å. The relationship between fractional solute clearance and molecular radius in other species is qualitatively similar to that of the rat (20, 157, 171, 382); however, there are significant quantitative differences beween species with respect to the molecular radii at which the fractional clearance deviates from one and zero. Of interest is the observation by Arturson et al. (20) that the clearance of various dextran fractions is lower in children than adults.

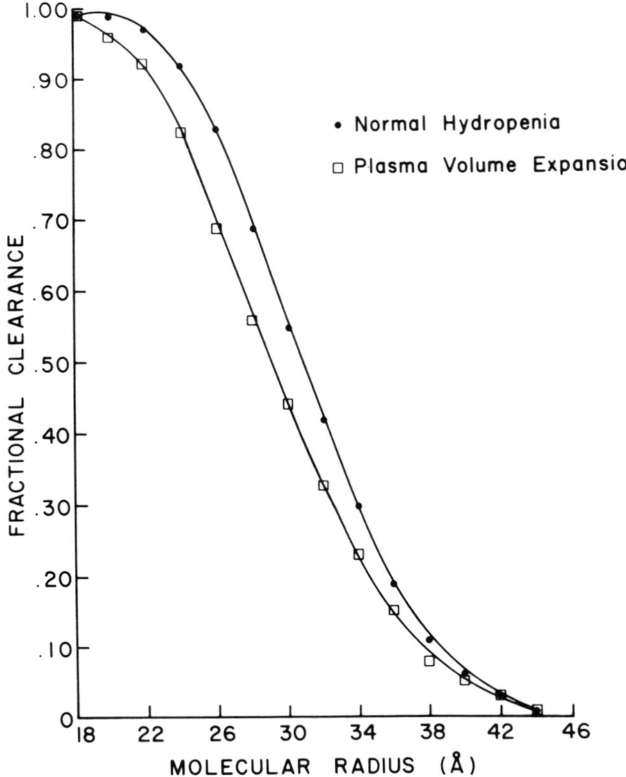

FIG. 24. Relationship between fractional solute clearance (neutral dextrans) and molecular radius in rat kidney glomerulus under control conditions and after plasma volume expansion. [Adapted from Chang et al. (83).]

As observed in other tissues, an inverse relationship exists between the sieving coefficient (fractional clearance) and capillary filtration rate—in this case, the glomerular filtration rate (GFR) (311). Figure 24 indicates that an increased GFR caused by plasma loading produces significant reductions in the fractional clearance of all but the smallest and largest dextrans studied (81, 83). The fact that fractional clearance is reduced when GFR is increased suggests that diffusion is an important component of transglomerular dextran transport under normal conditions (56,100). More importantly the absence of filtration rate independence of fractional clearances indicates that at a normal GFR, σ_d cannot be determined by the formula, one minus the sieving coefficient. Estimates of the reflection coefficient for the various dextran fractions have been made with mean values for other parameters in the Kedem-Katchalsky solute flux equation for normal and plasma-loaded states. The relationship thus obtained between σ and the dextran radius is essentially linear, ranging from 0.13 for a dextran radius of 22 Å and 0.91 for a 42-Å dextran in normal rats (83). The reflection coefficient is increased for any given solute radius in rats with experimentally induced glomerulonephritis (81).

Estimates of glomerular capillary pore size have been based on fractional clearances of neutral dextrans and PVP in several species (20, 81–83, 100, 171). The analyses employed to estimate pore sizes from clearance data are comparable to those used to predict pore size and relative numbers from the relationship between C_L/C_P and molecular radius in other tissues. In general most pore models constructed from the clearance data are consistent with a homoporous membrane composed of pores with radii of 45–50 Å (81, 83, 100, 171, 382).

Arturson et al. (20) explained their dextran-clearance data in humans with a heteroporous model that included two pore sizes: one system of pores with radii of 20–28 Å and an additional system of larger pores with radii up to 80 Å. The larger pores are relatively few in number with an approximate N_{lp}/N_{sp} =

1:10,000. An interesting feature of the pore models developed to describe dextran-clearance data is the prediction that 10% of the capillary surface area is occupied by pores (100), a value considerably larger than the ~0.1% usually predicted for other tissues (203). The pore sizes predicted for glomerular capillaries were compared with other tissues by applying the pore-stripping analysis to the data for neutral dextran clearance. It was found that neither the sieving data acquired at high GFR nor the reported reflection coefficients are consistent with any single- or multiple-pathway model. An explanation for this is not readily available, although there is the likely possibility that diffusion continues to be important in macromolecule transport at the GFRs studied. This is because the glomerular exchange-vessel surface area is disproportionately large relative to GFR.

The results of several physiological and ultrastructural studies indicate that molecular charge and configuration, in addition to molecular size, influence the rate of passage of macromolecules across glomerular capillaries (56, 57, 191, 316, 381). The observation that the sieving coefficient for albumin across the glomerulus is ~0.001, whereas the fractional clearance of a neutral dextran of the same effective molecular radius (36 Å) is 0.19, suggests that solute charge and/or configuration influence transglomerular solute fluxes (83, 112). Chang et al. (80) and Bohrer et al. (46) defined the role of solute charge in macromolecular transport by comparing the fractional clearance of neutral, anionic (sulfated), and cationic diethylaminoethyl cellulose dextrans over a wide range of molecular sizes (Fig. 25). The results clearly indicate that for a given molecular size the fractional clearance of the cationic solute exceeds that of the neutral solute. Conversely the clearance of anionic molecules is lower than that of neutral dextrans of equivalent molecular size. These results show that there are fixed, negatively charged components of the glomerular capillary wall that impede the movement of anionic macromolecules yet facilitate the movement of cationic macromolecules into the Bowman's space from the blood (57). Fractional-clearance studies on neutral, cationic, and anionic horseradish peroxidase also support this conclusion (315). In addition, studies indicate that positively charged macromolecules penetrate the glomerular basement membrane further than the anionic molecules do (314). The loss of the negative charge of the glomerular capillary wall in certain disease states is believed to account for the altered permselectivity for plasma proteins (57, 191).

Recent studies (47, 317) indicate that molecular parameters such as shape, flexibility, and deformability—in addition to solute size and charge—are important in the transport of macromolecules across glomerular capillaries. Simultaneous estimates of fractional clearance for two electrically neutral molecules with the same hydrodynamic radius, i.e., horseradish peroxidase (a globular protein) and dextran (a long-chain polymer), indicate that globular proteins undergo more restriction across the glomerular capillary wall than linear polymers do. This observation is consistent with evidence that the transport of linear polymers through gels (compared with globular proteins of equal radius) is facilitated by the process of reptation, which reduces the effective molecular radius (102, 191). The possibility that dextrans move end-on through the glomerular capillary may have important implications in the applicability of fractional-clearance data to pore theory.

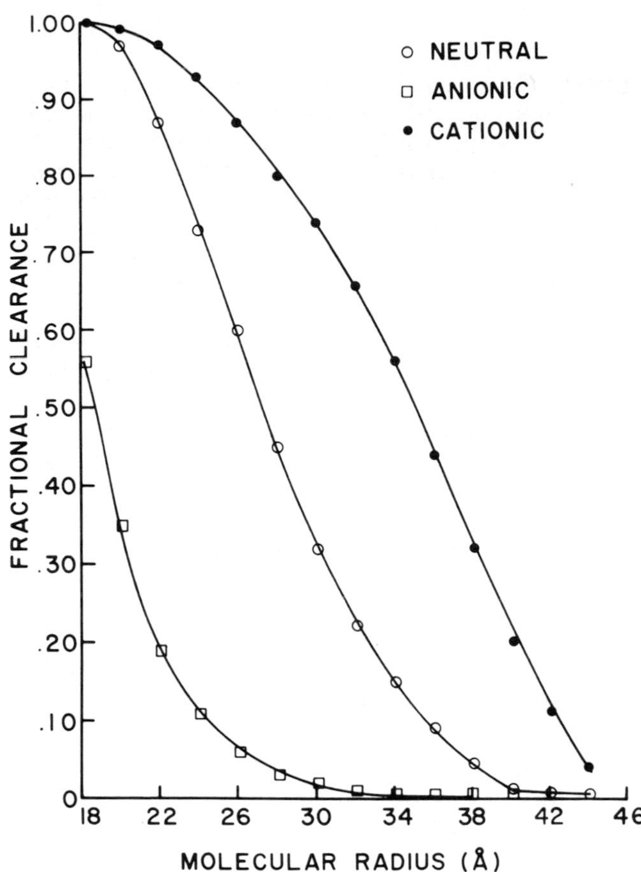

FIG. 25. Relationship between fractional solute clearance and molecular radius in rat kidney for neutral, anionic, and cationic dextrans. [Data from Chang et al. (80) and Bohrer et al. (46).]

Peritubular capillaries. Estimates of the restrictive properties exhibited by the fenestrated peritubular capillaries of the kidney toward macromolecules have been derived from the composition of renal lymph. Use of renal lymph to characterize the permeability properties of peritubular capillaries depends on the assumption that the tubular reabsorbate flows through that region of the cortical interstitium that is in communication with the lymph compartment (288). Since renal lymph originates mostly in the cortex (101), sieving coefficient data for macromolecules derived from lymph is generally assumed to provide an estimate of the restrictive properties of cortical peritubular capillaries.

The C_L/C_P value for total proteins in renal lymph is normally 0.38 in the dog (194, 198) and ranges between 0.29 and 0.39 in the rat (101, 158). Albumin C_L/C_P normally ranges between 0.29 and 0.33 in both rat and dog (101, 158, 206, 207). The ratio of albumin to globulin in rat renal lymph is ~2.1, while in plasma this ratio is 1.2 (158). Analysis of C_L/C_P for macromolecules of various sizes indicates selective restriction by the peritubular capillaries (Fig. 26). Data from the rat (101) show a steep fall in the permeation of neutral dextrans up to 42 Å, suggesting that there are restrictive porosities approximating this dimension. An extension of residual permeability beyond a 42-Å radius (as observed in lymph from other organs) cannot be ascertained in the rat because the largest solute studied had a radius of 42 Å. The data on neutral dextrans for the dog (158) are more consistent with a heteroporous membrane with the dimensions of the small pores exceeding those predicted from rat data. The discrepancy between the two sets of data may represent species differences or may reflect the inhomogeneity of the dextran fractions employed in the earlier dog studies (158). A consistent finding between the two studies is that the C_L/C_P value for albumin is considerably lower that that of the neutral-dextran fraction of equivalent molecular size, suggesting that molecular charge and/or shape are important determinants of sieving coefficients derived from renal lymph.

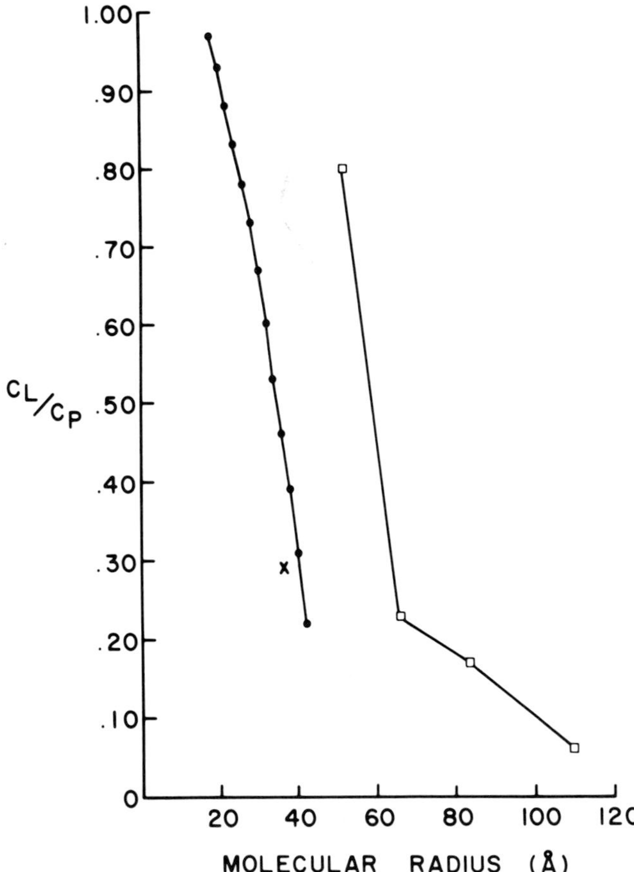

FIG. 26. Relationship between C_L/C_P for neutral dextrans and albumin (×) and molecular radius in peritubular capillaries of rat (●) and dog (□). [Data for rats from Deen et al. (101) and for dogs from Lebrie (206).]

Studies in rat kidney show that renal C_L/C_P values for various macromolecules are decreased when fluid reabsorption is induced by plasma or Ringer loading (101). Ringer loading produced significantly greater decreases in C_L/C_P and also resulted in much greater increases in lymph flow. In contrast to the inverse relationship between C_L/C_P and lymph flow observed with plasma or Ringer loading, elevations of renal vein pressure do not alter C_L/C_P in spite of up to tenfold increases in renal lymph flow (32, 383). This observation is often used to support the hypothesis that renal lymph is formed as a filtrate of postglomerular blood. However, it has been suggested that renal vein constriction damages the walls of peritubular capillaries, since erythrocyte extravasation and a fall in the ratio of albumin to globulin in lymph is observed with only partial renal vein occlusion (101).

Although direct estimates of σ_d for albumin in peritubular capillaries have not been reported, indirect approaches have been applied to data for lymph albumin clearance in the kidney in order to derive an approximation of σ_d (33, 101). These analyses suggest that σ_d for albumin in peritubular capillaries is at least 0.99. Because of the high σ_d values predicted, it is generally assumed that the movement of albumin from renal interstitium to blood by convection is negligible. If one assumes that renal (cortical) lymph is derived entirely from tubule reabsorbate not taken up by the peritubular capillaries, the net transcapillary protein flux and the convective flux from interstitium to blood can be estimated provided total renal lymph flow J_v, lymph protein concentration, plasma protein concentration, peritubular capillary absorption rate $J_{v,c}$, and the reflection coefficient are known. From two studies on rats (33, 101), values for J_v (0.20 ml·min^{-1}·100 g^{-1}), C_L (1.0 g/100 ml), C_P (2.0 g/100 ml), $J_{v,c}$ (60 ml·min^{-1}·100 g^{-1}), and σ_d (0.99) were acquired. By assuming that the convective flux can be described as J_v $(1 - \sigma)\overline{C}_P$ and net transcapillary albumin flux as $J_v \cdot C_L$, the convective flux of albumin from interstitium to blood is estimated to be ~6 times greater than the net transcapillary albumin flux. Even if C_L is used instead of $\overline{C}_P$ for estimating the convective flux, this analysis predicts that the protein flux from interstitium to blood is 3 times the net flux across the peritubular capillaries. Thus it is conceivable that significant quantities of proteins move from the renal interstitium into peritubular capillaries in spite of a high reflection coefficient simply because of the tremendous volume of fluid that is reabsorbed.

GASTROINTESTINAL ORGANS. *Small intestine.* It is generally considered that the capillaries of the intestine are permeable to macromolecules because of the normally high concentration of lymph protein and the fact that over 60% of the total capillary surface area is composed of fenestrated capillaries (79). In addition the hydraulic conductivity and filtration rate of intestinal capillaries are ~10 times greater than those of skeletal muscle, an organ containing exclusively continuous capillaries (319). Although all of these observations have generally led to the conclusion that intestinal capillaries are leaky, physiological studies indicate that intestinal capillaries offer more restriction to the movement of macromolecules than do the continuous capillaries of many other tissues (144).

The capillaries of the intestinal wall are ultrastructurally heterogeneous. The vessels of the mucosa and submucosa are fenestrated, whereas capillaries in the muscularis have a continuous endothelium. The contribution of the continuous capillaries to the overall permeability of the intestinal capillary bed is considered negligible by both electron microscopists and physiologists; however, there is no direct evidence supporting this assumption. Within the villi, fenestrated capillaries are concentrated immediately (0.5–2.0 μm) under the epithelium, and the fenestrations are preferentially oriented toward the base of the epithelium (79, 87, 190, 341, 345).

Stereological estimates of the number, dimensions, and distribution of endothelial fenestrae in the cat jejunum have led Casley-Smith and co-workers (79) to conclude that the fenestrated capillaries of the intestine correspond to "tunnel capillaries." According to this hypothesis, the physiological estimates of diffusion coefficients for small and large molecules are determined by an extravascular barrier, i.e., the inter-

TABLE 5. *Solute Concentration Ratios of Lymph to Plasma in Mammalian Gastrointestinal Organs*

	Stokes-Einstein Radius, Å	C_L/C_P	Ref.
Small intestine			
Human			
Total protein		0.59–0.62	
Albumin	37	0.68	403
Globulins		0.55	
Calf			
Total protein		0.57	
Albumin	37	0.71	338
Globulins		0.47	
Sheep			
Total protein		0.54	409
Dog			
Total protein		0.50–0.67	180, 407
Albumin	37	0.51–0.74	125, 364, 377
Globulins		0.40–0.45	119
α_1-Globulins		0.49	
α_2-Globulins		0.63	407
β_1-Globulins		0.70	
β_2-Globulins		0.50	
Orosomucoid	40	0.79	377
Transferrin	43	0.79	377
α_2-Macroglobulin	108	0.21	125
IgG	56	0.56	377
IgM	121	0.44	377
α_1-Antitrypsin	32.8	0.50	125
Haptoglobin	46	0.32	125
	20,000*	0.90	
	25,000*	0.60	
	35,000*	0.35	
Dextran	45,000*	0.22	19
	55,000*	0.13	
	65,000*	0.10	
	75,000*	0.10	
Cat			
Total protein		0.55–0.62	133, 159, 239
Albumin	37	0.53	143
Fractions			
I	37.5	0.50	
II	38	0.45	
III	39	0.43	
IV	42	0.35	143
V	45	0.26	
VI	76	0.24	
VII	96	0.25	
VIII	107	0.23	
IX	120	0.21	
Rat			
Total proteins		0.36–0.44	30,208
Stomach			
Dog			
Total protein		0.51	
Albumin	37	0.68	
Globulins		0.42	
α-Globulins		0.49	72
α_2-Globulins		0.62	
β-Globulins		0.35	
γ-Globulins	56	0.46	
Fibrinogen	108	0.39	
Cat			
Total protein		0.42	
Albumin	37	0.57	
Fractions			
I	37.5	0.55	
II	38	0.42	
III	39	0.35	
IV	42	0.36	281
V	45	0.25	
VI	76	0.38	
VII	96	0.24	
VIII	107	0.27	
XI	120	0.25	
Colon			
Dog			
Total proteins		0.52	
Albumin	37	0.68	318
β-Lipoprotein	120	0.20	

* Molecular weight.

stitial matrix. This hypothesis is not supported by experimental data.

Most physiological estimates of intestinal capillary permeability to macromolecules are based on concentration ratios of lymph to plasma. Table 5 provides the available data on solute concentration ratios in gastrointestinal organs of several mammalian species. Under normal experimental conditions the ratio for total protein in the intestine generally ranges between 0.50 and 0.65. There appears to be little variability in C_L/C_P for total protein between species, except for rat where normal values of 0.36–0.44 are acquired. Analyses of C_L/C_P for macromolecules of various sizes indicate selective restriction at the capillary wall in the intestine.

Approximations of the size and distribution of capillary pores in intestinal capillaries have been acquired from the relationship between C_L/C_P and solute radius. Figure 27 illustrates this relationship in dog (19, 125, 225) and cat (143) small intestines at normal capillary filtration rates. The data show a steep fall in permeation of solute in the size range below a radius of 60 Å. Above 60 Å there is an extension in residual permeability with little decrement in C_L/C_P for molecules with radii as large as 135 Å. The steep fall in C_L/C_P with solute radii below 60 Å suggests that there are restrictive porosities approximating this dimension. The constant residual permeability up to 135 Å (except for some of the dextran data) can be attributed to either large pores (>135-Å radius) or vesicular transport. From the data presented in Figure 27 the blood-lymph barrier of the small intestine can be described by an equivalent two-pore membrane with a small-pore radius of 50 Å and an additional set of larger pores with radii of 200 Å; here N_{lp}/N_{sp} = 1:1,280. The small pores account for 80% of the total pore area. Mayerson and co-workers (225) explained their C_L/C_P data for dextrans in the small intestine with a system of pores of 110-Å radius and capillary leaks of >140-Å radius. The small-pore system is considered to account for ~78% of the total capillary pore area, while the leaks (or vesicles) account for the remaining 22%.

All the data presented in Figure 27 were acquired at a normal capillary filtration rate. Figure 7 demonstrates the influence that capillary filtration rate exerts on the relationship between C_L/C_P and molecular radius in the small intestine (143). Although progres-

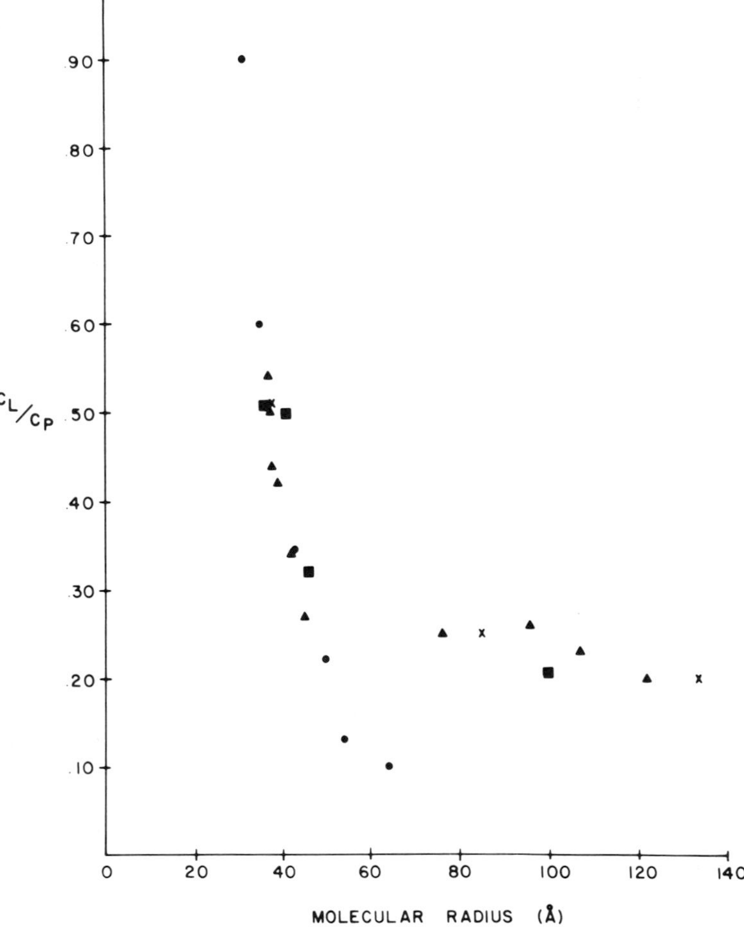

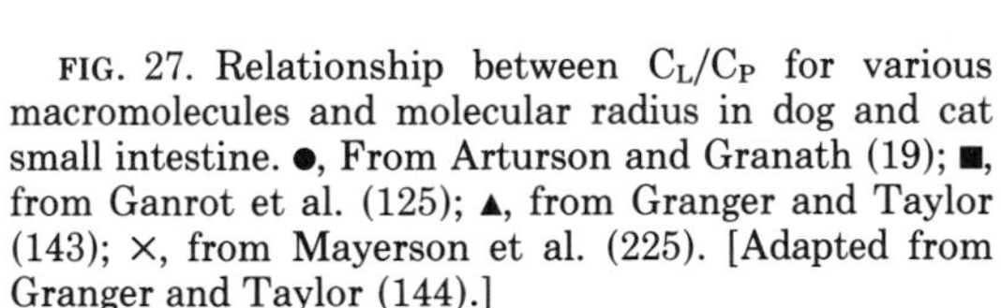
FIG. 27. Relationship between C_L/C_P for various macromolecules and molecular radius in dog and cat small intestine. ●, From Arturson and Granath (19); ■, from Ganrot et al. (125); ▲, from Granger and Taylor (143); ×, from Mayerson et al. (225). [Adapted from Granger and Taylor (144).]

sive elevations of lymph flow reduced C_L/C_P for each solute (as expected with restricted diffusion), the steep fall in C_L/C_P consistently occurred below 60 Å irrespective of filtration rate, suggesting that dimensions of the small pores remain constant at high lymph flows (and venous pressures). On the other hand the level of constant residual permeability for solute radii >60 Å progressively decreases as lymph flow rises. Applying the same two-pore model derived from Figure 27 to these data results in a predicted dramatic decrease in the ratio of large-pore (200-Å) to small-pore (50-Å) numbers as lymph flow is increased. A similar phenomenon is predicted from Grotte's (147) data from cervical lymph (Fig. 1). The effect of filtration rate on the relative number of pore sizes presumably reflects a repartitioning of filtration among various pores in this heteroporous capillary membrane.

Interest in the area of transcapillary fluid exchange in the small intestine has led to estimates of the osmotic reflection coefficient of intestinal capillaries. Estimates of σ_d for total protein by the formula $1 - (C_L/C_P)$ at high filtration rates vary between 0.72 and 0.92 in dogs (180, 407) and cats (133, 239). Some of the difference between the σ_d values presumably reflects the fact that the maximum filtration rates vary considerably between the studies. Thus some of these values are minimum estimates of σ_d. It is essential that capillary filtration rate be sufficiently high for lymph to reflect the ultrafiltrate of plasma in order to obtain a value for σ_d with the expression $1 - (C_L/C_P)$. To ensure that an ultrafiltrate of plasma is achieved in the intestine, lymph flow can be progressively elevated until it is established that C_L/C_P no longer changes with lymph flow, i.e., C_L/C_P is filtration rate independent. Figure 28 depicts the relationship between C_L/C_P and lymph flow in the small intestine of the cat (143) and rat (208). The relationship $\sigma_d = 1 - (C_L/C_P)$ (when C_L/C_P is filtration rate independent) predicts that σ_d is ~0.92 for total plasma proteins in both species. When the same analysis is applied to C_L/C_P (for total protein) and lymph flow data derived from cirrhotic patients, a value for σ_d of ~0.97 is predicted for the human small intestine (403). Thus the data from several mammalian species indicate that $0.90 < \sigma_d < 1.00$ for total plasma proteins in the small intestine. These findings suggest that the fenestrated capillaries of the small intestine may restrict macromolecules to a greater degree than capillaries in other organs, except for glomerular capillaries and those of the blood-brain barrier.

Estimates of σ_d for endogenous proteins of various sizes in the small intestine clearly demonstrate molecular sieving by intestinal capillaries (143, 144). The osmotic reflection coefficient is ~0.90 for albumin and rises progressively with molecular size up to β-lipoprotein, in which $\sigma_d = 0.99$. Renkin (306) has applied the principles of hydrodynamics and irreversible thermodynamics to data for the osmotic reflection coefficients of various protein fractions in the cat small intestine to estimate the dimension and number of transport pathways in intestinal capillaries. The results of this analysis for the small intestine suggest that the radii of the small-pore and large-pore systems are 47 and 200 Å, respectively (Fig. 9*D*). Ninety percent of the total hydraulic conductivity can be attributed to the small pores, while large pores account for 5% of the total. Values for A_{lp}/A_{sp} and N_{lp}/N_{sp} are 1:288 and 1:5,700, respectively. Recent estimates of *PS* for β-lactoglobulin A (27-Å radius) and inulin by indicator diffusion also predict a pore population of 47 Å in intestinal capillaries (283).

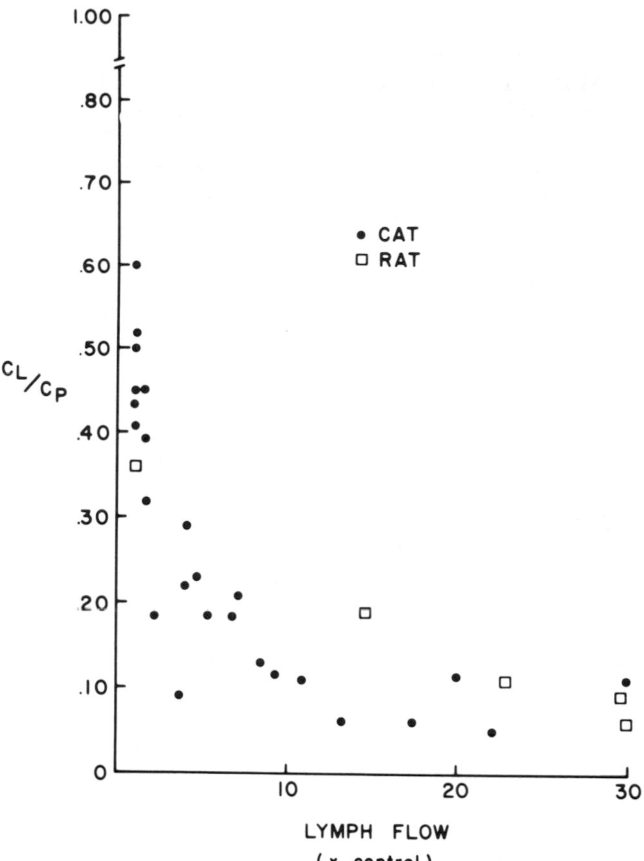

FIG. 28. Steady-state relationship between C_L/C_P for total proteins and lymph flow in the small intestines of cat and rat. [Data for cat from Granger and Taylor (143) and for rat from Lee (208).]

Many physiological and pharmacological interventions have been shown to alter the permeability of intestinal capillaries. Table 6 summarizes the available literature on σ_d estimates under various experimental conditions in the small intestine. Although the permeability responses of intestinal capillaries to various stimuli (histamine and bradykinin) are in general accord with those observed in other tissues, some of the responses are unique to this organ and deserve additional comment.

It is well documented that intestinal lymph flow

TABLE 6. *Physiological and Pharmacological Effects on Osmotic Reflection Coefficients of Intestinal Capillaries to Total Proteins*

	Reflection Coefficient	Ref.
Controls	0.92	133, 143
Isoproterenol	0.92	139
Ischemia (60 min)	0.59*	141
Ischemia (superoxide dismutase pretreatment)	0.86	140
Bradykinin	0.65*	139
Arterial hyperosmolarity (20 mM glucose)	0.64*	133
E. coli endotoxin	0.78*	140
Glucagon	0.81*	134
Fat absorption	0.70*	144
Cholecystokinin	0.89	138
Secretin	0.91	138
Histamine	0.56*	238
Cimetidine + histamine	0.90	238
Diphenhydramine HCl + histamine	0.56*	238
Ethylenediaminetetraacetate (intra-arterial)	0.73*	†
Goldblatt's hypertension	0.55*	32, 200

* Significant difference from control $P < 0.05$. †A. E. Taylor and D. N. Granger, unpublished observations.

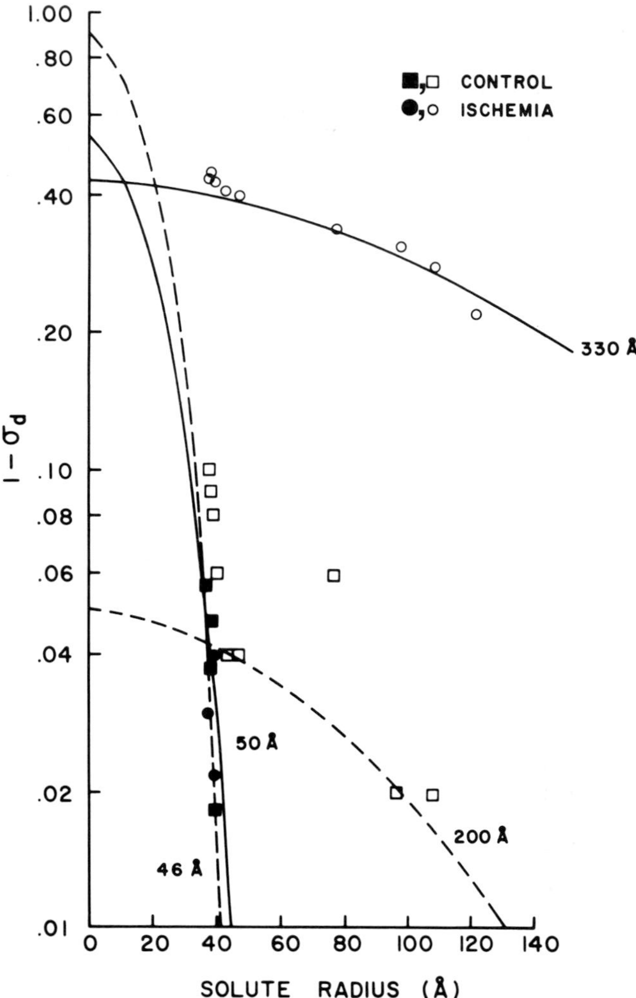

FIG. 29. Pore-stripping analysis of data for lymphatic protein flux from small intestine under control conditions (143) and after 1 h ischemia (141). Note that analysis predicts that ischemia selectively increases the size of large pores. [Data for control from Granger and Taylor (143) and for ischemia from Granger, Taylor, et al. (141).]

and lymphatic protein flux rise after a meal (28, 132). Results from studies of fluid absorption suggest that fat appears to be the most potent luminal stimulus for enhanced lymphatic protein flux (28). While there is some debate whether the rise in lymphatic protein flux in the intestines during absorption is due to alterations in capillary surface area or permeability (142), the reduction in σ_d during fat absorption suggests that intestinal capillary permeability can change significantly as a result of a normal physiological process, i.e., absorption.

The permeability response of intestinal capillaries to ischemia is also of interest. In many tissues (e.g., skeletal muscle) total or partial occlusion of the arterial inflow does not seem to affect macromolecular permeability. In the intestine, however, reperfusion after 1 h of ischemia (blood flow reduced to 30%–40% of normal level) significantly reduced the osmotic reflection coefficient for total proteins to a level comparable with that seen with local intra-arterial infusion of histamine or bradykinin (141). The data for σ_d of various endogenous protein fractions during ischemia provide a clear indication that molecular sieving by intestinal capillaries is significantly reduced as compared with control data (Fig. 29). Of particular interest is the effect of ischemia on the size and relative number of small and large pores. The analysis presented in Figure 29 suggests that the increased permeability present after ischemia can be attributed entirely to an increase in the dimensions of the large pores; the size of the large pores increases from 200 to 330 Å, while the small pores remain relatively constant at 47–50 Å. The ratio N_{lp}/N_{sp} increases from 1:35 to 1:7 during ischemia. Volumetric estimates of L_pS after intestinal ischemia suggest that total membrane hydraulic conductance increases by 70% (319). Ischemia appears to selectively influence the large-pore system through the release of superoxide radicals at the time of reperfusion (140).

In addition to lymph experiments there are several electron-microscope studies in the literature that describe the effect of a pharmacological or pathological intervention on intestinal capillary permeability. Perfusion of the fenestrated capillaries of the rat intestinal mucosa with histamine has been shown to cause partial removal of the fenestral diaphragms, occasional detachment of the endothelium from the basement membrane, and focal separation of the intercellular junctions (88). Histamine treatment allowed carbon particles to traverse the fenestrae; however, the basement membrane prevented most of the particles from entering the interstitium. Perfusion of the capillaries with ethylenediaminetetraacetate produced similar effects as histamine, yet the intensity of the structural alterations was greater (88). The ultrastructural alterations produced by histamine presumably account for the reduction in σ_d from 0.92 to 0.56 predicted from lymph protein studies (Table 6). Furthermore the effects of histamine on intestinal capillary permeability appear to be mediated through H_2 receptors (238).

There is also morphological evidence indicating that intestinal capillary permeability is increased (as judged by the restriction of carbon or ferritin particles) in early experimental hypertension (354), in acute angiotensin-induced hypertension (371, 372), and after intraluminal instillation of either cholera enterotoxin (97) or oil of mustard (173).

The relative contributions of diffusion and convection to macromolecule transport across intestinal capillaries have been estimated from data of lymphatic protein flux. From the relationship between lymphatic protein clearance and lymph flow in the intestines of cirrhotic patients, it has been suggested that diffusion is the dominant process in transcapillary protein exchange in the intestine (403). Using the Kedem-Katchalsky analysis for data of lymphatic protein flux in the cat ileum, one would predict that molecules the size of albumin cross intestinal capillaries primarily by convection at normal capillary filtration rates and that significant quantities of plasma proteins move by convection from interstitium to blood in the absorbing small intestine (137). The convective flux is also directionally opposite to diffusion in peritubular capillaries.

Stomach. Considerably less is known about the permeability characteristics of gastric capillaries to macromolecules, presumably because of the technical difficulties with obtaining gastric lymph (72). The data that are available on the composition of gastric lymph protein (Table 5) resemble those for the small intestine (72, 281). Estimates of the osmotic reflection coefficient for total proteins and several endogenous proteins of known molecular radius have been acquired by using the relationship between C_L/C_P and lymph flow. Assuming $\sigma_d = 1 - (C_L/C_P)$ when C_L/C_P is filtration rate independent, Perry and co-workers (279) derived σ_d values of 0.78, 0.73, and 0.91 for total proteins, albumin, and β-lipoprotein, respectively. Subjecting σ_d values for various plasma proteins to pore-stripping analysis (Fig. 30) suggests that the radii of small and large pores in stomach capillaries are 47 and 250 Å, respectively. Values for A_{lp}/A_{sp} and N_{lp}/N_{sp} are 1:92 and 1:2,600, respectively.

Davenport et al. (99) and Wood and Davenport (404) employed a different technique for estimating σ and *PS* for macromolecules in the stomach by using extraction values of radiolabeled albumin and fibrinogen. Their estimate of σ was based on the relation $1 - \sigma = J_s/J_v \cdot \overline{C}_s$. The transcapillary protein flux J_s was

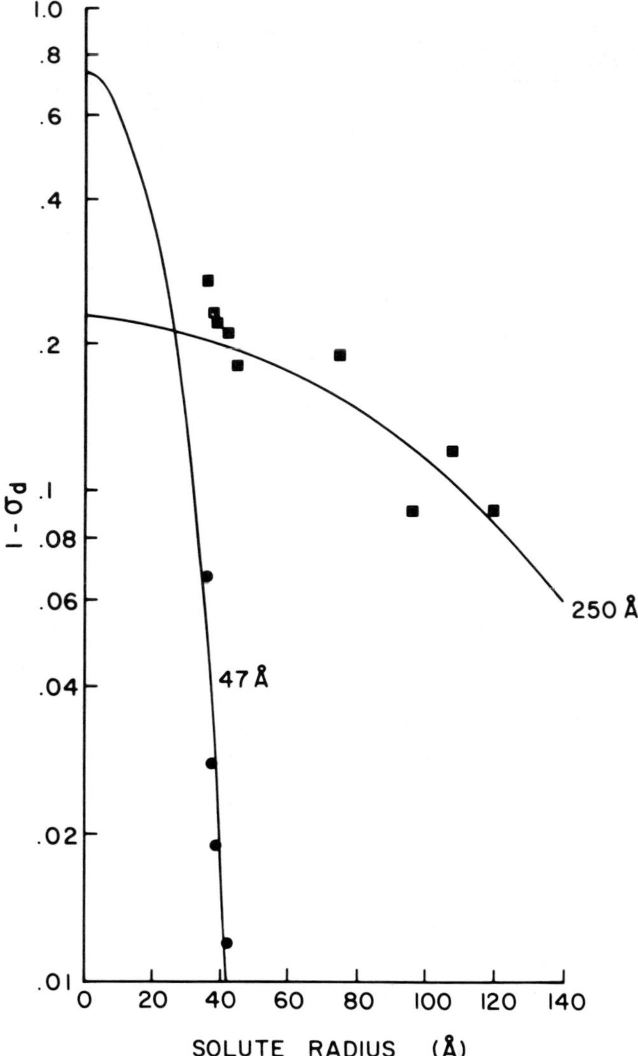

FIG. 30. Pore-stripping analysis of data for lymphatic protein from cat stomach. [Data from Perry, Crook, and Granger (284).]

derived from the extraction and arterial influx of labeled protein. Capillary filtration rate J_v was estimated from the difference in arterial inflow and venous outflow of blood. The activity of labeled proteins in a known volume of plasma was used to estimate $\overline{C}_s$. With this approach the authors acquired σ_d values of 0.70 and 0.90 for albumin and fibrinogen, respectively (98). These values were reduced to 0.40 and 0.70 after exposure of the gastric mucosa to 1,4-dithiothreitol, a sulfhydryl reducing agent. Permeability–surface area products for albumin (6.5×10^{-4} ml·s^{-1}·g^{-1} dry wt) and fibrinogen (2.3×10^{-4} ml·s^{-1}·g^{-1}) were derived by the indicator-dilution technique (99). The *PS* value for albumin in the stomach (0.80 ml·min^{-1}·100 g^{-1}) was much greater than the value calculated in studies of lymph protein flux in the small intestine (0.10 ml·min^{-1}·100 g^{-1}) (143).

Colon. The permeability of colonic capillaries to

endogenous macromolecules has been analyzed with data from lymphatic protein flux (318). The composition of lymph from the colon closely resembles that of the small intestine (see Table 5). Osmotic reflection coefficients have been determined in the colon for several endogenous protein fractions. The σ_d values for total protein (0.85), albumin (0.75), β-lipoprotein (0.98), and other protein fractions were generally less than those reported for the small intestine. Some discrepancy between σ_d values for large and small intestines may result from the fact that most colonic lymph appears to be derived from nonmucosal regions, whereas the opposite is generally considered true for the small intestine. Figure 31 illustrates the relationship between $1 - \sigma_d$ and molecular radius. From this relationship small and large pores with radii of 53 and 180 Å, respectively, are predicted. The ratios of A_{lp}/A_{sp} and N_{lp}/N_{sp} are 1:48 and 1:550, respectively.

Discontinuous Capillaries

Capillaries with discontinuous endothelia and no basement membrane are found in liver, spleen, and bone marrow. Although ultrastructural evidence suggests that discontinuous capillaries (sinusoids) are highly porous structures, the composition of lymph from these organs may provide useful information

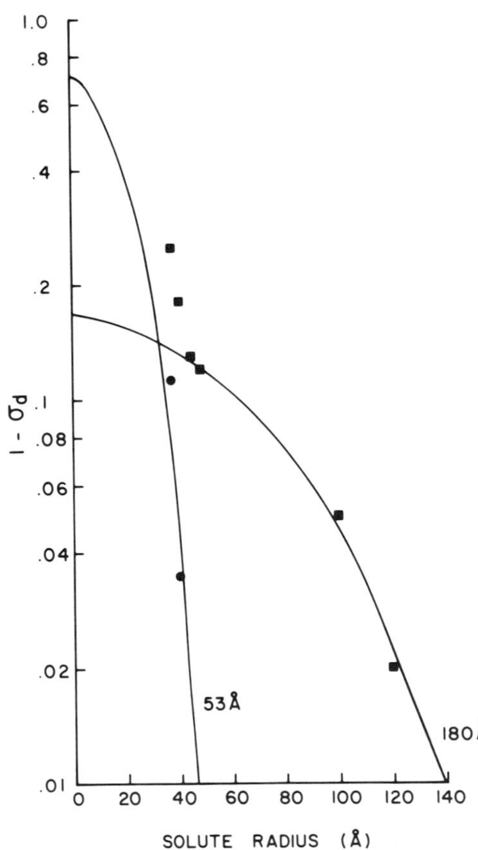

FIG. 31. Pore-stripping analysis of data for lymphatic protein from dog colon. [Data from Richardson, Granger, et al. (318).]

regarding the sieving characteristics of the barrier lying between the capillary and lymphatic walls, i.e., the interstitium.

LIVER. The important physiological characteristics of the permeability of liver sinusoids were first described by Starling (348) in his epochal studies on capillary filtration. Starling concluded that liver capillaries are normally the most permeable in the body based on his observation that the protein concentration in liver exceeds that of other tissues. After nearly a century Starling's original conclusions have not been refuted, and it is now generally accepted that, compared with other organs, the liver sinusoids are extremely permeable to macromolecules.

Hepatic lymph is unique because it flows at a high rate and has the greatest protein concentration of all regional lymphs. Under normal experimental conditions the ratio of total protein concentration in lymph to that in plasma generally ranges between 0.80 and 0.95 (Table 7), whereas a C_L/C_P value of 1.0 is commonly reported for albumin. In spite of the high C_L/C_P values for albumin and total protein, analyses of C_L/C_P for macromolecules of various sizes indicate that there is selectivity at the liver blood-lymph barrier under normal conditions (Fig. 32).

Grotte (147) analyzed the steady-state C_L/C_P of several dextran fractions (10,000–300,000 mol wt) from dog liver at normal capillary filtration rates and explained his findings with a model consisting of two sets of pores, i.e., a small-pore system with pore radii of 30–45 Å and one of large pores (leaks) of 250-Å radius. A value of 1:340 was obtained for N_{lp}/N_{sp} in liver capillaries. Mayerson and co-workers (225) studied C_L/C_P and the time of appearance of several large dextran fractions and radioiodinated serum albumin in lymph of the dog liver. From the rate of appearance of albumin and dextran (35,000 mol wt) in lymph, an equilibration time between plasma and lymph of 60–90 min was found for liver. The equilibration time in the liver is not significantly different from that in the intestine, yet it is substantially shorter than that in cervical lymph. Mayerson et al. (225) described their C_L/C_P data with a two-pore model comparable to Grotte's. The model included a small-pore system with pores of 110-Å radius and a large-pore system with pores of radii >140 Å. The large-pore system was considered to account for 66.7% of the effective pore area in hepatic sinusoids, while the small-pore system comprised the remaining area. It was also suggested that the large-pore population may well be involved with vesicular transport of macromolecules across the sinusoidal endothelium.

The more recent analyses of lymph protein composition in the liver (106, 135) have utilized endogenous plasma proteins of various molecular sizes (Fig. 33). Results of pore-stripping analysis, assuming that maximum selectivity is present at normal filtration rates, give data for C_L/C_P in the liver that are consistent

TABLE 7. *Solute Concentration Ratios of Lymph to Plasma in Mammalian Liver*

	Stokes-Einstein Radius, Å	C_L/C_P	Ref.
*Human**			
Total protein		0.90	
Albumin	37	1.00	403
Globulins		0.78	
Calf			
Total protein		0.81	
Albumin	37	0.94	338
Globulins		0.74	
Sheep			
Total protein		0.80	237
Dog			
Total protein		0.80–0.95	106, 201, 402
Albumin	37	0.80–1.00	106, 125, 225
Globulins		0.85	119
Orosomucoid	40	0.87	106
Transferrin	43	0.77	106
IgG	53	0.65	106, 377
α_2-Macroglobulin	108	0.51	106, 125
IgM	121	0.47	106, 125, 377
Haptoglobin	46	0.48	125
α_1-Antitrypsin	32.8	0.85	125
Dextran	10,000†	0.98–1.00	
	20,000†	0.98	
	25,000†	0.95	
	30,000†	0.98	
	35,000†	0.81	19, 147
	40,000†	0.67	
	45,000†	0.77	
	50,000†	0.71	
	55,000†	0.78	
	60,000†	0.84	
	65,000†	0.77	19, 147
	75,000†	0.77	
	100,000–180,000†	0.85–0.90	147
	200,000–300,000†	0.78–0.81	147
Cat			
Total protein		0.80	135
Albumin	37	0.90–0.92	135, 237
Fractions			
III	39	0.81	
IV	42	0.73	
V	45	0.68	
VI	76	0.55	135
VII	96	0.56	
VIII	107	0.50	
IX	124	0.47	
Globulins		0.86	237
Rabbit			
Total protein		0.86–0.90	
Albumin	37	0.87–0.96	384, 405
Globulins		0.70	
α-Globulins		0.75	
β-Globulins		0.71	405
γ-Globulins	56	0.74	
Lipoproteins			
	~200Å	0.70	
	~400Å	0.43	92
	~700Å	0.34	
PVP	38,000†	0.80	384
Rat			
Total protein		0.67	
Albumin	37	0.78	123
Globulins		0.59	

PVP, povidone (polyvinylpyrrolidone). * Ratio of concentrations in ascitic fluid to plasma. †Molecular weight.

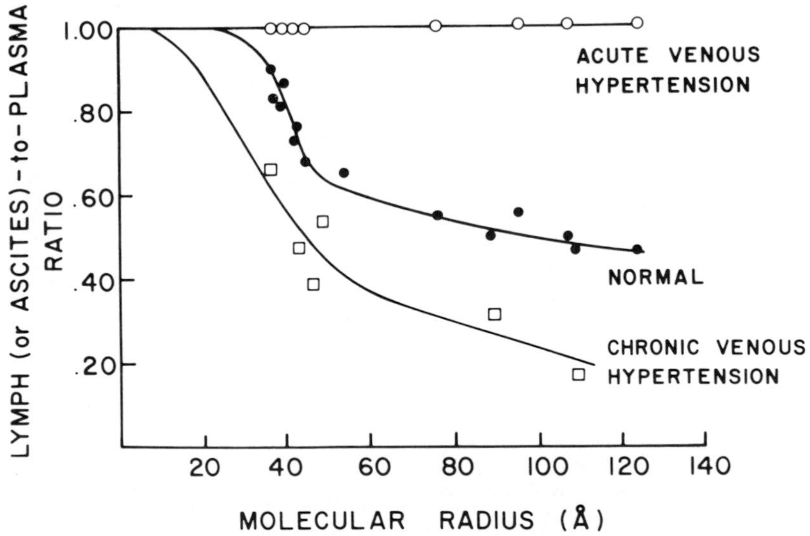

FIG. 32. Relationship between the ratio of lymph (○, ●) or ascites (□) to plasma for endogenous proteins and molecular radius in the normal liver [data from Dive et al. (106) and Granger, Taylor, et al. (135)], after acute venous hypertension [Granger, Taylor, et al. (135)], and during chronic venous hypertension [Roberts et al. (323)].

with a small-pore system of ~90-Å radii and a large-pore system of 330-Å radii. An approximate N_{lp}/N_{sp} of 1:46 would be predicted from such a two-pore system.

Although there is some discrepancy between the size and number of small and large pores in liver sinusoids, all estimates of pore sizes in the liver predict a relative abundance of large pores. In spite of this it is important to note that the magnitude of the physiological estimates of pore size are at least one-tenth

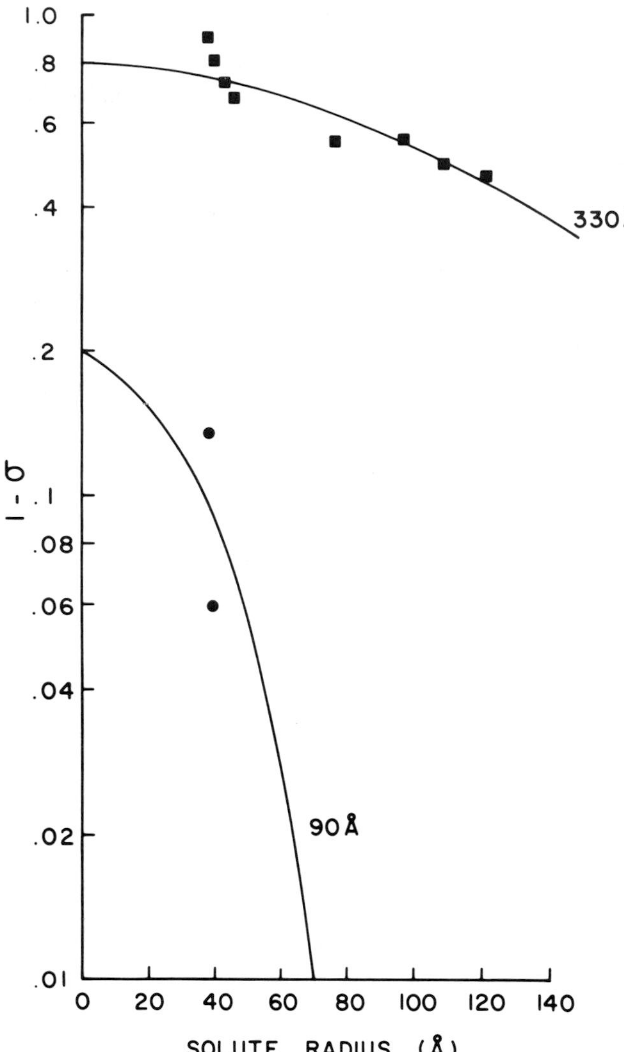

FIG. 33. Pore-stripping analysis of data for lymphatic protein flux in cat liver. [Data from Granger, Taylor, et al. (135).]

to one-fifth the pore dimensions predicted by electron microscopists (35, 188). Indeed the dimensions of the intercellular gaps in rat liver prompted Bennett and co-workers (35) to conclude that the sinusoidal endothelia "exercise no selective filtering effect on blood plasma constituents smaller than platelets." However, because of the following facts it is necessary to consider an alternative barrier to account for the selectivity observed with liver C_L/C_P data: *1)* the diameters of the sinusoid apertures range between 1,000 and 10,000 Å, *2)* the sinusoids lack a basement membrane, and *3)* there are relatively few vesicles within the sinusoidal endothelium. Recent evidence from cat liver (135) suggests that the interstitial matrix may serve as the limiting barrier for blood-to-lymph transport of macromolecules. It was observed that an increase in hepatic lymph flow due to acute hepatic vein occlusion produced an increase in C_L/C_P for total plasma proteins from a normal value of 0.82 to a value of 1.00 (135, 401). At this elevated venous pressure ascitic fluid was formed on the surface of the liver. The protein composition and concentration of the ascitic fluid were identical to those in lymph. In addition there was no evidence of selectivity in lymph for any of the macromolecules studied at high capillary filtration rates (Fig. 32).

Although there are several possible explanations for loss of selectivity at high flows of liver lymph, the most likely is that the sieve operating under normal conditions is located between the sinusoidal wall and the lymphatic vessel. The restrictive properties of the interstitium are generally ignored in organs where the capillary endothelium provides the limiting barrier to diffusion and convection of molecules; however, the extremely large gaps between sinusoidal endothelia may allow the interstitium to be the rate-limiting barrier to diffusion and convection in the liver (135). Because the excluded-volume phenomenon has been demonstrated for albumin in Disse's space, the liver interstitium may significantly restrict the movement of macromolecules (129, 280). Furthermore the degree of albumin exclusion in the liver interstitium decreases at elevated capillary filtration rates (280). In keeping with this hypothesis, one would predict that increasing the hydration of the interstitial matrix at elevated capillary filtration rates would result in a diminution of the restrictive properties of the interstitium, thereby accounting for the loss of selectivity seen at high venous pressures.

The permeability of the hepatic microvasculature to albumin has also been analyzed by Goresky (128–130) with the multiple-indicator–dilution technique. Labeled red cells, albumin, and sucrose were injected into the portal vein, and the hepatic venous-dilution curves were analyzed. Albumin was delayed in its passage through the liver, and the outflow pattern produced by the delay suggested that the extravascular distribution of albumin is flow limited. The existence of flow-limited distribution implies that the walls of the liver sinusoids do not restrict the movement of albumin from blood to interstitium. When this analysis was applied to the liver microcirculation of patients with cirrhosis of the liver, significantly different results were acquired (170). In the cirrhotic liver restricted permeability characteristics equivalent to those of continuous capillaries were discovered. These results indicate an evolution of liver capillaries from a completely permeant membrane under normal conditions to one displaying selective albumin restriction in cirrhosis.

Modification of the sieving properties of liver sinusoids during chronic disease states characterized by hepatic venous hypertension has also been demonstrated with C_L/C_P values and ratios of the protein concentration in ascites fluid to that in plasma. In contrast to the results acquired with acute hepatic vein occlusion in experimental animals, the total protein C_L/C_P was reduced from a normal value of 0.91 to a value of 0.54 in patients with hepatic cirrhosis (110). Furthermore there is evidence of selectivity at the sinusoidal wall (or interstitium) in cirrhotic livers: C_L/C_P for albumin was 0.66, whereas C_L/C_P for IgM was 0.29 (403). Although a complete electrophoretic analysis of the protein composition of cirrhotic liver lymph has not been undertaken, some information is available on ascitic fluid protein composition in patients with long-standing hepatic venous hypertension (323). The relationship between molecular radius and the protein concentration ratio of ascitic fluid to plasma (Fig. 32) supports the contention that the liver sinusoid evolves from being highly permeant under normal conditions to displaying selective solute restriction during chronic disease states accompanied by hepatic venous hypertension. Fibrotic bridging of the sinusoid, deposition of collagen fibers in Disse's space, or a greater filtration by the less-permeable peribiliary capillaries are thought to be structural counterparts to the physiological alterations of liver lymph in chronic disease states (399, 402).

An inherent assumption in much of the foregoing discussion is that liver lymph is a true representation of the transsinusoidal filtrate. A possible complication with this assumption is the contribution to hepatic lymph of a filtrate from the peribiliary capillary plexus. The peribiliary capillaries are continuous (374), and thus their sieving properties may be the same as those of skeletal muscle capillaries. Unfortunately the permeability and filtration characteristics of the peribiliary capillaries are unknown. Most investigators believe that the peribiliary capillary plexus contributes less than 10% of the total liver lymph flow measured from a hilar lymphatic, and this contribution is therefore considered insignificant. However, the assumption has never been verified experimentally. If filtration rate and permselectivity of the peribiliary capillaries are high, it is conceivable that lymph protein concentration and lymph flow data at normal pressures may not be truly representative of the filtration characteristics of the sinusoidal wall. The loss of permselectivity predicted from lymph data at high venous pressures may merely reflect a disproportionate rise in sinusoidal filtration relative to peribiliary filtration. To resolve this issue it is imperative that studies be designed to estimate the magnitude of the contribution of the peribiliary capillary filtrate to hepatic lymph (29).

Whole-Body Capillary Permeability

A large amount of published information concerning capillary permeability to macromolecules pertains to the permeability characteristics of either the whole body or a combination of organs. The most commonly employed techniques for evaluating capillary permeability in multiple-organ systems involve the analysis of plasma disappearance curves for radioactive macromolecules and of lymph protein flux from the thoracic duct.

The basic theory for analyzing plasma disappearance curves for maromolecules was developed by Sterling (353) and extended by others (38, 248). The method involves introducing a radioactive macromolecule into the circulation and evaluating its disappearance rate. Investigators have chosen to use the first hour of plasma disappearance curves to estimate capillary permeability and have coined the term *transcapillary escape rate* (TER) to describe the rapidity of macromolecule exchange across whole-body capillaries (266). In addition other components of the plasma disappearance curves have been used to estimate the total pool of macromolecules and their fractional catabolic rate. This technique has been especially useful for studying macromolecule permeability in various physiological and pathological conditions in humans. Essential hypertension (266, 268, 273), skin disease (276), exercise (195, 336), long-term juvenile diabetes (71, 271, 275), adult onset diabetes (36, 178), myxedema (267), the newborn state (175, 269), angiotensin II infusion (270, 274), hemophilia (241), amyotrophic lateral sclerosis (89), plasma volume expansion (274), idiopathic edema (325), and carbon monoxide poisoning (265, 272, 340) are all associated with an increased albumin TER in humans. In several of these studies IgG and IgM escape rates were also evaluated and compared with those of albumin (178, 270–272, 274). In general there is an inverse relationship between TER and macromolecule size. The use of larger proteins (immunoglobulins) allows a distinction to be made between alterations in capillary permeability and filtration rate when TER is varied.

Transcapillary escape rates of either radioactive albumin or Evans blue–albumin have also been used to assess capillary permeability in animals. The animal studies indicate that staphylococcal α-toxin (60), irradiation (85), kallikreins (215), hypertension in spontaneous hypertensive rats (322), thrombocytopenia (40), histamine (228), and hemorrhagic shock (1) cause TER to rise above control values. The ability of certain compounds to reverse the increased TER associated with various pathological states has been studied in both humans and animals. The α-toxin permeability changes were blocked by antihistamines (363), while the increased TER associated with human diabetes was less severe in insulin-responsive individuals (36). Although studies of whole-body capillary exchange are difficult to interpret with respect to transport mechanisms and sites of leakage, they remain one of the few techniques for assessing physiological and pathological alterations of capillary permeability in humans.

Another means of analyzing whole-body capillary permeability involves the measurement of lymph flow and composition in the thoracic duct (326, 409). It is not surprising that thoracic duct preparations have been widely used because of the ease of cannulating this lymphatic (it is the largest lymphatic in the body) and because of its high lymph flow (1 ml/min). The major portion of thoracic duct lymph originates in the gastrointestinal tract and liver, but the lower extremities also contribute to its composition and flow (37–39, 42, 185, 243, 287, 295, 403). In spite of this admixture the thoracic duct has proven to be useful in humans for estimating changes in the permeability of the liver and intestinal capillaries to macromolecules (403). However, results of studies of thoracic duct flux should be interpreted with caution when organs other than the liver or gastrointestinal tract are affected by experimental maneuvers or pathological states. An early paper on the effects of alterations in the composition of total protein, albumin, and β- and γ-globulins of thoracic duct lymph after administration of endotoxin illustrates this point (86). Although thoracic duct C_L/C_P and lymph flow increased after endotoxin, it is uncertain whether the increased lymph protein flux was due to an increase in the relative contribution of liver lymph (with a higher C_L/C_P) to thoracic duct flow or an increase in the permeability of capillaries in the gastrointestinal tract.

MECHANISMS OF TRANSCAPILLARY SOLUTE TRANSPORT

The mechanisms that account for the transfer of macromolecules across the capillary wall are poorly understood and are a matter of controversy. However, convection, diffusion, and vesicular exchange are accepted as the principal mechanisms involved. Convective transport is generally defined as that portion of total solute flux that is directly coupled to transcapillary volume flow, whereas transport by diffusion is considered as the solute flux that primarily depends on the transcapillary concentration gradient. That both processes are important in solute exchange is supported by the fact that the sieving coefficient for most macromolecules is significantly reduced as transcapillary volume flow is increased in all tissues except the noncirrhotic liver. With data acquired from a wide variety of physiological and ultrastructural approaches, numerous investigators contend that macromolecular transport across capillaries is predominantly convective (152, 204, 321, 328), while others hold that macromolecules move primarily by diffusion (278, 302, 312). Both of these views have been criticized on the grounds that the data on which they are based are indirect in nature.

Some researchers have used the relationship between lymphatic protein clearance and lymph flow to determine the dominant process moving proteins across the capillary wall (307, 403). In plotting this relationship a slope of 1 indicates that there is complete coupling of solute flow and volume flow (flow of undiluted plasma), whereas a slope of 0 indicates a complete independence of solute and volume flows. Although this analysis does provide a definitive answer regarding the relative contributions of diffusion and convection at the two extreme coupling slopes of 0 and 1, it is not possible from this analysis to precisely determine the relative diffusive and convective components for coupling slopes between 0 and 1. Data for solute and volume flows through capillaries with a high reflection coefficient may be misinterpreted when this analysis is applied (403). Figure 34 depicts the relationships predicted by Equation 9 between lymphatic solute clearance, relative convective flux, and lymph flow for various capillary osmotic reflection coefficients. As expected the coupling slope is 1.0 and convection accounts for the entire flux when $\sigma_d = 0$. When $\sigma_d = 0.50$ a limiting slope of 0.50 is achieved, and convection is the dominant process except at low lymph flows. Of particular interest are the data predicted for capillaries with $\sigma_d = 0.95$. In this instance solute clearance appears to be virtually uncoupled to flow except at low lymph flows. Although conventionally this seeming independence of clearance and lymph flow would be interpreted as indicating predominantly diffusive exchange (403), it is apparent that convective exchange accounts for most of the solute flux except at low lymph flows (where solute clearance and lymph

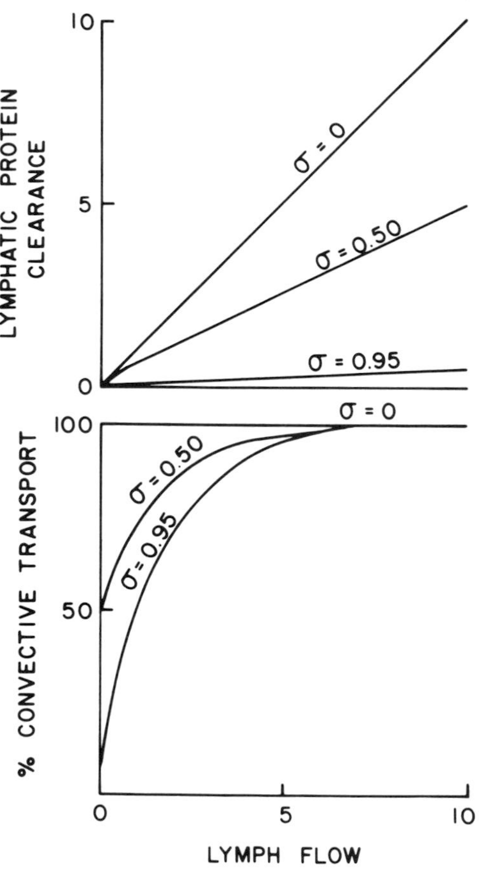

FIG. 34. Relationships between lymphatic protein clearance, % convective transport, and lymph flow predicted by Eq. 9 for osmotic reflection coefficients (σ) of 0, 0.50, and 0.95.

flow appear to be coupled). This analysis demonstrates that the relationship between lymphatic protein clearance and lymph flow alone does not allow one to readily dissociate convective and diffusive contributions even in a qualitative fashion.

Quantitative descriptions of the relative roles of diffusion and convection have been derived for a number of tissues by applying sieving data to the Kedem-Katchalsky flux relations or pore theory (Table 8). With few exceptions these analyses suggest that convection is the dominant mechanism for transport of macromolecules with dimensions similar to albumin across continuous, fenestrated, and discontinuous capillaries—accounting for 70%–100% of the total flux. Data acquired at various capillary filtration rates indicate that the relative contribution of convection increases (81, 312, 382) as transcapillary volume flow increases, while the diffusive contribution decreases with volume flow increase (Fig. 34). These findings are consistent with the theoretical prediction (see Fig. 5) that convection becomes the sole mechanism for transcapillary solute transport when the sieving coefficient of the solutes is unaltered by increases in capillary filtration rate. The fact that the sieving coefficient for larger macromolecules becomes filtration rate independent at a lower capillary filtration rate than smaller macromolecules supports the contention that the relative contribution of convection increases as the solute size increases (312, 382).

Although quantitative descriptions of membrane transport mechanisms based on pore theory and the Kedem-Katchalsky formulations provide results that are generally consistent from organ to organ, several assumptions inherent in each approach may limit their predictive value. Descriptions of membrane transport based on pore theory require assumptions about the geometric structure and uniformity of the pores, the total area of pores per unit path length, and the shape and rigidity of the solutes. Thus the accuracy of estimates of diffusion and convection based on pore theory is influenced to a large degree by the validity of estimates of membrane and solute characteristics. The fact that the membrane parameters based on pore theory (filtration coefficient, pore size, and area of pores/unit path length) can be derived from a single experimental condition is considered to be a practical advantage over the Kedem-Katchalsky solute flux formulation of Equation 2 (81, 82). However, accurate description of the permselective properties of the membrane demands that the sieving data be acquired under experimental conditions where diffusive exchange becomes infinitesimally small relative to convection (58).

In contrast to pore theory the Kedem-Katchalsky solute flux equation possesses the advantage of intuitive and computational simplicity. The Kedem-Katchalsky method differs from pore theory in that the geometric structure of the membrane need not be specified. Assessment of the relative contributions of diffusion and convection with the Kedem-Katchalsky relationship (Eq. 2) requires estimates of PS and σ, since other parameters in the equation are readily determined experimentally. These two unknown parameters can be calculated by using sieving data from two or more experimental states provided the capillary filtration rates are known. (See TECHNIQUES AND THEORETICAL BACKGROUND, p. 467, for description of estimation methods.) An inherent assumption with this approach is that membrane parameters are unchanged by the imposed experimental conditions required to alter capillary filtration rate (e.g., venous congestion, plasma volume expansion), but this assumption is not entirely supported by the available data (52, 53, 62, 368). Estimates of σ and PS for a wide range of capillary filtration rates made by the Kedem-Katchalsky solute flux equation suggest that both σ and PS increase as capillary filtration is enhanced. Solute movement across a heteroporous membrane with nonuniform pressure gradients would result in a similar rise in σ and PS without altering membrane porosity. There is also evidence suggesting that capillary permeability increases at elevated venous pressures (285, 312, 339).

Although the Kedem-Katchalsky and pore-theory approaches for separating diffusive and convective fluxes have unique assumptions and limitations, there are some premises common to both that may limit their predictive value. Diffusion and convection may not be as physically uncoupled as implied by the Kedem-Katchalsky and pore-theory equations. As il-

TABLE 8. *Relative Contributions of Diffusion and Convection in Transport of Macromolecules Across Capillary Walls*

Capillary Type	Organ	Solute	% Convection	% Diffusion	Ref.
Continuous	Skeletal muscle	Albumin	70	30	321
	Lung	Albumin	73	27	227
			76	24	262
	Subcutaneous tissue	Dextran, 42-Å radius	100	0	329
		Albumin	30	70	312
Fenestrated	Kidney (glomerulus)	Dextran, 37-Å radius	80	20	81
		PVP, 37-Å radius	82	18	382
	Small intestine	Total protein	85	15	136
Discontinuous	Liver	Albumin	~100	~0	165, 403

PVP, povidone (polyvinylpyrrolidone).

lustrated in Figures 5 and 34 diffusive exchange is heavily influenced by transcapillary volume flow. Alterations in transcapillary volume flow should significantly alter the concentration profile of macromolecules along the length of a pore and thereby alter their rates of diffusion. The expression for the solute concentration profile in the convective term of the solute flux equation also significantly influences the predictive value of these assessments. Investigators have employed arithmetical mean and integrated average concentrations as well as the plasma solute concentration as expressions for the solute concentration profile in the convective term (81, 101, 312, 368, 382). Use of the plasma solute concentration tends to enhance the predicted contribution of convective exchange, whereas the arithmetic mean concentration weights the assessment toward diffusion. The question of which expression for solute concentration profile should be used in the solute flux equation remains controversial.

TRANSPORT PATHWAYS

Since the introduction of electron microscopy, many investigators have attempted to define the structural equivalents to the small and large pores predicted by the pore theory of capillary permeability. Ultrastructural tracer studies and other morphological analyses have produced a detailed description of the nature, organization, and function of the structures that contribute to the transport characteristics of the capillary wall (35, 190, 259, 345). Although a few salient structural features of the capillary wall are encountered in every vascular bed, there are significant variations in these features from one vascular bed to another; this presumably accounts for regional differences in capillary permeability. Thus an attempt to correlate structural and physiological transport pathways for macromolecules can be made with reference to capillary types. Figure 35 illustrates the basic structural features of continuous, fenestrated, and discontinuous capillaries. For each capillary type specific pathways (or barriers) are designated that may play a role in capillary transport of macromolecules. Physiological transport pathways and their relative frequencies in several organs are presented in Table 9.

Continuous Capillaries

The continuous capillaries are the most widely distributed in mammalian tissues. They are found in

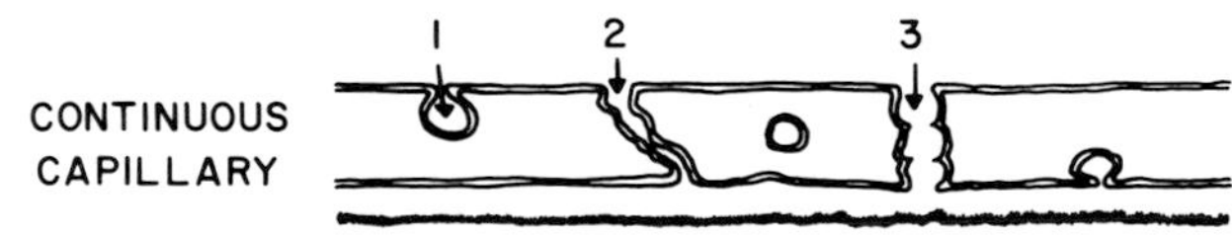

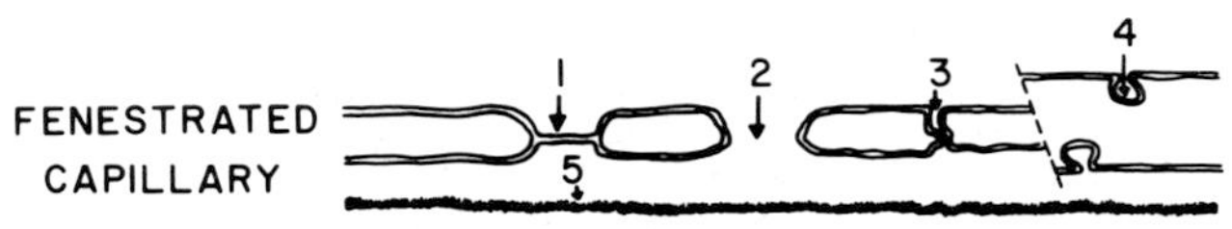

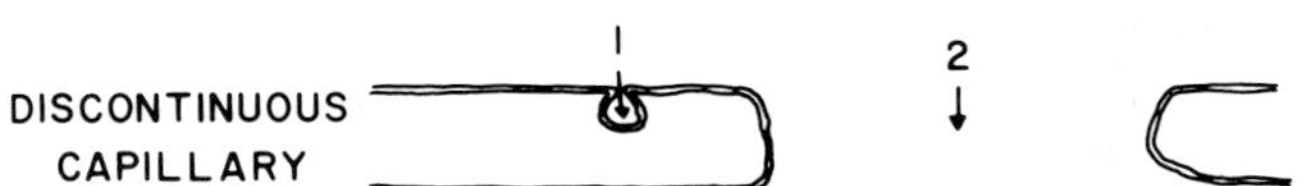

FIG. 35. Diagrammatic representation of possible transport pathways for macromolecules across continuous, fenestrated, and discontinuous capillaries. For the continuous capillary, pathways *1–3* denote pinocytotic vesicles, an intercellular junction, and a transendothelial channel, respectively. For the fenestrated capillary, pathways *1–5* denote diaphragmed fenestrae, open fenestrae, intercellular junctions, pinocytotic vesicles, and basement membrane, respectively. For the discontinuous capillary, pathways *1* and *2* represent pinocytotic vesicles and intercellular gaps, respectively.

TABLE 9. *Predicted Pore Sizes and Distribution in Various Capillary Beds*

	r_{sp}, Å	r_{lp}, Å	Fraction of Hydraulic Conductance			A_{lp}/A_{sp}	N_{lp}/N_{sp}	Fig.
			Small pores	Large pores	Other			
Dog								
Paw	47	195	0.820	0.130	0.05	1:114	1:2,064	ref. 283a
		280	0.815	0.185				12
Lung	80	200	0.80	0.16	0.04	1:31	1:195	17
Colon	53	180	0.71	0.17	0.12	1:48	1:550	31
Rat								
Skeletal muscle	67	220	0.65	0.018	0.33*	1:361	1:3,610	20
Human								
Blood:CSF barrier	70	180	0.86	0.10	0.04	1:52	1:345	22
Cat								
Small intestine	46	200	0.90	0.05	0.05	1:340	1:6,400	29
Stomach	47	250	0.75	0.23	0.02	1:92	1:2,600	30
Liver	90	330	0.20	0.80		1:3.4	1:46	33

r_{sp} and r_{lp}, Small-pore radius and large-pore radius, respectively. A_{lp}/A_{sp} and N_{lp}/N_{sp}, ratios of large-pore to small-pore areas and numbers, respectively. CSF, cerebrospinal fluid. Data in table derived from figures. *Value probably represents dilution caused by superfusion of muscle.

skeletal, heart, and smooth muscles, and in lung, skin, subcutaneous tissue, and serous and mucous membranes (35, 190). The transport pathways that may be important in macromolecule exchange in these capillaries include *1*) pinocytotic vesicles, *2*) intercellular junctions, and *3*) transendothelial channels.

1. A relatively large volume of the endothelial cell is occupied by pinocytotic vesicles with internal radii of ~250 Å. The vesicles are considered to move freely (by thermal kinetic energy) from one side to another and fuse with the plasma membrane, carrying either plasma or interstitial fluid. Ultrastructural tracer studies indicate that the vesicles participate in the transport of particles as large as 300 Å in diameter. The population density of vesicles within the endothelium increases from the arterial end to the venous end of the capillary. The overall density of vesicles also varies from one continuous capillary bed to another: vesicle population in muscle is greater than that in lung, which is greater than that in brain (73, 256, 257, 259, 298, 341, 346, 391).

2. Open intercellular junctions (maculae occludens) have been described in muscle capillaries. (Endothelial junctions in brain and lung capillaries are considered to be closed.) Ultrastructural tracer studies suggest that open intercellular junctions measure 20–60 Å in width. Intercellular junctions of arteriolar and capillary endothelia appear to be closed and are functionally impermeable to solutes with a diameter of 20 Å. However, 25%–30% of the junctions appear open in the endothelia of postcapillary venules (259, 298, 332, 341, 342, 398).

3. Patent transendothelial channels are formed by one or more vesicles that have opened simultaneously on both sides of the endothelium. The maximum internal diameters of these transient channels approach that of a single vesicle, i.e., 500 Å, yet the channels have strictures at their necks and at the points of fusion between vesicles that reduce the internal diameter to 100–400 Å. Occasionally the channel opening is provided with the equivalent of a stomatal diaphragm. The diaphragms have a porosity with an exclusion limit between molecular diameters of 50 and 110 Å. The relative frequency of transendothelial channels increases from the arterial end to the venous end of the capillary (73, 258, 259, 345).

Physiological estimates of transport pathways for macromolecules in continuous capillaries are generally consistent with small- and large-pore populations (Table 9). Estimates for small-pore radii range between 67 and 80 Å, while channels with radii of 200–280 Å are predicted for the large pores. Estimates of pore equivalents based on osmotic transients—made with macromolecules in heart, adipose tissue, lung, and mesentery—generally fall within the radius range of 55–70 Å (see REGIONAL DIFFERENCES IN CAPILLARY PERMEABILITY, p. 477.) Structural correlates to the physiological transport pathways are not readily apparent, and it is unlikely that the intercellular junctions are equivalents of the small and large pores. Nonetheless it is conceivable that there is a population of intercellular channels with dimensions comparable to these physiological estimates. Because of the rarity of such pathways, however, it is uncertain that they could be systematically found and identified. Yet the pinocytotic vesicles and transendothelial channels may well be the structural equivalents to large- and small-pore systems, respectively. The large-pore estimates for continuous capillaries (200–280 Å) are in reasonable agreement with the inner radius of an average vesicle (~250 Å).

Evidence for and against vesicular transport as a major pathway has been presented for continuous capillary beds (94, 313, 321). The transendothelial channel is a structural feature that may represent other (or alternate) large-pore and small-pore pathways. Transendothelial channels free of size-limiting structures (diaphragms and strictures) would possess an internal radius of ~200–250 Å and thus could be plausible candidates for the large-pore system involved in convective transport. The size-limiting structures of the transendothelial channels (particularly the stomatal diaphragms) may allow these structures to function as the small-pore system. The minimum internal radius of the channels produced by strictures (50–100 Å) and the limiting porosity of the stomatal diaphragms (up to 55-Å diam) are in reasonable agreement with the physiological estimates of small-pore size (67–80 Å). Although the transendothelial channel is one of the few reasonable correlates between morphological and physiological data, the significance of this transient pathway cannot be confirmed until more definitive data are acquired regarding its duration and frequency of occurrence.

Fenestrated Capillaries

The fenestrated capillaries are generally found in the intestinal mucosa, endocrine and exocrine glands, and the glomerular and peritubular capillaries of the kidney (35, 190). Because of the unique structure of fenestrated capillaries in the kidney, the following description of transport pathways is primarily limited to observations on gastrointestinal capillaries. The reader is referred to several treatises for a detailed description of structural transport pathways across glomerular capillaries (116, 191, 316, 381).

There are certain features of the fenestrated capillary wall that may serve as transport pathways for macromolecules: diaphragmed fenestrae, open fenestrae, intercellular junctions, pinocytotic vesicles, and basement membranes.

1. Fenestrae are circular openings with radii of 200–300 Å within the attenuated body of endothelial cells. Over 60% of the fenestrae are provided with an aperture or diaphragm similar in appearance to the stomatal diaphragm of the transendothelial channels.

Although the porosity of the diaphragms is unknown, these structures are considered to account for the observation that tracer molecules of 100-Å diameter or larger exit only through a relatively small fraction of the fenestral population. It is interesting that large dextran particles appear to unravel when passing through the fenestral diaphragm (35, 79, 87, 190, 259, 343, 345).

2. Fenestrae not subtended by a diaphragm appear to offer minimal restriction of transcapillary movement of macromolecules. Tracer molecules with radii between 25 and 150 Å readily permeate open fenestrae. The frequency of fenestrae (both open and diaphragmed) increases from the arterial end to the venous end of the capillary (87, 259, 343, 345).

3. Intercellular junctions are infrequent in fenestrated capillaries. Tracer molecules with radii as small as 25 Å do not permeate these junctions (87, 343).

4. Pinocytotic vesicles are found in relatively large numbers in fenestrated endothelia. Tracers with radii between 25 and 150 Å gain access to the vesicles. Ultrastructural tracer studies indicate that transport of macromolecules by vesicles is, at best, 3–8 times slower than exit through the fenestrae (87, 259, 343, 345).

5. The basement membrane surrounding fenestrated capillaries is formed by a layer of fine, fibrillar material similar to that around other capillaries. Although there are no structurally recognizable pathways across the basement membrane, there is evidence that this component reduces the rate of transport of large tracer particles. After penetration through the fenestrae, tracer particles (with radii of 62–150 Å) transiently accumulate in the subendothelial space against the basement membrane to form small clusters opposite permeable fenestrae. Particles with radii between 25 and 55 Å are not temporarily retained by the basement membrane (87, 343).

Physiological estimates of transport pathways for the fenestrated capillaries of stomach, small intestine, and colon are presented in Table 9. The data are consistent with small- and large-pore populations with radii of 46–53 Å and 180–250 Å, respectively. The structural equivalent of the large pores must clearly reside, to a large extent, at the open fenestrae (radii of 200–400 Å). The internal radii of the cytoplasmic vesicles (~250 Å) are also in reasonable agreement with the physiological large-pore estimates. Thus this structure may play a role, albeit small, in the transport of macromolecules across the fenestrated capillary. It is also plausible that differential porosities within the fibrillar structure of the basement membrane account for a component of the large-pore equivalency. Although the correlation of morphologically and physiologically defined pathways is reasonably clear for the large-pore system (343, 345), the structural equivalent to the small-pore system is not as readily apparent. The intercellular junctions are impermeable to solutes of 25-Å radius, making these structures unlikely candidates for small-pore equivalency. The porosity of the fenestral diaphragms is unknown, but it is generally considered that their porosity confirms them as the structural correlate to the small-pore system. The concept that the presence or absence of size-limiting structures within the fenestral diaphragms differentiates subpopulations corresponding to small- and large-pore systems (259, 345) seems tenable, yet the relative frequency of open and diaphragmed fenestrae appears to be much higher than the relative frequency of small and large pores predicted by the physiological data (Table 9).

Discontinuous Capillaries

The distribution of the discontinuous capillaries is more limited than other capillary types; they are found almost exclusively in the liver, spleen, and bone marrow (35, 190). These capillaries are characterized by an absence of a basement membrane. There are two structural features of the discontinuous capillary that may indicate its function as a transport pathway for macromolecules: pinocytotic vesicles and endothelial gaps. Pinocytotic vesicles are present in significant numbers in the endothelia of discontinuous capillaries, but they are considered to be negligible in macromolecule transport compared with endothelial gaps (35). Endothelial gaps are intercellular junctions with diameters ranging between 1,000 and 10,000 Å (35, 188, 289).

Correlation of physiological and morphological transport pathways across sinusoidal endothelia in discontinuous capillaries proves to be more difficult than for other capillary types. The extremely large intercellular gaps along with the absence of a basement membrane lead one to conclude that the sinusoidal wall exercises no selective filtering effect on even the largest proteins. However, the physiological data acquired when sieving is maximal between liver lymph and blood are consistent with small- and large-pore populations of 90- and 330-Å radii, respectively. The inconsistency between ultrastructural and physiological data suggests that a barrier lying past the sinusoidal wall accounts for the physiological pore predictions. The possibility that the interstitial matrix is the barrier was considered in LIVER, p. 500.

As a result of the early physiological studies of Pappenheimer and his associates (260) and the structural studies of Karnovsky (190), it was long supposed that the intercellular junctions are the structural counterparts to the small-pore system. However, in recent years the dimensions of the small pores have been revised upward, whereas newer ultrastructural tracer studies have led to a reduction in the predicted dimensions of the capillary intercellular junctions (259). From studies of macromolecules it is now reasonably clear that the intercellular junctions are unlikely counterparts of the small-pore system in all capillary beds. For continuous and fenestrated capillaries, size-limiting structures within transendothelial channels (diaphragms, strictures) and fenestrae (diaphragms) are invoked to explain the small-pore system predicted from physiological data (250). However, the porosity and frequency of such structures remain uncertain.

Pinocytotic vesicles and leaks (large intercellular gaps) were once the obvious correlates of the large-pore system. After many years of research, the existence of leaks in continuous capillaries remains unconfirmed; therefore patent transendothelial channels may be a viable alternative. The contribution of vesicles to the large-pore system is controversial, yet they remain a likely counterpart of the large-pore system in continuous capillaries. For fenestrated and discontinuous capillaries the structural equivalents of the large-pore system are fairly clear.

It is difficult to find even reasonable agreement between structural and physiological postulates for small- and large-pore systems, presumably because of the many inherent limitations of the techniques employed. Methodological problems associated with tissue fixation, exogenous electron-dense markers, and interpretation of tracer concentration profiles may limit the extrapolation of morphological findings to physiological data (75). Equally limiting are the problems associated with physiological studies: heterogeneity of capillary types within a tissue (e.g., lung and small intestine), restriction of macromolecules by barriers between the capillary wall and the lymphatic, a lymphatic concentrating ability, and non-steady-state conditions. Much of the physiological data thus far acquired (in the paw, lung, skeletal muscle, and kidney) does not lend itself to accurate pore estimates because reliable σ_d values are unavailable. Progress toward a more definitive correlation between structural and functional data depends on development of new approaches and refinement of existing techniques in both fields.

SUMMARY

This review of capillary permeability to macromolecules clearly indicates that much progress has been made in this area over the past 15 years. The original techniques and ideas of Landis and Pappenheimer (203) and Mayerson (224) have been refined and extended to many organ systems and single-capillary preparations. Although information has been obtained from several tissues through a wide variety of techniques, there is a relative paucity of knowledge on the permeability of skeletal, myocardial, and smooth muscle, as well as of adipose tissue and nonhepatic sinusoidal capillaries (e.g., spleen). Considerably more is known about the permeability of subcutaneous and pulmonary capillaries to large solutes; however, the bulk of the information derived from these tissues is only semiquantitative in nature. Those tissues that have afforded the most quantitive description of macromolecular permeability include the kidney (glomerular capillaries) and small intestine. In spite of the wealth of information available, only a small fraction is applicable to estimating the membrane parameters required to describe transcapillary solute movement, i.e., the reflection and permeability coefficients. Even in the kidney the available data do not help predict these parameters.

In most permeability studies the molecular probes and capillary pores have been treated as rigid structures exhibiting no net electrical charge. Data from the kidney clearly indicate that the electrical charge and configuration of macromolecules greatly influence transglomerular exchange. Since endogenous plasma proteins exhibit a wide spectrum of net electrical charges and configurations in physiological solutions, future emphasis should be placed on assessing whether the influences of solute charge and configuration on transcapillary exchange are exhibited in tissues other than the kidney. The need for such studies is exemplified by recent reports (280a, 367a) that capillaries in small intestine and lung behave as positive charged filters—findings opposite to those observed in the kidney and skeletal muscle.

The application of irreversible thermodynamics to biological membrane transport has led to a uniform description of the membrane parameters and forces involved in solute and solvent flows across the capillary wall. The Kedem-Katchalsky solute flux formulation (Eq. 2) has been extensively applied to macromolecule flux data because of its intuitive simplicity and convenient dissociation of diffusive and convective solute fluxes. However, recent evidence suggests that the Kedem-Katchalsky solute flux equation cannot accurately describe the data for transcapillary solute flux. Newer equations have been introduced that more accurately describe the data, but these equations do not allow for easy separation of diffusive and convective solute fluxes. Future emphasis should be placed on developing new theoretical and experimental approaches allowing for separation of these two components of flux as well as for separation of simple diffusion from vesicular exchange.

The ultimate goal of most investigations on the permeability of capillaries to macromolecules is to provide a physiological correlate to the transport pathways predicted by electron microscopists. Application of hydrodynamic pore theory to the data provides relatively consistent predictions for small-pore and large-pore dimensions and numbers for tissues within a given capillary type. In spite of the consistency of the predictions of pore size, much of the physiological data does not provide accurate pore estimates because reliable estimates of membrane reflection and permeability coefficients are unavailable. Future studies on macromolecule permeability should be designed to evaluate these membrane parameters, and studies should allow for individual assessment of solute size, charge, and configuration on transcapillary solute flux. Until the appropriate information has been obtained, it may be difficult to describe the mechanisms of macromolecule transport across capillaries under either normal or pathological conditions.

The authors are grateful to Drs. Peter R. Kvietys, James C. Parker, and Michael A. Perry for their helpful suggestions and criticisms. We also wish to thank Leigh Cosper and Carol Sims for their expert clerical help, and Penny Cook for her excellent illustrations.

Research was supported by National Heart, Lung, and Blood Institute Grants 15680, 22549, and 26441. Dr. Granger was a recipient of a Research Career Development Award from the National Heart, Lung, and Blood Institute.

APPENDIX A

Rutili et al. (329) have shown both mathematically and experimentally that $PS\Delta C \rightarrow 0$ when high volume flow (high lymph flows) occurs across capillary walls. This was the case when either the Kedem-Katchalsky [$\bar{C}_P = C_P$ or $(C_P + C_L)/2$] or the Patlak equations were used to estimate $PS\Delta C$ at high capillary filtration rates. How can the equations predict this behavior, since $PS\Delta C$ must approximate a constant at high volume flows? Consider the following analyses

$$J_s = (1 - \sigma)C_P J_v + PS\Delta C \quad (1A)$$

$$J_s = (1 - \sigma)\left(\frac{C_P + C_L}{2}\right)J_v + PS\Delta C \quad (2A)$$

and

$$J_s = (1 - \sigma)C_P J_v + \left(\frac{x}{e^x - 1}\right)PS\Delta C \quad (3A)$$

where x is the Péclet number. Using Equation 1A and incorporating C_P for the average concentration, $C_L/C_P \rightarrow 1 - \sigma$ at high volume flow

$$J_s = C_L J_v$$

$$= \left(\frac{C_L}{C_P}\right)C_P J_v + PS\Delta C$$

or

$$C_L J_v = C_L J_v + PS\Delta C$$

and therefore $PS\Delta C = 0$.

Using Equation 2A and the arithmetic average for $\bar{C}_P$, $C_L/C_P \rightarrow (1 - \sigma)/(1 + \sigma)$ at high volume flows and Equation 2A can be rewritten as

$$C_L J_v = \left[\frac{1 - \sigma)J_v}{2}\right](C_L + C_P) + PS\Delta C$$

$$= \left[\frac{(1 - \sigma)J_v C_P}{2}\right]\left[1 + \left(\frac{C_L}{C_P}\right)\right] + PS\Delta C$$

$$= \left[\frac{(1 - \sigma)J_v C_P}{2}\right]\left[1 + \left(\frac{1 - \sigma}{1 + \sigma}\right)\right] + PS\Delta C$$

$$= \left[\frac{(1 - \sigma)J_v C_P}{2}\right]\left(\frac{1 + \sigma + 1 - \sigma}{1 + \sigma}\right) + PS\Delta C$$

$$= \left[\frac{(1 - \sigma)J_v C_P}{2}\right]\left(\frac{2}{1 + \sigma}\right) + PS\Delta C$$

$$= \left(\frac{1 - \sigma}{1 + \sigma}\right)J_v C_P + PS\Delta C$$

or since $C_L/C_P = (1 - \sigma)/(1 + \sigma)$

$$J_s = \left(\frac{C_L}{C_P}\right)J_v C_P + PS\Delta C$$

and again, $PS\Delta C = 0$.

This behavior can be explained when the Patlak equation is written in the form designated as Equation 3A. The exponential term $x/e^x - 1$ approaches 0 as $J_v \rightarrow \infty$ and $PS\Delta C$ does not approach 0 but remains invariant. However, for the Kedem-Katchalsky formulation, $PS\Delta C$ contains $x/e^x - 1$ and must go to 0 at high volume flows. At first this appears to invalidate the Kedem-Katchalsky equation; however, A. K. Solomon (unpublished observations) has recently pointed out that if the friction between solute and solvent approaches ∞ by the Kedem-Katchalsky formulation, then permeability coefficient $P \rightarrow 0$. This is true of flow rates at high volume across any membrane permeable to the solute. The Kedem-Katchalsky formulations correctly describe sieving data, but the limiting C_L/C_P is different depending on the choice of $\bar{C}_P$. Furthermore $PS\Delta C$ really cannot equal 0 because PS is a constant and ΔC must approach a limiting value at high volume flows. The value of ΔC only appears to approach 0 because the term incorporates $x/(e^x - 1)$ into P when the Kedem-Katchalsky equations are used to predict J_s. Thus any attempt to separate diffusional and convective components of flux with these formulations is incorrect if $PS\Delta C$ is assumed to be constant.

APPENDIX B

Equations 9 and 66 from Levitt (210) represent the reflection coefficient σ_s and the drag function $G_\lambda(\beta)$ as

$$\sigma_s = 1 - 2\lambda^2 \int_0^{\lambda^{-1}-1} G\lambda(\beta)d\beta \quad (1B)$$

and

$$G\lambda(\beta) = \frac{2(1 - \frac{2}{3}\lambda^2 - 0.20217\lambda^5 - \gamma^2)}{1 - 0.75857\lambda^5} \quad (2B)$$

where λ = ratio of solute radius (a) to pore radius (R_p), β = ratio of distance from axis to center of solute (b) to solute radius (a), and γ = ratio of distance from axis to center of solute to radius of the pore.

The λ^5 terms are dropped from Equation 2B and the result is substituted into Equation 1B to yield

$$\sigma_s = 1 - 2\lambda^2 \int_0^{\lambda^{-1}-1} 2(1 - \tfrac{2}{3}\lambda^2 - \gamma^2)\beta d\beta$$

Since $\gamma = \beta a/R_p$

$$\sigma_s = 1 - 2\lambda^2 \int_0^{\lambda^{-1}-1} 2\left[1 - \tfrac{2}{3}\lambda^2 - \left(\frac{\beta a}{R_p}\right)^2\right]\beta d\beta$$

$$= 1 - 4\lambda^2 \left| \frac{\beta}{2} - \frac{\lambda^2\beta^2}{3} - \frac{\beta^4 a^2}{4R_p{}^2} \right|_0^{\lambda^{-1}-1}$$

$$= 1 - 4\lambda^2[(\tfrac{1}{2} - \tfrac{1}{3}\lambda^2)(\lambda^{-2} - 2\lambda^{-1} + 1)$$

$$- \tfrac{1}{4}\lambda^2(\lambda^{-4} + 4\lambda^{-3} + 6\lambda^{-2} - 4\lambda^{-1} + 1)]$$

$$= 1 - 4[\tfrac{1}{2} - \lambda + \tfrac{1}{2}\lambda^2 - \tfrac{1}{3}\lambda^2 + \tfrac{2}{3}\lambda^3$$

$$- \tfrac{1}{3}\lambda^4 - \tfrac{1}{4} + \lambda - \tfrac{3}{2}\lambda^2 + \lambda^3 - \tfrac{1}{4}\lambda^4]$$

$$= 1 - 4[\tfrac{1}{4} - \tfrac{4}{3}\lambda^2 + \tfrac{5}{3}\lambda^3 - \tfrac{7}{12}\lambda^4]$$

or

$$\sigma_s = \tfrac{16}{3}\lambda^2 - \tfrac{20}{3}\lambda^3 + \tfrac{7}{3}\lambda^4 \tag{3B}$$

This integration of Equation 1B derived by Levitt (210) was kindly provided by Dr. Robert Drake (107), in whose article Equation 3B appears.

REFERENCES

1. ABEL, F. L., AND M. B. WOLF. Increased capillary permeability to ^{125}I-labeled albumin during experimental hemorrhagic shock. *Trans. N. Y. Acad. Sci.* 35: 243–252, 1973.
2. ADAMSON, T. M., R. D. H. BOYD, J. R. HILL, I. C. S. NORMAND, E. O. R. REYNOLDS, AND L. B. STRANG. Effect of asphyxia due to umbilical cord occlusion in the foetal lamb on leakage of liquid from the circulation and on permeability of lung capillaries to albumin. *J. Physiol. London* 207: 493–505, 1970.
3. ALPERT, J. S., J. COFFMAN, M. C. BALODIMON, L. KONZ, AND J. S. SOELDNER. Capillary permeability and blood flow in skeletal muscle of patients with diabetes mellitus and genetic prediabetes. *N. Engl. J. Med.* 286: 454–460, 1972.
4. ALVAREZ, O. A., AND D. YUDILEVICH. Heart capillary permeability to lipid-insoluble molecules. *J. Physiol. London* 202: 45–48, 1969.
5. AMELANG, E., C. M. PRASAD, R. M. RAYMOND, AND G. J. GREGA. Interactions among inflammatory mediators on edema formation in the canine forelimb. *Circ. Res.* 49: 298–306, 1981.
6. ANDERSON, R. W., AND W. C. DEVRIES. Transvascular fluid and protein dynamics in the lung following hemorrhagic shock. *J. Surg. Res.* 20: 281–290, 1976.
7. APPELGREN, L., S. JACOBSSON, AND I. KJELLMER. Estimation of the protein concentration of the capillary filtrate by an isotope technique. *Acta Physiol. Scand.* 66: 353–361, 1966.
8. AREEKUL, S. Dynamics of transcapillary fluid exchange in the isolated rabbit ear. *Acta Soc. Med. Ups.* 74: 118–128, 1969.
9. AREEKUL, S. Reflection coefficients of neutral and sulphate-substituted dextran molecules in the isolated perfused rabbit ear. *Acta Soc. Med. Ups.* 74: 129–138, 1969.
10. AREEKUL, S. Effect of dextran 40 on the accumulation of ^{131}I-labelled human serum albumin in the isolated perfused rabbit ear. *Acta Soc. Med. Ups.* 74: 139–142, 1969.
11. ARESKOG, N. H., G. ARTURSON, AND G. GROTTE. Studies on heart lymph. *Acta Physiol. Scand.* 62: 209–217, 1964.
12. ARESKOG, N. H., G. ARTURSON, G. GROTTE, AND G. WALLENIUS. Studies on heart lymph. II. Capillary permeability of the dog's heart using dextran as a test substance. *Acta Physiol. Scand.* 62: 218–233, 1964.
13. ARFORS, K. E., G. ARTURSON, D. BERGQVIST, AND E. SVENSJÖ. Effect of inhibition of prostaglandin synthesis on microvascular haemostasis and macromolecular leakage. *Thromb. Res.* 8: 393–402, 1976.
14. ARFORS, K. E., G. RUTILI, AND E. SVENSJÖ. Microvascular transport of macromolecules in normal and inflammatory conditions. *Acta Physiol. Scand. Suppl.* 463: 93–103, 1979.
15. ARTURSON, G. The plasma kinins in thermal injury. *Scand. J. Clin. Lab. Invest. Suppl.* 107: 153, 1969.
16. ARTURSON, G. Prostaglandins in human burn-wound secretion. *Burns* 3: 112–117, 1977.
17. ARTURSON, G. Microvascular permeability to macromolecules in thermal injury. *Acta Physiol. Scand. Suppl.* 463: 111–122, 1979.
18. ARTURSON, G., N. A. ARESKOG, K. ARFORS, G. GROTTE, AND P. MALMBERG. The transport of macromolecules across the blood-lymph barrier. *Bibl. Anat.* 10: 228–233, 1969.
19. ARTURSON, G., AND K. GRANATH. Dextrans as test molecules in studies of the functional ultrastructure of biological membranes. *Clin. Chim. Acta* 37: 309–322, 1972.
20. ARTURSON, G., T. GROTH, AND G. GROTTE. Human glomerular membrane porosity and filtration pressure: dextran clearance data analyzed by theoretical models. *Clin. Sci.* 40: 137–158, 1971.
21. ARTURSON, G., T. GROTH, AND G. GROTTE. The functional ultrastructure of the blood-lymph barrier. Computer analysis of data from dog heart-lymph experiments using theoretical models. *Acta Physiol. Scand. Suppl.* 374: 1–29, 1972.
22. AUKLAND, K., AND H. O. FADNES. Protein concentration of interstitial fluid collected from rat skin by a wick method. *Acta Physiol. Scand.* 88: 350–358, 1973.
23. AUKLAND, K., AND H. M. JOHNSEN. Protein concentration and colloid osmotic pressure of rat skeletal muscle interstitial fluid. *Acta Physiol. Scand.* 91: 354–364, 1974.
24. AURSNES, I. Increased permeability of capillaries to protein during thrombocytopenia: an experimental study in the rabbit. *Microvasc. Res.* 7: 283–295, 1974.
25. BAKER, C. H. Nonhemodynamic effects of histamine on gracilis muscle capillary permeability. *J. Pharmacol. Exp. Ther.* 211: 672–677, 1979.
26. BAKER, P. L., M. KEUNZIG, AND L. F. PELTIER. Pulmonary lymph in experimental fat embolism. *Surgery* 69: 686–691, 1971.
27. BALLARD, K., AND W. PERL. Osmotic reflection coefficients of canine subcutaneous adipose tissue endothelium. *Microvasc. Res.* 16: 224–236, 1978.
28. BARROWMAN, J. A. *Physiology of the Gastro-Intestinal Lymphatic System.* London: Cambridge Univ. Press, 1978. (Physiol. Soc. Monog. 33.)
29. BARROWMAN, J. A., AND D. N. GRANGER. Hepatic lymph. In: *Hepatic Circulation in Health and Disease*, edited by W. W. Lautt. New York: Raven, 1981, p. 137–152.
30. BARROWMAN, J. A., AND K. B. ROBERTS. The role of the lymphatic system in the absorption of water from the intestine of the rat. *Q. J. Exp. Physiol.* 52: 19–30, 1967.
31. BASCH, A., AND G. I. FAZEKAS. Increased permeability of the blood-brain barrier following experimental thermal injury of the skin. *Angiologica* 7: 357–364, 1970.
32. BELL, D. R., M. J. KEYL, AND W. L. PERRY. Experimental study of sites of lymph formation in the canine kidney. *Invest. Urol.* 8: 356–362, 1970.
33. BELL, D. R., G. G. PINTER, AND P. D. WILSON. Albumin permeability of the peritubular capillaries in rat renal cortex. *J. Physiol. London* 279: 621–640, 1978.
34. BELL, D. R., P. D. WATSON, AND E. M. RENKIN. Exclusion of plasma proteins in interstitium of tissues from the dog hind paw. *Am. J. Physiol.* 239 (*Heart Circ. Physiol.* 8): H532–H538, 1980.
35. BENNETT, H. S., J. H. LUFT, AND J. C. HAMPTON. Morphological classification of vertebrate blood capillaries. *Am. J. Physiol.* 196: 381–390, 1959.

36. BERGLUND, B., S. EFENDÍC, T. STRANDELL, AND R. LUFT. Capillary permeability in healthy males with different insulin response to glucose. *Eur. J. Clin. Invest.* 9: 363–367, 1979.
37. BERGQVIST, D., E. SVENSJÖ, AND K. E. ARFORS. Effect of O-(β-hydroxyethyl)-rutoside (HR) on macromolecular leakage, thrombosis and haemostasis in experimental animals. *Upsala J. Med. Sci.* 83: 123–127, 1978.
38. BERSON, S. A., R. S. YALOW, S. S. SCHREIBER, AND J. POST. Tracer experiments with ^{131}I-labeled human serum albumin: distribution and degradation studies. *J. Clin. Invest.* 32: 746–768, 1953.
39. BINDER, A. S., K. NAKAHARA, K. OHKUDA, W. KAGELER, AND N. C. STAUB. Effect of heparin or fibrinogen depletion on lung fluid balance in sheep after emboli. *J. Appl. Physiol.: Respirat. Environ. Exercise Physiol.* 47: 213–219, 1979.
40. BLACKSHEAR, G., AND F. VARGAS. Filtration coefficient of heart capillaries obtained from osmotic and hydrostatic pressure gradients. *Microvasc. Res.* 17: 584, 1979.
41. BLAKE, L. H. Mathematical modeling of steady state fluid and protein exchange in lung. In: *Lung Biology in Health and Disease. Lung Water and Solute Exchange*, edited by N. C. Staub. New York: Dekker, 1978, vol. 7, p. 99–127.
42. BLAKE, L. H., AND N. C. STAUB. Pulmonary vascular transport in sheep: a mathematical model. *Microvasc. Res.* 12: 197–220, 1976.
43. BLAND, R. D., R. H. DEMLING, S. L. SELINGER, AND N. C. STAUB. Effects of alveolar hypoxia on lung fluid and protein transport in unanesthetized sheep. *Circ. Res.* 40: 269–273, 1977.
44. BLAND, R. D., AND D. D. MCMILLAN. Lung fluid dynamics in awake newborn lambs. *J. Clin. Invest.* 60: 1107–1115, 1977.
45. BØ, G., A. HAUGE, AND G. NICOLAYSEN. Alveolar pressure and lung volume as determinants of net transvascular fluid filtration. *J. Appl. Physiol.: Respirat. Environ. Exercise Physiol.* 42: 476–482, 1977.
46. BOHRER, M. P., C. BAYLIS, D. HUMES, R. J. GLASSOCK, C. R. ROBERTSON, AND B. M. BRENNER. Permselectivity of the glomerular capillary wall. Facilitated filtration of circulating polycations. *J. Clin. Invest.* 61: 72–78, 1978.
47. BOHRER, M. P., W. M. DEEN, C. R. ROBERTSON, J. L. TROY, AND B. M. BRENNER. Influence of molecular configuration on the passage of macromolecules across the glomerular capillary wall. *J. Gen. Physiol.* 74: 583–593, 1979.
48. BOONYAPRAKOB, U., P. M. TAYLOR, D. W. WATSON, V. WATERMAN, AND E. LOPATA. Hypoxia and protein clearance from the pulmonary vascular beds of adult dogs and pups. *Am. J. Physiol.* 216: 1013–1019, 1969.
49. BOWERS, R. E., K. BRIGHAM, AND P. J. OWEN. Salicylate pulmonary edema: mechanism in sheep and review of the clinical literature. *Am. Rev. Respir. Dis.* 115: 261–268, 1977.
50. BOYD, R. D. H., J. R. HILL, P. W. HUMPHREYS, I. C. S. NORMAND, E. O. R. REYNOLDS, AND L. B. STRANG. Permeability of lung capillaries to macromolecules in foetal and newborn lambs and sheep. *J. Physiol. London* 201: 567–588, 1969.
51. BRACE, R. A. Fitting straight lines to experimental data. *Am. J. Physiol.* 233 (*Regulatory Integrative Comp. Physiol.* 2): R94–R99, 1977.
52. BRACE, R. A., D. N. GRANGER, AND A. E. TAYLOR. Analysis of lymphatic protein flux data. II. Effect of capillary heteroporosity on estimates of reflection coefficients and PS products. *Microvasc. Res.* 14: 215–226, 1977.
53. BRACE, R. A., D. N. GRANGER, AND A. E. TAYLOR. Analysis of lymphatic protein flux data. III. Use of the nonlinear flux equation to estimate σ and PS. *Microvasc. Res.* 16: 297–303, 1978.
54. BRÅNEMARK, P.-I., R. EKHOLM, AND J. LINDHE. Colloidal carbon used for identification of vascular permeability. *Med. Exp.* 18: 139–150, 1968.
55. BRENNER, B. M., C. BAYLIS, AND W. M. DEEN. Transport of molecules across renal glomerular capillaries. *Physiol. Rev.* 56: 502–534, 1976.
56. BRENNER, B. M., M. P. BOHRER, C. BAYLIS, AND W. M. DEEN. Determinants of glomerular permselectivity: insights derived from observations in vivo. *Kidney Int.* 12: 229–237, 1977.
57. BRENNER, B. M., T. H. HOSTETTER, AND H. D. HUMES. Glomerular permselectivity: barrier function based on discrimination of molecular size and charge. *Am. J. Physiol.* 234 (*Renal Fluid Electrolyte Physiol.* 3): F455–F460, 1978.
58. BRESLER, E. H., AND L. J. GROOME. On equations for combined convective and diffusive transport of neutral solutes across porous membranes. *Am. J. Physiol.* 241 (*Renal Fluid Electrolyte Physiol.* 10): F469–F476, 1981.
59. BRESLER, E. H., E. A. MASON, AND R. P. WENDT. Appraisal of equations for neutral solute flux across porous sieving membranes. *Biophys. Chem.* 4: 229–236, 1976.
60. BRIGHAM, K. L., R. E. BOWERS, AND J. HAYNES. Increased sheep lung vascular permeability caused by *Escherichia coli* endotoxin. *Circ. Res.* 45: 292–297, 1979.
61. BRIGHAM, K. L., R. E. BOWERS, AND P. J. OWEN. Effect of antihistamines on the lung vascular response to histamine in unanesthetized sheep. *J. Clin. Invest.* 58: 391–398, 1976.
62. BRIGHAM, K. L., T. R. HARRIS, R. E. BOWERS, AND R. J. ROSELLI. Lung vascular permeability: inferences from measurements of plasma to lung lymph protein transport. *Lymphology* 12: 177–190, 1979.
63. BRIGHAM, K. L., AND P. J. OWEN. Mechanism of the serotonin effect on lung transvascular fluid and protein movement in awake sheep. *Circ. Res.* 36: 761–770, 1975.
64. BRIGHAM, K. L., AND P. J. OWEN. Increased sheep lung vascular permeability caused by histamine. *Circ. Res.* 37: 647–657, 1975.
65. BRIGHAM, K. L., W. C. WOOLVERTON, L. H. BLAKE, AND N. C. STAUB. Increased sheep lung vascular permeability caused by *Pseudomonas* bacteremia. *J. Clin. Invest.* 54: 792–804, 1974.
66. BRIGHAM, K. L., W. C. WOOLVERTON, AND N. C. STAUB. Reversible increase in pulmonary vascular permeability after *Pseudomonas aeruginosa* bacteremia in unanesthetized sheep. *Chest* 65, Suppl.: 51S–54S, 1974.
67. BRIGHTMAN, M. W. Ultrastructural characteristics of adult choroid plexus: relation to the blood-cerebrospinal fluid barrier to proteins. In: *The Choroid Plexus in Health and Disease*, edited by M. G. Netsky and S. Shuangshoti. Charlottesville: Univ. of Virginia Press, 1975, p. 86–112.
68. BRIGHTMAN, M. W., I. KLATZO, Y. OLSSON, AND T. S. REESE. The blood-brain barrier to proteins under normal and pathological conditions. *J. Neurol. Sci.* 10: 215–239, 1970.
69. BRIGHTMAN, M. W., S. I. RAPOPORT, AND T. S. REESE. Osmotic opening of tight junctions in cerebral endothelium. *J. Comp. Neurol.* 152: 317–326, 1974.
70. BRIGHTMAN, M. W., AND T. S. REESE. Junctions between intimately apposed cell membranes in the vertebrate brain. *J. Cell Biol.* 40: 648–677, 1969.
71. BRØCHNER-MORTENSEN, J., J. DITZEL, C. E. MOGENSEN, AND P. RØDBRO. Microvascular permeability to albumin and glomerular filtration rate in diabetic and normal children. *Diabetologia* 16: 307–311, 1979.
72. BRUGGEMAN, T. M. Plasma proteins in canine gastric lymph. *Gastroenterology* 68: 1204–1210, 1975.
73. BRUNS, R. R., AND G. E. PALADE. Studies on blood capillaries. II. Transport of ferritin molecules across the wall of muscle capillaries. *J. Cell Biol.* 37: 277–299, 1968.
74. BUCKLEY, I. K., AND G. B. RYAN. Increased vascular permeability: effect of histamine and serotonin on rat mesenteric blood vessels in vivo. Q. J. Exp. Physiol. 55: 329–347, 1969
75. BUNDGAARD, M. Transport pathways in capillaries—in search of pores. *Annu. Rev. Physiol.* 42: 325–326, 1980.
76. BUTLER, K., AND G. P. LEWIS. Effect of anti-inflammatory agents on the changes in local lymph after thermal injury. *Br. J. Pharmacol.* 45: 644–650, 1972.
77. BUTTERFIELD, J. D., AND C. P. MCGRAW. Free radical pathology. *Stroke* 9: 443–447, 1978.

78. CARTER, R. D., W. L. JOYNER, AND E. M. RENKIN. Effects of histamine and some other substances on molecular selectivity of the capillary wall to plasma proteins and dextran. *Microvasc. Res.* 7: 31–48, 1974.
79. CASLEY-SMITH, J. R., P. J. O'DONOGHUE, AND K. W. J. CROCKER. The quantitative relationships between fenestrae in jejunal capillaries and connective tissue channels: proof of "tunnel capillaries." *Microvasc. Res.* 9: 78–100, 1975.
80. CHANG, R. L. S., W. M. DEEN, C. R. ROBERTSON, AND B. M. BRENNER. Permselectivity of the glomerular capillary wall. III. Restricted transport of polyanions. *Kidney Int.* 8: 212–218, 1975.
81. CHANG, R. L. S., W. M. DEEN, C. R. ROBERTSON, AND B. M. BRENNER. Permselectivity of the glomerular capillary wall. Studies of experimental glomerulonephritis using neutral dextrans. *J. Clin. Invest.* 57: 1272–1286, 1976.
82. CHANG, R. L. S., C. R. ROBERTSON, W. M. DEEN, AND B. M. BRENNER. Permselectivity of the glomerular capillary wall to macromolecules. I. Theoretical considerations. *Biophys. J.* 15: 861–886, 1975.
83. CHANG, R. L. S., I. F. UEKI, J. TROY, W. M. DEEN, C. R. ROBERTSON, AND B. M. BRENNER. Permselectivity of the glomerular capillary wall to macromolecules. II. Experimental studies in rats using neutral dextran. *Biophys. J.* 15: 887–906, 1975.
84. CHEN, H. I., H. J. GRANGER, AND A. E. TAYLOR. Interaction of capillary, interstitial, and lymphatic forces in the canine hindpaw. *Circ. Res.* 39: 245–254, 1976.
85. CHERNOV, G. A., Z. I. SHEREMET, AND R. V. LENSKAYA. Effect of irradiation on vascular permeability and on blood mucopolysaccharide and serotonin levels. *Med. Radiol.* 9: 58, 1974.
86. CHIEN, S., D. G. SINCLAIR, R. J. DELLENBACK, C. CHANG, B. PERIC, S. USAMI, AND M. I. GREGERSEN. Effect of endotoxin on capillary permeability to macromolecules. *Am. J. Physiol.* 207: 518–522, 1964.
87. CLEMENTI, F., AND G. E. PALADE. Intestinal capillaries. I. Permeability to peroxidase and ferritin. *J. Cell Biol.*. 41: 33–58, 1969.
88. CLEMENTI, F., AND G. E. PALADE. Intestinal capillaries. II. Structural effects of EDTA and histamine. *J. Cell Biol.* 42: 706–714, 1969.
89. CONRADI, S., L. KAIJSER, AND L.-O. RONNEVI. Capillary permeability in ALS, determined through transcapillary escape rate of ^{125}I-albumin. *Acta Neurol. Scand.* 57: 257–261, 1978.
90. COURTICE, F. C. Lymph and plasma proteins: barriers to their movement throughout the extracellular fluid. *Lymphology* 4: 9–17, 1971.
91. COURTICE, F. C., E. P. ADAMS, AND J. DEMPSEY. The effect of ischaemia on acid phosphatase, β-glucuronidase and lactic acid dehydrogenase in lymph from hindpaw of the rabbit. *Lymphology* 5: 67–80, 1972.
92. COURTICE, F. C., AND D. G. GARLICK. The permeability of the capillary wall to the different plasma lipoproteins of the hypercholesterolaemic rabbit in relation to their size. *Q. J. Exp. Physiol.* 47: 221–227, 1961.
93. COURTICE, F. C., AND M. S. SABINE. Effect of different degrees of thermal injury on the transfer of proteins and lipoproteins from plasma to lymph in the leg of the hypercholesterolaemic rabbit. *Aust. J. Exp. Biol. Med. Sci.* 44: 37–44, 1966.
94. CRONE, C. Ariadne's thread—an autobiographical essay on capillary permeability. *Microvasc. Res.* 20: 133–149, 1980.
95. CRONE, C., AND N. A. LASSEN (editors). *Capillary Permeability.* Copenhagen: Munksgaard, 1970. (Alfred Benzon Symp. 2.)
96. CUNNINGHAM, A. L., AND J. V. HURLEY. Alpha-naphthylthiourea-induced pulmonary oedema in the rat: a topographical and electron-microscope study. *J. Pathol.* 106: 25–35, 1972.
97. DALLFORF, F. G., G. T. KEUSCH, AND H. L. LIVINGSTON. Transcellular permeability of capillaries in experimental cholera. *Am. J. Pathol.* 57: 153–160, 1969.
98. DAVENPORT, H. W., AND J. G. WOOD. Changes in gastric vascular permeability to plasma proteins during a model protein-losing state (Abstract). *Physiologist* 22(4): 26, 1979.
99. DAVENPORT, H. W., J. G. WOOD, T. M. BRUGGEMAN, AND I. L. DAVENPORT. Attempt to estimate changes in gastric vascular permeability to plasma proteins by intraarterial bolus injection of labeled fibrinogen and albumin (Abstract). *Physiologist* 21(4): 26, 1978.
100. DEEN, W. M., M. P. BOHRER, AND B. M. BRENNER. Macromolecule transport across glomerular capillaries: application of pore theory. *Kidney Int.* 16: 353–365, 1979.
101. DEEN, W. M., I. F. UEKI, AND B. M. BRENNER. Permeability of renal peritubular capillaries to neutral dextrans and endogenous albumin. *Am. J. Physiol.* 231: 283–291, 1976.
102. DE GENNES, P. G. Reptation of a polymer chain in the presence of fixed obstacles. *J. Chem. Phys.* 55: 572–579, 1971.
103. DEL MAESTRO, R. F., K. ARFORS, AND F. N. MCKENZIE. The effect of infusion solution temperature on albumin permeability through the intact and damaged blood-brain barrier. *Bibl. Anat.* 18: 229–232, 1979.
104. DEMLING, R. H., G. NIEHAUS, A. PEREA, AND J. A. WILL. Effect of burn-induced hypoproteinemia on pulmonary transvascular fluid filtration rate. *Surgery* 85: 339–343, 1979.
105. DIANA, J. N., S. C. LONG, AND H. YAO. Effect of histamine on equivalent pore radius in capillaries of isolated dog hindlimb. *Microvasc. Res.* 4: 413–437, 1972.
106. DIVE, C. C., A. NADALINI, AND J. F. HEREMANS. Origin and composition of hepatic lymph proteins in the dog. *Lymphology* 4: 133–139, 1979.
107. DRAKE, R., T. ADAIR, D. TRABER, AND J. GABEL. Contamination of caudal mediastinal node efferent lymph in sheep. *Am. J. Physiol.* 241 (*Heart Circ. Physiol.* 10): H354–H357, 1981.
108. DRAKE, R., AND E. DAVIS. A corrected equation for the calculation of reflection coefficients. *Microvasc. Res.* 15: 259, 1978.
109. DRAKE, R. E., AND A. E. TAYLOR. Tissue and capillary force changes during the formation of intra-alveolar edema. In: *Progress in Lymphology*, edited by R. C. Mayall and M. H. Witte. New York: Plenum, 1977, p. 13–17.
110. DUMONT, A. E., C. L. WITTE, AND M. H. WITTE. Protein content of liver lymph in patients with portal hypertension secondary to hepatic cirrhosis. *Lymphology* 8: 111–113, 1975.
111. DURBIN, R. P. Osmotic flow of water across permeable cellulose membranes. *J. Gen. Physiol.* 44: 315–326, 1960.
112. EISENBACH, G. M., J. B. VAN LIEW, AND J. W. BOYLAN. Effect of angiotensin on the filtration of protein in the rat kidney: a micropuncture study. *Kidney Int.* 8: 80–87, 1975.
113. ERDMANN, A. J., T. R. VAUGHAN, K. L. BRIGHAM, W. C. WOOLVERTON, AND N. C. STAUB. Effect of increased vascular pressure on lung fluid balance in unanesthetized sheep. *Circ. Res.* 37: 271–284, 1975.
114. FADNES, H. O. Protein concentration and hydrostatic pressure in subcutaneous tissue of rats in hypoproteinemia. *Scand. J. Clin. Lab. Invest.* 35: 441–446, 1975.
115. FADNES, H. O. Effect of increased venous pressure on the hydrostatic and colloid osmotic pressure in subcutaneous interstitial fluid in rats: edema-preventing mechanisms. *Scand. J. Clin. Lab. Invest.* 36: 371–377, 1976.
116. FARQUHAR, M. G. The primary glomerular filtration barrier—basement membrane or epithelial slits? *Kidney Int.* 8: 197–211, 1975.
117. FELGENHAUER, K. Protein size and cerebrospinal fluid composition. *Klin. Wochenschr.* 52: 1158–1164, 1974.
118. FEOLA, M., AND G. GLICK. Cardiac lymph flow and composition in acute myocardial ischemia in dogs. *Am. J. Physiol.* 229: 44–48, 1975.
119. FIELD, M. E., O. C. LEIGH, JR., J. W. HEIM, AND C. K. DRINKER. The protein content and osmotic pressure of blood serum and lymph from various sources in the dog. *Am. J. Physiol.* 110: 174–181, 1934.
120. FLYNN, S. B., AND D. A. A. OWEN. Effects of histamine on

skeletal muscle vasculature in cats. *J. Physiol. London* 265: 795–807, 1977.
121. Fox, J., F. Galey, and H. Wayland. Action of histamine on the mesenteric microvasculature. *Microvasc. Res.* 19: 108–125, 1980.
122. Friedman, J. J. Transcapillary protein leakage and fluid movement. Effect of venous pressure. *Microvasc. Res.* 12: 275–290, 1976.
123. Friedman, M., S. O. Byers, and C. Omoto. Some characteristics of hepatic lymph in the intact rat. *Am. J. Physiol.* 184: 11–17, 1956.
124. Ganrot, K., S. Jacobsson, and U. Rothman. Transcapillary passage of plasma proteins in experimental burns. *Acta Physiol. Scand.* 91: 497–501, 1974.
125. Ganrot, P. O., C. B. Laurell, and K. Ohlsson. Concentration of trypsin inhibitors of different molecular size and of albumin and haptoglobin in blood and lymph of various organs in the dog. *Acta Physiol. Scand.* 79: 280–286, 1970.
126. Garlick, D. G., and E. M. Renkin. Transport of large molecules from plasma to interstitial fluid and lymph in dogs. *Am. J. Physiol.* 219: 1595–1605, 1970.
127. Goldby, F. S., and L. J. Beilin. Relationship between arterial pressure and the permeability of arterioles to carbon particles in acute hypertension in the rat. *Cardiovasc. Res.* 6: 384–390, 1972.
128. Goresky, C. A. A linear method for determining liver sinusoidal and extravascular volumes. *Am. J. Physiol.* 204: 626–640, 1963.
129. Goresky, C. A. The nature of transcapillary exchange in the liver. *Can. Med. Assoc. J.* 92: 517–522, 1965.
130. Goresky, C. A. Uptake in the liver: the nature of the process. In: *Liver and Biliary Tract Physiology I*, edited by N. B. Javitt. Baltimore, MD: University Park, 1980, vol. 21, p. 65–102. (Int. Rev. Physiol. Ser.)
131. Gorin, A. B., J. Weidner, and N. C. Staub. Noninvasive measurements of altered protein permeability in lungs of sheep (Abstract). *Am. Rev. Respir. Dis.* 111: 941, 1975.
132. Granger, D. N. Intestinal microcirculation and transmucosal fluid transport. *Am. J. Physiol.* 240 (*Gastrointest. Liver Physiol.* 3): G343–G349, 1981.
133. Granger, D. N., J. P. Granger, R. A. Brace, R. E. Parker, and A. E. Taylor. Analysis of the permeability characteristics of intestinal capillaries. *Circ. Res.* 44: 335–344, 1979.
134. Granger, D. N., P. R. Kvietys, W. H. Wilborn, N. A. Mortillaro, and A. E. Taylor. Mechanism of glucagon-induced intestinal secretion. *Am. J. Physiol.* 239 (*Gastrointest. Liver Physiol.* 2): G30–G38, 1980.
135. Granger, D. N., T. Miller, R. Allen, R. E. Parker, J. C. Parker, and A. E. Taylor. Permselectivity of the liver blood-lymph barrier to endogenous macromolecules. *Gastroenterology* 77: 103–109, 1979.
136. Granger, D. N., and M. A. Perry. Interstitial-to-blood movement of plasma proteins. In: *Advances in Physiological Sciences. Microcirculation and Capillary Exchange*, edited by A. G. Kovach, H. Hamar, and L. Szabo. New York: Pergamon, 1981, vol. 7, p. 253–262.
137. Granger, D. N., M. A. Perry, P. R. Kvietys, and A. E. Taylor. Interstitium-to-blood movement of macromolecules in the absorbing small intestine. *Am. J. Physiol.* 241 (*Gastrointest. Liver Physiol.* 4): G31–G36, 1981.
138. Granger, D. N., M. A. Perry, P. R. Kvietys, and A. E. Taylor. Permeability of intestinal capillaries: effects of fat absorption and gastrointestinal hormones. *Am. J. Physiol.* 242 (*Gastrointest. Liver Physiol.* 5): G194–G201, 1982.
139. Granger, D. N., P. D. I. Richardson, and A. E. Taylor. The effects of isoprenaline and bradykinin on capillary filtration in the cat small intestine. *Br. J. Pharmacol.* 67: 361–366, 1979.
140. Granger, D. N., G. Rutili, and J. M. McCord. Superoxide radicals in feline intestinal ischemia. *Gastroenterology* 81: 22–29, 1981.
141. Granger, D. N., M. Sennett, P. McElearney, and A. E. Taylor. Effect of local arterial hypotension on cat intestinal capillary permeability. *Gastroenterology* 79: 474–480, 1980.
142. Granger, D. N., and A. E. Taylor. Effects of solute-coupled transport on lymph flow and oncotic pressures in cat ileum. *Am. J. Physiol.* 235 (*Endocrinol. Metab. Gastrointest. Physiol.* 4): E429–E436, 1978.
143. Granger, D. N., and A. E. Taylor. Permeability of intestinal capillaries to endogenous macromolecules. *Am. J. Physiol.* 238 (*Heart Circ. Physiol.* 7): H457–H464, 1980.
144. Granger, D. N., and A. E. Taylor. Permselectivity of intestinal capillaries. *Physiologist* 23(1): 47–52, 1980.
145. Grega, G. J., D. E. Dobbins, J. B. Scott, and F. J. Haddy. Effects of histamine and increased venous pressure on transmicrovascular protein transport. *Microvasc. Res.* 18: 95–104, 1979.
146. Grega, G. J., D. E. Dobbins, J. B. Scott, and F. J. Haddy. Interrelationship among histamine, various vasoactive substances, and macromolecular permeability in the canine forelimb. *Circ. Res.* 46: 264–275, 1980.
147. Grotte, G. Passage of dextran molecules across the blood-lymph barrier. *Acta Chir. Scand. Suppl.* 211: 1–84, 1956.
148. Guyton, A. C., and A. W. Lindsey. Effect of elevated left atrial pressure and decreased plasma protein concentration on development of pulmonary edema. *Circ. Res.* 1: 649–657, 1959.
149. Guyton, A. C., A. E. Taylor, R. E. Drake, and J. C. Parker. Dynamics of subatmospheric pressure in the pulmonary interstitial fluid. In: *Lung Liquids*, edited by R. Porter and M. O'Connor. New York: Elsevier, 1976, p. 77. (Ciba Found. Symp. 38.)
150. Haddy, F. J., and G. J. Grega. Effects of bradykinin on skin lymph flow and protein concentration in the dog forelimb. *Acta Physiol. Lat. Am.* 24: 469–474, 1974.
151. Haddy, F. J., J. B. Scott, and G. J. Grega. Effects of histamine on lymph protein concentration and flow in the dog forelimb. *Am. J. Physiol.* 223: 1172–1177, 1972.
152. Haddy, F. J., J. B. Scott, and G. J. Grega. Peripheral circulation: fluid transfer across the microvascular membrane. In: *Cardiovascular Physiology II*, edited by A. C. Guyton and A. W. Cowley. Baltimore, MD: University Park, 1976, vol. 9, p. 63–109. (Int. Rev. Physiol. Ser.)
153. Haggendal, E., and B. Johansson. On the pathophysiology of the increased cerebrovascular permeability in acute arterial hypertension in cats. *Acta Neurol. Scand.* 48: 265–270, 1972.
154. Haggendal, E., and B. Johansson. Effect of increased intravascular pressure on the blood-brain barrier to protein in dogs. *Acta Neurol. Scand.* 48: 271–275, 1972.
155. Haljamäe, H., and H. Fredén. Comparative analysis of the protein content of local subcutaneous tissue fluid and plasma. *Microvasc. Res.* 2: 163–171, 1970.
156. Hansson, H.-A., B. Johansson, and C. Blomstrand. Ultrastructural studies on cerebrovascular permeability in acute hypertension. *Acta Neuropathol.* 32: 187–198, 1975.
157. Hardwicke, J., B. Hulme, J. H. Jones, and C. R. Ricketts. Measurement of glomerular permeability to polydispersed radioactively-labelled macromolecules in normal rabbits. *Clin. Sci.* 34: 505–514, 1968.
158. Hargens, A. R., B. J. Tucker, and R. C. Blantz. Renal lymph protein in the rat. *Am. J. Physiol.* 233 (*Renal Fluid Electrolyte Physiol.* 2): F269–F273, 1977.
159. Hargens, A. R., and B. W. Zweifach. Transport between blood and peripheral lymph in intestine. *Microvasc. Res.* 11: 89–101, 1976.
160. Harris, T. R., D. Burks, and P. L. Custer. Coronary capillary permeability and tissue volumes for sucrose and water in dogs: a comparison of bolus and constant infusion multiple-indicator methods. *Cardiovasc. Res.* 12: 537–546, 1978.
161. Harris, T. R., C. Gervin, D. Burks, and P. Custer. Effects of coronary flow reduction on capillary-myocardial exchange in dogs. *Am. J. Physiol.* 234 (*Heart Circ. Physiol.* 3): H679–

H689, 1978.

162. HAUCK, G. Luminescence-microscopic evidence for the existence of a gradient of vascular permeability in the mesentery capillary bed. *Bibl. Anat.* 10: 221–224, 1969.
163. HAUCK, G. Permeability of the microvascular system. *Bibl. Anat.* 15: 202–205, 1977.
164. HAUCK, G., AND H. SCHRÖER. Vitalmikroskopische Untersuchungen zur Lokalisation der Eiweisspermeabilität an der Endstrombahn von Warmblütern. *Pfluegers Arch.* 312: 32–44, 1969.
165. HENRIKSEN, J. H., H. PARVING, N. A. LASSEN, AND K. WINKLER. Filtration as the main mechanism of increased protein extravasation in liver cirrhosis. *Scand. J. Clin. Lab. Invest.* 40: 121–128, 1980.
166. HOLCROFT, J. W., AND D. D. TRUNKEY. Pulmonary extravasation of albumin during and after hemorrhagic shock in baboons. *J. Surg. Res.* 18: 91–97, 1975.
167. HORTON, J. C., AND E. T. HEDLEY-WHITE. Protein movement across the blood-brain barrier in hypervolemia. *Brain Res.* 169: 610–614, 1979.
168. HOSSMANN, K. A., AND Y. OLSSON. The effect of transient cerebral ischemia on the vascular permeability to protein tracers. *Acta Neuropathol.* 18: 103–112, 1971.
169. HOSSMANN, K. A., AND Y. OLSSON. Influence of ischemia on the passage of protein tracers across capillaries in certain blood-brain barrier injuries. *Acta Neuropathol.* 18: 113–122, 1971.
170. HUET, P. M., C. A. GORESKY, AND J. O. LOUGH. Assessment of liver microcirculation in human cirrhosis. *J. Clin. Invest.* 70: 1234–1244, 1982.
171. HULME, B. Studies on glomerular permeability using inert polymers. *Congr. Nephrol.* 1: 3–8, 1975.
172. HULTSTRÖM, D., AND E. SVENSJÖ. Simultaneous fluorescence and electron microscopical detection of bradykinin induced macromolecular leakage. *Bibl. Anat.* 15: 466–468, 1977.
173. HURLEY, J. V., AND A. MCQUEEN. The response of the fenestrated vessels of the small intestine of rats to application of mustard oil. *J. Pathol.* 105: 21–29, 1971.
174. ILIFF, L. D. Extra-alveolar vessels and edema development in excised dog lungs. *Circ. Res.* 28: 524–532, 1971.
175. INGOMAR, C. H., J. G. KLEBE, AND P. BAEKGAARD. The transcapillary escape rate of T-1824 in healthy newborn infants. *Acta Paediatr. Scand.* 62: 617–620, 1973.
176. INOUE, S., R. P. MICHEL, AND J. C. HOGG. Zonulae occludentes in alveolar epithelium and capillary endothelium of dog lungs studied with the freeze-fracture technique. *J. Ultrastruct. Res.* 56: 215–225, 1976.
177. INTAGLIETTA, M. Evidence for a gradient of permeability in frog mesenteric capillaries. *Bibl. Anat.* 9: 465–468, 1967.
178. ISMAIL, A. A., K. KHALIFA, AND K. R. MADWAR. Capillary loss of radio-iodinated serum albumin in diabetics. *Lancet* 2: 810–813, 1965.
179. JACOBS, J. M. Vascular permeability and neurotoxicity. *Environ. Health Perspect.* 26: 107–116, 1978.
180. JOHNSON, P. C., AND D. R. RICHARDSON. The influence of venous pressure on filtration forces in the intestine. *Microvasc. Res.* 7: 296–306, 1974.
181. JOYNER, W. L. Effect of prostaglandins on macromolecular transport from blood to lymph in the dog. *Am. J. Physiol.* 232 (*Heart Circ. Physiol.* 1): H690–H696, 1977.
182. JOYNER, W. L., R. D. CARTER, G. S. RAIZES, AND E. M. RENKIN. Influence of histamine and some other substances on blood-lymph transport of plasma protein and dextran in the dog paw. *Microvasc. Res.* 7: 19–30, 1974.
183. JOYNER, W. L., R. D. CARTER, AND E. M. RENKIN. Influence of lymph flow rate on concentrations of proteins and dextran in dog leg lymph. *Lymphology* 6: 181–186, 1973.
184. JOYNER, W. L., E. SVENSJÖ, AND K. E. ARFORS. Simultaneous measurements of macromolecular leakage and arteriolar blood flow as altered by PGE_1 and β_2-receptor stimulant in the hamster cheek pouch. *Microvasc. Res.* 18: 301–310, 1979.
185. JUE, J., R. W. ENTRUP, M. HUGHES, G. NARANG, AND R. WÉGRIA. Rate of movement of interstitial fluid: a factor in the pathogenesis of edema. *Am. J. Physiol.* 218: 1003–1009, 1970.
186. JURCZAK, M. E. Effect of vibration stress on permeability of capillary endothelium for proteins. *Acta Physiol. Pol.* 24: 761–776, 1973.
187. KAHN, A., AND E. BRACHET. Some mediator of inflammation increases the permeability coefficient of albumin in the rat mesentery. *Bibl. Anat.* 15: 452–455, 1977.
188. KARDON, R. H., AND R. G. KESSEL. Three-dimensional organization of the hepatic microcirculation in the rodent as observed by scanning electron microscopy of corrosion casts. *Gastroenterology* 79: 72–81, 1980.
189. KARNOVSKY, M. J. The ultrastructural basis of capillary permeability studied with peroxidase as a tracer. *J. Cell Biol.* 35: 213–236, 1967.
190. KARNOVSKY, M. J. The ultrastructural basis of transcapillary exchanges. *J. Gen. Physiol.* 52: 641–696, 1968.
191. KARNOVSKY, M. J. The structural basis for glomerular filtration. In: *Kidney Disease: Present Status*, edited by Jacob Chung. Baltimore, MD: Williams & Wilkins, 1979, p. 1–41. (Int. Acad. Pathol. Monogr. Ser. 20.)
192. KEDEM, O., AND A. KATCHALSKY. Thermodynamic analysis of the permeability of biological membranes to non-electrolytes. *Biochim. Biophys. Acta* 27: 229–246, 1958.
193. KEDEM, O., AND A. KATCHALSKY. A physical interpretation of the phenomenological coefficients of membrane permeability. *J. Gen. Physiol.* 45: 143–179, 1961.
194. KEYL, M. J., R. T. DOWELL, AND A. A. YUNICE. Comparison of renal and cardiac lymph constituents. *Lymphology* 13: 158–160, 1980.
195. KIRSCHNER, H. Effect of physical training on the permeability of vascular bed to albumin labelled with T-1824. *Acta Physiol. Pol.* 27: 39–46, 1976.
196. KLINE, R. L., D. S. SAK, F. J. HADDY, AND G. J. GREGA. Pressure-dependent factors in edema formation in canine forelimbs. *J. Pharmacol. Exp. Ther.* 193: 452–459, 1975.
197. KLINE, R. L., J. B. SCOTT, F. J. HADDY, AND G. J. GREGA. Mechanism of edema formation in canine forelimbs by locally administered bradykinin. *Am. J. Physiol.* 225: 1051–1056, 1973.
198. KNOX, F. G., L. R. WILLIS, J. W. STRANDHOY, E. G. SCHNEIDER, L. G. NAVAR, AND C. E. OTT. Role of peritubule Starling forces in proximal reabsorption following albumin infusion. *Am. J. Physiol.* 223: 741–749, 1972.
199. LAINE, G. A., AND H. J. GRANGER. Myocardial Starling forces and lymphatic dynamics during venous hypertension. *Microvasc. Res.* 20: 116, 1980.
200. LAINE, G. A., AND H. J. GRANGER. Permeability of intestinal capillaries in chronic arterial hypertension. *Microvasc. Res.* 20: 116, 1981.
201. LAINE, G. A., J. T. HALL, S. H. LAINE, AND H. J. GRANGER. Transsinusoidal fluid dynamics in canine liver during venous hypertension. *Circ. Res.* 45: 317–323, 1979.
202. LANDIS, E. M. Heteroporosity of the capillary wall as indicated by cinematographic analysis of the passage of dyes. *Ann. NY Acad. Sci.* 116: 765–773, 1964.
203. LANDIS, E. M., AND J. R. PAPPENHEIMER. Exchange of substances through the capillary walls. In: *Handbook of Physiology. Circulation*, edited by W. F. Hamilton. Washington, DC: Am. Physiol. Soc., 1963, sect. 2, vol. II, chapt. 29, p. 961–1034.
204. LASSEN, N. A., H. H. PARVING, AND N. ROSSING. Filtration as the main mechanism of overall transcapillary protein escape from the plasma (Editorial). *Microvasc. Res.* 7: i–iv, 1974.
205. LATTA, H. Ultrastructure of the glomerulus and juxtaglomerular apparatus. In: *Handbook of Physiology. Renal Physiology*, edited by J. Orloff and R. W. Berliner. Washington, DC.: Am. Physiol. Soc., 1973, sect. 8, chapt. 1, p. 1–29.
206. LEBRIE, S. J. Renal peritubular capillary permeability to macromolecules. *Am. J. Physiol.* 213: 1225–1232, 1967.

207. LEBRIE, S. J., AND H. S. MAYERSON. Influence of elevated venous pressure on flow and composition of renal lymph. *Am. J. Physiol.* 195: 1037–1040, 1960.
208. LEE, J. S. Lymph pressure in intestinal villi and lymph flow during fluid secretion. In: *Tissue Fluid Pressure and Composition*, edited by A. R. Hargens. Baltimore, MD: Williams & Wilkins, 1981, p. 165–172.
209. LEVICK, J. R., AND C. C. MICHEL. Permeability of individually perfused frog mesenteric capillaries to T-1824 and T-1824-albumin as evidence for a large pore system. *Q. J. Exp. Physiol.* 58: 67–85, 1973.
210. LEVITT, D. G. General continuum analysis of transport through pores. *Biophys. J.* 15: 533–550, 1975.
211. LEWIS, G. P., AND N. J. P. WINSEY. The action of pharmacologically active substances on the flow and composition of cat hind limb lymph. *Br. J. Pharmacol.* 40: 446–460, 1970.
212. LIBERMANN, I. M., F. GONZALEZ, H. BRAZZUNA, H. GARCIA, AND D. LABUONORA. Fluid composition from implanted perforated capsules: an approach to interstitial fluid? *J. Appl. Physiol.* 33: 751–756, 1972.
213. LINDHE, J., AND P. I. BRÅNEMARK. Changes in vascular permeability after local application of sex hormones. *J. Periodontal Res.* 2: 259–265, 1967.
214. LINDQVIST, O., T. SALDEEN, E. SVENSJÖ, AND R. WALLIN. On the cause of increased vascular permeability in the delayed microembolism syndrome. *Bibl. Anat.* 16: 409–411, 1977.
215. MACFARLANE, N. A. A., I. H. MILLS, AND E. P. WRAIGHT. Increased vascular permeability produced by kallikrein infusions and its enhancement by nephrectomy. *J. Physiol. London* 231: 45P–47P, 1973.
216. MACIEJKO, J. J., D. L. MARCINIAK, E. F. GERSABECK, AND G. J. GREGA. Effects of locally and systemically infused bradykinin on transvascular fluid and protein transfer in the canine forelimb. *J. Pharmacol. Exp. Ther.* 205: 221–235, 1978.
217. MAJNO, G., S. M. SHEA, AND M. LEVENTHAL. Endothelial contraction induced by histamine-type mediators. *J. Cell Biol.* 42: 647–671, 1969.
218. MALIK, A. B. Pulmonary vascular response to increase in intracranial pressure: role of sympathetic mechanisms. *J. Appl. Physiol.: Respirat. Environ. Exercise Physiol.* 42: 335–343, 1977.
219. MALIK, A. B., AND H. VAN DER ZEE. Lung vascular permeability following progressive pulmonary embolization. *J. Appl. Physiol.: Respirat. Environ. Exercise Physiol.* 45: 590–597, 1978.
220. MALMBERG, P. Time course of enzyme escape via heart lymph following myocardial infarction in the dog. *Scand. J. Clin. Lab. Invest.* 30: 405–409, 1972.
221. MARCINIAK, D. L., D. E. DOBBINS, J. J. MACIEJKO, J. B. SCOTT, F. J. HADDY, AND G. J. GREGA. Effects of systemically infused histamine on transvascular fluid and protein transfer. *Am. J. Physiol.* 233 (*Heart Circ. Physiol.* 2): H148–H153, 1977.
222. MARCINIAK, D. L., D. E. DOBBINS, J. J. MACIEJKO, J. B. SCOTT, F. J. HADDY, AND G. J. GREGA. Antagonism of histamine edema formation by catecholamines. *Am. J. Physiol.* 234 (*Heart Circ. Physiol.* 3): H180–H185, 1978.
223. MASON, E. A., E. H. BRESLER, AND R. P. WENDT. Test of Onsager relation for ideal gas transport in membranes. *Trans. Faraday Soc. 2,* 68: 1938–1950, 1972.
224. MAYERSON, H. S. The physiologic importance of lymph. In: *Handbook of Physiology. Circulation*, edited by W. F. Hamilton. Washington, DC: Am. Physiol. Soc., 1963, sect. 2, vol. II, chapt. 30, p. 1035–1073.
225. MAYERSON, H. S., C. G. WOLFRAM, H. H. SHIRLEY, JR., AND K. WASSERMAN. Regional differences in capillary permeability. *Am. J. Physiol.* 198: 155–160, 1960.
226. MCNAMEE, J. E., AND F. S. GRODINS. Effect of histamine on microvasculature of isolated dog gracilis muscle. *Am. J. Physiol.* 229: 119–124, 1975.
227. MCNAMEE, J. E., AND N. C. STAUB. Pore models of sheep lung microvascular barrier using new data on protein tracers. *Microvasc. Res.* 18: 229–244, 1979.
228. MCQUEEN, A., AND J. V. HURLEY. Aspects of increased vascular permeability following the intradermal injection of histamine in the rat. *Pathology* 3: 191–202, 1971.
229. MEYER, E. C. Collection of pulmonary lymph in dogs. *J. Surg. Res.* 8: 544–550, 1968.
230. MEYER, E. C., AND R. OTTAVIANO. Right lymphatic duct distribution volume in dogs. Relationship to pulmonary interstitial volume. *Circ. Res.* 35: 197–203, 1974.
231. MEYRICK, B., J. MILLER, AND L. REID. Pulmonary oedema induced by ANTU, or by high or low oxygen concentrations in rat—an electron microscopic study. *Br. J. Exp. Pathol.* 53: 347–358, 1972.
232. MICHEL, C. C. Osmotic reflexion coefficients of single capillaries to myoglobin and serum albumin. *J. Physiol. London* 272: 95P–96P, 1977.
233. MICHEL, C. C. Measurement of permeability in single capillaries. *Arch. Int. Physiol. Biochim.* 86: 657–667, 1978.
234. MICHEL, C. C. Relative uniformity of pore size in frog mesenteric capillaries. *J. Physiol. London* 273: 46P–47P, 1978.
235. MICHEL, R. P., S. INOUE, AND J. C. HOGG. Pulmonary capillary permeability to HRP in dogs: a physiological and morphological study. *J. Appl. Physiol.: Respirat. Environ. Exercise Physiol.* 42: 13–21, 1977.
236. MILLER, G. L., R. L. KLINE, J. B. SCOTT, F. J. HADDY, AND G. J. GREGA. Effects of ischemia on forelimb weight and lymph protein concentration. *Proc. Soc. Exp. Biol. Med.* 149: 581–586, 1975.
237. MORRIS, B. The hepatic and intestinal contributions to the thoracic duct lymph. *Q. J. Exp. Physiol.* 41: 318–325, 1956.
238. MORTILLARO, N. A., D. N. GRANGER, P. R. KVIETYS, G. RUTILI, AND A. E. TAYLOR. Effects of histamine and histamine antagonists on intestinal capillary permeability. *Am. J. Physiol.* 240 (*Gastrointest. Liver Physiol.* 3): G381–G386, 1981.
239. MORTILLARO, N. A., AND A. E. TAYLOR. Interaction of capillary and tissue forces in the cat small intestine. *Circ. Res.* 39: 348–358, 1976.
240. NAKAMURA, Y., AND H. WAYLAND. Macromolecular transport in the cat mesentery. *Microvasc. Res.* 9: 1–21, 1975.
241. NERI SERNERI, G. G., G. F. GENSINI, AND R. A. GENSINI. Increased capillary permeability in haemophilia and afibrinogenaemia. *Acta Haematol.* 52: 336–344, 1974.
242. NICOLAYSEN, G., A. NICOLAYSEN, AND N. C. STAUB. A quantitative radioautographic comparison of albumin concentration in different sized lymph vessels in normal mouse lung. *Microvasc. Res.* 10: 138–152, 1975.
243. NIX, J. T., F. C. MANN, J. L. BOLLMAN, J. H. GRINDLAY, AND E. V. FLOCK. Alterations of protein constituents of lymph by specific injury to the liver. *Am. J. Physiol.* 164: 119–122, 1951.
244. NORTHOVER, A. N., AND B. J. NORTHOVER. Effect of vasoactive substances on rat mesenteric blood vessels. *J. Pathol.* 101: 99–107, 1970.
245. NORTHRUP, W. F., AND E. W. HUMPHREY. Pulmonary and systemic capillary permeability to protein following endotoxin. *Surg. Forum* 27: 65–67, 1976.
246. NORTHRUP, W. F., AND E. W. HUMPHREY. Albumin permeability in the pulmonary capillaries. *Surg. Forum* 28: 224–226, 1978.
247. NORTHRUP, W. F., AND E. W. HUMPHREY. Effect of hemorrhagic shock on pulmonary vascular permeability to plasma proteins. *Surgery* 83: 264–273, 1978.
248. NOSSLIN, B. Mathematical model of plasma protein turnover determined with ^{131}I-labeled protein. In: *Metabolism of Human Gamma Globulin* (γ_{ss}*-globulin*), edited by S. B. Anderson. Oxford, UK: Blackwell, 1964, p. 115–121.
249. OLSEN, F. Increased permeability for plasma components of the cerebral vessels during acute angiotensin hypertension in rats. *Acta Pathol. Microbiol. Scand.* 85: 572–576, 1977.
250. OLSSON, Y. Studies on vascular permeability in peripheral nerves. I. Distribution of serum albumin in normal, crushed and sectioned sciatic nerve. *Acta Neuropathol.* 7: 1–15, 1966.

251. OLSSON, Y. Studies on vascular permeability in peripheral nerves. IV. Distribution of protein tracers in the peripheral nervous system of various species. *Acta Neuropathol.* 17: 114–126, 1971.
252. OLSSON, Y., R. M. CROWELL, AND I. KLATZO. The blood-brain barrier to protein tracers in focal cerebral ischemia and infarction caused by occlusion of the middle cerebral artery. *Acta Neuropathol.* 18: 89–102, 1971.
253. OLSSON, Y., E. SVENSJÖ, K. E. ARFORS, AND D. HULSTRÖM. Fluorescein labelled dextrans as tracers for vascular permeability studies in the nervous system. *Acta Neuropathol.* 33: 45–50, 1975.
254. OLSZEWSKI, W. L., AND A. ENGESET. Capillary transport of immunoglobulins and complement proteins to the interstitial fluid and lymph. *Arch. Immunol. Ther. Exp.* 26: 57–65, 1978.
255. OLSZEWSKI, W. L., A. ENGESET, AND J. SOKOLOWSKI. Lymph flow and protein in the normal male leg during lying, getting up, and walking. *Lymphology* 10: 178–183, 1977.
256. PALADE, G. E. Transport in quanta across the endothelium of blood capillaries (Abstract). *Anat. Rec.* 136: 254, 1960.
257. PALADE, G. E. Blood capillaries of the heart and other organs. *Circulation* 24: 368, 1961.
258. PALADE, G. E., AND R. R. BRUNS. Structural modulations of plasmalemmal vesicles. *J. Cell Biol.* 37: 633–649, 1968.
259. PALADE, G. E., M. SIMIONESCU, AND N. SIMIONESCU. Structural aspects of the permeability of the microvascular endothelium. *Acta Physiol. Scand.* 463: 11–32, 1979.
260. PAPPENHEIMER, J. R., E. M. RENKIN, AND L. M. BORRERO. Filtration, diffusion and molecular sieving through peripheral capillary membranes: a contribution to the pore theory of capillary permeability. *Am. J. Physiol.* 167: 13–46, 1951.
261. PARKER, J. C., H. J. FALGOUT, R. E. PARKER, D. N. GRANGER, AND A. E. TAYLOR. The effect of fluid volume loading on exclusion of interstitial albumin and lymph flow in the dog lung. *Circ. Res.* 45: 440–450, 1979.
262. PARKER, J. C., R. E. PARKER, D. N. GRANGER, AND A. E. TAYLOR. Vascular permeability and transvascular fluid and protein transport in the dog lung. *Circ. Res.* 48: 545–561, 1981.
263. PARKER, R. E., R. J. ROSELLI, AND K. L. BRIGHAM. Effects of prolonged left atrial pressure elevation on lung microvascular protein sieving in unanesthetized sheep (Abstract). *Federation Proc.* 39: 279, 1980.
264. PARKER, R. E., R. J. ROSELLI, T. R. HARRIS, AND K. L. BRIGHAM. Effects of graded increases in pulmonary vascular pressures on lung fluid balance in unanesthetized sheep. *Circ. Res.* 49: 1164–1172, 1981.
265. PARVING, H.-H. The effect of hypoxia and carbon monoxide exposure on plasma volume and capillary permeability to albumin. *Scand. J. Clin. Lab. Invest.* 30: 49–56, 1972.
266. PARVING, H.-H., AND F. GYNTELBERG. Transcapillary escape rate and plasma volume in essential hypertension. *Circ. Res.* 32: 643–651, 1973.
267. PARVING, H.-H., J. M. HANSEN, S. L. NIELSEN, N. ROSSING, O. MUNCK, AND N. A. LASSEN. Mechanisms of edema formation in myxedema-increased protein extravasation and relatively slow lymphatic drainage. *N. Engl. J. Med.* 301: 460–465, 1979.
268. PARVING, H.-H., H. A. JENSEN, AND M. WESTRUP. Increased transcapillary escape rate of albumin and IgG in essential hypertension. *Scand. J. Clin. Lab. Invest.* 37: 223–227, 1977.
269. PARVING, H.-H., J. G. KLEBE, AND C. J. INGOMAR. Simultaneous determination of plasma volume and transcapillary escape rate with ^{131}I-labelled albumin and T-1824 in the newborn. *Acta Paediatr. Scand.* 62: 248–252, 1973.
270. PARVING, H.-H., S. L. NIELSEN, AND N. A. LASSEN. Increased transcapillary escape rate of albumin, IgG, and IgM during angiotensin-II-induced hypertension in man. *Scand. J. Clin. Lab. Invest.* 34: 111–118, 1974.
271. PARVING, H.-H., I. NOER, T. DECKERT, S. L. NIELSEN, J. LYRAGSOE, C. E. MOGENSEN, M. RÖRTH, P. A. SVENDSEN, J. TRAP-JENSEN, AND N. A. LASSEN. The effect of metabolic regulation on microvascular permeability to small and large molecules in short-term juvenile diabetics. *Diabetologia* 12: 161–166, 1976.
272. PARVING, H.-H., K. OHLSSON, H. J. BUCHARDT-HENSEN, AND M. RÖRTH. Effect of carbon monoxide exposure on capillary permeability to albumin and α_2-macroglobulin. *Scand. J. Clin. Lab. Invest.* 29: 381–388, 1972.
273. PARVING, H.-H., N. ROSSING, AND H. A. JENSEN. Increased metabolic turnover rate and transcapillary escape rate of albumin in essential hypertension. *Circ. Res.* 35: 544–552, 1974.
274. PARVING, H.-H., N. ROSSING, S. L. NIELSEN, AND N. A. LASSEN. Increased transcapillary escape rate of albumin, IgG, and IgM after plasma volume expansion. *Am. J. Physiol.* 227: 245–250, 1974.
275. PARVING, H.-H., N. ROSSING, AND E. SANDER. Increased metabolic turnover rate and transcapillary escape rate of albumin in long-term juvenile diabetes. *Scand. J. Clin. Lab. Invest.* 35: 59–66, 1975.
276. PARVING, H.-H., A.-M. WORM, AND N. ROSSING. Plasma volume, intravascular albumin and its transcapillary escape rate in patients with extensive skin disease. *Br. J. Dermatol.* 95: 519–523, 1976.
277. PATLAK, C. S., D. A. GOLDSTEIN, AND J. F. HOFFMAN. The flow of solute and solvent across a two-membrane system. *J. Theor. Biol.* 5: 425–442, 1963.
278. PERL, W. Convection and permeation of albumin between plasma and interstitium. *Microvasc. Res.* 10: 83–94, 1975.
279. PERL, W., P. CHOWDHURY, AND F. P. CHINARD. Reflection coefficients of dog lung endothelium to small hydrophilic solutes. *Am. J. Physiol.* 228: 797–809, 1975.
280. PERRY, M. A., J. A. BARROWMAN, P. R. KVIETYS, AND D. N. GRANGER. The exclusion phenomenon in the liver interstitium (Abstract). *Gastroenterology* 80: 1251, 1981.
280a. PERRY, M. A., J. J. BENOIT, P. R. KVIETYS, AND D. N. GRANGER. Restricted transport of cationic macromolecules across intestinal capillaries. *Am. J. Physiol.* 245 (*Gastrointest. Liver Physiol.* 8): G568–G572, 1983.
281. PERRY, M. A., W. J. CROOK, AND D. N. GRANGER. Permeability of gastric capillaries to small and large molecules. *Am. J. Physiol.* 241 (*Gastrointest. Liver Physiol.* 4): G478–G486, 1981.
282. PERRY, M., AND D. GARLICK. Transcapillary efflux of gamma globulin in rabbit skeletal muscle. *Microvasc. Res.* 9: 119–126, 1975.
283. PERRY, M. A., AND D. N. GRANGER. Permeability of intestinal capillaries to small molecules. *Am. J. Physiol.* 241 (*Gastrointest. Liver Physiol.* 4): G24–G30, 1981.
283a. PERRY, M. A., C. A. NAVIA, D. N. GRANGER, J. C. PARKER, AND A. E. TAYLOR. Calculation of equivalent pore radii in dog hind paw capillaries using endogenous lymph and plasma proteins. *Microvasc. Res.* 26: 250–253, 1983.
284. PETERSON, B. T., J. C. ROSS, AND K. L. BRIGHAM. Increased lung vascular permeability and lung water volume with elevated intracranial pressure (Abstract). *Federation Proc.* 39: 1140, 1980.
285. PIETRA, G. G., J. P. SZIDON, M. M. LEVENTHAL, AND A. P. FISHMAN. Hemoglobin as a tracer in hemodynamic pulmonary edema. *Science* 166: 1643–1646, 1969.
286. PIETRA, G. G., J. P. SZIDON, M. M. LEVENTHAL, AND A. P. FISHMAN. Histamine and interstitial pulmonary edema in the dog. *Circ. Res.* 29: 323–337, 1971.
287. PINARDI, G., E. LEAL, AND A. SALAS COLL. Vascular permeability to red blood cells and protein in hemorrhagic shock. *Acta Physiol. Lat. Am.* 17: 175–181, 1967.
288. PINTER, G. G., J. L. ATKINS, AND D. R. BELL. Albumin permeability times surface area (PS) product of peritubular capillaries in kidneys (Abstract). *Experientia* 15: 1045, 1974.
289. POULSEN, H. L. Interstitial fluid concentrations of albumin and immunoglobulin G in normal men. *Scand. J. Clin. Lab. Invest.* 34: 119–122, 1974.
290. PRITCHARD, J. S., AND G. D. LEE. Noninvasive measurement

of regional interstitial water spaces, capillary permeabilities and solute fluxes in the lung, using a radioisotope method. *Bull. Physio-Pathol. Respir.* 11: 137P–141P, 1975.

291. QUIN, J. W., AND A. D. SHANNON. The influence of the lymph node on the protein concentration of efferent lymph leaving the node. *J. Physiol. London* 264: 307–321, 1977.

292. RAPOPORT, S. I. *Blood-Brain Barrier in Physiology and Medicine.* New York: Raven, 1976.

293. RAPOPORT, S. I., M. HOI, AND I. KLATZO. Testing of a hypothesis for osmotic opening of the blood-brain barrier. *Am. J. Physiol.* 223: 323–331, 1972.

294. RAPOPORT, S. I., AND K. D. PETTIGREW. A heterogenous, pore-vesicle membrane model for protein transfer from blood to cerebrospinal fluid at the choroid plexus. *Microvasc. Res.* 18: 105–119, 1979.

295. RASIO, E. A., C. L. HAMPERS, J. S. SOELDNER, AND G. F. CAHILL, JR. Diffusion of glucose, insulin, inulin, and Evans blue protein into thoracic duct lymph of man. *J. Clin. Invest.* 6: 903–910, 1967.

296. RAYMOND, R. M., S. B. JANDHYALA, AND G. J. GREGA. Interrelationship among bradykinin, various vasoactive substances, and macromolecular permeability in the canine forelimb. *Microvasc. Res.* 19: 329–337, 1980.

297. REED, R. K., AND K. AUKLAND. Transcapillary fluid balance in immature rats. Interstitial fluid pressure, serum and interstitial protein concentration, and colloid osmotic pressure. *Microvasc. Res.* 14: 37–43, 1977.

298. REESE, T. S., AND M. J. KARNOVSKY. Fine structural localization of a blood-brain barrier to exogenous peroxidase. *J. Cell Biol.* 34: 207–217, 1969.

299. REICHEL, A., V. ROTHER, J. WERNER, AND F. REICHEL. On the transport of various endogenous plasma proteins from blood to peripheral lymph in man. *Lymphology* 9: 118–121, 1976.

300. RENKIN, E. M. Capillary permeability to lipid-soluble molecules. *Am. J. Physiol.* 168: 538–545, 1952.

301. RENKIN, E. M. Filtration diffusion and molecular sieving through porous cellulose membranes. *J. Gen. Physiol.* 38: 225–243, 1954.

302. RENKIN, E. M. Transport of large molecules across capillary walls. *Physiologist* 7: 13–28, 1964.

303. RENKIN, E. M. Multiple pathways of capillary permeability. *Circ. Res.* 62: 72–80, 1978.

304. RENKIN, E. M. Lymph as a measure of the composition of interstitial fluid. In: *Pulmonary Edema*, edited by A. P. Fishman and E. M. Renkin. Bethesda, MD: Am. Physiol. Soc., 1979, p. 145–159.

305. RENKIN, E. M. Relation of capillary morphology to transport of fluid and large molecules: a review. *Acta Physiol. Scand. Suppl.* 463: 81–91, 1979.

306. RENKIN, E. M. Ambiguities and errors in evaluation of capillary pore sizes. (Letter to the editor) *Am. J. Physiol.* 240 (*Heart Circ. Physiol.* 9): H145–H146, 1980.

307. RENKIN, E. M. Transport of proteins by diffusion, bulk flow and vesicular mechanisms. *Physiologist* 23(1): 57–61, 1980.

308. RENKIN, E. M., R. D. CARTER, AND W. L. JOYNER. Mechanism of the sustained action of histamine and bradykinin on transport of large molecules across capillary walls in the dog paw. *Microvasc. Res.* 7: 49–60, 1974.

309. RENKIN, E. M., F. E. CURRY, AND C. C. MICHEL. Failure of histamine, 5-hydroxytryptamine, or bradykinin to increase capillary permeability to plasma proteins in frogs: action of compound 48/80. *Microvasc. Res.* 8: 213–217, 1974.

310. RENKIN, E. M., AND D. G. GARLICK. Blood-lymph transport of macromolecules. *Microvasc. Res.* 2: 392–398, 1970.

311. RENKIN, E. M., AND J. P. GILMORE. Glomerular filtration. In: *Handbook of Physiology. Renal Physiology*, edited by J. Orloff and R. W. Berliner. Bethesda, MD: Am. Physiol. Soc., 1973, sect. 8, chapt. 9, p. 185–248.

312. RENKIN, E. M., W. L. JOYNER, C. H. SLOOP, AND P. D. WATSON. Influence of venous pressure on plasma-lymph transport in the dog's paw. Convective and dissipative mechanisms. *Microvasc. Res.* 14: 191–204, 1977.

313. RENKIN, E. M., P. D. WATSON, C. H. SLOOP, W. L. JOYNER, AND F. E. CURRY. Transport pathways for fluid and large molecules in microvascular endothelium of the dog's paw. *Microvasc. Res.* 14: 205–214, 1977.

314. RENNKE, H. G., R. S. COTRAN, AND M. A. VENKATACHALAM. Role of molecular charge in glomerular permeability. *J. Cell Biol.* 67: 638–646, 1975.

315. RENNKE, H. G., Y. PATEL, AND M. A. VENKATACHALAM. Effect of molecular charge in glomerular permeability. Clearance studies using neutral, anionic, and cationic horseradish peroxidase. *Kidney Int.* 13: 278–288, 1978.

316. RENNKE, H. G., AND M. A. VENKATACHALAM. Structural determinants of glomerular permselectivity. *Federation Proc.* 36: 2619–2626, 1977.

317. RENNKE, H. G., AND M. A. VENKATACHALAM. Glomerular permeability of macromolecules. Effect of molecular configuration on the fractional clearance of uncharged dextran and neutral horseradish peroxidase. *J. Clin. Invest.* 63: 713–717, 1979.

318. RICHARDSON, P. D. I., D. N. GRANGER, D. MAILMAN, AND P. R. KVIETYS. Permeability characteristics of colonic capillaries. *Am. J. Physiol.* 239 (*Gastrointest. Liver Physiol.* 2): G300–G305, 1980.

319. RICHARDSON, P. D. I., D. N. GRANGER, AND A. E. TAYLOR. Capillary filtration coefficient: the technique and its application to the small intestine. *Cardiovasc. Res.* 13: 547–561, 1979.

320. RIPPE, B., AND B. FOLKOW. Capillary permeability to albumin in normotensive and spontaneously hypertensive rats. *Acta Physiol. Scand.* 101: 72–83, 1977.

321. RIPPE, B., A. KAMIYA, AND B. FOLKOW. Transcapillary passage of albumin, effects of tissue cooling and of increases in filtration and plasma colloid osmotic pressure. *Acta Physiol. Scand.* 105: 171–187, 1979.

322. RIPPE, B., S. LUNDIN, AND B. FOLKOW. Plasma volume, blood volume and transcapillary escape rate (TER) of albumin in young spontaneously hypertensive rats (SHR) as compared with normotensive controls (NCR). *Clin. Exp. Hypertens.* 1: 39–50, 1978.

323. ROBERTS, S. H., D. L. KEPKAY, AND J. A. BARROWMAN. Proteins of ascitic fluid in constrictive pericarditis. *Am. J. Dig. Dis.* 23: 844–848, 1978.

324. ROUS, P., H. P. GILDING, AND F. SMITH. The gradient of vascular permeability. *J. Exp. Med.* 51: 807–830, 1930.

325. ROZTOČIL, K., I. PŘEROVSKÝ, I. OLIVA, K. HORKÝ, AND J. MAREK. Capillary diffusion capacity for I-131 and capillary filtration rate in female patients with idiopathic oedema. *Cor Vasa* 21: 43–50, 1979.

326. RUSSNYAK, I., M. FOLDI, AND G. SZABÓ (editors). *Lymphatics and Lymph Circulation: Physiology and Pathology* (2nd ed.). Oxford, UK: Pergamon, 1967, 971 p.

327. RUTILI, G., AND K.-E. ARFORS. Protein concentration in interstitial and lymphatic fluids from the subcutaneous tissue. *Acta Physiol. Scand.* 99: 1–8, 1977.

328. RUTILI, G., D. N. GRANGER, A. E. TAYLOR, J. C. PARKER, AND N. A. MORTILLARO. Analysis of lymphatic protein data. IV. Comparison of the different methods used to estimate reflection coefficients and permeability–surface area products. *Microvasc. Res.* 23: 347–360, 1982.

329. RUTILI, G., AND P. HAGANDER. Transport of macromolecules in subcutaneous tissue. *Acta Univ. Ups. Nova Acta Regiae Soc. Sci. Ups. Ser. V C* Suppl. 306: 1978.

329a. RUTILI, G., P. KVIETYS, J. C. PARKER, AND A. E. TAYLOR. Increased pulmonary microvascular permeability induced by α-naphthylthiourea. *J. Appl. Physiol.: Respirat. Environ. Exercise Physiol.* 52: 1316–1323, 1982.

330. SALDEEN, T. The microembolism syndrome. *Microvasc. Res.* 11: 227–259, 1976.

331. SCHAD, H., AND H. BRECHTELSBAUER. The effect of saline loading and subsequent anaesthesia on thoracic duct lymph,

transcapillary protein escape and plasma protein of conscious dogs. *Pfluegers Arch.* 378: 127–133, 1978.
332. Schneeberger, E. E. Ultrastructural basis for alveolar-capillary permeability to protein. In: *Lung Liquids*, edited by R. Porter and M. O'Connor. New York: Elsevier, 1976, p. 3–28. (Ciba Found. Symp. 38.)
333. Schneeberger, E. E., and M. J. Karnovsky. Substructure of intercellular junctions in freeze-fractured alveolar-capillary membranes of mouse lung. *Circ. Res.* 38: 404–411, 1976.
334. Schroer, M., and G. Hauck. Fluid and substance pathway through the extravascular space. *Bibl. Anat.* 15: 231–233, 1977.
335. Schultze, H. E., and J. F. Heremans. *Molecular Biology of Human Proteins.* New York: Elsevier, 1966, sect. 4, chapt. 3, p. 589–669.
336. Senay, L. C., Jr. Changes in plasma volume and protein content during exposures of working men to various temperatures before and after acclimatization to heat: separation of the roles of cutaneous and skeletal muscle circulation. *J. Physiol. London* 224: 61–81, 1972.
337. Sha'afi, R. I., G. T. Rich, D. C. Mikulecky, and A. K. Solomon. Determination of urea permeability in red cells by minimum method. A test of the phenomenological equations. *J. Gen. Physiol.* 5: 427–450, 1970.
338. Shannon, A. D., and A. K. Lascelles. A study of lipid absorption in young milk fed calves with the use of a lymphatico-venous shunt for the collection of thoracic duct lymph. *Aust. J. Exp. Physiol.* 20: 669–681, 1967.
339. Shirley, H. H., C. G. Wolfram, K. Wasserman, and H. S. Mayerson. Capillary permeability to macromolecules: stretched pore phenomenon. *Am. J. Physiol.* 190: 189–193, 1957.
340. Siggaard-Andersen, J., F. B. Petersen, T. I. Hansen, and K. Mellemgaard. Vascular permeability and plasma volume changes during hypoxia and carbon monoxide exposure. *Angiology* 20: 356–358, 1969.
341. Simionescu, M., N. Simionescu, and G. E. Palade. Morphometric data on the endothelium of blood capillaries. *J. Cell Biol.* 60: 128–137, 1974.
342. Simionescu, M., N. Simionescu, and G. E. Palade. Segmental differentiations of cell junctions in the vascular endothelium. The microvasculature. *J. Cell Biol.* 67: 863–885, 1975.
343. Simionescu, N., M. Simionescu, and G. E. Palade. Permeability of intestinal capillaries. Pathway followed by dextrans and glycogens. *J. Cell Biol.* 53: 365–392, 1972.
344. Simionescu, N., M. Simionescu, and G. E. Palade. Permeability of muscle capillaries to exogenous myoglobin. *J. Cell Biol.* 57: 424–436, 1973.
345. Simionescu, N., M. Simionescu, and G. E. Palade. Structural-functional correlates in the transendothelial exchange of water soluble macromolecules. *Thromb. Res.* 8: 257–269, 1976.
346. Simionescu, N., M. Simionescu, and G. E. Palade. Structural basis of permeability in sequential segments of the microvasculature. II. Pathways followed by microperoxidase across the endothelium. *Microvasc. Res.* 15: 17–36, 1978.
347. Starling, E. H. On the absorption of fluids from the connective tissue spaces. *J. Physiol. London* 19: 312–326, 1896.
348. Starling, E. H. *Principles of Human Physiology.* Philadelphia, PA: Lea & Febiger, 1915.
349. Staub, N. C. Steady state pulmonary transvascular water filtration in unanesthetized sheep. *Circ. Res.* 28, Suppl. 1: 135–139, 1971.
350. Staub, N. C. Pulmonary edema. *Physiol. Rev.* 54: 687–811, 1974.
351. Staub, N. C. Pulmonary edema due to increased microvascular permeability to fluid and protein. *Circ. Res.* 64: 48–56, 1979.
352. Staverman, A. J. Theory of measurement of osmotic pressure. *Rec. Trav. Chim. Pays-Bas* 70: 344–352, 1951.
353. Sterling, K. The turnover rate of serum albumin in man as measured by ^{131}I-tagged albumin. *J. Clin. Invest.* 30: 1228–1231, 1951.
354. Surtees, V. M., K. N. Ham, and J. D. Tange. Visceral oedema and increased vascular permeability in early experimental hypertension. *Pathology* 11: 663–670, 1979.
355. Svensjö, E. Bradykinin and prostaglandin E_1, E_2 and $F_{2\alpha}$-induced macromolecular leakage in the hamster cheek pouch. *Prostaglandins Med.* 1: 397–410, 1978.
356. Svensjö, E., and K.-E. Arfors. Dimensions of postcapillary venules sensitive to bradykinin and histamine-induced leakage of macromolecules. *Upsala J. Med. Sci.* 84: 47–60, 1979.
357. Svensjö, E., K.-E. Arfors, G. Arturson, and G. Rutili. Hamster cheek pouch preparation as a model for studies of macromolecular permeability of the microvasculature. *Upsala J. Med. Sci.* 83: 71–79, 1978.
358. Svensjö, E., K. E. Arfors, R. M. Raymond, and G. J. Grega. Morphological and physiological correlation of bradykinin-induced macromolecular efflux. *Am. J. Physiol.* 236 (*Heart Circ. Physiol.* 5): H600–H606, 1979.
359. Svensjö, E., C. G. A. Persson, and G. Rutili. Inhibition of bradykinin-induced macromolecular leakage from postcapillary venules by a β_2-adrenoreceptor stimulant, terbutaline. *Acta Physiol. Scand.* 101: 504–506, 1977.
360. Szabó, G., Z. Magyar, and E. Posch. The relationship between tissue fluid and lymph. *Lymphology* 9: 145–149, 1976.
361. Szabó, G., Z. Magyar, and A. Reffy. Lymphatic transport of enzymes after experimental myocardial infarction. *Lymphology* 7: 37–44, 1974.
362. Szidon, J. P., G. G. Pietra, and A. P. Fishman. Alveolar-capillary membrane and pulmonary edema. *N. Engl. J. Med.* 286: 1200–1204, 1972.
363. Szmigielski, S., K. Kwarecki, J. Jeljaszewicz, and C. Zak. Increased vascular permeability induced by staphylococcal alpha-toxin. *J. Pathol.* 106: 227–280, 1972.
364. Szwed, J. J., D. R. Maxwell, R. Elliott, and L. E. Redlich. Diuretics and small intestinal lymph flow in the dog. *J. Pharmacol. Exp. Ther.* 200: 88–94, 1977.
365. Taylor, A. E., and K. A. Gaar, Jr. Estimation of equivalent pore radii of pulmonary capillary and alveolar membranes. *Am. J. Physiol.* 218: 1133–1140, 1970.
366. Taylor, A., and H. Gibson. Concentrating ability of lymphatic vessels. *Lymphology* 8: 43–49, 1975.
367. Taylor, A. E., W. H. Gibson, H. J. Granger, and A. C. Guyton. The interaction between intercapillary and tissue forces in the overall regulation of interstitial fluid volume. *Lymphology* 6: 192–208, 1973.
367a. Taylor, A. E., and D. N. Granger. Equivalent pore modeling: vesicles and channels. *Federation Proc.* 42: 2440–2445, 1983.
368. Taylor, A. E., D. N. Granger, and R. A. Brace. Analysis of lymphatic protein flux data. I. Estimation of the reflection coefficient and permeability surface area product for total protein. *Microvasc. Res.* 13: 297–313, 1977.
369. Taylor, A. E., J. Parker, D. N. Granger, N. A. Mortillaro, and G. Rutili. Assessment of capillary permeability using lymphatic protein flux: estimation of osmotic reflection coefficient. In: *Basic Physiology*, edited by R. Effros. New York: Academic, 1981, p. 19–32.
370. Taylor, P. M., U. Boonyaprakob, D. W. Watson, and P. Fireman. Relative efflux of native proteins from the canine pulmonary vascular bed. *Am. J. Physiol.* 214: 1310–1314, 1968.
371. Thorball, N., and F. Olsen. The permeability pathways in the walls of intestinal submucosal arterioles in acute angiotensin-induced hypertension in rats. *Acta Pathol. Microbiol. Scand.* 82: 683–689, 1974.
372. Thorball, N., and F. Olsen. Ultrastructural pathological changes in intestinal submucosal arterioles in angiotensin-induced acute hypertension in rats. *Acta Pathol. Microbiol. Scand.* 82: 703–713, 1974.
373. Todd, T. R. J., E. Baile, and J. C. Hogg. Pulmonary capillary permeability during hemorrhagic shock. *J. Appl. Physiol.: Respirat. Environ. Exercise Physiol.* 45: 298–306, 1978.
374. Tompkins, C. L., and H. J. Granger. Ultrastructure of the

peribiliary capillary (Abstract). *Microvasc. Res.* 21: 261, 1981.

375. UHLEY, H. N., S. E. LEEDS, J. J. SAMPSON, AND M. FRIEDMAN. The cardiac lymphatics in experimental chronic congestive heart failure. *Proc. Soc. Biol. Exp. Med.* 131: 379–381, 1969.
376. ULLAL, S. R., T. KLUGE, W. KERTH, AND F. GERBODE. Changes in cardiac lymph of dogs during and after anoxia. *Ann. Surg.* 175: 472–477, 1972.
377. VAERMAN, J.-P., AND J. F. HEREMANS. Origin and molecular size of immunoglobulin-A in the mesenteric lymph of the dog. *Immunology* 18: 27–38, 1970.
378. VAN DER ZEE, H., A. B. MALIK, B. C. LEE, AND T. S. HAKIM. Lung fluid and protein exchange during intracranial hypertension and role of sympathetic mechanisms. *J. Appl. Physiol.: Respirat. Environ. Exercise Physiol.* 48: 273–280, 1980.
379. VARGAS, F. F., G. BLACKSHEAR, AND R. MAJERLE. Permeability and model testing of heart capillaries by osmotic and optical methods. *Am. J. Physiol.* 239 (*Heart Circ. Physiol.* 8): H464–H468, 1980.
380. VARGAS, F., AND J. A. JOHNSON. An estimate of reflection coefficient from rabbit heart capillaries. *J. Gen. Physiol.* 47: 667–677, 1964.
381. VENKATACHALAM, M. A., AND H. G. RENNKE. The structural and molecular basis of glomerular filtration. *Circ. Res.* 43: 337–347, 1978.
382. VERNIORY, A., R. DUBOIS, P. DECSODT, AND P. P. LAMBERT. Measurement of the permeability of biological membranes. *J. Gen. Physiol.* 62: 489–507, 1973.
383. VOGEL, G., K. GARTNER, AND M. ULBRICH. The flow rate and macromolecule content of hilar lymph from the rabbit's kidney under conditions of renal venous pressure elevation and restriction of renal function—studies on the origin of renal lymph. *Lymphology* 3: 136–143, 1974.
384. VOGEL, G., AND H. STRÖCKER. Regionale Unterschiede der Capillarpermeabilität. Untersuchungen über die Penetration von Polyvinylpyrrolidon und endogenen Proteinen aus dem Plasma in die Lymphe von Kanichen. *Pfluegers Arch. Gesamte Physiol. Menschen Tiere* 294: 119–125, 1967.
385. VREIM, C. E., K. OHKUDA, AND N. C. STAUB. Proportions of dog lung lymph in the thorax and right lymph ducts. *J. Appl. Physiol.: Respirat. Environ. Exercise Physiol.* 43: 874–898, 1977.
386. VREIM, C. E., P. D. SNASHALL, R. H. DEMLING, AND N. C. STAUB. Lung lymph and free interstitial fluid protein composition in sheep with edema. *Am. J. Physiol.* 230: 1650–1653, 1976.
387. VREIM, C. E., P. D. SNASHALL, AND N. C. STAUB. Protein composition of lung fluids in anesthetized dogs with acute cardiogenic edema. *Am. J. Physiol.* 231: 1466–1469, 1976.
388. WAGENSTEEN, O. D., E. LYSAKER, AND P. SAVARYN. Pulmonary capillary filtration and reflection coefficients in the adult rabbit. *Microvasc. Res.* 14: 81–99, 1977.
389. WARREN, M. F., AND C. K. DRINKER. The flow of lymph from the lungs of the dog. *Am. J. Physiol.* 136: 207–221, 1942.
390. WATSON, P. D., D. R. BELL, AND E. M. RENKIN. Early kinetics of large molecule transport between plasma and lymph in dogs. *Am. J. Physiol.* 239 (*Heart Circ. Physiol.* 8): H525–H531, 1980.
391. WEIBEL, E. R. Morphometry of pulmonary circulation. In: *Morphometry of the Human Lung.* New York: Academic, 1963.
392. WEIBEL, E. R., AND H. BACHOFEN. Structural design of the alveolar septum and fluid exchange. In: *Pulmonary Edema*, edited by A. P. Fishman and E. M. Renkin. Bethesda, MD: Am. Physiol. Soc., 1979, p. 1–20.
393. WELCH, K., AND H. DAVSON. The permeability of capillaries of the sciatic nerve of the rabbit to several materials. *Neurosurgery* 36: 21–26, 1972.
394. WELLS, F. R. Site of vascular response to thermal injury in skeletal muscle. *Br. J. Exp. Pathol.* 52: 292–305, 1971.
395. WENDT, R. P., E. KLEIN, E. H. BRESLER, F. F. HOLLAND, E. M. SEVINO, AND H. VILLA. Sieving properties of hemodialysis membranes. *J. Membr. Biol.* 5: 23–49, 1979.
396. WENDT, R. P., E. A. MASON, AND E. H. BRESLER. Effect of heteroporosity on flux equations for membranes. *Biophys. Chem.* 4: 237–247, 1976.
397. WIEDERHIELM, C. A. Transcapillary and interstitial transport phenomena in the mesentery. *Federation Proc.* 25: 1789–1798, 1967.
398. WILLIAMS, M. C., AND S. L. WISSIG. The permeability of muscle capillaries to horseradish peroxidase. *J. Cell Biol.* 66: 531, 1975.
399. WITTE, C. L., M. H. WITTE, AND A. E. DUMONT. The portal triad in hepatic cirrhosis. *Surg. Gynecol. Obstet.* 146: 965–974, 1978.
400. WITTE, C. L., M. H. WITTE, AND A. E. DUMONT. Lymph imbalance in the genesis and perpetuation of the ascites syndrome in hepatic cirrhosis. *Gastroenterology* 78: 1059–1068, 1980.
401. WITTE, C. L., M. H. WITTE, A. E. DUMONT, C. R. COLE, AND J. R. SMITH. Protein content in lymph and edema fluids in congestive heart failure. *Circulation* 40: 623–629, 1969.
402. WITTE, M. H., C. L. WITTE, AND A. E. DUMONT. Progress in liver disease: physiological factors involved in the causation of cirrhotic ascites. *Gastroenterology* 61: 742–750, 1971.
403. WITTE, M. H., C. L. WITTE, AND A. E. DUMONT. Estimates of net transcapillary water and protein flux in the liver and intestine of patients with portal hypertension from hepatic cirrhosis. *Gastroenterology* 80: 265–272, 1981.
404. WOOD, J. G., AND H. W. DAVENPORT. A method for measuring gastric vascular permeability to plasma proteins (Abstract). *Physiologist* 22(4): 135, 1979.
405. WOOLLEY, G., AND F. C. COURTICE. The origin of albumin in hepatic lymph. *Aust. J. Exp. Biol. Med. Sci.* 40: 121–128, 1962.
406. WORM, A. M. Capillary permeability of albumin in patients with skin disease. *Bibl. Anat.* 18: 47–49, 1979.
407. YABLONSKI, M. E., AND N. LIFSON. Mechanism of production of intestinal secretion by elevated venous pressure. *J. Clin. Invest.* 57: 904–915, 1976.
408. YIPINTSOI, T., R. TANCREDI, AND J. B. BASSINGTHWAIGHTE. Myocardial extractions of sucrose, glucose and potassium. In: *Capillary Permeability*, edited by C. Crone and N. A. Lassen. Copenhagen: Munksgaard 1970, p. 153–156. (Alfred Benzon Symp. 2.)
409. YOFFEY, J. M., AND F. C. COURTICE. *Lymphatics, Lymph and the Lymphomyeloid Complex.* London: Academic, 1970.
410. YOULTEN, L. J. F. Permeability to human serum albumin (HSA) and polyvinylpyrrolidone (PVP) of skeletal muscle (rat cremaster) blood vessel walls. *J. Physiol. London* 204: 112P–113P, 1969.
411. ZOLLINGER, R. M. Plasma volume and protein restoration after hemorrhage: role of the left thoracic duct versus transcapillary refilling. *J. Surg. Res.* 12: 151–160, 1972.

CHAPTER 12

The interstitium and microvascular exchange

JOEL L. BERT
RICHARD H. PEARCE

Departments of Pathology and Chemical Engineering, University of British Columbia, Vancouver, Canada

CHAPTER CONTENTS

Composition and Architecture of the Interstitial Space
Collagenous fibers
Elastic fibers
Hyaluronate and proteoglycans
Hyaluronate
Proteoglycans
Basement membrane
Interstitial plasma proteins
Physicochemical and Partition Properties of the Interstitium
Exclusion
Compartmentalization within the interstitium
Transport coefficients
Diffusion coefficients
Flow conductivity
Flow in the Interstitium
Interstitial Fluid and Lymph
Regulation Within the Interstitium
Computer Simulations of Microvascular Exchange
Summary

THIS CHAPTER reviews the current knowledge of the interstitial space and its role in microvascular exchange. This space is difficult to define rigorously, but operationally the interstitium is the connective tissue space outside the vascular and lymphatic systems and the cells. The information presented constitutes a survey of the chemical constitution and physicochemical properties of the components of the interstitium as well as of the architecture of the structural fibers of this space. Emphasis is on the effect of the interstitium on microvascular exchange of fluid and macromolecules. Current concepts discussed include compartmentalization of the interstitial space, flow through this space, and the self-regulating properties exhibited by it. Models used in descriptions of transport through the interstitial space are also presented.

COMPOSITION AND ARCHITECTURE OF THE INTERSTITIAL SPACE

Water and its dissolved constituents move from the blood plasma to lymph through a connective tissue space. In an avascular, acellular tissue such as dermis, tendon, or nucleus pulposus, this space may contain virtually all the water of the tissue; in a highly vascular or cellular tissue such as muscle, liver, lung, or kidney, this space may represent only a small fraction of the tissue water (68, 179). Thus in discussing the composition and architecture within this compartment, emphasis is given to those substances that are characteristic of the connective tissues (i.e., collagenous and elastic fibers, hyaluronate, and proteoglycans) as well as to the plasma proteins found in this space.

Collagenous Fibers

Conventional histological sections reveal that the interstitial space of most tissues contains long fiber bundles recognizable as collagenous fibers. Under the electron microscope these bundles, which have a roughly circular cross section, appear to contain masses of unit fibers with characteristic transverse banding at intervals of 65–70 nm. During the past two decades, chemical and physical analyses of proteins isolated from tissues rich in collagenous fibers have provided a detailed understanding of the organization down to the atomic level. The relevant data have been summarized in several thorough reviews (24, 91, 100, 114, 126).

The basic structural unit of the interstitial collagenous fiber is the collagen molecule, formerly known as tropocollagen. This cylindrical structure, 1.5 nm in diameter and 300 nm long, is a protein of molecular weight 285,000 composed of three peptidic α-chains coiled to form a triple helix. Each α-chain (mol wt 9.5 $\times 10^4$) is itself coiled over 95% of its length. Thus the three α-coils have a ropelike configuration. Short portions at both ends of the α-chains, known as telopeptides, do not possess this helical configuration. The collagen molecule is formed extracellularly from a precursor, procollagen, by removal of terminal peptides from both ends of the procollagen through the action of two proteases known as procollagen peptidases (24, 76). The enzyme lysyl oxidase generates aldehydes from the ϵ-amino groups of the lysyl and hydroxylysyl residues in the telopeptide region of the α-chain. The aldehydes react with adjacent peptide chains to form a variety of cross-linking structures that stabilize the collagen molecule (76, 99, 145, 170).

Five distinct types of collagen molecule, differing from each other in the composition of their constituent α-chains, have been characterized in the interstitial collagens (23, 100, 114). Type I is the sole collagen of tendon and bone and the principal collagen of dermis and most other connective tissues. It contains three α-chains, two designated $\alpha1(I)$ and one designated $\alpha2(I)$. These differ from each other in amino acid composition and sequence. Type II collagen is characteristic of cartilages and contains three identical α-chains designated $\alpha1(II)$, which are homologous to $\alpha1(I)$. Type III collagen is found in tissues mixed with other collagen types, principally in blood vessels and fetal dermis. It contains three $\alpha1(III)$ chains cross-linked in the helical region with disulfide bonds; such bonds are absent from type I and type II collagens. Trace amounts of type I trimer, containing three identical $\alpha1(I)$ chains, have been found in skin, embryonic tendon, and some other tissues. The interstitial form of type V collagen is believed to contain two $\alpha1(V)$ chains and one $\alpha2(V)$ chain, although some controversy remains about its structure (101). Each of these five types of collagen form molecules of similar structure and physical dimensions.

Collagenous fibers are formed by the interaction of collagen molecules to form an ordered array within which the molecules are arranged roughly parallel to the axis of the fiber. The organization of the molecules along the length of the fiber is well understood (Fig. 1). If D represents the interval of ~67 nm at which the staining pattern repeats along the fiber axis, the length of the collagen molecule is 4.4D. In the direction parallel to the axis each molecule is displaced by a distance D in relation to its neighbor, leaving a space 0.6D in length between adjacent molecules. Thus the pattern of molecules along the axis repeats at 5D intervals. The side-to-side interaction of the molecules necessary to produce this arrangement is stabilized by electrostatic and hydrophobic bonds between amino

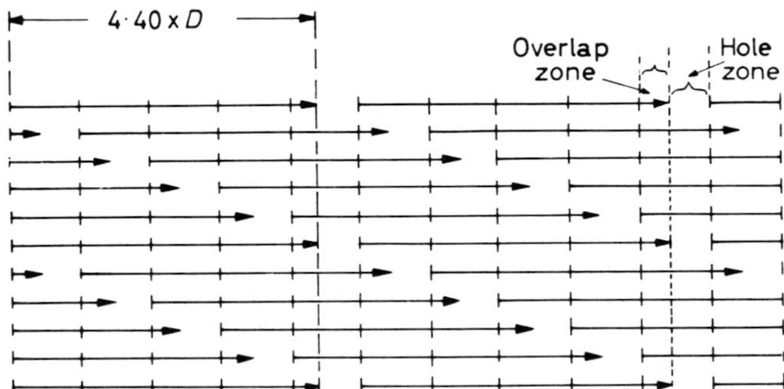

FIG. 1. Two-dimensional representation of the longitudinal arrangement of collagen molecules in a collagenous fiber. Displacement of nearest neighbors by a distance D results in the formation of a fiber of period D, with each period comprising an overlap zone of 0.4D and a hole zone of 0.6D. The pattern repeats at 5D intervals along the axis of any molecule. [From Hodge et al. (78).]

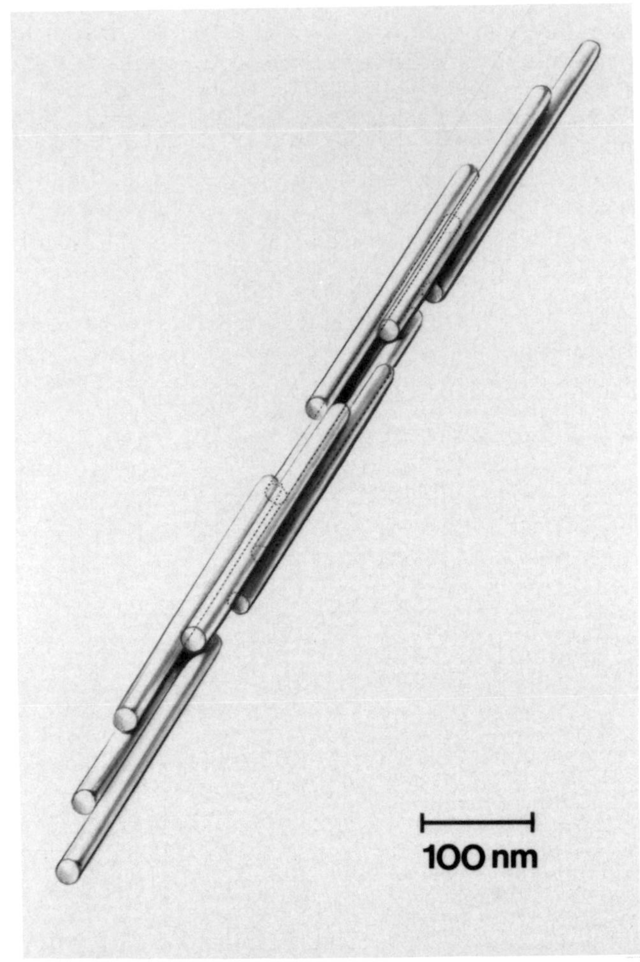

FIG. 2. Heuristic model of collagenous microfibril. [Adapted from Miller (112).]

acids on the outside of the molecule; the interval D corresponds to 234 amino acid residues (24, 90, 113).

The organization of the molecules perpendicular to the axis is less well established. Two models have been examined in some detail. Miller (112) described a heuristic model of a microfibril (Fig. 2) in which collagen molecules are arranged helically about an axis, five molecules per turn, providing a 5D repeating interval; such a structure would have a diameter of ~3.8 nm. Groups of four microfibrils combine to form a major subunit (49). These subunits combine to form the extended array of the collagenous fiber. Hulmes and Miller (80) subsequently proposed an approximately hexagonally packed crystalline array of collagen molecules with three Bragg planes spaced at distances of ~1.3 nm. Piez (138) pointed out that the two models may represent different views of the same structure. Current studies suggest that collagenous fibers form in vitro, beginning as a long thin fibril that then grows laterally to form a typical native fiber (138, 173, 176). Once assembled, these fibers are believed to be stabilized by intermolecular cross-links formed by mechanisms similar to those described for intramolecular cross-links (24, 99). The cylindrical collagenous fiber seen in the electron microscope is formed of these arrays of collagen molecules.

Only a few detailed studies of fiber size have been completed; the available data were summarized by Parry et al. (130). The average diameters of the fibers and their distribution varied widely among tissues and with the stage of development. The distributions were unimodal in the fetus and at senescence. Tissues subjected to high applied stress developed a bimodal distribution of fiber diameters, an observation interpreted by the authors as providing an optimal combination of tensile strength and resistance to damage by creep. Except in the cornea, the mass-weighted average diameter increased from birth to maturity and then decreased with approach to senescence. An analysis of data available for unimodal distributions demonstrated that fiber diameters clustered around values that were multiples of 8 nm, ranging from 16 to 48 nm (131). This finding was taken to indicate a unit structure comprising four 3.8-nm microfibrils as described by Fraser et al. (49). The diameters of the fibers recorded in electron micrographs may not correspond to their size in vivo. A comparison of electron-microscopic and X-ray–diffraction data for tendon has suggested that diameter values as measured in electron micrographs may be 20%–30% too small (37).

Bundles of parallel fibers are found in many tissues. Fiber bundles may be assembled into highly ordered arrays, as in cornea, or into feltlike mats randomly oriented parallel to the surface, as in dermis (68, 79, 179). No quantitative descriptions of the orientations of collagenous fiber bundles are available. The various levels of organization of collagenous fibers in tendon have been summarized in Figure 3, although the hierarchy of organization may differ in other tissues.

When considering their movement through the interstitial space, molecules' dimensions must be related to the dimensions and internal organization of the collagenous structures. Some data describing the accessible space *within* collagenous fibers are available. Hulmes and Miller (80) supported their model of quasi-hexagonal packing of fibers by a calculated collagen content of 0.54 ml collagen/ml; this value corresponds closely to published measurements. If water is assumed to occupy the remaining space, the interfibrillar water content would be 0.6 ml/g collagen. This value is substantially lower than the 1.14 ml/g collagen measured for reconstituted hide collagen by Katz and Li (87). However, the latter's system included spaces outside the fiber and did not correct for the possible steric exclusion of their polyethylene glycol probe.

Elastic Fibers

In contrast to the high tensile strength of collagenous fibers along their length, elastic fibers have a rubberlike consistency and impart this property to tissues rich in this component. Elastic fibers are the principal fibrous component of two tissues: in the elastic arteries, notably aorta, they represent 30%–60% of the dry weight and occur as cylindrical lamellae 2.5 μm thick; in the ligamentum nuchae from the neck of grazing animals, they represent 78%–80% of the dry weight and occur as fibers with 6.7-μm mean diameter. However, elastic fibers have been demonstrated in most connective tissues where they have

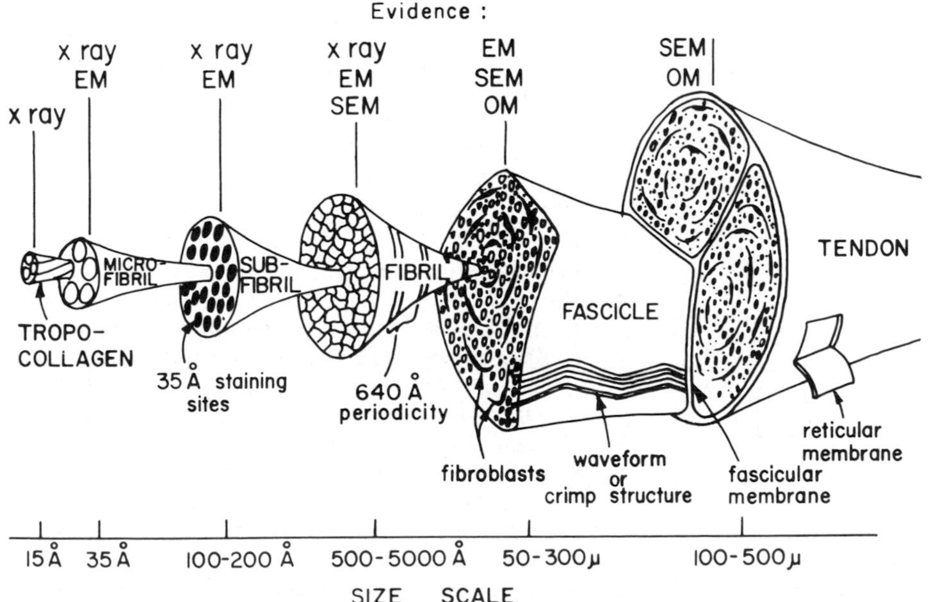

FIG. 3. Hierarchical organization of collagen in tendon. The type of instrument required to demonstrate each level of structure is indicated: OM, light microscope; SEM, scanning electron microscope; EM, transmission electron microscope; X ray, X-ray diffraction. Sizes of the various structures are shown. [From Kastelic et al. (85).]

been sought. For example, they account for 2%–5% of the dry weight of skin (48).

Definitive demonstration of elastic fibers in sections prepared for light microscopy requires special stains. In conventional preparations for electron microscopy, elastic fibers appear as amorphous masses surrounded by fine microfibrils. The microfibrils are the predominant component seen in the fetus. With maturation the microfibrils become infiltrated with an amorphous material until the microfibrils become obscured (48, 68, 179). Biochemists refer to these two structural components of the elastic fiber as microfibrillar protein and elastin, respectively. The microfibrillar protein can be solubilized, and its amino acid composition differs markedly from that of elastin. Over 95% of the amino acids of elastin are nonpolar, conferring on the protein a marked hydrophobic character. Elastin is composed of an extensive three-dimensional network of hydrophobic coils jointed at cross-links, and these cross-links comprise the amino acids desmosine and isodesmosine that are unique to elastin (46, 48, 157). In unstressed elastin the hydrophobic chains between the cross-links assume a random configuration. The application of force orients the chains, causing a loss of entropy and an associated release of heat, which is reabsorbed by the fiber if it is allowed to relax (53). On the other hand, some investigators believe that elastin is a mass of helical peptide coils (147, 174). Elastin arises from a molecule—tropoelastin—in which lysine residues serve as precursors to the desmosine and isodesmosine cross-links. The amino acid sequence of tropoelastin is almost completely known (157), although there is some evidence that more than one peptide chain may occur in elastic fibers (46). In the formation of elastin, some of the lysine residues of tropoelastin are converted to aldehydes by the enzyme lysyl oxidase, probably the same enzyme responsible for the formation of the cross-links in collagen. The aldehyde reacts with similar structures in its own and adjacent peptide chains; four such lysyl residues are required to form each desmosine. Many investigators believe that the microfibrillar protein contaminates many preparations of elastin (48, 157). The amino acid composition of elastin varies substantially in the evolutionary scale of species. These changes in composition are associated with marked changes in physical and mechanical properties of elastin (154).

Under physiological conditions unstressed elastic fibers contain ~0.56 ml water/ml elastin (54). Although most of this water is probably accessible to small molecules and ions (e.g., glucose, urea, sodium, and chloride), most larger moieties would be excluded because the apparent pore size of ligamentum nuchae elastin is ~1.6 nm (132).

Hyaluronate and Proteoglycans

Polysaccharides containing one of the amino sugars (i.e., hexosamines) have been recognized as characteristic components of the connective tissues and thus of the interstitial space. Such compounds, now known as glycosaminoglycans (GAGs), were formerly called acid mucopolysaccharides. With the probable exception of hyaluronate, the GAGs occur in tissues covalently bound to a polypeptide; such compounds are known as proteoglycans or, in the earlier literature, protein-polysaccharides. The contribution of these soluble, hydrophilic charged macromolecules to the physiological properties of the interstitium is profound and very different from that of the insoluble fibrous proteins, collagen and elastin. The characteristics contributed to the tissue by these polysaccharides are usually physicochemical in nature; those contributed by the fibers are structural. Unless special staining procedures are used, the proteoglycans are not apparent under the light or electron microscope and tend to be ignored by the general histologist. Thus much of what is known about their occurrence has been derived from chemical analysis.

HYALURONATE. Hyaluronate is an unbranched polysaccharide that is usually of high molecular weight and is found in most if not all tissues. Two thorough reviews summarize current knowledge relevant to interstitial mass transport (29, 94); the reader is referred to these for detailed information and references to the early literature. Hyaluronate is composed of alternating *N*-acetyl-D-glucosamine and D-glucuronic acid residues. Under physiological conditions the glucuronic acid is ionized. Thus the term *hyaluronate* more accurately describes its molecular state in vivo than does the term *hyaluronic acid.* The amount and molecular weight of hyaluronate varies widely from tissue to tissue (94, 97). Rooster comb and umbilical cord, tissues notably rich in this polysaccharide, contain 7.5 and 3 mg/g fresh wt, respectively (94); human plasma and urine each contain ~0.3 μg/ml (97). The concentration of hyaluronate in lymph is 10-fold higher than that in plasma, suggesting that the hyaluronate in the circulation comes from the tissues through the lymphatics (96).

Detailed physicochemical studies have shown that hyaluronate in physiological media forms an extended random coil. In the case of the hyaluronate of rooster comb ($\bar{M}_r \sim 7 \times 10^6$), it occupies a hydrodynamic volume of ~4 liter/g (187). Obviously solvent is the principal component of such a hyaluronate domain. The solvent water is believed to be held to the hyaluronate by hydrogen bonding. The mutual repulsion of the negative charges on the chains tends to expand the coil despite the excess of counterions in the hyaluronate domain (94). Solutions of hyaluronate are notably viscous even at low concentrations. A solution of undegraded umbilical cord hyaluronate in isotonic saline usually gels, i.e., behaves as a solid, at a concentration of 2–5 mg/ml. At concentrations just below those at which a gel forms, the viscosity of solutions rises sharply with concentration. This increase in viscosity has been attributed to entanglement of adjacent random coils, because the hydrodynamic volumes begin to overlap at these concentrations. This entanglement also contributes to the viscoelastic behavior of hyaluronate in this concentration range. Some workers believe that a form of interchain and/or intrachain binding also contributes to these phenomena (29). Changes in pH, which affect the ionization of the glucuronate residue, have a marked influence on the rheological properties of hyaluronate-solvent systems. For example, hyaluronate solutions of low concentration gel at a pH just below 3. The viscosity of hyaluronate solutions depends also on the molecular weight of the polysaccharide. In 0.15 M NaCl the intrinsic viscosity $[\eta]$ in milliliters per gram hyaluronate is described by the Mark-Houwink equation: $[\eta] = 0.012 M_r^{0.86}$, where M_r is molecular weight (187). At equilibrium and in the absence of other soluble macromolecules in the interstitium, the domain of hyaluronate would be limited only by the size of the extended molecule and the dimensions of the accessible space. For example, the maximum solvent volume that can be affected by the 0.3 mg of hyaluronate ($\bar{M}_r \sim 3 \times 10^5$) found in 1 g human dermis is 200 μl (106, 134).

The interaction of hyaluronate with other interstitial components affects its behavior in the tissue. In hyaline cartilage where much of the hyaluronate is bound in proteoglycan aggregates (see next section), the bound hyaluronate does not behave as if it were in solution. In other connective tissues, hyaluronate may be bound to fibronectin and, through this glycoprotein, to either cells or collagenous fibers (82, 150, 189). Binding affects the apparent specific volume and charge density of the hyaluronate. In tissues such as dermis and rooster comb the hyaluronate can be extracted quantitatively with isotonic saline, suggesting that in these tissues it is not bound to tissue structures (134, 168, 169).

PROTEOGLYCANS. Like hyaluronate, proteoglycans are distributed widely throughout the tissues of the body. The size and composition of the proteoglycans differ remarkably between tissues—in the number, type, and chain length of their component GAGs; in the length of their peptide cores; in their ability to aggregate either with themselves or with hyaluronate; and in their binding to other components of the tissue. Table 1 illustrates this diversity for a limited selection of proteoglycans. The chemical properties of the well-studied proteoglycans and the evidence supporting the accepted models of their structure have been the subject of several excellent reviews (69, 71, 72, 109, 116). Few general statements can be made that apply to such a diverse group of macromolecules.

Many of the known proteoglycans form aggregates in the presence of hyaluronate. As shown in Figure 4, the proteoglycan of bovine nasal cartilage contains a globular peptide attached to one end of the core protein. This peptide interacts with a sequence of five disaccharide units of the hyaluronate chain, and the interaction is stabilized by a link protein (72, 116). The size of the aggregate depends on the length of the

TABLE 1. *Molecular Characteristics of Selected Proteoglycans*

Tissue	$\bar{M}_r$	Glycosaminoglycan Chains: Type*	No. chains	$\bar{M}_r$	% of Proteoglycan	% Protein	Aggregate	Link	Ref.
Nasal cartilage (cattle)	2.5×10^6	Ch4S	100	$\sim 2 \times 10^4$	87	7	Present	Present	70
		KS	45	$\sim 6 \times 10^3$	6	($M_r \sim 3 \times 10^5$)			
Articular cartilage (human, age 20–40 yr)		ChS			42	34.7	Present	Present	8
		KS			24				
Intervertebral disk (human)		Ch6S		$\sim 2 \times 10^4$	42	20	Present		135
		KS		$\sim 1 \times 10^4$	38				
Dermis (pig)	7×10^4	DS	1	$\sim 2.6 \times 10^4$		60	Absent		31
Aortic intima (cattle)	2×10^6	Copolymer Ch4S (46%) Ch6S (47%) DS (7%)		$\sim 4 \times 10^4$		18	Present		121
Cornea (rhesus monkey)	1.2×10^5	Copolymer Ch (52%) Ch4S (31%) Ch6S (17%)		$\sim 5.5 \times 10^4$		70			75
		KS							
	5.5×10^4	KS	2	$\sim 7 \times 10^3$					
Glomerular basement membrane (rat)	1.3×10^5	HepS	4	$\sim 2.6 \times 10^4$					84
	1.3×10^5	ChS	4	$\sim 2.6 \times 10^4$					
Liver plasma membrane (rat)	7.5×10^4	HepS	4	$\sim 1.4 \times 10^4$		25 ($M_r \sim 1.9 \times 10^4$)			125

GAG, glycosaminoglycan; ChS, chondroitin sulfate; Ch, chondroitin; Ch4S, chondroitin 4-sulfate; Ch6S, chondroitin 6-sulfate; DS, dermatan sulfate; KS, keratan sulfate; HepS, heparan sulfate; $\bar{M}_r$, average mol wt. All percentages are wt/wt. * In the case of GAG copolymers, the percentage of GAG in copolymer is given.

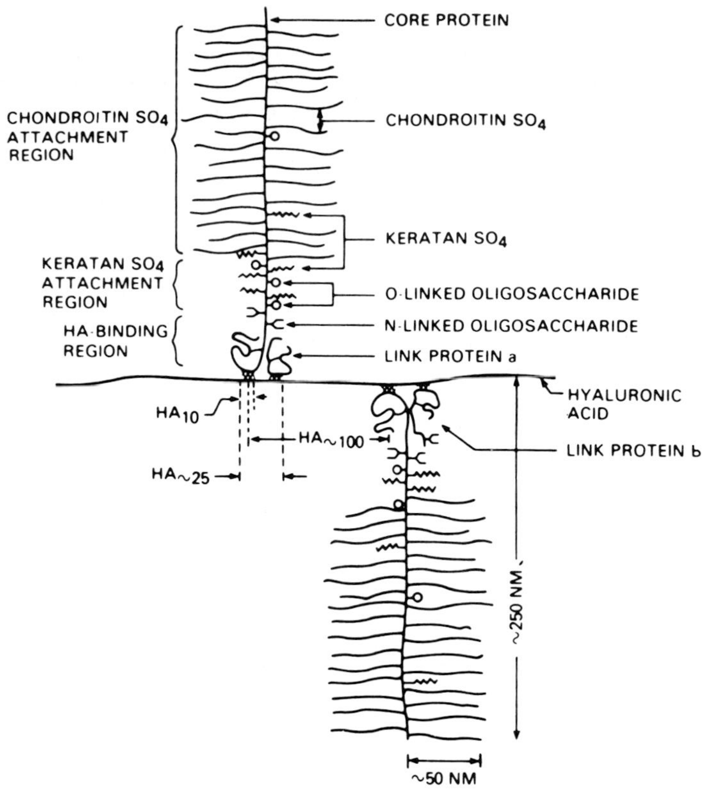

FIG. 4. Schematic model of the structure of cartilage proteoglycan aggregates. HA, hyaluronate. [From Hascall (71), reprinted by permission of John Wiley & Sons, Inc., © 1981.]

hyaluronate molecule. Aggregates containing over 100 proteoglycan monomers, each with $M_r \sim 2.5 \times 10^6$, have been observed in the electron microscope (70).

The properties of the proteoglycans relevant to interstitial physiology are their high charge density and hydrophilic character, the former arising principally from the ester sulfate and carboxyl groups attached to the GAG side chains and the latter from the hydrogen bonding of water to the carbohydrate residues of the GAGs. The proteoglycan monomer of bovine nasal cartilage has a mean hydrodynamic volume of 140 ml/g. Analysis of its physicochemical behavior suggests that its shape in solution is close to a sphere 40 nm in diameter (74). This hydrodynamic volume is much less than that of a hyaluronate of equivalent molecular weight, presumably because the attachment of many GAG chains to a polypeptide core limits the volume occupied by a given weight of the molecule. Under maximal compression in 0.5 M guanidinium chloride in the ultracentrifuge, the monomer occupied 30 ml/g (70). The intrinsic viscosity of the aggregate is about fivefold higher than that of the monomer. The viscosity of the aggregate depends on shear rate, and this suggests that it is asymmetric (73). In hyaline cartilage the proteoglycan is compressed to a volume less than one-fifth that at maximal expansion (71). The resulting extensive overlap causes the proteoglycan to behave as an extended three-dimensional network rather than as a discrete molecule (71). Scott et al. (160, 161) used a cationic dye to show that proteoglycan is bound to collagen at intervals corresponding to the repeat banding pattern. Poole et al. (139) used antibodies that bind both to the proteoglycan monomer and to the link protein to demonstrate a similar interaction between proteoglycan and collagen in the interterritorial region deep in articular cartilage. Long fibers of hyaluronate formed a lattice between collagenous fibers about which proteoglycan monomers aggregated in an organized structure. Proteoglycans containing dermatan sulfate and heparan sulfate are also tightly bound to collagenous fibers and can only be separated by methods capable of denaturing proteins (31, 84, 120, 137). Such binding between proteoglycans and collagenous fibers modifies the properties of both by providing a negatively charged environment around the fiber and by restricting the movement and domain of the proteoglycan.

The hyaluronate and proteoglycans of the interstitium are held in a meshwork of collagenous fibers. Principal support for this concept comes from the study of model systems. Fessler (43) showed that an intimate mixture of hyaluronate with thermally precipitated collagen formed a structure resistant to compression in the ultracentrifuge. The presence of the hyaluronate brought about a fourfold increase in the weight of solvent held within the pellet. The proteoglycan of bovine nasal cartilage showed a similar but more pronounced enhancement of solvent retention that increased with reduced ionic strength, as expected for a polyelectrolyte (35). In these systems the presence of hyaluronate or proteoglycan kept water in a state in which it was resistant to movement under external pressure. Maroudas (105) has shown for articular cartilage and intervertebral disks that the water content can be related to the fixed charge density of the tissue, a parameter considered a measure of GAG content. In the interstitial space both the local concentration of the trapped molecules and the Donnan effect contribute to the hydration of the tissue (29).

Basement Membrane

Basement membranes or basal laminae are sheets of extracellular matrix found wherever cells—other than connective tissue or blood cells—meet the interstitial space; these membranes surround the vessels of the microvasculature. At all sites basement membrane has two structurally distinct components: a central lamina densa 20–50 nm thick bounded on both sides by a lamina rara or lamina lucida about 10 nm thick, which doesn't stain as darkly as the lamina densa. One face of this structure adjoins cellular plasma membranes; the other borders the interstitium (41). Recent morphological, immunological, and biochemical studies have clarified the constitution of this structure (41, 61, 153, 164).

Collagen is a major component of basement membranes, but its composition and architecture in these structures differ markedly from those of the interstitial collagens. Type IV collagen, found in all basement membranes, is the principal component. Two $\alpha 1$(IV) chains and one $\alpha 2$(IV) chain form a triple-helical collagen molecule similar to that of the interstitial collagens, but the amino acid sequence is sufficiently different to limit the extent of the triple-helical regions. Furthermore the α-chains are longer than those of the interstitial collagens. The former make up a molecule of greater length cross-linked at the ends by disulfide bonds. The generally accepted architecture of the collagenous structure resembles a honeycomb (153, 164). Immunohistochemical studies suggest that the type IV collagen is located in the lamina densa. Other collagens, principally type V, have also been associated with basement membranes, but these are probably related more closely to nearby structures (153).

A heparan sulfate proteoglycan, described in Table 1, is associated with the collagenous meshwork of the lamina densa. Studies of the glomerular basement membrane have suggested that this proteoglycan may be responsible for the membrane's permeability properties (41, 164). The location of the heparan sulfate proteoglycan in the lamina densa may be related to its binding to collagen. A glycoprotein called laminin ($M_r - 1 \times 10^6$) has also been found in all basement membranes studied. Immunochemical procedures have localized this molecule in the lamina lucida. It is produced by epithelial and endothelial cells and facilitates the attachments of these cells to both type IV collagen and heparan sulfate proteoglycan (153, 164, 172). A currently accepted model of the basement membrane suggested by the observations just described is shown in Figure 5.

Interstitial Plasma Proteins

A major fraction of the body's plasma protein occurs extravascularly (e.g., 60% of the body's albumin), and because of this it forms a large interstitial reservoir. Skin is the tissue where these proteins have been studied most intensively. Extracts of skin prepared with physiological salt solutions contain proteins that are indistinguishable from those of the plasma by a variety of criteria, including electrophoresis on cellulose acetate or in polyacrylamide gels, or immunoelectrophoresis. Data have been obtained for rats, rabbits, cattle, and humans (1, 22, 30, 44, 81, 133, 134, 146, 169). The extravascular location of these proteins has been shown by the excess of plasma protein relative to hemoglobin in tissue extracts (22, 133, 134), by the entry of intravenously injected labeled albumin into tissue spaces (81, 88), and by direct observation of fluorescently labeled albumin, globulin, and fibrinogen in the extravascular space after intravenous injection (102). Much early work was well reviewed by Schultze and Heremans (159); more recent work relevant to albumin was discussed by Reeve (142). All the plasma proteins have been found extravascularly in tissues where they have been sought carefully, but most available data apply to connective tissues poor in proteoglycan. (However, refs. 2, 50 provide some data for tissues rich in proteoglycans.)

The plasma proteins are a diverse group of more than 100 different macromolecules; their structure and function have been reviewed in great detail by Putnam (141), among others. The data of Table 2 were chosen to illustrate this diversity for a group of six well-studied proteins. In any individual most of the plasma

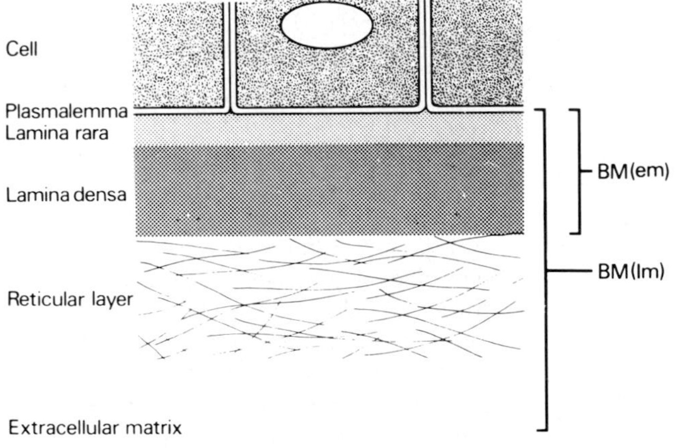

FIG. 5. Schematic representation of basement membrane structure. Single-layered basement membrane (BM) seen under the light microscope (lm) can be resolved into 3 zones under the electron microscope (em). Lamina rara and lamina densa seen in electron micrographs together constitute the basal lamina. [From Heathcote and Grant (77).]

proteins are monodisperse, homogeneous, and the products of single genes. Nevertheless circulating serum albumin occurs as a monomer, as a dimer, and as higher oligomers. Marked differences in the properties of a protein may also be found between species and between individuals of the same species; the latter polymorphism usually reflects genetic differences. The various plasma proteins differ in their mean concentrations in the plasma of normal individuals. Albumin in human serum may occur at a concentration of 55 g/liter, whereas enzymes, hormones, and other molecules with specific biological activities may be present in only trace amounts.

The physiological behavior of the plasma proteins is influenced profoundly by their physicochemical characteristics. Their molecular weights may vary from just over 5×10^3 (0.6S γ_2-globulin) to close to 1×10^6 (immunoglobulin M), with corresponding differences in size. Size is expressed as Stokes-Einstein radius (Table 2), which describes a sphere with an equivalent diffusion coefficient. The Stokes-Einstein radii for most plasma proteins range between 1 and 11 nm. Many plasma proteins have a relatively rigid three-dimensional conformation stabilized by intramolecular forces. Asymmetric species such as fibrinogen become oriented under shear stress like that encountered in the microcirculation. The asymmetry is expressed as the frictional ratio in Table 2; a spherical molecule has a frictional ratio of 1.00. The pH of plasma (~7.4) is well above the isoelectric point of most plasma proteins; as a result most of these molecules carry a net negative charge in the body. Because the interstitial hyaluronate, proteoglycans, and cells also carry an excess of fixed negative charges, the mutual repulsion of like charges inhibits the binding of proteins to these structures. An exception is immunoglobulin G: in many individuals a portion of the population of this protein may have an isoelectric point close to physiological pH. In normal individuals, immunoglobulin G is a heterogeneous mixture of antibodies each of which possesses a conformation related to its antigen. Thus immunoglobulin G is a poor choice for the probe in studies of the effects of protein size, charge, or shape on physiological properties of a plasma protein. The free-boundary electrophoretic mobility can be considered a measure of the charge density of a protein. The values of this mobility in Table 2 illustrate that the charge density is not related directly to the difference between pH 7.4 and the isoelectric point but rather to the number of titratable amino acids in the peptide chain. (However, many of the mobilities in Table 2 were not determined at physiological pH and ionic strength.) Each of these properties—homogeneity, size, asymmetry, and charge density—must be considered in the interpretation of experiments concerned with the interaction of plasma proteins with interstitial structures, and particularly with their transport through the interstitial space.

The whole-body metabolism and extravascular distribution of individual plasma proteins have usually been studied by intravenously injecting labeled protein and subsequently following the decay with time of the plasma radioactivity. These experiments are influenced by a number of factors: the quality of the labeled protein, the mixing time in the circulation, the rate of biosynthesis of the protein, the transcapillary exchange rate, and the catabolism of the protein. The methods of conducting the experiments and the mathematical analysis of the data have been reviewed by several authors in the book by Rothschild and Waldmann (149). The available data on the extravascular fraction of most plasma proteins come from such experiments and are uncertain because of the difficulties in deconvoluting the decay curves and in correcting the data for the release of label from the probe (143). The extravascular fractions of several plasma proteins that have been determined in this manner are listed in Table 2. An inverse relationship between extravascular fraction and the size (Stokes-Einstein radius) of the protein is apparent.

Few attempts have been made to measure the content of individual plasma proteins in various tissues. Some of the available data are summarized in Table 3. Rothschild et al. (148) measured the radioactivity of surgical specimens of human muscle and skin collected at intervals after the intravenous administration of labeled albumin. After a steady state had been

TABLE 2. *Physical Properties and Distribution of Selected Human Plasma Proteins*

Protein	Plasma Concentration Range,* g/liter	M_r* $\times 10^{-4}$	Stokes-Einstein Radius, nm	Frictional Ratio*	Isoelectric Point (pH)*	Electrophoretic Mobility,* $cm^2 \cdot V^{-1} \cdot s^{-1} \times 10^5$	Extravascular Fraction
Albumin	35–55	6.6	3.53	1.28	4.7	5.9	0.58
Transferrin	2–4	7.6	4.31	1.37	5.5	3.1	
Ceruloplasmin	0.15–0.60	13.0	5.67		4.4	5.2	
Immunoglobulin G	8–18	16	5.61	1.38	5.8–7.3	1.1	0.48
Fibrinogen	2.0–4.5	34	10.77	2.34	5.5	2.1	0.20
α_2-Macroglobulin	1.5–4.2	72.5	8.94	1.43	5.4	4.2	0.07

* Values from Putnam (141), corrected in some cases by more recent data (21). Values for Stokes-Einstein radii calculated from diffusion constants (141) by using the equation $r_s = kT/6\eta D$, where r_s is Stokes-Einstein radius, k is Boltzmann's constant, T is absolute temperature, η is viscosity of medium in poises, D is diffusion coefficient. Values for extravascular fraction (i.e., extravascular protein/total protein) taken or calculated from Rothschild and Waldmann (148).

attained (~5 days), the distribution of exchangeable albumin was calculated to be 40% in plasma, 18% in skin, and 15% in muscle. By direct extraction of tissues from nine donors, Katz et al. (89) found a mean and SD of 3.60 ± 1.15 mg extravascular albumin/g muscle and 8.41 ± 1.96 mg/g skin. The values in Table 3 were calculated from their published data for eight donors; the values are distinctly higher than those of Rothschild et al. for muscle but agree well for skin. Katz et al. also found that the extravascular albumin concentrations in human intestine and stomach lie between those for muscle and skin. Dewey (34) injected labeled albumin, γ-globulin, or a mixture of β- and γ-globulin intravenously into rats. He followed separately the attainment of a steady-state concentration of each of these proteins in spleen, lung, adrenal gland, liver, heart, kidney, ovaries, tibia, small intestine, stomach, lymph nodes, brain, Walker 256 sarcoma, muscle, fat, and skin. Over 90% of the extravascular plasma albumin was found in the last three tissues, although the amount in the fat was substantially less than that in muscle and skin. In the two latter tissues the content of γ-globulin was generally found to be less than that of albumin (Table 3). Katz et al. (88) measured the albumin content of plasma, carcass, and skin of rats and found that the distribution was 20%–25%, 35%–40%, and 20%–25%, respectively. Also, the content in these tissues was expressed relative to the interstitial water, the latter measured with both mannitol and sulfate. The albumin concentrations in the total interstitial water ranged from 50% to 61% of those in plasma, except in gut where the values ranged from 76% to 106%. Each of these studies indicated that a substantial fraction of the body's plasma proteins occur in the interstitial space, mainly in skeletal muscle and skin. Before the physiological importance of the interstitial plasma proteins can be clarified, much more information is needed about the concentrations of albumin and other plasma proteins in tissues of well-defined and uniform histological structure.

The physical properties of the plasma proteins in the interstitial space affect the physiology of this space in many ways. Because of its relative abundance, relatively low molecular weight, and high charge density (the latter contributing to its Donnan effect), albumin is the major contributor to the interstitial colloid osmotic pressure. Fibronectin, also known as cold-insoluble globulin, binds to collagen, fibroblasts, hyaluronate, and proteoglycans (82, 150, 189). The interstitial proteins return to the circulation via the lymph, and thus the interstitium acts as a reservoir of colloidally active molecules.

PHYSICOCHEMICAL AND PARTITION PROPERTIES OF THE INTERSTITIUM

Exclusion

Volume exclusion refers to a property of matter that prevents two materials from occupying the same space at the same time. The characteristic components of the interstitium of tissues have geometric shapes ranging from amorphous to well organized. The presence of these materials limits the extravascular, extracellular (i.e., interstitial) space accessible to a plasma protein or other macromolecule. A result of exclusion is that the concentration of a plasma protein in tissue fluid is higher than that obtained by simply dividing the extravascular, extracellular plasma protein content of the tissue by the extravascular, extracellular water content. This plasma protein concentration is one of the factors that determines the driving force for fluid and plasma protein transport in tissues; it is the effective concentration at which the plasma protein interacts with its environment.

Two models help describe interstitial exclusion: *1*) the rod-and-sphere model and *2*) the model of a sphere in a random network of rods. Figure 6 is an illustration of these two models and of a sphere excluding another sphere. In the rod-and-sphere model the space from which the center of the probe is excluded consists not only of the volume of the rod itself but also of an annulus of fluid surrounding the rod. This annulus has a thickness equal to the radius of the probe. Consequently the rod excludes a small probe from a small volume of annular fluid, whereas a larger probe is excluded from a much larger fluid volume. In the following analysis it is assumed that no binding of the probe to the excluding structures takes place. The rod-and-sphere representation is only applicable when end effects are negligible and when the center-to-center

TABLE 3. *Contents of Extravascular Plasma Proteins in Skin and Muscle*

	Skin		Muscle		Method	Ref.
	Albumin	IgG	Albumin	IgG		
Human	0.25–0.30		0.035		Count*	149
	0.27 ± 0.07(8)†		0.12 ± 0.06(8)†		Extraction‡	89
Rat	0.11 ± 0.02	0.11 ± 0.02	0.03 ± 0.01	0.02 ± 0.01	Count	34
	0.24		0.12		Extraction	88
Rabbit (hindlimb)	0.30 ± 0.01	0.20 ± 0.01	0.12 ± 0.01	0.07 ± 0.01	Extraction	9, 10

Contents in ml plasma/g tissue; expressed as mean, range, or mean ± SD (no.). IgG, immunoglobulin G. * Labeled protein injected intravenously; tissue and plasma sampled after steady state attained. † Calculated from authors' published data. ‡ Tissue extract and plasma analyzed for the protein.

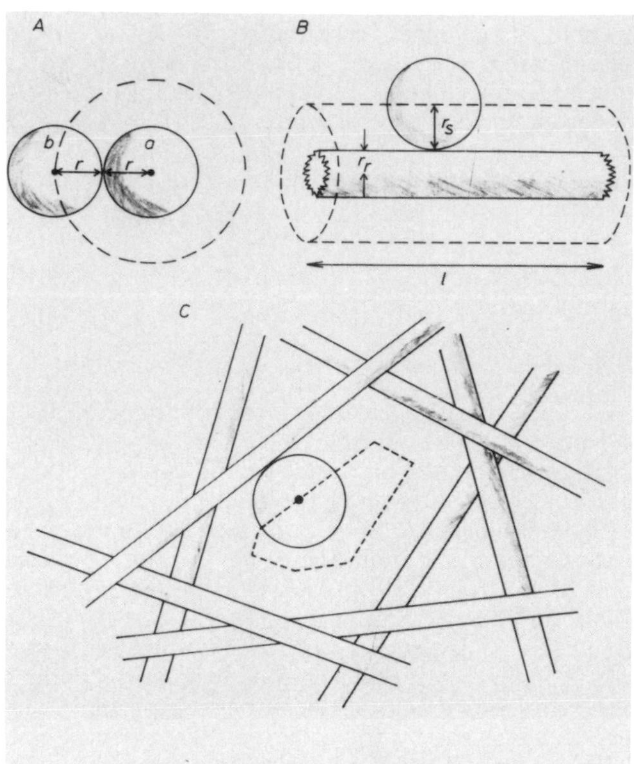

FIG. 6. *A*: steric exclusion of sphere *b* from the domain of sphere *a*. Center of *b* cannot come closer than $2r$ to center of *a* and therefore is excluded from a volume (*dotted*) that is 8 times larger than the volume of each sphere. *B*: steric exclusion of sphere of radius r_s from the domain of a rod with the radius r_r and length *l*. Excluded volume is equal to a cylinder of radius $r_s + r_r$ and length *l*. End effects have been disregarded. *C*: available space for a sphere in a random network of rods is equal to the volume (*dotted*) within which the center of the sphere can move freely. [From Comper and Laurent (29).]

spacing of the rods is greater than the sum of the diameters of the rod and the sphere. This latter constraint ensures that exclusion of a point in space is affected by only one rod and does not result from simultaneous exclusion exerted by neighboring rods. In this model the excluded volume per unit weight of rods, V_E, termed the *specific exclusion*, is

$$V_E = \pi L(r_s + r_r)^2 \quad (1)$$

where L = length of a unit weight of rod, r_r = radius of the rod, and r_s = radius of the molecular probe.

Ogston (122) determined the excluded-volume fraction, F_E of a sphere in a random network of rods to be

$$F_E = 1 - \exp[-\pi l(r_s + r_r)^2] \quad (2)$$

where l is the fiber length per unit volume of matrix. In this model also, the volume inaccessible to the probe is considered to be that space to which the center of the probe cannot gain access. The volume of distribution of the probe expressed as a fraction is simply 1-F_E. The random-network model has been used to describe the exclusion properties of biological macromolecules such as hyaluronate (29). If C_E is the concentration of the excluding fibers in weight per unit volume of matrix, then the following relationship exists

$$l = C_E L \quad (3)$$

For fibers that exclude probes independently

$$F_E = C_E V_E \quad (4)$$

and for randomly arranged fibers

$$F_E = 1 - \exp(-C_E V_E) \quad (5)$$

Most of our present knowledge of exclusion in tissues has been determined in the last decade and has been interpreted by using the rod-and-sphere or random-network models. From both Equations 1 and 2 it is clear that for a given system, increasing the size of the material being excluded lowers its available volume and results in greater exclusion. Table 4 shows values of exclusion or excluded-volume fraction for systems consisting of either a tissue or a collagenous fiber preparation and either a plasma protein or other molecular probe.

It is often a matter of convenience whether exclusion is expressed on the basis of the mass of excluding volume V_E or as a fractional volume F_E that is inaccessible to a probe. The description of exclusion as an absolute volume per unit weight of excluding material is a direct volumetric measure. The fraction of volume inaccessible to a probe due to the presence of some excluding material is not a direct volumetric measure but is useful because of similarities to partition in gel-exclusion chromatography. As a tissue swells it is not directly evident from F_E that the absolute excluded volume has changed. A more appropriate measure of changes in excluded volume for a system in which the excluding material is conserved is the direct measurement of V_E. However, when quantitating V_E one must be careful to describe the results based on a reference that includes the materials thought to be principally responsible for the exclusion properties of the tissue, such as fat-free, cell-free dry weight. However, neither V_E nor F_E relates exclusion to specific components of the interstitial matrix when these reference bases are used.

Ogston and Phelps (123) measured the partition, i.e., volume distribution, of serum albumin between a solution of hyaluronate and a buffered fluid phase to determine the exclusion properties of this plasma protein–polysaccharide system. A more detailed analysis of albumin exclusion by hyaluronate (93) resulted in an estimate of the size of the excluding structure. The extent to which hyaluronate in solution could exclude serum albumin is impressive. A 0.5% hyaluronate solution excluded serum albumin from 25% of the solution space, whereas a 1.5% hyaluronate concentration excluded serum albumin from 75% of the solution space. At this level of exclusion, and before the

TABLE 4. *Exclusion in Tissues and by Collagenous Fibers*

Excluding Material	Molecular Probe	F_E, ml/ml matrix	V_E, ml/g collagen	Comments	Ref.
Smooth muscle (dog)	Albumin	0.60		Based on sucrose space; equilibrium experiments	7
Liver (dog)	Albumin	0.30		Based on sucrose space; dilution technique	52
Corneal stroma (ox)	Albumin	0.9		Equilibrium experiments	107
Articular cartilage (human)	Dextran* (r_s = 2.0 nm)	0.9		Equilibrium experiments; series of dextrans	103
Lung (sheep)	Albumin	0.69† 0.81‡		Based on interstitial and plasma equivalence of probe concentration	162
Collagen preparation	Albumin		2.11	Equilibrium experiments based on osmotic pressure of albumin	185
Dermal collagen (human)	Dextran* (M_r-10^5)			Equilibrium experiment; series of dextrans; effect of PG and HA noted	136
Insoluble fibers			3.8		
Polymeric collagen			62.0		
Umbilical cord	Dextrans* (r_s = 5.5 nm)		3.1	Equilibrium experiment; series of dextrans; effect of PG and HA noted	111
Skin (rabbit)	Albumin	0.32		Cr-EDTA space; in vivo and in vitro studies	151
Polymeric collagen (calf tendon)	Albumin		33.6	Chromatography column	163
Lung (dog)	Albumin	0.38		Normal value; based on albumin concentration in lymph and on Tc-DTPA space; fluid volume loading studied	129
	Albumin	0.36		Normal value; based on albumin concentration in lymph and on Tc-DTPA space; vascular pressure changes studied	128
Collagenous fibers (human dermis)	Dextrans		4.2	Equilibrium experiment; V_E relatively constant for $r_s > 3.9$ nm	15
Hindpaw (dog)				Based on concentration in paw lymph and sucrose spaces	11
Skin	Albumin	0.25			
	Fibrinogen	0.35			
Tendon	Albumin	0.43			
	Fibrinogen	0.72			
Muscle	Albumin	0.35			
	Fibrinogen	0.70			
Toe pad	Albumin	0.08			
	Fibrinogen	0.67			
Intestine (cat)	Albumin	0.37		Based on lymph concentration and Tc-DTPA space	55
Skin (rabbit)	Albumin	0.50		Normal value; based on skin lymph concentration and Cr-EDTA space; increased venous pressure studied	10
	γ-Globulin	~0.50			
Muscle (rabbit)	Albumin	0.50		Normal values; based on muscle lymph concentration and Cr-EDTA space; increased venous pressure studied	9
	γ-Globulin	~0.50			
Hindpaw (rabbit)				Based on paw lymph concentration and Cr-EDTA space; fluid volume loading studied	117
Skin	Albumin	0.53			
	γ-Globulin	0.50			
Muscle	Albumin	0.47			
	γ-Globulin	0.50			
Dermal fibers (human)	Albumin		3.21	Equilibrium experiments; effect of organization noted	14
Dermis (human)	Albumin		1.62		

F_E, excluded-volume fraction; V_E, excluded volume; r_s, radius of the molecular probe; PG, proteoglycan; HA, hyaluronate; EDTA, ethylenediaminetetraacetate; DTPA, diethylenetriamine pentaacetic acid. * Example taken from a series of dextrans. † Based on sucrose space. ‡ Based on chloride space.

exclusion properties of collagenous fibers had been determined, it was reasonable to assume that hyaluronate and proteoglycans (51) were responsible for limiting the interstitial space accessible to a plasma protein.

When human articular cartilage (a tissue with a high polysaccharide content) was equilibrated in vitro with a solution containing a dextran 2 nm in radius, the molecular probe (dextran) was excluded from ~90% of the tissue space [Table 4; (103)]. This work typifies one approach to investigating the space accessible to a solute in a tissue. When a tissue is equilibrated with a solution containing a molecular probe, the space accessible to that molecular probe can be determined from the extravascular, extracellular water and probe content of the tissue and from the concentration of the molecular probe in the bathing solution. Because the accessible tissue fluid space and the external bathing solutions are in equilibrium, the probe concentrations in these two fluids are considered equal. If this is so, the accessible tissue fluid space equals the tissue probe content divided by the probe concentration in the external bathing solution. The excluded volume is simply the difference between the total interstitial and accessible volumes; the excluded-volume fraction is the ratio of excluded volume to total tissue volume.

In contrast to this type of equilibrium experiment with excised tissues, many steady-state measurements of space accessible to a molecular probe have been performed in vivo with animal models. In these experiments the macromolecular probe whose accessible space is being studied is administered intravascularly along with a labeled small solute. The small solute is used as a marker for the extracellular water in the tissue. After sufficient time for steady state to be reached, a differently labeled vascular probe is introduced and used to determine the plasma water content of the tissue. Tissue and blood samples are then removed and analyzed. By subtracting the value for vascular water from that for extracellular water the amount of interstitial water can be determined. The molecular probe content of the interstitium can be determined by subtracting its vascular content from its total tissue content. Additionally, if the concentration of the probe in lymph is *assumed* to be equal to its concentration in the accessible interstitial space, then the space accessible to the probe in the tissue can be determined by division of the interstitial probe content by the probe concentration in lymph. This space is the tissue distribution volume and can be compared with the total interstitial fluid space to determine the relative space inaccessible to the probe (i.e., the excluded volume). In earlier experiments the distribution volume of the probe in the tissue was taken relative to the plasma content of the probe (162). More recently investigators have chosen to relate probe or plasma protein concentration in the accessible interstitial space to its concentration in lymph (11). A further discussion of the equivalence of lymphatic and tissue concentrations of a plasma protein appears later. The results obtained by using these and other methods to determine F_E or V_E are shown in Table 4.

In many of these studies no attempt has been made to relate either the space accessible to a plasma protein or its excluded volume to content or organization of components characteristic of the tissue. Usually the proteoglycans and hyaluronate, whose specific excluded volumes are very high, have been assumed to play the principal role in limiting the volumes available to probes in tissues. The first studies of exclusion by collagenous fibers (111, 136, 185) demonstrated their potential importance in determining the space accessible to a plasma protein in a tissue. Subsequently other studies performed in our laboratory suggested that collagenous fibers may dominate the exclusion characteristics in certain tissues such as dermis (14). In addition a dependence of exclusion properties on collagenous fiber organization has been noted. Per unit weight, collagen in fiber preparations obtained from dermis exhibited significantly more exclusion than did the intact collagenous fibers of the tissue. The procedures used to make collagenous fiber preparations from the tissue had apparently reduced the organization of the collagen. The fact that a larger number of smaller fibers effects greater exclusion than an equal weight of a smaller number of larger fibers can be deduced from Equations 1 or 2. Figure 7 demonstrates this idea. Consequently, when studying the exclusion of collagenous fibers or collagen in tissue, one must note the organization or state of the collagen being studied. Those studies where collagenous organization may have been altered but not noted are of limited significance physiologically. The difference in volume excluded per gram collagen between collagenous structures and more organized collagenous tissue fibers is amplified in the studies of Pearce and Laurent (136) and Shaw and Schy (163). Both of these groups measured exclusion by polymeric collagen (collagen reduced to a microfibrillar state). The exclusion per gram collagen in this state is more than an order of magnitude greater than exclusion by the fibers found in the dermis from which the collagen was obtained (136). An advantage of the steady-state animal studies or excised-tissue studies of exclusion over those studies that use fiber preparations is that the question of physiological significance can usually be avoided. To date no definitive study of the relation between exclusion and tissue composition and structure has been made. This is not surprising, because the organization within the interstitium is not well defined.

Although there are many unanswered questions concerning exclusion by hyaluronate, proteoglycans, and collagenous fibers, even less is known about the exclusion properties of elastin. Elastin, which is usually present in very low concentrations in most tissues

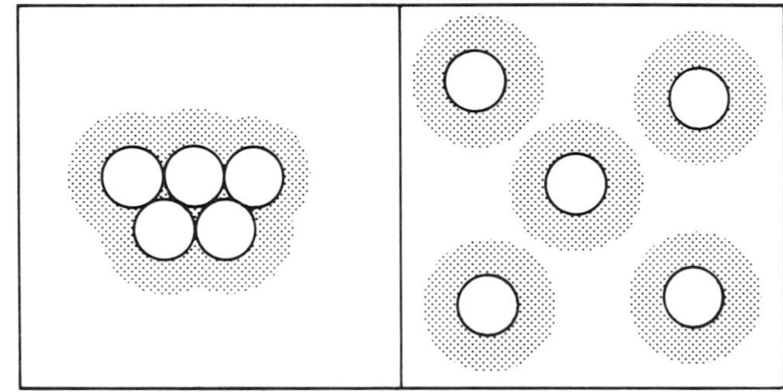

FIG. 7. Effect of the packing density of collagenous fibers on exclusion. *Stippled area*, fluid exclusion by collagenous fibers (*open circles*). Exclusion of fluid by closely packed fibers (*left*) is less than that by the same number of fibers loosely dispersed (*right*). [From Bert, Mathieson, and Pearce (14).]

(aorta and ligaments are notable exceptions), is believed to occur in relatively large fibers or lamellae (53). The characteristic size of the elastin fibers is several orders of magnitude greater than that of plasma proteins. At this level of organization the effective volume from which the plasma proteins are excluded by elastin is the volume of the fibers. Mathematically this is the case when $r_r \gg r_s$ in Equations 1 or 2. Therefore, due to the presence of elastin, the only water unavailable to a molecular probe the size of a plasma protein is the water involved in the elastin fiber structure. This has been estimated to be ~0.56 ml water/ml dry elastin (54). At its usually low concentration, elastin does not contribute significantly to exclusion of plasma proteins in most tissues.

The effect of the concentration of characteristic interstitial materials on exclusion is another unresolved area. A nonlinear relationship has been demonstrated for the exclusion of dextrans by different concentrations of hyaluronate (29). With regard to collagenous fibers, a linear relationship between volume inaccessible to various probes and collagen content has been demonstrated (14, 136). However, there is evidence for a nonlinear relationship based on collagen concentration for a mixed hyaluronate–collagenous fiber preparation (185). At the tissue level, corneal stroma (107) appears to exclude proteins from a constant volume as the tissue swells, whereas a slight decrease in exclusion of albumin was noted for lungs during fluid volume overloading (129). Clearly the effect of fiber concentration (or tissue swelling) on exclusion is tissue dependent. No definitive, generalized interpretations are warranted at present. An interesting observation was made that for probes larger than a critical size the accessible space in a tissue did not decrease significantly with increasing probe size (29, 67, 111, 151). A similar observation was made with collagenous fibers (15). These results imply that for probes up to a specific size, exclusion is effected by fibers with sizes comparable to those of the plasma proteins; exclusion seems also to be a strong function of probe size. For probes greater than this critical size, the effective excluding structures are very large compared with the probe. The water content of these larger structures appears to be the fluid volume inaccessible to the probes.

Compartmentalization Within the Interstitium

The outdated concept that the interstitium behaves as a well-mixed system has been replaced by multicompartment models of this tissue space. Presently a two-compartment model of the interstitium finds wide acceptance and use (6, 29, 144, 182). It includes the colloid-rich gel space containing the hydrophilic hyaluronate and proteoglycans at or near equilibrium with the colloid-poor, free-fluid space. The possibility that more than two compartments within the interstitium may explain experimental results more satisfactorily is not discounted. Two observations form a basis of the two-compartment model: *1*) dyes injected into the lymphatics appear initially in preferential channels in the interstitium (110) and *2*) investigations of the interstitium's structure have demonstrated restricted access of probes within the interstitial space (28). Under normal conditions a paucity of free fluid is thought to exist within the interstitium (64, 92).

In the two-compartment model the designation of free-fluid spaces and gel spaces (182) is somewhat arbitrary. Compartmentalization within the interstitium, based on exclusion, is an attractive alternative for which there is quantitative experimental evidence. The excluded volume in this alternate model is analogous to the gel space, but its size is a function of the size of the plasma protein or molecular probe being excluded. The free-fluid space corresponds to the accessible interstitial fluid volume. In the models based on either the gel space or excluded volume, the extracellular fluid within the interstitial space is continuous; thus fluid discontinuities occur only in definitions but not in fact.

In the presently accepted two-compartment model, the gel material is thought to be immobilized. Recent investigations indicate a significantly higher concentration of hyaluronate in lymph than in plasma (96). The hyaluronate in lymph may result from partial degradation of this material in the interstitium, or it may indicate that at least a portion of the interstitial hyaluronate is mobile. The presence of some mobile interstitial hyaluronate may warrant consideration of an additional gel compartment.

The interstitium may behave as a gel-exclusion chromatography column with respect to its effect on blood-to-lymph transport of plasma proteins or other macromolecules. It has been suggested (3) that this effect results from the existence of two compartments within the tissue space. Both the gel-space/free-fluid-space model and the available-volume/excluded-volume model would predict that a larger macromolecule would reach a steady state of transinterstitial transport faster than a smaller macromolecule. This results from the existence of a larger fluid space accessible to a small molecule than to a larger molecule and from the decreased mobility experienced by the smaller molecule in a portion of that space. It has been interpreted that relative to the larger molecule the velocity of the smaller molecule would be reduced. Recent experimental observations (11, 20) and theoretical predictions (178) tend to confirm the existence of at least two distinct phases based on the chromatographic effect associated with transinterstitial macromolecular transport.

Knowledge of the organization of these compartments within the interstitium is important to an understanding of transport through the tissue space. Whether the free fluid or available volumes are arranged in parallel or in series with respect to the overall direction of blood-to-lymph transport is not known. A consequence of the arrangement of the compartments, for example, is that sieving of macromolecules by the gel space is unlikely if the free-fluid space is arranged parallel to the direction of flow and so that it is continuous from blood to lymph. Alternatively, if the free-fluid and gel spaces are arranged in series, then plasma proteins (or macromolecules) must traverse each gel space during their journey across the interstitium. In this latter arrangement the plasma protein may be sieved or immobilized within the gel or excluding matrix. The manner in which compartments are arranged within the interstitium may have a pronounced effect on mass transport in the interstitium. Presently not enough information exists to determine the arrangement of interstitial compartments and to analyze the resultant effect on microvascular exchange.

Transport Coefficients

DIFFUSION COEFFICIENTS. Molecular diffusion results from the random kinetic motion of molecules. Table 5 lists the results of some attempts to quantify molecular diffusion of albumin and dextran within the interstitium of various tissues or in solutions of materials characteristic of the interstitium. It is well established that the interstitium is a heterogeneous space. Consequently a diffusion coefficient used to quantify the nonconvective movement of a molecule must be considered to be a macroscopic average for that tissue. The rate of diffusion in the interstitium is reduced compared with diffusion in fluid only; this is due to the presence of the polymeric materials characteristic of the interstitium and may result from frictional interactions or steric hindrance (29, 47, 124, 140).

To give an ideal characterization of solute diffusibility requires knowledge of the properties of both the solute (e.g., size, shape, and charge) and the tissue space (e.g., size, shape, organization, and charge distribution). In their studies with globular macromolecules and hyaluronate, Laurent et al. (95) draw attention to the similarity between diffusion and sedimentation and conclude that diffusion of the macromolecules within hyaluronate solutions does not depend primarily on frictional interactions; it appears instead to be controlled by steric considerations. In their work the reduction in the macromolecules' sedimentation rate (or similarly the reduction of the macromolecules' diffusion coefficients) was found to be directly proportional to the square root of the concentration of a hyaluronate. Starting with a stochastic model based on unit steps of the migrating species, Ogston et al. (124) obtained a relationship of the form described by Laurent et al. The equation derived by Ogston et al. describes the reduction in diffusion coefficient of a system of various solutes or plasma proteins that diffuse in solutions containing polymeric materials (e.g., hyaluronate and proteoglycans). They concluded that the form of the equation developed by Laurent et al. for hindered migration of a macromolecule in a hyaluronate solution could not be explained either by a reduction in available cross-sectional area or by hydrodynamic interactions between solute and solvent. Additional corroboration of the theoretical results obtained by Ogston et al. was provided in the work of Preston and Snowden (140). In his discussion of diffusion within the interstitium, Granger (58) concludes that reduction in diffusion coefficient in a tissue is greater than can be accounted for by exclusion of the same solute in that tissue. Further work is required.

With regard to the diffusion of plasma proteins in tissues, the relative effects of characteristic materials such as hyaluronate and proteoglycans, collagenous fibers, and elastin have not been determined. Several concepts that explain the reduction in diffusion coefficient effected by tissue components have been experimentally verified. The following observations are usually accepted as valid: *1*) reduction in diffusion coefficient is related directly to the size of the diffusing species and inversely to the relative hydration of the tissue and *2*) a number of fine fibers has a greater effect on reducing the diffusivity of a solute than does an equivalent mass of larger fibers. The latter point finds an analogy in the description of volume exclusion. Hyaluronate and proteoglycan chains are significantly smaller in equivalent diameter than are collagenous fibers and appear to occupy an inordinately large hydrodynamic volume (29). Thus many investigators have postulated that these ground substance materials are predominantly responsible for reduction in diffusion coefficients of probes in most tissues, although a definitive demonstration is lacking. Limited information exists concerning reduction in diffusion coefficients and the effect of electrostatic interactions between diffusing species and the matrix through which they migrate. Some investigators believe these interactions may have a significant effect (140). Maroudas (103) has characterized the reduction in diffusion coefficient on the basis of the fixed charged density of the matrix through which the solute

TABLE 5. *Relative Diffusion Coefficients of Albumin and Dextran in Hyaluronate and in Connective Tissues*

Molecular Probe	Network*	D/D_0†	Ref.
Albumin	1% (wt/vol) Hyaluronate	0.50	95
Albumin	Corneal stroma (rabbit)	0.10	108
Dextran (M_r-4.0 × 10^4)	Articular cartilage (human)	0.25	103
Albumin	Umbilical tissue (human)	0.25	59
Albumin	Mesentery (rat)	0.073	47

* All values at normal hydration if not otherwise indicated. † D, diffusion coefficient in network; D_0, diffusion in fluid only.

diffuses. The effects of electrochemical potentials on transport of materials through the interstitial space of connective tissues have recently been reviewed (62).

FLOW CONDUCTIVITY. The convective flow of a fluid resulting from a pressure gradient across a porous bed can be described by Darcy's law. For flow in one dimension only a hydraulic flow conductivity k/η can be defined as

$$\frac{k}{\eta} = \frac{q}{A(dP/dx)} \qquad (6)$$

where k/η has units of $cm^4 \cdot dyn^{-1} \cdot s^{-1}$, q is the volumetric flow rate of fluid in cm^3/s, A is the area in cm^2, and dP/dx is the hydrostatic pressure gradient across the material of interest in $dyn \cdot cm^{-2} \cdot cm^{-1}$. From Equation 6, k/η is the proportionality constant that relates fluid flow rate to a pressure gradient, and therefore it is a measure of the ability of a fluid to flow through a material.

Table 6 shows values of k/η for different animal tissues at normal conditions (i.e., with respect to water content). Early tissue permeability studies by Day (32, 33) established the relative resistance of different tissue components to flow in mouse fascia. Day believed that hyaluronic acid was primarily responsible for the resistance to fluid flow in this tissue. Quantitative results for fluid permeability were not determined directly, but the increase in permeability due to the action of hyaluronidase was clearly demonstrated. Day (33) described the fascia as a mesh or microfabric capable of segregating mobile macromolecules of sufficient size. He postulated that under normal circumstances hyaluronate occupies the holes in the mesh and thereby regulates the permeability of the tissue. Significant evidence now exists that relates the resistance of fluid flow through the interstitium to tissue hyaluronate and proteoglycan content. Maroudas (104), for example, demonstrated a decreasing relationship between k/η and the fixed charge density for articular cartilage, the fixed charge density being related to the presence of GAGs. She also found k/η to be a function of depth perpendicular to the articulating surface of the cartilage, demonstrating again the heterogeneous nature of the interstitium. Swabb et al. (167) report a direct decrease in k/η with increasing GAG concentration for a series of tissues. The main interest of Swabb et al. was to determine the relative importance of diffusive and convective modes of solute transport in tissues. In his review of permeability of corneal stroma and sclera, Fatt (42) discusses evidence that the resistance to flow in those tissues is primarily effected by hyaluronate and the proteoglycans, not by collagenous fibers. A similar general discussion of fluid flow as related to tissue components can be found in Granger's (58) review of the extracellular matrix. However, a different view is presented by Jackson and James (83), who measured the hydrodynamic resistance of hyaluronate solutions and concluded that this material offers only a fraction of the resistance to flow in tissues. Clearly the relationship between fluid conductivity and tissue composition is not resolved.

TABLE 6. *Flow Conductivities of Tissues*

Tissue	k/η, $cm^4 \cdot dyn^{-1} \cdot s^{-1}$ $\times 10^{13}$	Ref.
Subcutaneous tissue (rat)	60.0	167
Articular cartilage (human)	2.2	104
Umbilical cord (human)	200.0	59
Corneal stroma (human)	6.5	42
Sclera (human)	15.0	42
Aortic wall (rabbit)	15.8	175

A large body of information exists that directly relates k/η to tissue water content or hydration (42, 58, 104). In one review (13) the fluid conductivity of a series of tissues and other materials is shown to have a direct relationship with a power function of water content. This relationship is based on data covering nine orders of magnitude of k/η for biological tissues and some polymeric materials. This strong effect of hydration on k/η may cause problems when the conductance of these materials is experimentally measured. For example, if a tissue is deformable and changes volume by changing water content in response to applied pressure, then the permeability properties of that tissue also change as a function of pressure. This effect, termed *compaction*, is important in many membrane transport processes (12) and may influence the results of tissue perfusion studies.

The variability between experimental results for similar tissues points out the need for well-defined experiments. For example, from Guyton et al.'s (63) study of permeability in dog subcutaneous tissue, one can estimate that $k/\eta \sim 1.8 \times 10^{-9}$ $cm^4 \cdot dyn^{-1} \cdot s^{-1}$. This result is surprisingly more than two orders of magnitude greater than k/η reported for rat subcutaneous tissue (6, 167). The reason for these large differences is not clear.

Convective flow of fluid in the interstitium imparts mobility to solutes in that fluid. This flow-induced solute mobility thus becomes a mechanism by which solutes are transported. The way diffusive and convective components of solute transport are coupled is discussed in the chapters by Curry and by Crone and Levitt. The phenomenological approach of irreversible thermodynamics has been used successfully to describe transport across the capillary wall, but the convective transport of plasma proteins in tissues still needs to be studied. To date attempts at a rigorous mathematical description of convective macromolecular transport through a porous medium such as the interstitium have failed (36).

FLOW IN THE INTERSTITIUM

Until the last decade, the focus of studies of microvascular exchange has been on the properties of the capillary wall. This emphasis has resulted in the current state of limited information about the interstitium. This is particularly true with respect to understanding the practical hydrodynamics in this tissue space. Thus fluid flow in the interstitium is not well understood. Experiments have indicated that heterogeneity within the interstitium dominates its flow characteristics (11, 110, 118, 180). Reviews of microvascular exchange and discussions of flow within the interstitium have recently emphasized the importance of tissue heterogeneity (58, 65, 92, 178, 190).

A simple model that accounts for the heterogeneity of the interstitium is that of a structure composed of compartments. Only after such model representations are adopted can one begin to discuss the heterogeneous nature of flows in the interstitium. At present the most widely accepted of these compartment models makes use of gel spaces and free-fluid spaces. Very little attention has been paid to the nature of fluid flow in the gel space of the interstitium, but the free-fluid compartment has received more attention. Normally the free fluid is thought to be considerably less abundant but far more mobile than fluid in the gel space (26, 64). Rivulets (64) and unobstructed free-fluid channels have been observed in the interstitium (27, 118). However, there have been no successful attempts at measuring either the properties of these different pathways or their relative importance to overall fluid transport across the interstitium.

The organization of the compartments may complicate the description of flows in the interstitium. It is unclear whether the compartments containing the less mobile fluid are in a parallel or series arrangement with the preferential free-fluid channels (144). One can speculate that the tissue architecture consists of a mixture of these possibilities. However, it is often assumed that the free-fluid and gel compartments are in parallel with respect to the overall direction of fluid flow from blood to lymph (178) and that these compartments are in or near thermodynamic equilibrium (144, 182). Even under these conditions, it is unclear whether interstitial fluid flows through the gel space. Knowledge of the division of flow between free-fluid channels and across gel spaces is critical to an understanding of the formation of lymph. This is discussed in the next section. If the compartments in the interstitium are organized in a serial fashion, then fluid must pass through each of the compartments between the circulation and lymphatics. Clearly these different compartmental arrangements produce different microvascular exchange characteristics.

To further complicate the picture, Witte and Zenzes-Geprägs (188) observed that within the interstitium plasma proteins are not uniformly distributed, but that gradients in their concentration exist. Salathé and Venkataraman (156) accounted for this phenomenon by mathematical modeling of microvascular exchange, but their reasoning was different from that of Witte and Zenzes-Geprägs. The results of both of these studies indicated that spatial inhomogeneities of plasma protein concentration exist within the interstitium. The possibility that hyaluronate may be mobile within the interstitium further increases the complexity of this system. At present, an accurate description of flow in the interstitium would be not only very complicated but also unrealistic because of the lack of information about this space.

INTERSTITIAL FLUID AND LYMPH

In the absence of upsets, the microvascular exchange system is generally considered to be a dynamic system operating under steady-state or near steady-state conditions. The coupled convective and diffusive transport of fluid and macromolecules to, from, and across the interstitium occurs through a material with ill-defined transport pathways. To describe events occurring within the tissue space it is imperative to know the concentrations of osmotically active and/or transported macromolecules within this space. Although there have been no definitive measurements, it has often been assumed that the plasma protein concentration in the free-fluid space in the interstitium is the same as the plasma protein concentration in lymph.

The relationship between plasma protein concentrations in the interstitium and in prenodal lymph has been considered in several recent studies (6, 45, 119, 127, 144, 177, 183). To examine this relationship experimentally, representative samples of free fluid from the interstitium and from lymph must be collected. The three most commonly used methods for the collection of interstitial free fluid employ micropipettes (66, 152, 184), chronically implanted perforated capsules (25, 64), and implanted fibrous wicks (4, 39, 158). There are problems associated with each of these methods. In the following discussion the interstitial fluid referred to is that from the free-fluid space, and the lymph is the unmodified fluid obtained from initial lymphatics. If these fluids are to be compared, they should be collected, as much as possible, at the same time.

As reviewed by Renkin (144) and Aukland and Nicolaysen (6), capsules (originally designed for fluid pressure measurements) collect fluid that is slightly higher in macromolecular concentration than lymph; duration of capsule implantation is an important parameter. The use of wicks was also originally intended for tissue pressure measurements. The fluid collected by wicks (40) may not represent interstitial fluid accurately because of the action of the wicks as colloid osmometers, but experimental procedures have been designed to minimize this effect. The plasma protein concentration of the fluid collected with micropipettes resembles the concentration in lymph more closely than that collected by capsules or wicks (144). However, the possibility has been noted that suction applied to a micropipette in collection of fluid may drain fluid from other than the free-fluid space (6). Thus the rate at which fluid is collected may influence the concentration of a plasma protein. By using either wicks or micropipettes reasonable agreement between the plasma protein concentration in free fluid and lymph has been obtained (6). Each method has its drawbacks, but the micropipette method seems to collect fluid most representative of interstitial free fluid.

The accuracy of all of the above methods of collecting normal interstitial fluid suffers in varying degrees when there is tissue trauma. Edema, especially if localized to the site of collection, can result in nonrepresentative sampling. It is reasonable to expect that the free-fluid space increases during edema, thus facilitating the collection of this fluid. Furthermore when edema is present the interstitial plasma protein concentration in free fluid seems to be representative of lymph (177).

Other interactions that may affect the plasma protein concentration in the interstitium may occur at the site of the prenodal lymphatic vessels or in the lymph circulation. For example, if there is sieving at the lymphatic capillary wall, or if there is exchange between the fluid within the lymphatic vessels and that in the tissue interstitium, then both the interstitial and lymphatic plasma protein concentrations are affected. As plasma proteins or fluid travel from blood to lymph a series of barriers must be crossed, any of which may affect the protein concentrations in interstitial fluid and lymph. The evidence indicates that the plasma protein concentration in the interstitial free fluid is similar and its composition may be quite close to that of lymph. Nonetheless the equality between interstitial free fluid and lymph is still unproven; it finds wide use in the interpretation of experimental data, however.

Figure 8 is a representation of the interstitium with free-fluid and immobilized matrix spaces. The validity of the assumed identity between interstitial free fluid and lymph with respect to concentration of plasma proteins can be examined with the help of this figure. It shows a free-fluid space between two immobilized hydrophilic matrix spaces. Two sizes of plasma proteins are shown; the larger is excluded entirely from the matrix, whereas the smaller has some access. Therefore the distribution volume of the larger plasma protein is restricted to the free-fluid channel, and the distribution volume for the smaller plasma protein

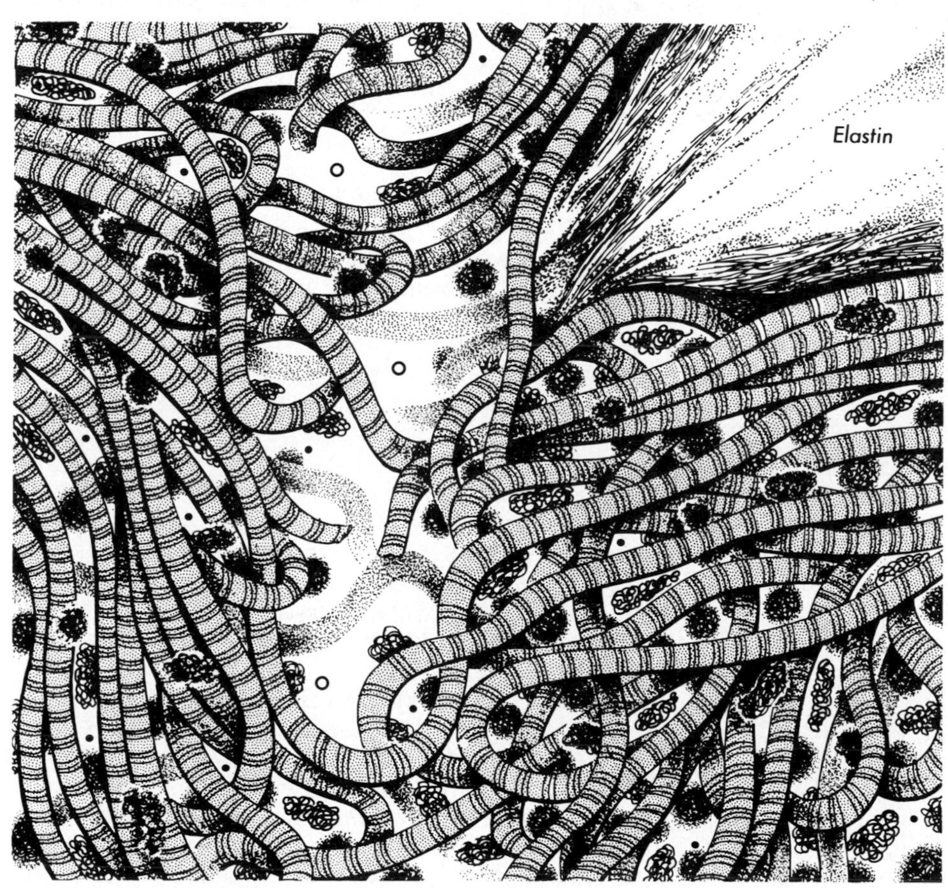

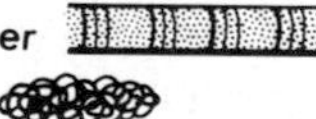

FIG. 8. Free-fluid channel between 2 hydrophilic gellike compartments. For this idealized case the larger of the 2 sizes of plasma proteins distributes only in the free-fluid channel. The smaller plasma protein has some access in the hydrophilic matrix. Hyaluronate is shown in the free-fluid channel. Figure is not to scale.

includes a portion of the immobilized matrix as well. At steady state the amount and concentration of plasma protein entering the interstitial space from the direction of the blood is equal to the amount of concentration leaving. If fluid flow occurs only in the free-fluid channel, then the concentration of each size of plasma proteins is identical in the free-fluid channel and in lymph. However, under the following conditions the concentrations of the plasma proteins in the free-fluid channel and in lymph are not equal: *1)* if fluid and/or solute flow within the immobilized matrix, 2) if there is a non-steady-state, and 3) if there is nonuniform protein distribution in the free-fluid channel (e.g., if the two sizes of plasma proteins have entirely different volumes of distribution within the channel through which fluid flows). Other, less probable scenarios could exist for the distribution, flow, and transport of fluid and plasma proteins in the interstitium. An additional complication may arise if there is reversible binding between some plasma proteins and the matrix. In the light of all of these reasonable possibilities, the conditions for equality between concentrations of plasma proteins in the free fluid and in lymph are restrictive.

The implications of assuming equality between interstitial plasma protein concentration in the free fluid and in lymph are far reaching. Using this assumption, experimental investigators seek to gain insight into what governs transport to, through, and from the interstitium. In the usual mathematical equations describing fluid or solute transport from blood to lymph or from blood to tissue, one of the driving forces is tissue colloid osmotic pressure. For example, fluid flow across a thin membrane has been described mathematically by using irreversible thermodynamics (86)

$$J_v = L_p A(\Delta P - \sum_i \sigma_i \Delta \Pi_i) \qquad (7)$$

where L_p is the hydraulic conductance (or permeability) in $cm^3 \cdot dyn^{-1} \cdot s^{-1}$, σ_i is the dimensionless reflection coefficient of the *i*th species, $\Delta\Pi_i$ is the difference in osmotic pressure of the *i*th species across the membrane in dyn/cm^2, ΔP is the hydrostatic pressure difference in dyn/cm^2, and A is the area of the membrane. The reflection coefficient represents the fraction of the solute rejected (reflected) at a membrane aperture and is a function of both the membrane and the solute. The osmotic pressure is a function of the concentration of the solute C_i; for dilute systems $\Pi_i = RTC_i$, where RT is the product of the gas constant and absolute temperature. When plasma protein concentrations in free fluid and lymph are assumed equal, one need only determine the colloid osmotic pressure in lymph to evaluate the colloid osmotic pressure in the tissue free fluid. Wiig et al. (186) and Guyton et al. (64) are among those who believe that the tissue forces influencing mass transport are the colloid osmotic and hydrostatic pressures. The algebraic sum of these two pressures are usually assumed equal for the tissue free fluid and gel space. The primary interest in this section is the colloid osmotic pressure of the tissue free fluid. If this is not assumed equal to the colloid osmotic pressure in lymph, it must be determined by measuring the volume exclusion and content of each plasma protein as well as the total volume of the interstitial fluid. Accurate values for interstitial volumes and plasma protein contents are far more difficult to obtain than are samples of lymph, from which colloid osmotic pressure can be determined directly. Therefore the justification for representing the colloid osmotic pressure for interstitial free fluid by that for lymph has a pragmatic basis. A similar practical approach is taken in some studies of interstitial exclusion. If lymph and free-fluid concentrations of plasma proteins are equal, then tissue exclusion of a plasma protein can be determined from measurement of tissue plasma protein content, interstitial water content, and lymph plasma protein concentration. Without assuming equality of lymph and free-fluid concentrations, measurement of total interstitial fluid and the difficult measurement of interstitial space accessible to a plasma protein are required in order to determine the exclusion properties of the tissue. Therefore the reasons for using the assumption are quite practical, especially because observations do show lymph and interstitial free fluid to be quite similar. Although the assumption has been used quite successfully, its validity is still uncertain. Further research is required.

REGULATION WITHIN THE INTERSTITIUM

The microvascular exchange system involves the circulation, the tissue space, and the lymphatics. This system can be characterized as highly interactive and nonlinear. One of the properties of the microcirculation vital to the survival of the organism is the ability of this mass-exchange system to respond to changes in its local environment while maintaining the various components of the system in a viable operating mode. Edema, the accumulation of fluid within the tissue, is the most frequent disturbance against which the tissue must regulate itself. The converse change in tissue fluid content (i.e., dehydration) may be just as damaging. The ability of the interstitium to respond to its environment by controlling its own properties is referred to as autoregulation. According to recent reviews (6, 64) stabilization of the interstitium has been assumed to occur through control of interstitial fluid volume. Many of these reviews focus on the regulation of tissue volume as it is effected by the organization and properties of the materials composing the interstitium (6, 57, 64). Two somewhat arbitrary factors are referred to when describing microvascular autoregulation: *1)* margin of safety and *2)* safety factor against edema. The margin of safety usually refers to a quantitative change in a particular parameter that must be exceeded before edema becomes apparent. On the other hand, the safety factors against edema usually refer to mechanisms operative within the system that tend to regulate the interstitial fluid volume relative to changes in its local environment. A thorough quantitative description of the latter incorporates the concept of margin of safety.

To explain how the interstitial fluid volume regulates itself, some basic concepts of microvascular exchange must be understood. Under normal conditions the microvascular exchange system can be characterized as a dynamic system assumed to be at or near steady state. Changes in the properties or driving forces of this system upset this dynamic steady state and force the system toward new steady-state conditions—with edema as a possible result. Changes in any of the pressures, concentrations, or permeability parameters in the mass-transfer exchange equations (e.g., Starling's hypothesis) or changes in the organization and/or makeup of the interstitium can upset this system. Some of the physicochemical properties of the interstitium that would oppose further changes in the microvascular exchange system after an upset or perturbation depend on the relationship between *1*) interstitial fluid volume and tissue pressure, *2*) lymph flow and either interstitial fluid volume or tissue pressure, and *3*) volume exclusion and interstitial fluid volume. The first property, often referred to as a compliance relationship, exerts control over edema formation by reducing driving forces due to hydrostatic pressure that occur between the circulation and the interstitium as the tissue swells. The monotonically increasing relationship between tissue hydrostatic pressure and interstitial fluid volume (i.e., the relationship has a positive slope) may be tissue dependent and quite different in different parts of the tissue pressure range. As a tissue swells and increases its volume in response to some perturbation, the tissue hydrostatic pressure increases. This increase tends to reduce further filtration into the tissue by reducing the hydrostatic pressure driving force between the circulation and the tissue. A second self-regulating property of the interstitium relies on the relationship between lymph flow and interstitial fluid volume. This relationship can also be described by a monotonically increasing function. Its effects on microvascular exchange have been reviewed by Granger (57). As the interstitial fluid volume increases and a tissue tends toward an edematous state, the concomitant increase in lymph flow tends to drain fluid from the tissue at an increased rate, thereby attempting to return the tissue to normal conditions.

The relationship between regulation of interstitial fluid volume and volume exclusion within the tissue is less clear. It is apparent that as the interstitial fluid volume increases, the space accessible to a plasma protein also increases in an approximately one-to-one relationship. This would be the case if the excluded volume were constant. Therefore any increase in normal interstitial fluid volume is likely to result in a similar increase in volume accessible to plasma proteins. If sieving of macromolecules takes place at the capillary wall, then the plasma protein concentration in the fluid entering the interstitial space is less than that in the circulation. When venous pressure is elevated, the plasma protein concentration of the fluid entering the interstitium is less than that entering under normal conditions. This is due to the increased contribution of the convective mechanism of transcapillary plasma protein transport. Additionally, as discussed by Curry in this *Handbook*, the relative increase in net fluid transport through pathways, which do not allow the larger molecules to pass, results in decreasing the plasma protein concentration of fluid entering the interstitium as venous pressure is increased. As the interstitial fluid volume increases, the fraction of its space accessible to a plasma protein increases. Because the fluid entering the accessible space is of reduced plasma protein concentration, the average concentration in the interstitium is decreased relative to normal. The tissue colloid osmotic pressure therefore decreases. Reduction in tissue oncotic pressure tends to decrease the driving force for the movement of fluid into the tissue, thereby regulating against further tissue changes. This entire phenomenon is termed *oncotic buffering* (57). Overall this mechanism depends on sieving at the capillary wall, exclusion within the tissue, and dilution of interstitial plasma proteins. The extent of self-regulation due to oncotic buffering depends on the type and magnitude of the perturbation disrupting the system.

For particular perturbations a combination of several factors may contribute to regulation of interstitial fluid volume. For example, if microvascular pressure is increased, possibly through venous congestion, an important regulatory mechanism termed *protein washdown* occurs (57). As discussed previously there is a decrease in plasma protein concentration in the fluid entering the tissue space as a result of increased sieving at the capillary wall. In addition there is an increase in interstitial fluid volume with the likelihood of an increase in lymph flow. The combination of decreased plasma protein concentration entering the interstitium and increased lymph flow results in a washout of plasma proteins from the interstitium (38, 57). Consequently the tissue colloid osmotic pressure decreases. This effect tends to reduce further changes to the interstitium resulting from increased hydrostatic pressure in the circulation.

The particular mechanisms that control interstitial fluid volume in different tissues and a quantitation of their effectiveness for various perturbations have been reported for various tissues relevant to study of the microcirculation: subcutaneous tissue and muscle (5), small intestine (56, 115), and lungs (165, 166, 171). The clinical impetus for studying the autoregulatory properties of the interstitium is the hope that management of edema in various tissues can be effected through positive manipulation of the environment responsible for these perturbed conditions.

In general it is difficult to quantify the safety factor against edema because of the complexity of the microcirculation. In experimental models or in clinical settings, for example, it is unlikely that only one variable can be changed at a time; thus uncertainty arises concerning causal relationships. Physiologists have recognized the difficulties in analyzing microvascular exchange and have used computer simulations to study this complex system (60, 64, 181, 183). From simulations of microvascular exchange, sensitivity analyses that avoid some of the drawbacks associated with experimental or clinical investigations can be performed. A sensitivity analysis consists of monitoring the relative change in a series of dependent variables when either one or a group of independent variables are changed from their normal value. The accuracy of the computer model defines the limits of this approach for investigating how the individual parts of the microvascular exchange system exert an autoregulatory response.

COMPUTER SIMULATIONS OF MICROVASCULAR EXCHANGE

The object of a computer simulation of microvascular exchange is to develop a model that describes the behavior of the system as a whole. This model is based on mathematical relationships that describe the operation and interaction of the components of the system. Each aspect that influences the behavior of a system is expressed mathematically and combined into an overall mathematical description. In addition to these relationships, initial and boundary conditions are required for a thorough description. This information is then programmed (i.e., converted into a format a computer can decipher), and with the aid of electronic computers (digital or analog), results for a variety of conditions (normal or pathological) can be obtained. Results can then be compared with clinical or experimental findings to determine the validity of the model.

Usually computer simulations are most appropriate for predicting trends in the behavior of a system and less useful for describing absolute values for systemic parameters. Typically only after the results of a computer simulation have been favorably compared with available information is the simulation used to predict the response of the system to changes. The extension of the computer simulation to this predictive mode provides hypothetical information that can be compared with experimental or clinical results as they become available, or the information can be used to help plan future investigations. A convenient aspect of computer simulations is their ability to be updated or fine-tuned as new information is acquired. When a computer simulation describes the operation of a system satisfactorily (either in a purely passive manner via negative feedback or by way of an active physiological response through changes either in input parameters or in coefficients of descriptive equations), it can be used to investigate autoregulation within that system.

Computer simulation of microvascular exchange can be separated conveniently into categories based on the roles of the various aspects of the exchange system. If one considers that the primary resistance to the movement of macromolecules and solvent results from a distribution of cylindrical channels in the capillary wall, then one adopts the pore-model approach [the basics of which were described by Landis and Pappenheimer (92)]. Pore models need not regard, but generally have regarded, the properties of the interstitium (except tissue hydrostatic pressure) as unimportant. If partition within the interstitium is considered, the plasma protein concentrations in lymph and in the free fluid of the interstitium are usually assumed to be equal. Typically these models have also been restricted to steady-state analysis. More recent simulations have tended to use a model of microvascular exchange based on compartmental units. Recent models (16, 17, 18, 60, 98, 155, 156, 178, 181, 183) have focused not only on steady-state results but also on the transient response effected by a perturbation. Wiederhielm's (183) second-generation computer simulation of transcapillary exchange in human skin and muscle not only investigates the transient response of several perturbations that eventually result in edemas but also examines the safety factors against edema operative in the microvascular exchange system. This simulation has been modified (16) to incorporate recent concepts in interstitial volume exclusion. A schematic of the modified program is shown in Figure 9. As described in the model, the properties of the interstitium affect microvascular exchange through the following relationships: *1*) tissue hydrostatic pressure P_t is determined directly from total interstitial fluid volume V_{TOT} through a tissue compliance relationship; *2*) the volume available to plasma proteins V_{AV} is the difference between V_{TOT} and the excluded volume V_E; *3*) Q_t, the plasma protein content, and V_{TOT}, the fluid content of the interstitium, are determined by mass balances around the interstitium; *4*) C_t, the plasma protein concentration of the fluid assumed to be the source of lymph, is Q_t/V_{TOT}; *5*) C_{AV}, the effective plasma protein concentration in the interstitial space, is Q_t/V_{AV}; and *6*) tissue osmotic pressure Π_t is determined directly from C_{AV}.

Figure 10 shows the transient response of several parameters to an increase in venous pressure from the normal value to an elevated one. The values of the parameters at time zero correspond to normal values predicted by the computer. From the predicted results one can assess the relative change in the parameters effected by a change in venous pressure. The sequence in which the parameters change is also predicted. In Figure 10 the interstitial volume and lymph flow rate,

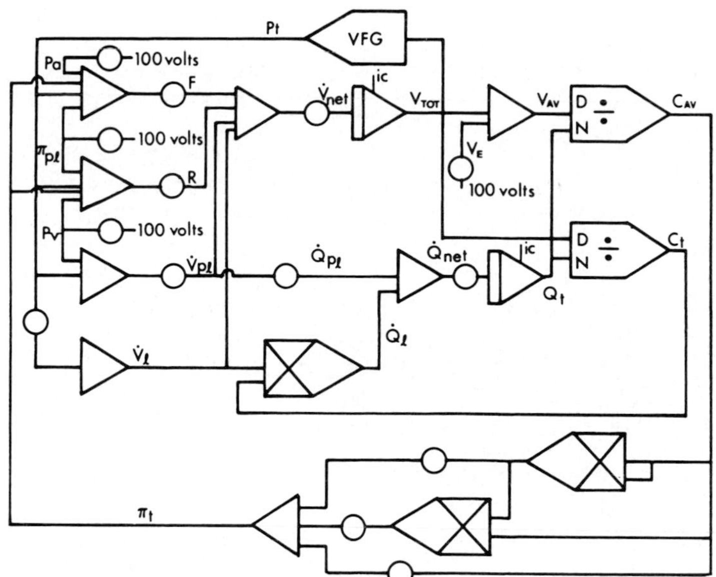

FIG. 9. Flowchart of a computer simulation of microvascular exchange based on constant volume exclusion in the interstitial space of human skin and muscle. Following the nomenclature of the original article, variables are P, pressure (mmHg); Π, colloid osmotic pressure (mmHg); V, volume (liters); $\dot{V}$, volume flow rate (ml/h); Q, protein mass (g); $\dot{Q}$, protein flux (g/h); C, concentration (g/100 ml); F, filtration rate (ml/h); R, reabsorption rate (ml/h). Subscripts are a, arterial; v, venous; pl, plasma; t, tissue; *l*, lymph; net, summation in tissue; TOT, total in tissue; AV, available in tissue; E, excluded in tissue. Abbreviations are VFG, variable function generator; ic, initial conditions; N, numerator; and D, denominator. [From Bert and Pinder (16).]

which are directly related, respond more quickly to a change in venous pressure than do tissue plasma protein content and clearance. A minimum value for interstitial plasma protein content is also evident ~20 h after the perturbation. This slight overshoot results from tissue plasma protein and total interstitial volume having different characteristic response times. Results similar to those shown in Figure 10, but for other parameters (e.g., changes in pressures, concentrations, permeability), have been obtained.

With the aid of computer simulations, other individual aspects of exchange within the microcirculation can be investigated. For example, the effects on microvascular exchange of the following have been studied: *1*) the role of lymphatic permeability and/or plateauing of lymph flow (17) and *2*) the variance of plasma protein concentration in the fluid that forms lymph from those concentrations based on available and total interstitial fluid volumes (18). The latter simulation was performed to investigate the assumptions concerning which interstitial fluid compartments are the source of lymph. A sensitivity analysis employing a computer simulation of pulmonary microvascular exchange has been reported (19). In this study the effects of small changes in a series of dependent variables (i.e., pressures, permeability properties, and concentrations) on other parameters of the system have been investigated. The results clearly demonstrate the highly interactive, complex nature of the system.

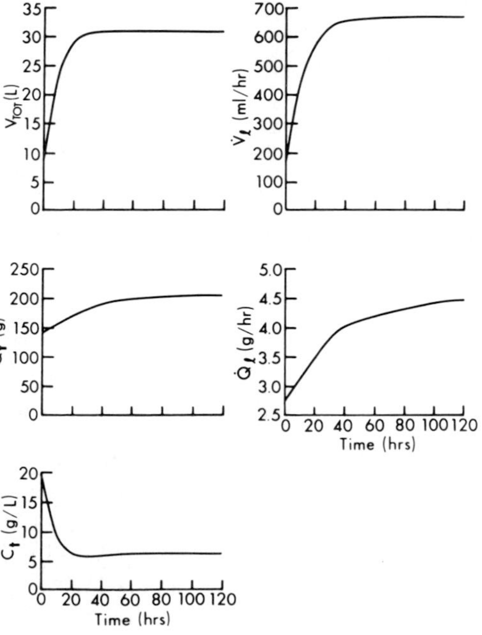

FIG. 10. Transient responses of microvascular variables to a step change in venous pressure from 12 to 27 mmHg. V_{TOT}, total interstitial volume; Q_t, plasma protein content of tissue; C_t, plasma protein concentration in total interstitial volume; $\dot{V}_l$, lymph flow rate; and $\dot{Q}_l$, plasma protein clearance in lymph. Results are from an analog computer simulation of microvascular exchange in skin and muscle. [From Bert and Pinder (16).]

Because of the complexity of the microvascular exchange system and as a result of the experimental and clinical difficulties encountered in obtaining meaningful data, it is understandable that more accurate descriptions of the autoregulatory behavior have not yet been reported and that computer simulations have been employed. The recent trend in computer simulations of assigning a much more important role to the interstitium, even to the point of predominance, reflects an increased understanding of this part of the overall blood-to-lymph transport system. Depending on the scope of the attempt to model microvascular exchange, different properties of the interstitium have been used. The inclusion of these properties in a simulation of microvascular exchange is in marked contrast to models based primarily on lymph as a measure of events occurring at the capillary

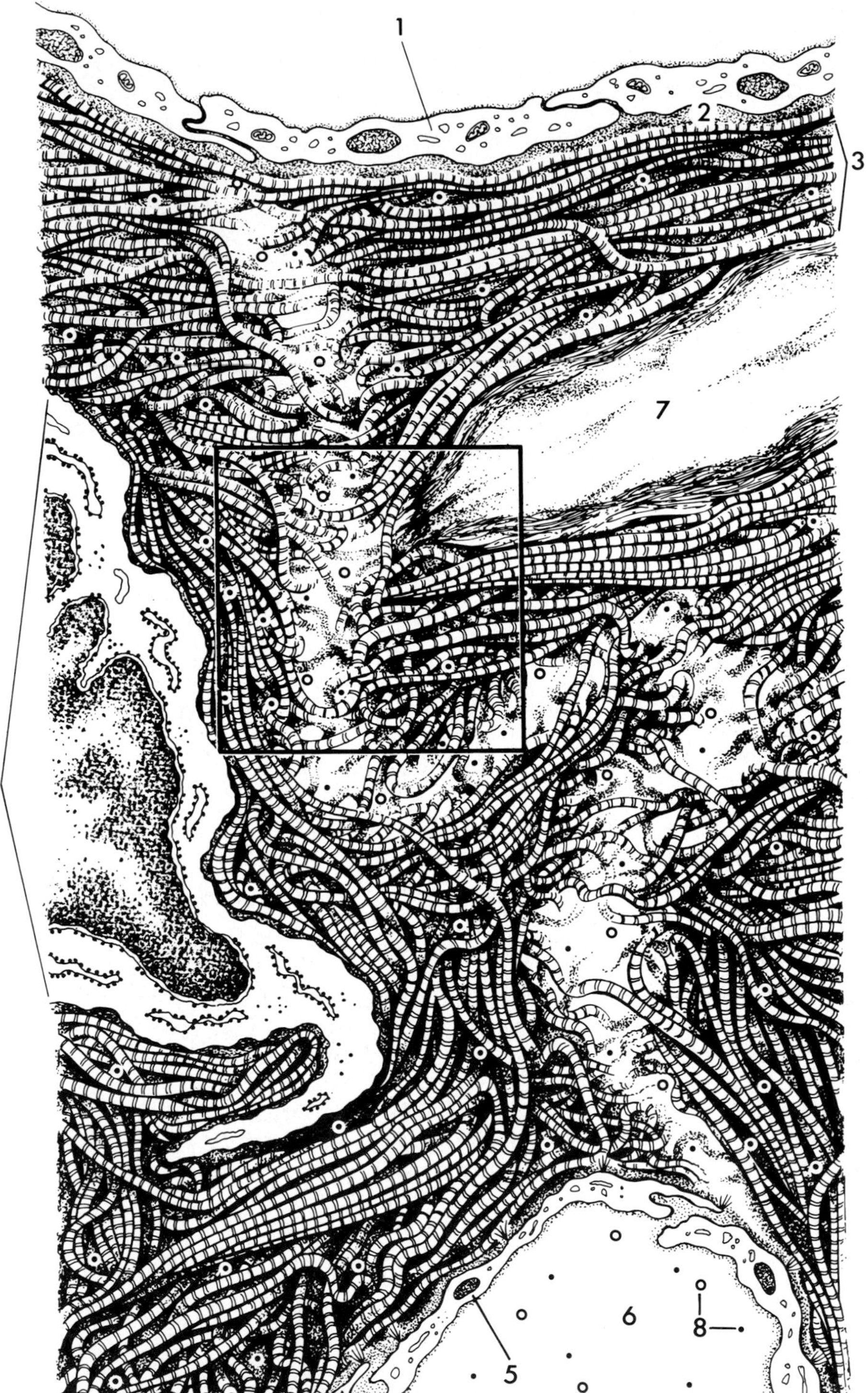

FIG. 11. Overall representation of a blood-to-lymph pathway (not to scale). Numbers represent the following: *1)* endothelial cell in capillary wall, *2)* basement membrane, *3)* gel-like, hydrophilic interstitial matrix, *4)* interstitial cell, *5)* terminal lymphatic cell, *6)* prenodal lymphatic fluid, *7)* elastic fiber, and *8)* two sizes of plasma proteins. (Magnification of rectangular inset appears in Fig. 8.)

wall, with a negligible role attributed to the interstitium.

Simulations like those just described have the capacity to incorporate new information. When the roles of all components of this system—the interstitium in particular—are better understood, fluid and plasma protein distribution and transport in the microcirculation can be described more accurately.

SUMMARY

From the time fluid or solute leaves the plasma and crosses the capillary wall and basement membrane and until it enters the lymphatic system, it moves within the domain of the interstitium. This tissue space may contain water, small solutes, plasma proteins, fibrous structural components such as collagen and elastin, hydrophilic polymers such as hyaluronate and proteoglycans, fat, and cells. These materials are arranged in a three-dimensional matrix. Parts of this tissue space are well organized and other parts appear amorphous. The exact nature of the interstitium is tissue dependent but can usually be described as heterogeneous and deformable. A large fraction of the plasma proteins and fluid reservoirs of the body are found in the interstitium of connective tissues. The manner in which the interstitium moderates changes in plasma volume or plasma protein content is of great interest to health care personnel.

Molecular transport of materials occurs in the direction of decreasing chemical potential of the material being transported. In addition specific convective flow patterns exist within the tissue space, generally in the direction of blood to lymph. Interstitial fluid containing solutes may be exposed to *1*) environments with high electrical charge densities due to the presence of hyaluronate and/or proteoglycans packed in a meshwork of collagenous fibers, *2*) free-fluid channels that may or may not contain mobile hydrophilic macromolecules, or *3*) cells. Figure 11 is a representation of transinterstitial pathways for fluid and solute transport from blood to lymph. Two factors determine the transport pathway: *1*) the resistance to flow offered by the materials characteristic of the interstitium and *2*) the spatial differences in chemical potential of fluid and solutes. The heterogeneous nature of the interstitium makes several different tortuous pathways available to fluid and solutes on their journey from blood to lymph. The interstitial compartments can be defined most easily in terms of composition and organization within the tissue. The interstitium is not a static stucture; rather it undergoes deformation in response to stresses, i.e., mechanical pressures or flows. This compliant nature of the interstitium affects its transport properties. Evidence exists that some of the hydrophilic, macromolecular components of the interstitium (in particular, hyaluronate) are not conserved within the tissue but instead cross the lymphatic boundary.

Transinterstitial exchange of materials can be the result of convective and/or diffusive mechanisms. Not all of the extravascular, extracellular fluid volume of the tissue is accessible to plasma proteins. This volume restriction (i.e., exclusion) concentrates the interstitial plasma proteins in a volume smaller than the total interstitial fluid. The effective concentration of the interstitial plasma proteins is therefore greater than the apparent concentration.

The microvascular exchange system is highly interactive, nonlinear, and complex. The interstitium, previously thought to be only a well-mixed storage chamber for fluid and solutes, is now recognized to have important physicochemical characteristics that not only determine the distribution of fluid and solutes in tissues but also govern the rate of transport of these materials from blood to lymph. The increased attention that the interstitium has received in the last two decades has resulted in greater understanding of microvascular exchange. The work is ongoing.

The manuscript was reviewed critically by a number of colleagues: Mark E. Adams, Paul Bornstein, Don Brooks, Ray Curry, John Gosline, Ken Pinder, E. M. Renkin, and Anders Tengblad. Their constructive comments have helped immensely. Theresa Crawford provided some references to the proteoglycan literature, J. M. Mathieson checked the bibliography, Bruce Stuart drew Figures 8 and 11, and Penny Ma was primarily responsible for typing the manuscript.

Research has been supported by the National Science and Engineering Research Council of Canada and the British Columbia Health Care Research Foundation.

REFERENCES

1. ADELMANN, B., H. MARQUARDT, AND K. KUHN. Investigations on non-collagenous proteins in rat skin. *Biochemistry* 346: 282–296, 1966.
2. ANDERSON, J. G. Glycoproteins of the connective tissue matrix. *Int. Rev. Connect. Tissue Res.* 7: 251–322, 1976.
3. ARTURSON, G., T. GROTH, AND G. GROTTE. The functional ultrastructure of the blood-lymph barrier. Computer analysis of data from dog heart-lymph experiments using theoretical models. *Acta Physiol. Scand. Suppl.* 374: 1–30, 1972.
4. AUKLAND, K., AND H. O. FADNES. Protein concentration of interstitial fluid collected from rat skin by a wick method. *Acta Physiol. Scand.* 88: 350–358, 1973.
5. AUKLAND, K., H. O. FADNES, H. NODDELAND, AND R. K. REED. Edema-preventing mechanisms in subcutis and skeletal muscle. In: *Tissue Fluid Pressure and Composition*, edited by A. R. Hargens. Baltimore, MD: Williams & Wilkins, 1981, p. 87–93.
6. AUKLAND, K., AND G. NICOLAYSEN. Interstitial fluid volume: local regulatory mechanisms. *Physiol. Rev.* 61: 556–643, 1981.
7. BARR, L., AND R. L. MALVIN. Estimation of extracellular spaces of smooth muscle using different-sized molecules. *Am. J. Physiol.* 208: 1042–1045, 1965.
8. BAYLISS, M. T., AND M. VENN. Chemistry of human articular cartilage. In: *Studies in Joint Disease*, edited by A. Maroudas and E. J. Holborow. Tunbridge Wells, UK: Pitman, 1980, vol. I, p. 2–58.
9. BELL, D. R., AND R. J. MULLINS. Effects of increased venous pressure on albumin- and IgG-excluded volumes in skin. *Am. J. Physiol.* 242 (*Heart Circ. Physiol.* 11): H1038–H1043, 1982.
10. BELL, D. R., AND R. J. MULLINS. Effects of increased venous pressure on albumin- and IgG-excluded volumes in muscle. *Am. J. Physiol.* 242 (*Heart Circ. Physiol.* 11): H1044–H1049, 1982.
11. BELL, D. R., P. D. WATSON, AND E. M. RENKIN. Exclusion of plasma proteins in interstitium of tissues from the dog hind paw. *Am. J. Physiol.* 239 (*Heart Circ. Physiol.* 8): H532–H538, 1980.
12. BERT, J. L. Membrane compaction: a theoretical and experimental explanation. *Polym. Lett.* 7: 685–691, 1969.
13. BERT, J. L., AND I. FATT. Relation of water transport to water content in swelling biological membranes. In: *Surface Chemistry of Biological Systems*, edited by M. Blank. New York: Plenum, 1970, p. 287–294.
14. BERT, J. L., J. M. MATHIESON, AND R. H. PEARCE. The exclusion of human serum albumin by human dermal collagenous fibers and within human dermis. *Biochem. J.* 201: 395–403, 1982.
15. BERT, J. L., R. H. PEARCE, J. M. MATHIESON, AND S. J.

WARNER. Characterization of collagenous meshworks by volume exclusion of dextrans. *Biochem. J.* 191: 761–768, 1980.

16. BERT, J. L., AND K. L. PINDER. An analog computer simulation showing the effect of volume exclusion on capillary fluid exchange. *Microvasc. Res.* 24: 94–103, 1982.
17. BERT, J. L., AND K. L. PINDER. Lymph flow characteristics and microvascular exchange: an analog computer simulation. *Lymphology* 15: 156–162, 1982.
18. BERT, J. L., AND K. L. PINDER. From which compartment in the interstitium does lymph originate? *Microvasc. Res.* 26: 116–121, 1983.
19. BERT, J. L., AND K. L. PINDER. Pulmonary microvascular exchange: an analog computer simulation. *Microvasc. Res.* In press.
20. BILL, A. Plasma protein dynamics: albumin and IgG capillary permeability, extravascular movement and regional blood flow in unanesthetized rabbits. *Acta Physiol. Scand.* 101: 28–42, 1977.
21. BLOMBACK, B., AND L. A. HANSON (editors). *Plasma Proteins.* Chichester, UK: Wiley, 1979.
22. BOAS, N. F. Distribution of hexosamine in electrophoretically separated extracts of rat connective tissue. *Arch. Biochem. Biophys.* 57: 367–375, 1955.
23. BORNSTEIN, P., AND H. SAGE. Structurally distinct collagen types. *Annu. Rev. Biochem.* 49: 957–1003, 1980.
24. BORNSTEIN, P., AND W. TRAUB. The chemistry and biology of collagen. In: *The Proteins* (3rd ed.), edited by H. Neurath and R. L. Hill. New York: Academic, 1979, vol. IV, p. 411–632.
25. BRACE, R. A. The chronically implanted capsule: interstitial fluid pressure and solute concentration measurements. In: *Tissue Fluid Pressure and Composition*, edited by A. R. Hargens. Baltimore, MD: Williams & Wilkins, 1981, p. 233–245.
26. BRACE, R. A., AND A. C. GUYTON. Interstitial fluid pressure: capsule, free fluid, gel fluid, and gel absorption pressure in subcutaneous tissue. *Microvasc. Res.* 18: 217–228, 1979.
27. CASLEY-SMITH, J. R. The fine structure and functioning of tissue channels and lymphatics. *Lymphology* 12: 177–183, 1980.
28. CHASE, W. H. Extracellular distribution of ferrocyanide in muscle. *Arch. Pathol.* 67: 525–532, 1959.
29. COMPER, W. D., AND T. C. LAURENT. Physiological function of connective tissue polysaccharides. *Physiol. Rev.* 58: 255–315, 1978.
30. COOPER, D. R., AND P. JOHNSON. The soluble proteins of bovine hide. I. Extraction by aqueous sodium chloride. *Biochim. Biophys. Acta* 26: 317–329, 1957.
31. DAMLE, S. P., L. CÖSTER, AND J. D. GREGORY. Proteodermatan sulfate isolated from pig skin. *J. Biol. Chem.* 257: 5523–5527, 1982.
32. DAY, T. D. Connective tissue permeability and the mode of action of hyaluronidase *Nature London* 166: 785–786, 1950.
33. DAY, T. D. The permeability of the interstitial connective tissue and the nature of the interfibrillary substance. *J. Physiol. London* 117: 1–8, 1952.
34. DEWEY, W. C. Vascular-extravascular exchange of I^{131} plasma proteins in the rat. *Am. J. Physiol.* 197: 423–431, 1959.
35. DISALVO, J., AND M. SCHUBERT. Interaction during fibril formation of soluble collagen with cartilage proteinpolysaccharide. *Biopolymers* 4: 247–258, 1966.
36. DULLIEN, F. A. L. *Porous Media. Fluid Transport and Pore Structure.* New York: Academic, 1979.
37. EIKENBERRY, E. F., B. B. BRODSKY, A. S. CRAIG, AND D. A. D. PARRY. Collagen fibril morphology in developing chick metatarsal tendon. 2. Electron microscope studies. *Int. J. Biol. Macromol.* 4: 393–398, 1982.
38. FADNES, H. O. Effect of increased venous pressure on the hydrostatic and colloid osmotic pressure in subcutaneous interstitial fluid in rats: edema-preventing mechanisms. *Scand. J. Clin. Lab. Invest.* 36: 371–377, 1976.
39. FADNES, H. O. Colloid osmotic pressure in interstitial fluid and lymph from rabbit subcutaneous tissue. *Microvasc. Res.* 21: 390–392, 1981.
40. FADNES, H. O., AND K. AUKLAND. Protein concentration and colloid osmotic pressure of interstitial fluid collected by the wick technique. Analysis and evaluation of the method. *Microvasc. Res.* 14: 11–25, 1977.
41. FARQUHAR, M. G. The glomerular basement membrane. A selective macromolecular filter. In: *Cell Biology of Extracellular Matrix*, edited by E. D. Hay. New York: Plenum, 1981, p. 335–378.
42. FATT, I. *Physiology of the Eye: An Introduction of the Vegetative Functions.* Boston, MA: Butterworths, 1978.
43. FESSLER, J. H. A structural function of mucopolysaccharide in connective tissue. *Biochem. J.* 76: 124–132, 1960.
44. FLEISCHMAJER, R., AND S. KROL. Non-collagenous proteins of human dermis. *J. Invest. Dermatol.* 48: 359–363, 1967.
45. FÖLDI, M. Physiology and pathophysiology of lymph flow. In: *Lymphedema*, edited by L. Clodius. Stuttgart, West Germany: Thieme, 1977, p. 1–11.
46. FOSTER, J. A. Elastin structure and biosynthesis: an overview. *Methods Enzymol.* 82: 559–570, 1982.
47. FOX, J. R., AND H. WAYLAND. Interstitial diffusion of macromolecules in the rat mesentery. *Microvasc. Res.* 18: 255–276, 1979.
48. FRANZBLAU, C., AND B. FARIS. Elastin. In: *Cell Biology of Extracellular Matrix*, edited by E. D. Hay. New York: Plenum, 1981, p. 65–93.
49. FRASER, R. D. B., A. MILLER, AND D. A. D. PARRY. Packing of microfibrils in collagen. *J. Mol. Biol.* 83: 281–283, 1974.
50. FRICKE, R. Serum proteins in connective tissues. In: *Protides of the Biological Fluids*, edited by H. Peeters. Amsterdam: Elsevier, 1962, p. 249–252.
51. GERBER, B. R., AND M. SCHUBERT. The exclusion of large solutes by cartilage proteinpolysaccharide. *Biopolymers* 2: 259–273, 1964.
52. GORESKY, C. A. The nature of transcapillary exchange in the liver. *Can. Med. Assoc. J.* 92: 517–522, 1965.
53. GOSLINE, J. M. The physical properties of elastic tissues. *Int. Rev. Connect. Tissue Res.* 7: 211–249, 1976.
54. GOSLINE, J. M. The temperature-dependent swelling of elastin. *Biopolymers* 17: 697–707, 1978.
55. GRANGER, D. N., N. A. MORTILLARO, P. R. KVIETYS, G. RUTILI, J. C. PARKER, AND A. E. TAYLOR. Role of the interstitial matrix during intestinal volume absorption. *Am. J. Physiol.* 238 (*Gastrointest. Liver Physiol.* 1): G183–G189, 1980.
56. GRANGER, D. N., N. A. MORTILLARO, P. R. KVIETYS, AND A. E. TAYLOR. Regulation of interstitial fluid volume in the small bowel. In: *Tissue Fluid Pressure and Composition*, edited by A. R. Hargens. Baltimore, MD: Williams & Wilkins, 1981, p. 173–183.
57. GRANGER, H. J. Role of the interstitial matrix and lymphatic pump in regulation of transcapillary fluid balance. *Microvasc. Res.* 18: 209–216, 1979.
58. GRANGER, H. J. Physicochemical properties of the extracellular matrix. In: *Tissue Fluid Pressure and Composition*, edited by A. R. Hargens. Baltimore, MD: Williams & Wilkins, 1981, p. 43–61.
59. GRANGER, H. J., J. DHAR, AND H. I. CHEN. Structure and function of the interstitium. In: *Proc. of the Workshop on Albumin*, edited by J. T. Sgouris and A. Rene. Bethesda, MD: Natl. Heart and Lung Inst., 1975, p. 114–124.
60. GRANGER, H. J., AND A. P. SHEPHERD. Dynamics and control of the microcirculation. *Adv. Biomed. Eng.* 7: 1–63, 1979.
61. GRANT, M. E., J. G. HEATHCOTE, AND R. W. ORKIN. Current concepts of basement-membrane structure and function. *Biosci. Rep.* 1: 819–842, 1981.
62. GRODZINSKY, A. J. Electromechanical and physicochemical properties of connective tissue. *Crit. Rev. Biomed. Eng.* 9: 133–199, 1983.
63. GUYTON, A. C., K. SCHEEL, AND D. MURPHREE. Interstitial fluid pressure. III. Its effect on resistance to tissue fluid mobility. *Circ. Res.* 19: 412–419, 1966.
64. GUYTON, A. C., H. J. GRANGER, AND A. E. TAYLOR. *Circula-*

tory Physiology II. Dynamics and Control of the Body Fluids. Philadelphia, PA: Saunders, 1975.
65. HADDY, F. J., J. B. SCOTT, AND G. J. GREGA. Peripheral circulation: fluid transfer across the microvascular membrane. In: *Cardiovascular Physiology II*, edited by A. C. Guyton and A. W. Cowley, Jr. Baltimore, MD: University Park, 1976, vol. 9, p. 63–109. (Int. Rev. Physiol. Ser.)
66. HALJAMÄE, H., AND H. FREDEN. Comparative analysis of the protein content of local subcutaneous tissue fluid and plasma. *Microvasc. Res.* 2: 163–171, 1970.
67. HALLÉN, A. Application of Ion Exchange Chromatography to the Study of Connective Tissue Glycosaminoglycans. Uppsala, Sweden: Univ. Upsaliensis, 1974. Dissertation.
68. HAM, A. W., AND D.H. CORMACK. *Histology* (8th ed.). Philadelphia, PA: Lippincott, 1979.
69. HARDINGHAM, T. E. Proteoglycans: their structure, interactions and molecular organization in cartilage. *Biochem. Soc. Trans.* 9: 489–497, 1981.
70. HASCALL, V. C. Interaction of cartilage proteoglycans with hyaluronic acid. *J. Supramol. Struct.* 7: 101–120, 1977.
71. HASCALL, V. C. Proteoglycans: structure and function. In: *Biology of Carbohydrates*, edited by V. Ginsburg. New York: Wiley, 1981, vol. 1, p. 1–49.
72. HASCALL, V. C., AND J. H. KIMURA. Proteoglycans: isolation and characterization. *Methods Enzymol.* 82: 769–800, 1982.
73. HASCALL, V. C., AND S. W. SAJDERA. Protein polysaccharide complex from bovine nasal cartilage. The function of glycoprotein in the formation of aggregates. *J. Biol. Chem.* 244: 2384–2396, 1969.
74. HASCALL, V. C., AND S. W. SAJDERA. Physical properties and polydispersity of proteoglycan from bovine nasal cartilage. *J. Biol. Chem.* 245: 4920–4930, 1970.
75. HASSELL, J. R., D. A. NEWSOME, AND V. C. HASCALL. Characterization and biosynthesis of proteoglycans of corneal stroma from Rhesus monkey. *J. Biol. Chem.* 254: 12346–12354, 1979.
76. HEATHCOTE, J. G., AND M. E. GRANT. Extracellular modification of connective tissue proteins. In: *The Enzymology of Post-Translational Modification of Proteins*, edited by R. B. Freedman and H. C. Hawkins. London: Academic, 1980, vol. 1, p. 457–506.
77. HEATHCOTE, J. G., AND M. E. GRANT. The molecular organization of basement membranes. *Int. Rev. Connect. Tissue Res.* 9: 191–264, 1981.
78. HODGE, A. J., J. A. PETRUSKA, AND A. J. BAILEY. The subunit structure of the tropocollagen macromolecule and its relation to various ordered aggregation states. In: *Structure and Function of Connective and Skeletal Tissue*, edited by S. Fitton Jackson, R. D. Harkness, S. M. Partridge, and G. R. Tristram. London: Butterworths, 1965, p. 31–41.
79. HOLBROOK, K. A. A histological comparison of infant and adult skin. In: *Neonatal Skin. Structure and Function*, edited by H. Maibach and E. K. Boisits. New York: Dekker, 1982, p. 3–31.
80. HULMES, D. J. S., AND A. MILLER. Quasi-hexagonal molecular packing in collagen fibrils. *Nature London* 282: 878–880, 1979.
81. HUMPHREY, J. H., A. NEUBERGER, AND D. J. PERKINS. Observations on the presence of plasma proteins in skin and tendon. *Biochem. J.* 66: 390–399, 1957.
82. HYNES, R. O. Fibronectin and its relation to cellular structure and behavior. In: *Cell Biology of Extracellular Matrix*, edited by E. D. Hay. New York: Plenum, 1981, p. 295–334.
83. JACKSON, G. W., AND D. F. JAMES. The hydrodynamic resistance of hyaluronic acid and its contribution to tissue permeability. *Biorheology* 19: 317–329, 1982.
84. KANWAR, Y. S., V. C. HASCALL, AND M. G. FARQUHAR. Partial characterization of newly synthesized proteoglycans isolated from the glomerular basement membrane. *J. Cell Biol.* 90: 527–532, 1981.
85. KASTELIC, J., A. GALESKI, AND E. BAER. The multicomposite structure of tendon. *Connect. Tissue Res.* 6: 11–23, 1978.
86. KATCHALSKY, A., AND P. F. CURRAN. *Nonequilibrium Thermodynamics in Biophysics.* Cambridge, MA: Harvard Univ. Press, 1965.
87. KATZ, E. P., AND S. T. LI. The intermolecular space of reconstituted collagen fibrils. *J. Mol. Biol.* 73: 351–369, 1973.
88. KATZ, J., G. BONORRIS, S. GOLDEN, AND A. L. SELLERS. Extravascular albumin mass and exchange in rat tissues. *Clin. Sci.* 39: 705–724, 1970.
89. KATZ, J., G. BONORRIS, AND A. L. SELLERS. Extravascular albumin in human tissues. *Clin. Sci.* 39: 725–729, 1970.
90. KÜHN, K. Relationship between amino acid sequence and higher structures of collagen. *Connect. Tissue Res.* 10: 5–10, 1982.
91. KÜHN, K., AND R. W. GLANVILLE. Molecular structure and higher organization of different collagen types. In: *Biology of Collagen*, edited by A. Viidik and J. Vuust. London: Academic, 1980, p. 1–14.
92. LANDIS, E. M., AND J. R. PAPPENHEIMER. Exchange of substances through the capillary walls. In: *Handbook of Physiology. Circulation*, edited by W. F. Hamilton. Washington, DC: Am. Physiol. Soc., 1963, sect. 2, vol. II, chapt. 29, p. 961–1034.
93. LAURENT, T. C. The interaction between polysaccharides and other macromolecules. The exclusion of molecules from hyaluronic acid gels and solutions. *Biochem. J.* 93: 106–112, 1964.
94. LAURENT, T. C. Structure of hyaluronic acid. In: *Chemistry and Molecular Biology of the Intercellular Matrix*, edited by E. A. Balazs. London: Academic, 1970, vol. 2, p. 703–732.
95. LAURENT, T. C., I. BJÖRK, A. PIETRUSZKIEWICZ, AND H. PERSSON. On the interaction between polysaccharides and other macromolecules. II. The transport of globular particles through hyaluronic acid solutions. *Biochim. Biophys. Acta* 78: 351–359, 1963.
96. LAURENT, U. B. G., AND T. C. LAURENT. On the origin of hyaluronate in blood. *Biochem. Int.* 2: 195–199, 1981.
97. LAURENT, U. B. G., AND A. TENGBLAD. Determination of hyaluronate in biological samples by a specific radioassay technique. *Anal. Biochem.* 109: 386–394, 1980.
98. LEONARD, J. I., AND P. H. ABBRECHT. Dynamics of plasma-interstitial fluid distribution following intravenous infusions in dogs. An experimental and computer simulation study. *Circ. Res.* 33: 735–748, 1973.
99. LIGHT, N. D., AND A. J. BAILEY. Molecular structure and stabilization of the collagen fibre. In: *Biology of Collagen*, edited by A. Viidik and J. Vuust. London: Academic, 1980, p. 15–38.
100. LINSENMAYER, T. F. Collagen. In: *Cell Biology of Extracellular Matrix*, edited by E. D. Hay. New York: Plenum, 1981, p. 5–37.
101. LINSENMAYER, T. F., J. M. FITCH, T. M. SCHMID, N. B. ZAK, E. GIBNEY, R. D. SANDERSON, AND R. MAYNE. Monoclonal antibodies against chicken type V collagen: production, specificity, and use for immunocytochemical localization in embryonic cornea and other organs. *J. Cell Biol.* 96: 124–132, 1983.
102. MANCINI, R. E., O. VILAR, J. M. DELLACHA, O. W. DAVIDSON, C. J. GOMEZ, AND B. ALVAREZ. Extravascular distribution of fluorescent albumin, globulin and fibrinogen in connective tissue structures. *J. Histochem. Cytochem.* 10: 194–203, 1962.
103. MAROUDAS, A. Distribution and diffusion of solutes in articular cartilage. *Biophys. J.* 10: 365–379, 1970.
104. MAROUDAS, A. Biophysical chemistry of cartilaginous tissues with special reference to solute and fluid transport. *Biorheology* 12: 233–248, 1975.
105. MAROUDAS, A. Physical chemistry of articular cartilage and the intervertebral disc. In: *The Joints and Synovial Fluid*, edited by L. Sokoloff. New York: Academic, 1980, vol. 2, p. 239–291.
106. MATHIESON, J. M., AND R. H. PEARCE. The isolation of minimally degraded hyaluronate from rat skin. *Biochem. J.* 161: 419–424, 1977.
107. MAURICE, D. M. The physical state of water in the corneal stroma. In: *The Cornea. Macromolecular Organization of a Connective Tissue*, edited by M. E. Langham. Baltimore, MD:

Johns Hopkins Univ. Press, 1969, p. 193–204.

108. MAURICE, D. M., AND P. G. WATSON. The distribution and movement of serum albumin in the cornea. *Exp. Eye Res.* 4: 355–363, 1965.
109. MCDEVITT, C. A. The proteoglycans and the intervertebral disc in ageing and osteoarthritis. In: *Tissue Repair and Regeneration*, edited by L. E. Glynn. Amsterdam: Elsevier, 1981, p. 111–143.
110. MCMASTER, P. D., AND R. J. PARSONS. Physiological conditions existing in connective tissue. I. The method of interstitial spread of vital dyes. *J. Exp. Med.* 69: 247–264, 1939.
111. MEYER, F. A., M. KOBLENTZ, AND A. SILBERBERG. Structural investigation of loose connective tissue by using a series of dextran fractions as non-interacting macromolecular probes. *Biochem. J.* 161: 285–291, 1977.
112. MILLER, A. Molecular packing in collagen fibrils. In: *Biochemistry of Collagen*, edited by G. N. Ramachandran and A. H. Reddi. New York: Plenum, 1976, p. 85–136.
113. MILLER, A. Structural studies on connective tissue. In: *Biology of Collagen*, edited by A. Viidik and J. Vuust. London: Academic, 1980, p. 39–52.
114. MILLER, E. J., AND S. GAY. Collagen: an overview. *Methods Enzymol.* 82: 3–32, 1982.
115. MORTILLARO, N. A., AND A. E. TAYLOR. Interaction of capillary and tissue forces in the cat small intestine. *Circ. Res.* 39: 348–358, 1976.
116. MUIR, I. H. M. The chemistry of the ground substance of joint cartilage. In: *The Joints and Synovial Fluid*, edited by L. Sokoloff. New York: Academic, 1980, vol. 2, p. 27–94.
117. MULLINS, R. J., AND D. R. BELL. Changes in interstitial volume and masses of albumin and IgG in rabbit skin and skeletal muscle after saline volume loading. *Circ. Res.* 51: 305–313, 1982.
118. NAKAMURA, Y., AND H. WAYLAND. Macromolecular transport in the cat mesentery. *Microvasc. Res.* 9: 1–21, 1975.
119. NICOLAYSEN, G. Protein concentration in lymph. *Lymphology* 11: 143–146, 1978.
120. ÖBRINK, B. Polysaccharide-collagen interactions. In: *Structure of Fibrous Biopolymers*, edited by E. D. T. Atkins and A. Keller. London: Butterworths, 1975, p. 81–92.
121. OEGEMA, T. R., JR., V. C. HASCALL, AND R. EISENSTEIN. Characterization of bovine aorta proteoglycan extracted with guanidine hydrochloride in the presence of protease inhibitors. *J. Biol. Chem.* 254: 1312–1318, 1979.
122. OGSTON, A. G. The spaces in a uniform random suspension of fibres. *Trans. Faraday Soc.* 54: 1754–1757, 1958.
123. OGSTON, A. G., AND C. F. PHELPS. The partition of solutes between buffer solutions and solutions containing hyaluronic acid. *Biochem. J.* 78: 827–833, 1961.
124. OGSTON, A. G., B. N. PRESTON, AND J. D. WELLS. On the transport of compact particles through solutions of chain-polymers. *Proc. R. Soc. London Ser. A* 333: 297–316, 1973.
125. OLDBERG, A., L. KJELLÉN, AND M. HÖÖK. Cell-surface heparan sulfate. Isolation and characterization of a proteoglycan from rat liver membranes. *J. Biol. Chem.* 254: 8505–8510, 1979.
126. OLSEN, B. R. Collagen biosynthesis. In: *Cell Biology of Extracellular Matrix*, edited by E. D. Hay. New York: Plenum, 1981, p. 139–177.
127. OLSZEWSKI, W. L. Collection and physiological measurements of peripheral lymph and interstitial fluid in man. *Lymphology* 10: 137–145, 1977.
128. PARKER, J. C., H. J. FALGOUT, F. A. GRIMBERT, AND A. E. TAYLOR. The effect of increased vascular pressure on albumin-excluded volume and lymph flow in the dog lung. *Circ. Res.* 47: 866–875, 1980.
129. PARKER, J. C., H. J. FALGOUT, R. E. PARKER, D. N. GRANGER, AND A. E. TAYLOR. The effect of fluid volume loading on exclusion of interstitial albumin and lymph flow in the dog lung. *Circ. Res.* 45: 440–450, 1979.
130. PARRY, D. A. D., G. R. G. BARNES, AND A. S. CRAIG. A comparison of the size distribution of collagen fibrils in connective tissues as a function of age and a possible relation between fibril size distribution and mechanical properties. *Proc. R. Soc. London Ser. B* 203: 305–321, 1978.
131. PARRY, D. A. D., AND A. S. CRAIG. Electron microscope evidence for an 80 Å unit in collagen fibrils. *Nature London* 282: 213–215, 1979.
132. PATRIDGE, S. M. Diffusion of solutes in elastin fibres. *Biochim. Biophys. Acta.* 140: 132–141, 1967.
133. PEARCE, R. H., AND B. J. GRIMMER. The nature of the ground substance. In: *Advances in Biology of Skin. The Dermis*, edited by W. Montagna, J. P. Bentley, and R. L. Dobson. New York: Appleton-Century-Crofts, 1970, vol. X, p. 89–101.
134. PEARCE, R. H., AND B. J. GRIMMER. Age and the chemical constitution of normal human dermis. *J. Invest. Dermatol.* 58: 347–361, 1972.
135. PEARCE, R. H., AND B. J. GRIMMER. The chemical constitution of the proteoglycan of human intervertebral disc. *Biochem. J.* 157: 753–763, 1976.
136. PEARCE, R. H., AND T. C. LAURENT. Exclusion of dextrans by meshworks of collagenous fibres. *Biochem. J.* 163: 617–625, 1977.
137. PEARSON, C. H., AND G. J. GIBSON. Proteoglycans of bovine periodontal ligament and skin. Occurrence of different hybrid-sulphated galactosaminoglycans in distinct proteoglycans. *Biochem. J.* 201: 27–37, 1982.
138. PIEZ, K. A. Structure and assembly of the native collagen fibril. *Connect. Tissue Res.* 10: 25–36, 1982.
139. POOLE, A. R., I. PIDOUX, A. REINER, AND L. ROSENBERG. An immunoelectron microscope study of the organization of proteoglycan monomer, link protein, and collagen in the matrix of articular cartilage. *J. Cell Biol.* 93: 921–937, 1982.
140. PRESTON, B. N., AND J. MCK. SNOWDEN. Diffusion properties in model extracellular systems. In: *Biology of Fibroblast*, edited by E. Kulonen and J. Pikkarainen. London: Academic, 1973, p. 215–230.
141. PUTNAM, F. W. (editor). *The Plasma Proteins. Structure, Function and Genetic Control.* New York: Academic, 1975.
142. REEVE, E. B. Interstitial albumin. In: *Albumin Structure, Function and Uses*, edited by V. M. Rosenoer, M. Oratz, and M. A. Rothschild. Oxford, UK: Pergamon, 1977, p. 283–303.
143. REEVE, E. B., AND A. Y. CHEN. Regulation of interstitial albumin. In: *Plasma Protein Metabolism. Regulation of Synthesis, Distribution, and Degradation*, edited by M. A. Rothschild and T. Waldmann. New York: Academic, 1970, p. 89–109.
144. RENKIN, E. M. Lymph as a measure of the composition of interstitial fluid. In: *Pulmonary Edema*, edited by A. P. Fishman and E.M. Renkin. Bethesda, MD: Am. Physiol. Soc., 1979, p. 145–159.
145. ROBINS, S. P. Analysis of the crosslinking components in collagen and elastin. *Methods Biochem. Anal.* 28: 329–379, 1982.
146. RODERMUND, O.-E. Zur Verteilung von Plasmaprotein in Blut und Haut. *Arch. Klin. Exp. Dermatol.* 237: 684–689, 1970.
147. ROSENBLOOM, J. Elastin: biosynthesis, structure, degradation and role in disease processes. *Connect. Tissue Res.* 10: 73–91, 1982.
148. ROTHSCHILD, M. A., A. BAUMAN, R. S. YALOW, AND S. A. BERSON. Tissue distribution of ^{131}I labeled human serum albumin following intravenous administration. *J. Clin. Invest.* 34: 1354–1358, 1955.
149. ROTHSCHILD, M. A., AND T. WALDMANN (editors). *Plasma Protein Metabolism. Regulation of Synthesis, Distribution, and Degradation.* New York: Academic, 1970.
150. RUOSLAHTI, E., E. G. HAYMAN, M. PIERSCHBACHER, AND E. ENGVALL. Fibronectin: purification, immunochemical properties and biological activities. *Methods Enzymol.* 82: 803–831, 1982.
151. RUTILI, G. Transport of Macromolecules in Subcutaneous Tissue Studied by FITC-Dextrans. Uppsala, Sweden: Univ. Upsaliensis, 1978. Dissertation.

152. RUTILI, G., AND K. E. ARFORS. Fluorescein-labelled dextran measurement in interstitial fluid in studies of macromolecular permeability. *Microvasc. Res.* 12: 221–230, 1976.
153. SAGE, H. Collagens of basement membranes. *J. Invest. Dermatol.* 79: 51S–59S, 1982.
154. SAGE, H. Structure-function relationships in the evolution of elastin. *J. Invest. Dermatol.* 79: 146S–153S, 1982.
155. SALATHÉ, E. P., AND R. VENKATARAMAN. Role of extravascular protein in capillary-tissue fluid exchange. *Am. J. Physiol.* 234 (*Heart Circ. Physiol.* 3): H52–H58, 1978.
156. SALATHÉ, E. P., AND R. VENKATARAMAN. Interaction of fluid movement and particle diffusion across capillary walls. *J. Biomech. Eng.* 104: 57–62, 1982.
157. SANDBERG, L. B., N. T. SOSKEL, AND J. G. LESLIE. Elastin structure, biosynthesis, and relation to disease states. *N. Engl. J. Med.* 304: 566–579, 1981.
158. SCHOLANDER, P. F., A. R. HARGENS, AND S. L. MILLER. Negative pressure in the interstitial fluid of animals. *Science* 161: 321–328, 1968.
159. SCHULTZE, H. E., AND J. F. HEREMANS. *Molecular Biology of Human Proteins.* Amsterdam: Elsevier, 1966.
160. SCOTT, J. E. Collagen-proteoglycan interactions. Localization of proteoglycans in tendon by electron microscopy. *Biochem. J.* 187: 887–891, 1980.
161. SCOTT, J. E., C. R. ORFORD, AND E. W. HUGHES. Proteoglycan-collagen arrangements in developing rat tail tendon. An electron-microscopical and biochemical investigation. *Biochem. J.* 195: 573–581, 1981.
162. SELINGER, S. L., R. D. BLAND, R. H. DEMLING, AND N. C. STAUB. Distribution volumes of [^{131}I]albumin, [^{14}C]sucrose and ^{36}Cl in sheep lung. *J. Appl. Physiol.* 39: 773–779, 1975.
163. SHAW, M., AND A. SCHY. Molecular distribution within a collagen gel column. *J. Chromatogr.* 170: 449–452, 1979.
164. STANLEY, J. R., D. T. WOODLEY, S. I. KATZ, AND G. R. MARTIN. Structure and function of basement membrane. *J. Invest. Dermatol.* 79: 69S–72S, 1982.
165. STAUB, N. C. Pulmonary edema due to increased microvascular permeability to fluid and protein. *Circ. Res.* 43: 143–151, 1978.
166. STAUB, N. C. Pulmonary edema: physiologic approaches to management. *Chest* 74: 559–564, 1978.
167. SWABB, E. A., J. WEI, AND P. M. GULLINO. Diffusion and convection in normal and neoplastic tissues. *Cancer Res.* 34: 2814–2822, 1974.
168. SWANN, D. A. Studies on hyaluronic acid. I. The preparation and properties of rooster comb hyaluronic acid. *Biochim. Biophys. Acta* 156: 17–30, 1968.
169. SWEENY, P. R., R. H. PEARCE, AND H. G. VANCE. The chemical anatomy of rat skin. *Can. J. Biochem. Physiol.* 41: 2307–2326, 1963.
170. TANZER, M. L., AND J. H. WAITE. Collagen cross-linking. *Coll. Relat. Res.* 2: 177–180, 1982.
171. TAYLOR, A. E., F. GRIMBERT, G. RUTILI, P. KVIETYS, AND J. C. PARKER. Pulmonary edema: changes in Starling forces and lymph flow. In: *Tissue Fluid Pressure and Composition*, edited by A. R. Hargens. Baltimore, MD: Williams & Wilkins, 1981, p. 135–143.
172. TIMPL, R., H. ROHDE, L. RISTELI, U. OTT, P. G. ROBEY, AND G. R. MARTIN. Laminin. *Methods Enzymol.* 82: 831–838, 1982.
173. TRELSTAD, R. L., AND F. H. SILVER. Matrix assembly. In: *Cell Biology of Extracellular Matrix*, edited by E. D. Hay. New York: Plenum, 1981, p. 179–215.
174. URRY, D. W., AND M. M. LONG. On the conformation, coacervation and function of polymeric models of elastin. *Adv. Exp. Med. Biol.* 79: 685–714, 1977.
175. VARGAS, C. B., F. F. VARGAS, J. G. PRIBYL, AND P. L. BLACKSHEAR. Hydraulic conductivity of the endothelial and outer layers of the rabbit aorta. *Am. J. Physiol.* 236 (*Heart Circ. Physiol.* 5): H53–H60, 1979.
176. VEIS, A. Collagen fibrillogenesis. *Connect. Tissue Res.* 10: 11–24, 1982.
177. VREIM, C. E., P. D. SNASHALL, R. H. DEMLING, AND N. C. STAUB. Lung lymph and free interstitial fluid protein composition in sheep with edema. *Am. J. Physiol.* 230: 1650–1653, 1976.
178. WATSON, P. D., AND F. S. GRODINS. An analysis of the effects of the interstitial matrix on plasma-lymph transport. *Microvasc. Res.* 16: 19–41, 1978.
179. WEISS, L. *Histology; Cell and Tissue Biology* (5th ed.). New York: Elsevier, 1983.
180. WIEDERHIELM, C. A. Transcapillary and interstitial transport phenomena in the mesentery. *Federation Proc.* 25: 1789–1798, 1966.
181. WIEDERHIELM, C. A. Dynamics of transcapillary fluid exchange. *J. Gen. Physiol.* 52: 29S–63S, 1968.
182. WIEDERHIELM, C. A. The interstitial space. In: *Biomechanics: Its Foundations and Objectives*, edited by Y. C. Fung, N. Perrone, and M. Anliker. Englewood Cliffs, NJ: Prentice-Hall, 1972, p. 273–286.
183. WIEDERHIELM, C. A. Dynamics of capillary fluid exchange: a nonlinear computer simulation. *Microvasc. Res.* 18: 48–82, 1979.
184. WIEDERHIELM, C. A. The servo-micropipette pressure recording system and the bat wing preparation. In: *Tissue Fluid Pressure and Composition*, edited by A. R. Hargens. Baltimore, MD: Williams & Wilkins, 1981, p. 247–254.
185. WIEDERHIELM, C. A., AND L. L. BLACK. Osmotic interaction of plasma proteins with interstitial macromolecules. *Am. J. Physiol.* 231: 638–641, 1976.
186. WIIG, H., R. K. REED, AND K. AUKLAND. Micropuncture measurement of interstitial fluid pressure in rat subcutis and skeletal muscle: comparison to wick-in-needle technique. *Microvasc. Res.* 21: 308–319, 1981.
187. WIK, K. O. Physicochemical Studies on Hyaluronate. Uppsala, Sweden: Univ. Upsaliensis, 1979. Dissertation.
188. WITTE, S., AND S. ZENZES-GEPRÄGS. Extravascular protein measurements in vivo and in situ by ultramicrospectrophotometry. *Microvasc. Res.* 13: 225–231, 1977.
189. YAMADA, K. M. Fibronectin and other structural proteins. In: *Cell Biology of Extracellular Matrix*, edited by E. D. Hay. New York: Plenum, 1981, p. 95–114.
190. ZWEIFACH, B. W., AND A. SILBERBERG. The interstitial-lymphatic flow system. In: *Cardiovascular Physiology III*, edited by A. C. Guyton and D. B. Young. Baltimore, MD: University Park, 1979, vol. 18, p. 215–260. (Int. Rev. Physiol. Ser.)

CHAPTER 13

Modeling in the analysis of solute and water exchange in the microvasculature

JAMES B. BASSINGTHWAIGHTE | Department of Bioengineering and Biomathematics, University of Washington, Seattle, Washington

CARL A. GORESKY | Department of Medicine and Physiology, McGill University and Montreal General Hospital, Montreal, Canada

CHAPTER CONTENTS

General Considerations
- Structural arrangements in capillary-tissue units
- Diffusion in blood and tissue
- Permeation

General Approaches to Blood-Tissue Exchange
- Model-free stochastic descriptions of transport functions in linear, stationary systems
- Distributed and lumped systems
- Influences of flow and diffusion on blood-tissue exchange
- Regional variation within an organ
- Relationship between center of mass of tracer in an organ and its movement in relation to flow
- The multiple-indicator-dilution technique

Steady-State Capillary-Tissue Exchange Modeling
- The modeling process
  - The model as a hypothesis
  - Degrees of freedom in fitting models to data
  - The model in the process of experiment design
  - Sensitivity functions
  - Model validation and distance functions
- Capillary–interstitial fluid exchange
  - General expression
  - Single-capillary–interstitial fluid model
  - Whole-organ capillary–interstitial fluid models: homogeneous flow
  - Whole-organ capillary–interstitial fluid models: heterogeneous flows
- Cell–interstitial fluid–capillary exchange
  - Single-capillary–interstitial fluid–cell model
  - Behavoir of the model
  - Multicapillary–interstitial fluid–cell–organ model with heterogeneous flow
- Cell–interstitial fluid–capillary systems with saturable transport mechanisms
  - General characteristics of facilitated transport processes
  - Saturable systems that are nonlinear to tracer
- Homogeneous and heterogeneous systems with diffusional shunting of tracers

Modeling of Perturbed States: Osmotic and Pressure Transients
- Importance of analysis of transient states
- Single-capillary–interstitial fluid–cell model
- Features of the analysis
  - Solute buffering
  - Tissue elasticity
  - Other secondary influences
  - Parameter estimates
  - Estimation of hydraulic conductivity, solute reflection coefficient, and solute permeability
- Shortcomings of current models

The Relation of Modeling Parameters to Understanding Exchange Processes

Summary

THE USE OF MODELING in the analysis of blood-tissue exchange rests on previous physiological observations. Although Krogh (109) developed an equation describing the elements of capillary-tissue exchange of oxygen and Bohr (33) considered the effects of a barrier in pulmonary gas exchange, each of these developments was rooted in inferences derived from experimental data and was only as complete as the physiological observations were. Subsequently much data describing capillary function have accumulated, and capillary physiology has arrived at the stage where the basic principles relating capillary flow and exchange have been developed. It is the purpose of this chapter to communicate these principles.

Problems occur because the systems being analyzed are physically complex, and even when the ideas being pursued are quite straightforward, their final application may not be easy. It is not that the listing of the phenomena or even the writing of equations for appropriate approximate situations is so difficult but that solutions to the equations are difficult to find and present to others in a useful form. This difficulty has inhibited the development of the field. Krogh's work, summarized in his monograph (109), defined the phenomena involved rather well, and Schmidt (182) later described them with some exactitude. However, Schmidt failed to find solutions to the equations except for two oversimplified and therefore not very useful cases.

The principle of conservation of mass, as applied to indicator-dilution data, was utilized by Fick (62), Stewart (202, 204, 205), and Hamilton et al. (85) for the estimation of blood flow. This principle led to the generalizations by Stephenson (201), Meier and Zierler (134), Zierler (243–249), and Bergner (29), who more clearly defined both the advantages and restrictions of this approach. All of these generalizations are structure-free in the sense that they do not depend on the physical nature of the organ or system being observed; one exception is that the system must be of constant volume and that there can be no shifts in internal behavior or fluctuations in flow during the period of observation. The great advantage of indicator-dilution methods for measuring flow (104, 233) has been their adherence to conservation of mass.

The introduction of structure into a system description can be subtle. Zierler (247) used general stochastic formulations of transit times from inflow to outflow to describe the behavior of a pair of tracers introduced simultaneously, one remaining intravascular (reference tracer) and the other penetrating a region inaccessible to the reference tracer (diffusible tracer). As part of this description he sought to separate the outflow profile of the permeating tracer into two parts: *1*) the part that arrives at the outflow without ever leaving the vasculature and *2*) the part that leaves the vasculature and returns later. Without a clear model of the underlying processes, it was not possible to develop the criteria necessary for defining the two components of the diffusible label curve (the throughput and returning moieties).

Sheppard was the first to develop a complete analytical expression for a model of capillary-tissue exchange across a capillary barrier (181, 188). Models are desired because, although their form is necessarily simpler than that of the living system, they are explicitly formulated paradigms that can be tested experimentally. Sheppard's model was pioneering but remained unused for many years, perhaps because it was published in a journal not read by experimentalists or perhaps because it was only later appreciated that its spatially distributed form was essential. Subsequently, Renkin (165, 166) and Crone (45) independently reinvented the equation for a limiting case in which there was no return of tracer to the capillary, and they began to define the limited conditions under which this approximation could be utilized. At the same time Goresky (72) developed the delayed-wave, flow-limited case (the high-permeability extreme) and applied it to the liver. A few years later Goresky et al. (78, 79) and Bassingthwaighte et al. (19) reexplored the underlying differential equations. The former group obtained an analytical solution for the limiting case of zero axial diffusion and developed guidelines for the use of expressions for both throughput and returning components. Ziegler and Goresky (241) were then able to apply these in the estimation of the myocardial capillary permeability to sucrose. The subsequent development of such models for analysis is the focus of this presentation. Their use in estimating transport rates of substrates and ions lends an impetus to physiological explorations that was not felt so urgently in past decades.

A feature of the modeling process is that it leads to recognition of different hierarchical levels of physiological phenomena. For example, in our capillary-tissue models the capillary permeability is considered simply as a phenomenological coefficient and is not expressed by the relationship between a molecule (modeled by a particle with size, shape, charge, etc.) and the channel (modeled by a cylindrical pore, a slit, or a meshwork) through which it may move. This level of modeling is usually reserved for the examination of the relationships between, for example, the permeabilities of a set of molecules at a variety of flows, derived from experimental data. If it is found in a computational process that much of the computing time is being spent on a single element in the model, then it is useful to substitute for this often deeper hierarchical level with some simpler approximating expression. For example, one can use capillary-tissue models to analyze sets of tracer data to provide estimates of cellular permeabilities at different concentration levels; where saturation effects are found, this set of estimates can in turn be analyzed with any of several models for carrier-mediated transmembrane transport. The use of both levels of modeling for the analysis of a single set of tracer data would not usually enable one to find parameters describing the saturation effects.

Another feature of modeling analysis that emerges is that when one has a comprehensive model of a system, the degrees of freedom in fitting the model to the data are greatly reduced. With well-defined models and with particular sets of experimental data, the range of estimates of the parameter values often becomes very limited. This occurs because the influences of each parameter on particular parts of a model function have positive and negative associations with the influences of other parameters. The narrowness of ranges of parameter values in a model is reassuring for two contrasting reasons: *1*) it gives one confidence that the estimate is precise in terms of the chosen model or *2*) it can lead to reasonably prompt rejection of a model when sets of parameters for a group of experiments can be recognized as unrealistic by virtue of reference to some more fundamental principle.

Capillary-tissue exchange is described here from the viewpoint of the whole organ by considering the organ to be composed of arteries, veins, and an immense number of capillary-tissue units, each comprising a capillary, a capillary wall, interstitial fluid region, and parenchymal cells. Although details of convection, diffusion, and permeation of salts, substrates, and water in these units are emphasized, a broader view forces one to consider the heterogeneities in properties, functions, and interactions between capillary-tissue units. Each model must be tested by experiments probing its various aspects. The probing proceeds via more and more comprehensive tests, and the usual outcome is the demonstration of some inadequacy of the model and the development of either a more complex model or a different one altogether.

GENERAL CONSIDERATIONS

Structural Arrangements in Capillary-Tissue Units

The cells of an organ are arranged in a fashion more or less unique to the organ's particular function. Muscle cells are joined together in longitudinal arrays in order to exert tension on contraction, glandular cells are arranged in lobules around a secretory duct, and cells of the intestinal villi form peninsulas that provide a large surface area to the gut. Excretory organs like the liver, kidney, and lung have specialized units maximizing the surface area of the layer of cells that eliminate material into the effluent bile, urine, or air. In each case the capillary bed is structured so as to minimize diffusion distances between the flowing blood and the cells it serves (see Fig. 1).

Diffusion is too slow for transport over distances larger than a cell or two. Accordingly convection is the essential delivery process, and through evolution, diffusion distances have been minimized. In his study of the diffusion of oxygen and lactic acid, Hill (90) wrote:

> A cylinder 1 cm in diameter composed of material similar to frog's nerve, if suddenly placed in oxygen, would take 185 minutes to attain 90 percent of its full saturation with that gas. An actual nerve 0.7 mm thick would take 54 seconds for the same stage of saturation to be reached. A single nerve fibre 7 μm thick would take only 5.4 milliseconds. Again, the rapidity of diffusion attainable in systems of small dimensions is the basis of the capillary circulation, and therewith of the whole design of the larger animals.

Since convection requires a pressure gradient and a fluid pathway must have continuity, the arrangement of capillaries in long arrays between cells satisfies both these needs and the need for short intercapillary distances. Thus capillaries are long, often hundreds of microns or even a few millimeters, but the distances between them are the dimensions of one or two of the organ's cells. In each organ the capillaries take on the arrangement best serving the organ's particular needs. This is natural in an embryological sense because the capillary buds work their way through tissues that are already somewhat developed.

Vascular units in each organ tend to assume a particular form and tend to be replicated with about the same dimensions throughout an organ. Such units have been well defined for the liver (157), the mesentery (37, 65), the rete mirabile of the eel swim bladder (158, 206), and the wing of the bat (138, 224), but complete descriptions are not readily available for all organs. Even when the anatomical arrangements have been examined in considerable detail [the kidney (27), the heart (24, 89), and the lung (193, 221)], a clear-cut definition of the functional vascular unit may be lacking. No matter what the details of the form are, it seems likely that neighboring structurally similar units have similarities in flow and transit times. If they did not, the system's efficiency for oxygen delivery would be reduced. On the other hand, some sacrifice of moment-to-moment efficiency may be needed to provide stability and security over a lifetime.

One can envisage an ideal capillary-tissue unit of the form shown in Figure 1, known as the Krogh cylinder model since Krogh's use of it in his calculations on oxygen delivery (108, 109). This arrangement only exists if the branching from an arteriole to a set of capillaries occurs over very short distances compared with the lengths of the capillaries. This occurs in the liver with the confluence of the hepatic arterioles and the portal venules at the entrance to the sinusoids (135). In the heart each large group of capillaries is fed by an arteriole that goes through three to four orders of branching within ~40–80 μm on the way to the capillaries. The venular confluences are almost as rapid (24). Structurally, because the inter-

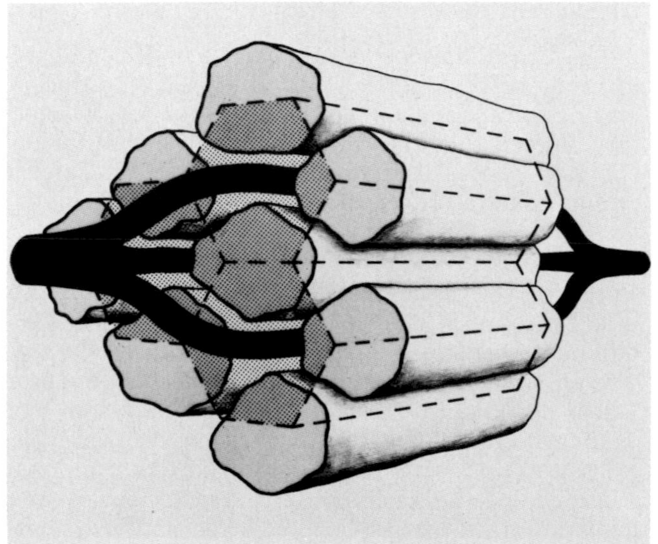

FIG. 1. Concurrent arrangement of capillaries and muscle fibers in myocardium. Krogh capillary-tissue hexagons with uniform dimensions and flows. Exchange occurs only in capillary-tissue regions and not in large vessels. A fundamental prerequisite is that flows in adjacent capillaries and volumes in adjacent capillary-tissue regions are similar. Therefore, although there are concentration gradients both radially and longitudinally in the tissue, there are no gradients across the interface between regions. In such a circumstance the local region can be modeled as a composite of capillaries all having identical behavior. [From Grabowski and Bassingthwaighte (80).]

capillary distances are quite uniform and the arteriolar-venular distances very long (~800–1,000 μm) compared with the size of the branching region, the unit is similar to the idealized diagram in Figure 1. Even so, some skepticism about the idealized capillary-tissue cylinder model should be retained because neither the geometry nor the capillary velocities are necessarily uniform. An example of this is the variation in atrial myocardial capillaries (38, 88).

A real limitation to modeling in terms of Krogh cylinders is the occurrence of regions where diffusional shunting may occur, where arterioles and venules are close together, where there are different blood velocities in neighboring capillaries, or where the beginnings and endings of neighboring capillaries are offset from one another. Where such geometrical situations are frequent, solute (or tracer) may bypass the capillary-exchange region altogether or may take a shortcut from the upstream end of one capillary to the downstream end of another. When this occurs, the capillary-tissue units cannot be considered independent and an assembly of such units must be modeled. Deviations from the idealized unit are expected to be most evident for highly diffusible substances and less so for large hydrophilic molecules. Although the liver and heart microvasculatures can be described by parallel capillary-tissue units, the capillaries of bone (130), brain (82), and mesentery (65) have much more variable arrangements.

Diffusion in Blood and Tissue

The Brownian motion of particles under bombardment by solvent particles is the basis of diffusion, leading to randomized molecular dispersion. Einstein (55) showed that the diffusion coefficient D for uncharged spheres is inversely related to the particle radius a and to the viscosity η of the medium

$$D = RT/6\pi a \eta N_A \qquad (1)$$

where R is the gas constant, T is absolute temperature, π is 3.1416, and N_A is Avogadro's number. Thus the diffusion coefficient, measured experimentally, can give an indication of the size of a molecule. Equation 1 does not take into account electric charges on ions or the adherence of water molecules to charged molecules. Friction with other solute particles and any reduction of the mobility of water molecules in a relatively fixed matrix (e.g., collagen and glycosaminoglycans) reduce the effective diffusivity even further. [See Robinson and Stokes (168) for discussion of ionic diffusion.]

Crank (44) gives equations for diffusion in many situations. A simple but often useful calculation is the time constant τ for radial-diffusion equilibration throughout a cylindrical region of radius r_0 from an axial source

$$\tau = r_0^2/D \qquad (2)$$

where D is the effective diffusion coefficient in the radial direction. At time $t = \tau$ the average concentration in the cylinder is 99% of that at the axis and the minimum concentration at the outside is 97%. Other cases can be defined for other geometries.

Radial concentration gradients within a microvascular capillary of radius r_C may usually be considered negligible (7, 154); the radial relaxation times $\tau = r_C^2/D$ are short. With $r_C = 4$ μm (for a large capillary) and $D = 0.7 \times 10^{-5}$ cm^2/s (for a molecule the size of sucrose), $\tau = 0.023$ s, which is very short compared with capillary transit times. Actual relaxation times must be still shorter; red blood cells speed up radial equilibration by causing circulation within plasmatic gaps.

Axial dispersion in the capillary occurs as a result of several processes: axial diffusion; the rotation of erythrocytes, which stir the plasma locally (121); and via the differences in velocities in the flow streamlines. Dispersion tends to be diminished by radial diffusion between streamlines (212). Axial dispersion is offset by the segmenting of the flow stream by red cells to form plasmatic gaps, as occurs for the flow of bubbles in tubes (69, 154). Within the plasmatic gaps between the red cells the fluid rotates to bring the axial fluid to the capillary surface and vice versa, thereby enhancing radial equilibration. (See the chapter by Chien et al. in this *Handbook* for an overview of particle movement in small tubes.)

Axial diffusion is not nearly sufficient to bring about equilibration between inflow and outflow ends of the capillary, the time constant for equilibration being ~1,000 s. Therefore an axially distributed model is important for tissues with long capillaries; a first-order, lumped-compartment model, which assumes complete equilibration from end to end, is generally quite unsuitable.

Diffusion through tissue is slower than through water or plasma because of a number of factors: partial or complete exclusion from cells, molecular exclusion from a portion of the tissue water, tortuous pathways, steric hindrance, and solute binding. The bulk diffusion coefficient D_b (cm^2/s) is an experimental value, with the tissue considered as a homogeneous medium. For a steady-state flux across a plane sheet

$$D_b = \frac{\text{flux (mol/s)} \cdot \text{thickness (cm)}}{\text{concn difference (mol/cm}^3) \cdot \text{sheet area (cm}^2)} \qquad (3)$$

The delay in initial diffusional flux across a thick sheet with or without binding sites is shown by experiments in which tracer is added to a well-stirred solution on one side of a plane sheet and its concentration measured as a function of time in a well-stirred chamber of fixed volume on the other side. These data give estimates of transverse or radial rather than axial diffusion coefficients because the capillaries and muscle fibers are parallel to the surface of the sheet. A diagram of transients in intratissue concentration profiles and the resultant concentration in the unlabeled chamber is shown in Figure 2.

Page and Bernstein (141), Suenson, Richmond, and Bassingthwaighte (209), and Safford, Bassingthwaighte, and Bassingthwaighte (179, 180) used this approach with a sheet of heart muscle. An example of the data is shown in Figure 3. Bulk diffusion coefficients for sucrose and sodium were ~6% of the free-diffusion coefficient. The interstitial diffusion coefficient D_I is

$$D_I = D_b/A_D \tag{4}$$

where A_D is the fraction of the extracellular space available for diffusion. Values for D_I were 25% of D_0, the free-diffusion coefficient in water.

Diffusion is slowed similarly in gels (66), particularly by hyaluronates (140). Much of this is due to molecular exclusion (i.e., volume exclusion). The excluded-volume fraction v_{excl} can be estimated experimentally from the known concentration of the solute C in the water fraction of the matrix and from the effective osmotic concentration C′ estimated from the observed osmotic pressure of the solute in the matrix (139)

$$v_{excl} = 1 - C/C' \tag{5}$$

Interstitial exclusion for large molecules can be estimated from experimental data. The method requires estimation of the extracellular volume of distribution V'_{ECF} for both the large molecule and for a small extracellular reference tracer for which v_{excl} is negligible [e.g., sucrose, L-glucose, and cobaltic-ethylenediaminetetraacetate (32)]. The intravascular volume of distribution V'_C in the same piece of tissue must also be estimated. From these the calculation is

$$v_{excl} = 1 - \frac{V'_{ECF}\ (\text{solute}) - V'_C}{V'_{ECF}\ (\text{sucrose}) - V'_C} \tag{6}$$

The exclusion phenomenon has been thoroughly studied not only in gels (2, 117, 118, 146, 186, 228) but also in tissues (31, 39, 51, 72, 197, 212). Curry, in his chapter in this *Handbook* and in reference 49, traces the development of expressions for diffusion in a fiber matrix from the work of Ogston et al. (139).

Further developments should allow for heterogeneity of the meshwork. The normal state of randomness means that intermolecular distances cannot be uniform, so that in a meshwork of relatively fixed molecules there must be regions of high exclusion and low diffusivity as well as areas of low exclusion and high diffusivity. Wiederhielm (226) suggested a two-phase interstitium with gel and fluid phases, although we prefer to consider the system as a continuum—a gel with spatial variations in local composition. Because of the nonlinearities of the relationships, the observable overall average values of the diffusivities are different from those in a uniformly dense matrix.

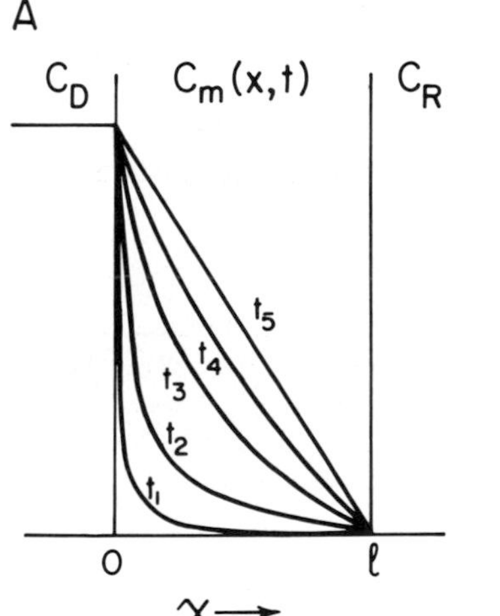

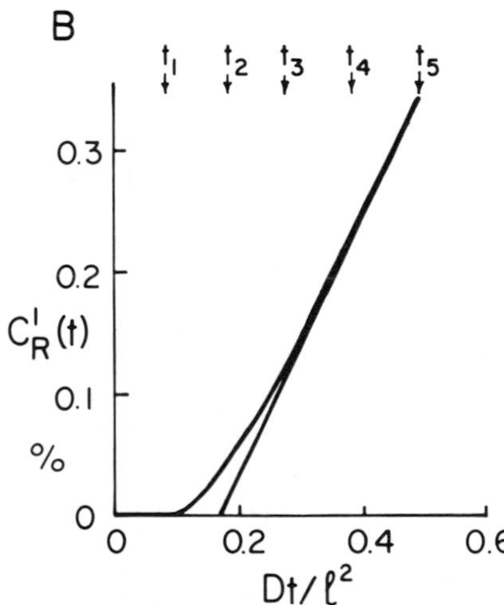

FIG. 2. Transient for diffusion across a planar sheet of thickness l between well-stirred chambers: "donor" chamber D and "recipient" chamber R. *A*: concentration in donor chamber C_D labeled at $t = 0$ is held constant; concentration in unlabeled recipient compartment C_R rises with time but remains so low (<0.5% of C_D) that it may be considered zero relative to tissue concentrations. Concentration profiles within the sheet of myocardium C_m are shown at 4 times approaching steady state; t_5 is at pseudo–steady state. *B*: concentration in recipient chamber C'_R (where $C'_R = 100\ C_R/C_D$) shows delay and then gradual rise to pseudo–steady state. The abscissa is time, rendered dimensionless by multiplying by the diffusion coefficient in the sheet and dividing by the thickness squared. The x-intercept to which the straight line is extrapolated gives an estimate of the volume of distribution of tracer in tissue; the slope of the line gives an estimate of the diffusion coefficient. The phrase *pseudo–steady state* is used because $C'_R(t)$ is a straight line only for very low values before flux from R to D becomes significant. If regions D and R were well mixed, then both C_D and C_R would show exponential-like time courses, the earliest part of which is shown here.

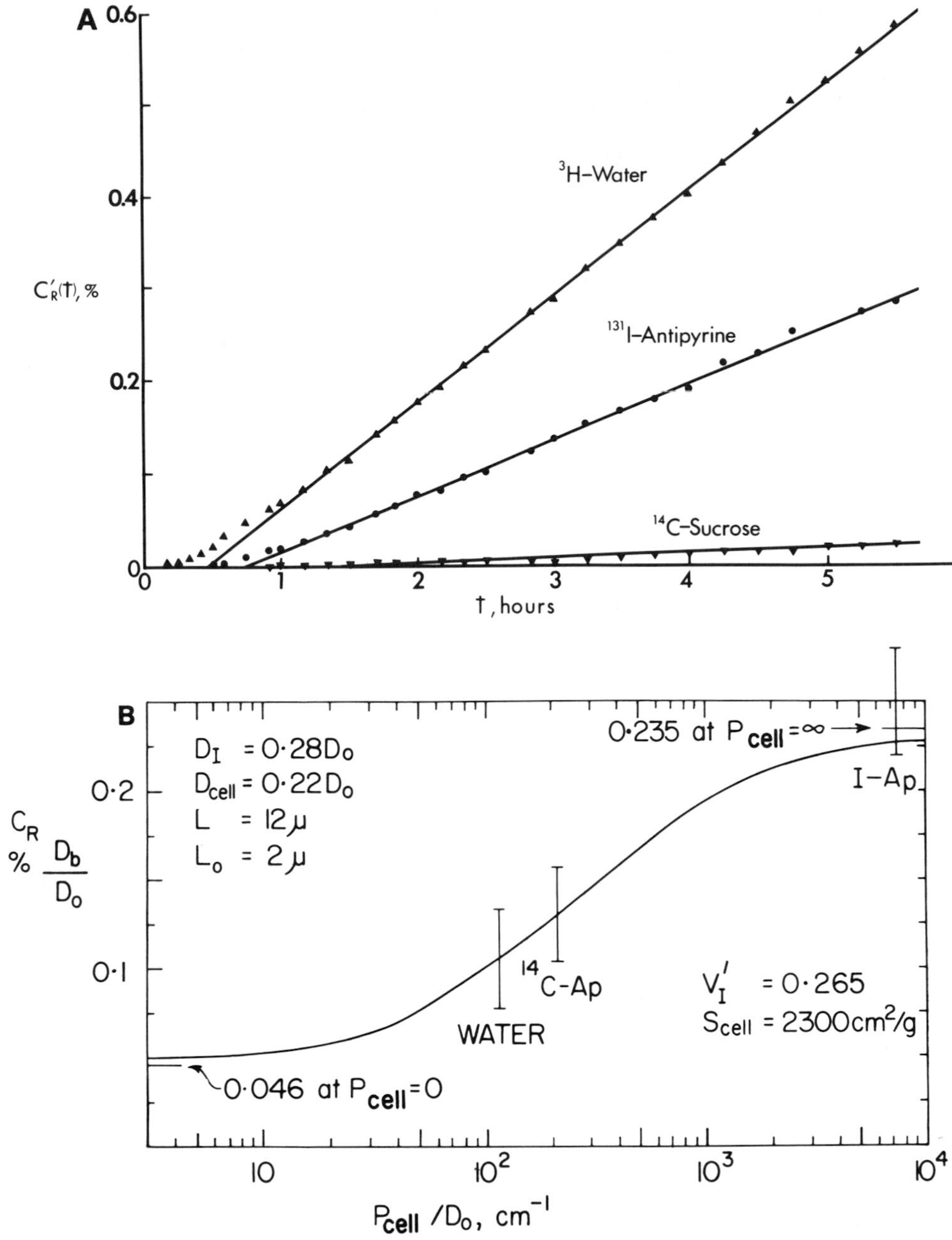

FIG. 3. Diffusion of labeled water, iodoantipyrine, and sucrose across sheet of right ventricular myocardium of ferret heart. *A*: experimental lines for tracer concentration in recipient chamber $C'_R(t)$ as a fraction of initial concentration in chamber to which tracer was added at $t = 0$. Sheet thickness was 1.4 ± 0.2 mm (mean ±SD, $n = 32$); water content was 0.82 ml/g; temperature was 23°C. Bulk diffusion coefficients (from slopes) for [^{3}H]water, ^{131}I-antipyrine, and [^{14}C]sucrose were 2.39, 1.22, and 0.14 × 10^{-6} cm^2/s. Fitting the sucrose curve with the equation for a plane sheet of uneven thickness (209) gives a fractional area for extracellular (i.e., interstitial) diffusion A_D of 0.24 and an effective diffusion coefficient of sucrose in the extracellular fluid D_I of 0.58 × 10^{-6} cm^2/s, or D_I/D_0 = 0.25, where D_0 is the coefficient of free diffusion. If A_D and D_I/D_0 for [^{3}H]water and ^{131}I-antipyrine are the same and intracellular diffusion is at the same rate, the estimates of sarcolemmal permeability–surface area products for [^{3}H]water and ^{131}I-antipyrine are 5.7 and 4.0 ml·g^{-1}·min^{-1}. *B*: relationship between D_b/D_0 (where D_b is bulk diffusion coefficient) and P_{cell}/D_0 (where P_{cell} is cell permeability). *Curve*, relationship for a medium composed of evenly dispersed permeable cells of width L and with spacing L_0 between them; D_I and D_{cell} (intracellular diffusion coefficient) have a cross-sectionally weighted average of 0.235D_0 when there is no permeability barrier. *Vertical bars*, SD of D_b/D_0. Higher lipid permeability of ^{131}I-antipyrine (I-Ap) compared with water and [^{14}C]antipyrine (^{14}C-Ap) contributes to its higher overall intratissue diffusivity. V'_I, apparent interstitial volume of distribution; S_{cell}, surface area of parenchymal cells.

Species variation in exclusion is particularly notable for ions, presumably because interstitial macromolecules are charged and net effective charges vary. For example, Macchia et al. (131) report that the sulfate space and sucrose space of the left ventricular myocardium are 0.204 ± 0.022 (SD) and 0.205 ± 0.019 in nephrectomized rats, and 0.105 ± 0.019 and 0.150 ± 0.022 in gastrocnemius muscle, with $n = 10$ in all cases. In contrast they found that in toad semitendinosus muscle the sulfate space is 110% of the sucrose space—a statistically significant deviation, this time in the direction opposite to that in rat gastrocnemius. The deviations in chloride space observed by Haljamäe et al. (84) in subcutaneous tissues in dog and rabbit are similar in direction to those for sulfate in rat gastrocnemius. However, the observations in heart and in toad semitendinosus demonstrate the dangers of generalizing.

For a solute that binds during its transfer, the initial delay (time lag) for diffusion across a sheet (as in Fig. 2) depends on the free concentration of the solute and the affinity of the binding site, the relative amount bound being much higher at low concentrations of solute. The varied delays (the intercept on the time axis in Fig. 2) for calcium in myocardium over a wide range of steady-state calcium concentrations were interpreted by Safford and Bassingthwaighte (180) in terms of two immobile first-order binding sites for calcium. This was the minimum number of sites distinguishable in their somewhat "noisy" kinetic data. The binding sites may be on the intercellular connective tissue molecules (100) or on the cell surfaces (21, 115).

Attachment to the binding site of a larger molecule reduces solute diffusivity; the effective diffusivity D' of a moving front of tracer is calculated from the diffusivities of the free species in the tissue D and of the various bound species D_{B_i} as follows

$$D' = \frac{D + \Sigma D_{B_i} R_i}{1 + \Sigma R_i} \tag{7}$$

where R_i is the concentration-dependent value for the ratio of the concentration of solute bound at the site i to that of the free species. When only the free species is mobile, this reduces to

$$D' = D\left(\frac{1}{1 + \Sigma R_i}\right) \tag{8}$$

where D' is the effective diffusivity of the concentration front as before. Behind the front the effective tracer diffusivity becomes higher as the specific activity of the tracer attached to the binding sites rises toward that at the source of the tracer. As steady state is approached, D' increases to D, the value of which then depends only on the area and steric hindrances in the diffusion space because at this point equilibration with binding sites is complete.

When there is a constant concentration of the mother substance (the substance being traced), facilitated diffusion of a tracer is faster than that given by Equation 7 because both the bound and free species diffuse. The steady-state expression becomes

$$D' = D + \Sigma D_{B_i} R_i \tag{9}$$

Even when the binding sites are on large molecules with low diffusion coefficients (low D_{B_i}), the facilitation may be physiologically important. As with facilitation of oxygen diffusion by hemoglobin, calcium diffusion intracellularly must be facilitated by the presence of calmodulin or parvalbumin (177, 220).

There is, however, a paucity of data on intracellular diffusion coefficients (D_{cell}) because of the difficulty in estimating the role of membranes (e.g., plasmalemma or intercalated disks) in the transport. Kushmerick and Podolsky (112) estimated D_{cell}/D_0 to be 41%–56% for K^+, Na^+, sucrose, sorbitol, and adenosine 5′-triphosphate (ATP) along the axis of skinned single fibers of frog skeletal muscle; a D_{cell}/D_0 value for Ca^{2+} of less than 2% was estimated. Using $D_{cell}/D_0 = 1/2$, Weidmann (222) calculated the resistance of the intercalated disks of ventricular myocardial fiber bundles for K^+. Weingart (223) did the same for tetraethylammonium, Imanaga (94) for Procion yellow in Purkinje fibers, and Pollack (151) for fluorescein transport in the arteriovenous nodal tissue. The low diffusion coefficient for Ca^{2+} is easily understood in view of the multitude of specific binding sites available to it. Less easily understood is Kushmerick and Podolsky's (112) observation in some experiments that there were fast and slow components that could not be explained by the presence of binding sites, as in Equation 7. Rather their results suggest diffusion along two paths in parallel. The concentration-distance profiles of Imanaga (94) and Weingart (223) are also better fitted by an equation for the sum of two interacting diffusional processes (J. B. Bassingthwaighte and R. E. Safford, unpublished observations). Axial diffusion in heart muscle fibers could be faster than radial diffusion because of the orientation of the meshwork parallel to myofibrils. Nevertheless it would be unexpected for diffusion in general to be very much faster in intracellular regions, with their high protein concentrations, than in the interstitial space.

The diffusion of a variety of small solutes in solutions corresponding to intracellular contents has been explored. In a 33% hemoglobin solution Redwood et al. (160) found $D/D_0 = 0.50$ for water, 0.47 for formamide, and 0.52 for acetamide. Longmuir and Roughton (129) showed $D/D_0 = 0.25$ for oxygen in 35% hemoglobin when the hemoglobin is inactivated to stop oxygen binding and to be higher when binding occurs. Thus the solute diffusion is facilitated by the additional diffusion of the oxyhemoglobin, as also occurs with intact erythrocytes (207). Garrick et al. (67) found $D_{cell}/D_0 = 0.4–0.5$ for the monohydric alcohols in 33% hemoglobin solutions; in plasma, where the protein concentration is lower, values are ~0.8. For the intracellular contents of lysed lung cells D_{cell}/D_0 averages 0.28 both for water and the small monohydric alcohols (68).

In a medium of cells dispersed in an interstitial matrix, diffusion may occur solely through the extracellular space or through both the cellular and extracellular regions in parallel and in series. Stroeve et al. (208) gave the expressions for diffusion through a medium containing spheres in which there was diffusion and consumption. Redwood et al. (160) described extracellular diffusion parallel to and in equilibrium with intracellular diffusion and permeation in series. Safford, Bassingthwaighte, and Bassingthwaighte (179), in analyzing experiments on water diffusion in the myocardium, extended the model to include restricted permeation of the sarcolemma and extracellular and intracellular diffusion in series as well as in parallel. The higher the permeability, the greater the contribution of intracellular diffusion to the overall diffusion coefficient D_b. In this analysis, Safford et al. ignored the presence of the capillaries as hindrances, a conceptual shortcoming justified by the vessels' small volumes (<4% of the tissue and much smaller in diameter than the myocytes), the short intracapillary diffusion time, and the high permeability of capillary walls compared with myocytes.

To show the effects of permeability Winget and Bassingthwaighte (231) examined the diffusion of ^{131}I-labeled antipyrine, [^{14}C]antipyrine (whose lipid solubility is much less than that of iodoantipyrine), water, and sucrose through a sheet of right ventricular myocardium in the same type of experiment as that diagramed in Figure 2. A set of raw data is shown in Figure 3*A*. Figure 3*B* shows the average values of the ratios of bulk diffusion coefficients to free-diffusion coefficients. For both antipyrine and water these were twice what would be predicted from the sucrose curves to be due to extracellular diffusion. For ^{131}I-antipyrine, with its higher lipid solubility, the average ratio was over 4 times that expected to be due to extracellular diffusion alone. Intracellular diffusion obviously contributed more to the latter.

The dissipation of gradients by diffusion over radial intercapillary distances of the dimensions encountered in a richly perfused tissue such as the heart occurs in milliseconds, but over millimeter distances diffusion is too slow to be useful for metabolic substrates. For example, Patlak and Fenstermacher (145)

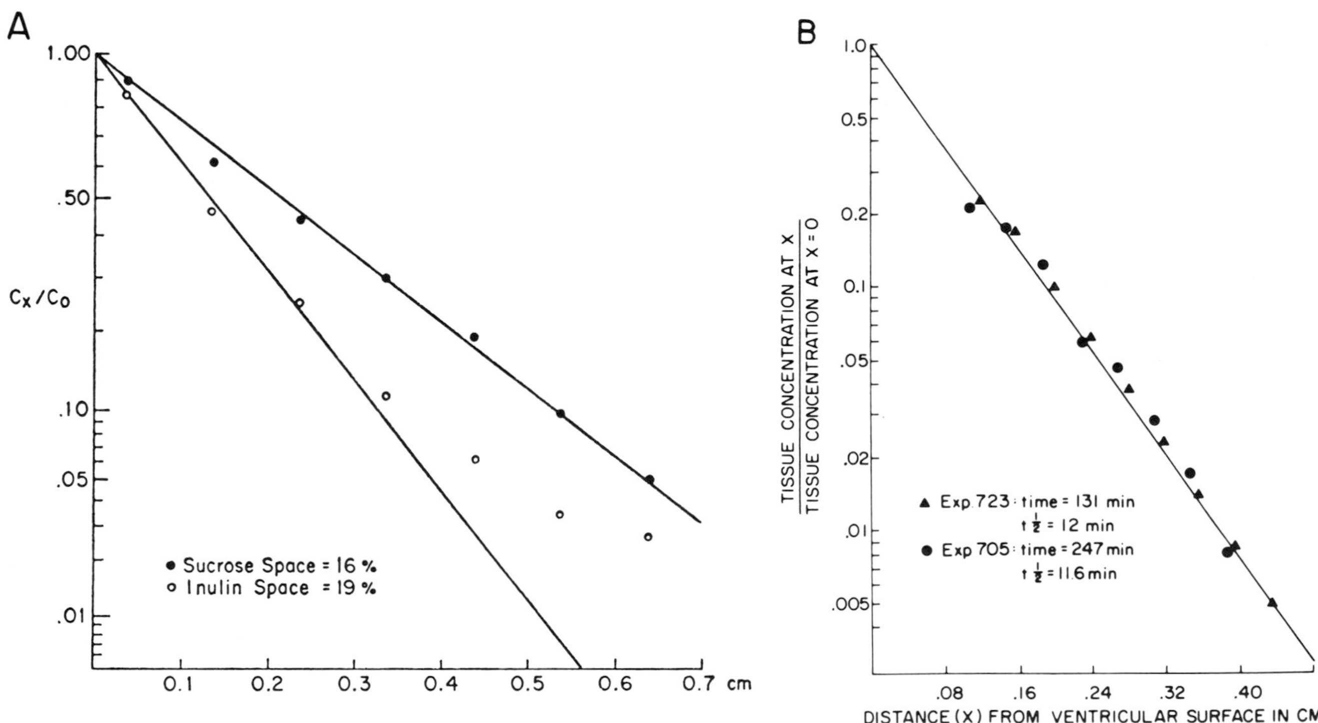

FIG. 4. Dog caudate nucleus concentration-distance profiles after 4 h ventriculocisternal perfusion during which a constant concentration of solute is presented to surface of 3rd ventricle. Ordinates are concentration at distance x into the brain (C_x) divided by surface concentration (C_0). *A*: inverse complementary error function plots of tissue concentration profiles for [^{14}C]sucrose and [^{3}H]inulin. Slopes of lines provide estimates of D_b, assuming that there is no loss of tracer into the capillary blood [Eq. 19 of Patlak and Fenstermacher (145)]. *B*: semilog plot of [^{14}C]urea concentrations at two different times, showing attainment of steady state. The single exponential form, a front unchanging in position with time, indicates that a balance between diffusional inflow into the tissue and removal by the vascular system has been attained. [From Patlak and Fenstermacher (145).]

obtained the spatial profiles of concentration in brain tissue after perfusing the third ventricle of an anesthetized dog with tracer so that the surface concentration was constant. The brain ependyma facing the cerebrospinal fluid is quite permeable, unlike that of the capillaries, so that sucrose enters the extracellular fluid spaces of the brain parenchyma freely. In the absence of consumption of the tracer and of washout by the blood flowing through the capillaries (these are essentially impermeable to sucrose in the brain), the profile of concentration as a function of time and distance from the surface gives a measure of the effective diffusion coefficient. The tissue concentration profile in such an experiment, 4 h after beginning a perfusion, is shown in Figure 4*A*. Estimates of the bulk diffusion coefficient for sucrose, corrected for the fractional surface area for diffusion A_D and made at various times after starting cisternal perfusion, were similar. An average for the ratio $(D_b/A_D)/D_0$ is 0.43. The constancy of this ratio with time is evidence that removal (by permeation of capillaries) is negligible.

The movement of a concentration front by diffusion is slowed whenever indicator is consumed by cells or removed continuously by any mechanism. When the rate of removal and the concentration of tracer at the brain surface are constant, then after a time the diffusion front stabilizes at a position where the total removal rate equals the flux into the region. Patlak and Fenstermacher (145) found that the concentration-distance profiles for urea (Fig. 4*B*) no longer changed after 2 h but that the rate of attainment of this stable position for the front was slower than if there had been no loss of tracer. A similar situation occurs for oxygen in tissues, where concentration-distance profiles of constant shape are expected wherever there is constant delivery by flow and diffusion and removal by oxygen consumption.

Diffusion coefficients have been estimated in less cellular and less vascular tissues by optical techniques. Wiederhielm (225) observed the spreading of the intratissue concentration profiles for light-absorbing dyes in the bat wing as a function of distance from a capillary. He used the change in the profile for patent blue V dye (580 mol wt) as a function of time to calculate its diffusion coefficient (Fig. 5). Wiederhielm also observed that a dye that binds to the interstitial matrix (methylene blue, 374 mol wt) diffuses much more slowly. Nakamura and Wayland (137) also used video time-lapse photography of the omentum to demonstrate regions of capillary permeation and to estimate diffusion coefficients.

Steric factors and their influences on diffusion are analytically difficult to deal with. Recently Curry and Michel (48, 49) put together an expression for movement of spheres through a gel space that is a composite of the Renkin (163) expression for microporous transport and the formulas of Ogston, Preston, and Wells (139) for transport through gels. Although the formula is perhaps more empirical than deductive, Curry shows that it works pretty well.

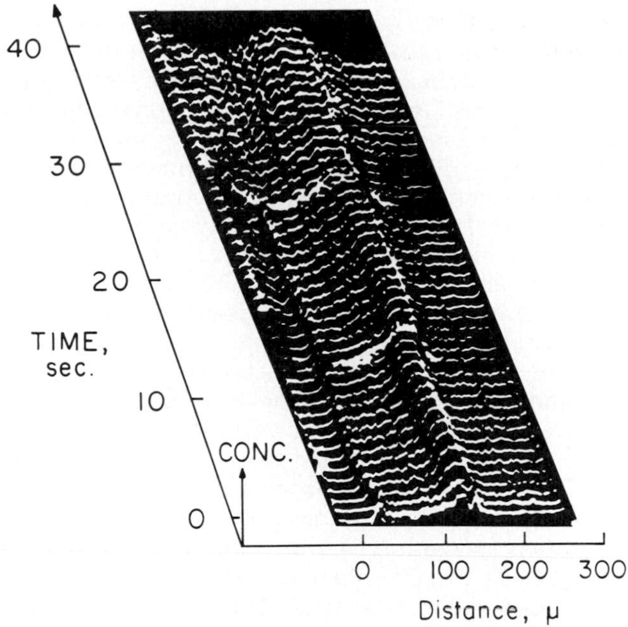

FIG. 5. Three-dimensional recordings of optical-density changes produced by diffusion of patent blue V in frog mesentery. Rate of spreading into tissue gives an estimate of bulk diffusion coefficient. In this instance the average of 4 determinations was $D_b = 0.3 \times 10^{-6}$ cm^2/s. [Adapted from Wiederhielm (225).]

New mathematical descriptions are needed for transport in the interstitial space. For a randomly structured gel one would think it useful to account for the fluctuations in density of the meshwork: randomness by definition implies that there are variations in mesh density—aggregations and rarefactions. These give strong variations in the structuring of the water, molecular exclusion, frictional effects, pathway tortuosity, effective viscosity of the water, and solute-solute interactions. In dense meshes there are regions accessible to solute but with only one entrance so that it is in effect a dead-end pore, which is kinetically equivalent to a binding site. Fluctuations of the meshwork may also imply the existence of pockets into which the solute may enter at limited periods and then be retained for some time before exit again becomes possible; this is a modified dead-end pore or transient diffusion pathway. Any nonrandomness of the meshwork implies the likelihood of anisotropy of diffusion coefficients. This seems highly likely in ordered cells and tissues such as heart muscle. (A possible way of examining this would be to use elongated molecules, measuring their diffusion coefficients in different directions.) DeGennes (50) has described the reptation of long, flexible polymer molecules into gels as the lengthwise protrusion of the molecule between the strands of the mesh. Laurent et al. (119) found this to be an appropriate explanation for dextrans diffusing in hyaluronate solutions. [See also the review by Comper and Laurent (42).] One can see that the difference in diffusion coefficient for an elongated molecule in a direction parallel to the fiber direction compared with that in the transverse direction might be quite great.

Structuring of the diffusion environment is clearly present in some situations, and sometimes this is the likely explanation for experimentally observed differences between axial and transverse diffusion rates. Diffusion along partially communicating parallel paths (extracellular and cellular) may account for this. Another factor may be parallel movement by convection and diffusion. Thus Nakamura and Wayland (137) and Wiederhielm (225) have recognized convection as a source of movement parallel to the direction of fibers in the extracellular space, whereas Anversa et al. (5) see it as movement toward the endocardium.

There is a strong axial orientation of collagen and other fibers in the interstitium parallel to the muscle cells, just as for myofilament structures intracellularly; thus there may be fewer impedances (both outside and inside cells) to diffusion in the parallel direction compared with that in the transverse direction. In addition the microstructure of the interstitial network is notably random and may result in higher tortuosities than would occur parallel to myofilaments. Winegrad et al. (230) presented electron micrographs showing a very fine and dense array of filaments in the interstitium linking one cell to another and linking sarcolemma to collagen fibers. These would be highly impeding and thus probably explain our observations that $D_I/D_0 = 25\%$. Although it is clear that the transverse diffusion path length is increased by the need to go around cells, a calculation based on a symmetrical aggregate of smooth-walled cells in parallel does not reduce D_I/D_0 to 25%. A more correct explanation must be that the observed coefficient results from the macrotortuosity caused by the cells and the microtortuosity induced by the presence of the microfilaments, glycosaminoglycans, and collagen fibers in the interstitium. Similarly the cytoplasmic microtrabeculae observed with the high-voltage electron microscope by Wolosewick and Porter (232) and displayed with great clarity in stereo images must be major contributors to the intracellular impedance to diffusion.

In summary, the types of phenomena that influence the dispersion of solutes in tissue include *1*) size, shape, and flexibility of the solute molecule; *2*) water viscosity, temperature, and adherence to other molecules or surfaces; *3*) volume exclusion; *4*) friction with macromolecules; *5*) the presence of binding sites; *6*) anisotropy of tissue structures; *7*) heterogeneity of meshworks of molecules; *8*) consumption of the diffusing species; and *9*) the presence of convection.

The purpose of these detailed considerations of diffusion in the capillary, interstitial fluid, and cell is to provide a background for determining the influences of intraregional diffusion on the rates of transport between blood, interstitium, and cell. In particular one wants to know where detailed diffusional considerations must be incorporated into the transport models and where simpler approximations can justifiably be used. Complete analytical, mathematical descriptions for the conceptually simple Krogh cylinder models that incorporate radial and axial diffusion gradients have only recently been derived (120). The numerical schema developed previously in their absence to describe changes in concentration profiles with time can be very tedious to compute, even for steady state [e.g., the treatment by Reneau et al. (161) for oxygen consumption]. Numerical solutions needed for the analysis of data for indicator-dilution transients or osmotic transients are also slow to compute because of the complexity of the waveform. Profiles of concentration as a function of distance in a capillary-tissue cylinder can be calculated for two different times to determine if the intratissue radial-diffusion relaxation times are short compared with capillary transit time (i.e., for a substance with a low diffusion coefficient). The solutions in Figure 6, calculated numerically by Bassingthwaighte et al. (19), demonstrate the presence of both axial and radial gradients for such a substance. When the mathematical solutions effectively show only axial concentration gradients, the modeling can be greatly simplified by approximating the radial gradients to zero.

Axial gradients cannot be ignored, except in extreme circumstances. The use of distributed modeling, allowing concentration gradients between inflow and outflow, is essential whenever $L^2/D_C > \bar{t}_C$, where L is capillary length, D_C is intracapillary diffusion coefficient, and $\bar{t}_C$ is the capillary mean transit time. Ordinarily $L^2/(D_C\bar{t}_C) \sim 1{,}000$ s, and thus a model lumping the capillary blood and interstitial fluid into single compartments, uniform from end to end, would not in general be a good descriptor of the system. Because capillaries are on the order of 1 mm long, an index of the contribution of axial diffusion to capillary traversal can be obtained from the sucrose concentration-position profile in Figure 4*A*. The sucrose front in this case has risen to only 12% of the source concentration at 0.5 mm in 4 h.

The next question is whether or not one can neglect radial gradients within regions. In Figure 7 the spatial profile of concentrations, calculated numerically, is shown for a capillary-tissue region characterized by a permeability barrier at the capillary wall and short dimensions in the radial direction, so that only very small radial gradients develop in the tissue. These types of radial gradients can be ignored justifiably and computations simplified greatly by considering the interstitial fluid concentrations to be radially uniform at each axial position. For tissues with large intercapillary distances, however, an approximation of instantaneous radial diffusion is not adequate; thus for each

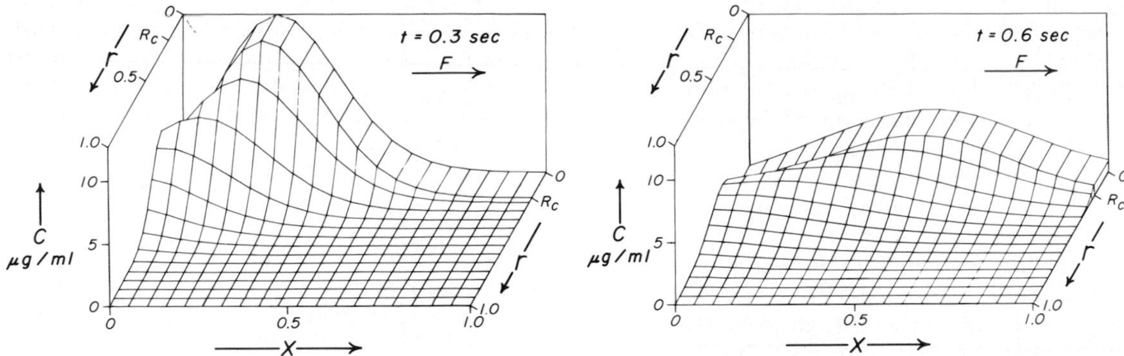

FIG. 6. Concentration profiles in capillary and tissue when exchange is diffusion limited. Only one-half of capillary-tissue region is shown. Capillary is the region on part of plot farthest away, from 0 to R_C, where R_C is capillary radius. Flow is from *left* to *right*; profile within capillary is flat radially. Tissue region is closer to observer. Parameters for solution were capillary transit time $\tau_C = 0.4$, $R_C = 4$ μm, tissue cylinder radius $R = 20$ μm, capillary length $L_C = 100$ μm, flow F = 300 ml·100 g^{-1}·min^{-1}, tissue diffusion coefficient (either axial $D_{I,x}$ or radial $D_{I,r}$) $D_T = D_{I,x} = D_{I,r} = 2 \times 10^{-7}$ cm²/s, axial intracapillary diffusion coefficient (in plasma) $D_C = 1 \times 10^{-6}$ cm²/s, and permeability $P = 10^{-2}$ cm/s (or permeability-surface area product PS = 3,000 ml·ml^{-1}·min^{-1}). The *x-r* plane is labeled 1.0, 1.0 at $x = L_C$, $r = R$. "Snapshots" of the concentration matrix at 0.3 s (*left panel*) and 0.6 s (*right panel*) after introduction of a 0.01-s pulse injection at the input show that resistance to passage through the capillary wall at this high P is negligible but that the low tissue diffusion coefficient results in a "trailing wave" of concentration in the tissue. [From Bassingthwaighte et al. (19).]

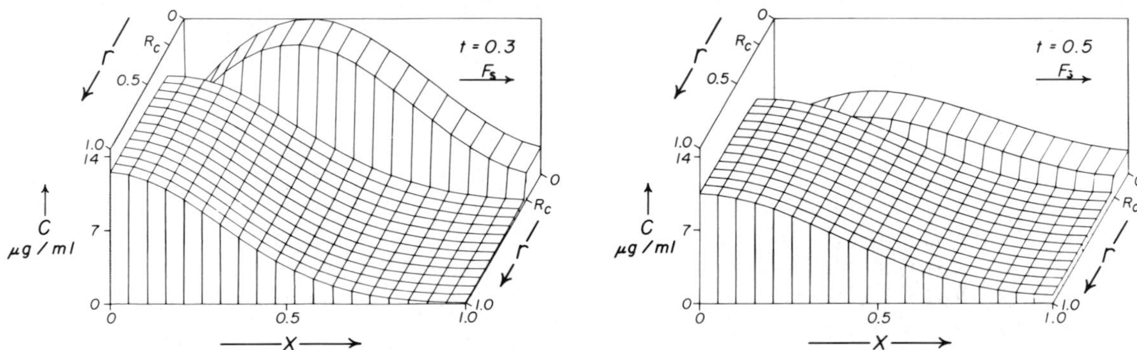

FIG. 7. Concentration profiles in capillary-tissue cylinder when exchange is limited primarily by capillary endothelial layer. Parameters are similar to those in Fig. 6 except that R is lower (10 μm), P is lower (2.5 × 10^{-3} cm/s), and $D_{I,r}$ is higher (1.0 × 10^{-5} cm²/s); thus tissue profiles are flat radially. Discontinuity at the capillary wall persists for most of the capillary transit even at this high ratio of capillary PS and flow of solute-containing mother fluid F_S ($PS_C/F_S = 8.2$). [From Bassingthwaighte (12), by permission of the American Heart Association, Inc.]

tissue and each solute a calculation of radial relaxation time should be made. Interstitial gradients in organs of high capillarity with intercapillary half-distances of 10–25 μm (heart, liver, lung, kidney cortex) have short relaxation times for small solutes, even when D_I/D_O is reduced to ~25%. For example, for sucrose in the heart at 37°C and $D_I/D_O = 0.226$ [from Safford, Bassingthwaighte, and Bassingthwaighte (179)], $D_O = 7.2 \times 10^{-6}$ cm²/s at 37°C and r_{in} and r_{out} = 2.5 and 10 μm (24) for the inner and outer radii of a hollow cylinder representing the interstitial region

$$\tau = \frac{(r_{out} - r_{in})^2}{D_I} = \frac{[(10-2.5)\times 10^{-4}]^2}{0.226\times 7.2\times 10^{-6}} = 0.35\,\text{s} \quad (10)$$

This time, for a complete cylinder, is a significant fraction of capillary transit time; thus some concern about the validity of assuming instantaneous radial equilibration should be retained. On the other hand, the myocytes occupy the bulk of the space farthest from the capillaries, so that most of the interstitial space is <1–2 μm away. If $r_{out} - r_{in}$ were 2 μm, then τ would be 0.025 s for sucrose; for ions and substrates of metabolic interest it would be even smaller. With values of τ < 2.5% of the capillary transit time, the neglect of radial gradients introduces only minuscule errors into estimates of barrier effects at the capillary wall and parenchymal cell membrane.

Within the cells the distances are larger. Considering myocardial cells as cylinders of 10-μm radius (probably somewhat of an overestimate because of indentations in the cell surface) supplied from the surface, the relaxation time would be r^2/D. For glucose this would be $\sim 10^{-6}/(0.25 \times 8.6 \times 10^{-6})$ or 0.47 s. This is small compared with the time constant of entry of solutes into the cell V'_{cell}/PS_{cell}, where V'_{cell} is the intracellular volume of distribution and PS_{cell} is the cell's permeability–surface area product. Therefore the establishment of intracellular concentration gradients can almost certainly be considered negligible. The arguments for ignoring radial gradients are applied to formulating versions of the Krogh cylinder model simplified from that shown in Figures 6 and 7.

Permeation

The unidirectional rate of solute movement across a barrier down a concentration gradient is defined by a proportionality factor between the flux and the driving force. This factor is the permeability of the barrier. It is a conductance, and thus with higher permeability there is more flux. It is also the reciprocal of a resistance, and therefore the flux (a current) can be regarded as being related to the concentration on one side of the barrier (a potential) via this coefficient in a variant of Ohm's law

$$P(\text{cm/s}) = \frac{\text{flux (mol/s)}}{\text{area (cm}^2)\cdot\text{concn (mol/ml)}} \qquad (11)$$

This expression is analogous to Equation 3. Permeability has the dimensions of a diffusion coefficient divided by a distance ($\text{cm}^2 \cdot \text{s}^{-1} \cdot \text{cm}^{-1}$) and can be considered as a diffusive velocity (cm/s), a view that is applicable to a homogeneous plane membrane but not to heterogeneous or multilayer barriers.

A net flux J_{net} from side 1 to side 2 of a membrane is simply the difference between the two opposite unidirectional fluxes J_{12} and J_{21}

$$J_{net} = J_{12} - J_{21} \qquad (12)$$

and can be estimated directly by using Equation 11

$$\begin{aligned} J_{net} &= PSC_1 - PSC_2 \\ &= PS\Delta C \end{aligned} \qquad (13)$$

where S is the surface area of the membrane (cm^2), C is solute concentration, and $\Delta C = C_1 - C_2$. Equation 13 demonstrates that the physicochemical parameter governing the flux is PS—not permeability (P) alone. The components P and S are not separable by measurement of the flux.

A key advantage in using tracers is that nonlinear processes are made linear. Take the case where rate constant k for a special transport mechanism depends on the concentration C of the mother substance, i.e., $k = k(C)$, indicating k to be a function of C

$$\frac{dC}{dt} = -k(C)\cdot C \qquad (14)$$

When tracer of concentration C* is being transported by the same process in the presence of nontracer mother substance, the rate constant is determined by the sum of the tracer and nontracer concentrations

$$\frac{dC^*}{dt} = -k(C + C^*)\cdot C^* \qquad (15)$$

However, by the definition of a tracer that says that C^*/C is negligible (ordinarily the ratio is $<1/10^{16}$), the rate constant is independent of C*

$$\frac{dC^*}{dt} = -k(C)\cdot C^* \qquad (16)$$

This extends to cases of facilitated transport, with rate constants that depend on concentrations on both sides of a membrane—not only of the substance of interest but also of any other substance having an affinity for the transport site

$$\frac{dC_1^*}{dt} = -k(C_1, C_2, \cdots C_n)\cdot C_1^*(t) \qquad (17)$$

where C_i values, for $i = 2\text{–}n$, are the concentrations of other substances attaching to the transport site. Steady state means steady concentrations of all substances affecting the transport site, and again transport of the tracer is linear. When concentration varies along the length as a result of consumption, the rate constant varies concurrently.

GENERAL APPROACHES TO BLOOD-TISSUE EXCHANGE

Model-Free Stochastic Descriptions of Transport Functions in Linear, Stationary Systems

The basis of analysis in this section is the assumption that the system is linear and stationary. In a linear system if two inputs are given together, the output is the simple sum of the individual responses. The condition of linearity is fulfilled by using tracer in a system with constant chemical composition. "Stationarity" simply means that the distribution of transit times (governed by flow, distribution of flows, etc.) is not changing during the period of observation.

A stochastic description is very general and thus is a good introduction to the design and analysis of experiments, whereas the deterministic approach provides a mechanism for interpreting the data in terms of specific physical models. The approaches are not mutually exclusive: deterministic physical models are simply special cases of the more general stochastic approach, and combinations are common. The stochastic approach given here follows that of Meier and Zierler (134) and Zierler (243, 245–249), who have expressed the concepts in terms that describe experimental data well.

What follows assumes that the tracer-solute combination entering the tissue is not transformed or lost and does not have its properties changed in any way.

The principles outlined are based on the conservation of material. In Figure 8 a linear, stationary system is defined accurately and in a general way for a simple system with a single inflow and a single outflow. Stationarity implies constant flow. Defining the unit impulse input as a Dirac delta function $\delta(t)$ (a thin spike with unit area but of infinitely narrow width occurring at time zero) the unit impulse response or transport function $h(t)$ is the frequency function of transit times or the probability density function of transit times from the input point to the outflow. It embodies the delay and dispersion of each element of tracer. It has the shape of the concentration-time curve $C_V(t)$ that would be obtained by flow-proportional sampling at the output following an ideal impulse input $\delta(t)$ at the inflow, with flow-proportional labeling across the cross section of the stream of the entrance [as defined by Gonzalez-Fernandez (70)] and no recirculation. Under such conditions

$$h(t) = F \cdot C_V(t)/q_0 \tag{18}$$

where F is the constant flow in ml/s, $C_V(t)$ is concentration in the outflow in g/ml or disintegrations$\cdot$min$^{-1}\cdot$ml^{-1}, and q_0 is the dose in grams or disintegrations/min of indicator injected at $t = 0$ into the inflow. The term $h_R(t)$ is used for transport functions of a nonpermeant reference molecule. A nonpermeant reference molecule is used in combination with a test molecule in studies of tracer extraction during transcapillary passage.

The time integral of the probability density function $h(t)$ is unity. Thus flow can be calculated from the integral of $C_V(t)$, the area under the concentration-time curve. Equation 19 from Stewart (202–204) shows this relationship

$$F = q_0 \Big/ \int_0^\infty C_V(t)dt \tag{19}$$

The relation between inflow and outflow is completely defined when $h(t)$ is known, so that $C_{out}(t)$ can be calculated from $C_{in}(t)$ by the convolution integral

$$C_{out}(t) = C_{in}(t) * h(t) = \int_0^t C_{in}(t-\tau) \cdot h(\tau)d\tau \tag{20}$$

The asterisk is used here as an abbreviation for convolution. The convolution of a given transport function with a variety of inputs is illustrated in Figure 9.

Where there is more than one process producing the dispersion, the overall output is independent of the order of these processes. This is particularly important in analyses designed to separate the dispersive effects of transport in large vessels from those of processes at the level of capillaries. It is also important when dispersion is caused by tracer injection or sample collection. Generally the sample collection system is experimentally accessible, and its characteristics (in terms of delay and dispersion) are then easily taken into account (190). The input to the system may also be accessible, and if this input is observed by sampling, the effects of the sampling system here must also be taken into account. Dispersal at the input and output tends to slur high-frequency features of $h(t)$ and degrades the accuracy attainable in recapitulating the original $h(t)$. From this point of view the experimental $h(t)$ is most cleanly defined when the injection technique and the sample collecting system cause the least possible dispersion.

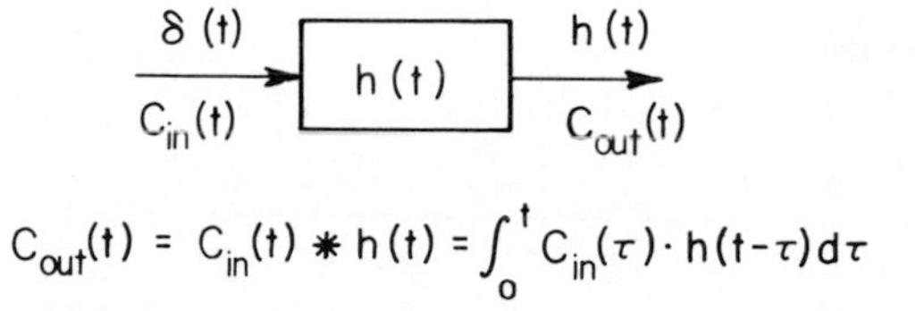

$$C_{out}(t) = C_{in}(t) * h(t) = \int_0^t C_{in}(\tau) \cdot h(t-\tau)d\tau$$

FIG. 8. Linear stationary system with response to an ideal impulse input $\delta(t)$, which at the entrance is the transport function $h(t)$. When the input is of another form $C_{in}(t)$, then the outflow response $C_{out}(t)$ is the convolution (*) of $C_{in}(t)$ and $h(t)$. τ, Variable for the integration.

Deconvolution can be used to identify $h(t)$ when $C_{in}(t)$ and $C_{out}(t)$ are known precisely enough and when $C_{in}(t)$ is not too dispersed. An example of this is shown in Figure 10 for the transcoronary transport function in dogs. The input and output curves, recorded at the aortic root and in the coronary sinus with identical, fairly rapid sampling systems, are used to compute the transcoronary $h(t)$. The convolution of $h(t)$ with $C_{in}(t)$ provides a curve (crosses) that almost coincides with the recorded C_{out} (continuous curve), demonstrating that the estimated $h(t)$ is an accurate description of the intravascular transport function.

In general, deconvolution is difficult because it is inherently a differentiating process that is mathematically unstable (10) and is therefore very susceptible to noise in the data and to computer round-off error. An approach to limiting the effects of noise in the data has been to use smooth functions as descriptors of experimental curves (see refs. 16, 77). Another approach is to assume that $h(t)$ is composed of a sum of narrowly dispersed functions with differing mean delay times and to determine the weighting function itself by iterative trials, checking the accuracy of estimation of $h(t)$ by reconvolution (107). This has the advantages of being stable and providing estimates of $h(t)$ that do not show oscillations in the tails of the curves. Nevertheless the approach is not completely general; more research on this topic would be useful.

The response of the organ $h(t)$ to the ideal tracer impulse input $\delta(t)$ at the entrance is related in a theoretically precise fashion to information obtainable from the tracer content of the organ and from the cumulative outflow. Both of these can be measured experimentally, as suggested by the diagram in Figure 11. The content of the γ-emitting tracer within the organ can be recorded via a detector placed over the

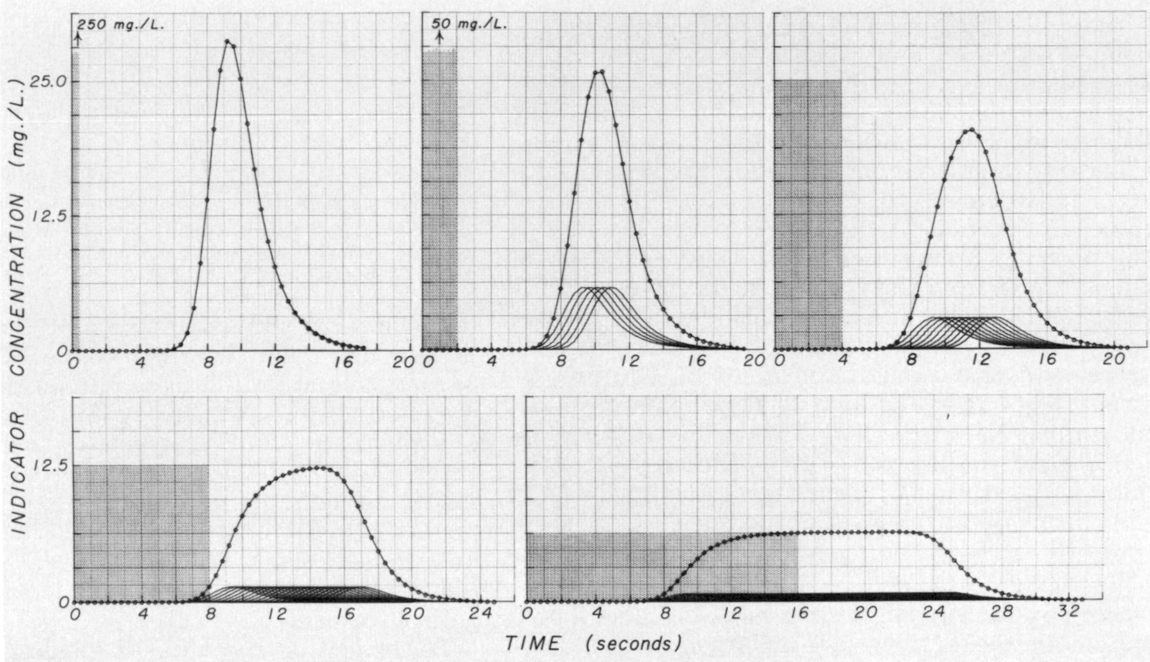

FIG. 9. Example of convolution: deformation of square input functions $C_{in}(t)$ of varied duration by a linear system with transport function h(t). Responses of model of vascular segment to injection of same total amount (10 mg) of indicator at different constant rates. Total flow through vascular segment was constant 100 ml/s during injection and during inscription of each curve. Each injection was considered as a sequence of 0.4-s pulses, the amplitudes of which were inversely related to the number of pulses required to inject the 10 mg. In the 5 panels there were 1, 5, 10, 20, and 40 pulses so that the injection rates were 25.0, 5.0, 2.5, 1.25, and 0.625 mg/s, respectively. If input had ideal mixing at injection site, curves at arterial end of segment are represented by *stippled rectangular areas*. Responses to each of these pulses individually have the shape of h(t) and are shown by the *continuous lines* in each panel. The sum of these responses (*circles*) is the output curve $C_{out}(t)$ resulting from the convolution. The slowest injection rate resulted in a primary $C_{out}(t)$ curve from which flow can be estimated by using equations describing the constant-rate injection. [From Bassingthwaighte (10).]

organ, represented in the diagram by the volume V. Given a unit impulse input, the residue curve R(t) begins at $t = 0$ with a unit content of tracer, which later appears in the outflow. In the ideal state where the outflow concentration is measured at exactly the exit from the organ, the outflow response h(t) is the negative of the derivative of the residue fraction R(t)

$$h(t) = -dR(t)/dt \tag{21}$$

In practice, any delay or dispersion between the organ and the outflow sampling point distorts this relationship in a way predictable from the transport function of the system lying between the exit and the outflow detection point. For the purposes of this chapter this nonideality is considered negligible, although it is difficult to avoid experimentally. There are the normal experimental problems in eliminating inaccuracies in observed curves of tracer content or outflow concentration-time curves and of knowing exactly from the outflow curves the fraction of the dose remaining in the organ. Therefore in some situations the simultaneous use of outflow and residue detection is helpful.

In Figure 11 the organ is idealized as having a constant volume V with a constant inflow and outflow F in ml/s. When a sudden slug or impulse input of tracer of quantity q_0 is injected into the inflow, the quantity of tracer $q(t)$ contained in the volume V can be estimated by external detection of the radiation. When the tracer detection is of equal efficiency throughout V, the residue function can be taken directly from the recorded signal, which is proportional to $q(t)$

$$R(t) = \frac{q(t)}{q_0} \quad \text{or} \quad \frac{kq(t)}{kq_0} \tag{22}$$

where k, the efficiency of detection, is constant and q_0 is the amount in the system at $t = 0$. From either h(t) or R(t), the other overall stochastic functions can be determined, as in Figure 12.

The cumulative-residence-time distribution function of the system is H(t), a dimensionless value representing the fraction of injectate collected at time t in a container into which all the outflow is emptying.

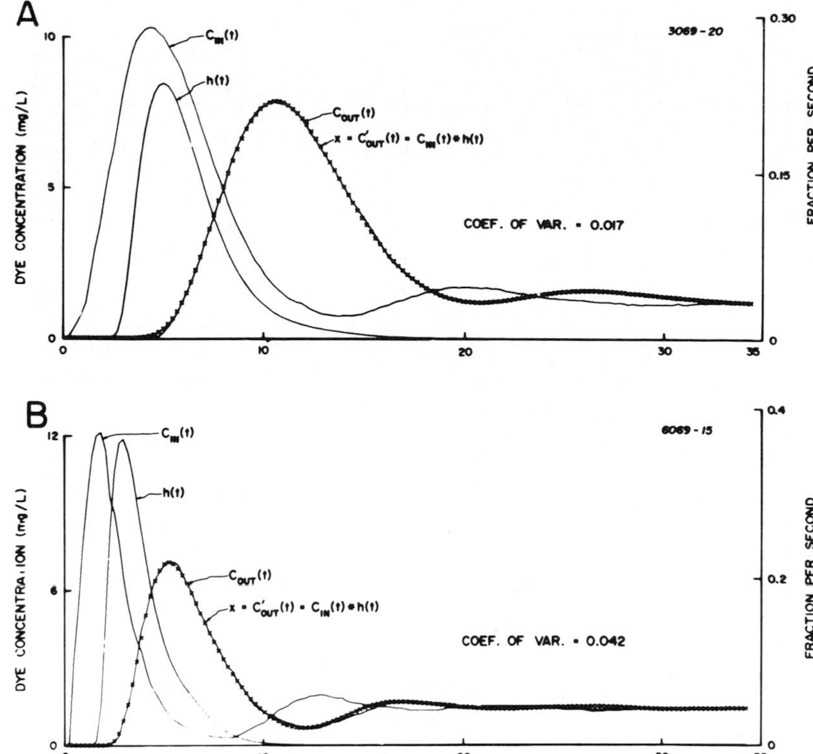

FIG. 10. Two sets of dilution curves sampled from the aortic root $C_{in}(t)$ and coronary sinus $C_{out}(t)$ and the calculated transcoronary transport functions h(t). The *crosses* are the calculated output given by convolution of the recorded $C_{in}(t)$ curve and the calculated transport function $C'_{out}(t)$, and they closely approximate the observed $C_{out}(t)$ curve. Mean transit times are 6.1 and 3.6 s for *A* and *B*, respectively. Input and output sampling systems had identical transport functions (with mean transit times of 0.8–1.6 s) so that the deconvolution of the sampled dilution curves gives an estimate of h(t) that is theoretically identical to that between the two intravascular sampling points. [From Knopp, Bassingthwaighte, et al. (107), © 1976, with permission from Pergamon Press, Ltd.]

It is also the response to a unit step input and is the area of h(t) up to any particular time

$$H(t) = \int_0^t h(\lambda)d\lambda \tag{23}$$

where λ is the variable used for the time integration.

The residue function (also dimensionless) is the complement of H(t), i.e., R(t) = 1 − H(t). It represents the fraction of injectate remaining in the organ at time t following indicator entry at t = 0. It is the probability of a particle residing in the organ for time t or longer. Because h(t) is the frequency of particles leaving the system, the residue function is one minus the sum of all of the tracer that has escaped

$$R(t) = 1 - \int_0^t h(\lambda)d\lambda \tag{24}$$

The rate of escape of particles, as a fraction of those present, is also a useful measure (23). The reader may be familiar with rate of escape in the special case of an exponential rate constant for a single mixing chamber. The fractional escape rate is the instantaneous rate of loss of tracer divided by the amount of tracer remaining in the organ at that moment. After an impulse input the specific fractional escape rate is $\eta(t)$, also known as the emergence function, where

$$\eta(t) = -\frac{dq(t)/dt}{q(t)} \tag{25}$$

or

$$\eta(t) = h(t)/R(t) \tag{26}$$

The emergence function is the fraction of the particles residing in the system for t seconds, which exits in the tth second. In chemical engineering this is known as the intensity function (189) and in population statistics or renewal theory as the risk function, the death rate of those living at age t. Other useful forms of $\eta(t)$ are

$$\eta(t) = \frac{-dR(t)/dt}{R(t)} \tag{27}$$

$$= -d[\ln R(t)]/dt \tag{28}$$

$$= h(t) \bigg/ \left[1 - \int_0^t h(\lambda)d\lambda\right] \tag{29}$$

$$= C_V(t) \bigg/ \left[\int_0^\infty C_V(t)dt - \int_0^t C_V(\lambda)d\lambda\right] \tag{30}$$

Equation 28 shows that $\eta(t)$ is the local logarithmic slope at time t on a semilog plot. Use of the slope of R(t) has the disadvantage that one must calculate a derivative from inevitably noisy data. Equation 30 is used when one records outflow concentration-time curves $C_V(t)$. Here it is necessary to exclude recirculation from the estimation of the area under the curve to $t = \infty$. A way of avoiding errors at the tail of h(t) is to use a combination of techniques, as represented by

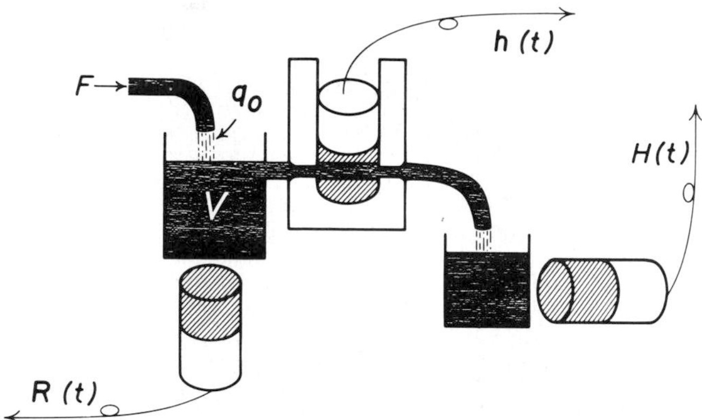

FIG. 11. Experimental approaches to measuring the response of a system to slug injection of the tracer dose. *Striped cylinder* (*lower left*) represents an idealized γ-detector providing a signal proportional to the amount of indicator $q(t)$ contained in the organ of volume V at time t. Initial amount of tracer is q_0. This signal directly provides an estimate of the proportion of injected indicator present in the system, i.e., the residue function $R(t)$. The uppermost detector provides a signal from the outflow proportional to the effluent concentration-time curve and to $h(t)$. The right-hand detector provides a signal proportional to the cumulative fraction of tracer leaving the system $H(t)$. This can be measured only by complete collection in a nonrecirculating system. F, flow. [From Bassingthwaighte and Holloway (18), by permission of Grune & Stratton, Inc.]

Equation 26. At any time prior to recirculation the integral of $h(t)$ is $H(t)$, or $1 - R(t)$

$$1 - R(t) = \int_0^t C_V(\lambda)d\lambda \Big/ \int_0^\infty C_V(t)dt \qquad (31)$$

This may then be used to calculate $\eta(t)$

$$\eta(t) = \frac{h(t)}{R(t)} \qquad (32)$$

$$= C_V(t) \Big/ \left[\int_0^t C_V(\lambda)d\lambda/[1-R(t)]\right] \Big/ R(t) \qquad (33)$$

$$= C_V(t)\cdot[q_0-q(t)] \Big/ \left[\int_0^t C_V(\lambda)d\lambda\right]\cdot q(t) \qquad (34)$$

where $C_V(t)$ is obtained by intravascular sampling or continuous detection, and $q(t)$ is determined by external detection.

In modeling a single unit in a whole organ it is important to distinguish the influences of those regions, arteries, and veins in which there is little or no separation of tracers of differing molecular characteristics from those where separation occurs, i.e., the capillary-tissue exchange regions. This is diagramed in Figure 13 for a unit consisting of an arterial segment, its cognate bed in the capillary-tissue exchange region, and its venous drainage. The assumption implicit in such a diagram is that the dispersion and delay in the arterial system (its transport function) are mathematically independent of the form of the transport function in the capillary-tissue region as well as independent of the form of the transport function describing venous drainage. The assumption permits calculation of the overall $h(t)$ by the convolution of arterial, capillary, and venous transport functions $h_A * h_C * h_V$ whenever the system is stationary. A change in flow to a new steady flow would change the transport functions and mean transit times in all three regions proportionately if their relative volumes did not change. An organ is an aggregate of such units; the problem of formulating how the sum of these units makes up the whole and of defining the flow linkage within this aggregate involves additional considerations. These are outlined in the sections on modeling whole-organ outflow dilution curves.

From the observed transport function $h(t)$ one can calculate its moments with respect to the time axis. These include the mean transit time and the variance, which is analogous to the moment of inertia. These give further information of a general kind when indicator is not removed within the system. The zeroth moment is the area

$$A = \int_0^\infty h(t)dt = 1.0 \qquad (35a)$$

When it is not practical experimentally to sample the outflow until all tracer has left the system, the area under the density function $h(t)$ is incomplete experimentally. However, mass conservation still prevails at any time T

$$\int_0^T h(t)dt + R(T) = 1.0 \qquad (35b)$$

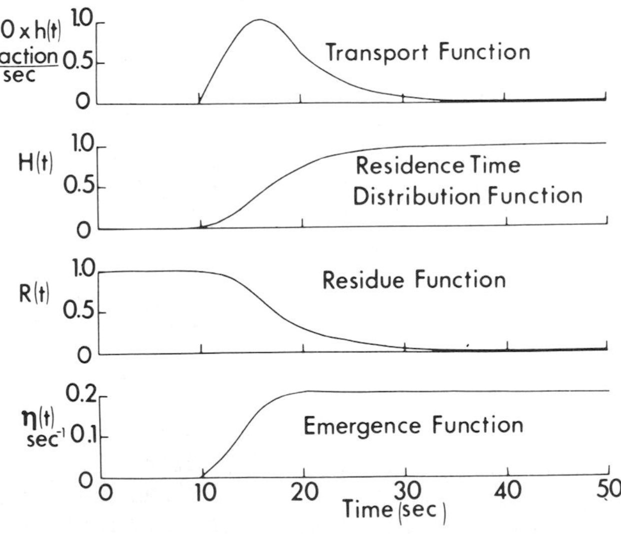

FIG. 12. Mass transport through a stationary system: relationships between $h(t)$, $H(t)$, $R(t)$, and the emergence function $\eta(t)$. The curve of $h(t)$ is in this instance given by a lagged normal density curve (16) having a relative dispersion of 0.33 and a skewness of 1.5. However, the theory is general and applies to $h(t)$ curves of all shapes. The tail of this $h(t)$ curve becomes exponential in form, and hence $\eta(t)$ becomes constant. Mean transit time $\bar{t}$ given by Eq. 36.

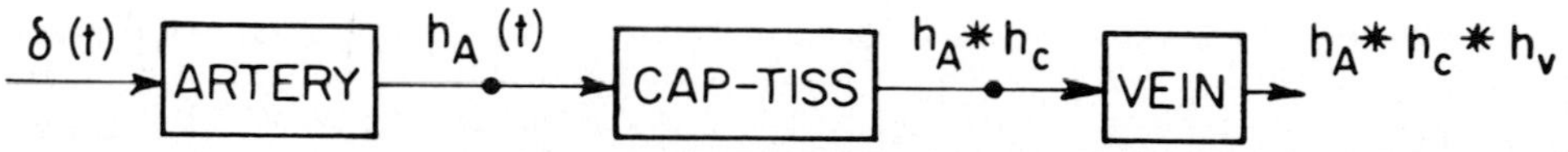

FIG. 13. Microcirculatory unit within an organ with the transport functions of arterial inflow $h_A(t)$, capillary-tissue unit h_C, and venous outflow $h_V(t)$ assumed to be mathematically independent but having a common flow. If one assumes independence the convolution integration can be applied but is not justifiable as a complete generality. $\delta(t)$, Impulse input.

It is sometimes necessary to distinguish between a tracer such as D-[^{14}C]glucose and the label ^{14}C. A parallel conservation relation holds for label and also applies to the case in which label is removed within the system. The outflow total at any time T equals the difference between the input and the amount retained in the system. If label is converted and sequestered so that it remains in the system, the final outflow recovery is incomplete.

The mean transit time $\bar{t}$ for a tracer conserved in the system is the first moment of the probability density function h(t)

$$\bar{t} = \int_0^\infty t \cdot \mathrm{h}(t)\mathrm{d}t \tag{36a}$$

Note that the integration is for infinite time, i.e., there can be no recirculation of indicator. To obtain the data base to determine the moments of in vivo dilution curves, one must either prevent recirculation by surgical maneuvers or guess that the tail of the dilution curve has a specific form. The most common form of extrapolation is that proposed by Hamilton et al. (85) in which the tail of the curve is predicted to follow a single exponential time course. The first moment can also be calculated directly by integration of the residue function

$$\bar{t} = \int_0^\infty \mathrm{R}(t)\mathrm{d}t \tag{36b}$$

The tail of the residue function curves can also be extrapolated, exponentially or otherwise. Some of the various alternatives were described and tested by Bassingthwaighte et al. (22).

The mean transit time may also be calculated directly from the outflow concentration-time curve

$$\bar{t} = \int_0^\infty t \cdot \mathrm{C_V}(t)\mathrm{d}t \Big/ \int_0^\infty \mathrm{C_V}(t)\mathrm{d}t \tag{36c}$$

When the indicator is partially consumed, this calculation gives a systematically smaller value than it does in the absence of consumption simply because the consumption of molecules residing for a longer time in the system is greater than that for particles having a shorter exposure to the sites of consumption.

The mean-transit-time volume V, also known as the Stewart-Hamilton volume or "needle-to-needle" volume is

$$\mathrm{V} = \mathrm{F} \cdot \bar{t} \tag{37}$$

When the system has a single entrance and a single exit, V is the volume of the system into which indicator can become distributed, i.e., the volume of distribution. This volume is underestimated if indicator is consumed because the calculation of $\bar{t}$ is invalid, being underestimated to a variable degree. The definition is also less precise when the system has a number of outflows. For example, when sampling a peripheral artery after an injection of tracer into the right atrium, V is the volume lying between the right atrium and all the points in the circulatory system to which the $\bar{t}$ is the same as it is to the sampled artery (13).

The higher moments also describe h(t). The useful forms are the moments around the mean, the nth central moment μ_n being

$$\mu n = \int_0^\infty (t - \bar{t})^n \cdot \mathrm{h}(t)\mathrm{d}t \tag{38}$$

Numerical forms of this computation are given by Bassingthwaighte (13). The standard deviation SD is $\mu_2^{1/2}$, the square root of the variance of h(t). It provides a measure of the temporal spread or dispersion of h(t). The relative dispersion SD/$\bar{t}$ is particularly useful; it is the standard deviation divided by the mean transit time, which gives a measure of the relative spread. Within the vascular system a bolus of indicator undergoes a spatial spreading. It expands as the centroid of the bolus moves along the flow path so that the temporal spread (SD) gives only a measure of the time the dispersed bolus takes to pass by the observation point. The value for SD/$\bar{t}$ reflects the spatial dispersion in a manner that is more or less independent of the flow. If flow characteristics, such as velocity profiles and the regional distribution of flows, remain constant over a range of flows, then SD/$\bar{t}$ is also constant (independent of flow) over that range, since SD and $\bar{t}$ change proportionately.

Two other standard parameters that utilize the third and fourth moments for their computation are skewness and kurtosis; they are useful in describing density functions. Each is calculated as the nth central moment divided by the standard deviation raised to the power n

$$\beta_{n-2} = \mu_n/(\mathrm{SD})^n \tag{39}$$

The skewness β_1 (i.e., the value of the expression when $n = 3$) is a measure of asymmetry. Right skewness is indicated by a positive β_1 and left skewness by a negative β_1. The skewness of most circulatory transport functions has a value on the order of +1.0 (16). The value for kurtosis β_2 (Eq. 39, with $n = 4$) can be used to evaluate the degree of deviation from a Gaussian probability density function. The kurtosis has values of 3.0 for a Gaussian function, >3.0 for leptokurtic (sharp-pointed) density functions, and <3.0 for platykurtic (flat-topped) functions.

Distributed and Lumped Systems

When the tracer methodology is used to examine a system, due regard must be given to the manner in which an organ handles the substance being traced, i.e., the mother substance. If the substance being traced is not removed in net fashion by the organ and if the input concentration of this substance does not change, its concentrations at input and output are the same and its concentration throughout the organ is everywhere in equilibrium with that value. If, on the other hand, the material being traced is removed steadily by the organ, there are steady-state gradients in the concentration of mother substance from input to exit.

Consider first the simpler case, in which the concentrations of mother substance are the same everywhere. If one has sufficient information on spatial profiles, the concentration of tracer in any such three-dimensional system may be represented as $C(x, y, z, t)$. Such a system is "distributed in space," and spatial profiles are expected to change with time after an impulse input of tracer. If differences in tracer concentration from one point to another were dissipated instantaneously by extremely rapid diffusion to give a uniform concentration, then the system could be considered lumped and the concentration could be represented as $C(t)$, omitting the spatial features. For the second more complex case, in which there is consumption of mother substance and thus steady-state concentration gradients in mother substance, the system is much more complex for tracer because tracer is consumed as well. Concentration gradients of tracer cannot be dissipated, even by rapid diffusion. In this situation the local consumption rates are likely to be concentration dependent. Nevertheless all of the local rates are still linear with respect to tracer, but there is a gradient or heterogeneity in these local rates so that the overall rate is a composite.

In *Diffusion in Blood and Tissue* (see p. 552), data were presented indicating that axial dimensions of a capillary and diffusion coefficients are such that diffusional processes could not possibly cause instantaneous dissipation of axial or lengthwise gradients. Thus for neither the inert nor the consumed tracer does lumped-system analysis that uses $C(t)$ (i.e., compartmental analysis) represent $C(x, y, z, t)$ and provide an accurate description of blood-tissue exchange. The inadequacy of lumped models becomes particularly evident when tracer data are obtained with a high degree of resolution early in time. It is clear that compartmental models cannot be appropriately fitted to sets of outflow dilution curves when there has been any substantial passage of tracer across the capillary wall during a single passage. On the other hand, there is one situation in which lumped-model analysis may become realistic. If, after a step infusion of nonconsumed tracer, the permeability of the capillary is so low that the proportion of tracer lost during a single passage is small enough that the plasma concentration of tracer remains virtually the same from input to outflow, this now virtually uniform plasma pool exchanges with its accessible extravascular space. Then, if the radial dimensions of that space are such that radial gradients are not established, this slow process corresponds to a compartmental description. For example, the compartmental model can be usefully employed to describe exchange of labeled protein across the wall of a capillary that is poorly permeable to it.

Reduction in complexity is ordinarily necessary to analyze observed data and to develop models that are not hopelessly complex. This was the aim of those who initially tried to use lumped-model analysis to describe blood-tissue exchange. However, for quantitative accuracy and deeper understanding of the physiological processes, it is necessary to emphasize the distributed nature of the system. The main problem with the lumped analyses is that they cannot account for transport lags or axial gradients in tracer concentration. These occur during all tracer transients, and in most capillary-tissue units the gradients persist for a long time. In systems with long capillaries, three-dimensionality can be represented by $C(x, y, z, t)$ or, where cylindrical geometry is applicable, by $C(x, r, \theta, t)$ where r is radial distance from a capillary axis and θ is angular position. If the gradients are concentric around the axis, $C(x, r, \theta, t)$ reduces to $C(x, r, t)$, and in the special case where there are no gradients perpendicular to the capillary axis this would reduce to $C(x, t)$. This latter representation is adequate for tracers whose local exchange is very fast compared with axial movement, i.e., whose transport is flow limited (see *Influences of Flow and Diffusion on Blood-Tissue Exchange*, p. 567). Where there are diffusional limitations, the radial dependency must be recognized by using $C(x, r, t)$. A special case of radial diffusion gradients occurs when there are barriers (e.g., capillary wall and cell membrane) across which there are concentration differences. If within each region (capillary, interstitial space, and cell) there are no radial gradients, then $C(x, r, t)$ in these three regions can be legitimately represented by $C_C(x, t)$, $C_I(x, t)$, and $C_{cell}(x, t)$. Theoretically this situation is close to the compartmental analysis in emphasizing the barriers between regions, but it differs importantly in retaining axial dependency on the lengthwise position x along the capillary-tissue unit. Forker and Luxon (64) have made a comparison of distributed versus lumped models for hepatic transport.

The axial gradients in mother substance, which

evolve when there is a consumption along the capillary length, impose an analogous pattern on the distribution of tracer. The pattern that evolves in space is mirrored by the distribution of tracer and after a steady input of tracer is found to define the outlines of microcirculatory units in an organ. Figure 14 displays such a pattern for the uptake of labeled galactose by the hepatocytes in liver microcirculatory lobules.

Influences of Flow and Diffusion on Blood-Tissue Exchange

When flow is relatively low the velocity of blood within capillaries is also low; also the time available for exchange between blood and tissue becomes relatively long so that concentration gradients between blood and tissue tend to be well dissipated. The local concentrations at each point approach or achieve equilibrium. On the other hand, at very high flows with short intracapillary dwell times for intravascular tracer, there is insufficient time for equilibration; concentration differences between the blood and tissue persist whenever either of these is changing. These phenomena are represented in a general way in Figure 15 by the clearance-flow diagram of Renkin (164).

In the figure the ordinate represents the fraction of those solute molecules delivered to an organ or region of an organ that exchanges with the tissue during a single passage. The abscissa is the flow relative to the exchange; this may be described as convective flux divided by exchange flux, or as intracapillary velocity divided by permeability. The three zones include *1*) zone I, a region of flow-limited exchange where flow is the factor retarding delivery to tissue and where diffusion, permeation, or membrane transport radially are relatively so fast that there is local equilibrium between blood and tissue; *2*) zone II, a region of combined flow limitation and diffusion limitation in which exchange rates are lower than the limit imposed by either flow (the sloping line) or by diffusion (the

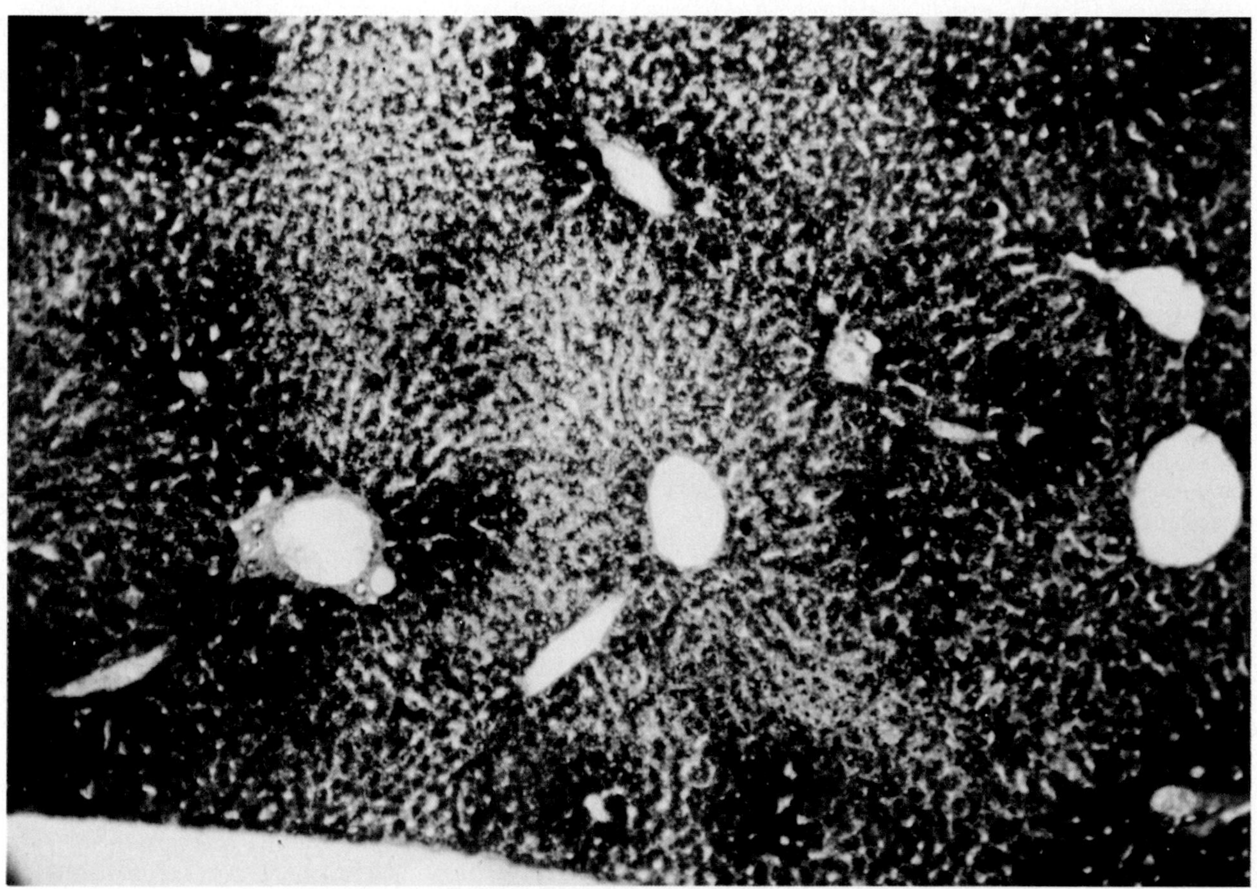

FIG. 14. Autoradiograph of liver 2 min after intravenous injection of tracer D-[^{3}H]galactose. In the absence of loading, galactose is extracted almost completely from blood during its passage through the liver. After the introduction of tracer into the circulation, a substantial proportion of the extracted activity has been converted into glycogen, revealing the axial gradient for nontracer galactose. This activity is visible on the slide (the black granules result from exposure of the radiographic emulsion) in relation to the pink-stained glycogen granules. The heaviest deposition occurs near the inflow (portal venules and hepatic arterioles) and provides a clear outline of the microcirculatory unit in the liver—the hepatic lobule or acinus. [From Goresky et al. (73).]

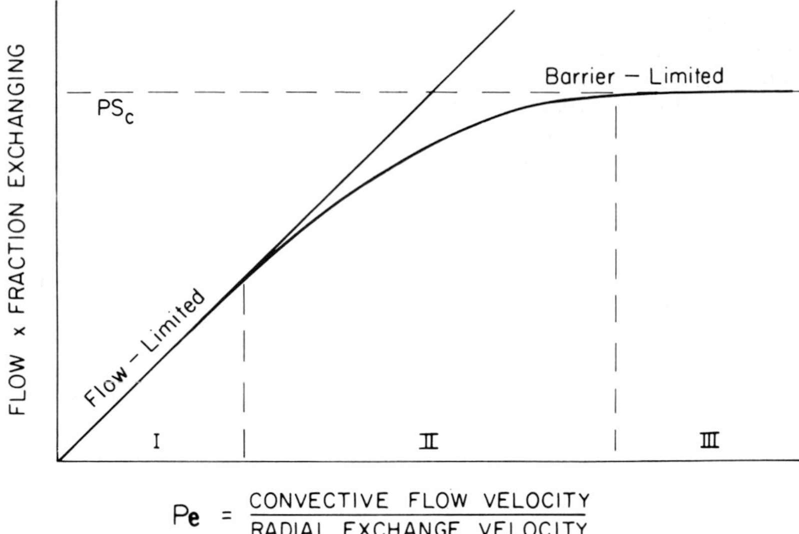

FIG. 15. General relationship between the fraction of solute exchanging and flow through a capillary-tissue region. Ordinate, the product of flow and the fraction of solute molecules exchanging with the tissue during a single transcapillary passage. Amount exchanging depends on rate of delivery to the region via flow, time for exchange, and permeability of the barrier bounding the flow stream. Fraction exchanging diminishes at higher flows. Abscissa, the Péclet number Pe, i.e., the ratio of convective velocity to diffusive velocity. (For a single-barrier situation the abscissa would be equivalent to F_S/PS_C.) The diagram applies to systems in which there is no exchange between inflow and outflow regions. Generally, zone I is flow-limited exchange, zone III is barrier-limited exchange, and zone II is a combination of both. Expressing these generalities as specific rates of transport or fractional escape rates depends on the blood-tissue exchange model and the location of the mass of indicator. The form of the diagram is similar to Renkin's (164) diagram of clearance versus flow, a special case in which material leaving the capillary does not return. (See *Extraction during transcapillary passage*, p. 582.) PS_C, capillary permeability–surface area product; F_S, flow of solute-containing mother fluid.

horizontal line); and *3*) zone III, a region of barrier-limited exchange where low rates of permeation, diffusion, or membrane transport govern the fluxes between blood and tissue and in which increases in flow do not increase solute delivery to the tissue.

These governing principles apply to both distributed and lumped systems. For example, consider a flow stream through a gel with no barrier between the convective and stagnant regions. The abscissa would be the velocity of the streaming fluid (cm/s) divided by the ratio of the diffusion coefficient in the gel to the distance over which diffusion occurs, D/L (cm/s). Alternatively, if a barrier between the flow stream and the extravascular region is the factor that limits radial exchange, then the abscissa is F_S/PS_C, the flow of solute-containing mother fluid divided by the capillary permeability–surface area product. The abscissa corresponding to the flow-limited range extends from 0 to ~0.1, and the barrier-limited range is >50 (each to within <1% of its asymptotic limit). Thus there is a 500-fold range in between in which both flow and diffusion radially influence the exchange. The flow-limited region applies to solute with high lipid solubility and high diffusion coefficients. This region is emphatically not a region of exponential washout in any organ studied so far, but rather it is the delayed-wave, flow-limited region defined by Goresky (72) and explored in the earlier experiments by Chinard et al. (41).

These generalities need modification whenever axial diffusion or diffusional exchange between inflow and outflow becomes significant. The effects are discussed in *Homogeneous and Heterogeneous Systems with Diffusional Shunting of Tracers*, p. 606.

Regional Variation Within an Organ

Local variations within an organ indicate that it is unwise to assume the rates of exchange in any organ to be uniform. Perhaps the easiest feature to identify and to account for is regional variation in flow.

Wide variations in rates of xenon washout after small local intratissue injections in the heart were observed by Bassingthwaighte et al. (22). This caused them to abandon the local-injection technique in favor of intra-arterial injection for the estimation of myocardial blood flow. Microsphere deposition has demonstrated that the heterogeneity of flow within the heart is considerable (56, 184, 235) and that there is some degree of stability in this heterogeneity. The spatial variation in regional flows in the heart shows about a four- to fivefold range of local flows with moderate temporal fluctuations locally around a more or less stable pattern (ref. 14 and R. B. King, J. B.

Bassingthwaighte, J. R. S. Hales, and L. B. Rowell, unpublished data). A representative distribution is shown in Figure 16.

These microsphere-deposition densities do not provide very high resolution, representing flows in pieces of tissue weighing, at the smallest, 0.1–0.2 g. In the heart, for instance, these sample sizes should be compared with the size of the metabolic units consisting of the capillary bed associated with a single arteriole. The photographs of Steenbergen et al. (200) of fluorescence heterogeneity in the epicardium of hypoxic rat hearts demonstrate grain sizes of about 1 mm [see also Barlow and Chance (8)]. These demonstrate not only the localization and size of the units but some degree of stability, in that the same regions fluoresced first each time after reduction in oxygen supply.

The heterogeneity of regional flows in the heart has been emphasized here only because the heart has been relatively thoroughly studied and because it illustrates a large degree of nonuniformity in an anatomically uniform organ that is relatively highly perfused and has a constant, high metabolic need. The relative dispersion (SD/mean) of the flows is 25%–35%, and this degree of dispersion immediately raises the question of whether this heterogeneity must be accounted for in the analysis. Rose and Goresky (171) and M. Levin and J. B. Bassingthwaighte (unpublished data) have demonstrated with model analysis that failure to account for heterogeneity introduces systematic errors in parameter estimates, a point to be discussed in detail in *Homogeneous and Heterogeneous Systems With Diffusional Shunting of Tracers*, p. 606.

Heterogeneity of flows has not been systematically studied in most organs, but it is important to assess. Other heterogeneities, in volumes of distribution for example (F. Gonzalez and J. B. Bassingthwaighte, unpublished data), are beginning to be researched. Although it has long been recognized that there are permeability gradients along a capillary (178, 225), the unidirectional flux from blood to interstitial fluid space is governed completely by the average permeability in each capillary (11). What may be important is regional variation in the capillary permeability–surface area products or in volumes of distribution, since the effect of these on exchange rate may be just as important per fractional change as is the influence of flow. At another level, when metabolic uptake processes are being examined, the distribution and activity of the intracellular enzymes underlying the uptake process are important. Experimental methods producing the appropriate information are needed.

Relationship Between Center of Mass of Tracer in an Organ and Its Movement in Relation to Flow

Movement of tracer in an organ at any time depends on its location. To simplify: if tracer is in the inflowing blood then one expects some of it to escape into the extravascular space and some to remain intravascular and to leave with the effluent blood. If the tracer is mainly in the tissue and not in the inflowing blood, it tends to enter the bloodstream and be washed out. These truisms can be extended to give some qualitative ways of expressing the expected behavior and to suggest some exact calculations for particular situations.

To begin with a straightforward situation, consider the behavior of a tracer not undergoing net removal in an organ composed of a set of regions having different flows. Let the organ be uniformly labeled with tracer at $t = 0$, and then begin washout with inflowing arterial blood containing no tracer. As a first

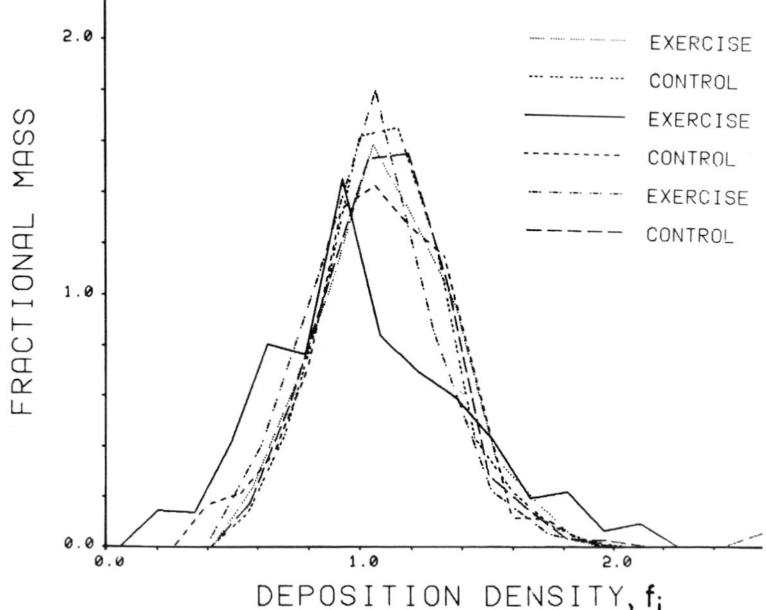

FIG. 16. Probability density functions of microsphere concentrations (indicating relative regional flows) in the left ventricular myocardium in an awake baboon at rest and during leg exercise. Abscissa, density of deposition relative to mean density and interpreted as f_i, the flow in the *i*th group of regions divided by the mean flow. Ordinate, fraction of the left ventricular mass having a specific flow. In general, these density functions tended to have relative dispersions of 30%–35%, to be symmetrical or slightly skewed in either direction (but consistent for each animal), and to be leptokurtic (high peaked) with skewness, i.e., β_2 values > 4.0.

case, consider the exchange between blood and tissue to be flow limited in all regions, even those with the highest flow. Then tracer washes out of each region at a rate governed by the regional flows F, in milliliters blood per unit tissue mass per minute. At any time prior to the shortest transit time, the emerging blood contains tracer at the initial concentration; it is washed out continuously. However, flow then carries tracer-free blood into various regions at differing rates. The high-flow regions are first cleared of tracer, so that the content of these areas diminishes; the high-flow regions initially contribute the most tracer to the outflow. When the tracer content of the high-flow regions becomes low, the observed tracer outflow is dominated by washout from low-flow regions. Thus in a heterogeneous organ the initial rate of washout is the highest, and then it decreases continuously until in the final phases the washout rate is that of the slowest region. Initially the mass of intraorgan tracer is evenly distributed. As washout proceeds with time the center of mass of tracer shifts more and more to the low-flow regions, ending up in the region of lowest flow.

Consider a second flow-limited case, this time with a pulse of tracer in the incoming blood. In the beginning the label is delivered to each unit of tissue in proportion to the regional flow. The label pulse is transported more rapidly through the high-flow regions, and the early part of the outflow profile is dominated by these regions just as it was in the preequilibrated case. Later, after the peak of the density function has been passed, the efflux of tracer corresponds to regions of lower flow; the final efflux comes from the region of slowest flow. In this case the center of mass of tracer is initially biased by the delivery (proportional to flow per gram) to the high-flow regions rather than being uniformly distributed, and similarly the center is shifted with time to the low-flow regions.

The completely barrier-limited case is a unique situation: the efflux of tracer occurs at a rate completely governed by the value of PS_C. Efflux is independent of flow. Thus, where preequilibrated tissue is being perfused with tracer-free blood, in the completely barrier-limited case there is no diminution in washout rate due to heterogeneity of flow. Any diminution must be attributed to *1*) heterogeneity of PS_C, *2*) other diffusional limitation, or *3*) heterogeneity of local extravascular volumes of distribution. The dominating rate in a purely barrier-limited situation is the regional value of PS_C/V_I, where V_I is interstitial volume of distribution.

The mixed-flow and barrier-limited state is still simple in this conceptual view. In a heterogeneous system the rate of entry or washout is always higher when flow is higher (Fig. 15) until the maximum rate of exchange is limited by the barrier. However, a doubling of flow in one region compared with another less than doubles the rate of delivery to or efflux from the tissue. This means that in the case of uniform initial labeling or of impulse-input labeling the diminution in efflux rates as the center of retained mass shifts toward the low-flow regions is not as great as the change in flow. In both cases the degree of barrier limitation in low-flow regions is less than in high-flow regions; therefore the clearance is a higher fraction of the flow, and in the case of inflow labeling proportionately less enters the tissue in the high-flow regions than does in the totally flow-limited case.

The conceptual relationship between the location of tracer and flow also applies to single capillary-tissue units. In a long capillary-tissue cylinder any tracer that is in the blood near the upstream end of the capillary has a higher chance of entry into the tissue than tracer that is near the outflow. This is also true of tracer in the extravascular space. Tracer entering the blood from the upstream end of the tissue has a higher probability of reescape into the tissue than does tracer entering the blood from the downstream end of the tissue. In general, because capillaries have such great lengths, axial diffusion has only a modest influence on outflow profiles; most of the tracer in the upstream end of the tissue is carried to the downstream end by convection (i.e., by flow).

The concept of center of mass for tracer is particularly useful in situations where diffusional shunting may occur. When tracer is in the inflow region and there is some diffusional shunting to the outflow region, the early escape or washout rate is higher than is otherwise expected. As a corollary, tracer that is within the organ tends to be retained later by the same diffusional shunt mechanism. In this case the idea of a long, straight capillary-tissue region does not work well, and "close to the exit" needs to be interpreted in terms of average time required to reach the exit rather than in terms of the distance that the blood must travel.

Combinations of diffusional and flow effects can be summarized by considering the location of the center of mass of retained tracer and its probability of escape. As an example, consider the experiments of Setchell et al. (185) on the washout of krypton after its injection into the inflow of a ram's testis. In this organ the inflow and outflow vessels form an extended rete of countercurrently exchanging vessels. Washout was found to be monoexponential over a four-decade range of tracer content in the tissue. This does not imply that regional flows in the testis are not heterogeneous or that the flow per unit volume is estimable from the washout rate; rather it means that the center of mass of retained tracer reaches and maintains a constant position. The diffusional shunting from outflow venules to inflow arterioles in the extended vascular rete is quite efficient, so that escaping tracer is delivered back into the testis. With this the washout becomes monoexponential whether or not there are nonuniformities of concentration in the tissue, as long as there is good transverse exchange in the rete. There is no equivalent lumped-compartment model that would give an accurate representation of this type of regional washout process.

The Multiple-Indicator–Dilution Technique

The multiple-indicator–dilution technique, introduced by Chinard et al. (41), is based on the use of multiple, simultaneous controls. It has been developed to facilitate the comparisons of tracers differing with respect to the rates at which they penetrate capillary walls or cell membranes or with respect to their volumes of distribution. Appropriate controls are those giving refined information on a specific part of the system that is relevant to the transport of a test solute with more complicated transport.

The technique is either to inject as a bolus or infuse at constant rate into the inflow a set of tracers of differing molecular characteristics. For example, in designing an experiment to assess the transcapillary exchange of D-glucose, one uses a reference tracer that does not escape from the blood (usually albumin) and may use, in addition, a similar permeant solute, L-glucose, for which the cellular uptake is zero. Displacements of the outflow pattern of the L-glucose from that of the intravascular reference are then interpreted as resulting from the transcapillary exchange, and differences between D-glucose and L-glucose are indicative of uptake by cells. A set of dilution curves for five substances is shown in Figure 17. Such curves are obtained by collecting a sequence of blood samples taken at short intervals at known times (0.2 to a few seconds apart) and measuring their contained tracer concentrations. The data give information from which $h(t)$ is calculable for each tracer. Alternatively the residue functions for the reference and diffusible tracers $R_R(t)$ and $R_D(t)$ are recorded by use of an external, multichannel, γ-detector analyzer system. From the pairs or multiples of curves obtained simultaneously the investigator can derive information on the features of the system that have led to the separation of the tracers. For example, from the difference between the curves (outflow or residue) for the reference intravascular marker and for the permeant tracer, the investigator may attempt via modeling to extract an estimate of the rate of blood-tissue exchange of the test substance. From differences in mean transit times and the measurement of the flow provided by the curves, he can obtain estimates of mean-transit-time volumes, which reflect the volumes of distribution of the tracers. By far the most definitive and satisfactory way to obtain estimates of the important exchange rates and volumes, however, has been to fit the observed dilution curves with models for blood-tissue exchange.

The intravascular reference curve is highly important because it describes all the dispersion within the vascular system; it is highly desirable that the reference indicator be carried in the bloodstream in exactly the same way as the tracer of interest is, i.e., having the same intravascular volume of distribution, axial and radial diffusivity, etc. For organs such as heart and brain, albumin or larger molecules serve adequately as references for small hydrophilic solutes that

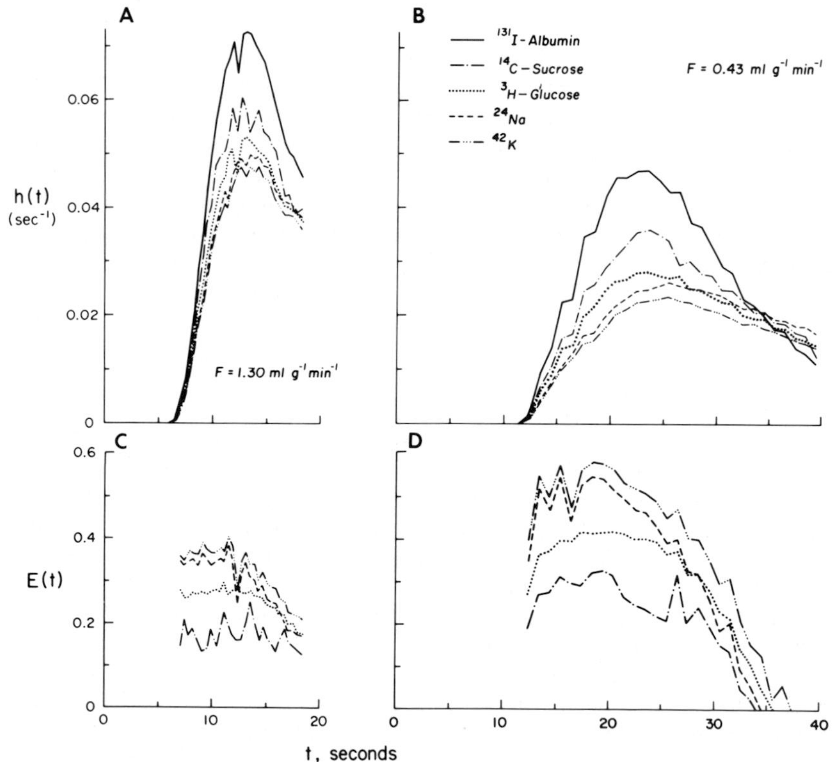

FIG. 17. Transcapillary extraction of solutes shown in sets of indicator-dilution curves $h(t)$ obtained simultaneously by sequential sampling of the coronary sinus outflow from a blood-perfused dog heart at 2 different plasma flows (F). *A*: $F = 1.30\ ml \cdot g^{-1} \cdot min^{-1}$; *B*: $F = 0.43\ ml \cdot g^{-1} \cdot min^{-1}$. *C* and *D*: corresponding fractional extractions $E(t)$ are higher at the lower flow.

do not enter erythrocytes, as long as differences in intravascular diffusivity are unimportant. In the liver, albumin escapes freely from the sinusoids, and thus its capillary permeability cannot be measured. This kind of behavior can also be used to advantage, however. In the liver, sucrose does not enter cells, and its movement through the liver is dominated by convection along the sinusoid; therefore it serves well as an extracellular reference for the estimation of cellular influx rates of tracers of similar size that are taken up by the liver. Sometimes two or more reference tracers are needed simultaneously. In the experiments of Kuikka, Bouskela, and Bassingthwaighte (111) the estimates of cellular uptake and return flux of D-glucose to the blood required albumin as the intravascular reference, L-glucose as an extracellular marker with PS_C the same as for D-glucose, and 2-deoxy-D-glucose as one having a similar (slightly higher) cellular uptake rate but a much lower cellular efflux. Each dilution curve for a reference tracer gives redundant information on the parts of the system that are common to two or more tracers; thus the accuracy of the estimates of the model parameters is much improved. The use of multiple simultaneous functions that must all be fitted by the model is the strongest technique for demonstrating shortcomings of the models, yet at the same time it is one of the strongest techniques for showing the self-consistency of a model.

STEADY-STATE CAPILLARY-TISSUE EXCHANGE MODELING

The Modeling Process

THE MODEL AS A HYPOTHESIS. The model itself is merely the formulation of a hypothesis from which predictions are made and compared with real-world behavior. Like any simplification, the model is a parsimonious and somewhat erroneous description. The overall objective of the process is to maintain the minimal level of complexity that provides the desired minimization of error. Modifying the model to reduce the difference between model and physiological observation ordinarily requires making the model more complex. Thus one must usually overcome the psychological (and economic) barriers to abandoning simplicity to attain increased realism. Because in biological modeling it is the approach to realism (evaluation with experimental data) that brings insight into the unknown aspects of the system, the sacrifice of simplicity and of the easily taught homilies becomes an unavoidable feature of the quest for reality. Bekey (28) emphasizes that each phase of development of the model must be compared with the real situation and that the model can be regarded as valid only to the extent that it corresponds to reality.

The design of a model inevitably involves a compromise between an attempt to describe the whole complexity of the real system and one's ability or willingness to deal with this complexity. In choosing a usable design one tends to define a model within a given hierarchical level. For example, in this presentation models span two hierarchical levels—the capillary and organ levels—but modeling of either the whole-body distribution (a broader hierarchical level) or the mechanisms of permeation or convection (a narrower, mechanistic level) is avoided. While so restricting ourselves we hope to see the capillary and organ models incorporated as elements of whole-body kinetic modeling and to see the parameters obtained by capillary modeling (such as permeabilities) used to test or to explain models of molecular penetration across capillary walls.

Like any hypothesis, a working model is a best guess for the purposes of the moment and should be regarded as a stepping stone. As one attempts to achieve a deeper level of insight into the behavior of a system, it may be possible to envisage two or more models that may be tested. These alternative hypotheses can be tested by designing experiments that distinguish between them. This is where models have their greatest advantage: a set of experiments can be mimicked via model simulations to determine which types of experiments are most sensitive to the distinctions between these models or most sensitive to the accurate estimation of some parameter. For example, the impulse-injection, multiple-tracer outflow dilution curve experiment gives primary sensitivity to estimates of PS_C, whereas the residue-detection technique is much more suited to direct estimation of residual cellular content and the intracellular volume of distribution V_{cell}.

DEGREES OF FREEDOM IN FITTING MODELS TO DATA. The fitting of *complete* models to sets of data greatly increases the accuracy of parameter estimation. Complete models that fulfill the requirements of physical laws, such as conservation of mass, are much more constrained than partial models describing part of the data. An integrated model, whose behavior must by definition be self-consistent, has a much reduced number of degrees of freedom. Degrees of freedom in a complex, integrated model are difficult to define because the standard statistical definitions are not applicable.

An intuitive approach to defining the degrees of freedom for a set of five indicator-dilution curves obtained simultaneously is as follows. Each concentration-time curve contains a few items of information, fewer than the number of data points (usually 30–60 points), since the points must be interdependent to form smooth curves. The shapes of the curves are too complex to be described by simple functions defined by three or four parameters [e.g., a lagged normal density curve (16) or a gamma variate function (213)]. Therefore a minimum of five or six independent items of information are provided by an individual outflow dilution curve. However, when one has four simultaneously recorded indicator-dilution curves, there are not 20 or 24 information items in the data; some are interdependent. For example, vascular dispersion is common to all four curves, and thus the total is perhaps only 15 independent items of information. In fitting the models to the four curves, some parameters have values in common for all four tracers; regional flows, vascular volumes, and the interstitial space are often the same for all the permeating tracers. Therefore, perhaps only eight parameters are to be independently evaluated from the 15 or so items of information in the data. As a result there are fewer model parameters than there are items of information. The extra information helps narrow the limits on the values of the parameters.

THE MODEL IN THE PROCESS OF EXPERIMENT DESIGN. Expressing a model as a hypothesis identifies the model's role in the design of experiments. This is closely related to parameter estimation in that to derive the value for a parameter (e.g., cell permeability) by fitting model function to data, the experiment must be designed so that the influence of a particular component of the system (e.g., a resistive barrier or a volume of distribution) on the observable data can be detected and quantitated. The eccentricity of a chicken egg, for example, is not measured by photographing the silhouette from one end.

SENSITIVITY FUNCTIONS. A key to both experimental design and parameter evaluation is sensitivity analysis (122), which is the use of the sensitivity functions to ascertain the degree of each parameter's influence on the form of the function predicted by the model hypothesis. The estimation of values of the parameters of a model depends on the parameters being independent of each other both mathematically and observationally. The principle is that the estimation of n parameters requires at least n separate and independent items of information. Sensitivity functions are sets of functions, one function for each independent free parameter, which define the relative change of amplitude of each part of a model function as a function of a change in a parameter (see Fig. 22). For a time-dependent function $h(t)$ the sensitivity functions are

$$S_i(t) = \frac{\partial h(t, \vec{p})}{\partial p_i} \quad \text{for } p_j \text{ constant}, j \neq i \qquad (40)$$

with other parameters constant, where p_i is the value of the ith parameter and $\vec{p}$ is the vector of all the parameters. Any two parameters that are interdependent have identical or algebraically related sensitivity functions. For success in the practical effort of estimating the values of various parameters separately, these sensitivity functions must be of distinctly different form.

MODEL VALIDATION AND DISTANCE FUNCTIONS. The testing of the hypothesis is equivalent to validating a model by comparing it with the observations, the best tests being those that utilize many sets of data from a variety of different experiments or observational viewpoints. Measuring the goodness of fit of a hypothesis to observations involves the computation of a distance function, which measures the disparity at points of time between predicted and observed function values. Curiously enough the distance function is most subject to the investigator's choice; it is selected by whim, intuition, or mathematical logic. It may be the linear difference between predicted and observed values, the squared differences, the areas, or the weighted sums or integrals of differences. The coefficient of variation (CV) is very commonly used to judge the goodness of fit between data and model. It is a measure of the squared differences and is most suitable where errors in the observations have a Gaussian distribution around the "true" or expected value

$$CV = \sqrt{\Sigma(\hat{Y}_i - Y_i)^2/(n - 1)}/(\Sigma\hat{Y}_i/n) \qquad (41)$$

where the $\hat{Y}_i(t)$ are the values of the model function at time t and the $Y_i(t)$ are the observed data points of which there are n. The CV is minimal at the best fit. Another useful measure is the correlation coefficient r, which is maximal at the best fit, i.e., it is as close to unity as possible

$$r^2 = 1 - \sum_i [Y(t_i) - \hat{Y}(t_i)]^2/\Sigma[Y(t_i) - \bar{Y}]^2 \qquad (42)$$

where $\bar{Y}$ is the average value of the model function $\hat{Y}(t)$ over the time span of the observed data

$$\bar{Y} = \frac{1}{n}\sum_{i=1}^{i=n} \hat{Y}(t_i) \qquad (43)$$

Both CV and r are designed to have values independent of the number of data points in the computation. However, both are subject to the problem that a single wild point has an unduly large influence and tends to bias the fit and the estimates of the parameters.

Minimization of an overall coefficient of variation has no straightforward justification and would be erroneous when one part of the data is more accurate than other parts. In the absence of more refined and general approaches to the problem, the investigator can only weight the distance functions in proportion to the accuracy of the data and with respect to the sensitivity functions of the parameters of primary importance to the form of the data. The CV or r values can be used to report the goodness of fit of the whole function or functions whether or not one has attempted to minimize the least-squares distance by minimizing CV or maximizing r.

Capillary–Interstitial Fluid Exchange

GENERAL EXPRESSION. Many specific cases can be described by a fairly general model for exchange among capillaries, interstitial fluid, and cells. The differential equations for concentration at any point might be phrased

$$\underset{\text{(local)}}{\text{concn}} = \underset{\text{(radial and axial)}}{-\text{diffusional flux}} - \underset{\text{(radial)}}{\text{permeation}} - \underset{\text{(axial)}}{\text{convection}} - \underset{\text{(local)}}{\text{consumption}} \tag{44}$$

All of these processes remove solute from any particular location. In terms of cylindrical geometry around the axis of a capillary, assuming radial symmetry without azimuthal gradients in concentrations, this becomes Equation 45 (see below), where C is concentration, x and r are axial and radial positions, t is time, D_x and D_r are axial and radial diffusion coefficients, and PS/V is the ratio of permeability–surface area product for each barrier divided by the volume bounded by the nearest membranes. The PS/V term accounts for the discontinuity in the radial concentration-distance profile. The term $P_1(x)$ denotes the apparent permeability for flux in an outward direction at axial position x and $P_2(x)$ that in the centripetal direction. The concentration on the *cis* side of the membrane is $C(x, r_-, t)$, where r_- is the position just to the axial side of the membrane and $C(x, r_+, t)$ is that on the *trans* side farther from the axis. The axial velocity $v_F(x, r)$ is radius dependent if there is an axicentric velocity profile and x dependent if there is axial variation in the space available for flow. The total flow across any plane orthogonal to the x axis is considered constant (i.e., the system is stationary). The metabolic rate constant K (for burning or consuming, excreting, or binding infinitely tightly) possibly depends on concentration and axial and radial position. It could be zero order (where the product $K \cdot C$ is constant) or first order (where K is independent of concentration), or it could demonstrate saturation kinetics as for a carrier-mediated process. The expressions containing D_r would not be used at a permeability barrier; rather one would use the term containing PS/V.

In the process of taking the general formulation of Equation 45 and transforming it into a practical model, some explicit assumptions must be made. Expressing the model in terms of cylindrical geometry has already involved two of these: *Assumption 1*, that the capillary extends from inflow to outflow in a line straight enough that radial fluxes are apparently independent of axial fluxes, and thus the system behaves as if there were radial symmetry; and *Assumption 2*, that the system is linear, stationary, and mass conservative when there is no consumption of tracer.

SINGLE-CAPILLARY–INTERSTITIAL FLUID MODEL. *Mathematical definition.* The assumptions made in formulating a simple single-capillary–interstitial fluid exchange model and using it as an analog to a whole organ are as follows:

1. Straight system with radial symmetry
2. Linearity and stationarity hold
3. Convection only in capillary
4. Rapid intracapillary radial diffusion
5. Negligible axial diffusion
6. No capacitance in the capillary wall
7. First-order tracer transport
8. Axially uniform capillary permeability–surface area product (PS_C)
9. Plasma concentrations as a basis
10. Rapid interstitial radial diffusion
11. Uniform dimensions in capillary-tissue units
12. Uniform flows in capillary-tissue units

Assumption 3 distinguishes between two regions: the capillary, in which there is flow, and the interstitial fluid, which is assumed to be stagnant. *Assumption 4* states that within the capillary, on the basis of the small radial dimension and short diffusional relaxation time, radial concentration gradients are completely dissipated. Therefore $C_C(x, r, t)$ can be written $C_C(x, t)$, a reduction from the model used for Figures 6 and 7. *Assumption 5*, that axial diffusion is negligible ($D_x = 0$), simplifies the computation greatly and is justified in terms of molecular diffusion when capillaries are long. Bolus flow in the capillaries (154) interrupts the flow profiles: the red cells, which fill the lumen and are deformed by flow through the capillary, retard spreading of the material along the length of the capillary. In contrast to present assumptions, axial diffusion has been retained in some models to provide a vehicle for describing axial dispersive effects (12, 19). Perl and Chinard (148) used axial dispersion to approximate transorgan dispersion as a

$$\frac{\partial C(x, r, t)}{\partial t} = \underset{\substack{\text{(axial}\\\text{diffusion)}}}{+D_x \frac{\partial^2 C}{\partial x^2}} + \underset{\text{(radial diffusion)}}{D_r \left[\frac{\partial^2 C}{\partial r^2} + \frac{1}{r}\frac{\partial C}{\partial r}\right]} - \underset{\text{(permeation)}}{\frac{S(x)}{V(x)} [P_1(x) \cdot C(x, r_-, t) - P_2(x) \cdot C(x, r_+, t)]}$$
$$- \underset{\text{(axial convection)}}{\frac{v_F(x, r)\partial C(x, r_-, t)}{\partial x}} - \underset{\text{(local metabolism)}}{\frac{K(C, x, r)}{V(x)} \cdot C(x, r, t)} \tag{45}$$

whole, which included flow heterogeneity. If bolus flow is so dominant that axial dispersion is negligible for all tracers, the velocity profile in the capillary could be considered flat. This case is termed *piston flow*, or *plug flow*. Here $v_F(x, r)$ becomes $v_F(x)$, and if the capillary has a uniform diameter it becomes simply v_F. This assumption has been the key to obtaining analytical solutions (78, 79, 181). With these assumptions the intravascular transport processes for molecules of differing diffusivity must be considered identical.

Assumption 6 is that the wall that bounds the capillary is of negligible thickness (or volume) so that there is no capacitance for tracer. According to *Assumption 7* transcapillary tracer transport is a first-order process with a limited concentration range of mother substance for any nonlinear process. The values P_1S_C and P_2S_C are used for the exchange in and out of the capillary; the P and S are kinetically inseparable in these models and no distinction can be made between passive and facilitated transport without doing experiments at more than one concentration. *Assumption 8* is that PS is uniform along the length of the capillary, i.e., that the sites of permeation are uniformly dispersed. This makes it possible to obtain analytical solutions (79, 172, 181), although this is not necessary for obtaining numerical solutions (12, 19). Deviations from this assumption, such as increasing the permeability at the venous end [in accordance with the observations of Rous et al. (178) and of Wiederhielm (225)] only slightly affect the shapes of the outflow dilution curves (12) but greatly affect the shape of extravascular spatial concentration profiles (19).

The steady-state condition means that volumes are constant. These are the volumes of distribution of the tracer solute (i.e., virtual volumes) and are not the real volumes occupied by the water in the capillary or interstitial fluid. The magnitude of the virtual volume depends on the definition of the concentration. According to *Assumption 9* the concentration in the capillary C_C is defined as the moles of solute per liter plasma and, assuming the activity coefficient in the plasma to be unity, all other concentrations and partition coefficients are related to the plasma. Then $C_C(x, t)$ represents the concentration and the activity in the plasma, and $V_C(1 - \text{Hct})$ is the plasma space available to the solute, where Hct is the hematocrit (corollary to *Assumption 9*). Further corollaries to *Assumptions 7* and *9* are that $C_I(x, t)$, the activity in the apparent interstitial volume of distribution V_I' would at equilibrium be equal to $C_C(x, t)$, which by inference defines V_I' as being the virtual volume of interstitial fluid having an activity equal to that in plasma. When there is a concentrative process at the membrane either due to a specialized transport process or to solubility differences in interstitial fluid and plasma, then the ratio of the apparent volume of distribution in interstitial fluid to the actual volume is given by $v_I = V_I'/V_I$, where v_I is the fraction of V_I accessible to solute. This therefore gives an overall composite measure of volume exclusion, solubility (or binding), and concentrative asymmetric transport across the capillary wall.

When the capillary is situated in a well-perfused organ with a dense capillary network in which there is flow in all of the capillaries, the half-distance between the capillaries is so small that the time for equilibration of the concentration of the diffusible substance in the lateral direction is a negligible fraction of the transit time along the capillary. This means that the diffusible substance in the extravascular space equilibrates virtually instantaneously in the lateral direction. Therefore *Assumption 10* allows $C_I(x, r, t)$ to be written $C_I(x, t)$ because there are no concentration gradients in the extravascular space in a direction perpendicular to the capillary axis. This model is appropriate only for the well-perfused visceral organs. It could not be applied to poorly perfused tissues, such as cool skin or resting skeletal muscle, where there would be significant concentration gradients in the extravascular space due to the large diffusion distances between capillaries in which there is flow.

Assumption 11 is that the capillary and tissue dimensions are uniform. When the volumes per unit length in capillary, interstitial fluid, and cell are constant, one can use the characteristic ratios $\gamma = V_I'/V_C'$ and $\Theta = V_{cell}'/V_C'$ where V_I' is apparent volume, and intracapillary velocity is constant along the length.

Uniform regional flows (*Assumption 12*) mean that all neighboring capillaries behave alike, having identical spatial concentration profiles at all times so that there are no gradients in concentration from one unit to another and no net exchange between them.

The result of all these specific simplifications (*Assumptions 1–12*) is a capillary–interstitial fluid model described by a pair of partial differential equations. For the capillary of length L, and with S_C as capillary surface area

$$\frac{\partial C_C(x, t)}{\partial t} = -\frac{S_C}{V_C'}[P_1C_C(x, t) - P_2C_I(x, t)] - \frac{F_SL}{V_C'}\frac{\partial C_C(x, t)}{\partial x} \tag{46}$$

The axial velocity v_F in Equation 45 is given by F_SL/V_C', where F_S is the flow of solute-containing mother fluid ($\text{ml}\cdot\text{g}^{-1}\cdot\text{min}^{-1}$), calculated from the blood flow F_B (ml/min) divided by the organ mass W (g) and from Hct. This calculation excludes the fraction of the organ volume that consists of large, nonexchanging vessels v_{LV} (ml/ml). An estimate of L is not needed for the fitting of outflow dilution curves because the outflow represents the integral over the distance from

$x = 0$ to $x = L$, and the comparison with the reference curve is the critical feature of the analysis

$$F_S = F_B(1 - Hct + v_{RBC} \cdot Hct)/[W(1 - v_{LV})] \quad (47)$$

In Equation 46 V_C' is the volume of distribution in the capillary space (ml/g) calculated from the total capillary volume V_C (ml/g tissue), excluding large vessels. The fractional volume of capillary available to solute is given by v_C

$$\begin{aligned} V_C' &= v_C V_C \\ &= V_C(1 - Hct + v_{RBC} \cdot Hct) \end{aligned} \quad (48)$$

Numerical solutions for the concentrations within the capillary and interstitial spaces at any time t were presented by Bassingthwaighte et al. (19) with the radial and axial diffusion terms retained. By omitting the diffusional terms Goresky et al. (79) were able to obtain analytical expressions for these concentrations (Eqs. 26 and 27 in ref. 79). These equations are similar to those at the outflow (Eq. 53 in this chapter). The time for the pulse to reach position x is x/v_F, or $(x/L)\tau$, where τ is the capillary transit time. The capillary concentration is composed of an impulse (spike) at this point and a wave of returning material at positions upstream from it

$$C_C(x, t) = \frac{q_0}{F_S} e^{-\frac{PS_C}{F_S}\frac{x}{L}} \delta\left(t - \frac{x\tau}{L}\right) + \frac{q_0}{F_S} e^{-\frac{PS_C}{V_I'}[t - (1-\gamma)x\tau/L]} \frac{PS_C}{\sqrt{F_S V_I'(Lt/x - \tau)}} \cdot I_1\left[2PS_C \sqrt{\left(t - \frac{x\tau}{L}\right)\frac{x}{L} \Big/ (F_S V_I')}\right] S\left(t - \frac{x\tau}{L}\right) \quad (51)$$

where v_{RBC} is the fractional volume of distribution of the tracer in the erythrocytes. Although the definition of v_C in Equation 48 assumes instantaneous equilibration between plasma and erythrocytes, this is an invalid premise when the plasma-RBC exchange rates are slow. When the rates are very slow, v_{RBC} may be considered zero for the analysis of multiple-indicator-dilution curves, but the approaches of Goresky et al. (74) and of Roselli and Harris (174, 175) are required for intermediate rates.

For the interstitial space

$$\frac{\partial C_I(x, t)}{\partial t} = \frac{S_C}{V_I'} [P_1 C_C(x, t) - P_2 C_I(x, t)] \quad (49)$$

The equations are relatively simple due to the approximation that radial-diffusion gradients within capillary or interstitial spaces are small (7, 154). The term V_I' is the apparent volume of distribution in the interstitial space and is the product $v_I V_I$ where V_I (ml/g) is the anatomical estimate of interstitial fluid space and v_I is the fraction of V_I accessible to solute; v_I is the composite product of three factors: *1*) an interstitial space/plasma partition coefficient, *2*) a fractional unexcluded volume, and *3*) one plus the ratio of bound solute to free solute in the interstitial space.

Substitution for the expression $P_1C_C - P_2C_I$ in Equation 46 from Equation 49 leads to the conservation expression

$$\frac{\partial C_C}{\partial t} + \frac{F_S L}{V_C'} \frac{\partial C_C}{\partial x} + \frac{V_I}{V_C'} \frac{\partial C_I}{\partial t} = 0 \quad (50a)$$

or in the notation of Rose, Goresky, and Bach (172)

$$\frac{\partial u}{\partial t} + v_F \frac{\partial u}{\partial x} + \gamma \frac{\partial v}{\partial t} = 0 \quad (50b)$$

where u and v are capillary and interstitial concentrations, v_F is intracapillary velocity, and $\gamma = V_I'/V_C'$.

The delayed Dirac delta function $\delta(t - x\tau/L)$ exists when $t = x\tau/L$ and is zero at all other times; its time integral is zero prior to $x\tau/L$ and becomes unity thereafter. The delayed unit step function $S(t - x\tau/L)$ is unity for times greater than $x\tau/L$ and zero at earlier times. The term $I_1(y)$ is a first-order modified Bessel function of argument y, and q_0 is input quantity of tracer. The concentration in the interstitial space, which evolves in parallel fashion, lacks the impulse response

$$C_I(x, t) = \frac{q_0}{F_S} e^{-\frac{PS_C}{V_I'}[t - (1-\gamma)x\tau/L]} \cdot I_0\left[2PS_C \sqrt{\left(t - \frac{x\tau}{L}\right)\frac{x}{L} \Big/ F_S V_I'}\right] \cdot S(t - x\tau/L) \quad (52)$$

where $I_0(y)$ is a zero-order modified Bessel function of argument y.

Behavior of the model. Spatial profiles. To illustrate how these two profiles change as a function of time, Goresky et al. (79) computed a set of numerical examples (Fig. 18). These demonstrate that when PS_C/F_S is small, a major part of the material remains confined to the impulse (sliding along the capillary with velocity v_F) and emerges at the outflow in the delayed impulse $\delta(t - \tau)$, i.e., it does not enter the extravascular space. The material that enters the interstitial space and returns to the capillary emerges at the outflow as the tail function. When the permeability is high, the loss from the intravascular impulse function is so large that the area under it becomes negligible during its passage along the capillary. The exchanging material spreads into the extravascular space and appears to move along toward the exit with time, both inside the capillary and in the extravascular space. The extravascular concentration profile for the exchanging material $C_I(x, t)$ appears to fall behind that of the intravascular material $C_C(x, t)$ in space. The mode of representation used (neglecting radial concentration gradients) is suitable because instantaneous lateral equilibration is assumed to occur within each region, i.e., no lateral concentration gradient is assumed to be present. The discontinuity between the intravascular and extravascular concentration profiles is situated at the capillary barrier. At the higher values of permeability ($PS_C/F_S = 15$ in Fig. 18, *right panel*), the profiles are somewhat similar to those shown in Figure 7 in which the radial gradients in the interstitial fluid are very small.

Outflow responses. From the model the time-domain solution for the unit impulse response at the outflow at $x = L$ is the concentration-time curve $C(t) = C_C(L, t) = q_0 h_C(t)/F_S$, where q_0 is the mass of tracer in an impulse injection at the inflow at $t = 0$. The expression for the outflow has the same two main components as the parent expression: *1*) a throughput component of tracer carried to the outflow without traversing the capillary wall and *2*) a returning fraction (or tail function) composed of tracer that has left the capillary and returned, to exit from the unit at the outflow

$$h_C(t) = \frac{F_S \cdot C_C(L, t)}{q_0} = e^{-P_1S_C\tau/V'_C}\delta(t - \tau) + e^{-P_2S_Ct/V'_I} \cdot e^{-\tau(P_1S_C/V'_C - P_2S_C/V'_I)} \cdot \left(\frac{P_1S_C}{V'_C} \cdot \frac{P_2S_C}{V'_I}\tau\right) \sum_{n=0}^{\infty} \frac{1}{n!(n+1)!} \cdot \left(\frac{P_1S_C}{V'_C} \cdot \frac{P_2S_C}{V'_I}\tau[t - \tau]\right)^n S(t - \tau) \quad (53)$$

When the P values are equal, when the summation is included in a first-order modified Bessel function, and when $\tau = V'_C/F_S$, this simplifies further to

$$h_C(t) = e^{-PS_C/F_S}\delta(t - \tau) + e^{-(PS_C/V'_I)[t - \tau(1 - \gamma)]} \cdot \frac{PS_C}{[F_S V'_I (t - \tau)]^{1/2}} \cdot I_1\{2PS_C[(t - \tau)/F_S V'_I]^{1/2}\} S(t - \tau) \quad (54)$$

Note that replacement of Equation 53 by 54 does not result in any loss of generality: in each term where P_2 appears it is paired with V'_I. Therefore in the case where there is asymmetry of transcapillary permeability, the virtual volume of the interstitial region is the passive equilibrative volume multiplied by the factor P_1/P_2. By definition $V'_I = v_I V_I$, a partitioning factor times the physical volume, and thus v_I is the nonexcluded fraction times P_1/P_2. In the steady state the ratio of solute activities in interstitial fluid and capillary plasma would be P_1/P_2.

This equation was developed earlier by Sangren and Sheppard (181) and Sheppard (188), the latter giving the correct solution. The first component, which contains the delayed Dirac delta function $\delta(t - \tau)$, is a spike at the capillary transit time τ; it contains the throughput fraction of tracer $\exp(-PS_C/F_S)$, which becomes zero with a very high PS_C or low flow. The escaping (or "extracted") fraction is $1 - \exp(-PS_C/F_S)$, which is the area of the second portion of the curve. This second term [as indicated by the delayed unit step $S(t - \tau)$, which is the integral of $\delta(t - \tau)$] exists only for times after $t = \tau$, i.e., after $\tau = 1$. The permeability notation used here is readily translated into the terminology used by Goresky et al. (79)

$$V'_I/V'_C = \gamma \quad (55)$$

$$P_1S_C/F_S = \frac{P_1S_C}{V'_I} \cdot \frac{V'_I}{V'_C} \cdot \frac{V'_C}{F_S} = k_1\gamma\tau \quad (56)$$

$$P_2S_C/V'_I = k_2 \quad (57)$$

where k_1 and k_2 are rate constants.

The first-order modified Bessel function with the argument y is computed for the bracketed term at each time t. When the argument is small, an ordinary series definition of $I_1(y)$ is adequate

$$I_1(y) = y/2 \sum_{n=0}^{\infty} \frac{(y/2)^{2n}}{n!(n+1)!} = y/2 + \left(\frac{y/2}{2}\right)^3 + \left(\frac{y/2}{2!3!}\right)^5 + \left(\frac{y/2}{3!4!}\right)^7 + \ldots \quad (58)$$

However, when k_1 and k_2 are large and the value of the argument y in the Bessel function $I_1(y)$ is greater than ~12, this form fails to converge quickly. The tail function can then be computed by using the asymptotic form of the Bessel function

$$I_1(y) = \frac{e^y}{\sqrt{2\pi y}}\left[1 - \frac{(4 - 1)}{8y \cdot 1!} + \frac{(4 - 1)(4 - 9)}{(8y)^2 2!} - \frac{(4 - 1)(4 - 9)(4 - 25)}{(8y)^3 3!} + \ldots\right] \quad (59)$$

[Polynomial approximations are given by Abramowitz and Segun (1) and are accurate and faster to compute.]

The model described by Equations 53 and 54 is similar to the numerical model developed by Bassingthwaighte et al. (19) except that the latter retains both axial diffusion in capillary and interstitial fluid and radial-diffusion gradients in the interstitial fluid. A still later model (12) retains only the axial diffusion terms and is very fast to compute.

Normalized outflow concentration-time curves for a single-capillary–interstitial fluid unit with plug flow are shown in Figure 19 for cases with increasing permeability. The outflow profile of a diffusible substance from a single barrier-limited capillary consists

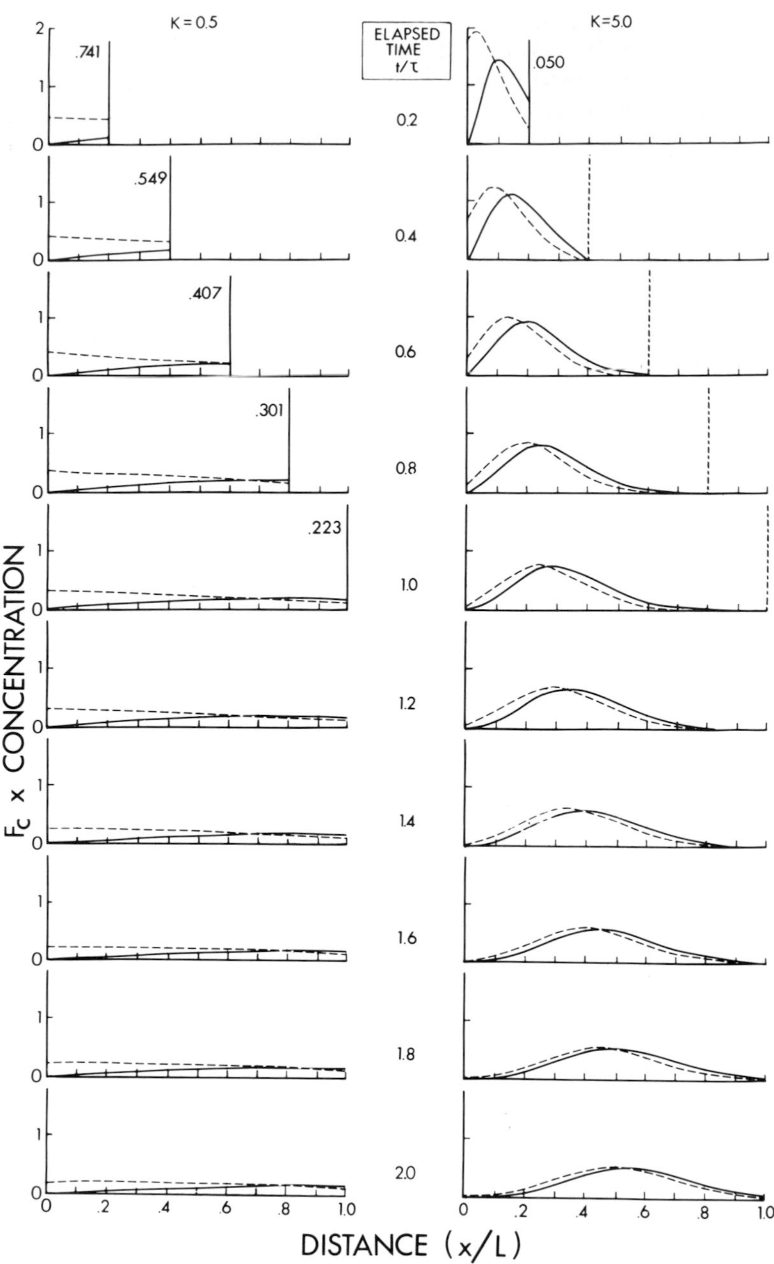

FIG. 18. Solutions for an axially distributed capillary-tissue model showing concentration profiles along the length of the capillary. Distance axis is normalized so that the abscissa is x/L. Ordinate is either $F_SC_C(x, t)$ or $F_SC_I(x, t)$, where C_C and C_I are tracer concentration in capillary and interstitial fluid. The case is taken in which the system is nonconcentrative, i.e., $P_1 = P_2 = P$ and $\gamma = 3.0$, where P_1 and P_2 are apparent permeability for flux in an outward and centripetal direction and γ is the ratio V_I'/V_C'. (V_I' and V_C' are the apparent volumes of distribution of interstitial fluid and capillary.) Time scale has been normalized to t/τ (τ = capillary transit time), and changes in length profiles (intravascular and extravascular) are illustrated at normalized time intervals of 0.2 for both a small metabolic rate constant ($K = 0.50$ or $PS_C/F_S = 1.5$, *left panel*) and a moderately large metabolic rate constant ($K = 5.0$ or $PS_C/F_S = 15$, *right panel*). *Solid line*, intravascular profile; *broken line*, extravascular profile. Impulse function (*vertical line*) remains intravascular during its propagation along the capillary in these instances. Number on each panel represents proportion of total material introduced that is still traveling in the damped impulse function within the capillary. When this area is less than 0.01 of the total, the impulse function is illustrated by a *broken* (rather than *solid*) *vertical line*. [From Goresky et al. (79), by permission of the American Heart Association, Inc.]

of a damped impulse function, which emerges at the capillary transit time τ and is followed by a tail function that is spread out in time. Prior to time τ, nothing appears at the outflow. The tail function is zero until the time τ, as indicated by the term $S(t - \tau)$ in Equation 54. It becomes finite thereafter and contains two major terms that decay with time: the exponential leading term beginning $\exp[-(PS_C/V_I')t \ldots]$, a more slowly decaying middle term $PS_C/(t - \tau)^{1/2}$, and a first-order modified Bessel function, which increases progressively as the value of the argument increases. With higher capillary permeability the area under the impulse function decreases, as dictated by the exponent $-PS_C/F_S$ in the first term of Equation 54. The area under the tail function simultaneously increases. Because it is difficult to perceive how this function changes in form, the series of numerical examples in Figure 19 serves to illustrate the influences of PS_C and V_I'. We have used two different values of the γ ratio, 3 and 10. The value $\gamma = 3$ corresponds roughly to that which would be found in a solid visceral organ for an extracellular substance such as sucrose; the value $\gamma = 10$ corresponds to the value for a substance such as labeled water, distributing freely into the total water of the organ. Capillaries with equivalent permeabilities are compared in these two instances, i.e., the damping factors in the first term of Equation 54, $\exp[-(PS_C/F_S)]$, are made equal. When the capillary is a right circular cylinder of radius r_C, then $S_C = 2\pi r_C L$, $V_C = \pi r_C^2 L$, $k_1\gamma = 2P/r_C$, and $k_1\gamma\tau = (PS_C/V_C')\cdot(V_C'/F_S) = PS_C/F_S$.

In Figure 19 the *top panels*, labeled $PS/F = 0$,

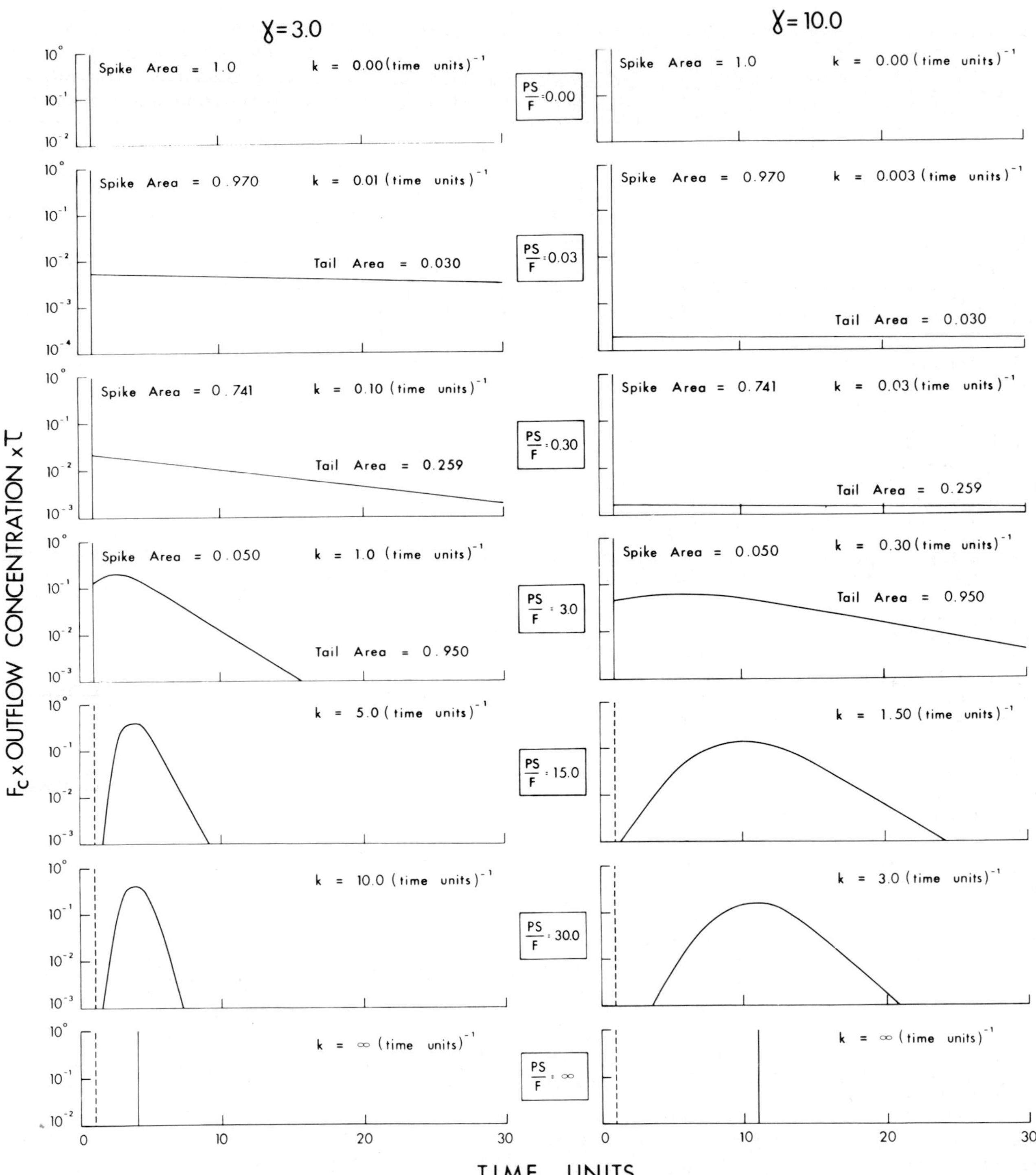

FIG. 19. Outflow profile for substances undergoing passive barrier-limited distribution in response to a unit impulse input. Area under each curve is unity. Abscissa is normalized to t/τ, and ordinate correspondingly becomes $F_S\tau C_C(L, t)$, where the L indicates that this is the concentration at the outflow end, at $x = L$. Abscissa scale is linear; ordinate scale is logarithmic. Separate sets of data are displayed for $\gamma = 3$ and 10. In each case, capillaries with equal PS_C/F_S (which is $k\gamma\tau$, where $k = PS_C/V_I'$) values are displayed in these semilogarithmic plots. Permeability values increase from *top* to *bottom*, and lowest panels display the asymptotic case, i.e., flow-limited distribution. The first part of the illustrated output, in the cases with low permeability, is an impulse function with normalized area $\exp(-PS_C/F_S)$. It is difficult to illustrate this form, which theoretically has an infinitely large magnitude and infinitesimally small duration. Thus a *vertical line* has simply been placed at the site of the function with a number representing its normalized area. When spike area is less than 0.01 of the total, a *broken* (rather than *solid*) *line* was used. [From Goresky et al. (79), by permission of the American Heart Association, Inc.]

correspond to the case in which $PS_C = 0$. The reference vascular impulse emerges at the normalized transit time 1.0 with undiminished area, and there is of course no tail function. In the *lower panels* the mean transit time of the diffusible substance $\bar{t}_D$ is fixed by the value for γ

$$\bar{t}_D = \tau(1 + \gamma) \tag{60}$$

When the major proportion of the outflow profile is localized to the spike, the tail function has a large dispersion and appears as a low-magnitude single exponential with a large time constant. As the permeability is increased the proportion of the output emerging in the throughput spike diminishes progressively until it becomes an insignificant fraction. The tail function then reshapes into a peaked function with less and less dispersion and finally approaches an asymptote at the delayed-wave, flow-limited case (72)—a spike of unit area—at the normalized time $(1 + \gamma)$ along the abscissa. The time of the peak of the tail function becomes imperceptibly different from that of the initial spike until a preponderant part of the area is localized to the tail function. The peak then begins to shift to the right in time, increase in magnitude, and approach the position of the delayed impulse function.

This characteristic behavior of the ideal single-capillary–interstitial fluid unit is not seen directly as such in experimental curves because of dispersion of the input to the capillaries and because of the heterogeneity of regional flows. Nevertheless the case of the delayed impulse function at the highest PS_C is supported by fitting Goresky's flow-limited model (72) to sets of dilution curves in the liver.

Experimentally, if the permeability is very low, the low-magnitude exponential tail function may not be easily resolvable and at time τ the outflow profile may appear to consist of only an impulse with area $\exp(-k_1\gamma\tau)$. In their multiple-indicator–dilution studies in the kidney, Chinard et al. (40) observed low recoveries of labeled albumin with respect to labeled red cells at the outflow; they considered only the early extrapolated parts of the curves. A mechanism like the one described here may account for their observations when it is distributed over the whole labeled-albumin dilution curve.

WHOLE-ORGAN CAPILLARY–INTERSTITIAL FLUID MODELS: HOMOGENEOUS FLOW. *Mathematical definition.* Single-capillary models can be used as components of whole organ models under specific constraints and with additional assumptions or experimentally acquired information. First, there is the constraint that the total volume or mass of the organ must include the capillary-tissue units as well as the arteries and veins. Tissue is defined here as being composed of capillary-tissue units, i.e., capillary blood plus interstitium plus cells; large nonexchanging vessels are excluded. This definition is arbitrary but is useful when making comparisons between organs having differential ratios for the volume of a large vessel to the volume of functional tissue. A simple configuration of one whole-organ model with a single artery and vein is diagramed in Figure 13.

In experiments on a single organ, values can be obtained for the total blood flow F_B (ml/s), the organ mass W (g), and the density ρ (g/ml). Other experiments can provide values for the fraction of the organ volume consisting of the blood in the nonexchanging vessels of the inflowing arterial and outflowing venous system, v_{LV} (ml blood/ml organ). These vessels are defined as separate from the tissue. To conserve volume and mass the sum of the volumes (ml/g) of the exchanging regions V_C, V_I, and V_{cell} must be the reciprocal of the specific gravity

$$V_C + V_I + V_{cell} = 1/\rho \tag{61}$$

Useful values for the heart are $\rho = 1.063$ g/ml (237), $V_C = 0.03–0.04$ ml/g (24, 136), $V_I = 0.15$ ml/g [from Polimeni's (150) value of 0.19 ml/g for extracellular space $V_I + V_C$], and $v_{LV} \sim 0.11$ ml blood/ml organ (refs. 93 and 224 and F. Gonzalez and J. B. Bassingthwaighte, unpublished data). The traditional view of fitting capillary-tissue units together is to consider them as hexagons, as shown in Figure 1. The slightly longer diffusion distances from the capillary to the corners of the hexagon appear inconsequential because they are compensated for by azimuthal diffusion in addition to radial diffusion (71).

The volume of a hexagonal capillary-tissue unit V_h is defined by the intercapillary half-distance $r_{1/2}$ and the capillary length L so that $V_h = 2\sqrt{3}r_{1/2}^2L$. Thus a capillary mean transit time for blood $\bar{t}_C$ is given by the capillary volume divided by the capillary flow, calculated as a whole-organ average

$$\bar{t}_C = \frac{V_C}{V_h} \cdot \frac{W(1 - v_{LV})}{\rho F_B} \tag{62}$$

When the capillary and large-vessel hematocrits are the same, $\bar{t}_C$ is identical to τ in Equation 53. If the intracapillary hematocrit Hct_C is smaller than the large-vessel hematocrit Hct_{LV} (as appears to be the usual case), then $\tau > \bar{t}_C$ for solutes not entering red cells

$$\tau = \bar{t}_C(1 - Hct_{LV})/(1 - Hct_C) \tag{63}$$

However, this is of no consequence to the estimation of PS_C from the magnitude of the nonextracted fraction of tracer because such a correction for τ in Equation 53 would be exactly canceled by the same correction for the volume of distribution within the capillary V'_C. Similarly, any error in estimates of capillary length or of intercapillary distance has no influence on the estimation of PS_C; the exponent of the first term of Equation 53 reduces to the familiar form $-PS_C/F_S$ and is uninfluenced by the details of the intraorgan structure. However, the return flux from interstitial fluid to capillary is influenced by V_I', and therefore this is an important parameter to be optimized in fitting model solutions to dilution curves.

A model solution from Bassingthwaighte (12) that takes intravascular dispersion into account is shown in Figure 20. The input function to the single-capillary–interstitial fluid unit is a dispersed concentration-time curve such as might be expected after traversal of the arterial inflow (9). It has the shape of the normalized outflow dilution curve for the reference $h_R(t)$, but it is shifted to the left by one capillary transit time. The curve $h_D(t)$ is the transport function for a tracer that permeates the capillary membrane; $h_D(t)$ is shown for five values of permeability. As PS_C increases, the height of the initial peak of $h_D(t)$—which is dominated by the throughput fraction (the nonexchanging tracer)—diminishes; more and more of the tracer goes into the returning or tail component. The form of the tails is easier to see on the semilog plots. The characteristic time for escape from the capillary is V_C'/PS_C; the time available for escape is the capillary transit time τ_C. Thus the fractional escape or extraction is governed by the ratio $\tau_C/(V_C'/PS_C)$, which simplifies to PS_C/F_S. Similar descriptive illustrations of the effects of hematocrit, flow, large-vessel volume, capillary volume, and permeability gradients are given by Bassingthwaighte (12).

Estimation of capillary PS and interstitial volume. The essence of the foregoing discussion is that the information desired lies in the interrelations between the curves for labeled vascular reference and the curves for diffusible label. When the organ is being perfused in such a way that the capillary transit times are everywhere the same, this information can be obtained straightforwardly. Because the intracapillary transport function $h_{C,R}(t)$ (a special case of Equation 54, with $PS_C = 0$) is a pure delay function $\delta(t - \tau_C)$, the observed shift of the curve for the reference tracer $h_R(t)$ can be shifted back by one capillary transit time τ_C so that the input function [the transport function

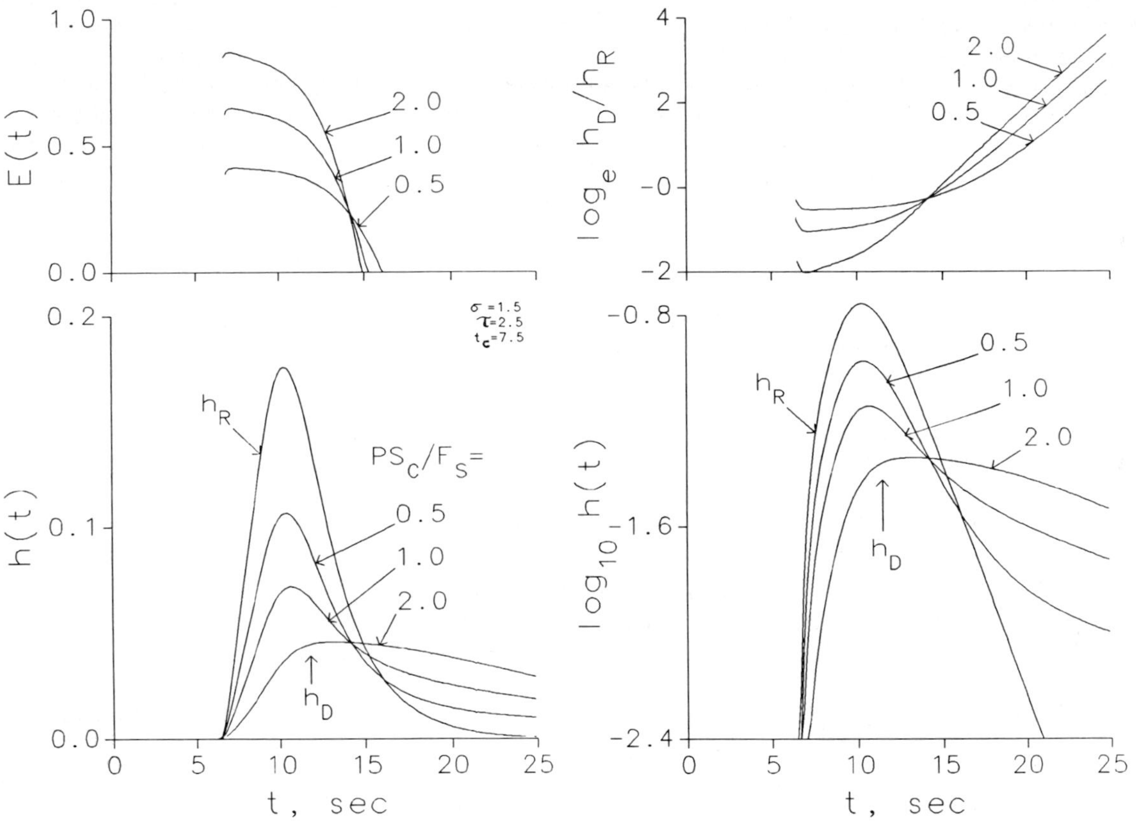

FIG. 20. Solutions for single-capillary–tissue model (12) with a dispersed input function and varied permeabilities; $h_R(t)$ and $h_D(t)$ are transport functions for nonpermeant reference-molecule and permeant tracer. *Left panels*: normalized responses $h_R(t)$ and 3 curves of $h_D(t)$ are shown on a linear scale for 3 values of permeability with $F_S = 1\ ml \cdot g^{-1} \cdot min^{-1}$; $PS_C/F_S = 0.5$, 1, and 2; and $\gamma = 6$, where $\gamma = V_I'/V_C'$. Curves of $h_D(t)$ show diminution in size of throughput component at higher PS_C. At even higher PS_C apparent instantaneous extraction $E(t)$ approaches unity, at which level the early upslope data are insensitive to the value of PS_C. *Right panels*: logarithmic ordinate scaling of $h_R(t)$ and $h_D(t)$ for the same 3 permeabilities shows the influences of the shapes of the curves' tails. Log ratio $\log_e[h_D(t)/h_R(t)]$ appears linear with lower permeabilities. This occurs because in this model each element of tracer traverses the same capillary with the same transit time. Shape of the function of log ratio versus time corresponds to that found by Martín and Yudilevich (132) in isolated perfused dog heart.

of the large vessels $h_{LV}(t)$] is $h_R(t + \tau_C)$. [The commutative property of convolution in linear systems allows the reordering of $h_V(t)$ and $h_C(t)$.] Since $h_R(t + \tau_C) * \delta(t - \tau_C) = h_R(t)$, the reference curve is always exactly fitted by the model. The reflux from interstitial fluid to capillary is governed by PS_C/V_I'; adjusting PS_C to fit the early part of the indicator-dilution curves and V_I' for the later portion usually gives good fit. For example, the anatomical volume, the unprimed V_I, can be estimated from V_C' for sucrose, for which the transcapillary wall transport is passive and the interstitial volume exclusion small. An example of the single-capillary (homogeneous-organ) model fitted to data in the heart is shown in Figure 21.

This formulation of the homogeneously perfused organ is suitable for any type of serial or parallel arrangement of arteries and veins; the full variety of possibilities is always accounted for by the observed $h_R(t)$ whenever the capillary–interstitial fluid units are identical in flow and other parameters. Parallel arrangements in the arterial and venous systems become consequential only when there is a heterogeneous population of capillary-tissue units and a systematic relationship between the form of various $h_{LV}(t)$ values or their mean transit times in large vessels with those in their cognate capillary-tissue units (see WHOLE-ORGAN CAPILLARY–INTERSTITIAL FLUID MODELS: HETEROGENEOUS FLOWS, p. 588).

The estimation of parameters with this model is best done by direct fitting of the curves, as illustrated in Figure 21. To optimize the fit of the model to the curves the two parameters PS_C and V_I' (or γ) are adjusted. There are two for each tracer that permeates the capillary wall.

The influences of these two parameters in the shape of $h_D(t)$ are distinctly different, as is illustrated by their sensitivity function in Figure 22. At early times on the upslope of $h_D(t)$ the fitting is influenced by PS_C alone, as anticipated by Crone (45). At later times V_I' also influences the height of the model $h_D(t)$ but with a magnitude and sign that is independent of the influence of PS_C. For example, as $\partial h_D(t)/\partial PS_C$ goes through a change of sign at $t \sim 15$ s, the influence of an increase in PS_C no longer causes $h_D(t)$ to diminish in height, but to increase. At this particular moment, since $h_D(t)$ is a smooth curve, the value of V_I' is the only influence on the height of $h_D(t)$. At this instant the influence of an increase in V_I' is to diminish $h_D(t)$, as indicated by the negative value for $\partial h_D/\partial \gamma$. The physical reason is that return flux is slower with a larger interstitial volume. In general the value of PS_C/V_I' is the dominant influence on $h_D(t)$ throughout the tail of the curve; at long times both have an influence in the same direction because any material that enters the extravascular region must eventually return.

Extraction during transcapillary passage. The early

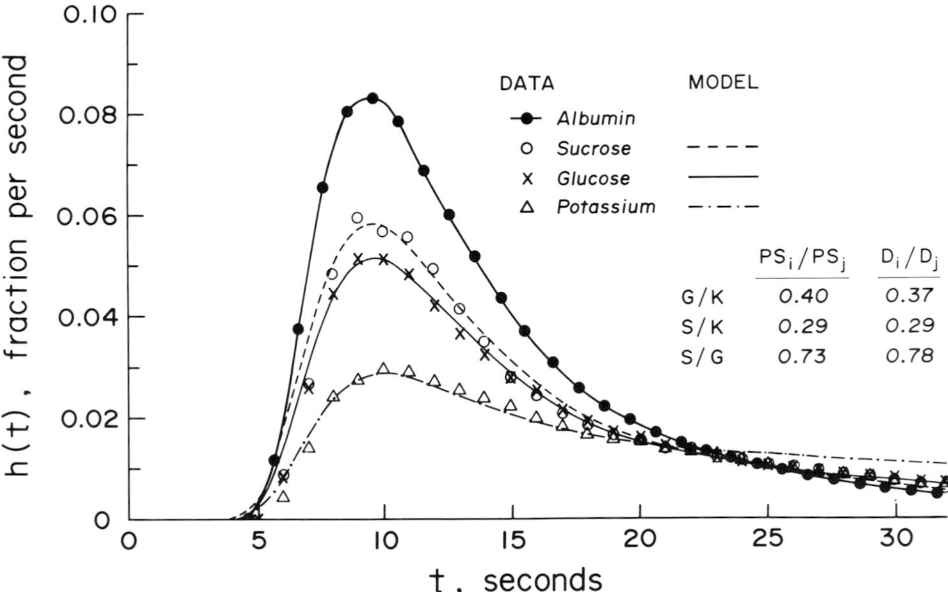

FIG. 21. Fitting of a model for homogeneously perfused organ (of configuration shown in Fig. 13) to outflow dilution curves from an isolated blood-perfused dog heart after intra-aortic injection of tracer albumin, sucrose (S), glucose (G), and potassium (K). Capillary-tissue unit consists of capillary and interstitial space only; thus cellular uptake of glucose and potassium is not accounted for. Excellence of fit despite the model's inability to account for heterogeneity of flows is probably due to use of the vasodilator dipyridamole. Rose, Goresky, et al. (170, 173) observed that dipyridamole reduces normal heterogeneity. Ratios of apparent permeabilities for the various solutes were indistinguishable from ratios of free-diffusion coefficients, suggesting that there was no steric hindrance. The conclusion is not firm, however; data of this kind need reappraisal with modeling that includes both cell entry (for glucose and potassium) and heterogeneity of flows; note the failure to fit the tail of the potassium curve.

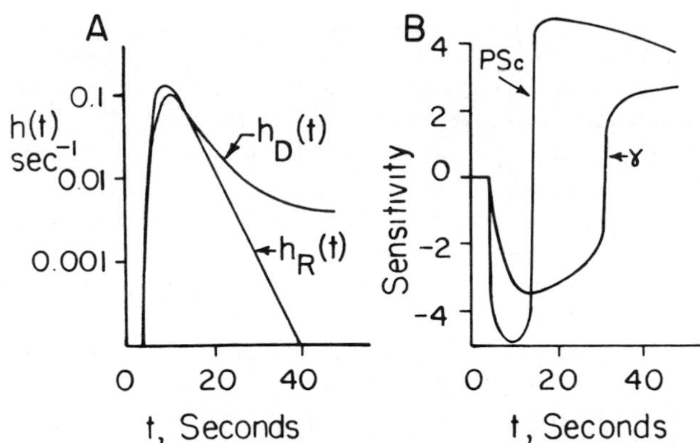

FIG. 22. Sensitivity functions for adjustable parameters PS_C and V_I' in capillary-tissue exchange model for the homogeneously perfused organ in Fig. 13. *A*: outflow responses for reference solutes $h_R(t)$ and permeating solutes $h_D(t)$. *B*: sensitivity functions showing influence of increase in PS_C and V_I' (where $\gamma = V_I'/V_C$) on the height of $h_D(t)$ over the first 10 s. PS_C, capillary permeability–surface area product; V_I', apparent interstitial volume of distribution.

goal of using single-capillary–interstitial fluid models was to estimate PS_C from tracer extraction after a bolus injection, as proposed by Chinard et al. (41) and Crone (45). This was not the only type of suitable experiment. Renkin (165, 166) had developed an equation (see Eq. 68) for the estimation of potassium permeability in skeletal muscle capillaries by using a steady-infusion technique. Guller, Bassingthwaighte, et al. (83) showed that the fractional extraction can be calculated from the venous outflow curves or from the residue functions R(t). Estimating an extraction or "exchanging fraction" is to estimate a unidirectional flux from blood to tissue and so to obtain an estimate of the conductance of the capillary wall for the solute. There are two main difficulties with using a simple, direct interpretation of an extraction. *1*) If the system is mass conservative (doesn't lose material), then all of the tracer reaches the outflow and there is zero overall extraction. Thus this extraction is quite different from the steady-state arteriovenous difference for a consumed substance. *2*) The reflux of the permeant or diffusible tracer from tissue to blood contributes to the tail of $h_D(t)$ before the complete passage of the reference curve $h_R(t)$, sometimes as early as the peak or late upslope of the dilution curve. Thus some special approximation (i.e., "modeling" in the broader sense) is needed to separate the throughput and returning components.

Some standard ways of calculating an exchange fraction from the observed dilution curves are illustrated in Figure 23. The most common is the instantaneous extraction E(t) proposed by Crone (45)

$$E(t) = [h_R(t) - h_D(t)]/h_R(t) = 1 - h_D(t)/h_R(t) \quad (64)$$

Guller, Bassingthwaighte, et al. (83) used an analogous calculation from residue functions [E′(t)] based on the fact that, as stated in Equation 22, the outflow h(t) is equal to the negative of the slope of the residue functions

$$E'(t) = 1 - dR_D(t)/dR_R(t) \quad (65)$$

where $R_D(t)$ and $R_R(t)$ are the residue functions for diffusible and reference tracers. Lassen and Crone (116) introduced the "area fraction" or net extraction $E_{net}(t)$

$$E_{net}(t) = 1 - \int_0^t h_D(\lambda)d\lambda \Big/ \int_0^t h_R(\lambda)d\lambda \quad (66)$$

usually calculating it over the interval from the appearance to the peak of the reference curve. Here λ is the variable used for the time integration. From the residue functions, this is

$$E'_{net}(t) = \frac{R_D(t) - R_R(t)}{1 - R_R(t)} \quad (67)$$

$E'_{net}(t)$ becomes identical to $R_D(t)$ when all the refer-

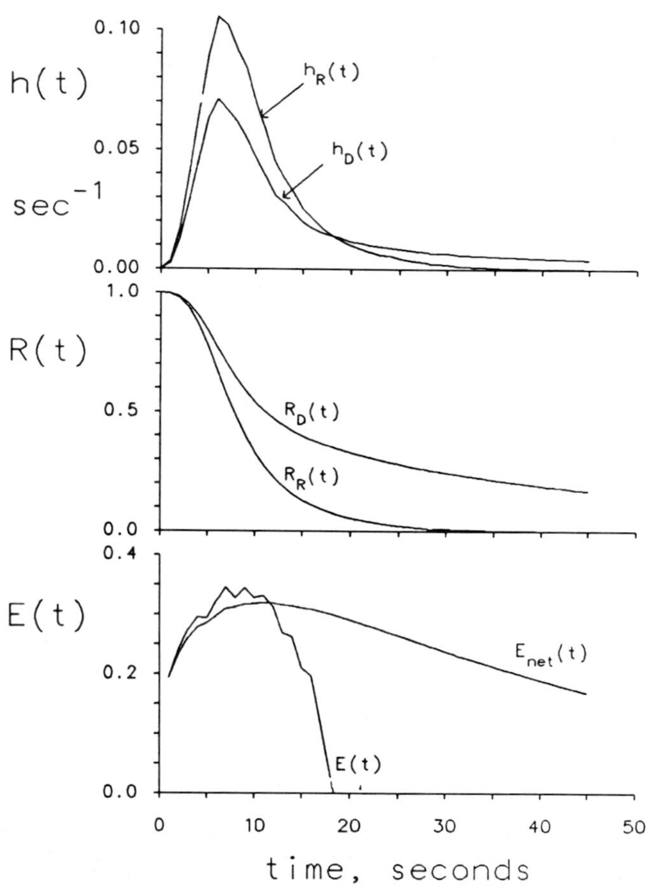

FIG. 23. Calculations of various so-called extractions of permeant tracer from impulse responses and residue functions. Outflow dilution curves obtained by sampling from dog coronary sinus after injecting into left main coronary artery ^{131}I-albumin for $h_R(t)$ and [^{14}C]sucrose for $h_D(t)$. For times beyond 35 s the tails were extrapolated exponentially. h(t), Transport function; R(t), residue function; $R_D(t)$ and $R_R(t)$, residue functions for permeating solute and reference; E(t) and $E_{net}(t)$, instantaneous and net extractions.

ence tracer has emerged from the organ. The Crone-Renkin equation (45, 165) can be used to calculate PS_C from E, given that PS_C represents a unidirectional flux

$$PS_C = -F_S \cdot \ln(1 - E) \tag{68}$$

How to use this is the difficult question. The usual approach has been to pick a value of E(t) at early times in the hope that return flux from interstitial space to blood is negligible. Bassingthwaighte (12) advocated using an E_{max}, the maximum of smoothed values of E(t) or E′(t) occurring on the upslope of $h_R(t)$ or up to about the time of the peak of $h_R(t)$ or to the steepest portion of $R_R(t)$, on the basis that this would average over some heterogeneity of flows if it were present. Guller, Bassingthwaighte, et al. (83) found that Equations 64–67 give similar estimates of early extraction for sodium in the blood-perfused dog heart; however, they observed that Equation 68 gives underestimates of PS_C compared with the values obtained by fitting the full model to the dilution curves. This means that there is some return flux that reduces E(t) to levels below what would be expected if the efflux from blood to interstitial space were unidirectional. They showed that for sodium in the heart a modification of Equation 68 could be used with good accuracy

$$PS_C = - F_S \cdot \ln(1 - 1.14\ E_{max}) \tag{69}$$

where the factor 1.14 was derived from the model fitting with $V_I' = 0.21$ ml/g. The expression is inaccurate with extractions greater than 60%, i.e., at low flows or high ratios of PS_C/F_S. The generality of this type of expression has not been shown, and it can be predicted that the factor is different for substances with cellular uptake or with different volumes of distribution in the interstitial fluid space. In general the curves of E(t) that Crone (45) obtained for small solutes in the brain and that Yudilevich and co-workers (3, 132, 239, 240) and Bassingthwaighte and co-workers (11, 83, 238) obtained in the heart were fairly flat for times preceding t_p, the time of the peak of $h_R(t)$. It is seen from the modeling that when this occurs the estimates of PS_C are not much underestimated, although there is a systematic bias toward underestimation because of the contribution to $h_D(t)$ of the return flux from the tissue.

Martín and Yudilevich (132) attempted to offset the influence of return of tracer from extravascular space into the capillary by extrapolating the indicator outflow concentrations back to the appearance time

$$E(0) = \lim_{t \to t_a} [1 - C_D(t)/C_R(t)] \tag{70}$$

where t_a is the time of appearance of the tracers in the outflow and $C_D(t)$ and $C_R(t)$ are the concentrations of diffusible and reference tracers. This does not directly account for the backdiffusion process but does introduce smoothing by extending a line through the early data points. Implicit in this equation is the idea that in a dilution curve the influence of throughput components can most easily be isolated by examining the earliest parts of the curves. It is assumed that no contamination by returning material is evident there. The problem with the expression is that when heterogeneity of flows is present, the earliest points may correspond to the shortest capillary transit times and these are then not representative of the average over the whole organ (170). The idea is of course an extension of the Crone approach in which only the initial term of the outflow response from the single-capillary–interstitial fluid model described by Equation 54 is considered; the return flux from tissue is ignored. Because in Equation 54 $C_D(t)$ and $C_R(t)$ are scaled by the same factor to give $h_D(t)$ and $h_R(t)$—special cases of $h_C(t)$—Equation 70 can be written

$$1 - E = h_D(t_a)/h_R(t_a) = e^{(-PS_C/V'_C)\tau_a} \tag{71}$$

where τ_a is the capillary transit time corresponding to the appearance time t_a. More generally, this expression has usually been written

$$1 - E = h_D(t)/h_R(t) = e^{-PS_C/F_S} \tag{72}$$

The Crone-Renkin expression (Eq. 68) is derived from this by taking the natural logarithm of each side of the equation. In this form, when the equation has been applied to whole-organ dilution curves, an average capillary transit time is implicitly considered.

From the point of view of tissue deposition the case of no return flux can be examined further to define its asymptotic patterns of behavior. Because the relative amount of tracer being delivered to one region versus another is proportional to flow to the region, the amount deposited in the tissue is the product of $E \cdot F_S$ and the area under the input concentration-time curve $C_{in}(t)$. In the limit of low flow and long transit time the extraction becomes complete ($E \rightarrow 1$) and $E \cdot F_S$ becomes unity. The tracer then behaves in a delayed-wave, flow-limited fashion. In the limit of high flow and short transit time, PS_C/F_S becomes small and the asymptote of the product $E \cdot F_S$ at high flows is PS_C

$$\begin{aligned} E \cdot F_S &= F_S(1 - e^{-PS_C/F_S} \\ &= F_S\left\{1 - \left[1 - \frac{PS_C}{F_S} + \left(\frac{PS_C}{F_S}\right)^2 - \ldots\right]\right\} \\ &= F_S\left(\frac{PS_C}{F_S} + \text{vanishingly small terms}\right) \\ &= PS_C \end{aligned} \tag{73}$$

Thus when F_S/PS_C is high, E versus F_S is hyperbolic and $E \cdot F_S$ approaches the high-flow asymptote PS_C. (An example of this behavior is illustrated in Fig. 15.) This result provides a warning to those who use the relative amount of tracer deposited as an indicator of relative regional flow because at high flows and low permeabilities the deposition ($E \cdot F_S$) is independent of flow; it is limited by the barrier permeability.

Sensitivities to parameter estimation. The measurable range of the permeability–surface area products is relatively limited. If PS_C is very low then the extraction is low. The estimation of PS_C depends on there being a measurable distance between $h_R(t)$ and $h_D(t)$, whether fitting with a model or estimating an extraction, and therefore it involves quantitating a small difference between two large numbers with substantial scatter. In practice the two dominant experimental errors are in the quantitation of the relative doses of the injected tracers (q_0 values) and in pipetting accurate sample volumes. Both errors are usually small. The error in q_0 changes the relative height of $h_D(t)$ and $h_R(t)$ and therefore is highly influential when PS_C is small. Errors in sample volume cause irregularities in the curves $h_R(t)$ and $h_D(t)$, as shown in Figure 17, but since the sample volume is the same for all tracers contained in each sample, this introduces no error into the calculation of $E(t)$. When the dimensionless ratio PS_C/F_S is quite small, then the approximate Crone-Renkin equation for PS_C (Eq. 68)—which applies to the throughput component only—is nearly correct and may be preferable for its simplicity.

When PS_C/F_S is large, permeability–surface area products can be measured accurately only when the flow-limited extreme is also defined and accessible. In its absence, when PS_C/F_S is large, estimation of the permeability–surface area product tends to become unreliable when the extraction exceeds 90%. An E of 0.9 in Equation 68 gives $PS_C/F_S = 2.3$, which is quite low. It is probably more than a coincidence that the range of PS_C/F_S values easily measured with this technique (~0.1–2) encompasses the range pertinent for small hydrophilic solutes. Teleologically the rationale may be that it is useful for substrate transport that PS_C be as high as possible yet low enough that transcapillary protein transport be minimized for osmotic control and minimization of the protein load in the lymph. Such a generality would support the commonality of values for PS_C/F_S in various tissues despite large differences in flow, capillary surface area, and PS_C. In other words, PS_C tends to be higher in organs with high flows per unit mass of tissue.

Estimation of PS_C is most accurate when heterogeneity is minimal and the initial extractions are 10%–40%. Dispersion in the venous outflow and sampling system tends to reduce the accuracy of the estimates and also introduces a bias toward underestimation by causing the returning tail of material in interstitial fluid to be mixed with the throughput component and thus lowering the early values of $E(t)$ (12). Heterogeneity of regional flows has a similar effect (M. Levin and J. B. Bassingthwaighte, unpublished observations).

Obviously there is overlap between the influence of PS_C and that of V_I as demonstrated by the sensitivity functions in Figure 22. The influences on $h_D(t)$ are similar early and opposite later. When V_I is small, the negative components of the sensitivity to PS_C and to V_I are abbreviated and the positive components are earlier and closer together. In the extreme of V_I close to zero, PS_C could not be distinguished from zero no matter what its value because $h_D(t)$ would be nearly superimposed on $h_R(t)$.

Unrealistic reduction to a lumped model. Compartmental (lumped) models are commonly used because of their convenience in defining systems. Their application to biological problems is illustrated by the works of Bohr (33), Smith and Morales (191, 192), Kety (103), Solomon (194), Berman (30), and Jacquez (96). The equations are linear, ordinary differential equations with constant coefficients, which are relatively easily solved to provide analytical solutions composed of exponential functions. Despite these advantages compartmental models commonly are not suitable to the physiological situation and are therefore sometimes misleading. The basic assumptions of compartmental modeling are as follows:

1. Each compartment is wholly and instantaneously mixed so that the concentration within it is uniform at all times.

2. The system is in a steady state with respect to mother substance so that tracer exchange rates are first order.

3. The volumes and exchange rates between compartments are constant.

The most common misuse of compartmental analysis is its application to systems failing to meet the first condition. For example, it is obvious from observing indicator-dilution curves in the circulation (see Figs. 10, 17, and 21) that the plasma is not an instantaneously mixed compartment, and yet this is commonly assumed in pharmacokinetic modeling. A further condition therefore merits listing:

4. When the time required for complete mixing in a volume is very short compared with the time constant of the fastest exchange process, then condition 1 is reasonably well fulfilled.

How to calculate "very short" is the next question. Perhaps a safe rule of thumb might be defined as follows. *1*) Let t_{mix} be the time required for concentration differences in different parts of a system to become <1%. *2*) Let the time constant for the fastest process be $\tau = V/PS$ or V/F_S. *3*) A very short mixing time is $t_{mix} < 0.1\tau$.

Whether this is too "safe" or not depends on the accuracy needed and on the physiological situation. It can be stated categorically that PS_C for small solutes is far too high to permit reasonable use of compartmental analysis. For example, for glucose with myocardial $PS_C = 0.3\ ml \cdot g^{-1} \cdot min^{-1}$ and $V_C = 0.03$ ml/g, $V_C/PS_C = 0.1\ min = 6\ s = \tau$. Diffusional mixing for glucose would take 4 time constants or $4L^2/D = 4 \times (0.1\ cm)^2/(0.5 \times 10^{-5}\ cm^2/s) = 8 \times 10^3$

s = t_{mix}. Thus $t_{mix} > 1{,}000\tau$, which demonstrates that one primary condition for compartmental analysis is not satisfied.

A continuous removal process—substrate consumption, for example—produces axial gradients in capillary and interstitial concentrations, particularly when the capillary permeability and the rate of consumption are high. Again the compartmental assumption of uniform concentration is violated.

Misuse of compartmental models for capillary-tissue exchange. In Figure 24*A* the response to an impulse input is shown for a traditional two-compartment

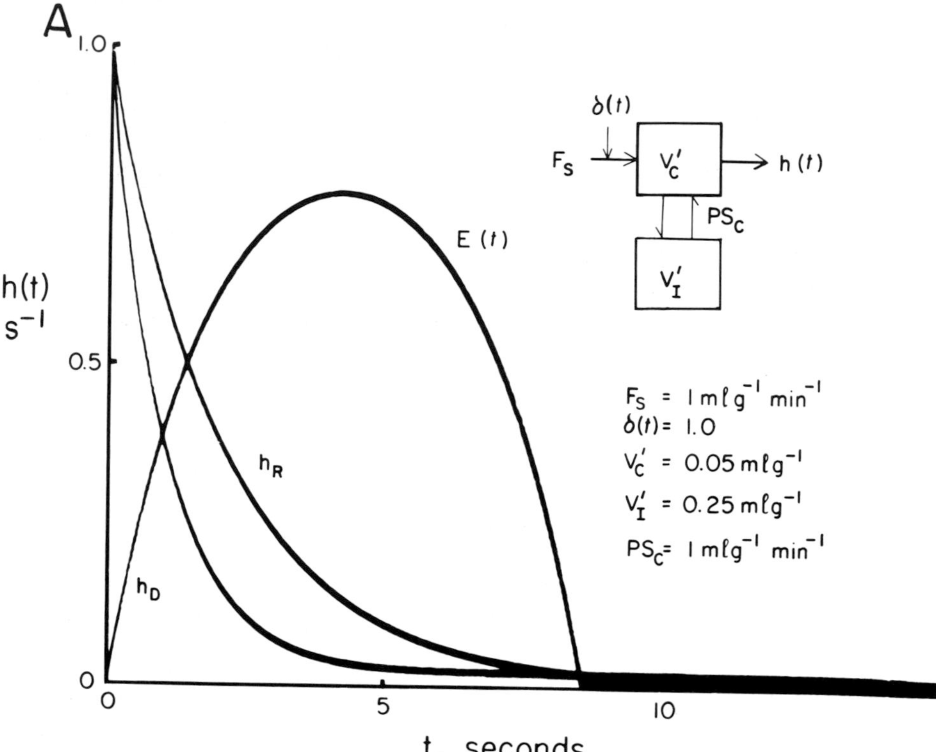

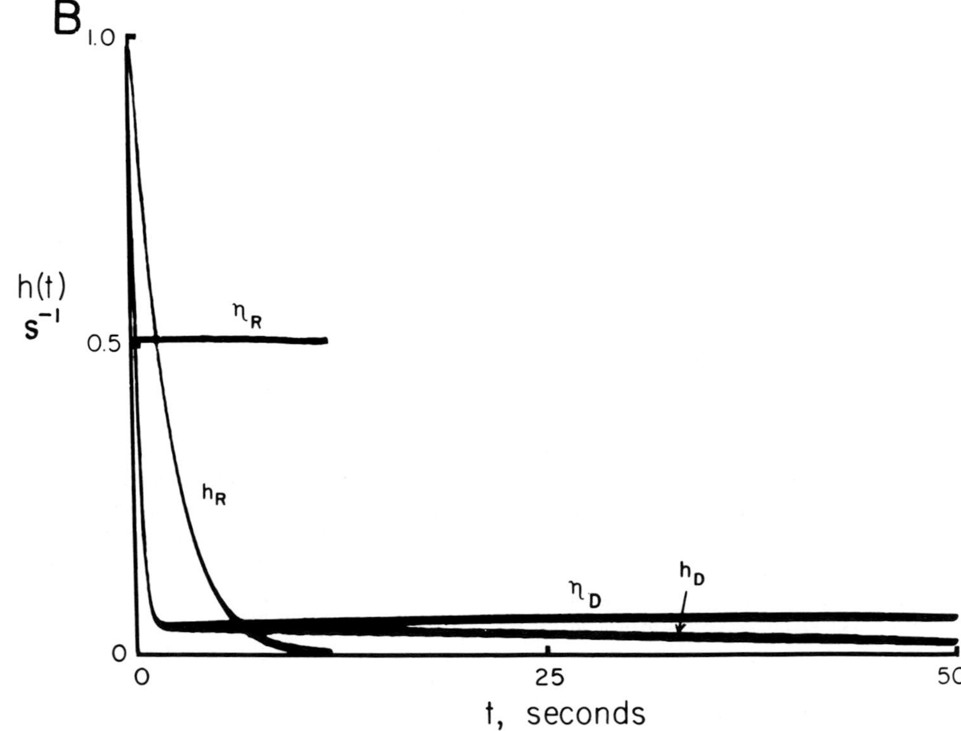

FIG. 24. Solutions for a lumped, 2-compartment model for capillary–interstitial fluid exchange. *A*: given impulse input $\delta(t)$, impulse response for an intravascular reference indicator $h_R(t)$ is a single exponential equal to $(F_S/V_C')\exp(-F_S \cdot t/V_C')$, where t is time and V_C' is the intracapillary volume of distribution. Response for the permeant tracer $h_D(t)$ has a more rapid initial component and a long tail of tracer returning from the interstitial fluid. Instantaneous extraction E(t) has a form that cannot be readily interpreted because it has no period of constancy; it is not suitable for use in the expression $PS_C/F_S = -\ln(1 - E)$. *B*: fractional escape rates [from emergence function $\eta(t)$] are more revealing of the nature of the system. For the reference tracer, $\eta_R(t)$ is constant at F_S/V_C' or 20/min. For the permeant, $\eta_D(t)$ quickly falls below even the rate of escape from the interstitium, given by PS_C/V_I' (where V_I' is the apparent interstitial volume of distribution) because the washout is both flow limited and barrier limited, as in zone II of Fig. 15.

system. Consider the flowing compartment into which label is introduced to be the capillary blood and the second compartment to be the interstitial space. The response for the intravascular tracer is a monoexponential indicator-dilution curve but that for the permeating tracer has a sharper, earlier phase and a much slower, late washout phase. The extraction calculated from such a pair of curves has a gradually rising value initially and a well-defined peak. These curves differ from experimental dilution curves in their shapes. The spatial elements present in the distributed modeling provide for the transport lags defined by flow and allow generation of curves that fit experimental data quite well.

A similar sort of problem occurs in the description of fractional escape rates or emergence functions (Eq. 26) for this two-compartment system. For the reference tracer introduced after an impulse injection into a first-order mixing chamber, the escape rate $\eta_R(t)$ is the flow divided by the capillary volume. Because the impulse response for the permeating tracer has at least two exponential components, η_D initially declines from a high rate of escape to a tail portion showing a constant rate of escape (see Fig. 24*B*). The final emergence rate, being limited by the permeability, is close to PS_C/V'_I. If the capillary permeability were very high, then the fractional escape rate $\eta(t)$ for this two-compartment model would be close to that given by Perl and Chinard (148) when axial diffusion is infinitely rapid, i.e., it would be given by the Kety expression for compartmental washout (104). In general one may say that the maximum rate of washout is either $F_S/(V'_C + V'_I)$ or PS_C/V'_I, but at intermediate values it is lower than the lesser of these. The Krogh cylinder (distributed) models have the same extremes of values when the washout rate is from the extravascular region, but the intermediate cases are quite different from the compartmental models because the fastest transit time from inflow to outflow is V'_C/F_S—not instantaneous—and the intravascular and extravascular dispersions are smaller.

Satisfactory applications of compartmental models. Several general statements that may be of value in helping to determine when compartmental models may be used are given here with the idea that it is commonly helpful to be able to use very simple, easily manipulated models even when they are not necessarily completely correct.

1. When a single process dominates. When an exchange rate or a flow is so low that all others are relatively rapid, then a consortium of processes tends to become monoexponential. Therefore this limiting rate constant can be estimated. A case in point is the washout of a substance of very low permeability (e.g., a protein) from the interstitial space, in which case the washout rate is PS_C/V'_I. This washout rate constant is the same under this condition in a distributed capillary–interstitial fluid model as it is in a compartmental model. The implication is clear, i.e., that the flow does not influence the washout. Thus an experimental test for the adequacy of a compartmental model is to increase the flow: if the washout does not increase, then one can be assured that it is barrier limited. There is a problem, however, with using this test in an organ such as the heart, because increasing the flow may make more capillaries functional. This increases the functional surface area S_C, thus making the test appear invalid when in fact it may be valid.

2. When dominating rate constants differ by an order of magnitude. The separation of exponential time constants when the observed curve contains a set of exponentials is mathematically reasonable when the data are virtually noiseless and the time constants differ by at least a factor of four. When there is any significant noise in the data, even if the data have been obtained over extended periods of time with many observations, the rate constants should differ by a larger factor, more nearly a factor of 10. An example of this is given by Rogus and Zierler (169) in which they observed washout of ^{24}Na over a period of many hours from rat skeletal muscle. Three time constants were clearly distinguishable and led to the development of a model of sodium in the sarcoplasm, the sarcoplasmic reticulum, and the extracellular space. The rate constants for exchange were so different that there seemed to be little problem in concluding that specific barriers were providing the limitation to washout and that these were mathematically distinguishable from each other.

3. When models are used purely as descriptors of data. If descriptive equations suffice without the need for interpretation, then conditions 1 and 2 are of no consequence. Most washout processes show continuous curvature on semilogarithmic plots and thus lend themselves to being described by sums of exponentials, as if they were made up of an aggregate of first-order washout processes in parallel. In testing different methods of estimating coronary blood flow by the washout of diffusible indicators, Bassingthwaighte et al. (22) fitted the downslopes of xenon and antipyrine washout curves with one or two exponentials; they found that their washout almost never required three exponentials to obtain very good fits. The descriptions with two exponentials gave estimates of the areas of the curves. Therefore flow could be best estimated from the exponentials as well as by the "height-over-area" technique of Zierler (247)—not by representing the physiological system but simply by curve fitting.

4. When models are used as components of spatially distributed systems. A distributed system can often be described well by a multicompartmental model. The simplest example is that a model composed of 5–30 similar compartments in series (an *N*th-order Poisson process) has an impulse response that can be readily fitted to observed indicator-dilution curves for albumin. The same principle applies to models for blood-

tissue exchange. For example, the distributed capillary–interstitial fluid model of Bassingthwaighte (12) was computed by using 20–60 compartments in the capillary, exchanging with the same number of interstitial fluid compartments. This numerical approach, combined with a convective shift of the contents of the capillary, provided a solution in a limiting case closely approximating the correct analytical solution given by Sheppard (188) and by Goresky et al. (79).

Equations for simple compartmental systems were provided by Solomon (194). An extensive and powerful capability for analyzing complex compartmental systems has been built up by Berman (30) and his colleagues during the past two decades and is available on many computers as Simulation Analysis and Applied Mathematics (SAAM). His general approach has been well described, although the details of the methodology are not readily available. Excellent reference works on compartmental analysis are those of Sheppard (188) and Jacquez (96).

WHOLE-ORGAN CAPILLARY–INTERSTITIAL FLUID MODELS: HETEROGENEOUS FLOWS. *Various mathematical definitions.* The variety among models for heterogeneous networks is mainly in the relationship between the capillary-tissue units and the larger conduit vessels. (For highly diffusible solutes like dissolved gases, exchange between arterial and venous vessels may also play a role, but this is considered in *Homogeneous and Heterogeneous Systems With Diffusional Shunting of Tracers*, p. 606.) Heterogeneity of the exchange process depends solely on the capillary flows; the overall transport function from artery to vein is an aggregate of many units, as is diagramed in Figure 13. The choice of a heterogeneous model therefore depends on the relationship between the large vessels and the capillaries. This relationship is governed by a combination of anatomical and rheological considerations. Local metabolic need is probably the underlying determinant of local blood flow and therefore limits the heterogeneity. Microsphere distributions give the dispersion of capillary flows but do not answer the question of how much of the spread of an indicator-dilution curve is due to dispersion along a single pathway as opposed to variation among parallel large-vessel pathways.

Here knowledge of the dispersive characteristics of a single large-vessel pathway is some help. The most dispersive situation is Newtonian (parabolic) flow; the least dispersive is that for a single vessel with a flattened velocity profile. With Newtonian flow the ratio of maximum to mean velocity is 2.0 and the relative dispersion of transit times ($SD/\bar{t}_C$) is greater than 100%. (It is not formally calculable because of failure of the integral in Eq. 38 to converge.) The observations in single arteries show a ratio of maximum to mean velocity of 1.6–1.7 (averaging 1.65) and a relative dispersion of 16%–18% (9). The flattest velocity profiles are observed at extremely high Reynolds numbers: in water with Re = 400,000 a ratio of maximum to mean velocity of 1.23 was observed by Prandtl and Tietjens (153). The dispersion of transit times from input to the microvascular unit and from the microvascular unit to the output becomes an important parameter in describing events in a simple microvascular unit.

There is no model that exactly describes all vascular networks. The architecture of the vasculature is specific to each organ and the range of forms is large; at one extreme there may be a succession of branches from a single trunk (pine-tree type) and at the other a dichotomous branching (elm-tree or lung airway types), as well as any of many intermediate combinations. As a result it is difficult to relate the transit times in large vessels to transit times in specific microvascular units. A number of simple, flexible, yet relatively realistic models that span the spectrum of possibilities are illustrated in Figures 25–28. These must not be taken too literally but should be related to the specific vascular bed under study.

At one extreme is the relatively simple and useful model assuming the independence of transport in capillaries from that in large vessels, as diagramed in Figure 25. The principle is that dispersion and delay in the arterial and venous components of the organs' vasculature are not related to the transit time through the individual capillary. The rationalization is based on observations in the heart [such as in the figures of Bassingthwaighte et al. (24)] that intercapillary distances and lengths appear to be similar in regions at the base and at the apex, i.e., whether linked to short or long arterial vessels. In addition, flows per gram of tissue in the various regions do not depend on the length of the supplying arteries.

When arterial, venous, and capillary transport functions h_A, h_V, and h_C are independent, convolution of the transport processes of the separate axial segments of the system is appropriate. The total transport function $h(t)$ is

$$h(t) = h_A(t) * \left[\sum_{i=1}^{N} w_i f_i \Delta f_i h_{C_i}(t) \right] * h_V(t) \qquad (74)$$

where the weighted summation of all the individual capillary transport functions [$h_{C_i}(t)$ values] is the overall capillary transport function $h_C(t)$. The weighting function $w_i f_i \Delta f_i$ is composed of the product of w_i, the fraction of the organ having a flow f_i; the flow f_i, which is the local flow divided by the mean flow for the organ and is dimensionless; and Δf_i, which is the width of the ith class of relative flows. Convolution is commutative, i.e., the sequence of operations can be taken in any order, and for large vessels

$$h_{LV}(t) = h_A(t) * h_V(t) \qquad (75)$$

The transport function of the set of capillaries in parallel is the sum of their individual transport func-

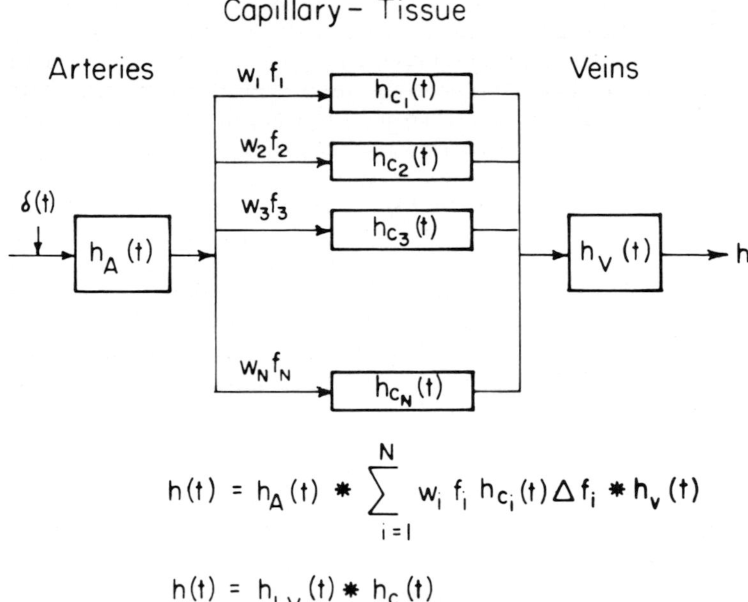

FIG. 25. Model for exchange in an organ in which the transport functions of the arteries and veins $h_A(t)$ and $h_V(t)$ are independent of those in a set of capillary-tissue regions, the $h_{C_i}(t)$ values. Capillary-tissue regions are considered to be alike except for their relative flows f_i (local flow divided by mean organ flow). Fraction of organ mass having flow f_i is $w_i \Delta f_i$, so that the fraction of tracer traversing a region with flow f_i is $w_i f_i \Delta f_i$. Each path denotes a convolution ($*$) of the linear processes given in the boxes. $\delta(t)$, Impulse input.

tions, weighted by the relative amount of flow through each type of pathway

$$h_C(t) = \sum_{i=1}^{N} w_i f_i \Delta f_i h_{C_i}(t) \tag{76}$$

The convolution integral represented by Equation 74 implies that all capillary transit times are convoluted with all elements in the distribution of large-vessel transit times, i.e., there are no preferential associations between particular large-vessel and capillary transit times. When $h_C(t)$ is for a single dispersionless capillary (i.e., when the transit time τ_C is the same in all capillaries), $h_{LV}(t)$ is the shape of the reference concentration-time curve $h_R(t)$ shifted to the left by one capillary transit time: $h_R(t) = h_{LV}(t - \tau_c)$. Conversely in the hypothetical extreme in which there is no dispersion within large vessels and all have identical transit times τ_{LV}, $h_C(t)$ would have the shape of the reference concentration-time curve shifted to the left by the large-vessel transit time: $h_R(t) = h_C(t - \tau_{LV})$ (79).

The physiological situation in the heart is intermediate, with variations occurring in both large-vessel and capillary transit times. Two approaches have been used. M. Levin and J. B. Bassingthwaighte (unpublished data) have assumed that large-vessel and capillary transit times are independent and that the distribution of regional flows given by microsphere-deposition densities (see Fig. 16) represents capillary flows (R. B. King, J. B. Bassingthwaighte, J. R. S. Hales, and L. B. Rowell, unpublished data). The distribution of relative capillary transit times is calculated as the reciprocal of the distribution of relative capillary flows, given that the volume of capillaries per unit mass of tissue V_C (ml/g tissue) is everywhere the same. (Less restrictive assumptions can be used equally well.) With V_C constant the *i*th capillary transit time is

$$\tau_{C_i} = V_C/F_i \tag{77}$$

where F_i is the local blood flow ($ml \cdot g^{-1} \cdot min^{-1}$). For an aggregate of nondispersive capillaries, the distribution of the capillary transit time for the reference tracer $h_{C,R}(t)$ is

$$h_{C,R}(t) = \Sigma w_i f_i (\Delta f_i / \Delta \tau_{C_i}) \delta(t - \tau_{C_i}) \tag{78}$$

where $\Delta f_i / \Delta \tau_i$ is the interval width in the histogram representation of flows divided by the same for the transit times. The weighting function of the relative flows (cf. Fig. 16) makes Equation 75 exact. The average capillary transit time $\bar{\tau}_C$ can be calculated directly from the experimental measurements when one has an anatomical estimate of V_C

$$\begin{aligned} \bar{\tau}_C &= \frac{V_C}{F_B/W} \\ &= \frac{V_C(\text{ml/g}) \cdot W(\text{heart wt, g}) \cdot 60(\text{s/min})}{F_B(\text{ml/min blood flow})} \end{aligned} \tag{79}$$

From myocardial preparations with silicone-casted capillaries Bassingthwaighte et al. (24) estimated V_C to be 0.035 ml/g. The individual-pathway capillary transit times τ_{C_i} can then be calculated by using f_i, the ratio of the regional flow to the mean flow

$$\tau_{C_i} = \bar{\tau}_C / f_i \tag{80}$$

For the model with independent $h_{LV}(t)$ and $h_C(t)$ the mathematical form of the input to all of the capillaries is $h_{LV}(t)$. Because superposition (linearity and stationarity) applies and the assumption of independence of the two distributions has been made, the observed outflow dilution curve for the intravascular reference tracer $h_R(t)$ is the convolution of capillary and large-vessel transport functions, as indicated by combining Equations 71 and 72

$$h_R(t) = h_{C,R}(t)*h_{LV}(t) \tag{81}$$

Because $h_{C,R}(t)$ and $h_R(t)$ are known, $h_{LV}(t)$ can be obtained by using this equation (M. Levin and J. B. Bassingthwaighte, unpublished data).

The second approach to handling flow heterogeneity is that adopted by Rose and Goresky (170). The method uses outflow dilution curves for labeled sucrose, a tracer that cannot enter cells (Fig. 26). The rationale followed the observation that after vasodilation both the reference albumin and sucrose curves showed less dispersion and a change in their shapes relative to one another. The instantaneous extraction rises steeply during the upslopes of dilution curves in the normal, relatively vasoconstricted state; but with vasodilation the E(t) curve becomes completely flat. It was inferred that in the control situation the capillary transit times represented by the first outflow samples are short, whereas later points on $h_R(t)$ and $h_D(t)$ represent outflow from capillaries with progressively longer transit times. Longer intracapillary dwell time permits greater extraction. Assuming a constant PS_C for all pathways allows a very direct calculation of the relative capillary transit times if it is further assumed that all the tracer molecules emerging at each particular time t_i are from capillaries with a single transit time τ_{C_i}. Perforce from this assumption, all pathways are secondarily assumed to be nondispersive, and as a further direct consequence a transit time τ_{LV_i} is defined for any large vessel by the capillary-tissue transit time τ_{C_i}

$$\tau_{LV_i} + \tau_{C_i} = t_i \tag{82}$$

where t_i is the time of arrival of the intravascular (undispersed) reference tracer at the outflow, having

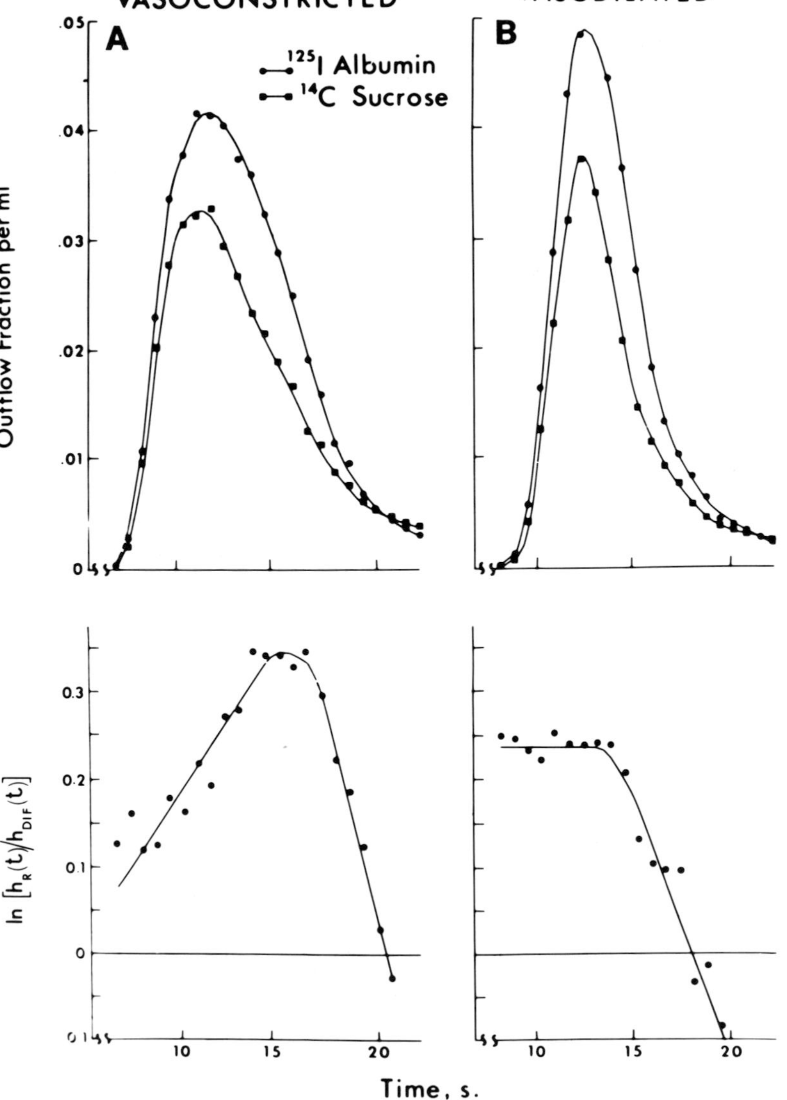

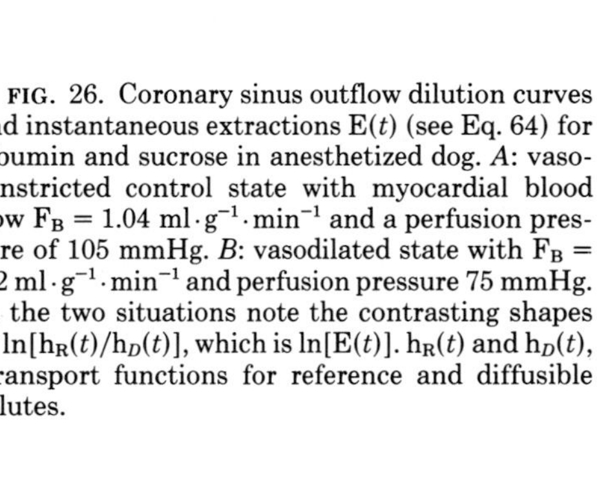
FIG. 26. Coronary sinus outflow dilution curves and instantaneous extractions E(t) (see Eq. 64) for albumin and sucrose in anesthetized dog. *A*: vasoconstricted control state with myocardial blood flow $F_B = 1.04\ ml \cdot g^{-1} \cdot min^{-1}$ and a perfusion pressure of 105 mmHg. *B*: vasodilated state with $F_B = 1.2\ ml \cdot g^{-1} \cdot min^{-1}$ and perfusion pressure 75 mmHg. In the two situations note the contrasting shapes of $\ln[h_R(t)/h_D(t)]$, which is $\ln[E(t)]$. $h_R(t)$ and $h_D(t)$, Transport functions for reference and diffusible solutes.

traversed the ith group of pathways. Because of this one-to-one relationship between large-vessel and capillary transit times, this is called the flow-coupled model. The fraction of injected tracer entering the ith pathway is $h_R(t_i)dt$.

A linear relationship between τ_{LV_i} and τ_{C_i} is constrained by the shortest transit time, i.e., the appearance time t_a

$$t_a = \tau_{LV_{min}} + \tau_{C_{min}} \quad (83)$$

and

$$\tau_{C_i} = a + b(t_i - t_a) \quad (84)$$

where a and b are constants.

Then all the data points of $h_R(t)$ and $h_D(t)$ are used to define a value for PS_C/V'_C for sucrose by using the expression

$$\ln\left[\frac{h_R(t)}{h_D(t)}\right] = \frac{PS_C}{V'_C}\,\tau_{C_i} \quad (85)$$

which is a variant of the Crone-Renkin expression; the left side is $\ln(1 - E)$ and the right side is PS_C/F_{S_i}. Equations 84 and 85 can be combined

$$\ln\left[\frac{h_R(t_i)}{h_D(t_i)}\right] = \frac{PS_C}{V'_C}\,a + \frac{PS_C}{V'_C}\,b(t_i - t_a) \quad (86)$$

When these relations are fitted to a pair of labeled albumin and sucrose outflow dilution curves from the heart, four unambiguous parameters are found (see ref. 170 and the chapter by Rose and Goresky in this *Handbook*). Two describe the capillary transit time heterogeneity, and two are related to the permeability of the capillary to sucrose and to its extravascular space of distribution. The first two are the intercept (at outflow appearance) and initial slope, respectively, of the plot described by Equation 86. The second two are the PS_C (for sucrose) per unit interstitial space, and the plasma flow per unit interstitial space.

Analyses like these carried out by Rose and Goresky (170) and Rose et al. (173) showed that changes in the estimated heterogeneity of capillary transit times make important contributions to the shaping of the autoregulatory plateau. Heterogeneity was maximal when the preparation was overperfused and minimal when the vascular resistance was minimized as a result of increased metabolic demand.

The flow-coupled transport model diagramed in Figure 27 need not be restricted to dispersionless transport; the more general formulation allows dispersive intravascular transport in each pathway. To define it mathematically the form of the dispersion must be assumed or estimated by using additional information. For example, one approach is to assume a constant relative dispersion in the pathways; then the pathway impulse responses have similar shapes, the absolute dispersions being defined by the mean transit time of the ith path. For each individual serial pathway, convolution holds

$$h_{R_i}(t) = h_{LV_i}(t) * h_{C_i}(t) \quad (87)$$

The total outflow is the weighted sum of the parallel pathway outputs

$$h(t) = \Sigma w_i f_i [h_{LV_i}(t) * h_{C_i}(t)]\Delta f_i \quad (88)$$

This approach could be incorporated directly into the analysis if the weighting function of the individual pathways were known—for example, from microsphere-deposition densities (M. Levin and J. B. Bassingthwaighte, unpublished data). The minimal and maximal regional flows are estimated from a distribution such as that in Figure 16. The shortest and longest capillary mean transit times are then estimated from the known mean flow $\overline{F}_S$ by using an assumed volume V'_C

$$\overline{\tau}_{C_{min}} = V'_C/(f_{max} \cdot \overline{F}_S) \quad (89)$$

$$\overline{\tau}_{C_{max}} = V'_C/(f_{min} \cdot \overline{F}_S) \quad (90)$$

The assumption implicit in these equations is that

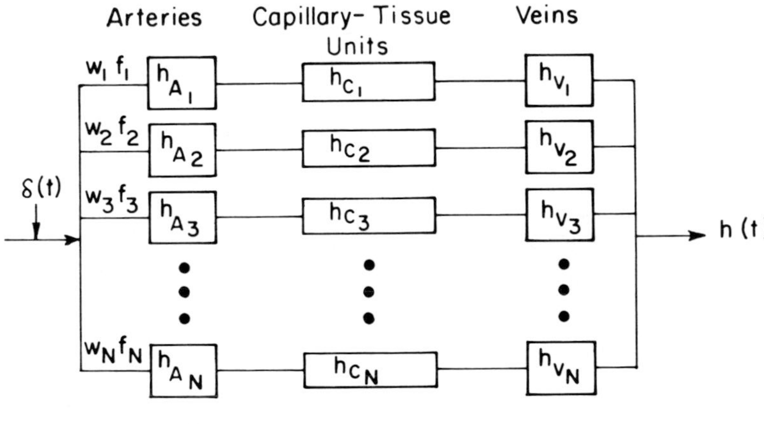

FIG. 27. Capillary-tissue transport model with specifically defined relationships between transit times in large vessels and in capillaries. In the special case of this model used by Rose and Goresky (170, 171) they considered all intravascular pathways to be nondispersive so that $h_{R_i}(t) = \delta(t - \tau_{LV_i} - \tau_{C_i})$, where $h_{R_i}(t)$ is the transport function for an individual pathway and τ_{LV_i} and τ_{C_i} are the sum of the arterial and venous transit times and the capillary transit time for pathway i. The more general form (defined in equation at *bottom* of figure) would allow for any form of h_A, h_C, or h_V that is linear, stationary, and mass conservative. It describes dispersive or nondispersive transport.

flow is utilizing all parts of the capillary bed, i.e., that the anatomical estimate corresponds to physiological reality. From Equations 83 and 84 and the appearance and disappearance times derived from the outflow dilution curve for the simultaneously injected vascular reference, one can obtain values for a slope and intercept equivalent to the a and b of Equation 84. From these values the density function of regional capillary flows can be derived. With this a comparison of the observed microsphere density functions with those expected on the basis of a set of outflow dilution curves can be carried out. In the nondispersive case the frequency function of capillary transit times can be mapped into the obverse flow domain by utilizing the expected relation

$$h_R(t_i')\Delta t_i = w_i(f_i)\Delta f_i \tag{91}$$

where t_i' is a time intermediate between t_{max} [the longest time at which $h_R(t)$ is nonzero] and t_a [the appearance time of $h_R(t)$]

$$t_i' = (t_{max} - t_i)/(t_{max} - t_a) \tag{92}$$

where t_i is the time of emergence of a particular tracer molecule. The skewed distribution of capillary transit time becomes symmetric in the microsphere flow domain. The dispersive case is not so simply stated but is analogous. The relations provide a frequency distribution of flows that can be compared with the microsphere data, but the comparison remains to be made.

It might be expected that changes in heterogeneity detected over the autoregulatory range would again be as just described. One might also expect that in a highly vasodilated state some degree of flow heterogeneity would still be present, and although recognizable in the microsphere data, might not be recognizable by the dilution approach.

Bronikowski et al. (35) carried out a theoretical examination of the form of the function $(PS_C/V_C)\cdot\tau_C(t)$ for the randomly coupled case and found that outflow times order the mean values for $\tau_C(t)$ such that, when there is a substantial heterogeneity of capillary transit times, a rising function results—much like that predicted for the flow-coupled case. This study indicates that the rising function cannot be used to distinguish between the flow-coupled and randomly coupled extremes. It also indicates that $\tau_C(t)$ is expected to vary systematically with time as originally predicted by Rose and Goresky (170). Variation with heterogeneity is expected to occur whether or not random coupling or flow coupling are present. The problem remains to discover the degree of determinism in the system.

A next stage of generality is shown by a model with partial interdependence of transit times in large vessels and capillaries, as in Figure 28. The models of Figures 25 and 27 are at opposite ends of a spectrum of models having varying degrees of interdependence of large-vessel and capillary transit times. Because of lack of detailed information on intraorgan dispersion, the more general model of Figure 28 requires assumptions about either the forms of the large-vessel transport functions $h_{LV_j}(t)$ and their relationship to each other or of the probability density functions for the distribution from each of the $h_{LV_j}(t)$ values to the $h_{C_i}(t)$ values. (The subscripts j and i are used for large-vessel and capillary indices, respectively.) The v_i values give the fraction of total flow going to each of the large-vessel pathways (and are equivalent to the w_if_i values, although they cannot be measured directly). The $u_{j,i}$ values give the fraction of the jth large-vessel pathway going to the ith capillary pathway. Although this model formulation is manageable with very few additional parameters defining the distributions u and v, limitations imposed by the network structure would be more useful. The models of the microvasculature as randomized branching networks presented by Levin and Popel (123) may be useful in this regard, but they are probably best designed for description of individual organs.

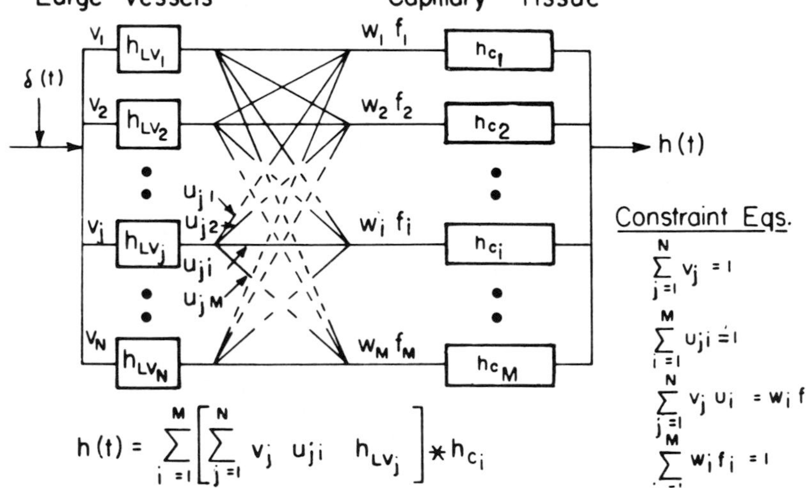

FIG. 28. Capillary-tissue transport model with variable degree of association between transport functions of large vessels and capillaries. The large-vessel transit times, with fractions of flow v_j through the N independent pathways, may be nondispersive [i.e., $h_{LV_j}(t) = \delta(t - \tau_{LV_j})$] or dispersive. Flow from the jth large-vessel pathway is distributed among M capillary-tissue units, the distribution being defined by the $u_{j,i}$ to the ith of the M units. The distribution functions, the u_j's, may differ from each other in the most general case, but such a degree of generality is probably not useful. When they are nondispersive, when $N = M$, $u_{j,i} = 1.0$ for all $j = i$, and $u_{j,i} = 0$ for all $j \neq i$, then this model is identical to that in Fig. 26 and that of Rose and Goresky (170). When all $h_{LV_j}(t)$ values are dispersive and identical, then the model is the same as that in Fig. 25.

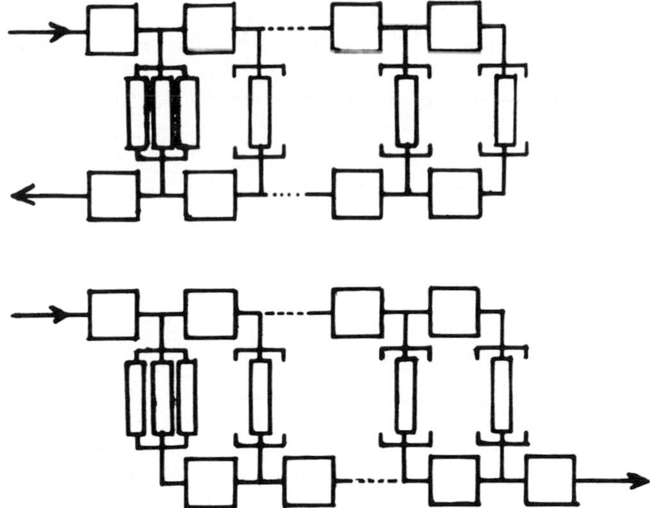

FIG. 29. Examples of alternative models for the arrangement of arteries, capillary-tissue units, and veins in an organ. Heterogeneity of flow in capillary-tissue units indicated by triplication of elongated units on diagram; in actuality more elements are likely to be needed. Each box represents a distributed element with dispersion, not a first-order compartment. *Top*: diagram for an extended organ (e.g., a leg) with arterial inflow and venous outflow in proximity. *Bottom*: diagram for an organ with inflow and outflow separated (e.g., in the liver and parts of the heart). Either of these (or others) might be considered as a component of an aggregate of such units in parallel.

The anatomy of the vascular network may suggest other variations, such as those diagramed in Figure 29. An organ like the heart contrasts with the leg, in which the distances the blood travels through large vessels are quite different. In the heart, capillaries serve relatively uniformly sized regions of tissue. Within the arteries and the veins of the heart there is dispersion due to the velocity profile, axial and radial diffusion, turbulence or disturbed flow, and eddy and cross-stream mixing, all of which result in intra-arterial and intravenous dispersion. Relative intra-arterial dispersion has been found to be ~16%–18% (9), intra-aortic dispersion to be 50% (15), transpulmonary dispersion to be 50% (195), and transcoronary dispersion to be 40% (107). The models should account for this overall transport heterogeneity when realistic values for the dispersion of 16%–20% along individual pathways are used. Therefore alternative models are diagramed in Figure 29. The equations are not as simple as for those in Figures 25 and 27, but there is some resemblance. For example, the model in Figure 29*B* becomes identical to that in Figure 25 if the convolution of the arterial transport function $h_A(t)$ for the individual pathway with the transport function through the veins $h_V(t)$ is the same in all regions. This is reasonable, since even though the arteries have a different velocity of flow than the veins, the relative dispersion and skewness of the transport functions may well be reasonably similar. Therefore, unless the volumes on the venous side versus the arterial side are quite different from one region to another, the total transfer functions should be fairly similar and thus similar to the model of Figure 25. This type of model would not serve at all for the leg, but it makes better sense for the heart where the arterial inflow and the venous outflow are separated.

There are thus various ways of describing heterogeneity—all imperfect. It should be emphasized that the best configuration is different for each organ. A combination of two or even three of these different arrangements of the microvasculature may be needed for satisfactory analysis of all the phenomena involved. The form of the heterogeneity almost certainly influences the parameter values for the exchange processes, and the degree of heterogeneity is demonstrably important.

Influences of heterogeneity on estimates of capillary PS and interstitial volumes. This is an area in which further quantitative studies are needed. At this stage it is clear that failure to account for heterogeneity gives systematic errors in the estimates of parameter values. Although the various models of heterogeneity must differ quantitatively, the errors in estimating PS_C and V'_I from single-capillary models compared with the appropriate multicapillary models are in the same direction even if not to the same degree.

It should be appreciated that a multicapillary model may not necessarily give a remarkably better fit to the data than a single-capillary model does, although in our experience it is always somewhat better. The key is that only by the fitting of a multicapillary model can one account for the observed variation in regional flows as well as the observed sets of dilution curves. One fits the observed microsphere-deposition density function or other heterogeneity descriptor and the exchange parameters of the multiple-indicator–dilution curves simultaneously. Use of flow distributions reduces the number of degrees of freedom in fitting models to data, but the reassuring result has been that despite this the closeness of fit has been improved. This is illustrated in Figure 30 for coronary outflow dilution curves for L-glucose by using the model in which $h_{LV}(t)$ and $h_C(t)$ are independent (as in Fig. 25). From one experiment of J. Kuikka, M. Levin, and J. B. Bassingthwaighte (unpublished data) a pair of curves for albumin $h_R(t)$ and L-glucose $h_D(t)$ are shown fitted with single-capillary and multicapillary models. (The L-glucose does not enter the cells.) In the *left panel* the glucose curve is fitted by a single-capillary model (i.e., all capillaries have the same flow and transit time) so that the input to the capillary is a curve of exactly the same shape as the experimentally recorded $h_R(t)$ curve except that it is shifted to the left by exactly the capillary transit time τ, which in this case is 3.64 s.

The *middle panel* shows the fit of the multicapillary model to the same data, the f_i values describing the relative regional flows being taken from the microsphere-deposition densities. The estimated parameter

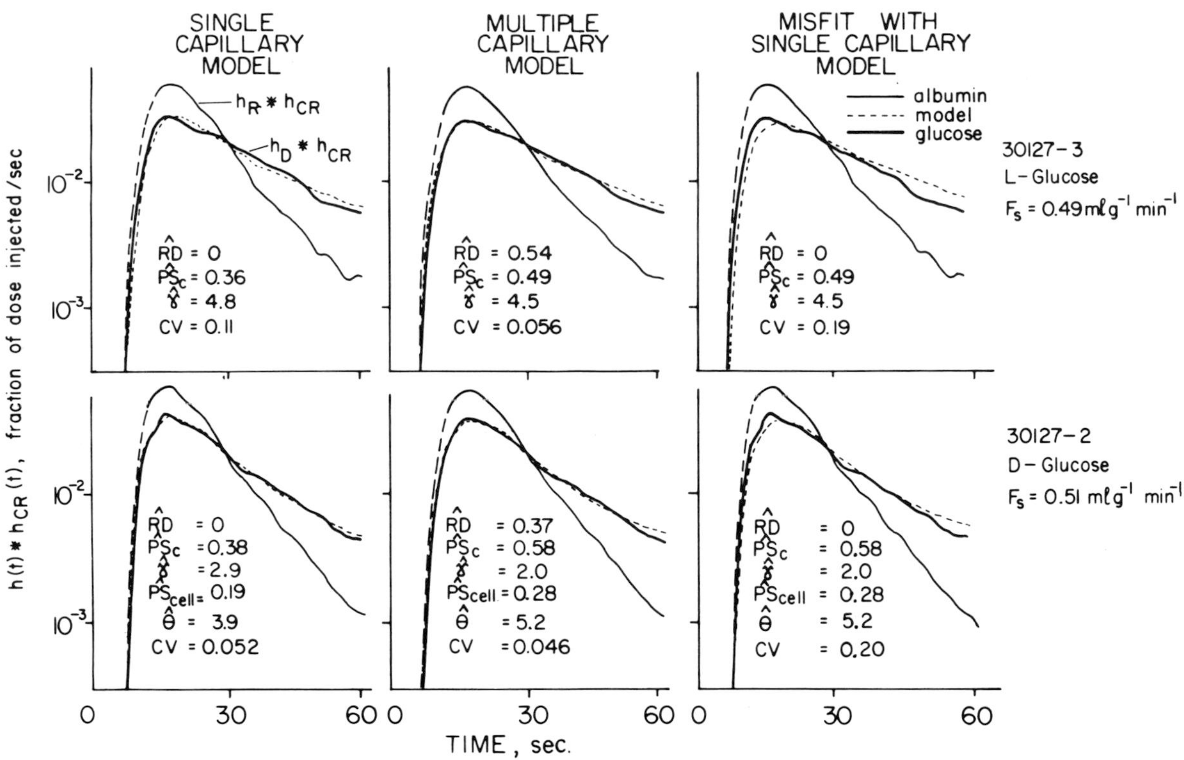

FIG. 30. Coronary outflow indicator-dilution curves for albumin $h_R(t)$ and permeant tracer glucoses $h_D(t)$; L-glucose in *upper panels* and D-glucose in *lower panels* from isolated blood-perfused dog heart. Curves fitted with single-capillary and multicapillary models. Experimental glucose curves fitted with single-capillary models (*left panels*) and the multicapillary model with independence of large-vessel and capillary transport functions (*middle panels*). In both cases the observed reference curve $h_R(t)$ was used to define the input to the capillaries. *Right panels*, parameter values obtained from the multicapillary model used to produce a model curve for $h_D(t)$ based on a single capillary (i.e., uniform flow). Marked difference from the experimental curve for $h_D(t)$ illustrates the importance of using the multicapillary model. Parameters with carets denote estimates. $h_{C,R}(t)$, Distribution of capillary transit time for reference tracer; $\widehat{RD}$, relative dispersion; $\gamma = V'_I/V'_C$; $\Theta = V'_{cell}/V'_C$; F_S, plasma flow; CV, coefficient of variation.

values are different from those obtained by using the single-capillary model, which always gives underestimates of PS_C. The fitting with the multicapillary model is closer, particularly around the peak and the early, critically important part of the downslope of $h_D(t)$.

The *right panels* of Figure 30 demonstrate the inadequacy of the single-capillary model. Taking the viewpoint that the "correct" parameter values are those listed in the *middle panels* of Figure 30, these values are used in the single-capillary model to provide a solution for $h_D(t)$. The fit is poor and the coefficient of variation is large. We conclude that the single-capillary model is not as suitable as the multicapillary model.

To evaluate the influence of heterogeneity on the estimate of PS_C with greater precision, a pseudo-Gaussian variation in flows (Gaussian with seven class sizes) was assumed and a set of test curves was generated by using specific values of F_S, PS_C, and γ but with different relative dispersions of the flows ranging from 0 up to 50%. The best fits of a single-capillary model to the pseudoexperimental test case with seven pathways were obtained, and the results are shown in Figure 31.

The value of PS_C is consistently underestimated when a single-capillary model is used to fit the multicapillary data, and the error increases with increasing heterogeneity. Because this test is on noise-free "data" generated from a seven-pathway model, any random error in actual data may give larger errors.

The next question is whether the degree of error in $\widehat{PS}_C$ (estimated PS_C) is different in differing ranges of the true values of PS_C. For example, because the Crone-Renkin equation (Eq. 72) is less subject to error in situations of uniform flow at low values of PS_C and smaller initial apparent extractions, it might be anticipated that the error in estimating PS_C with a single-capillary model might be less when $PS_C/\overline{F}_S$ is small. However, Figure 31*B* shows that when there is significant heterogeneity the error in PS_C is least around $PS_C/F_S = 1$. The rationale is that at this level there is the best compensation for the diminished extraction in high-flow regions and the return flux in low-flow regions. The figure shows that PS_C was underestimated particularly at both low and high values of PS_C.

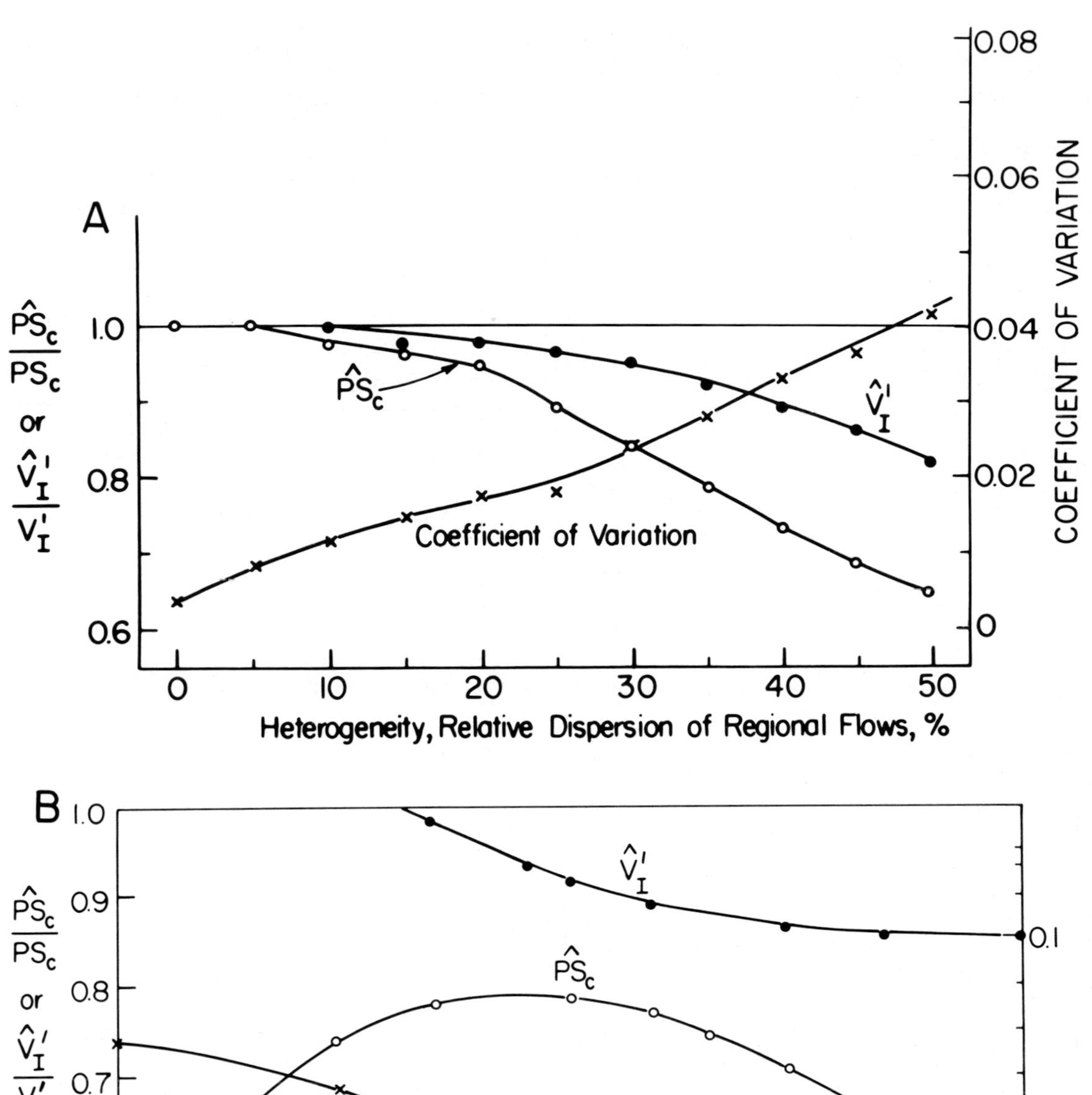

FIG. 31. Underestimation of PS_C and V'_I by using a single-capillary model to fit a multicapillary heterogeneous flow system. *A*: "data" curves generated from a multicapillary model with fixed PS_C and V'_I but with heterogeneity of regional flows. Input function defining the large-vessel transport function $h_{LV}(t)$ was a lagged normal density curve (16) with the parameters of the curve fixed at $\bar{t}$ = 10 s, RD = 0.18, and skewness β_1 = 1.16. Parameters with carets denote estimates; those without carets stand for true values. Abscissa, RD of flows, i.e., standard deviation divided by mean flow. Capillary–interstitial fluid–cell model generated with PS_C = 1.0 ml·g^{-1}·min^{-1}, V'_I/V_C = 5.0, and F_S = 1.0 ml·g^{-1}·min^{-1}. The heterogeneity model is one with parallel, noninteractive units of varied flows all having the same large-vessel transport function (see Fig. 25). *B*: there is relatively constant error in $\widehat{PS}_C$ estimates (over a middle range of values) of 0.3–3.0 ml·g^{-1}·min^{-1}. Multicapillary test data generated with RD of regional flows of 35%, with PS_C different for each case.

It is interesting that the underestimation was fairly constant over the physiological range of maximum interest: 22%–30% over the range of $0.3 < PS_C < 3.0$ $ml \cdot g^{-1} \cdot min^{-1}$.

Although the potential importance of heterogeneity of flows on the estimation of transport parameters such as PS_C has been appreciated for a long time (17, 47), the quantitative effect of choosing different spatially distributed, dispersive models such as those diagramed in Figures 25 and 28 remains a topic for future research.

Guller, Bassingthwaighte, et al. (83) did make comparisons between the estimates of PS_C obtained from the Crone-Renkin equation (Eq. 72) and those obtained from whole-organ studies, but only for homogeneous flow. Rose and Goresky (170) compared the estimates of PS_C obtained from a multicapillary model (reduced from that shown in Figure 27 and having nondispersive transport in each pathway) with estimates from a single-capillary model. They found that the latter technique gave very much lower estimates of PS_C.

The choice of model influences both the susceptibility to error and the systematic nature of such errors at different ranges of parameter values. Error is likely to be greatest when a part of the data is analyzed by analogy with a part of a model rather than by fitting the whole of the observed data with a complete and self-consistent model. For example, by analogy with the two-compartment model of Figure 24, some investigators (e.g., ref. 183) have attempted to analyze residue function curves from organs in terms of two exponential components and thus to estimate PS_C and V'_I. The results presented in those studies look reasonably self-consistent, but an ordered study of inherent systematic and statistical errors or of regions of applicability versus inadequacy has not been undertaken. As noted in the legend to Figure 24 the extraction, $E(t)$, cannot be easily translated into physiological parameter estimates, nor does extrapolation of the residue functions $R_D(t)$ yield good estimates of the single-pass extraction for calculating PS_C by the Crone-Renkin equation (Eq. 72), although the estimates may not be far wrong when PS_C is small.

Cell–Interstitial Fluid–Capillary Exchange

SINGLE-CAPILLARY–INTERSTITIAL FLUID–CELL MODEL. *Mathematical definitions.* The extension of the model to provide for transport across cell membranes utilizes the general concepts of the convection-permeation-diffusion approach given in Equations 44 and 45. Conn and Robertson (43) developed a three-compartment model for potassium exchange, which lacked the critical feature of axial distribution. Renkin's (165, 166) model for potassium exchange with the cells of skeletal muscle incorporated the axial distribution but only one membrane barrier. Sheehan and Renkin (187) reanalyzed the data and accounted for both capillary and cell barriers, but they considered the interstitial fluid and cell regions as lumped compartments rather than spatially distributed regions.

The first definitive extension of the axially distributed models to account for uptake by cells was that of Ziegler and Goresky (242), which they designed for the analysis of rubidium uptake in the heart during the first minute. However, because it did not account for reflux from the cell, it was unsuitable for the analysis of data obtained over longer times. Thus it could not be used for the analysis of potassium reflux from myocardial cells by Tancredi, Yipintsoi, and Bassingthwaighte (210). Tancredi et al. accounted for reflux in the same way as Sheehan and Renkin (187), but the former had the advantage of having the early, transient outflow dilution curves from which to estimate PS_C separately.

The first analytical distributed model accounting for uptake into and reflux from the cells was that of Rose, Goresky, and Bach (172). The model had the advantage of being expressed in the form of an analytical solution (albeit with series expansions) and thereby mathematically displaying some of its features. Later models solved numerically lacked this feature but were slightly more general. For example, the model of Roselli and Harris (174, 175) accounted for intravascular tracer transport in erythrocytes as well as in plasma, and that of J. B. Bassingthwaighte, B. Winkler, and R. Kern (unpublished data) retained terms for axial diffusion in all three regions. The latter is as fast to compute numerically as is the analytical solution and appears to be at least as accurate in calculating the limiting cases, which are the only situations, apart from the estimation of areas and mean transit times, where checks can be made on the accuracy of either the analytical or numerical solutions. The analytical solution is emphasized here because one can see the mathematical features of the system's behavior in this solution.

The form of the single-capillary–interstitial fluid–cell unit is shown in Figure 32. The general expressions in Equations 44 and 45 remain suitable, and the specific equation for the capillary region (Eq. 46) remains unchanged. If the axial-diffusion term with diffusion coefficient D_C (in cm^2/s) is left in to illustrate its form, Equation 46 would read

$$\frac{\partial C_C(x,t)}{\partial t} = -\frac{F_S L}{V'_C}\frac{\partial C_C}{\partial x} - \frac{S_C}{V'_C}(P_1 C_C - P_2 C_I) + D_C \frac{\partial^2 C_C}{\partial x^2} \tag{93}$$

The exchange between interstitial fluid and cell requires an additional term; thus Equation 49 becomes

$$\frac{\partial C_I(x,t)}{\partial t} = \frac{S_C}{V'_I}(P_1 C_C - P_2 C_I) - \frac{S_{cell}}{V'_I}(P_3 C_I - P_4 C_{cell}) + D_I \frac{\partial^2 C_I}{\partial x^2} \tag{94}$$

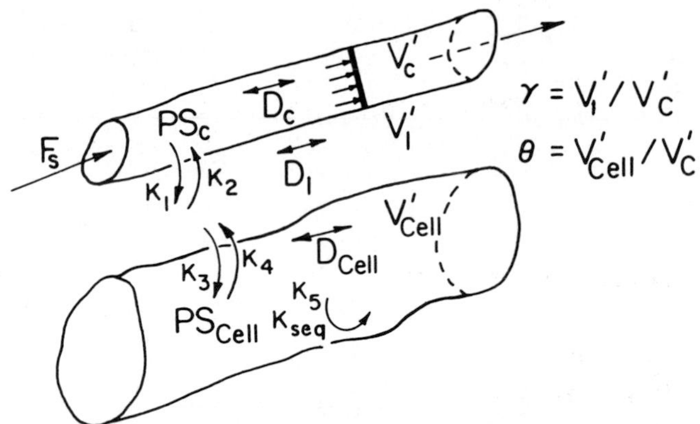

FIG. 32. Model of spatially distributed single-capillary–interstitial fluid–cell model for solute exchanges. The underlying premise is that capillaries are too long for instantaneous axial diffusion to bring about equilibration of concentrations from end to end, although radial equilibration is rapid. The model allows one to define mathematically an array of capillary-tissue units such as those shown in Fig. 1. The K's are rate constants used by Rose, Goresky, and Bach (172). k_{seq}, Sequestration rate constant.

$$h_C(t) = e^{-k_1\gamma\tau}\delta(t-\tau) + e^{-k_1\gamma\tau}\cdot\Bigg[\Bigg\{e^{d(t-\tau)}\sqrt{\gamma k_1 k_2 \tau A'/(t-\tau)}\; I_1[2\sqrt{\gamma k_1 k_2 \tau A'(t-\tau)}] + e^{f(t-\tau)}\sqrt{\gamma k_1 k_2 \tau B'/(t-\tau)}\; I_1[2\sqrt{\gamma k_1 k_2 \tau B'(t-\tau)}]\Bigg\}S(t-\tau) + \int_\tau^t e^{d(\lambda-\tau)}\sqrt{\gamma k_1 k_2 \tau A'/(\lambda-\tau)}\; I_1[2\sqrt{\gamma k_1 k_2 \tau A'(\lambda-\tau)}] \cdot e^{f(t-\lambda)}\sqrt{\gamma k_1 k_2 \tau B'/(t-\lambda)}\; I_1[2\sqrt{\gamma k_1 k_2 \tau B'(t-\lambda)}]d\lambda\Bigg] \tag{97}$$

where S_{cell} and S_C are the surface areas of the parenchymal cells of the organ and the capillary (cm²/g). Permeability terms (in cm/s) include P_1 and P_2, the apparent permeabilities at the axial position in an outward and centripetal direction; P_3, the permeability for entry into the cell; and P_4, the permeability for exit from the cell. The term $C_{cell}(x, t)$ is the concentration of the labeled solute within the cell that is available for reflux to the interstitial space, and C_I and V_I' are the interstitial concentration and apparent interstitial volume of distribution. Inside the cell

$$\frac{\partial C_{cell}(x,t)}{\partial t} = \frac{S_{cell}}{V'_{cell}}(P_3C_I - P_4C_{cell}) - k_{seq}C_{cell} + D_{cell}\frac{\partial^2 C_{cell}}{\partial x^2} \tag{95}$$

where k_{seq} [ml/(g·s)] is a first-order clearance or unidirectional removal by binding, burning, or otherwise consuming or sequestering within the cell. The terms C_{cell}, D_{cell}, and V'_{cell} are intracellular concentration, diffusion coefficient, and volume of distribution. Because axial diffusion does not have a marked effect when capillaries are long, the diffusion terms can be omitted to obtain analytical solutions. As before, one can substitute Equation 95 into Equation 94 and the result into Equation 93 to obtain the conservation expression, which in the absence of axial-diffusion terms is

$$\frac{\partial C_C}{\partial t} + \frac{F_S L}{V_C}\frac{\partial C_C}{\partial x} + \gamma\frac{\partial C_I}{\partial t} + \Theta\left(\frac{\partial C_{cell}}{\partial t} + k_{seq}C_{cell}\right) = 0 \tag{96}$$

where $\gamma = V_I'/V_C'$ and $\Theta = V'_{cell}/V_C'$.

The solutions for the spatial concentration-distance profiles and for the concentration-time curves in the capillary outflow are more complicated than those of Equation 54 for the capillary–interstitial fluid model, but the same ideas are evident. The capillary concentration-time curve at the outflow from a single capillary after an impulse input at its entrance (where $k_1 = P_1S_C/V_I'$, $k_2 = P_2S_C/V_I'$, $k_3 = P_3S_{cell}/V_I'$, $k_4 = P_4S_{cell}/V_I'$, and $k_5 = k_{seq}$) is described as Equation 97 above.

The term $I_1[y]$ is a first-order modified Bessel function with argument y, d and f are the roots of the quadratic equation, and A' and B' are constants

$$s^2 + [k_2 + k_3 + (\gamma/\Theta)k_4 + k_5]s + (\gamma/\Theta)k_2k_4 + k_2k_5 + k_3k_5 = 0$$

$$A' = \frac{d + (\gamma/\Theta)k_4 + k_5}{d - f}$$

$$B' = \frac{f + (\gamma/\Theta)k_4 + k_5}{f - d}$$

In Equation 97, $\delta(t - \tau)$ is the Dirac delta function delayed one capillary transit time, $S(t - \tau)$ is the unit step function starting at $t = \tau$ and being zero previously, and λ is a dummy variable of integration in the integral concerning the intracellular accumulation.

Equation 97 has five main components. The first term is the throughput or spike component defining the fraction of tracer that passes along the capillary without escaping into the tissue. The second and third terms are dominated by events in the interstitial fluid, i.e., the escape from interstitial fluid back to the capillary with a characteristic rate of PS_C/V_I' and permeation into the cell with a characteristic rate of

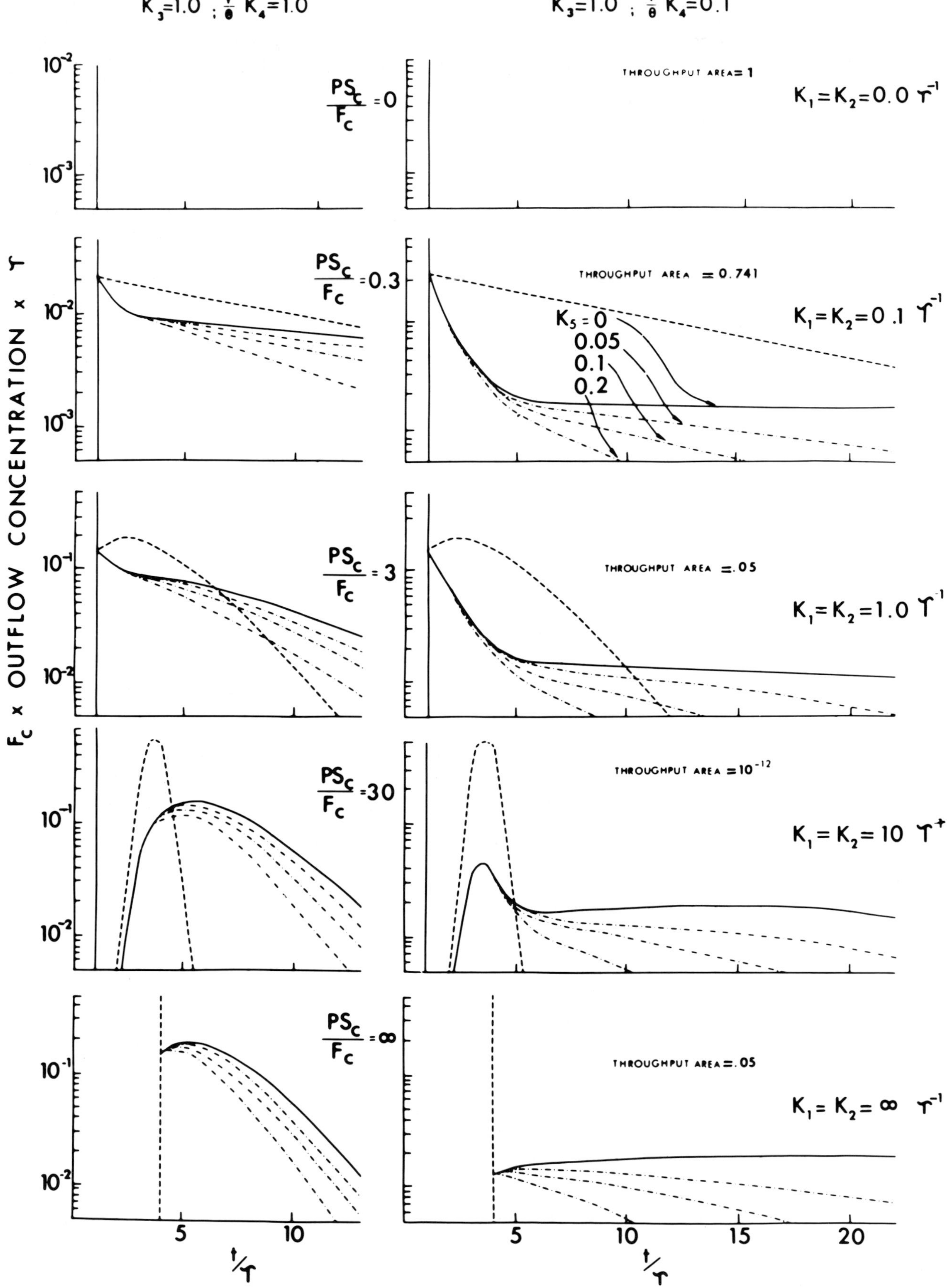

K3=1.0 ; γ/θ K4=1.0
K3=1.0 ; γ/θ K4=0.1
PSc/Fc =0
THROUGHPUT AREA= 1
K1=K2=0.0 τ⁻¹
PSc/Fc =0.3
THROUGHPUT AREA = 0.741
K5=0
0.05
0.1
0.2
K1=K2=0.1 τ⁻¹
PSc/Fc = 3
THROUGHPUT AREA =.05
K1=K2=1.0 τ⁻¹
PSc/Fc =30
THROUGHPUT AREA =10⁻¹²
K1=K2=10 τ⁺
PSc/Fc =∞
THROUGHPUT AREA=.05
K1=K2=∞ τ⁻¹
Fc x OUTFLOW CONCENTRATION x τ
10⁻²
10⁻³
10⁻¹
5
10
15
20
t/τ

PS_{cell}/V'_I. The terms on the fourth and fifth lines relate the balance between the influx into and the loss from the cell with characteristic rate constants of PS_{cell}/V'_C and k_5 (the rate constant for sequestration). The integral is a convolution of the two terms in the braces on the second and third lines. Because the extent of reflux from the cell and of the sequestration or metabolism opposing the reflex depend on the total accumulation at each moment, these latter terms are a part of an integral that requires evaluation at each time point in the solution. Thus this computation is rather costly in computer time. It is for this reason that numerical solutions can be computed more quickly.

BEHAVIOR OF THE MODEL. The outflow concentration-time curves from a single capillary after an impulse input at the entrance to the capillary have primary features similar to those shown for the capillary–interstitial fluid unit in Figure 19, i.e., a spike of unextracted solute and a tail of solute returning from the extravascular region. The form of the tail is influenced by the rates of permeation of the cell, reflux from the cell (which depends on cell volume), and the rate of incorporation into forms that do not escape from the cell, as shown in Figure 33.

The upper dashed lines represent the cases with no cell entry, i.e., $PS_{cell} = 0$ or $k_3 = 0$. The solid lines in the figure represent the outflow for the case with $k_{seq} = 0$ (no metabolism) but with cell entry and reflux. The lower, more widely spaced dashed lines show responses for three finite rates of cell metabolism, at 0.05, 0.1, and 0.2 s^{-1}.

The *left panels* of Figure 33 represent cases with increased values of PS_C but with constant values of PS_{cell} and F_S, $\gamma = 3.0$, and V'_{cell}/V'_C (i.e., $\Theta) = \gamma$. This is a smaller volume for cells than one finds in most tissues but serves to illustrate the various forms of the returning tail. The effect of increasing rates of intracellular sequestration (k_5 or k_{seq}) is to reduce the tail concentrations, particularly at later times. The sequestration or metabolism is considered as a first-order process; longer availability means greater loss to metabolism and therefore less return of tracer because there is no provision for the reflux of metabolites or the release of sequestered material in any form. (These are features that are needed in some future, further developed models.) A comparison of the peak values of the tail component of the dilution curve at the downstream exit of the capillary $C_C(L,t)$ is shown in the three *lower panels*. The peaks are demonstrated to be higher than those for the two *upper panels*: the tracer must escape from the capillary to participate in reflux from interstitial fluid and cell.

In the *right panels* of Figure 33 the cell volume was increased by a factor of 10 while other parameter values were unchanged. The effect is to retard the reflux so that the concentration levels are lowered and the curves are extended in time. Because of the longer intracellular retention, the solute is available longer for metabolism and the fraction metabolized is greater. In special cases a compartmental analogue would be very similar: if the capillary transit times were 1/10 of V'_I/PS_C, and V'_{cell}/PS_{cell} were another 10-fold longer, then three phases of washout would be separable. With very long retention the axial diffusion terms would play a greater role in evening out the intratissue concentration gradients. However, because of the unidirectional nature of the flow the gradients do not vanish; instead at later times an increasing fraction of the tracer accumulates near the outflow end of the tissue. The reason is that the flow carries tracer (which has returned from the tissue near the upstream end of the capillary) downstream until it reescapes into the tissue, and this tends to empty the upstream end of the tissue of contained tracer. The only factor offsetting this is axial diffusion, which causes net movement of tracer from the high-concentration region near the outflow in an upstream direction within the extravascular regions. These opposing factors bal-

FIG. 33. Outflow concentration-time curves for substances undergoing passive barrier-limited distribution at the capillary and concomitant exchange with the cell at the tissue cell membrane in response to a unit impulse input. Area under each curve is unity. Abscissa is normalized to t/τ, which is time divided by the capillary transit time, and ordinate correspondingly becomes $F_C\tau u(L,t)$; F_C is same as F_S in text, and $u(L,t)$ is the outflow concentration-time curve. In all cases the capillary membrane has been assumed to be equilibrative ($k_1 = k_2$) and $\gamma = 3.0$, where k's are rate constants and $\gamma = V'_I/V'_C$. *Left panels*, for an equilibrative tissue cell membrane ($k_3 = k_4 = 1.0$) with $\gamma/\Theta = 1.0$; *right panels*, for the equivalent case with the cell volume expanded by a factor of 10 (i.e., $\gamma/\Theta = 0.1$) and an equilibrative cell membrane ($k_3 = k_4 = 1.0$); $\Theta = V'_{cell}/V'_C$. Abscissa scale is linear; ordinate scale is logarithmic. In each case, capillaries with equal PS_C/F_C values are displayed on the two sides of the plots, and the panels are arranged in order of increasing membrane permeability from *top* to *bottom*. *Upper dashed lines*, output if no cells are present ($k_3 = k_4 = 0$). *Solid lines*, output that occurs with tissue cells present but no intracellular sequestration. *Lower dashed lines* (more widely spaced), output for different degrees of intracellular metabolic sequestration (i.e., varying values of k_5). The first part of the illustration output, in the cases with low permeability, is an impulse function with a normalized area, $\exp(-k_1\gamma\tau)$ or $\exp(-PS_C/F_C)$. It is difficult to illustrate this form, which theoretically has an infinitesimally small duration. A *vertical line* has simply been placed at the site of the function with a number representing its normalized area. When the spike area is less than 0.01 of the total, a *broken line* rather than *solid line* has been used. In the *bottom panel*, when the capillary permeability has been allowed to become infinite, the throughput area refers to the label emerging in the delayed impulse function. [From Rose, Goresky, and Bach (172), by permission of the American Heart Association, Inc.]

ance to maintain a concentration profile with its peak at the outflow end of the capillary-tissue unit. (See *Relationship Between Center of Mass of Tracer in an Organ and Its Movement in Relation to Flow*, p. 569.)

When the permeabilities are very high, the system reduces to the traveling-wave behavior of the Goresky (72) model in which the impulse input travels along the capillary-tissue unit as an undispersed spike (when there is no axial diffusion) at a rate proportional to the flow divided by the sum of the volumes of distribution in the capillary, interstitial fluid, and cell. The impulse input appears at the outflow as a delayed spike, as shown in the *lower panels* of Figure 19. With an infinitely high value of PS_{cell} and with $V'_{cell} = V'_I$, the limiting case for the volumes in the *left panel* of Figure 33 would be a spike at $t/\tau = 7$; for the *right panel* the analogous case would be a spike at $t/\tau = 34$, at $(V'_C + V'_I + V'_{cell})/V'_C$.

MULTICAPILLARY–INTERSTITIAL FLUID–CELL–ORGAN MODEL WITH HETEROGENEOUS FLOW. *Whole-organ formulation.* For the purposes of illustration the discussion here is of the randomly coupled case, in which whole-organ arterial and venous transport functions are considered independent of the capillary transit times. This is the model in Figure 25, defined by Equation 74. The flow-coupled approach, a specific case of the model of Figure 27 with nondispersive intravascular transport, could also be used. Convenient distributions that fit the distributions of capillary transit times or microsphere distributions are Gaussian, gamma variate (213), and a lagged normal density curve (16).

Behavior of the whole-organ model. The behavior of the multicapillary–interstitial fluid–cell model over a range of cellular uptake rates without return flux from the cell is shown in Figure 34. In this case with PS_{cell}(in) finite and PS_{cell}(out) = 0, the transport through the single-capillary–interstitial fluid–cell units can be described by the equation of Goresky et al. (79). With PS_{cell}(in) = 0, i.e., no cellular uptake, the individual-pathway models become the same as those described in Outflow responses, p. 577.

Having efflux from the cell set to zero is equivalent to putting $V'_{cell}/V'_C = \infty$, in which case the intracellular concentration remains at zero and there is no gradient for reflux. With intermediate values of PS_{cell}(in) from 0.25 to 8 ml·g^{-1}·min^{-1}, the height of the peak of $h_D(t)$ is little affected; however, the downslope region beyond $t = 20$ s is greatly lowered by cellular uptake in the absence of return flux from the cells. With $PS_{cell} = \infty$ the cellular uptake removes from the interstitial fluid all the tracer that escapes from the capillary; in each pathway the $h_{D_i}(t)$ has a shape identical to $h_{R_i}(t)$ but scaled down according to the relation

$$\frac{h_{D_i}(t)}{h_{R_i}(t)} = e^{-PS_C/F_{S_i}} \tag{98}$$

This is the basis for the classic Crone-Renkin expression (refs. 45, 165, 166; Eq. 72) for estimating capillary permeability in the absence of return flux from interstitial fluid to capillary. The flow-weighted sums of

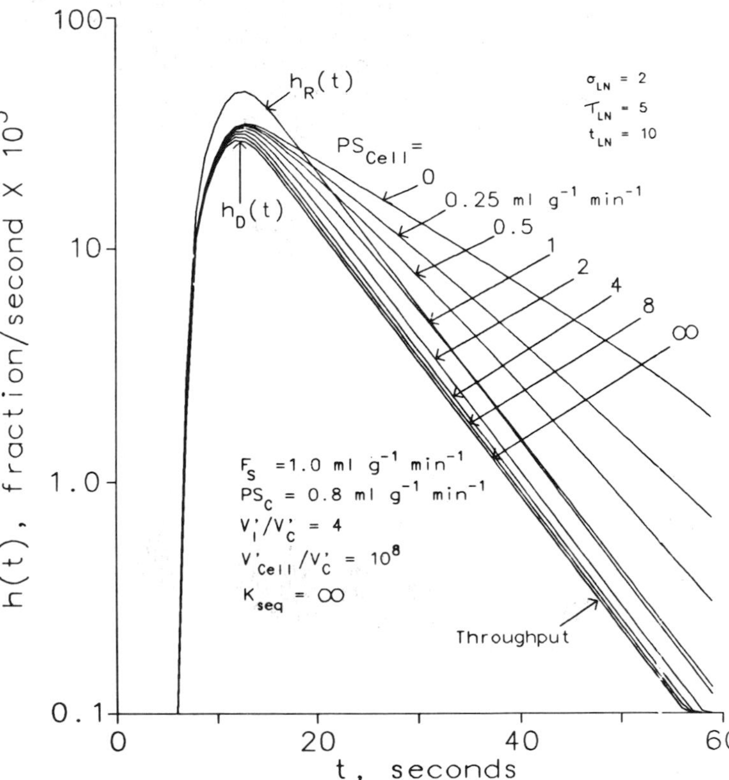

FIG. 34. Effect of cell uptake on shape of outflow dilution curve. Multicapillary model solutions from a whole-organ model for capillary permeation and cellular uptake without return flux from the cell but with return flux from the interstitial fluid to the capillary. Heterogeneity of flows was defined by a Gaussian distribution with a relative dispersion of flows of 30%, approximated by partitioning total flow into 7 pathways of different flows [Levin, Kuikka, and Bassingthwaighte (122)]. There are 8 solutions drawn for different values of PS_{cell}; $h_R(t)$ were all identical, but $h_D(t)$ were influenced strongly by the rate of cellular influx PS_{cell}, all other parameters being constant. Organ structure is that of Fig. 25 with independence of $h_C(t)$ and $h_{LV}(t)$. The large-vessel transport $h_{LV}(t)$ is a lagged normal density curve with a relative dispersion of 36% and a mean transit time of 15 s.

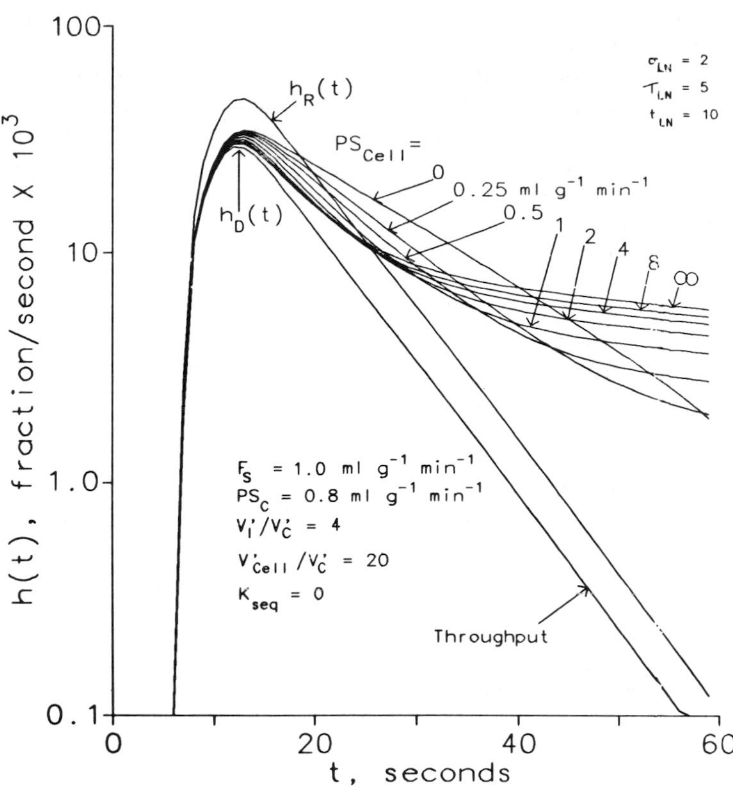

FIG. 35. Effect of cell exchange on shape of outflow dilution curve. Multicapillary model solutions for capillary permeation and cellular entry with return flux from cell to interstitial fluid and no consumption of tracer; PS_{cell} is same in both directions, and parameter values and heterogeneity are same as for Fig. 34.

the family of $h_{D_i}(t)$ are $h_D(t)$, whose shape is different from that of $h_R(t)$ in the presence of heterogeneity because the fraction of tracer lost into the cells is greater in low-flow pathways than in high-flow pathways. This is the throughput component in this and the following situations.

The effects of bidirectional flux across the cell membrane on the shape of the outflow dilution curves are illustrated in Figure 35. While Figure 34 shows a model suitable for a substance strongly bound intracellularly with no tracer escaping from the cell, the situation portrayed in Figure 35 (having the return flux) is a more suitable example for D-glucose. The curve for $PS_{cell} = 0$ would be suitable for L-glucose, which—as long as it does not enter cells at all—would serve as the best conceivable reference tracer for the estimation of D-glucose entry into the cell. With a constant V'_{cell} (in this case $V'_{cell}/V'_C = \Theta = 20.0$), $PS_C(\text{in}) = PS_C(\text{out})$, and the intracellular sequestration or consumption rate k_{seq} set to zero, all curves show separation with nonzero PS_{cell} from the curve for which $PS_{cell} = 0$. Later the return flux from the cell for tracer that has entered the cell results in the model curve crossing above that for tracer that does not enter ($PS_{cell} = 0$). This is markedly different from the nonreturn behavior shown in Figure 34, where the separation continuously increases. The mean transit time in the capillary–interstitial fluid–cell unit for the tracer that can enter the cells is $(V'_C + V'_I + V'_{cell})/\overline{F}_S$, as compared with $V'_C/\overline{F}_S$, the capillary transit time when it is restricted to the vascular space.

Any consumption or sequestration within the cell reduces the return flux from the cell and might appear to be either a loss of tracer (a nonconservative system) or a further enlargement of the volume of distribution if there are binding sites from which the tracer would eventually be released. The rate of sequestration is considered to be important in influencing the retention of ^{18}F-labeled 2-deoxy-D-glucose in the brain but has not been assessed for circumstances where there are serial capillary and cell membrane barriers preceding the reactions along the glycolytic pathway. For the solutions in Figure 35 the consumption was set equal to zero.

The effect of intracellular consumption of the tracer depends on the rate of entry into the cell, as shown in Figure 36. For the model solutions we used more or less typical values for PS_C and PS_{cell} and several different values for the first-order consumption, ranging up to a value of 1 s^{-1}, at which rate there is almost no return flux from the cell. Because k_{seq} represents a unidirectional flux without a return flux, at high values of k_{seq} all intracellular tracer is sequestered and none is available for reflux from cell to interstitial fluid to capillary. Here the curves are the same as those in Figure 34. In other words, any intracellular consumption reduces the return flux from cell to interstitial fluid, lowering the tail of the curve below that given in Figure 35 (no consumption); in the extreme—with 100% consumption or binding—consumption lowers the tail to the limits allowed by the rate of entry into the cell (see Fig. 34).

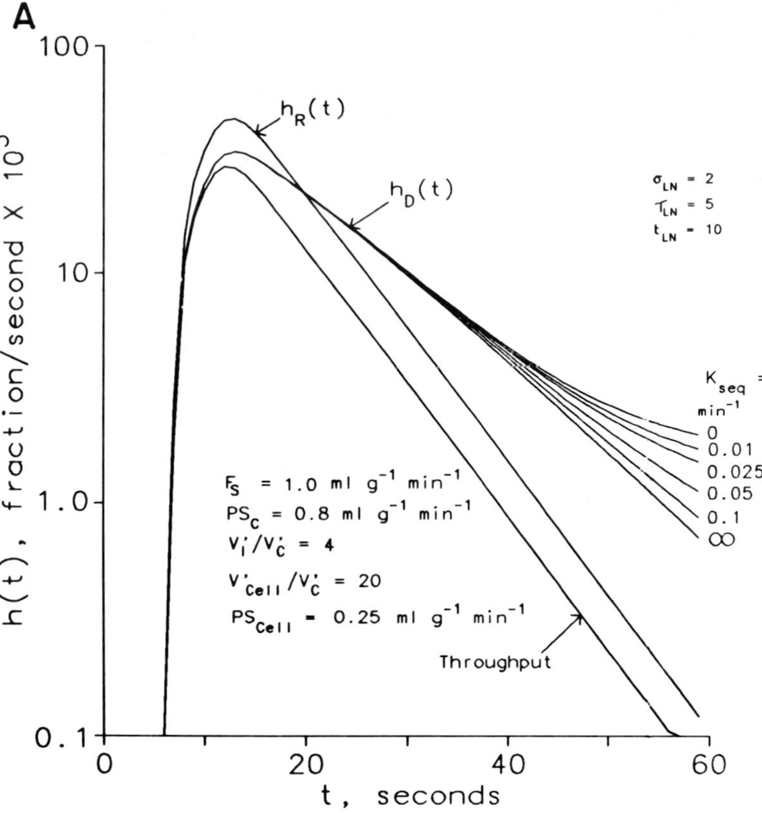

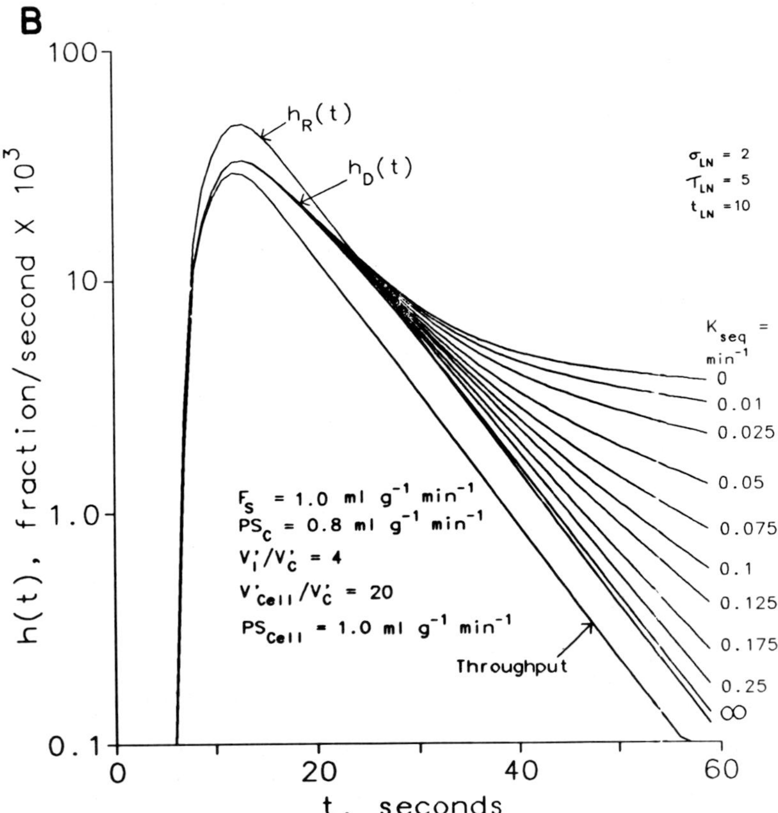

FIG. 36. Effect of intracellular consumption on shapes of tails of outflow dilution curves in a heterogeneous flow, multiple-unit, capillary–interstitial fluid–cell model. Increasing rates of consumption reduce reflux from cell into outflow, lowering the tails of the curves. *A*: with $PS_{cell} = 0.25\ ml \cdot g^{-1} \cdot min^{-1}$, the possible range of influences of k_{seq} ~20% around the 60th s. *B*: with $PS_{cell} = 1.0\ ml \cdot g^{-1} \cdot min^{-1}$, the range of influence of k_{seq} is several times as great.

The directional influences of PS_{cell} and k_{seq} on the dilution curves are shown in Figures 33–35. The effect is all on the tails of the curves and not on the upslopes and peaks of the curves. The effect of V'_{cell} is similar to that of k_{seq} on the downslope phase of the curves, but because enlarging V'_{cell} only retards the efflux, there is a late phase of return flux from the cell to the outflow that allows one to distinguish intracellular volume effects from an irreversible sequestration. The key to the unraveling of the relative effects of the various parameters on the model solutions to be fitted to the data is that each parameter influences different parts of the outflow dilution curves in different ways. Thus each parameter has a unique influence on the curve, independent of all the other parameters. The relative influences are given by the sensitivity functions shown in Figure 37 for a model solution suitable for D-glucose, i.e., including cell influx, efflux, and consumption.

Parameter estimation: fitting models to dilution curves. In fitting the data, the estimated value of PS for outward flux from the cell $\widehat{PS}_{cell}(out)$ is set equal to $\widehat{PS}_{cell}(in)$; for this equality the permeability–surface area product is defined as $\widehat{PS}_{cell}$. For systems involving transmembrane transporters (carrier-facilitated or active transport mechanisms), the conductances (permeabilities) for influx and efflux (P_3 and P_4 in Eq. 95) usually differ. Nevertheless in the modeling, P_3 and P_4 can be treated as identical; their ratio P_3/P_4 is inferred by the ratio of the estimate obtained for the apparent cellular volume of distribution V'_{cell} to the passive equilibrative volume of distribution for the solute inside the cell. Unfortunately this latter value is seldom known a priori: it is influenced by any molecular-exclusion phenomena, by ratios of solubilities and fractional adsorption, or by binding inside versus outside the cells. The situation is similar to that described for transcapillary permeation (see Outflow responses, p. 577). When the passive equilibrative volume of distribution inside the cell is equal to the anatomical volume V_{cell} and when the solute in the blood is limited to the plasma volume V_P, then by definition

$$\Theta = \frac{V'_{cell}}{V'_C} = \frac{P_3}{P_4} \cdot \frac{V_{cell}}{V_P} \tag{99}$$

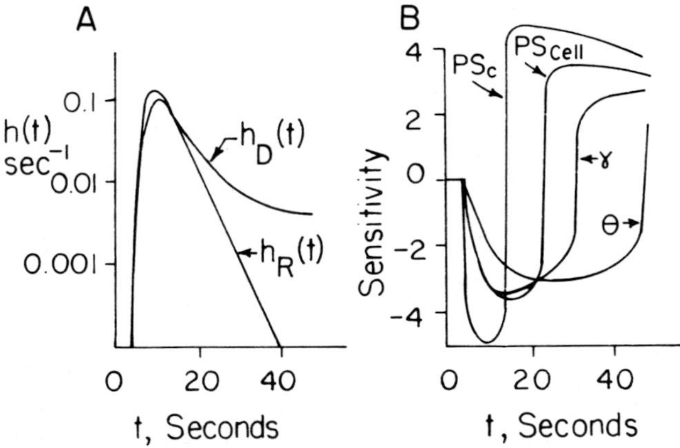

FIG. 37. Impulse responses and sensitivity functions for capillary–interstitial fluid–cell model solutions with parameter values suitable for D-glucose in the heart. Sensitivity functions are all different, indicating the independence of the parameters in shaping the model solutions. Note that Θ and sequestration rate constant k_{seq} have little influence at early times and more influence later, suggesting the importance of avoiding (or accounting for) recirculation. Parameter values used to generate model solutions are mean values for best fit to D-glucose experimental curves. $\gamma = V'_I/V'_C$.

In Figure 38 solutions for the multicapillary model are fitted to coronary sinus outflow dilution curves for D-glucose and L-glucose. The upslope and peak values of the two curves coincide; they diverge on the downslope. The fundamental assumption made in the analysis is that there is no entry of L-glucose into the parenchymal cells because their transport mechanism is stereospecific for D-glucose. This in essence allows L-glucose to be used as a second reference substance, one that is confined to extracellular space and whose permeation through the capillary endothelial layer is either very close to or identical to that of D-glucose. In the brain the situation is different. There the endothelial barrier of the capillary is relatively impermeable to molecules the size of glucose; D-glucose reaches the parenchymal cells via a stereospecific capillary transport mechanism in the brain, which carries this substrate through these cells (46). The possibility of stereospecificity was retained in this analysis. As expected, no significant differences between the D-isomer and the L-isomer for either PS_C or V'_I are shown. The results also indicate that the evaluation of the cellular parameters for D-glucose (PS_{cell} and V'_{cell}) is not influenced by interaction with the evaluation of the more accessible parameters PS_C and V'_I. This is a nice confirmation of the adequacy of the fitting technique, and it is what one would predict from the sensitivity functions shown in Figure 37. The sensitivity functions for the several parameters are all differently shaped and have different regions of maximal sensitivity.

In this type of modeling the accuracy of parameter estimation is not the same for all parameters but depends on the form of the model and on the precise nature of the experiment. An example is that the estimation of PS_{cell} is rather tenuous if PS_C is so low that the return flux into the outflow is very low and much delayed. Similarly the estimation of k_{seq} is greatly hampered by low conductances across either the capillary or cell membranes.

In such circumstances it is most useful to bring other information into the analysis. Intracellular consumption may best be calculated from arteriovenous differences. The consumption rate $F_B(C_A - C_V)/W$—where C_A and C_V are arterial and venous concentrations, F_B is blood flow, and W is organ mass—has the

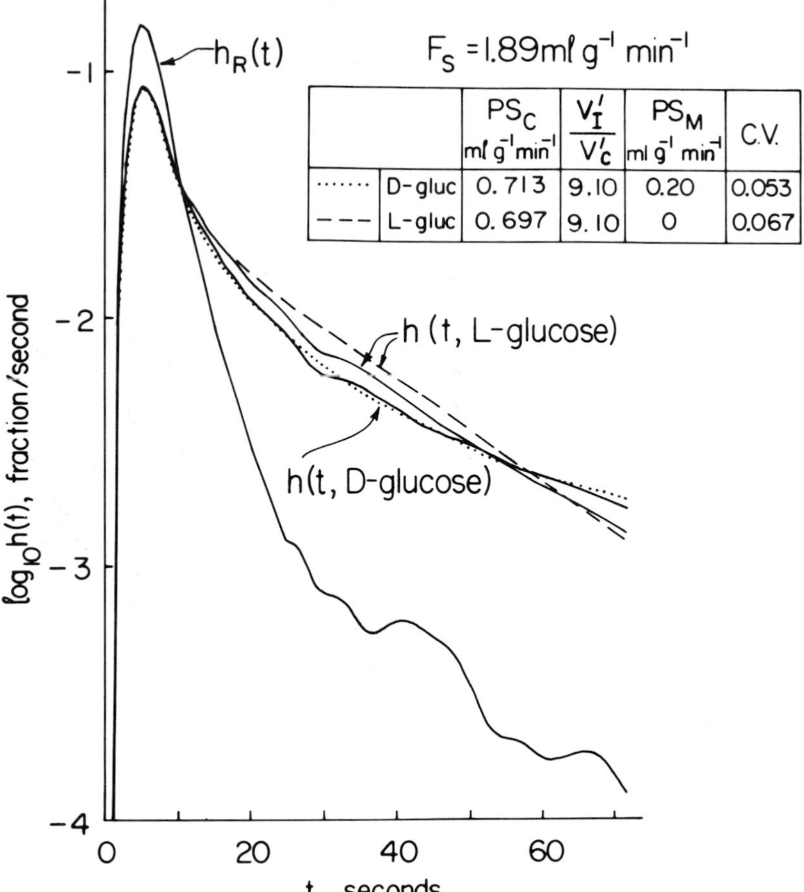

FIG. 38. Rabbit coronary sinus outflow dilution curves $h_D(t)$ for D-glucose and L-glucose, fitted with the model, and reference albumin curve $h_R(t)$. *Continuous lines*, data tabulated (or plotted) at 1-s intervals; *dashed* and *dotted lines*, model solutions fitted to D-glucose and L-glucose. Best-fit parameters indicated in the table at *top*. A common value for γ was used for simultaneous optimization of both diffusible curve fits. CV, coefficient of variation.

same value as the product $k_{seq}\overline{C}_{cell}V'_{cell}$ (in mol·g⁻¹·s⁻¹), which improves the estimates of k_{seq} and Θ. The product $k_{seq}V'_{cell}$ is equivalent to a PS, and $k_{seq}\overline{C}'_{cell}V'_{cell}$ is a clearance.

The description of outflow dilution or residue function curves by a multicapillary–interstitial fluid–cell model has some useful predictive features ,which help in the choice of a tracer to suit a specific purpose. For example, for the estimation of regional flows one wants a tracer with maximal transmembrane conductances and maximal retention within the tissue; thallium is one that is commonly used in gamma imaging for regional flow estimation in the heart because it exhibits these features (149). Little and Bassingthwaighte (128a) have found desmethylimipramine to be nearly 100% extracted and strongly retained in the heart—the closest marker yet to the ideal "molecular microsphere." For the estimation of PS_C or changes in PS_C with physiological conditions, one wants to have a situation in which the estimation is not marred by excessive return flux from interstitial fluid to capillary. Thus PS_C/F_S should be chosen to provide extractions of 20%–60%, and if possible there should be some uptake by the cell to retard the return flux.

Cell–Interstitial Fluid–Capillary Systems With Saturable Transport Mechanisms

GENERAL CHARACTERISTICS OF FACILITATED TRANSPORT PROCESSES. The equations presented in *Cell–Interstitial Fluid–Capillary Exchange*, p. 596, are quite applicable to systems in which there are active or facilitated transport mechanisms, provided that the concentration of the nontracer mother substance is constant along the length of each capillary. In this case the transmembrane conductance for the tracer (PS) is governed by the concentration of the mother substance and is the same everywhere within the system. This renders the system linear (see *Permeation*, p. 560).

Although active and facilitated transport mechanisms are usually complex in the sense that the mechanisms of transmembrane movement may consist of several steps, the general principles and a typical mode of behavior are exhibited by a simple approximation analogous to that used to describe Michaelis-Menten enzyme kinetics. In this situation the flux J_S (in mol·s⁻¹·cm⁻²) across a membrane per square centimeter of surface area can be considered to be governed by the molar concentration of the transported solute C, the maximum transport rate V_{max} (in $mol \cdot s^{-1} \cdot cm^{-2}$), and the concentration K_m at which the transport rate is half maximal

$$J_S = \frac{V_{max} \cdot C}{K_m + C} \quad (100)$$

This is a saturating function with two extremes. At very low substrate concentrations C, the transport rate is a linear function of C; when C is very high, the rate approaches an asymptote at its maximum, i.e., V_{max}. When a competitor for the transport site is present in concentration C_I and is transported at half-maximal rate at concentration K_I, the transport rate of the substrate J_S is modified by the presence of the competitor according to

$$J_S = \frac{V_{max} \cdot C}{C + K_m(1 + C_I/K_I)} \quad (101)$$

The presence of the competitor lowers the observed rate of transport of the substrate because some of the competitor binds to the carrier and fewer carrier molecules are available to bind the substrate.

The estimates of permeability P obtained from modeling analysis of indicator-dilution curves for tracers depend on the concentration of the nontracer mother substance having concentration C and not on the concentration of tracer per se. The unidirectional flux of tracer J_S^* is given by

$$J_S^* = P \cdot C^* \quad (102)$$

By analogy with the preceding equations this implies that the tracer flux per unit tracer concentration J_S^*/C^* is P and therefore that

$$P = \frac{V_{max}}{K_m + C} \quad (103)$$

When a series of experiments is done at differing concentrations C of the mother substance, the estimates of P for tracer diminish as a function of C (see Fig. 39). The K_m is given by the concentration at which P is half its maximum value. Thus the tracer modeling reveals the kinetics of the nontracer mother substance even when the system is nonlinear. For more complex transport mechanisms the interpretation of the observed P values requires something more than the simple plot shown, but in principle the same approach applies. For example, observations of PS_{cell} plotted versus C as in Figure 39 might simply be fitted with the equation for the transport model to obtain estimates of the parameters governing the transport. This then also serves as an example of the use of parameters obtained by use of one level of modeling (the capillary–interstitial fluid–cell model) to provide data interpretable at another hierarchical level of modeling (the transport mechanism itself).

The approach just described is one-sided; it is adequate when concentrations on the other side of the membrane do not influence the apparent PS_{cell}. Since concentrations on the *trans* side usually influence availability of a transporter molecule at the *cis* side of the membrane, the above approach should be regarded as a simplified special case.

SATURABLE SYSTEMS THAT ARE NONLINEAR TO TRACER. For systems in which there is no consumption of the solute the rate constant for any facilitated or active transport system is the same throughout the

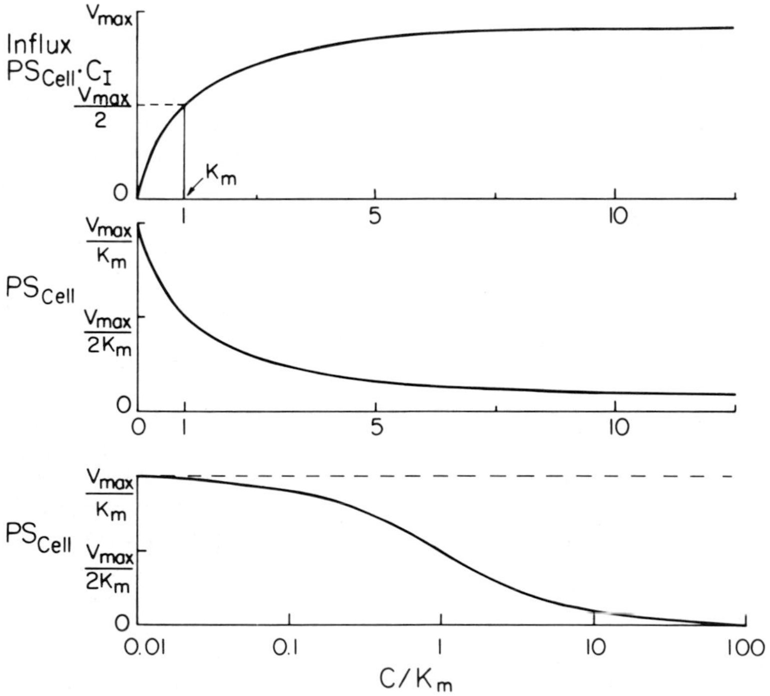

FIG. 39. Cellular influx and PS_{cell} versus concentration. PS_{cell} diminishes as a function of concentration if the transport mechanism is saturable. The mechanism here is analogous to a first-order Michaelis-Menten reaction for enzyme kinetics. More complex reactions would be expected to give curves of different form. C_I, interstitial concentration; V_{max}, maximum transport rate; K_m, concentration at which transport rate is half maximal. S_{cell} is not affected by changes in concentration and in the heart is ~2,000 cm^2/g.

system. In contrast, when the nontracer mother substance is consumed, there must be a constant arteriovenous gradient for the solute during the steady state. Because the concentration nearer the arteriolar end of the capillary is higher than that nearer the venous end, the degree of saturation of the transport process must be higher at the arteriolar end than further downstream. The question is whether this is of practical consequence or whether the experimental and analytical techniques simply yield an estimate of the average along the capillary.

Nonlinearities associated with tracer handling may then occur at three levels: *1*) in the capillary, in association with its falling bulk concentration profile; *2*) at the level of the cell entry or PS_{cell} process; and *3*) at the level of the intracellular sequestration process. Goresky et al. (73) found, in the case of galactose, that the intracellular disposal mechanism saturated at a much lower concentration than did the liver cell entry process. They also pointed out the difficult problem of picking the intermediate mean concentrations in capillary and cell to which it is appropriate to relate the saturation characteristics of either mechanism. At a theoretical level the case of dual saturation has not been explored in detail. Despite this, one can develop some expectations of the nature of the effects with saturation at either site. The sequestration and membrane transport effects have generally been found to be paired in such a way that in a single-indicator–dilution experiment the capillary and interstitial concentrations do not sweep across a wide range with respect to the K_m, and thus saturation effects are not seen. They are revealed better by a set of experiments encompassing a wide range of steady-state concentrations. Nevertheless one would expect relative cell uptake to be higher near the venous outflow. Conversely Linehan et al. (127, 128) have attempted to explore the saturating transport process for prostaglandins across pulmonary endothelium by use of a bolus-dose approach. Tracer plus nontracer prostaglandin is injected along with a labeled-albumin vascular reference. With the large change in bolus concentration during passage, qualitative effects suggesting intrapassage saturation are seen and qualitative analyses based on upslope and peak outflow concentrations are carried out. Two difficult problems emerge at an analytical level when one attempts to exploit this situation. The first is that the concentration in the bolus facing the barrier is not known; knowledge of this is of course essential if the data are to be utilized to derive parameters applicable to the steady-state situation. The second is that the effect of heterogeneity of capillary transit times becomes difficult to separate from concentration effects.

Goresky et al. (75) have explored in some detail the kinetics of saturable removal (i.e., sequestration) of tracer during blood-tissue exchange under conditions in which nonsaturating transfer occurs at the level of the tissue barriers. As expected from the qualitative arguments just given, the uptake of tracer is predicted to be, in general, relatively greater toward the venous end of the capillary, even though the absolute uptake is somewhat less. Axial concentration profiles vary from exponential at the low concentration ranges (where the system is linear) to small-scale linear decreases at the higher concentration ranges (where the system is saturated). When an effective barrier is present, the concentration drops abruptly across the barrier and parallel profiles develop in the cell and adjacent space. The logarithmic average bulk concentration from each experiment $(C_{in} - C_{out})/(\ln C_{in} - \ln C_{out})$ is found to be the concentration for the sequestration mechanism appropriate for use in Equation 100 to derive the characteristic parameters of the mechanism from a set of experimental data. Goresky et al. (76) were able to apply this approach of nonlinear uptake modeling during the steady state to the estimation of kinetic parameters for ethanol uptake in the liver.

The problem of detailed consideration of the nonlinearities of both membrane transfer and metabolic sequestration mechanisms is mathematically difficult. At this time experimental data exhibiting both have usually been analyzed without accounting for nonlinearity.

Homogeneous and Heterogeneous Systems With Diffusional Shunting of Tracers

The presence of adjacent vascular counterflows provides an anatomical basis for diffusional shunting. At the capillary level these kinds of structures have evolved in an organized way in some areas, and when flow progresses from inflow channels to outflow channels (in a U-shaped countercurrent fashion), these counterflows preserve concentration gradients along their length (the osmolality gradient in the renal medulla, the oxygen gradient along the rete mirabile of the swim bladder of the eel, etc.). When the continuous-counterflow mechanism is unhooked and the organized channels in either direction are counterperfused, the equations describing the combined permeabilities of the barriers between the flows become extremely simplified and permeability values can be obtained by use of end concentration values (158). The discovery of diffusional shunts within other kinds of tissues is a more challenging issue. Staggering of input and output sites of concurrently perfused capillary bundles could provide a suitable anatomical base for small-scale shunting, if it is present. At the larger vascular level the potential for communication exists between small arterioles and accompanying venules. Apparent oxygen transfer has been observed from arteriole to venule in the pathways supplying the hamster cheek pouch (52). The question is whether, in a more richly perfused organ like the heart, the phenomenon occurs in a physiologically important proportion.

The question has been partially examined in the heart. It is the potential diffusional shunting of gases of metabolic importance that is of particular interest here. Roth and Feigl (176) have searched directly for large-vessel shunting by seeking evidence of early emergence of hydrogen gas, the most diffusible substance known, after its simultaneous injection with labeled red cells and albumin. A very small proportion (0.1% of the normalized peak for vascular reference tracer) was found to emerge in the coronary sinus blood prior to the vascular reference labels.

The lack of a label behaving in a delayed-wave, flow-limited fashion in the heart makes it difficult to look for shunting within the tissue. Nevertheless some observations have been made that suggest that there may be some intratissue diffusional shunting. Bassingthwaighte and Yipintsoi (23, 234) carried out a set of labeled-iodoantipyrine dilution experiments in isolated hearts perfused at varying flows and found that when residue functions were normalized with respect to flow, they tended to superimpose with no systematic differences, demonstrating flow-limited washout without either barrier limitation or diffusional shunting. Labeled-water and labeled-iodoantipyrine curves were similar at high flows. However, at low flows the labeled water (the more diffusible label) exhibited an initial component emerging more rapidly than the iodoantipyrine. Xenon curves, when normalized for flow, exhibited a behavior similar to that of the labeled water; an accelerated early washout was evident at low flows. The relatively more rapid emergence of the more diffusible labels at low flows than at high flows has been interpreted to indicate that intratissue diffusional shunting may be present and that it becomes more visible when flows are slow and time for diffusional transfers is allowed.

The potentials for shunting thus differ in various tissues. Scrutiny of structure at the levels necessary to define the potential for intratissue shunting requires both the definition of the underlying structure and the in vivo definition of the underlying flow patterns.

MODELING OF PERTURBED STATES: OSMOTIC AND PRESSURE TRANSIENTS

Importance of Analysis of Transient States

Osmotic and pressure changes have been used extensively to probe the behavior of the vascular system through the use of a wide variety of methods. Here the emphasis is on their use in obtaining information on permeabilities, reflection coefficients, and filtration coefficients. Tracer techniques applied during physicochemical steady-state situations do not lend themselves to the measurement of either reflection or filtration coefficients, which in general are derived from estimates of net fluxes rather than unidirectional fluxes. In the osmotic-transient approach to the estimation of capillary permeability, a nontracer (osmotic) amount of solute is introduced into the artery leading to an organ. Capillary permeability to the particular solute is inferred from measurement of the time course of rates of water transport out of or into the organ or tissue bed. Transport is induced by step changes in perfusate osmolarity [the weight-transient procedure of Vargas and Johnson (218)] or from measurement of the time-varying hydrostatic pressure required to prevent weight changes [the isogravimetric procedure of Pappenheimer et al. (143)]. Interpretation of such data requires realistic mathematical modeling to yield valid estimates of permeability. The evolution of modeling in this area has been slow; however, advances have been encouraged both by the development of new general ideas and by recognition of apparent inadequacies in earlier conceptual approaches to the interpretation of data. The topic is also reviewed in the chapter by Crone and Levitt in this *Handbook*.

Use of osmotic driving forces for exploring the characteristics of the microcirculation was given a great thrust forward by Pappenheimer and his colleagues (142–144). The principles that Starling (196) had proposed as governing water exchange, i.e., that water flux is proportional to the difference between osmotic and pressure gradients across the capillary wall, were explored by Krogh et al. (110) in studies of human forearm capillaries. Landis (113) developed a technique for directly observing volume changes in single capillaries, thereby allowing estimation of the filtration coefficient of the capillary wall; his approach has stood the test of time. (Modern direct techniques are reviewed in the chapter by Michel in this *Handbook*.)

The approach of Pappenheimer and colleagues was to use isolated organs (the perfused hindlegs of cats and dogs) in which the weight loss due to step increases in perfusate osmolarity was offset by raising the venous pressure to maintain the constancy of organ weight. Perhaps the most stimulating part of their effort was the analysis. They observed that highly lipid-soluble molecules exerted no effective transcapillary osmotic pressure, whereas hydrophilic molecules did. Furthermore large hydrophilic molecules provoked greater water flux than did small molecules of equal molarity. The derived relationships between actual and potential solvent flow and solute penetration led to the concept that, whereas lipophilic molecules traverse the whole area of the capillary wall—endothelial cells plus aqueous channels—hydrophilic molecules traverse only the aqueous channels. The channel widths were estimated to be <5 nm on the basis of an accompanying analysis of hydrodynamic pore theory. This development is thoroughly reviewed by Landis and Pappenheimer (114), and the subsequent developments on porous transport are reviewed in the chapters by Curry and by Taylor and Granger in this *Handbook*.

Ussing (214) and Grim (81) refined the analytical approach of Pappenheimer and his co-workers by observing that, for a selectively permeable membrane like that of capillaries, the van't Hoff relationship between osmotic pressure and solute concentration difference must be replaced by the irreversible thermodynamic relationship [see Kedem and Katchalsky (102) and Katchalsky and Curran (101)] between osmotic pressure and the product of the reflection coefficient and the solute concentration difference (198). Chinard et al. (41) also recognized the importance of solute buffering in transcapillary exchange, although their quantitative statements did not incorporate the concept of the reflection coefficient. Vargas and Johnson (218, 219) and Farmer and Macey (57–60) independently applied the Kedem-Katchalsky equations (in which solute and solvent transport are coupled) to osmotic weight transients of rabbit hearts and osmotic volume transients of bovine and human red cells, respectively. Farmer and Macey considered the effects of solvent drag and the presence of an impermeant second solute.

Vargas and Johnson (218, 219) developed a new experimental approach. One of the problems with Pappenheimer's hindlimb preparation was that there was variation in vascular volume as venous pressure was changed to maintain the isogravimetric state. To avoid the problem, Vargas and Johnson perfused isolated rabbit hearts at constant arterial pressure. They made step increases in perfusate osmolarity while continuously recording the heart weight. On the basis that the weight loss in response to a step increase in osmolarity (with urea, sucrose, raffinose, and inulin) represented water loss from a single compartmental extravascular region, they extrapolated the rates of weight loss over the first 20–40 s back to the start of the step to obtain the initial rate. This was interpreted by a simplified form of the Kedem-Katchalsky expressions, assuming that the weight loss represented water flux across a single membrane in a single solute-solvent system

$$J_{C,W} = L_{pC}\sigma_S \Delta C_S RT \qquad (104)$$

where $J_{C,W}$ is water flux across the capillary wall per unit surface area, L_{pC} is the hydraulic conductivity or filtration coefficient of the capillary wall, σ_S is the reflection coefficient of solute whose concentration step change is ΔC_S, and R and T are the gas constant and the absolute temperature. Vargas and Johnson determined L_{pC} from experiments by using albumin and assuming its reflection coefficient to be unity. The value for ΔC_S was known and that for $J_{C,W}$ estimated from the extrapolated rate of weight loss; thus σ_S could be calculated. After a step change in osmolarity the net water flux diminishes nearly exponentially. From the rate constant they estimated PS_C/V'_I. Thus σ_S and PS_C were estimated from a pair of osmotic-transient weight-loss curves.

Osmotic buffering was not accounted for in the analyses by Pappenheimer or by Vargas and Johnson, although the latter (219) did argue that it should be negligibly small. Starling (196) had recognized that the presence of nonpermeating, osmotically active solutes would oppose water movement. Wiederhielm (226), using a computer simulation of transcapillary exchange that allowed interstitial volume to vary, established that on sudden, moderate reduction (or increase) of capillary hydrostatic pressure the reabsorption (or filtration) of water from (or into) capillaries is buffered by a simultaneous rise (or fall) in interstitial protein concentration.

The importance of buffering of permeant solute in the microcirculation appears first to have been recognized by Keys (105). Keys argued quantitatively that the establishment of transient, filtration-retarding osmotic gradients of electrolytes across capillary membranes prevents enormous shifts of water from occurring in humans during exercise and standing. Keys (106) seems also to have been first to employ the osmotic-transient approach (volume transients in perfused gill preparation), though he lacked a detailed model for solute transport. [Interestingly, Keys had a difficult time getting his ideas across. He left the United States to work with A. Krogh in Copenhagen in the early 1930s and there started his studies on osmotic influences in fish gills. Then he undertook further work with H. Barcroft at Cambridge and at the Harvard Fatigue Laboratory. His paper (105) was presented at the Faraday Society after preprints had been distributed. Krogh, unable to attend, sent a highly critical, uncomplimentary, and largely incorrect critique, but he did point out that exchange with cells was important. J. H. Schulman seemed to think that Keys' results were due to surface effects, whereas T. Teorell attributed them to electrical charge effects and W. Wilbrandt to an ion transport system. Now, however, Keys' interpretation is recognized as correct and the phenomenon as important.]

The more modern bolus-dilution experiments of Effros (53) showed the effects of tissue buffering in dramatic form. A hypertonic intra-arterial bolus drew fluid from the tissue, transiently diluting the otherwise constant plasma concentrations of nonpermeant molecules. Immediately thereafter, there was a rebound in their concentrations to above-normal levels as the tissue regained the lost fluid and returned to the previous steady state. The events took place over some seconds, and the rapidity of these exchanges provides an index of the large rate of water movement that can be induced by osmotic forces.

Other phenomena came to be considered as well. Many solutes penetrate parenchymal cells slowly or not at all. The retardation of water fluxes by cell membranes also damps the responses. In the experiments of Grabowski and Bassingthwaighte (80), interstitial and intracellular mechanical forces were also consistently evident. After an osmotic weight loss, there is a partial regain in weight in the absence of electrochemical driving forces for the transport of water, demonstrating the effects of tissue elasticity. Yipintsoi and Knopp (236) carried out tracer-dilution and osmotic weight-transient estimations of capillary permeability in rabbit hearts. They suggested that solvent-drag and solute-solute interactions are unimportant for small molecules but significant for larger ones and that heterogeneity of flow can also be expected to influence the fluxes.

Very high osmolarity can itself change permeabilities. Rapoport (155) showed that huge osmotic transients create a condition in which materials usually excluded by the cerebral capillary do enter the brain. Rapoport et al. (156) found that a large osmotic bolus (~750 mosM) disrupts the continuity of the cerebral capillaries (which have few vesicles and therefore little extra membrane) and allows large molecules to permeate. Likewise, in the countercurrent perfused rete mirabile of the eel, Rasio, Bendayan, and Goresky (158, 159) found that with addition of 350-mM sucrose to the perfusing buffer, permeabilities to urea and albumin increased by ~65%, whereas water permeability decreased by 30%. In this preparation, where vesicles are present in the capillaries, no disruption of the interendothelial junction was evident; rather an increase in the number of capillary endothelial vesicles was found. More moderate changes in osmolarity (50 mosM vs. 350 mosM) used in flux experiments (80, 218) would not be expected to produce discernible changes in permeability.

There is a critical need to reexamine the analytical approaches to the estimation of capillary permeabilities and reflection coefficients. The evidence is that osmotic-transient and tracer-transient experiments performed simultaneously on isolated rabbit hearts perfused with Tyrode's solution (25) yield apparently different estimates of permeabilities and of channel dimensions. The real conundrum was that the analysis of transients in organ weight with step changes in osmolarity by using the analyses of Vargas and Johnson (218, 219) gave threefold higher estimates of permeability than did the analysis of the tracer transients with Equation 54. The same osmotic-transient analysis gave an opposing result: reflection coefficients were found that suggested that penetration occurred through narrow channels with diameters on the order of 5 nm, whereas the tracer permeabilities suggested large aqueous pathways with little steric hindrance. The contradictory nature of the deductions, the one method showing higher permeabilities but smaller pores than the other, pointed out the need to further refine the methods of analysis. The difference must be an analytical artifact.

Single-Capillary–Interstitial Fluid–Cell Model

The modeling of osmotic fluxes, which is basically similar to that for tracers in steady-state situations, must account for volume changes and their sequelae (elastic forces, multisolute buffering and exchange, and water permeation of barriers), and for partial flow limitation to exchange (the equivalent of "backdiffusion" explained by Eq. 54).

The tissue is considered to consist of a single hexagonal column (Fig. 1) in accordance with results from Krogh (108) and others concerned with water and solute exchanges in muscular or other tissue [e.g., Bassingthwaighte et al. (19) and Johnson and Wilson (99)]. The solute exchanges are the same as diagramed in Figure 32. For simplicity the central capillary is taken to be a rigid, circular cylinder of constant length surrounded by interstitium and cells whose volumes are variable. Capillary filtration, permeability, reflection coefficients, and surface area for exchange are constants in time and position along the capillary. The exchanges of solute and solvent are assumed to occur across a barrier of the type described by Kedem and Katchalsky (102). In this context, parallel transport via pathways common to solute and water versus those available only to water are not treated explicitly, although the estimated parameters can be reinterpreted appropriately if the fraction of solvent traversing endothelial cells as opposed to aqueous pathways is known. The analysis therefore provides values of L_p, P_C and σ_S for the overall capillary membrane. The tissue cell membranes, impermeable to the test solutes selected, have a water permeability and surface area for water exchange that are also independent of time and axial location. The model is axisymmetric, and radial diffusion within each region is considered to be rapid compared with convection, as estimated by Aroesty and Gross (7) and by Bassingthwaighte (12).

The restricting nature of these and some lesser assumptions discussed in the following pages show that this model should be regarded as requiring still further development, even though we believe these assumptions provide a substantial advance over earlier ones. The equations are necessarily nonlinear because of the simultaneous changes in volumes and concentrations.

As in the analyses of tracer transients (Eq. 97), a two-barrier, spatially-distributed system is defined. Capillary dimensions are assumed not to change (V_C = constant), and thus solute flux per unit surface area $J_{C,S}$ is defined at each point x along the capillary at each time t. Three driving forces (which appear as separate terms on the right-hand side of the equation) are involved: *1*) solvent drag with water flux, *2*) permeation according to the solute's concentration gradient, and *3*) solute movement in response to the movements of other solutes that interact by solute-solute friction

$$J_{C,S_1}(x, t) = J_{C,W} \frac{(C_{C,S_1} + C_{I,S_1})}{2} (1 - \sigma_{C,S_1}) + P_{C,S_1}(C_{C,S_1} - C_{I,S_1}) + \sum_{i=2}^{i=n} P_{C,S_iS_1}(C_{C,S_i} - C_{I,S_i}) \tag{105}$$

where P_{C,S_iS_1} is a solute-drag permeability quantitating solute-solute interactions. The term $J_{C,W}$ is the water flux per unit capillary area across the capillary membrane and like $J_{C,S}$ is defined at each position x along the capillary

$$J_{C,W}(x, t) = L_{pC}\left[p_C - p_I - \sum_{i=1}^{i=n} \sigma_{C,S_i} RT(C_{C,S_i} - C_{I,S_i})\right] \quad (106)$$

The reflection coefficients and the permeabilities, otherwise complex, are directly interpretable when solvent and solutes traverse the same pathway. Here C_{C,S_1} and C_{I,S_1} are capillary and interstitial concentrations of the solute S_1, σ_{S_i} is the reflection coefficient of each solute at the capillary wall, L_{pC} is the capillary filtration coefficient, P_{C,S_1} is capillary permeability to solute S_1, and P_{C,S_iS_1} is a solute-drag permeability (the effect of flux of each other solute S_i on the solute S_1 driven by the gradient for S_i). The terms p_C and p_I are capillary and interstitial pressures in mmHg. Solute flux expressions are written for albumin, a test solute (e.g., sucrose), sodium chloride (a representative of the permeant solutes in the normal perfusate and interstitium), and the larger molecules confined to the interstitial space that exert an osmotic pressure. Data must be obtained for permeabilities and reflection coefficients for each of the mobile solutes (albumin, sucrose, and sodium chloride) in each of the membranes in the same preparation to arrive at a self-consistent description. In the capillary the pressure is assumed to decrease from inflow to outflow with a constant capillary axial conductance g_C ($cm^4 \cdot g^{-1} \cdot s^{-1} \cdot mmHg^{-1}$)

$$\frac{\partial p_C}{\partial x} = \frac{v_F(x, t)V_C}{g_C L} \quad (107)$$

where $x = 0$ is inflow and $x = L$ (capillary length) is the outflow. These flux expressions, together with initial conditions, define the concentration and velocity changes in the same way as in the general expression in Equation 45

$$\frac{\partial C_{C,S_1}(x, t)}{\partial t} + \frac{\partial(v_F C_{C,S_1})}{\partial x} - D_C \frac{\partial^2 C_{C,S_1}}{\partial x^2} = -\frac{S_C}{V_C} J_{C,S} \quad (108)$$

and

$$\frac{\partial v_F}{\partial x} = \frac{-S_C}{V_C} J_{C,W} \quad (109)$$

where at the entrance to the capillary the intracapillary fluid velocity v_F is $F_S L/V_C$ just as in Equation 96, since there are no erythrocytes present. Here S_C is the capillary surface area, and V_C is the capillary volume. The second term on the left side of the equation accounts for the changing linear velocity with volume fluxes across the capillary membrane. The third term is axial intracapillary diffusion with coefficient D_C.

In the interstitial space a similar set of expressions governs the water and solute fluxes and the concentrations and volumes at the axially distributed locations

$$\frac{\partial C_{I,S_1}(x, t)}{\partial t} - D_I \frac{\partial^2 C_{I,S_1}}{\partial x^2} = \frac{S_C}{V_I} J_{C,S_1} - \frac{C_{I,S_1}}{V_I} \cdot \frac{\partial V_I}{\partial t} - \frac{S_{cell}}{V_I} J_{cell,S_1} \quad (110)$$

$$\frac{\partial V_I(x, t)}{\partial t} = S_C \cdot J_{C,W} - S_{cell} \cdot J_{cell,W} - g_I \frac{\partial p_I}{\partial x} \quad (111)$$

where V_I is interstitial volume, S_{cell} is surface area of the parenchymal cells, $J_{cell,W}$ is water flux ($ml \cdot cm^{-2} \cdot s^{-1}$) from interstitial fluid into parenchymal cells, and J_{cell,S_1} is the flux of solute from interstitial fluid into cells. The parameter g_I is the product of filtration conductance in the axial direction and cross-sectional surface area of the interstitial space; the last term in Equation 111 is the axial interstitial fluid flux. The volume equation neglects the partial molar volumes of the solutes whose concentrations change. The interstitial pressure at each position x changes with the volume change from the steady state [initial volume is $V_I(x, 0)$ and initial pressure is $p_I(x, 0)$]

$$p_I(x, t) = Y_I[V_I(x, t) - V_I(x, 0)] + p_I(x, 0) \quad (112)$$

The value Y_I is a linear approximation to the tissue elasticity coefficient ($mmHg/cm^3$) and is the change in pressure per unit change in volume.

As does flux across the capillary membrane, solute flux across the cell membrane has three terms: solvent drag, solute permeation, and solute-solute interactions. Because there may be active or passive transport carriers at the membrane, this is recognized as a simplification. For each solute

$$J_{cell,S_1}(x, t) = J_{cell,W} \frac{(C_{I,S_1} + C_{cell,S_1})}{2}(1 - \sigma_{cell,S_1}) + P_{cell}(C_{I,S_1} - C_{cell,S_1}) + \sum_{i=2}^{i=n} P_{cell,S_iS_1}(C_{I,S_i} - C_{cell,S_i}) \quad (113)$$

The water flux into the cell $J_{cell,W}$ is similarly governed by the osmotic pressure differences and to a minor extent by hydrostatic pressures p_I and p_{cell}

$$J_{cell,W}(x, t) = L_{p\,cell}\left[p_I - p_{cell} - \sum_{i=1}^{i=n} \sigma_{cell,S_i} RT(C_{I,S_i} - C_{cell,S_i})\right] \quad (114)$$

where $L_{p\,cell}$ is the filtration coefficient for the cell membrane. For the hydrophilic solutes used for characterizing the capillary membrane, the reflection coefficients for the solutes were all assumed to be unity; i.e., it was assumed that there is no transmembrane solute flux for sucrose, raffinose, and inulin.

The intracellular pressures are calculated in the style of the interstitial pressures, and since it is not known whether the elasticity of cells Y_{cell} differs from that for the interstitial fluid, similar values are used in the equation

$$p_{cell}(x, t) = Y_{cell}[V_{cell}(x, t) - V_{cell}(x, 0)] + p_{cell}(x, 0) \tag{115}$$

The volume flux results in changes in intracellular concentrations even if the total solute content changes only slightly because the J_{cell,S_i} are small.

$$\frac{\partial C_{cell,S_1}(x, t)}{\partial t} - D_{x,cell}\frac{\partial^2 C_{cell,S_1}}{\partial x^2} = -\frac{C_{cell,S_1}}{V_{cell}} \cdot \frac{\partial V_{cell}}{\partial t} + \frac{S_{cell}}{V_{cell}} J_{cell,S_1} \tag{116}$$

$$\frac{\partial V_{cell}(x, t)}{\partial t} = S_{cell} \cdot J_{cell,W} - g_{cell}\frac{\partial p_{cell}}{\partial x} \tag{117}$$

where g_{cell} is the conductance for volume flux in the axial direction inside cells; it is included for completeness although it is probably close to zero.

The integral of all the volume changes over time gives the total weight change, which can be fitted by parameter adjustment to the observed weight-transient curves for a set of different solutes, including the nonpermeant albumin, and for intravascular pressure changes. The values for elasticity coefficients Y_I and Y_{cell} can be expected to depend on the absolute volumes, increasing as the spaces become distended; however, they are considered constants over a limited range. Because the coefficients in the equations are time varying, it is likely that solutions for these simultaneous equations can only be obtained numerically. Omission of the diffusional terms simplifies the computation considerably, but the nonlinearities in volumes, pressures, and intracapillary velocity make it highly unlikely that analytical solutions can be developed. Grabowski and Bassingthwaighte (80) solved the flux and concentration expressions numerically for three solutes in the capillary (albumin, native solute, and a test solute), four in the interstitial fluid (the same three plus an immobile solute), and one in the cells (immobile). They assumed that none of the test solutes crossed the parenchymal cell membranes during the time course of the observations.

The most important factor in the application of these equations is that they must be fitted to a set of experimental data for at least three solutes: an intravascular reference that does not penetrate the capillary wall; one or more solutes that enter the interstitial fluid but not the cells; and sodium chloride, because it is the dominant species in capillary and interstitial fluid. To interpret an individual weight-transient curve in terms of the equations, one needs information provided only by other solutes of differing characteristics, just as is the case for the tracer technique. Thus the reflection coefficient of sodium chloride and its interstitial volume of distribution are needed to interpret the weight transient for a step change in intravascular osmolarity due to an impermeant species. These measures as well as pressure step changes are used to estimate L_{pC}. When the reflection coefficient for sodium chloride and the volumes V_I and V_{cell} are known reasonably accurately, then the pressure transient and albumin osmotic transients yield essentially the same values for L_{pC}. Because the experiments with various solutes and pressures cannot be done closer than a few minutes apart, the analysis depends on the preparation remaining stable long enough to make a whole set of observations. Thus the analysis involves solving the set of simultaneous equations for one test solute plus those for the resident native solute and the impermeant solutes in each region to fit the weight-transient curve. Then each one of a set of solute transients fitted individually is refitted with the more refined parameter estimates obtained from the others. This iterative approach improves the estimates with each rotation through the set of curves fitted by the model until a self-consistent set of parameters is obtained to fit all the data of pressure and weight changes for all the solutes. This was done by Grabowski and Bassingthwaighte (80).

Features of the Analysis

In practice the analysis can be carried out only as just described, by the sequential and then iterative fitting of several sets of data obtained from a single preparation. They cannot be fitted simultaneously because, for a given step change in concentration in the inflowing perfusate, time-course changes in weight and pressure are found that are unique to the particular intervention. To illustrate the influences of the phenomena involved, various parameters for the weight transients are shown, for example, responses in the heart to a step increase of 50-mM sucrose. It is important to remember, however, that in such analysis one should put equal emphasis on data collected after step increments and decrements in osmolarity, as Grabowski and Bassingthwaighte (80) did. Analysis only of step increments not only risks bias in the interpretation and parameter estimates but means throwing away half the data; in the experiments both upsteps and downsteps must be performed to reach a starting point for the next step increment with a different solute.

For practical reasons in computing solutions the equations were simplified. Axial-diffusion terms were omitted but approximated by using a small number of elements (5–15) of the three regions in the axial dimension. When there are few elements in a numerical

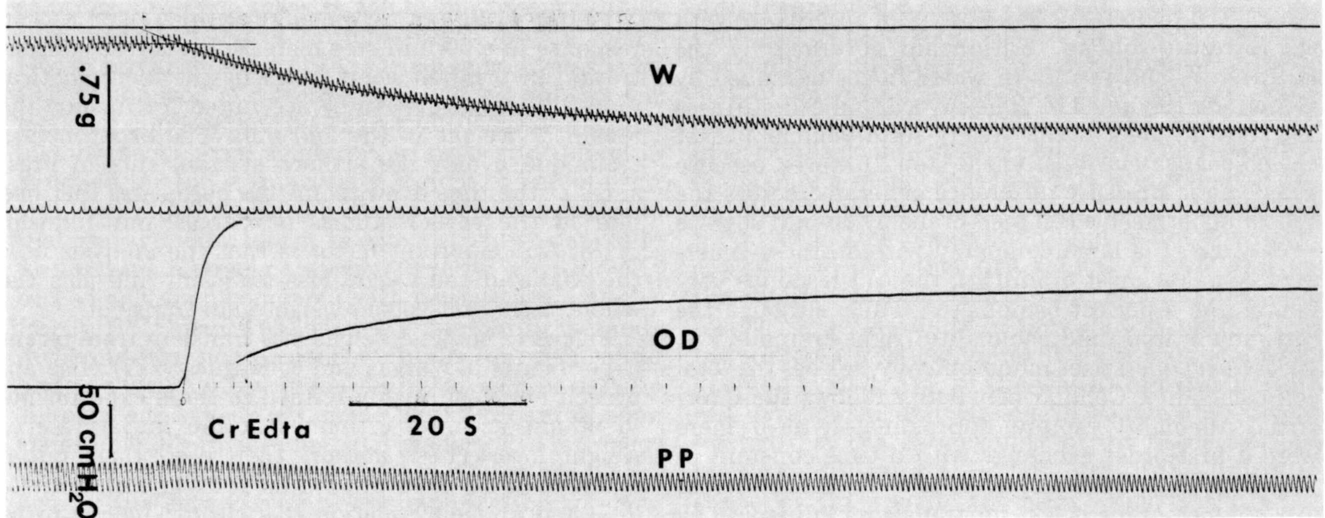

FIG. 42. Osmotic weight-loss transient in rabbit heart perfused with Tris-Ringer's solution. Heart was suspended from the apex, draining openly to prevent fluid accumulation and stimulated 90 times/min. W, weight; PP, perfusion pressure. A 25-mosM step increase in osmolarity due to Cr-EDTA (chromium-ethylenediaminetetraacetate) was induced via a rapid mixing chamber about 0.2 ml upstream from the heart, giving a sharp concentration front. Concentration of Cr-EDTA in the outflow was measured optically; OD, optical density. Note the sharp, smooth onset of weight loss. [From Vargas et al. (217).]

is augmented by the transient reduction in interstitial volume but diminished by any solvent drag. The countergradient retards water loss to an increasing extent (the buffering action) such that after several seconds the resident permeant solute (principally sodium chloride) is actually able to leave the interstitium faster than water! The interstitial impermeant solute continues its buffering action throughout the entire weight transient.

Figure 43 shows the model solution for the weight response fitted to the weight curve obtained after a 50-mM step increase in sucrose concentration. The model solutions for the concentrations of the native resident solute in interstitial fluid and in the capillary are shown for a position 60% of the length along the capillary (at $x = 0.60L$). That the concentration in interstitial fluid should rise as a consequence of water flux into the capillary is understandable. Within the capillary there is an exceedingly short period of dilution followed by a rising concentration of sodium chloride that is due to the combination of the large amount of sodium chloride with the water flux across the wall plus sodium chloride flux down its diffusion gradient.

If there were no solutes—permeant or impermeant—in the interstitial fluid or if a resident solute had a reflection coefficient of zero, then the only forces opposing the emptying of the interstitial fluid into the capillary would be mechanical. Moreover, even if there were a permeant resident solute with a nonzero reflection coefficient, it would exert no force to restore the interstitial fluid volume at the end of the transient. Thus again the mechanical restoring force—tissue

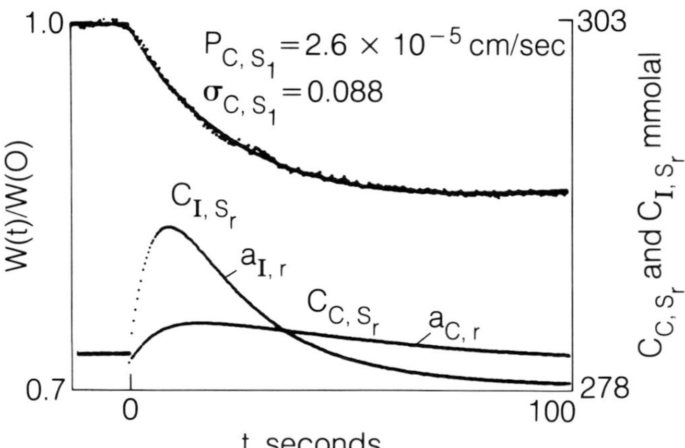

FIG. 43. Experimental weight transient in rabbit heart perfused with Tyrode's solution. Response $W(t)$ is to a step increase from 0 to 50 mmol/kg sucrose (test solute) at $t = 0$; $W(0)$ is mass at $t = 0$. *Smooth curve* is a model solution that best fits the data giving values for reflection coefficient σ_{C,S_1} and permeability P_{C,S_1} for sucrose; correlation coefficient was 0.994. Changes in activities of the resident solute in capillary $a_{C,r}$ and in interstitial fluid $a_{I,r}$ shown for the position 60% along the capillary. They diminish the initial rate of water loss because the transcapillary membrane activity gradient for the resident solute opposes ΔC_S, the gradient for the test solute. This is the "osmotic buffering" effect. [Data from Grabowski and Bassingthwaighte (80).]

elasticity—is needed to explain the weight-regain phase seen in Figure 41. Naturally the cellular concentrations also buffer the water loss, and the buffering is more effective there because solutes cannot escape from the cell.

TISSUE ELASTICITY. The stiffness of the extravascular

region is an important secondary factor, providing for a restoring force in situations where osmotic forces are absent. Elasticity is to be expected in a tissue that regains its shape after distortion. The shape of the heart is restored after each beat. A well-known experiment illustrates the power of the restoring forces: a heart cleanly removed from a rat and placed in oxygenated perfusate continues to beat for a considerable time. With each beat the heart "jet-propels" itself around the bath; the ventricles fill during each diastole solely because of the elastic recoil to the filled state. During each filling phase the intraventricular pressure and the intratissue pressure must be transiently negative. The rapidity of the restoration of shape by the elastic recoil indicates the importance of its role when there are volume or shape changes in the ventricle.

Vargas and Blackshear (215) measured intratissue pressures via fine needles inserted into the ventricular wall of isolated rabbit hearts. Their estimates of tissue stiffness (the reciprocal of compliance) averaged about 1.2 mmHg per 1% change in heart volume. This is effectively a rather stiff tissue (unlike mesentery); the effect of lesser degrees of stiffness is shown in Figure 44. The influence on regain of weight in model solutions at Y_{cell} and Y_I of 0.6 and 0.3 mmHg per 1% volume change, respectively, is considerable compared with the solution with zero stiffness. At the end of 3 min a stiffness of 0.6, half of that estimated by Vargas and Blackshear (216), caused a 25% return of weight toward the initial value. Because of a lack of information, the stiffnesses of cells and interstitium have been assumed to be the same.

OTHER SECONDARY INFLUENCES. We have expressed concern that osmotic-transient experiments might create artifactually large channels for permeation caused by shrinkage of the endothelial cells. Bassingthwaighte et al. (25) carried out a series of indicator-dilution experiments in rabbit hearts to measure the permeability of the capillary wall to tracer sucrose and inulin. These were carried out along with osmotic-transient experiments, the indicator-dilution curves being done before, during, and after a series of changes in osmolarity by using both step increases and decreases. The results are illustrated in Figure 45. There was no statistically significant influence of the change in osmolarity on the tracer permeabilities (i.e., with the levels of osmotic challenge utilized, no detectable change in the physical characteristics of the passages through the capillary wall was found).

The same data illustrate another point about the relative importance of convection and diffusion in solute flux. The solvent-drag term in Equation 105 (first term on the right side) is an important one conceptually, although it is not the dominant term. The second term, diffusive permeation, is the larger factor. The data in Figure 45 show that the permeabilities of tracer sucrose estimated during the ON-transients (step increase in perfusate osmolarity) are not different from those during the OFF-transient (step decrease in osmolarity). In the ON-transient the water flux opposes the tracer flux, and during the OFF-transient it assists. The absence of a difference means that the solvent-drag term is much smaller than the diffusive term. With tracer inulin the evidence is not clear, but there may be a solvent-drag effect. It makes sense that a larger molecule has lower diffusivity, and at the same time the greater friction with water makes solvent drag more important.

PARAMETER ESTIMATES. In the rabbit heart Grabowski and Bassingthwaighte (80) found the values for P_C and σ_S for the capillary membrane shown in Table 1. These permeabilities are higher and the reflection coefficients lower than the values initially estimated by Vargas and Johnson (218, 219) with their less refined analysis. More recently estimates of reflection coefficients in the heart obtained by Vargas and Blackshear (216) with data that provided good estimates of water flux at time zero have been of the same order of magnitude. The values they found were $\sigma_{NaCl} = 0.063$ and $\sigma_{suc} = 0.16$. They also used optical detection of the dilution of dye in the effluent to estimate water flux. The estimation of permeabilities depends on the time course of solute exchange across the capillary membrane, and it is therefore necessary to use the initial 20–60 s of the weight-transient data. As a consequence the secondary influences of buffering, elasticity, and other factors play an important role even though they have no influence at $t = 0$. Thus it is not surprising that the value of 10×10^5 cm/s for sucrose permeability estimated by Vargas et al. (217) by use of an approach neglecting the secondary influences is apparently too high. [They used a capillary surface area of 560 cm^2/g of heart tissue; we would prefer 500 cm^2/g (24), a small difference.]

Using the method of initial water loss (Eq. 104), Vargas and Blackshear (216) performed an experi-

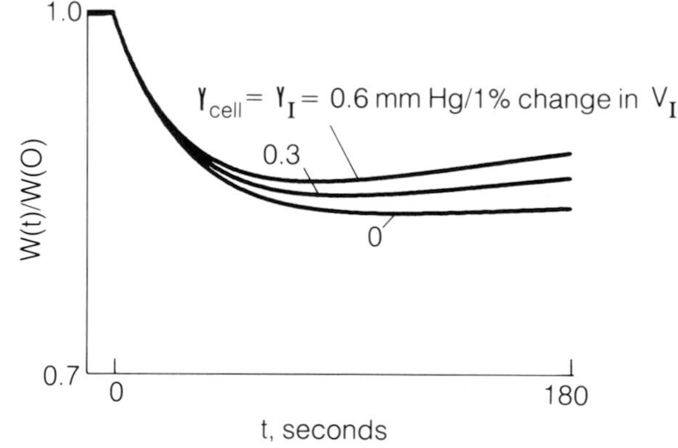

FIG. 44. Influence of tissue stiffness on weight transient. Same conditions as in Fig. 43 except that $Y_I = Y_{cell} = 0.6$, 0.3, and 0 mmHg/1% change in interstitial volume V_I. Note that when $Y_{Cell} = Y_I = 0$ there is almost no weight regain; the barely discernible return phase is due to buffering by interstitial proteins that become relatively concentrated by the water loss.

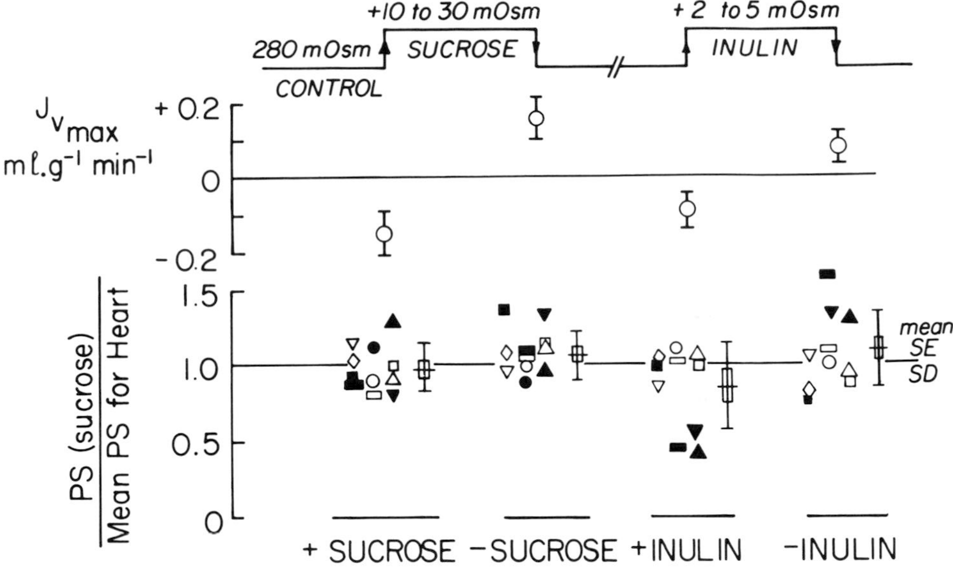

FIG. 45. Estimates of PS_C for [^{14}C]sucrose during step increases and decreases in osmolarity with sucrose and inulin in 11 rabbit hearts perfused with Tyrode's solution. Ordinate, individual estimates of PS_C divided by the mean value of PS_C obtained in the same heart during the osmotic weight transients. *Symbols* indicate different experiments. *Bars* on $J_{V\max}$, the initial rate of weight loss, indicate ± 1 SD (n = 11). In 5 of these hearts the inulin osmotic transients preceded the sucrose transients. To *right* of each group of observations are given the group mean (*horizontal bar*) ± SE (*height of open rectangles*) and ± SD (*vertical lines with small bars at ends*). Data indicate that solvent-drag effects are statistically insignificant.

ment to directly estimate the ratio $\sigma_{suc}/\sigma_{NaCl}$. Instead of making single-solute step changes in osmolarity, they changed both sodium chloride and sucrose concentrations simultaneously over a range of ratios of the concentration changes. By diminishing the concentration of one solute at the same moment as increasing the concentration of the other, a series of estimates of $J_{C,W}$ were obtained from different starting concentrations. The principle is that if there is no net water flux then the ratio of concentration changes equals the rate of change in reflection coefficients, i.e., $\Delta C_{C,NaCl}/\sigma_{NaCl} = \Delta C_{C,suc}/\sigma_{suc}$. The ratio $\sigma_{suc}/\sigma_{NaCl} = 2.9$, the reciprocal of the intercept in Figure 46. This ratio is probably more accurate than that which could be calculated from Table 1 because Vargas and Blackshear's experiments used simultaneous changes in the concentrations of the two solutes to focus on the ratio of reflection coefficients, whereas the data summarized in Table 1 were from separate osmotic transients. From an estimate of $\sigma_{suc} = 0.16$ the slope of Figure 46 gives an estimate of $\sigma_{NaCl} = 0.063$.

ESTIMATION OF HYDRAULIC CONDUCTIVITY, SOLUTE REFLECTION COEFFICIENT, AND SOLUTE PERMEABILITY. Some of the features of the modeling analysis are illustrated in Figure 47, although the details of the iterative process are not discussed here. The responses to only two solutes are shown, but the responses to several, both ON- and OFF-transients, were analyzed in each heart. Figure 47*A* is a response to a 1-mM step decrement in albumin concentration; both step decrements and increments should be analyzed for completeness and as a check on the adequacy of the analysis. If only the responses of one direction are used, there is an inevitable bias. If responses in both directions cannot be fitted with the model over the time course of the observed responses, the model is inadequate. As one can expect from Equation 106, the estimates of L_p and σ_S are to some extent interdependent. Figure 47*B* shows that for a given parameter set the very earliest part of each weight-transient curve could be fitted with little apparent error with quite a range of values of L_p and σ_S, as long as the product $\sigma_S L_p$ is held constant. The sucrose weight response is first fitted by using the value of L_p obtained from joint analysis of the response to albumin washout shown in Figure 47*A*—assuming σ_{alb} = 1 and using σ_{NaCl} obtained from a response to sodium chloride. Values for P_S (solute permeability) and σ_S are adjusted to fit the model to the data. With P_S constant, L_p and σ_S are changed by a factor of one-fifth and five, then vice versa to produce the two other curves (σ_S = 0.02 and σ_S = 0.5), which fit the data almost as well. Of

TABLE 1. *Permeabilities and Reflection Coefficients of Various Solutes*

	P_C, $10^5 \times$ cm/s	σ_S
Sodium chloride	6.0	0.08
Sucrose	2.4	0.14
Raffinose	2.0	0.19
Inulin	0.6	0.46

Data from Vargas and Blackshear (216).

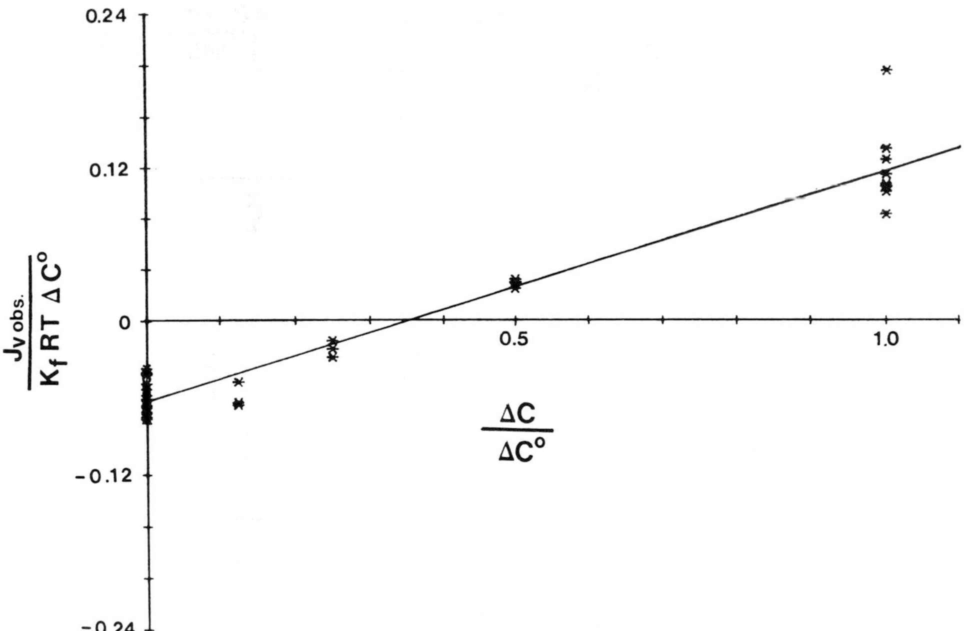

FIG. 46. Initial water fluxes in rabbit hearts perfused with Ringer's solution when step changes of NaCl and sucrose are made simultaneously in the same or in opposite directions, adding or offsetting their effects. $J_{V_{obs}}$ is initial rate of weight loss due to changes in capillary sucrose concentration (ΔC). ΔC°, capillary sucrose concentration cryoscopically isosmotic with the NaCl concentration with which the heart was equilibrated prior to the change. Abscissa, ΔC/ΔC°. Intercept on the abscissa at zero flow indicates ΔC relative to ΔC°, which suffices to balance the opposing concentration difference of NaCl. $K_f = L_{pC}$, the filtration coefficient; RT, product of gas constant and absolute temperature. [From Vargas and Blackshear (216).]

course the cost of changing σ_S is having unrealistic values of L_p, which could not fit an albumin experiment; moreover values of $\sigma_S = 0.02$ or 0.5 would be incompatible with observations on the same heart with larger and smaller solutes. Figure 47*C* shows the sensitivity to σ_S alone where all other parameters are held constant, and Figure 47*D* shows the same for P_S. Analysis of a set of experiments on one isolated heart preparation with different test solutes shows the expected decrease in P_S and increase in σ_S with increasing solute size.

The major point is that L_p must be determined either by the use of a test solute whose reflection coefficient is known or with a set of test solutes with a wide range of σ_S values, of which at least one is quite large. Moreover this must be done while accounting for buffering by resident solutes, and therefore the analysis technique must be iterative, rotating sequentially through a set of data on osmotic transients induced by albumin, sodium chloride (or the solutes of Tyrode's solution), and some other solutes of intermediate size. Determining L_p by raising capillary pressure and measuring the weight gain does not obviate the need to measure the σ_S and P values of the buffering solutes. Only when the whole of a set of osmotic-transient data from a particular experimental preparation is analyzed with a common set of parameter values can the modeling analysis be considered self-consistent. Naturally also, the most demanding tests of the model itself are provided by large sets of data coming from one preparation.

SHORTCOMINGS OF CURRENT MODELS. Although the heart and the liver may be the organs to which these axially distributed capillary–interstitial fluid–cell models are the most applicable, the use of a single-unit model neglects potentially important anatomical and physiological heterogeneities that exist in aggregates of such simple systems. These include variability in myocardial cell diameters, intercapillary distances, capillary diameters, branching, and functional capillary lengths (24); differences in capillary density in different regions of the organ (136, 167); dependence on oxygen supply (133); and variability in pressures and flows (229), P_S (5, 87, 95, 178), L_p (225), and σ_S (199). These factors need to be borne in mind, especially because the introduction of a change in osmolarity often changes the overall vascular resistance (86).

Johnson et al. (98) have argued that flow is not likely to influence the interpretation of the data because at the high perfusion rates they used (generally above 5 $ml \cdot min^{-1} \cdot g^{-1}$), transcapillary exchanges of medium-sized hydrophilic solutes are more barrier limited than flow limited. This would be the case if the solute's clearance were barrier limited as on the plateau of clearance at high flow (Fig. 15). For the same reason variations in the local ratios of capillary

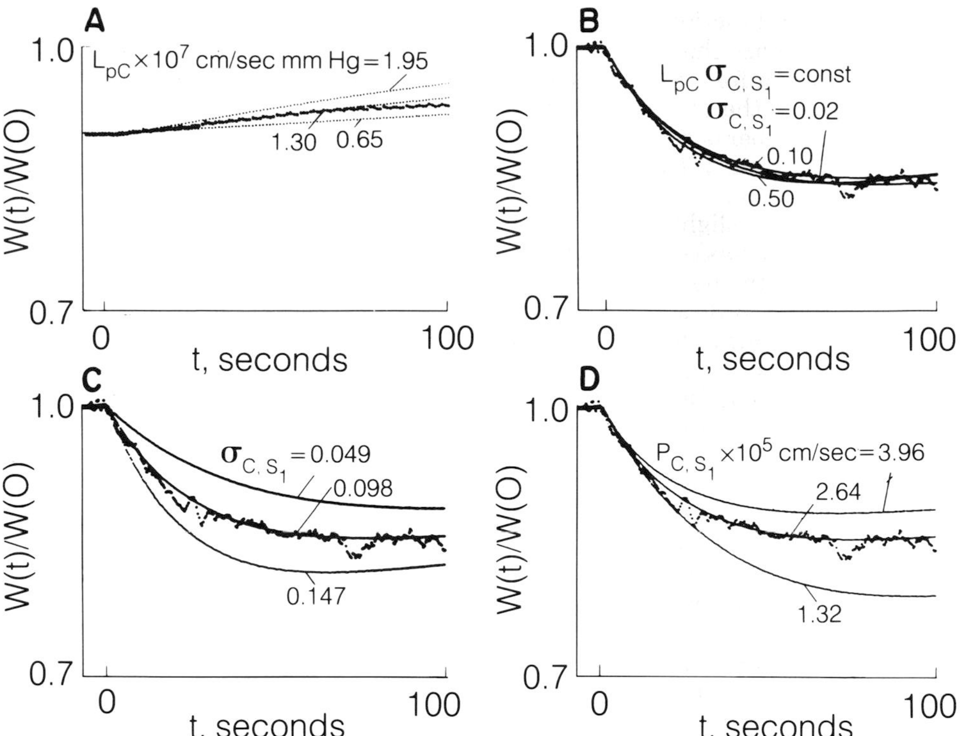

FIG. 47. Interrelationships between capillary hydraulic conductivity L_{pC}, solute reflection coefficient σ_{C,S_1}, and solute permeability P_{C,S_1} on fitting transient responses to osmolarity step changes of 1-mM albumin and 50-mM sucrose in perfused rabbit heart. This is a "worst case" situation in which the curves of mass, W, divided by mass at $t = 0$, W(0), are extremely noisy. *A*: weight responses W(t) to step decrease of 1-mM albumin. Variations of ±50% in L_{pC} strongly influence the model curves of W(t). An $L_{pC} = 1.3 \times 10^7\ \mathrm{cm \cdot s^{-1} \cdot mmHg^{-1}}$ gives the best fit to the data. *B*: weight response to a 50-mM step increase in sucrose concentration. This exceedingly and atypically noisy curve illustrates that parameter evaluation can be reasonable despite such extreme noise. The 50% variations in σ_{C,S_1} around the best fit show large differences. *C*: with a constant product $\sigma_{C,S_1} \cdot L_{pC}$ the sensitivity to variation in either σ_{C,S_1} or L_{pC} is low because they appear as a product in the equation for water flux across capillary wall/unit surface area, $J_{C,w}$; L_{pC} must therefore be determined separately from σ_{C,S_1}. *D*: the 50% variations in P_{C,S_1} give influences as large as those of σ_{C,S_1}. Whereas σ_{C,S_1} strongly influences the initial slope and shape of W(t) near $t = 0$, the influence of P_{C,S_1} occurs later and has a different form. [Data and analyses from Grabowski and Bassingthwaighte (80).]

volume to extravascular region are not very important. The influences of cyclical variations in flow with each heartbeat and associated fluctuations in transcapillary exchange have been calculated by Bassingthwaighte et al. (19) as having a negligible influence on the exchange of tracer solutes at high heart rates. But low-frequency fluctuations in flow may be more important. The influence of the known heterogeneities in local volumes of distribution (F. Gonzalez and J. B. Bassingthwaighte, unpublished data) has yet to be assessed. Multicapillary modeling for osmotic transients is needed just as it was for tracer transients by M. Levin and J. B. Bassingthwaighte (unpublished data).

The modeling does not answer several questions related to submicroscopic inhomogeneities of the capillary barrier itself. Ignoring the vesicular transport of large protein molecules (36, 63) is probably justified because the transport is slow (see the chapter by Michel in this *Handbook*). The parallel transport of water through clefts and across endothelial cells is another story, however, and is considered in some detail in the chapter by Curry in this *Handbook*. Parallel transport routes introduce the possibility of inhomogeneities in concentrations at the micron level, for example, by the formation of standing gradients in regions near entrances to interendothelial clefts. Such phenomena affect the interpretation of observed values of σ_S, L_p, and P_S, although exactly how has not been theoretically determined.

The consideration of barrier inhomogeneity, large concentration changes, and submicroscopic concentration gradients within regions brings into question the wholehearted applicability of the phenomenological equations of Kedem and Katchalsky (102). These are generally considered valid for sufficiently small concentration differences among fractions. For large fluxes of solute and solvent the coefficients L_p, P_S, and σ_S become functions of the fluxes and no longer nicely characterize the barrier in question. The quantitative criterion for sufficient smallness of the fluxes is the value of the Péclet number relative to unity. The Péclet number is defined as the ratio of convective to diffusive effects within a hypothetical pore pathway: $L_p\sigma_S RT\Delta C_S(1 - \sigma_S)/P_S$. Values for the Péclet number are only slightly below unity, and therefore the Kedem-Katchalsky relationships are only marginally applicable to the transport of small permeating solutes. For 0.5-mM albumin the value of the Péclet number is 100, calculated by assuming $P_{alb} = 10^{-8}$ cm/s [from the data of Areskog et al. (6)] and $\sigma_{alb} = 1.0$. This indicates that the Kedem-Katchalsky relationships are not applicable to albumin transport, which is dominated by convection (see the chapter by Curry in this *Handbook*). Even so, equations based on pore models (4, 26, 124, 126, 149) have been used in specific situations to interpret the observed phenomenological coefficients σ_S, P_S, and L_p in terms of estimates of the radii of channels composed of sets of uniformly sized cylindrical pores.

Recently Lewellen (125), in collaboration with W. Stewart and E. Lightfoot at the University of Wisconsin, completed a new approach to the analysis of the phenomena associated with a spherical molecule traversing a cylindrical pore. Although mathematically complex and computationally tedious, the method is general and allows for considerable further development for nonspherical molecules and for other geometries of the passage. Lewellen's results are the most accurate to date; they serve to check previous computations at a few ratios of sphere to pore radius, but more computations are needed. Bean's (26) curves for reflection coefficients appear to be nearly correct, although this result is somewhat fortuitous because two errors in opposite directions almost completely canceled. However, Bean's permeability calculations appear incorrect; those of Anderson and Quinn (4) are more accurate. The fiber-matrix model of Curry and Michel (49) is a step in the direction of analyzing the physical situation more realistically but is not yet set in a self-consistent framework. This is a field for further research.

One should not be left with the impression that the membranes (of capillary wall or cell) are the sole barriers to exchange of solutes and water. The matrix of interstitial and intracellular proteins is also resistant, as suggested in *Diffusion in Blood and Tissue*, p. 552. This can be demonstrated even in the heart, where intracapillary diffusion distances are so short that diffusional equilibration for tracers must occur in several milliseconds. Consider the solute antipyrine. Renkin (162) showed that neither antipyrine nor the even more lipid-soluble 4-aminoantipyrine causes an osmotic transient when a step in concentration of 25 mM was made in the perfusate to skeletal muscle at relatively low flows. The conclusion was that the membrane permeability is so high that no osmolarity difference across a membrane can persist long enough to induce a volume flux. This idea is fully compatible with the observations of Yipintsoi and Bassingthwaighte (234) that tracer iodoantipyrine transport is almost flow limited in its exchange in the heart; the washout curves showed very close similarity in shape over a wide range of flows, indicating the absence of diffusional influences.

Bassingthwaighte et al. (20) used a much larger step (90 mM) in perfusate osmolarity with 4-aminoantipyrine and antipyrine and observed in rabbit hearts at 37°C that both solutes induce weight transients of the form shown in the preceding illustrations. The weight changes were small, about one-fourth of those produced by 40-mM sucrose. The two antipyrines caused the same magnitudes of response at 37°C and were only slightly different at 25°C, but at 15°C the antipyrine transient was considerably larger than that for 4-aminoantipyrine. The interpretation is that at 37°C there is an osmotic effect for both and that there is no effective membrane barrier for either. At 15°C the solubility of antipyrine in the lipid bilayers is much less, and the membrane barrier then contributes significantly to the production of an osmolarity gradient and the weight transient.

How can there be an osmotic transient in a system having no membrane barriers? The answer is that it is not the barriers per se that are important but rather the presence of a matrix of immobile or relatively immobile impeding substances. After a step increase in antipyrine concentration in the perfusate to an organ, the antipyrine diffuses down its concentration gradient, being opposed as it goes by friction with water and with the immobile substances. Water also diffuses down its concentration gradient, being opposed by friction with the antipyrine and the immobile substances. The friction of water with antipyrine and of antipyrine with water must have the same frictional coefficient. Therefore if only these two species were present, the forces would be equal and opposite and there would be no net volume flux; the reflection coefficient would be zero. However, in the presence of a third substance, a transient occurs. If the frictional coefficient of antipyrine with the substance is larger than that of water with the substance, which is to be expected because antipyrine is larger than water, then a weight-loss transient must occur. A weight-gain transient would occur in the (unreasonable) situation in which the substance's frictional coefficient with antipyrine is less than that with water. This generality should be true for any ternary system. The conclusion is that osmotic-transient phenomena do not require the presence of a membrane but that interstitial and intracellular macromolecules have an analogous effect on water and solute movement. These effects are similar to the events described by Curry and Michel (49) for their fiber-matrix model of a capillary pore;

the difference is that the concept need not be limited to finite pores but may be expanded to any open meshwork.

THE RELATION OF MODELING PARAMETERS TO UNDERSTANDING EXCHANGE PROCESSES

It has generally been assumed that if one could obtain a refined set of parameters for a set of molecular probes spanning a wide range, one would be able to use the sequential change in parameters with change in probe properties to gain insight into the properties of capillary membranes, interstitium, parenchymal cellular membranes, internal cellular milieu, and intracellular metabolic processes. In the past the efforts at this level have been concentrated particularly on relating permeability values to the size of molecular probes. Much theoretical superstructure has been built up, primarily on the basis of early and more superficial analyses of osmotic-transient experiments. The reliability of all such efforts has been in question: one would expect tracer and osmotic-transient estimates of permeability to be the same, but the earlier theories used for the analysis of experiments did not give this required result. The model evaluation outlined in this chapter indicates that finding self-consistent osmotic and tracer values for permeability of capillary membranes, for instance, can probably be achieved. Once this has occurred, modeling at both higher and lower hierarchical levels should become more accurate. In terms of permeability of hydrophilic solutes the question remains as to whether or not the estimates of permeability decrease (indicating the existence of a single class of aqueous transcapillary channels, not necessarily uniformly sized) or whether several classes or a spectrum are involved. The analyses of osmotic transients indicate permeation by restricted diffusion, whereas early analyses of multiple-indicator–dilution experiments (carried out prior to the development of the multicapillary modeling described in this chapter) would suggest wide, unrestricted channels. The demand arising from such contradictions is of course that both the data sets and the modeling utilized to frame either point of view be reexamined. Finally, when all of the available experimental and analytical methods yield the same values for a permeability, the level of confidence in the result can rise to the point where interpretations in terms of mechanisms or membrane structure can be really encouraged. Nevertheless a final reminder: helpful as models may be, they must never be cast in bronze but rather serve as transient hypotheses or descriptors of the current state of thinking. Their improvement or replacement depends on each investigator thinking beyond the model. Although modeling is useful in assisting intuition, it is the common sense of the investigator that guides research forward.

SUMMARY

The modeling of blood-tissue exchange processes has made some headway over the past two decades, but there is much more to do. Improvements in the models (e.g., inclusion of factors such as heterogeneities and interaction between unlike capillary-tissue units) are not all that is needed. In addition the approaches to model application, model development and use in experiment design, model computation, and methods of fitting models to data need further elaboration.

The utility of the modeling process is not in doubt. It provides insights that can be obtained in no other way and raises new questions that are the fuel for progress in this area. With new insight, based on relatively simple concepts that become generally accepted, there emerge more complex issues; often these can then be approached directly. At the same time limitations in previous conclusions often become obvious.

The modeling pursued here applies primarily to the interface between blood and tissue. It therefore provides for integration of physiological and biochemical events and can also be used to describe the functional characteristics of a particular process that is part of a larger system. In the converse direction it can be used to gain insight into the nature of the structure of a barrier. Knowledge gained by analysis of blood-tissue exchange is therefore expected to provide one of the large-scale unifying concepts in biology.

The assistance of Edith Boettcher, Geraldine Crooker, Kalee Larsen, and Paddy O'Brien in the preparation of the manuscript and of Hedi Nurk in the preparation of the illustrations is greatly appreciated.

James B. Bassingthwaighte was Visiting Professor of Medicine and Physiology, McGill University, Montreal, 1979–1980.

Research was supported by the Louis and Artur Lucian Award of McGill University and by grants from the National Institutes of Health (HL-19139 and HL-19135), the Medical Research Council of Canada, and the Quebec Heart Foundation.

REFERENCES

1. ABRAMOWITZ, M., AND I. A. SEGUN. *Handbook of Mathematical Functions.* New York: Dover, 1968.
2. AITKEN, A., AND R. M. BARRER. Transport and solubility of isomeric paraffins in rubber. *Trans. Faraday Soc.* 51: 116–130, 1955.
3. ALVAREZ, O. A., AND D. L. YUDILEVICH. Heart capillary permeability to lipid-insoluble molecules. *J. Physiol. London* 202: 45–58, 1969.
4. ANDERSON, J. L., AND J. A. QUINN. Restricted transport in small pores: a model for steric exclusion and hindered particle motion. *Biophys. J.* 14: 130–150, 1974.
5. ANVERSA, P., F. GIACOMELLI, J. WIENER, AND D. SPIRO.

Permeability properties of ventricular endocardium. *Lab. Invest.* 28: 728–734, 1973.

6. ARESKOG, N. H., G. ARTURSON, G. GROTTE, AND G. WALLENIUS. Studies on heart lymph. II. Capillary permeability of the dog's heart, using dextran as a test substance. *Acta Physiol. Scand.* 62: 218–223, 1964.
7. AROESTY, J., AND J. F. GROSS. Convection and diffusion in the microcirculation. *Microvasc. Res.* 2: 247–267, 1970.
8. BARLOW, C. H., AND B. CHANCE. Ischemic areas in perfused rat hearts: measurement by NADH fluorescence photography. *Science* 3: 909–910, 1976.
9. BASSINGTHWAIGHTE, J. B. Plasma indicator dispersion in arteries of the human leg. *Circ. Res.* 19: 332–346, 1966.
10. BASSINGTHWAIGHTE, J. B. Circulatory transport and the convolution integral. *Mayo Clin. Proc.* 42: 137–154, 1967.
11. BASSINGTHWAIGHTE, J. B. Blood flow and diffusion through mammalian organs. *Science* 167: 1347–1353, 1970.
12. BASSINGTHWAIGHTE, J. B. A concurrent model for extraction during transcapillary passage. *Circ. Res.* 35: 483–503, 1974.
13. BASSINGTHWAIGHTE, J. B. The measurement of blood flows and volumes by indicator dilution. In: *Medical Engineering*, edited by C. D. Ray. Chicago, IL: Year Book, 1974, p. 246–260.
14. BASSINGTHWAIGHTE, J. B. Physiology and theory of tracer washout techniques for the estimation of myocardial blood flow: flow estimation from tracer washout. *Prog. Cardiovasc. Dis.* 20: 165–189, 1977.
15. BASSINGTHWAIGHTE, J. B., AND F. H. ACKERMAN. Mathematical linearity of circulatory transport. *J. Appl. Physiol.* 22: 879–888, 1967.
16. BASSINGTHWAIGHTE, J. B., F. H. ACKERMAN, AND E. H. WOOD. Applications of the lagged normal density curve as a model for arterial dilution curves. *Circ. Res.* 18: 398–415, 1966.
17. BASSINGTHWAIGHTE, J. B., W. A. DOBBS, AND T. YIPINTSOI. Heterogeneity of myocardial blood flow. In: *Myocardial Blood Flow in Man: Methods and Significance in Coronary Disease*, edited by A. Maseri. Torino, Italy: Minerva Med., 1972, p. 197–205.
18. BASSINGTHWAIGHTE, J. B., AND G. A. HOLLOWAY, JR. Estimation of blood flow with radioactive tracers. *Semin. Nucl. Med.* 6: 141–161, 1976.
19. BASSINGTHWAIGHTE, J. B., T. J. KNOPP, AND J. B. HAZELRIG. A concurrent flow model for capillary-tissue exchanges. In: *Capillary Permeability*, edited by C. Crone and N. A. Lassen. Copenhagen: Munksgaard, 1970, p. 60–80. (Alfred Benzon Symp. 2.)
20. BASSINGTHWAIGHTE, J. B., P. LEWELLEN, AND R. KERN. Induction of osmotic weight transients in the absence of permeability barriers (Abstract). *Proc. Int. Congr. Physiol. Sci., 28th, Budapest, 1980*, vol. 26, p. 315.
21. BASSINGTHWAIGHTE, J. B., AND H. REUTER. Calcium movements and excitation-contraction coupling in cardiac cells. In: *Electrical Phenomena in the Heart*, edited by W. C. DeMello. New York: Academic, 1972, p. 353–395.
22. BASSINGTHWAIGHTE, J. B., T. STRANDELL, AND D. E. DONALD. Estimation of coronary blood flow by washout of diffusible indicators. *Circ. Res.* 23: 259–278, 1968.
23. BASSINGTHWAIGHTE, J. B., AND T. YIPINTSOI. The emergence function: effects of flow and capillary-tissue exchange in the heart. In: *Capillary Permeability*, edited by C. Crone and N. A. Lassen. Copenhagen: Munksgaard, 1970, p. 239–252. (Alfred Benzon Symp. 2.)
24. BASSINGTHWAIGHTE, J. B., T. YIPINTSOI, AND R. B. HARVEY. Microvasculature of the dog left ventricular myocardium. *Microvasc. Res.* 7: 229–249, 1974.
25. BASSINGTHWAIGHTE, J. B., T. YIPINTSOI, AND T. J. KNOPP. Effect of transcapillary osmotic fluxes on tracer flux in rabbit hearts (Abstract). *Microvasc. Res.* 17: S85, 1979.
26. BEAN, C. P. The physics of porous membranes—neutral pores. In: *Membranes*, edited by G. Eisenman. New York: Dekker, 1972, vol. I, p. 1–54.
27. BEEUWKES, R., III. Efferent vascular patterns and early vascular-tubular relations in the dog kidney. *Am. J. Physiol.* 221: 1361–1374, 1971.
28. BEKEY, G. A. Models and reality: some reflections on the art and science of simulation. *Simulation* 29: 161–164, 1977.
29. BERGNER, P.-E. E. Dynamic aspects of a method in tracer kinetics. *Exp. Cell Res.* 17: 328–335, 1959.
30. BERMAN, M. The formulation and testing of models. *Ann. NY Acad. Sci.* 108: 182–194, 1963.
31. BERT, J. L., R. H. PEARCE, J. M. MATHIESON, AND S. J. WARNER. Characterization of collagenous meshworks by volume exclusion of dextrans. *Biochem. J.* 181: 761–768, 1980.
32. BLOOM, G., AND J. A. JOHNSON. A model for osmotically induced weight transient in the isolated rabbit heart. *Microvasc. Res.* 22: 64–79, 1981.
33. BOHR, C. Über die spezifische Tätigkeit der Lungen bei der respiratorischen Gasaufnahme und ihr Verhalten zu der durch die Alveolarwand stattfindenden Gasdiffusion. *Skand. Arch. Physiol.* 22: 221–280, 1909.
34. BRIDGE, J. H. B., M. BERSOHN, F. GONZALEZ, AND J. B. BASSINGTHWAIGHTE. Synthesis and use of radio cobaltic EDTA as an extracellular marker in rabbit heart. *Am. J. Physiol.* 242 (*Heart Circ. Physiol.* 11): H671–H676, 1982.
35. BRONIKOWSKI, T. A., J. H. LINEHAN, AND C. A. DAWSON. A mathematical analysis of the influence of perfusion heterogeneity on indicator extraction. *Math. Biosci.* 52: 27–51, 1980.
36. BRUNS, R. R., AND G. E. PALADE. Studies on blood capillaries. II. Transport of ferritin molecules across the wall of muscle capillaries. *J. Cell Biol.* 37: 277–299, 1968.
37. CHAMBERS, R., AND B. W. ZWEIFACH. Topography and function of the mesenteric circulation. *Am. J. Anat.* 75: 173–205, 1944.
38. CHANG, B.-L., T. YAMAKAWA, J. NUCCIO, R. PACE, AND R. J. BING. Microcirculation of left atrial muscle, cerebral cortex and mesentary of the cat: a comparative analysis. *Circ. Res.* 50: 240–249, 1982.
39. CHEN, H. I., H. J. GRANGER, AND A. E. TAYLOR. Interaction of capillary, interstitial and lymphatic forces in the canine hindpaw. *Circ. Res.* 39: 245–254, 1976.
40. CHINARD, F. P., T. ENNS, AND M. F. NOLAN. The arterial hematocrit and the separation of red cells and plasma in the dog kidney. *Am. J. Physiol.* 207: 128–132, 1964.
41. CHINARD, F. P., G. J. VOSBURGH, AND T. ENNS. Transcapillary exchange of water and of other substances in certain organs of the dog. *Am. J. Physiol.* 183: 221–234, 1955.
42. COMPER, W. D., AND T. C. LAURENT. Physiological function of connective tissue polysaccharides. *Physiol. Rev.* 58: 255–315, 1978.
43. CONN, H. L., JR., AND J. S. ROBERTSON. Kinetics of potassium transfer in the left ventricle of the intact dog. *J. Appl. Physiol.* 181: 319–324, 1955.
44. CRANK, J. *The Mathematics of Diffusion* (2nd ed.). Oxford, UK: Clarendon, 1975.
45. CRONE, C. The permeability of capillaries in various organs as determined by the use of the "indicator diffusion" method. *Acta Physiol. Scand.* 58: 292–305, 1963.
46. CRONE, C. Facilitated transfer of glucose from blood into brain tissue. *J. Physiol. London* 181: 103–113, 1965.
47. CRONE, C. Capillary permeability. In: *The Inflammatory Process* (2nd ed.), edited by B. W. Zweifach, L. Grant, and R. T. McCluskey. New York: Academic, 1973, vol. 2, p. 95–119.
48. CURRY, F. E. Is the transport of hydrophilic substances across the capillary wall determined by a network of fibrous molecules. *Physiologist* 23(1): 90–93, 1980.
49. CURRY, F. E., AND C. C. MICHEL. A fiber matrix model of capillary permeability. *Microvasc. Res.* 20: 96–99, 1980.
50. DEGENNES, P. G. Reptation of a polymer chain in the presence of fixed obstacles. *J. Chem. Phys.* 55: 572–579, 1971.
51. DEWEY, W. C. Vascular-extravascular exchange of I^{131} plasma proteins in the rat. *Am. J. Physiol.* 197: 423–431, 1959.
52. DULING, B. R., AND R. M. BERNE. Longitudinal gradients in periarteriolar oxygen tension: a possible mechanism for the

participation of oxygen in local regulation of blood flow. *Circ. Res.* 27: 669–678, 1970.

53. EFFROS, R. M. Osmotic extraction of hypotonic fluid from the lungs. *J. Clin. Invest.* 54: 935–947, 1974.
54. EINSTEIN, A. Über die von der molekularkinetischen Theorie der Wärme geforderte Bewegung von in ruhenden Flüssigkeiten suspendierten Teilchen. *Ann. Phys. Leipzig* 17: 549–560, 1905.
55. EINSTEIN, A. Elementare Theorie der Brownschen Bewegung. *Z. Elektrochem.* 14: 235–239, 1908.
56. FALSETTI, H. L., R. J. CARROLL, AND M. L. MARCUS. Temporal heterogeneity of myocardial blood flow in anesthetized dogs. *Circ. Res.* 52: 848–853, 1975.
57. FARMER, R. E. L., AND R. I. MACEY. A perturbation method of determining transport parameters of erythrocytes (Abstract). *Biophys. Soc., 11th Annu. Meet., Houston, 1967*, p. 6.
58. FARMER, R. E. L., AND R. I. MACEY. Perturbation of red cell volume: rectification of osmotic flow. *Biochim. Biophys. Acta* 196: 53–65, 1970.
59. FARMER, R. E. L., AND R. I. MACEY. Perturbation of red cell volume: constancy of membrane transport parameters for certain slow penetrants. *Biochim. Biophys. Acta* 255: 502–516, 1972.
60. FARMER, R. E. L., AND R. I. MACEY. Perturbation of red cell volume. Determination of membrane transport parameters for rapid penetrants. *Biochim. Biophys. Acta* 290: 290–299, 1972.
61. FENSTERMACHER, J. D., D. P. RALL, C. S. PATLAK, AND V. A. LEVIN. Ventriculocisternal perfusion as a technique for analysis of brain capillary permeability and extracellular transport. In: *Capillary Permeability*, edited by C. Crone and N. A. Lassen. Copenhagen: Munksgaard, 1970, p. 483–490. (Alfred Benzon Symp. 2.)
62. FICK, A. Über die Messung des Blutquantums in den Herzventrikeln. *Verhandl. Phys. Med. Ges. Wurzburg* 2: XVI, 1870.
63. FLOREY, H. W. Address of the President, Sir Howard Florey, at the Annual Meeting. *Proc. R. Soc. London Ser. A* 265: 1–14, 1961.
64. FORKER, E. L., AND B. LUXON. Hepatic transport kinetics and plasma disappearance curves: distributed modeling vs. conventional approach. *Am. J. Physiol.* 235 (*Endocrinol. Metab. Gastrointest. Physiol.* 4): E648–E660, 1978.
65. FRASHER, W. G., AND H. WAYLAND. A repeating modular organization of the microcirculation of cat mesentery. *Microvasc. Res.* 4: 62–76, 1972.
66. FRIEDMAN, L., AND E. O. KRAMER. The structure of gelatin gels from studies of diffusion. *J. Am. Chem. Soc.* 52: 1295–1304, 1930.
67. GARRICK, R. A., B. C. PATEL, AND F. P. CHINARD. Permeability of dog erythrocytes to lipophilic molecules: solubility and volume effects. *Am. J. Physiol.* 238 (*Cell Physiol.* 7): C107–C113, 1980.
68. GARRICK, R. A., AND W. R. REDWOOD. Membrane permeability of isolated lung cells to nonelectrolytes. *Am. J. Physiol.* 233 (*Cell Physiol.* 2): C104–C110, 1977.
69. GOLDSMITH, H. L., AND S. G. MASON. The flow of suspensions through tubes. I. Single spheres, rods, and discs. *J. Colloid Sci.* 17: 448–476, 1962.
70. GONZALEZ-FERNANDEZ, J. M. Theory of the measurement of the dispersion of an indicator in indicator-dilution studies. *Circ. Res.* 10: 409–428, 1962.
71. GONZALEZ-FERNANDEZ, J. M., AND S. E. ATTA. Transport and consumption of oxygen in capillary-tissue structures. *Math. Biosci.* 2: 225–262, 1968.
72. GORESKY, C. A. A linear method for determining liver sinusoidal and extravascular volumes. *Am. J. Physiol.* 204: 626–640, 1963.
73. GORESKY, C. A., G. G. BACH, AND B. E. NADEAU. On the uptake of materials by the intact liver—the transport and net removal of galactose. *J. Clin. Invest.* 52: 991–1009, 1973.
74. GORESKY, C. A., G. G. BACH, AND B. E. NADEAU. Red cell carriage of label—its limiting effect on the exchange of materials in the liver. *Circ. Res.* 36: 328–351, 1975.
75. GORESKY, C. A., G. G. BACH, AND C. P. ROSE. The effects of saturating metabolic uptake on space profiles and tracer kinetics. *Am. J. Physiol.* 244 (*Gastrointest. Liver Physiol.* 3): G215–G232, 1983.
76. GORESKY, C. A., E. R. GORDON, AND G. G. BACH. Uptake of monohydric alcohols by liver: demonstration of a shared enzymatic shape. *Am. J. Physiol.* 244 (*Gastrointest. Liver Physiol.* 3): G198–G214, 1983.
77. GORESKY, C. A., AND M. SILVERMAN. Effect of correction of catheter distortion on calculated liver sinusoidal volumes. *Am. J. Physiol.* 207: 883–892, 1964.
78. GORESKY, C. A., W. H. ZIEGLER, AND G. G. BACH. Barrier-limited distribution of diffusible substances from the capillaries in a well-perfused organ. In: *Capillary Permeability*, edited by C. Crone and N. A. Lassen. Copenhagen: Munksgaard, 1970, p. 172–184. (Alfred Benzon Symp. 2.)
79. GORESKY, C. A., W. H. ZIEGLER, AND G. G. BACH. Capillary exchange modeling—barrier-limited and flow-limited distribution. *Circ. Res.* 27: 739–764, 1970.
80. GRABOWSKI, E. F., AND J. B. BASSINGTHWAIGHTE. An osmotic weight transient model for estimation of capillary transport parameters in myocardium. In: *Microcirculation*, edited by J. Grayson and W. Zingg. New York: Plenum, 1976, vol. 2, p. 29–50.
81. GRIM, E. Relation between pressure and concentration difference across membranes permeable to solute and solvent. *Proc. Soc. Exp. Biol. Med.* 83: 195–200, 1953.
82. GRUNEWALD, W. The influence of the threedimensional capillary pattern on the intercapillary oxygen diffusion—a new composed model for comparison of calculated and measured oxygen distribution. In: *Oxygen Supply*, edited by M. Kessler. Baltimore, MD: University Park, 1973, p. 5–17.
83. GULLER, B., T. YIPINTSOI, A. L. ORVIS, AND J. B. BASSINGTHWAIGHTE. Myocardial sodium extraction at varied coronary flows in the dog: estimation of capillary permeability by residue and outflow detection. *Circ. Res.* 37: 359–378, 1975.
84. HALJAMÄE, H., A. LINDE, AND B. AMUNDSON. Comparative analyses of capsular fluid and interstitial fluid. *Am. J. Physiol.* 227: 1199–1205, 1974.
85. HAMILTON, W. F., J. W. MOORE, J. M. KINSMAN, AND R. G. SPURLING. Studies on the circulation. IV. Further analysis of the injection method, and of changes in hemodynamics under physiological and pathological conditions. *Am. J. Physiol.* 99: 534–551, 1931.
86. HARVEY, R. B. Vascular resistance changes produced by hyperosmotic solutions. *Am. J. Physiol.* 199: 31–34, 1960.
87. HAUCK, G., AND H. SCHRÖER. Vital mikroskopische Untersuchungen zur Lokalisation der Eiweisspermeabilität an der Endstrombahn von Warmblütern. *Pfluegers Arch.* 312: 32–44, 1969.
88. HELLBERG, K., A. RICKART, AND R. BING. Direct observations of the coronary microcirculation in the arrested and beating heart (high speed cine). *Federation Proc.* 30: 613a, 1971.
89. HENQUELL, L., AND C. R. HONIG. Intercapillary distances and capillary reserve in right and left ventricles: significance for control of tissue Po_2. *Microvasc. Res.* 12: 35–41, 1976.
90. HILL, A. V. The diffusion of oxygen and lactic acid through tissues. *Proc. R. Soc. London Ser. B* 104: 39–96, 1928.
91. HILL, A. V. The state of water in muscle and blood and the osmotic behaviour of muscle. *Proc. R. Soc. London Ser. B* 106: 477–505, 1930.
92. HINKE, J. A. M. Solvent water for electrolytes in the muscle fiber of the giant barnacle. *J. Gen. Physiol.* 56: 521–541, 1970.
93. HIRCHE, H. J., AND W. LOCHNER. Messung der Durchblutung und der Blutfüllung des coronaren Gefässbettes mit der Teststoffinjektions-methode am narkotisierten Hund bei geschlossenem Thorax. *Pfluegers Arch. Gesamte Physiol. Menschen Tiere* 274: 624–632, 1962.
94. IMANAGA, I. Cell-to-cell diffusion of procion yellow in sheep and calf Purkinje fibers. *J. Membr. Biol.* 16: 381–388, 1974.
95. INTAGLIETTA, M. Evidence for a gradient of permeability in frog mesenteric capillaries. *Bibl. Anat.* 9: 465–468, 1967.

96. JACQUEZ, J. J. *Compartmental Analysis in Biology and Medicine—Kinetics of Distribution of Tracer-Labeled Materials.* Amsterdam: Elsevier, 1972.
97. JOHNSON, J. A., AND G. BLOOM. Permeability and reflection coefficients from osmotic transients—extravascular factors. *Microvasc. Res.* 22: 80–92, 1981.
98. JOHNSON, J. A., G. BLOOM, S. ANDERSON, AND K. MCEVOY. Intracapillary events in osmotic weight transients. *Microvasc. Res.* 22: 93–109, 1981.
99. JOHNSON, J. A., AND T. A. WILSON. A model for capillary exchange. *Am. J. Physiol.* 210: 1299–1303, 1966.
100. JOSEPH, N. R., M. B. ENGEL, AND H. R. CATCHPOLE. Homeostasis of connective tissues. II. Potassium-sodium equilibrium. *Arch. Pathol.* 58: 40–58, 1954.
101. KATCHALSKY, A., AND P. F. CURRAN. *Nonequilibrium Thermodynamics in Biophysics.* Cambridge, MA: Harvard Univ. Press, 1965.
102. KEDEM, O., AND A. KATCHALSKY. Thermodynamic analysis of the permeability of biological membranes to non-electrolytes. *Biochim. Biophys. Acta* 27: 229–246, 1958.
103. KETY, S. S. Measurement of regional circulation by the local clearance of radioactive sodium. *Am. Heart J.* 38: 321–328, 1949.
104. KETY, S. S., AND C. F. SCHMIDT. The nitrous oxide method for the quantitative determination of cerebral blood flow in man: theory, procedure, and normal values. *J. Clin. Invest.* 27: 476–483, 1948.
105. KEYS, A. The apparent permeability of the capillary membrane in man. *Trans. Faraday Soc.* 33: 930–939, 1937.
106. KEYS, A. The properties of the gill membranes of fishes. *Trans. Faraday Soc.* 33: 972–981, 1937.
107. KNOPP, T. J., W. A. DOBBS, J. F. GREENLEAF, AND J. B. BASSINGTHWAIGHTE. Transcoronary intravascular transport functions in normal dogs obtained via a stable deconvolution technique. *Ann. Biomed. Eng.* 4: 49–59, 1976.
108. KROGH, A. The number and distribution of capillaries in muscles with calculations of the oxygen pressure head necessary for supplying the tissue. *J. Physiol. London* 52: 409–415, 1919.
109. KROGH, A. *The Anatomy and Physiology of Capillaries* (revised ed.) New Haven, CT: Yale Univ. Press, 1929.
110. KROGH, A., E. M. LANDIS, AND A. H. TURNER. The movement of fluid through the human capillary wall in relation to venous pressure and to the colloid osmotic pressure of the blood. *J. Clin. Invest.* 11: 63–95, 1932.
111. KUIKKA, J., E. BOUSKELA, AND J. B. BASSINGTHWAIGHTE. D-, L-, and 2-deoxy-D-glucose uptake in the isolated blood perfused dog hearts. *Bibl. Anat.* 18: 239–242, 1979.
112. KUSHMERICK, M. J., AND R. J. PODOLSKY. Ionic mobility in muscle cells. *Science* 166: 1297–1298, 1969.
113. LANDIS, E. M. Micro-injection studies of capillary permeability. II. The relation between capillary pressure and the rate at which fluid passes through the walls of single capillaries. *Am. J. Physiol.* 82: 217–238, 1927.
114. LANDIS, E. M., AND J. R. PAPPENHEIMER. Exchange of substances through the capillary walls. In: *Handbook of Physiology. Circulation*, edited by W. F. Hamilton. Washington, DC: Am. Physiol. Soc., 1963, sect. 2, vol. II, chapt. 29, p. 961–1034.
115. LANGER, G. A., AND J. S. FRANK. Lanthanum in heart cell culture: effect on calcium exchange correlated with its localization. *J. Cell Biol.* 54: 441–455, 1972.
116. LASSEN, N. A., AND C. CRONE. The extraction fraction of a capillary bed to hydrophilic molecules: theoretical considerations regarding the single injection technique with a discussion of the role of diffusion between laminar streams (Taylor's effect). In: *Capillary Permeability*, edited by C. Crone and N. A. Lassen. Copenhagen: Munksgaard, 1970, p. 48–59. (Alfred Benzon Symp. 2.)
117. LAURENT, T. C. The interaction between polysaccharides and other macromolecules. IX. The exclusion of molecules from hyaluronic acid gels and solutions. *Biochem. J.* 93: 106–112, 1964.
118. LAURENT, T. C., AND J. KILLANDER. A theory of gel filtration and its experimental verification. *J. Chromatogr.* 14: 317–330, 1964.
119. LAURENT, T. C., B. N. PRESTON, H. PERTOFT, B. GUSTAFSSON, AND M. MCCABE. Diffusion of linear polymers in hyaluronate solutions. *Eur. J. Biochem.* 53: 129–136, 1975.
120. LENHOFF, A. M., AND E. N. LIGHTFOOT. The effects of axial diffusion and permeability barriers on the transient response of tissue cylinders. I. Solution in transform space. *J. Theor. Biol.* 97: 663–677, 1982.
121. LEONARD, E. F., E. F. GRABOWSKI, AND V. T. TURITTO. The role of convection and diffusion on platelet adhesion and aggregation. *Ann. NY Acad. Sci.* 201: 329–342, 1972.
122. LEVIN, M., J. KUIKKA, AND J. B. BASSINGTHWAIGHTE. Sensitivity analysis in optimization of time-distributed parameters for a coronary circulation model. *Med. Prog. Technol.* 7: 119–124, 1980.
123. LEVIN, M., AND A. S. POPEL. Simulation of flow in stochastic microvascular networks (Abstract). *Microvasc. Res.* 23: 263, 1982.
124. LEVITT, D. G. General continuum analysis of transport through pores. I. Proof of Onsager's reciprocity postulate for uniform pore. II. Nonuniform pores. *Biophys. J.* 15: 533–563, 1975.
125. LEWELLEN, P. C. Hydrodynamic Analysis of Microporous Mass Transport. Madison: Univ. of Wisconsin, 1982. PhD thesis.
126. LIGHTFOOT, E. N., J. B. BASSINGTHWAIGHTE, AND E. F. GRABOWSKI. Hydrodynamic models for diffusion in microporous membranes. *Ann. Biomed. Eng.* 4: 78–90, 1976.
127. LINEHAN, J. H., AND C. A. DAWSON. A kinetic model of prostaglandin metabolism in the lung. *J. Appl. Physiol.: Respirat. Environ. Exercise Physiol.* 47: 404–411, 1979.
128. LINEHAN, J. H., C. A. DAWSON, AND V. M. WAGNER-WEBER. Prostaglandin E_1 uptake by isolated cat lungs perfused with physiological salt solution. *J. Appl. Physiol.: Respirat. Environ. Exercise Physiol.* 50: 428–434, 1981.
128a. S. E. LITTLE AND J. B. BASSINGTHWAIGHTE. Plasma-soluble marker for intraorgan regional flows. *Am. J. Physiol.* 245 (*Heart Circ. Physiol.* 14): H707–H712, 1983.
129. LONGMUIR, I. S., AND F. J. W. ROUGHTON. The diffusion coefficients of carbon monoxide and nitrogen in haemoglobin solutions. *J. Physiol. London* 118: 264–275, 1952.
130. LOPEZ-CURTO, J. A., J. B. BASSINGTHWAIGHTE, AND P. J. KELLY. Microvascular anatomy of the adult canine tibial diaphysis. *J. Bone Jt. Surg.* 62: 1362–1369, 1980.
131. MACCHIA, D. D., E. PAGE, AND P. I. POLIMENI. Interstitial anion distribution in striated muscle determined with [^{35}S]sulfate and [^{3}H]sucrose. *Am. J. Physiol.* 237 (*Cell Physiol.* 6): C125–C130, 1979.
132. MARTÍN, P., AND D. YUDILEVICH. A theory for the quantification of transcapillary exchange by tracer-dilution curves. *Am. J. Physiol.* 207: 162–168, 1964.
133. MARTINI, J., AND C. R. HONIG. Direct measurement of intercapillary distance in beating rat heart in situ under various conditions of O_2 supply. *Microvasc. Res.* 1: 244–256, 1969.
134. MEIER, P., AND K. L. ZIERLER. On the theory of the indicator-dilution method for measurement of blood flow and volume. *J. Appl. Physiol.* 6: 731–744, 1954.
135. MOTTA, P., M. MUTO, AND T. FUJITA. *The Liver: An Atlas of Scanning Electron Microscopy.* Tokyo: Igaku Shoin, 1978.
136. MYERS, W. W., AND C. R. HONIG. Number and distribution of capillaries as determinants of myocardial oxygen tension. *Am. J. Physiol.* 207: 653–660, 1964.
137. NAKAMURA, Y., AND H. WAYLAND. Macromolecular transport in the cat mesentery. *Microvasc. Res.* 9: 1–21, 1975.
138. NICOLL, P. A., AND R. L. WEBB. Blood circulation in the subcutaneous tissue of the living bat's wing. *Ann. NY Acad. Sci.* 46: 697–709, 1946.
139. OGSTON, A. G., B. N. PRESTON, AND J. D. WELLS. On the transport of compact particles through solutions of chain-polymers. *Proc. R. Soc. London Ser. A* 333: 297–316, 1973.

140. OGSTON, A. G., AND T. F. SHERMAN. Effects of hyaluronic acid upon diffusion of solutes and flow of solvent. *J. Physiol. London* 156: 67–74, 1961.
141. PAGE, E., AND R. S. BERNSTEIN. Cat heart muscle *in vitro*. V. Diffusion through a sheet of right ventricle. *J. Gen. Physiol.* 47: 1129–1140, 1964.
142. PAPPENHEIMER, J. R. Passage of molecules through capillary walls. *Physiol. Rev.* 33: 387–423, 1953.
143. PAPPENHEIMER, J. R., E. M. RENKIN, AND L. M. BORRERO. Filtration, diffusion and molecular sieving through peripheral capillary membranes. A contribution to the pore theory of capillary permeability. *Am. J. Physiol.* 167: 13–46, 1951.
144. PAPPENHEIMER, J. R., AND A. SOTO-RIVERA. Effective osmotic pressure of the plasma proteins and other qualities associated with the capillary circulation in the hindlimbs of cats and dogs. *Am. J. Physiol.* 152: 471–491, 1948.
145. PATLAK, C. S., AND J. D. FENSTERMACHER. Measurement of dog blood-brain transfer constants by ventriculocisternal perfusion. *Am. J. Physiol.* 229: 877–884, 1975.
146. PEARCE, R. H., AND T. C. LAURENT. Exclusion of dextrans by meshworks of collagenous fibres. *Biochem. J.* 163: 617–625, 1977.
147. PERL, W. Modified filtration-permeability model of transcapillary transport—a solution of the Pappenheimer pore puzzle? *Microvasc. Res.* 3: 233–251, 1971.
148. PERL, W., AND F. P. CHINARD. A convection-diffusion model of indicator transport through an organ. *Circ. Res.* 22: 273–298, 1968.
149. POHOST, G. M., N. M. ALPERT, J. S. INGWALL, AND H. S. STRAUSS. Thallium redistribution: mechanisms and clinical utility. *Semin. Nucl. Med.* 10: 70–93, 1980.
150. POLIMENI, P. I. Extracellular space and ionic distribution in rat ventricle. *Am. J. Physiol.* 227: 676–683, 1974.
151. POLLACK, G. H. Intercellular coupling in the atrioventricular node and other tissues of the rabbit heart. *J. Physiol. London* 255: 275–298, 1976.
152. POLLOCK, F., AND J. J. BLUM. On the distribution of a permeable solute during Poiseuille flow in capillary tubes. *Biophys. J.* 6: 19–29, 1966.
153. PRANDTL, L., AND O. G. TIETJENS. *Applied Hydro- and Aeromechanics*. New York: McGraw-Hill, 1934.
154. PROTHERO, J., AND A. C. BURTON. The physics of blood flow in capillaries. I. The nature of the motion. *Biophys. J.* 1: 565–579, 1961.
155. RAPOPORT, S. I. Effect of concentrated solutions on blood-brain barrier. *Am. J. Physiol.* 219: 270–274, 1970.
156. RAPOPORT, S. I., W. R. FREDERICKS, K. OHNO, AND K. D. PETTIGREW. Quantitative aspects of reversible osmotic opening of the blood-brain barrier. *Am. J. Physiol.* 238 (*Regulatory Integrative Comp. Physiol.* 7): R421–R431, 1980.
157. RAPPAPORT, A. M., Z. J. BOROWY, W. M. LOUGHEED, AND W. N. LOTTO. Subdivision of hexagonal liver lobules into a structural and functional unit. *Anat. Rec.* 119: 11–34, 1954.
158. RASIO, E. A., M. BENDAYAN, AND C. A. GORESKY. Diffusion permeability of an isolated rete mirabile. *Circ. Res.* 41: 791–798, 1977.
159. RASIO, E. A., M. BENDAYAN, AND C. A. GORESKY. The effect of hyperosmolality on the permeability and structure of the capillaries of the isolated rete mirabile of the eel. *Circ. Res.* 49: 661–676, 1981.
160. REDWOOD, W. R., E. RALL, AND W. PERL. Red cell membrane permeability deduced from bulk diffusion coefficients. *J. Gen. Physiol.* 64: 706–729, 1974.
161. RENEAU, D. D., JR., D. F. BRULEY, AND M. H. KNISELY. A mathematical simulation of oxygen release, diffusion, and consumption in the capillaries and tissue of the human brain. In: *Chemical Engineering in Medicine and Biology*, edited by D. Hershey. New York: Plenum, 1967, p. 135–241.
162. RENKIN, E. M. Capillary and cellular permeability to some compounds related to antipyrine. *Am. J. Physiol.* 173: 125–130, 1953.
163. RENKIN, E. M. Filtration, diffusion, and molecular sieving through porous cellulose membranes. *J. Gen. Physiol.* 38: 225–243, 1954.
164. RENKIN, E. M. Effects of blood flow on diffusion kinetics in isolated, perfused hindlegs of cats: a double circulation hypothesis. *Am. J. Physiol.* 183: 125–136, 1955.
165. RENKIN, E. M. Transport of potassium-42 from blood to tissue in isolated mammalian skeletal muscles. *Am. J. Physiol.* 197: 1205–1210, 1959.
166. RENKIN, E. M. Exchangeability of tissue potassium in skeletal muscle. *Am. J. Physiol.* 197: 1211–1215, 1959.
167. REYNOLDS, S. R. M., M. KIRSCH, AND R. J. BING. Functional capillary beds in the beating KCl-arrested and KCl-arrested-perfused myocardium of the dog. *Circ. Res.* 6: 600–611, 1958.
168. ROBINSON, R. A., AND R. H. STOKES. *Electrolyte Solutions* (2nd ed.). London: Butterworths, 1959.
169. ROGUS, E., AND K. L. ZIERLER. Sodium and water contents of sarcoplasm and sarcoplasmic reticulum in rat skeletal muscle: effects of anisotonic media, ouabain and external sodium. *J. Physiol. London* 233: 227–270, 1973.
170. ROSE, C. P., AND C. A. GORESKY. Vasomotor control of capillary transit time heterogeneity in the canine coronary circulation. *Circ. Res.* 39: 541–554, 1976.
171. ROSE, C. P., AND C. A. GORESKY. Constraints on the uptake of labeled palmitate by the heart—the barriers at the capillary and sarcolemmal surfaces and the control of intracellular sequestration. *Circ. Res.* 41: 534–545, 1977.
172. ROSE, C. P., C. A. GORESKY, AND G. G. BACH. The capillary and sarcolemmal barriers in the heart—an exploration of labeled water permeability. *Circ. Res.* 41: 515–533, 1977.
173. ROSE, C. P., G. C. GORESKY, P. BELANGER, AND M. CHEN. Effect of vasodilation and flow rate on capillary permeability surface product and interstitial space size in the coronary circulation—a frequency domain technique for modeling multiple dilution data with Laguerre functions. *Circ. Res.* 47: 312–328, 1980.
174. ROSELLI, R. J., AND T. R. HARRIS. A four phase model of capillary tracer exchange. *Ann. Biomed. Eng.* 7: 203–238, 1979.
175. ROSELLI, R. J., AND T. R. HARRIS. The effects of red cell and tissue exchange on the evaluation of capillary permeability from multiple indicator data. *Ann. Biomed. Eng.* 7: 239–282, 1979.
176. ROTH, A. C., AND E. O. FEIGL. Diffusional shunting in the canine myocardium. *Circ. Res.* 48: 470–480, 1981.
177. ROUFOGALIS, B. D. Regulation of calcium translocation across the red blood cell membrane. *Can. J. Physiol. Pharmacol.* 57: 1331–1349, 1979.
178. ROUS, P., H. P. GILDING, AND F. SMITH. The gradient of vascular permeability. *J. Exp. Med.* 51: 807, 1930.
179. SAFFORD, R. E., E. A. BASSINGTHWAIGHTE, AND J. B. BASSINGTHWAIGHTE. Diffusion of water in cat ventricular myocardium. *J. Gen. Physiol.* 72: 513–558, 1978.
180. SAFFORD, R. E., AND J. B. BASSINGTHWAIGHTE. Calcium diffusion in transient and steady states in muscle. *Biophys. J.* 20: 113–136, 1977.
181. SANGREN, W. C., AND C. W. SHEPPARD. Mathematical derivation of the exchange of a labeled substance between a liquid flowing in a vessel and an external compartment. *Bull. Math. Biophys.* 15: 387–394, 1953.
182. SCHMIDT, G. W. A. A mathematical theory of capillary exchange as a function of tissue structure. *Bull. Math. Biophys.* 14: 229–264, 1952.
183. SEJRSEN, P. Single injection, external registration method for measurement of capillary extraction. In: *Capillary Permeability*, edited by C. Crone and N. A. Lassen. Copenhagen: Munksgaard, 1970, p. 256–260. (Alfred Benzon Symp. 2.)
184. SESTIER, F. J., R. R. MILDENBERGER, AND G. A. KLASSEN. Role of autoregulation in spatial and temporal perfusion heterogeneity of canine myocardium. *Am. J. Physiol.* 235 (*Heart Circ. Physiol.* 4): H64–H71, 1978.
185. SETCHELL, B. P., G. M. H. WAITES, AND G. D. THORBURN.

Blood flow in the testis of the conscious ram measured with krypton—effects of heat, catecholamines and acetylcholine. *Circ. Res.* 18: 755–763, 1966.

186. SHAW, M. Interpretation of osmotic pressure in solutions of one and two nondiffusible components. *Biophys. J.* 16: 43–57, 1976.
187. SHEEHAN, R. M., AND E. M. RENKIN. Capillary, interstitial, and cell membrane barriers to blood-tissue transport of potassium and rubidium in mammalian skeletal muscle. *Circ. Res.* 30: 588–607, 1972.
188. SHEPPARD, C. W. *Basic Principles of the Tracer Method.* New York: Wiley, 1962.
189. SHINNAR, R., AND P. NAOR. Residence time distribution in systems with internal reflux. *Chem. Eng. Sci.* 22: 1369–1381, 1967.
190. SILVERMAN, M., AND C. A. GORESKY. A unified kinetic hypothesis of carrier mediated transport: its applications. *Biophys. J.* 5: 487–509, 1965.
191. SMITH, R. E., AND M. F. MORALES. On the theory of blood-tissue exchanges. I. Fundamental equations. *Bull. Math. Biophys.* 6: 125–131, 1944.
192. SMITH, R. E., AND M. F. MORALES. On the theory of blood-tissue exchanges. II. Applications. *Bull. Math. Biophys.* 6: 133–139, 1944.
193. SOBIN, S., H. M. TREMER, AND Y. L. FUNG. Morphometric basis of the sheet-flow concept of the pulmonary alveolar microcirculation in the cat. *Circ. Res.* 26: 397–414, 1970.
194. SOLOMON, A. K. Compartmental methods of kinetic analysis. In: *Mineral Metabolism: An Advanced Treatise*, edited by C. L. Comar and F. Bronner. New York: Academic, 1960, vol. I, pt. A, p. 119–167.
195. SPANGLER, R. D., T. YIPINTSOI, T. J. KNOPP, R. L. FRYE, AND J. B. BASSINGTHWAIGHTE. Pulmonary mean-transit-time blood volumes in anesthetized dogs. *J. Appl. Physiol.* 30: 56–63, 1971.
196. STARLING, E. H. On the absorption of fluids from the connective tissue spaces. *J. Physiol. London* 19: 312–326, 1896.
197. STAUB, N. C. The forces regulating fluid filtration in the lung. *Microvasc. Res.* 15: 45–55, 1978.
198. STAVERMAN, A. J. The theory of measurement of osmotic pressure. *Rec. Trav. Chim. Pays Bas Belg.* 70: 344–352, 1951.
199. STAVERMAN, A. J. Non-equilibrium thermodynamics of membrane processes. *Trans. Faraday Soc.* 48: 176–185, 1952.
200. STEENBERGEN, C., G. DEELEUW, C. BARLOW, B. CHANCE, AND J. R. WILLIAMSON. Heterogeneity of the hypoxic state in perfused rat heart. *Circ. Res.* 41: 606–615, 1977.
201. STEPHENSON, J. L. Theory of the measurement of blood flow by the dilution of an indicator. *Bull. Math. Biophys.* 10: 117–121, 1948.
202. STEWART, G. N. Researches on the circulation time in organs and on the influences which affect it. *J. Physiol. London* 15: 1–89, 1894.
203. STEWART, G. N. The measurement of the output of the heart (Abstract). *Science* 5: 137, 1897.
204. STEWART, G. N. Researches on the circulation time and on the influences which affect it. IV. The output of the heart. *J. Physiol. London* 22: 159–183, 1897.
205. STEWART, G. N. Researches on the circulation time and on the influences which affect it. V. The circulation time of the spleen, kidney, intestine, heart (coronary circulation) and retina, with some further observations on the time of the lesser circulation. *Am. J. Physiol.* 58: 278–295, 1921.
206. STRAY-PEDERSEN, S., AND A. NICOLAYSEN. Qualitative and quantitative studies of the capillary structure in the rete mirabile of the eel, *Anguilla vulgaris L. Acta Physiol. Scand.* 94: 339–357, 1975.
207. STROEVE, P., C. K. COLTON, AND K. A. SMITH. Steady state diffusion of oxygen in red blood cell and model suspensions. *AIChE J.* 22: 1133–1142, 1976.
208. STROEVE, P., K. A. SMITH, AND C. K. COLTON. An analysis of carrier facilitated transport in heterogeneous media. *AIChE J.* 22: 1125–1132, 1976.
209. SUENSON, M., D. R. RICHMOND, AND J. B. BASSINGTHWAIGHTE. Diffusion of sucrose, sodium and water in ventricular myocardium. *Am. J. Physiol.* 227: 1116–1123, 1974.
210. TANCREDI, R. G., T. YIPINTSOI, AND J. B. BASSINGTHWAIGHTE. Capillary and cell wall permeability to potassium in isolated dog hearts. *Am. J. Physiol.* 229: 537–544, 1975.
211. TAYLOR, A. E., AND R. E. DRAKE. Fluid and protein movement across the pulmonary microcirculation. In: *Lung Biology in Health and Disease. Lung Water and Solute Exchange*, edited by N. C. Staub. New York: Dekker, 1977, vol. 7, p. 129–166.
212. TAYLOR, G. I. Dispersion of soluble matter in solvent flowing slowly through a tube. *Proc. R. Soc. London Ser. B* 219: 186–203, 1953.
213. THOMPSON, H. K, G. F. STARMER, R. E. WHALEN, AND K. D. MCINTOSH. Indicator transit time considered as a gamma variate. *Circ. Res.* 14: 502–515, 1964.
214. USSING, H. H. Transport through biological membranes. *Annu. Rev. Physiol.* 15: 1–20, 1953.
215. VARGAS, F. F., AND G. L. BLACKSHEAR. Transcapillary osmotic flows in the in vitro perfused heart. *Am. J. Physiol.* 240 (*Heart Circ. Physiol.* 9): H448–H456, 1981.
216. VARGAS, F. F., AND G. L. BLACKSHEAR. Secondary driving forces affecting transcapillary osmotic flows in perfused heart. *Am. J. Physiol.* 240 (*Heart Circ. Physiol.* 9): H457–H464, 1981.
217. VARGAS, F. F., G. L. BLACKSHEAR, AND R. J. MAJERLE. Permeability and model testing of heart capillaries by osmotic and optical methods. *Am. J. Physiol.* 239 (*Heart Circ. Physiol.* 8): H464–H468, 1980.
218. VARGAS, F. F., AND J. A. JOHNSON. An estimate of reflection coefficients for rabbit heart capillaries. *J. Gen. Physiol.* 47: 667–677, 1964.
219. VARGAS, F. F., AND J. A. JOHNSON. Permeability of rabbit heart capillaries to nonelectrolytes. *Am. J. Physiol.* 213: 87–93, 1967.
220. VINCENZI, F. F., AND T. R. HINDS. Calmodulin and plasma membrane calcium transport. In: *Calcium and Cell Function*, edited by W. Y. Cheung. New York: Academic, 1980, vol. I, p. 128–165.
221. WEIBEL, E. R. *Morphometry of the Human Lung.* New York: Academic, 1963.
222. WEIDMANN, S. The diffusion of radiopotassium across intercalated disks of mammalian cardiac muscle. *J. Physiol. London* 187: 323–342, 1966.
223. WEINGART, R. The permeability to tetraethylammonium of ions of the surface membrane and the intercalated disks of sheep and calf myocardium. *J. Physiol. London* 240: 741–762, 1974.
224. WIEDEMAN, M. P. Dimensions of blood vessels from distribution artery to collecting vein. *Circ. Res.* 12: 375–378, 1963.
225. WIEDERHIELM, C. A. Transcapillary and interstitial transport phenomena in the mesentery. *Federation Proc.* 25: 1789–1798, 1966.
226. WIEDERHIELM, C. A. Dynamics of transcapillary fluid exchange. *J. Gen. Physiol.* 52: 29–63, 1968.
227. WIEDERHIELM, C. A. Dynamics of capillary fluid exchange: a nonlinear computer simulation. *Microvasc. Res.* 18: 48–82, 1979.
228. WIEDERHIELM, C. A., AND L. L. BLACK. Osmotic interaction of plasma proteins with interstitial macromolecules. *Am. J. Physiol.* 231: 638–641, 1976.
229. WIEDERHIELM, C. A., AND B. V. WESTON. Microvascular, lymphatic and tissue pressures in the unanesthetized mammal. *Am. J. Physiol.* 225: 992–996, 1973.
230. WINEGRAD, S., A. WEISBERG, AND G. MCCLELLAN. Are restoring forces important to relaxation? *Eur. J. Cardiol.* 11, Suppl: 59–65, 1980.
231. WINGET, R. R., AND J. B. BASSINGTHWAIGHTE. Diffusion of antipyrine and water through myocardium (Abstract). *Federation Proc.* 37: 314, 1978.
232. WOLOSEWICK, J. J., AND K. R. PORTER. Microtrabecular

lattice of the cytoplasmic ground substance. *J. Cell Biol.* 82: 114–139, 1979.

233. WOOD, E. H. (editor). Symposium on use of indicator-dilution technics in the study of the circulation. *Circ. Res.* 10: 373–581, 1962.
234. YIPINTSOI, T., AND J. B. BASSINGTHWAIGHTE. Circulatory transport of iodoantipyrine and water in the isolated dog heart. *Circ. Res.* 27: 461–477, 1970.
235. YIPINTSOI, T., W. A. DOBBS, JR., P. D. SCANLON, T. J. KNOPP, AND J. B. BASSINGTHWAIGHTE. Regional distribution of diffusible tracers and carbonized microspheres in the left ventricle of isolated dog hearts. *Circ. Res.* 33: 573–587, 1973.
236. YIPINTSOI, T., AND T. J. KNOPP. Simultaneous permeability estimation by osmotic transient and tracer diffusion techniques (Abstract). *Biophys. J.* 12: 137a, 1972.
237. YIPINTSOI, T., P. D. SCANLON, AND J. B. BASSINGTHWAIGHTE. Density and water content of dog ventricular myocardium. *Proc. Soc. Exp. Biol. Med.* 141: 1032–1035, 1972.
238. YIPINTSOI, T., R. G. TANCREDI, D. R. RICHMOND, AND J. B. BASSINGTHWAIGHTE. Myocardial extractions of sucrose, glucose, and potassium. In: *Capillary Permeability*, edited by C. Crone and N. A. Lassen. Copenhagen: Munksgaard, 1970, p. 153–156. (Alfred Benzon Symp. 2.)
239. YUDILEVICH, D. L., AND O. A. ALVAREZ. Water, sodium, and thiourea transcapillary diffusion in the dog heart. *Am. J. Physiol.* 213: 308–314, 1967.
240. YUDILEVICH, D. L., AND P. M. DE JULIÁN. Potassium, sodium, and iodide transcapillary exchange in dog heart. *Am. J. Physiol.* 208: 959–967, 1965.
241. ZIEGLER, W. H., AND C. A. GORESKY. Transcapillary exchange in the working left ventricle of the dog. *Circ. Res.* 29: 181–207, 1971.
242. ZIEGLER, W. H., AND C. A. GORESKY. Kinetics of rubidium uptake in the working dog heart. *Circ. Res.* 29: 208–220, 1971.
243. ZIERLER, K. L. A simplified explanation of the theory of indicator-dilution for measurement of fluid flow and volume and other distributive phenomena. *Johns Hopkins Med. J.* 103: 199–217, 1958.
244. ZIERLER, K. L. Theory of the use of arteriovenous concentration differences for measuring metabolism in steady and nonsteady states. *J. Clin. Invest.* 40: 2111, 1961.
245. ZIERLER, K. L. Circulation times and the theory of indicator-dilution methods for determining blood flow and volume. In: *Handbook of Physiology. Circulation*, edited by W. F. Hamilton. Washington, DC: Am. Physiol. Soc., 1962, sect. 2, vol. I, chapt. 18, p. 585–615.
246. ZIERLER, K. L. Theoretical basis of indicator-dilution methods for measuring flow and volume. *Circ. Res.* 10: 393–407, 1962.
247. ZIERLER, K. L. Theory of use of indicators to measure blood flow and extracellular volume and calculation of transcapillary movement of tracers. *Circ. Res.* 12: 464–471, 1963.
248. ZIERLER, K. L. Circulation times and the theory of indicator-dilution methods for determining blood flow and volume. *Circ. Res.* 12: 585–615, 1963.
249. ZIERLER, K. L. Equations of measuring blood flow by external monitoring of radioisotopes. *Circ. Res.* 16: 309–321, 1965.

Index

Adenine nucleotides
  metabolism by vascular endothelial cells, 143
Adenosine
  metabolism by vascular endothelial cells, 143
Adipose tissue
  adipocytes, vascular morphology of, 949–950
  capillary permeability to macromolecules in, 488
  microcirculation of, 949–967
    adrenergic innervation of, 950
    adrenergic innervation of, regional differences in, 953
    β-adrenoreceptors in, types, 952–953
    α- and β-adrenoreceptors in, distribution of, 952
    basic hemodynamics of, 951–952
    cholinergic innervation of, 950
    circulating catecholamines in control of, 960
    CNS control of, 961
    effect of hypotension and hemorrhagic shock on, 962–963
    effect of reduced ambient temperature on, 963
    hormonal control of, 960–961
    local control of, 959–960
    methods of investigation of, 950–951
    neurotensin, role in control of, 960–961
    relation to adipocytes, 949–950
    relation to whole-body physiology, 961–963
    release and metabolism of adrenergic transmitter in, 954
    vascular actions of sympathetic nerve stimulation, 954–959
    vascular morphology of, 949–950
Adrenal glands
  capillary bed and portal circulation of, 1041–1042
Aging
  capillary changes with, 183–184
Altitude, high
  see also Anoxia
  capillary growth during exposure to, 190
Amino acids
  carrier-mediated transport across blood-brain barrier, 984–985
  involvement in capillary growth, 202
Anesthesia
  effect on microvessel pressures, 264–265
Angiogenesis factor: *see* Growth substances
Angiotensin-converting enzyme: *see* Kininase II
Anoxia
  hypoxia, involvement in capillary growth, 202–203
Antigens
  on surface of vascular endothelial cells, 141–142
Aqueous humor
  drainage of, 1024–1029
    outflow resistance, 1028–1029
    outflow via Schlemm's canal, 1024–1028
    outflow via uveoscleral routes, 1028
  formation of, 1021–1023
    measurement of rate of formation, 1024
    modification in anterior chamber, 1021–1022
    rate-influencing factors, 1022–1023
  properties and movements of, 1019–1020
Arterioles
  ultrastructural organization of, 67–69
Arteriovenous anastomosis
  ultrastructural organization of, 78
Ascitic fluid
  generation and reabsorption of, 706–707

Basement membrane
  of interstitial space, 527
Bats: *see* Chiroptera
Biological transport
  see also Capillary permeability; Cell membrane permeability
  active transport in endothelium, 448–449
  cell entry processes in liver, 707–709
    carrier-mediated membrane transport, 707–709
    general background, 707
  flux of small solutes across blood-joint barrier, 931–935
    carrier-mediated transport? 934–935
    drug transport, 935
    estimation of permeability–surface area product of blood-joint barrier, 932–934
    methods of flux measurement, 932
    theoretical considerations, 931–932
  in adipose tissue, 949–967
  mass transport in synovial joints in relation to blood flow, 917–947
  membrane transport in transcapillary exchange, 320–327
    application of membrane-transport equations to steady-state ultrafiltration, 326–327
    experimental demonstration of reciprocity, 327
    Staverman-Kedem-Katchalsky equations, 321–324
    thermodynamic equations within membranes, 324–326
  of macromolecules and particulate matter out of joint cavity, 938
  protein flux from plasma to synovial fluid, 935–938
    evidence for restricted diffusion, 936–937
    modeling permeability of blood-joint barrier, 937–938
    synovial fluid:plasma concentration ratios, 935–936
  solute exchange between synovial fluid and epiphysial cartilage, 940–941
    effects of high charge density, 940
    nutritional routes and metabolic activity of cartilage, 940
    steric exclusion and restricted diffusion in cartilage, 940–941
  solute transport from plasma to chondrocyte, 941–942
    fluid-to-cartilage flux, 941–942
    plasma-to-fluid flux, 941
  solute transport from synovial interface to cartilage interface, 938–940
    importance of motion for transport through joint space, 939–940
    inadequacy of diffusional flux through joint space, 938–939
Blood
  flow in small tubes, 217–249
    pulsatile flow, 239–241
    pulse wave propagation in microvessels, 241
    relevance to blood flow in vivo, 244
    viscoelastic properties of blood, 239–241
  rheological properties of, 219–220, 277–278
  rheology as mechanism of microvascular control, 275–276
  rheology in vivo, macrocirculatory studies of, 278–279
Blood-brain barrier
  facilitated transport in endothelium, 446–448

Blood brain barrier (*continued*)
transfer across, 969–1000
amino acids, 984–985
carrier-mediated transport, 982–985
cerebral blood flow, 976–977
drugs and partition hypothesis, 987–988
enzymatic trapping, 988–989
extracellular compounds, 979
inorganic ions, 985–987
monocarboxylic acids, 985
monosaccharides, 983–984
other organic compounds, 985
transcellular diffusion, 979–982
water, 977–979
transfer across, alterations in, 989–996
arterial hypertension, 993–994
general considerations, 989
hypercapnia, 994
models of barrier opening, 995–996
osmotic imbalance, 989–993
seizures, 994–995
transfer across, methods of quantifying, 970–976
brain-uptake index, 972–973
brain washout time, 975
external-registration technique, 973–974
general considerations, 970–971
indicator-diffusion technique, 971–972
intravenous administration methods, 974–975
ventriculocisternal perfusion, 975–976
Blood cells
see also Blood platelets; Erythrocytes; Leukocytes
rheological properties of, 220–225
suspensions of, flow through branched tubes, 241–243
effects of blood cell eccentricity in feeding vessel on cell distribution, 243
effects of discharge ratio on cell distribution, 241–242
effects of entrance geometry and flow on cell distribution, 243
Blood circulation
see also Cerebrovascular circulation; Coronary circulation; Liver circulation; Microcirculation
blood flow and mass transport in synovial joints, 917–947
control of blood flow, 920–921
measurement methods of synovial blood flow, 920
continuous portal circulations, 1041–1042
adrenal, 1041–1042
neurohypophysis, 1042
pancreas, 1042
convergent portal circulations, 1038–1041
hypothalamus and adenohypophysis, 1038–1039
kidney, 1039–1040
liver, 1038
lymphatic system, 1041
testis, 1040–1041
uterus and ovary, 1040
in bronchi, 903–904
in capillaries, 268–270
in humans, 269–270
in eyes, 1001–1034
anatomy, 1001–1005
blood flow, 1008–1009
control by autonomic nerves, 1012–1015
control by facial nerve, 1015
control by oculomotor nerve, 1014–1015
control by sympathetic nerves, 1012–1014
control of blood flow, 1009–1012
control of optic nerve blood flow, 1011–1012
control of retinal blood flow, 1011
control of uveal blood flow, 1011
effects of O_2 and CO_2, 1016
nutrition of retina, 1020
O_2 supply, 1012
optic nerve blood vessels, 1005
pressure in intraocular arteries, 1005–1006
pressure in intraocular veins, 1006–1008
retinal blood vessels, 1002–1004
role of prostaglandins and sensory nerves, 1015
uveal blood vessels, 1004–1005
macrocirculatory studies of in vivo blood rheology, 278–279
miscellaneous portal circulations, 1042–1043
portal circulations and countercurrent mechanisms, 1044–1045
portal circulations, classification of, 1035–1043
portal circulations, sites in which they may occur, 1043–1044
other organs, 1044
stomach, 1043
sweat glands, 1043–1044
Blood-joint barrier: *see* Joints
Blood platelets
properties of, effects of alterations on tube flow, 238
rheological properties of, 225
role in pathogenesis of disseminated intravascular coagulation, 1062–1063
Blood pressure
see also Capillary pressure; Hypertension; Hypotension; Venous pressure
in intraocular blood vessels, 1005–1008
influence on trans-synovial flow, 928
microvessel pressures, 26, 252–265, 632–634
anesthesia and, 264–265
effect of systemic hypertension, 265
in control of microcirculation and blood-tissue exchange, 632–634
in intestinal muscle and mucosal microcirculation of rat, 26
measurement, 254–255
modular configuration of network, 253
shunts, 264
systemic pressure dissipation, 255–258
systemic pressure versus, 259–261
terminology, 253–254
variability, 258–259
pressure-flow relations in microcirculation, 251–307
systemic pressure dissipation in microvessels, 255–258
branching considerations, 256–257
effect of vessel dimensions, 255–256
pressure distribution in successive segments, 257–258
venous vessels, 258
systemic pressure vs. microvessel pressure, 259–261
Blood pressure determination
early measurements of capillary pressure, 261–262
mercury manometer, use by Poiseuille in 1828, 2–3
Blood proteins
flux across blood-joint barrier into synovial fluid, 935–938
evidence for restricted diffusion, 936–937
modeling permeability of blood-joint barrier, 937–938
synovial fluid:plasma concentration ratios, 935–936
interstitial plasma proteins, 527–529
contents in skin and muscle, 529
Blood vessels
see also Arterioles; Coronary vessels; Microcirculation; Muscles, smooth, vascular; Retinal vessels; Veins
endothelium of, physiology and biochemistry, 103–164
angiogenic studies, 113–117
biosynthesis in subendothelium, 119–123, 147
biosynthesis of releasable products, 123–126
cell surface antigens, 141–142
cell surface enzymes, 140–141
cell surface molecules related to thrombosis, 141
contractile pathophysiology of endothelial cells, 131
contraction of endothelial cells, 128–130, 147
enzyme activities of endothelial cells in tissue culture, 145–146
growth control in endothelial cell cultures, 109–113, 146

Blood vessels (*continued*)
in vitro endothelial cell technology, 105–109
membrane-associated activities, 136–142
metabolism of circulating vasoactive agents, 142–144
motility of endothelial cells, 127–136, 147
other cell surface molecules, 142
other metabolic activities, 144–146
receptor mediation of nonvasoactive substances, 139–140
receptor mediation of vasoactive substances, 136–139
regeneration of endothelial cells, 118–119
regulation of pericytes, 130–131
regulation of postcapillary venule junctions, 131–136
wall, role in pathogenesis of disseminated intravascular coagulation, 1064–1065
Blood volume
in adipose tissue, 952
microvascular volume controlling microcirculation and blood-tissue exchange, 634–635
Bronchi
blood circulation in, 903–904

Capillaries
see also Capillary permeability; Capillary pressure
architectural and flow characteristics in, 32
capillary beds and portal circulations, 1035–1046
circulation studies by Poiseuille in 1833–1835, 3–4
density in different tissues, comparison of, 166–172
relation to fibers in various regions of heart, 169
relation to fibers in various skeletal muscles, 170
electrical resistance of walls, measurement in study of capillary permeability, 442–443
endothelial cell enzyme activities, 144–145
flow in, 268–270
of humans, 269–270
growth and adaptation of, 165–216
growth and its inhibition, factors in, 199–205
growth during prenatal and postnatal development, 180–184
central nervous system, 182
changes with aging, 183–184
heart, 182
retina, 183
skeletal muscle, 182–183
skin, 183
growth in normal adult tissues, 184–190
during exposure to high altitude, 190
in cardiac muscle during exercise, 188–189
in heart during long-term bradycardial pacing, 189–190
in skeletal muscle during long-term electrical stimulation, 185–188
in skeletal muscle during training, 185
growth inhibition, factors in, 205
growth of, chemical factors in, 200–203
fibroblast growth factor, epidermal growth factor, polypeptides, amino acids, and prostaglandins, 202
hormones, 202
hypoxia, 202–203
mast cells and histamine, 201
other factors contained in blood, 201
substances released from leukocytes, 201
tumor angiogenic factor, 199, 201–202
growth of, mechanical factors in, 203–205
growth of, techniques used in evaluation of, 172–180
chick chorioallantoic membrane, 180
diffusion chambers, 179
electron microscopy, 172–173
light microscopy, 172
rabbit cornea, 179
rabbit ear chambers, 178–179
studies with incorporation of [^{3}H]thymidine, 173–176
tissue chambers and avascular regions, 177–180
tissue cultures, 176–177
growth under pathological conditions, 190–199
diabetes mellitus, 198
healing of skin wounds and grafts, 197–198
hypertrophy and atrophy, 190–194
muscle wound healing and regeneration, 195–197
psoriasis, 198
retrolental fibroplasia, 198–199
tumors, 199, 201–202
wound healing and regeneration, 194–198
microcirculation and blood-tissue exchange, control of, 627–687
active hyperemia in, 651–657
blood flow autoregulation, 642–646
capillary pressure autoregulation, 646–647
local control of microcirculation and transport, 642–650
mechanisms of autoregulation, 648–650
metabolic regulation, 651–663
microvascular nerve networks, 673–674
nervous control, 663–674
parasympathetic cholinergic vasodilatation, 672
physical factors controlling flow and exchange, 629–642
reactive hyperemia in, 657–659
responses to venous pressure elevation, 648
role of endothelial cells, 628–629
role of pericytes, 628
role of smooth muscle, 627–628
series and parallel microvascular components, 629
stimuli for metabolic vasodilatation, 659–663
sympathetic adrenergic vasoconstrictor nerves, 663–671
sympathetic cholinergic vasodilator nerves, 671–672
vasomotor nerves and transmitters, 672–673
of lung, ultrastructure of, 868–874
recruitment of, 270–271
surface area in adipose tissue, effects of sympathetic nerve stimulation on, 954
surface area in relation to capillary permeability, 433–436
synovial, morphology of, 918–920
ultrastructural organization of, 69–73
continuous capillaries, 70–71
discontinuous capillaries (sinusoids), 72–73
fenestrated capillaries, 71–72
Capillary permeability
active transport in endothelium, 448–449
blood-tissue exchange in heart, tracer-transient analysis of, 786–797
catecholamines, 795–796
effect of coronary blood flow and vascular resistance on, 789–790
free fatty acids, 792–795
glucose, 795
implications of reconstructions arising from analyses for hypotheses on metabolic regulation of coronary blood flow, 796–797
modeling of, 786–789
multiple-tracer approach, 786
water, 790–792
capillary pressure, regulated? 397–398
channels conducting fluid through capillary walls, properties of, 398–403
deductions concerning nature of fluid-conducting pathways, 402–403
effects of macromolecules on hydraulic conductivity, 401–402
evidence for an exclusive water channel, 400
filtration rates and filtration coefficients in single vessels, 398–400
charge, role in, 358–363
concentration and potential profiles near membranes, 360–362
critique of Donnan-distribution calculations, 360
Donnan distribution, 359
Donnan potential and osmotic pressure, 359–360

Capillary permeability (*continued*)
effect of charge on selectivity of capillary wall, 363
interactions of charged solutes in cylindrical pores, 362–363
determination of, methods, 413–429
determination of, principal considerations in, 412–413
diffusion mechanism of, 310–316
diffusion across thin membranes, 313
diffusion with superimposed convective solute transport, 313–314
hydrodynamic description of diffusion coefficients, 312–313
partition of solute flux into convective and diffusive components, 314–316
stochastic description of diffusion coefficients, 310–312
fiber-matrix model of, 351–358
exclusion and diffusion in hyaluronic acid networks, 354
permeability coefficients of membranes containing fibrous networks, 354–355
pore and fiber-matrix models applied to capillary transport, 357–358
reflection coefficients in fibrous networks, 356–357
restricted diffusion, 353–354
spaces within fibrous networks, 352–353
steric exclusion, 353
water flow through fibrous networks, 355–356
filtration coefficients in organs and tissues, 386–389
fluid balance in organs and tissues, 389–398
adjustments of filtration rate after changes in venous pressure, 392–396
fluid balance and capillary pressure in tissues at low venous pressures, 390–392
steady-state reabsorption of fluid into vascular system, 396–397
techniques for measuring Starling forces, 389–390
fluid movements through capillary walls, 375–409
in adipose tissue, effects of sympathetic nerve stimulation on, 954–958
functional aspects, 958
net transvascular movement of fluid, 958–959
possible effector mechanisms, 956–958
in brain, facilitated transport in endothelium, 446–448
in eye, 1016–1019
measurements in single capillaries, 383–386
hydraulic conductivity in mammalian and avian capillaries, 383–384
hydraulic conductivity in microperfused frog capillaries, 384–386
mechanics and thermodynamics of, 309–374
background, 310
membrane transport, 320–327
application of membrane-transport equations to steady-state ultrafiltration, 326–327
experimental demonstration of reciprocity, 327
Staverman-Kedem-Katchalsky equations, 321–324
thermodynamic equations within membranes, 324–326
multiple pathways for, 370
pore theory of, 327–351
osmotic flow, 344–349
Poiseuille's law, 327–330
pore diffusion, 330–334
pore theory, 334–336
pore theory of ultrafiltration, 339–344
slit geometry, 349
solvent drag, 336–339
rate-limiting processes in blood-tissue exchange, 429–431
lipophilic solutes, 430–431
water permeability, 431
relation to capillary surface area, 433–436
single-capillary studies of, 439–446
dye-diffusion studies, 443–444
electrical resistance of capillary walls, 442–443
gradient of permeability, 444–445
interstitial-diffusion method, 441, 445–446
results, 441–442
sac method, 440–441
single-injection technique, 440
solute and water exchange in microvasculature, modeling in analysis of, 549–626
general approaches to blood-tissue exchange, 560–572
general considerations, 551–560
modeling of perturbed states, osmotic and pressure transients, 607–620
relation of modeling parameters to understanding exchange processes, 620
Starling's hypothesis of, formulation of, 375–377
filtration theory, 375–376
reabsorption of tissue fluid into blood, 376–377
Starling's hypothesis of, general and theoretical considerations, 379–383
coupling of fluid filtration to solute permeability, 381
general implications, 379–381
osmotic pressure of protein solutions, 381–383
Starling's hypothesis of, quantitative support for, 377–379
fluid movements, protein osmotic pressure, and mean capillary pressure in intact and perfused tissues, 378–379
pressure and filtration rates in single capillaries, 377–378
steady-state capillary-tissue exchange modeling, 572–607
capillary–interstitial fluid exchange, 574–596
cell–interstitial fluid–capillary exchange, 596–604
cell–interstitial fluid–capillary systems with saturable transport mechanisms, 604–606
homogeneous and heterogeneous systems with diffusional shunting of tracers, 606–607
modeling process, 572–573
studies of, interpretation, 449–455
background, 449–450
equivalent model of hydrophilic channel, 450–453
other approaches to equivalent slit widths, 453–455
thermodynamic principles of, 316–320
entropy generation and dissipation of free energy, 316–317
entropy generation and fluxes and forces across membranes, 317–318
molecular viewpoint, some elementary statistical mechanical concepts, 319–320
Onsager's law, thermodynamic relations for passive solute and water flows across membranes, 318–319
to ions and small molecules in eye, 1017–1019
to macromolecules, 467–520
across continuous capillary beds, 477–491, 506–507
across discontinuous capillaries, 500–503, 508–509
across fenestrated capillary beds, 491–500, 507–508
experimental approaches, 468–477
in adipose tissue, 488
in colon, 499–500
in eye, 1017
in kidney glomerular capillaries, 492–493
in kidney peritubular capillaries, 493–494
in liver, 500–503
in lung, 480–485
in myocardium, 488
in nervous system, 488–490
in skeletal muscle, 485–488
in small intestine, 495–499
in stomach, 499
in subcutaneous tissue, 477–480
intravital microscopy studies, 490–491
lymph studies, 469–474, 477–504
mechanisms of transcapillary solute transport, 504–506
microscopic visualization of macromolecule leakage, 469
osmotic transients, 468–469
plasma disappearance curves for radioactive macromolecules, 469
pore estimates, 474–477
regional differences, 477–504

Capillary permeability (*continued*)
theoretical considerations, 468
transport pathways, 506–509
whole-body capillary permeability, 503–504
to small solutes, 411–466
to solutes in lung, 888–892
high-molecular-weight solutes, 891–892
low-molecular-weight solutes, 888–891
transport rates in vivo, capillary diffusion capacities, 431–433
vesicle and lipophilic-solute transport, 363–370
effect of hydrostatic pressure on vesicular transport, 368
measurement of transcapillary exchange, vesicle transport vs. ultrafiltration, 366–368
movement of vesicles within cytoplasm, 366
permeability coefficients for small lipid-soluble solutes, 369–370
tissue-to-blood transport of macromolecules, 368
transport of small lipid-soluble solutes via cell membrane pathways, 368–369
vesicle filling, 364–366
vesicular exchange, transcytosis, 364
whole-organ studies, 413–429
blood-clearance techniques, 414–419
blood transients, 427–429
diffusion methods, 414–423
osmotic methods, 423–429
tissue transients, 423–427
tissue-uptake techniques, 419–423
whole-organ studies, data from, 437–439
diffusion permeabilities, 437–438
permeability ratios, 438
reflection coefficients, 438–439
Capillary pressure
and fluid exchange, 263
autoregulation in control of microcirculation and blood-tissue exchange, 646–647
drop within capillary network, 262
early measurements of, 261–262
in humans, 263–264
in tissues at low venous pressure, fluid balance and, 390–392
is it regulated? 397–398
isogravimetric pressures, 262
local regulation of, 262–263
measurements in study of Starling's hypothesis of capillary permeability, 377–379
techniques for measuring Starling's forces, 389–390
Carbon dioxide
see also Hypercapnia
effects on blood circulation in eye, 1016
role in local control of gastric microcirculation, 811–812
Cartilage, articular
see also Growth plate
chondrocytes, solute transport from plasma to, 941–942
interface of, solute transport from synovial interface to, 938–940
importance of motion for transport through joint space, 939–940
inadequacy of diffusional flux through joint space, 938–939
Catecholamines
see also Epinephrine; Norepinephrine
role in control of adipose tissue circulation, 960
steady-state extraction and tissue levels in myocardium, 785–786
tracer-transient analysis of blood-tissue exchange in heart, 795–796
CCK: *see* Cholecystokinin
Cell membrane permeability
limited RBC permeability, modifying effect on flow-limited exchange processes in liver, 733–741
thiourea studies, 733–735
of microvascular endothelium, 81–91
lipids and lipid-soluble molecules, 81
water and water-soluble molecules, 81–91
Central nervous system
prenatal and postnatal development of, capillary growth during, 182
role in control of adipose tissue circulation, 961
Cerebrospinal fluid
see also Blood brain barrier
macromolecule concentration and capillary permeability, 488–490
Cerebrovascular circulation
capillaries of CNS, growth during prenatal and postnatal development, 182
microscope studies of, 30–32
relation to blood-brain transfer, 976–977
Chick embryo
chorioallantoic membrane in studies of capillary growth, 180
Chiroptera
wing microcirculation, architecture of, 27–29
Cholecystokinin
role in gastric microcirculation, 811
role in intestinal microcirculation, 827
role in pancreatic microcirculation, 839
Clostridiopeptidase A
biosynthesis in vascular endothelium, 123
CNS: *see* Central nervous system
Collagen
collagenous fibers in interstitial space, 521–523
Collagenase: *see* Clostridiopeptidase A
Colon
capillary permeability to macromolecules in, 499–500
Colony-stimulating factor
biosynthesis in vascular endothelium, 126
Complement
role in pathogenesis of disseminated intravascular coagulation, 1063–1064
Computers
simulations of microvascular exchange, 540–542
Connective tissue
of microvascular wall, ultrastructure correlated with function, 65–67
connective tissue cells, 65–67
elastic fibers, 65
nerves, 67
Cornea
rabbit cornea technique for study of capillary growth, 179
Coronary circulation
blood flow and vascular resistance, effect on blood-tissue exchange in myocardium, 789–790
autoregulation, 789
heterogeneity of local blood flow, 789–790
recruitment of capillaries, 790
metabolic regulation of, implications of reconstructions arising from transient analyses of blood-tissue exchange in heart for hypotheses on mechanism of, 796–797
Coronary vessels
capillary growth during exercise, 188–189
capillary growth during long-term bradycardial pacing, 189–190
capillary growth during prenatal and postnatal development, 182
microcirculation, comparison of differentiation and growth of, 184
microcirculation of myocardium, 20–21
microcirculatory anatomy, 782

Diabetes mellitus
vascular growth in, 198
Digestion
vascular reactions of intestinal microcirculation during, 833–836
Disseminated intravascular coagulation
etiological considerations, 1057

Disseminated intravascular coagulation (*continued*)
historical background on, 1047–1048
pathogenesis of microcirculatory changes in, 1057–1069
fibrinolysis, 1068–1069
formation of microthrombi, 1066–1068
initiating events, 1058–1066
role of complement, 1063–1064
role of mast cells, 1065–1066
role of platelets, 1062–1063
role of reticuloendothelial system and fixed macrophages, 1061–1062
role of vascular wall, 1064–1065
pathology and pathophysiology of, 1055–1057
Drugs
transport across blood-brain barrier, 987–988
transport across blood-joint barrier, 935

Ear, external
rabbit ear chambers for study of capillary growth, 178–179
Elastase: *see* Pancreatopeptidase
Elastic tissue
in interstitial space, 523–524
of microvascular wall, 65
Electrical stimulation
long-term stimulation of skeletal muscles, capillary growth during, 185–188
of sympathetic nerves, vascular actions on adipose tissue, 954–959
capillary surface area, 954
net transvascular movement of fluid, 958–959
permeability, 954–958
resistance, 954
Endocytosis
processes in microvascular endothelium, 78–79
Endothelium
active transport in, 448–449
facilitated transport in, 446–448
of microvascular wall, structural correlations in basic processes of, 78–91
endocytosis and transcytosis, traffic of membranes, 78–81
permeability of lipids and lipid-soluble molecules, 81
permeability of water and water-soluble molecules, 81–91
synthetic and metabolic activities, 78
of microvascular wall, ultrastructure and functional correlations, 42–63
cell surface biochemistry, 52–59
coated pits and coated vesicles, 43–44
cytoskeleton and endothelial contractility, 47–51
differentiations of endothelium, 60–63
fenestrae, 47
general structure, 42–51
growth and regeneration, 59
intercellular junctions, 59–60
other organelles, 51
plasma membrane, 43
plasmalemmal vesicles, 44–45
subendothelial matrix, 63–64
transendothelial channels, 45–47
of vascular wall, physiology and biochemistry of, 103–164
angiogenic studies, 113–117
biosynthesis in subendothelium, 119–123, 147
biosynthesis of releasable products, 123–126
cell contraction, 128–130, 147
cell motility, 127–136, 147
cell regeneration, 118–119
cell surface antigens, 141–142
cell surface enzymes, 140–141
cell surface molecules related to thrombosis, 141
endothelial cell, role in microvascular control, 628–629
endothelial contractile pathophysiology, 131
enzyme activities of endothelial cells in tissue culture, 145–146
growth control in endothelial cell cultures, 109–113, 146
in vitro endothelial cell technology, 105–109
membrane-associated activities, 136–142
metabolism of circulating vasoactive agents, 142–144
other cell surface molecules, 142
other metabolic activities, 144–146
pericyte regulation, 130–131
pericyte role in microvascular control, 628
receptor mediation of nonvasoactive substances, 139–140
receptor mediation of vasoactive substances, 136–139
regeneration and growth of endothelium in large blood vessels, 198
regulation of postcapillary venule junctions, 131–136
Endotoxins
induction of disseminated intravascular coagulation, 1049–1050
Enzymes
enzymatic trapping system in transfer across blood-brain barrier, 988–989
Epidermal growth factor
involvement in capillary growth, 202
Epinephrine
see also Norepinephrine
role in intestinal microcirculation, 827–828
Epiphyseal cartilage: *see* Growth plate
Erythrocytes
in splenic pulp, 766–772
mechanism of RBC concentration, 766–768
physical environment, harmful or not? 768–770
selective retention of immature and abnormal RBCs by splenic filter, 770–772
limited RBC permeability, modifying effect on flow-limited exchange processes in liver, 733–741
theoretical examination of effects on distribution of tracer in otherwise flow-limited case, 735–739
thiourea studies, 733–735
use of RBC carriage modeling to analyze outflow dilution curves for labeled thiourea, 739–741
macrorheology of RBC suspensions in narrow tubes, 228–234
cell screening and plasma skimming, 231–232
experimental studies, 228–231
nonaxisymmetric flow, 234
pressure-flow relations, 232–234
relative velocity of cells and suspending medium, 232
semiempirical theories, 234
theoretical considerations, 231–234
microrheology in narrow tubes, 225–228
cell aggregation, 226–227
cell concentration and cell migration, 225–226
cell deformation and cell rotation, 226
cell velocity, 225
interactions of cells with tube walls, 227–228
properties of, effects of alterations on tube flow, 235–237
aggregation, 235–237
deformability, 235
rheological properties of, 220–222
Exertion
capillary growth in cardiac muscle during exercise, 188–189
Extremities
capillary permeability in, adjustments of filtration rate after changes in venous pressure, 394–396
Eye
see also Aqueous humor; Cornea; Intraocular Pressure; Retina; Uvea; Vitreous body
blood circulation in, 1001–1034
anatomy, 1001–1005
blood flow, 1008–1009
control by autonomic nerves, 1012–1015
control by facial nerve, 1015
control by oculomotor nerve, 1014–1015
control by sympathetic nerves, 1012–1014

Eye (*continued*)
control of blood flow, 1009–1012
control of optic nerve blood flow, 1011–1012
control of retinal blood flow, 1011
control of uveal blood flow, 1011
effects of O_2 and CO_2, 1016
nutrition of retina, 1020
O_2 supply, 1012
optic nerve blood vessels, 1005
pressure in intraocular arteries, 1005–1006
pressure in intraocular veins, 1006–1008
retinal blood vessels, 1002–1004
role of prostaglandins and sensory nerves, 1015
uveal blood vessels, 1004–1005
blood vessel permeability in, 1016–1019
to ions and small molecules, 1017–1019
to macromolecules, 1017
tissue fluids of, 1019–1020

Facial nerve
control of blood circulation in eye, 1015
Factor VIII
biosynthesis in vascular endothelium, 123
Fatty acids, nonesterified
steady-state extraction and tissue levels in myocardium, 784–785
tracer-transient analysis of blood-tissue exchange in heart, 792–795
Fatty tissue: *see* Adipose tissue
Fibrinolysis
development during pathogenesis of microcirculatory changes in disseminated intravascular coagulation, 1068–1069
Fibroblast growth factor: *see* Growth substances
Fibronectin
biosynthesis in vascular endothelium, 123–124

Gastrin
role in gastric microcirculation, 810–811
Gastrointestinal motility
influence on gastrointestinal blood flow, 839–840
Gastrointestinal system
see also Digestion; Intestines; Stomach
blood flow in relation to function in, 839–850
influence of gastrointestinal motility, 839–840
influence on actively absorbed solutes, 846–848
influence on passively absorbed solutes, 840–846
influence on secretion, 848–850
microcirculation of, 799–836
anatomy and function of vascular beds, 800–802
study with clearance methods, 802–803
study with microspheres, 803–804
Glucose
steady-state extraction and tissue levels in myocardium, 782–783
tracer-transient analysis of blood-tissue exchange in heart, 795
Gravitation
effect on pulmonary hemodynamics, 884–886
Growth plate
solute exchange between synovial fluid and, 940–941
effect of high charge density, 940
nutritional routes and metabolic activity of cartilage, 940
steric exclusion and restricted diffusion in cartilage, 940–941
Growth substances
involvement in capillary growth, 201–202
fibroblast growth factor, 202
tumor angiogenic factor, 201–202

Hamster cheek pouch
microcirculation in, 26–27

Heart
see also Coronary vessels; Myocardium
development of, capillary density in relation to fiber density in, 168
various regions of, capillary density in relation to fiber density in, 169
Heart conduction system
long-term bradycardial pacing in rabbits, capillary growth in heart during, 189–190
Heart enlargement
capillary growth in, 190–194
Hematoencephalic barrier: *see* Blood-brain barrier
Hemodynamics
see also Blood pressure; Blood volume; Vascular resistance
in individual microvessels, 282–291
apparent viscosity, 284–286
branch points and bifurcations, 289–291
microvessel hematocrit, 286–288
phenomena related to shear rate, 288–289
pressure gradients, 282–284
resistance vs. luminal diameter, 284
of adipose tissue microcirculation, 951–952
exchange, 951–952
plasma volume and interstitial space, 952
resistance, 951
of gastric microcirculation, 804–806
of intestinal microcirculation, 812–820
capacitance function, 820
exchange function, 816–820
resistance function, 812–816
of microcirculatory networks, mathematical modeling of, 291–295
discrete-network models, 294–295
distributive models, 292–294
lumped-parameter models, 290–292
of pancreatic microcirculation, 836–837
capacitance function, 837
exchange function, 837
resistance function, 836–837
of pulmonary microcirculation, 879–887
effect of gravity, 884–886
effect of lung inflation, 883–884
hydrostatic pressure, 879–883
passage of cells through lungs, 886–887
parameters of microcirculation, network distributions of, 279–283
intravascular pressure, 279–280
ratio of precapillary resistance to postcapillary resistance, 282–283
volumetric flow rates, 281–282
Hepatic artery
buffer response in control of liver blood supply, 692–695
Histamine
role in capillary growth, 201
role in local control of gastric microcirculation, 811
Homeostasis
tissue homeostasis, pressure-flow relations in extravascular systems, 295–299
extravascular flow system, 299
interstitial transport, 297–298
interstitium, 295
lymphatic pressures, 296–297
terminal lymphatics, 295–296
tissue pressure, 298–299
Hormones
involvement in capillary growth, 202
Hyaluronic acid
in interstitial space, 524–525
Hydrostatic pressure
intra-articular, influence on trans-synovial flow, 927–928
Hypercapnia
effect on transfer across blood-brain barrier, 994

Hypertension
effect on microvessel pressures, 265
effect on transfer across blood-brain barrier, 993–994
Hypotension
effect on adipose tissue circulation, 962–963
Hypothalamus
capillary bed and portal circulation of, 1038–1039
Hypoxia: *see* Anoxia

Indicator-dilution techniques
in measurement of hepatic blood flow, 698
multiple-indicator–dilution studies of hepatic acinar structure, 698–704
establishing behavior of reference substances in liver, 699–700
excluded-volume effect in interstitial space, 703–704
fractional composition of liver, 702–703
modeling of flow-limited exchange in liver, 700–702
multiple-indicator–dilution technique, 699
Inflammation
acute inflammatory reaction, pathology and pathophysiology of, 1048–1049
Intercellular junctions
of endothelium of microvascular wall, 59–60
postcapillary venule junctions, regulation of, 131–136
Interstitial space
composition and architecture of, 521–529
basement membrane, 527
collagenous fibers, 521–523
elastic fibers, 523–524
hyaluronate, 524–525
interstitial plasma proteins, 527–529
proteoglycans, 525–527
of adipose tissue, 952
physicochemical and partition properties of, 529–535
compartmentalization within interstitium, 533–534
diffusion coefficients, 534–535
exclusion, 529–533
flow conductivity, 535
transport coefficients, 534–535
role in microvascular exchange, 521–547
computer simulations, 540–542
flow in interstitium, 535–536
interstitial fluid and lymph, 536–538
regulation within the interstitium, 538–540
Intestinal absorption
actively absorbed solutes, influence of intestinal blood flow on, 846–848
experimental observations, 846–847
intestinal countercurrent multiplier, 847–848
theoretical considerations, 846
passively absorbed solutes, influence of intestinal blood flow on, 840–846
experimental observations, 841–842
intestinal countercurrent exchanger, 842–846
theoretical considerations, 840–841
Intestinal mucosa
microcirculation of, 23–26
Intestine, small
capillary permeability to macromolecules in, 495–499
microcirculation of, 23–26
Intestines
see also Colon
capillary permeability in, adjustments of filtration rate after changes in venous pressure, 396
microcirculation of, 812–836
autoregulation of blood flow, 828–833
basic hemodynamics, 812–820
hormonal control of, 827–828
local chemical control of, 828–829
local nervous control of, 829
nervous vasoconstrictor fibers of, 823–827
nervous vasodilator fibers of, 821–823
role of secretin, cholecystokinin, and epinephrine in, 827–828
vascular reactions during digestion, 833–836
secretion by, influence of intestinal blood flow on, 849
Intraocular pressure
episcleral venous pressure, measurement of, 1023
measurement of, 1023
outflow resistance, determination of, 1023–1024, 1028–1029
Ions
inorganic ion transport across blood-brain barrier, 985–987
permeability of intraocular blood vessels to, 1017–1019

Joints
see also Cartilage, articular; Synovial fluid
blood flow and mass transport in, 917–947
blood-joint barrier, flux of small solutes across, 931–935
carrier-mediated transport? 934–935
drug transport, 935
estimation of permeability–surface area product, 932–934
methods of flux measurement, 932
theoretical considerations, 931–932
blood-joint barrier, structure of, 918–920
morphology of synovial capillaries, 918–920
ultrastructure of intimal layer, 918
resting and moving joints, fluid balance in, 930–931
solute transport from plasma to chondrocyte, 941–942
fluid-to-cartilage flux, 941–942
plasma-to-fluid flux, 941
solute transport from synovial interface to cartilage interface, 938–940
importance of motion for transport through joint space, 939–940
inadequacy of diffusional flux through joint space, 938–939
synovial blood flow, 920–921
control of, 920–921
measurement of, 920
transport of macromolecules and particulate matter out of joint cavity, 938
trans-synovial flow, control of, 927–930
algebraic analysis of, 929–930
influence of blood pressure, 928
influence of intra-articular hydrostatic and oncotic pressure, 927–928
influence of plasma oncotic pressure, 928–929

Kidney
capillary bed and portal circulation of, 1039–1040
capillary permeability to macromolecules in, 492–494
glomerular capillaries, 492–493
peritubular capillaries, 493–494
Kininase II
metabolism by vascular endothelial cells, 143–144

Lactates
steady-state extraction and tissue levels in myocardium, 783–784
Leukocytes
factors involved in capillary growth, 201
properties of, effects of alterations on tube flow, 237–238
rheological properties of, 223–225
Limbs: *see* Extremities
Lipids
permeability through endothelial cell membrane of microvascular wall, 81
Liver
see also Liver circulation
acinar structure of, physiological explorations of, 698–707

Liver (*continued*)
changes in fractional composition of and blood flow to liver during acute hepatic venous congestion, 704
excluded-volume effect in interstitial space, 703–704
fractional composition, 702–703
generation and reabsorption of ascitic fluid, 706–707
lymph flow, 704–706
modeling of flow-limited exchange, 700–702
multiple-indicator–dilution studies establishing behavior of reference substances, 699–700
multiple-indicator–dilution technique, 699
blood supply of, general characteristics of control of, 692–696
arterial buffer response, 692–695
blood volume, 695–696
capillary permeability to macromolecules in, 500–503
cell entry processes in, 707–709
carrier-mediated membrane transport, 707–709
general background, 707
exchange at cell surface of, effective blood-tissue interface, 709–717
concentrative entry processes, 710–715
nonconcentrative entry processes, 715–717
Liver circulation
anatomy of microcirculation, 690–692
capillary beds and portal circulation, 1038
cellular entry with intracellular metabolic sequestration or biliary secretion under steady-state conditions, 717–730
cellular removal with barrier at cell membrane, 721–730
cellular removal with no barrier at cell membrane, 718–721
general considerations, 717–718
cellular entry with intracellular removal under substrate non-steady-state conditions, 730–733
bolus-dose indicator-dilution studies, 732–733
intravenous disappearance curves, 730–732
control of, general characteristics of, 692–696
arterial buffer response, 692–695
blood volume, 695–696
flow-limited exchange processes, modifying effect of limited RBC permeability on, 733–741
theoretical examination of effects on distribution of tracer in an otherwise flow-limited case, 735–739
thiourea studies, 733–735
use of RBC carriage modeling to analyze outflow dilution curves for labeled thiourea, 739–741
measurement of blood flow, 696–698
flow estimates based on clearance measurements, 696–697
indicator-dilution measurements, 698
partition of hepatic blood flow, 698
microcirculatory events, 689–743
physiological explorations of acinar structure, 698–707
Lung
capillary permeability in, adjustments of filtration rate after changes in venous pressure, 392–393
capillary permeability to macromolecules in, 480–485
microcirculation of, 865–915
architecture of, 874–877
dimensions of microcirculatory bed, 877–879
effect of gravity on pulmonary hemodynamics, 884–886
effect of lung inflation on pulmonary hemodynamics, 883–884
hemodynamics of, 879–887
hydrostatic pressure in, 879–883
passage of cells through lungs, 886–887
relationship to macrocirculation, 865–868
ultrastructure of pulmonary capillaries, 868–874
solute and water transfer in, 887–903
filtration coefficient, 892–894
interstitial compartment, 896–901
lymphatic functions, 901–903
pulmonary capillary permeability to solutes, 888–892
reflection coefficient, 894–896
Starling relationship, 887–888
Lymph
analysis in studies of capillary permeability to macromolecules, 469–474, 477–504
and interstitial fluid in microvascular exchange, 536–538
circulation of, 33–38
hepatic lymph flow, 704–706
Lymphatic system
capillary beds and convergent portal circulation of, 1041
extravascular systems, pressure-flow relations in, 295–299
extravascular flow system, 299
interstitial transport, 297–298
interstitium, 295
lymphatic pressures, 296–297
terminal lymphatics, 295–296
tissue pressure, 298–299
function in relation to solute and water transfer in lung, 901–903
lymphatic vessels of spleen, 752–753
lymphatic vessels, structure and distribution of, 33–38

Macromolecules
capillary permeability to, 467–520
across continuous capillary beds, 477–491, 506–507
across discontinuous capillaries, 500–503, 508–509
across fenestrated capillary beds, 491–500, 507–508
experimental approaches in study of, 468–477
in adipose tissue, 488
in colon, 499–500
in intraocular blood vessels, 1017
in kidney glomerular capillaries, 492–493
in kidney peritubular capillaries, 493–494
in liver, 500–503
in lung, 480–485
in myocardium, 488
in nervous system, 488–490
in skeletal muscle, 485–488
in small intestine, 495–499
in stomach, 499
in subcutaneous tissue, 477–480
intravital microscopy studies, 490–491
lymph studies, 469–474, 477–504
mechanisms of transcapillary solute transport, 504–506
microscopic visualization of macromolecule leakage, 469
osmotic transients, 468–469
plasma disappearance curves for radioactive macromolecules, 469
pore estimates, 474–477
regional differences in, 477–504
theoretical considerations, 468
transport pathways, 506–509
whole-body capillary permeability, 503–504
effects on hydraulic conductivity of capillary walls, 401–402
exchange across microcirculation, 467–520
transport out of joint cavity, 938
Macrophages
role in pathogenesis of disseminated intravascular coagulation, 1061–1062
Macrorheology: *see* Rheology
Manometry
mercury manometer, use by Poiseuille for measurement of arterial pressure, 2–3
Mast cells
role in capillary growth, 201
role in pathogenesis of disseminated intravascular coagulation, 1065–1066
Membranes
permeability of, characterization by Poiseuille's law and Fick's law, 8–9
Mesentery
microcirculation in cat, 21–23

Microcirculation
see also Arterioles; Arteriovenous anastomosis; Capillaries; Venules
and blood-tissue exchange, control of, 627–687
architectural and flow characteristics of, 13–33
bat wing, 27–29
brain, 30–32
cardiac muscle, 20–21
cat mesentery, 21–23
hamster cheek pouch, 26–27
skeletal muscle, 13–20
skin, 29–30
small intestine muscle and mucosa, 23–26
blood flow in, 265–271
flow distribution, 267
general considerations, 265–266
microvessel number, 270
velocity relationships, 266–267
blood flow in, rheological behavior of, 277–295
background, 277–279
conceptual framework, 277
hemodynamics in individual microvessels, 282–291
mathematical modeling of network hemodynamics, 291–295
network distributions of hemodynamic parameters, 279–283
changes in disseminated intravascular coagulation induced by endotoxins, pathogenesis of, 1057–1069
fibrinolysis, 1068–1069
formation of microthrombi, 1066–1068
initiating events, 1058–1066
development of, 165–216
differentiation and growth of, comparison, 184
events in liver and spleen, 689–780
growth under pathological conditions, 190–199
in disseminated intravascular coagulation induced by endotoxins, 1047–1076
microvascular control mechanisms, 271–277
ancillary factors, 275
blood rheology, 275–276
central vs. local, 272
myogenic adjustments, 272–273
O_2 tension and local adjustments, 274–275
sympathetic innervation, 276–277
vascular tone, 271–272
vasomotion, 273–274
microvascular endothelium, structural correlations in basic processes of, 78–91
endocytosis and transcytosis, traffic of membranes, 78–81
permeability of lipids and lipid-soluble molecules, 81
permeability of water and water-soluble molecules, 81–91
synthetic and metabolic activities, 78
microvascular endothelium, ultrastructure of, 42–63
cell surface biochemistry, 52–59
differentiations of endothelium, 60–63
general structure, 42–51
growth and regeneration, 59
intercellular junctions, 59–60
microvascular exchange, role of interstitium in, 521–547
computer simulations, 540–542
flow in interstitium, 535–536
interstitial fluid and lymph, 536–538
regulation within the interstitium, 538–540
microvascular wall, ultrastructure correlated with function, 41–101
basal lamina, subendothelial matrix, and pericytes, 63–64
connective tissue cells, 65–67
elastic fibers, 65
endothelium, 42–63
smooth muscle cells, 64
microvessel pressures, 252–265
anesthesia and, 264–265
effect of systemic hypertension, 265
measurement, 254–255
modular configuration of network, 253
shunts, 264
systemic pressure dissipation, 255–258
systemic pressure versus, 259–261
terminology, 253–254
variability in, 258–259
of adipose tissue, 949–967
adrenergic innervation of, 950
adrenergic innervation of, regional differences in, 953
β-adrenoreceptors in, types, 952–953
α- and β-adrenoreceptors in, distribution of, 952
basic hemodynamics of, 951–952
cholinergic innervation of, 950
circulating catecholamines in control of, 960
CNS control of, 961
effect of hypotension and hemorrhagic shock on, 962–963
effect of reduced ambient temperature on, 963
hormonal control of, 960–961
local control of, 959–960
methods of investigation of, 950–951
neurotensin, role in control of, 960–961
relation to adipocytes, 949–950
relation to whole-body physiology, 961–963
release and metabolism of adrenergic transmitter in, 954
vascular actions of sympathetic nerve stimulation, 954–959
vascular morphology of, 949–950
of blood and lymph, pressure-flow relations in, 251–307
of gastrointestinal tract, 799–836
anatomy and function of vascular beds, 800–802
study with clearance methods, 802–803
study with microspheres, 803–804
of intestines, 812–836
autoregulation of blood flow, 828–833
basic hemodynamics, 812–820
hormonal control of, 827–828
local chemical control of, 828–829
local nervous control of, 829
nervous vasoconstrictor fibers of, 823–827
nervous vasodilator fibers of, 821–823
role of secretin, cholecystokinin, and epinephrine in, 827–828
vascular reactions during digestion, 833–836
of lung, 865–915
architecture of, 874–877
dimensions of microcirculatory bed, 877–879
effect of gravity on pulmonary hemodynamics, 884–886
effect of lung inflation on pulmonary hemodynamics, 883–884
hemodynamics of, 879–887
hydrostatic pressure in, 879–883
passage of cells through lungs, 886–887
relation to macrocirculation, 865–868
relation to solute and water transfer, 887–903
ultrastructure of pulmonary capillaries, 868–874
of pancreas, 836–839
anatomy of, 836
basic hemodynamics, 836–837
hormonal and local control of, 838–839
nervous control of, 837–838
role of cholecystokinin in, 839
role of secretin in, 838–839
sympathetic control of, 838
vagal control of, 838
of spleen, 743–773
changes arising from cell trapping and from splenic contraction or distension, 772–773
fast and slow circulations and mathematical model, 754–760
kinetics, 753–766
methodology, 743–744, 753–754
morphology, 743–753
vascular compartments and cellular factors, morphological counterparts to mathematical model, 760–766

Microcirculation (*continued*)
of stomach, 804–812
autoregulation of blood flow, 812
basic hemodynamics, 804–806
CO_2 and O_2 in local control of, 811–812
histamine in local control of, 811
hormonal control of, 809–811
nervous control of, 806–809
role of gastrin and pentagastrin in, 810–811
role of secretin and cholecystokinin in, 811
sympathetic control of, 807–809
vagal control of, 806–807
research contributions of Poiseuille, 1–10
capillary circulation studies, 3–4
liquid movements through tubes of small diameter, 4–8
mercury manometer and measurement of arterial pressure, 2–3
Poiseuille's law for characterization of membrane permeability, 8–9
pressures and flows in venous system, 3
solute and water exchange in microvasculature, modeling in analysis of, 549–626
terminology of, 12–13
Microrheology: *see* Rheology
Microscopy
electron microscopy, 41–101, 172–173, 868–874
in evaluation of capillary growth, 172–173
of microvascular wall, functional correlations of, 41–101
of pulmonary capillaries, 868–874
historical background on, 11–12
Microspheres
in study of gastrointestinal microcirculation, 803–804
Models
fiber-matrix model of transcapillary exchange, 351–358
application to capillary transport, 357–358
exclusion and diffusion in hyaluronic acid networks, 354
permeability coefficients of membranes containing fibrous networks, 354–355
reflection coefficients in fibrous networks, 356–357
restricted diffusion, 353–354
spaces within fibrous networks, 352–353
steric exclusion, 353
water flow through fibrous networks, 355–356
mathematical model of splenic microcirculation, 754–766
mathematical models of microcirculatory network hemodynamics, 291–295
discrete-network models, 294–295
distributive models, 292–294
lumped-parameter models, 290–292
modeling in analysis of solute and water exchange in microvasculature, 549–626
approaches to blood-tissue exchange, 560–572
general considerations, 551–560
modeling of perturbed states, osmotic and pressure transients, 607–620
relation of modeling parameters to understanding exchange processes, 620
modeling of blood-tissue exchange in heart, 786–789
formulation of transform of whole-organ impulse response, 788
optimization of model parameters, 788–789
time-domain formulation of exchange in capillary-tissue unit, 786–788
modeling of flow-limited exchange in liver in studies of hepatic acinar structure, 700–702
of blood-brain barrier opening, 995–996
pore model applied to capillary transport, 357–358
RBC carriage modeling in analysis of liver outflow dilution curves for labeled thiourea, 739–741
steady-state capillary-tissue exchange modeling, 572–607
capillary–interstitial fluid exchange, 574–596
cell-interstitial fluid–capillary exchange, 596–604
cell–interstitial fluid–capillary systems with saturable transport mechanisms, 604–606
homogeneous and heterogeneous systems with diffusional shunting of tracers, 606–607
modeling process, 572–573
Monosaccharides
carrier-mediated transport across blood-brain barrier, 983–984
Muscles
capillary density in relation to fibers in, 170
capillary permeability to macromolecules in, 485–488
content of extravascular plasma proteins in, 529
cremaster muscle, microcirculation of, 13–15
extensor hallucis proprius muscle, microcirculation of, 18
gracilis muscle, microcirculation of, 17–18
long-term electrical stimulation of, capillary growth during, 185–188
prenatal and postnatal development of, capillary growth during, 182–183
smooth, vascular, 64, 272–273, 627–628
cells in microvascular wall, 64
myogenic adjustments in microvascular control, 272–273
role in control of microcirculation and blood-tissue exchange, 627–628
spinotrapezius muscle, microcirculation of, 18–20
tenuissimus muscle, microcirculation of, 15–17
training in normal adults, capillary growth during, 185
wound healing and regeneration in, capillary growth during, 195–197
Muscular atrophy
capillary exchange, cellular entry, and metabolic sequestration processes in, interactions between, 781–798
capillary growth in, 190–194
capillary permeability to macromolecules in, 488
microcirculation of, 20–21
steady-state extractions and tissue levels of metabolites and catecholamines in, 782–786
catecholamines, 785–786
free fatty acids, 784–785
glucose, 782–783
lactate, 783–784
O_2, 785
Myocardium
blood-tissue exchange in, tracer-transient analysis of, 786–797
catecholamines, 795–796
effect of coronary blood flow and vascular resistance on, 789–790
free fatty acids, 792–795
glucose, 795
implications of reconstructions arising from transient analyses for hypotheses on mechanism of metabolic regulation of coronary blood flow, 796–797
models, 786–789
multiple-tracer approach, 786
water, 790–792

Neoplasms
capillary growth in, 199, 201–202
Nervous system
see also Central nervous system; Parasympathetic nervous system; Sympathetic nervous system
capillary permeability to macromolecules in, 488–490
control of microcirculation and blood-tissue exchange, 663–674
microvascular nerve networks, 673–674
vasomotor nerves and transmitters, 672–673
Neurons, afferent
role in blood circulation in eye, 1015
Neuroregulators
adrenergic transmitter in adipose tissue, release and metabolism of, 954

Neuroregulators (*continued*)
role in control of microcirculation and blood-tissue exchange, 672–673
Neurotensin
role in control of adipose tissue circulation, 960–961
Norepinephrine
metabolism by vascular endothelial cells, 143

Oculomotor nerve
control of blood circulation in eye, 1014–1015
Optic nerve
blood flow to, control of, 1011–1012
blood vessels of, 1005
Osmolar concentration
osmotic imbalance, effects on transfer across blood-brain barrier, 989–993
Osmotic pressure
intra-articular oncotic pressure, influence on trans-synovial flow, 927–928
measurements in study of Starling's hypothesis of capillary permeability, 378–379, 390
of protein solutions in study of capillary permeability, 381–383
plasma oncotic pressure, influence on trans-synovial flow, 928–929
Ovary
capillary bed and portal circulation of, 1040
Oxygen
see also Anoxia
effects on blood circulation in eye, 1016
O_2 tension and local adjustments in microvascular control, 274–275
role in local control of gastric microcirculation, 811–812
tissue levels in myocardium, 785

Pancreas
capillary beds and portal circulation of, 1042
microcirculation of, 836–839
anatomy of, 836
basic hemodynamics of, 836–837
hormonal and local control of, 838–839
nervous control of, 837–838
role of cholecystokinin in, 839
role of secretin in, 838–839
sympathetic control of, 838
vagal control of, 838
secretion by, influence of gastrointestinal blood flow on, 849–850
Pancreatopeptidase
biosynthesis in vascular endothelium, 123
Parasympathetic nervous system
see also Vagus nerve
cholinergic innervation of adipose tissue, 950
cholinergic vasodilatation in control of microcirculation and blood-tissue exchange, 672
Pentagastrin
role in gastric microcirculation, 810–811
Peptides
polypeptides, involvement in capillary growth, 202
Permeability, capillary: *see* Capillary permeability
Physical education and training
capillary growth in skeletal muscles of normal adults during, 185
Pituitary gland
capillary bed and portal circulation of, 1038–1039, 1042
adenohypophysis, 1038–1039
neurohypophysis, 1042
Plasminogen activators
biosynthesis in vascular endothelium, 124
Polypeptides: *see* Peptides
Portal circulations: *see* Blood circulation
Pressure
see also Blood pressure; Hydrostatic pressure; Intraocular pressure; Manometry; Osmotic pressure
pressure-flow relations in extravascular systems, 295–299
extravascular flow system, 299
interstitial transport, 297–298
interstitium, 295
lymphatic pressure, 296–297
terminal lymphatics, 295–296
tissue pressure, 298–299
Prostaglandins
biosynthesis in vascular endothelium, 124–126
metabolism by vascular endothelial cells, 144
role in blood circulation in eye, 1015
role in capillary growth, 202
Proteoglycans
an interstitial space, 525–527
Psoriasis
vascular growth in, 198

RBCs: *see* Erythrocytes
Receptors, adrenergic
β-adrenoreceptors in adipose tissue microcirculation, types of, 952–953
α- and β-adrenoreceptors in adipose tissue microcirculation, distribution of, 952
Receptors, endogenous substances
nonvasoactive substances, mediation by vascular endothelial cells, 139–140
vasoactive substances, mediation by vascular endothelial cells, 136–139
Reticuloendothelial system
role in pathogenesis of disseminated intravascular coagulation, 1061–1062
Retina
nutrition of, 1020
Retinal vessels
anatomy of, 1002–1004
blood flow in, control of, 1011
capillary growth during prenatal and postnatal development, 183
Retrolental fibroplasia
capillary growth in, 198–199
Rheology
blood flow in microcirculation, 277–295
background, 277–279
conceptual framework, 277
hemodynamics in individual microvessels, 282–291
mathematical modeling of network hemodynamics, 291–295
network distributions of hemodynamic parameters, 279–283
blood flow in small tubes, 217–249, 277–278
effect of alterations of blood cell properties on tube flow, 235–239
effect of RBC aggregation, 235–237
effect of RBC deformability, 235
generalized Fåhraeus effect, 238–239
leukocytes, 237–238
platelets, 238
pulsatile flow, 239–241
pulse wave propagation in microvessels, 241
relevance to blood flow in vivo, 244
rheological properties of blood, 219–220, 277–278
rheological properties of blood cells, 220–225
viscoelastic properties of blood, 239–241
blood flow in vivo, macrocirculatory studies, 278–279
blood rheology as mechanism of microvascular control, 275–276
flow of blood cell suspensions through branched tubes, 241–243
effect of blood cell eccentricity in feeding vessel on cell distribution, 243

Rheology (*continued*)
effect of discharge ratio on cell distribution, 241–242
effect of entrance geometry and flow on cell distribution, 243
macrorheology of RBC suspensions in narrow tubes, 228–234
cell screening and plasma skimming, 231–232
experimental studies, 228–231
nonaxisymmetric flow, 234
pressure-flow relations, 232–234
relative velocity of cells and suspending medium, 232
semiempirical theories, 234
theoretical considerations, 231–234
microrheology of RBCs in narrow tubes, 225–228
cell aggregation, 226–227
cell concentration and cell migration, 225–226
cell deformation and cell rotation, 226
cell velocity, 225
interactions of cells with tube walls, 227–228
of tube flow, 217–219
definitions, 217–218
steady flow of Newtonian fluids through unbranched tubes, 218–219
Poiseuille's law, 4–8, 327–330
effect of pressure, 6–8
effect of temperature, 5–6
variations in tube diameter and ellipticity, 5

Secretin
role in gastric microcirculation, 811
role in intestinal microcirculation, 827
role in pancreatic microcirculation, 838–839
Seizures
effect on transfer across blood-brain barrier, 994–995
Serotonin
metabolism by vascular endothelial cells, 143
Shock, hemorrhagic
effect on adipose tissue circulation, 962–963
Shwartzman phenomenon
local reaction induced by endotoxins, 1050–1055
Skin
content of extravascular plasma proteins in, 529
healing of skin wounds and grafts, capillary growth during, 197–198
microcirculation of, 29–30
prenatal and postnatal development of, capillary growth during, 183
Spleen
arterial circulation of, 744–746
functions and gross structure of, 741–743
intermediate circulation of, open or closed? 748–752
lymphatic vessels of, 752–753
microcirculation of, kinetics, 753–766
fast and slow circulations and mathematical model, 754–760
methodology, 753–754
vascular compartments and cellular factors, morphological counterparts to mathematical model, 760–766
microcirculation of, morphology, 743–753
methodology, 743–744
microcirculatory changes arising from cell trapping and from splenic contraction or distension, 772–773
after sequestration of abnormal cells, 772
contracted spleen, 772
dilated spleen, 772–773
pulp of, blood in, 766–772
mechanism of RBC concentration, 766–768
physical environment, harmful to RBCs or not? 768–770
selective retention of immature and abnormal RBCs by splenic filter mechanism, 770–772
venous circulation of, 746–748
Stomach
capillary permeability to macromolecules in, 499
microcirculation of, 804–812
autoregulation of blood flow, 812
basic hemodynamics, 804–806
CO_2 and O_2 in local control of, 811–812
histamine in local control of, 811
hormonal control of, 809–811
nervous control of, 806–809
role of gastrin and pentagastrin in, 810–811
role of secretin and cholecystokinin in, 811
sympathetic control of, 807–809
vagal control of, 806–807
possible site for portal circulation, 1043
secretion by, influence of gastrointestinal blood flow on, 848–849
Sweat glands
possible site for portal circulation, 1043–1044
Sympathetic nervous system
adrenergic innervation of adipose tissue, 950
regional differences in, 953
in control of blood circulation in eye, 1012–1014
in control of gastric microcirculation, 807–809
in control of microcirculation and blood-tissue exchange, 663–672
adrenergic vasoconstrictor nerves, 663–671
cholinergic vasodilator nerves, 671–672
stimulation of, vascular actions on adipose tissue, 954–959
capillary surface area, 954
net transvascular movement of fluid, 958–959
permeability, 954–958
resistance, 954
sympathetic innervation in microvascular control, 276–277
Synovial fluid
filtration fraction of, 923–924
fluid balance in resting and moving joints, 930–931
origin and composition, 922–923
pressure-angle relationships, 924–925
pressure-volume relationships and compartmentation of, 925–927
protein flux from plasma into, 935–938
evidence for restricted diffusion, 936–937
modeling permeability of blood-joint barrier, 937–938
synovial fluid:plasma concentration ratios, 935–936
rate of formation, 923
solute exchange between epiphyseal cartilage and, 940–941
effect of high charge density, 940
nutritional routes and metabolic activity of cartilage, 940
steric exclusion and restricted diffusion in cartilage, 940–941
solute transport from plasma to chondrocyte, 941–942
fluid-to-cartilage flux, 941–942
plasma-to-fluid flux, 941
subatmospheric pressure of, 924

Temperature
reduced ambient temperature, effect on adipose tissue circulation, 963
Testis
capillary bed and portal circulation of, 1040–1041
Thermodynamics
of transcapillary exchange, 309–374
entropy generation and dissipation of free energy, 316–317
entropy generation and fluxes and forces across membranes, 317–318
molecular viewpoint, some elementary statistical mechanical concepts, 319–320
Onsager's law, thermodynamic relations for passive solute and water flows across membranes, 318–319
thermodynamic equations within membranes, 324–326
Thiourea
in study of modifying effect of limited RBC permeability on flow-limited exchange processes in liver, 733–735

Thiourea (*continued*)
labeled thiourea outflow dilution curves from liver, analysis by use of RBC carriage modeling, 739–741
Thrombosis
cell surface molecules of vascular endothelium related to, 141
microthrombi, formation in microcirculation in disseminated intravascular coagulation, 1066–1068
Thymidine
incorporation studies in evaluation of capillary growth, 173–176
Tissue culture
endothelial cell culture studies, growth control factors, 109–113, 146–147
cell surface protein, 111–112
extracellular matrix, 111, 146
growth factors, 113, 147
shape, 109–110
variant endothelial cells, 112–113
endothelial cells in, enzyme activities of, 145–146
in studies of capillary growth, 176–177
of vascular endothelium, technology of, 105–109
criteria for cell identification, 107–109
history and state of the art, 105–107
Transcapillary exchange: *see* Capillary permeability

Uterus
capillary bed and portal circulation of, 1040
Uvea
blood flow in, control of, 1011
blood vessels of, 1004–1005

Vagus nerve
control of gastric microcirculation, 806–807
control of pancreatic microcirculation, 838
Vascular resistance
coronary, effect on blood-tissue exchange in myocardium, 789–790
of adipose tissue microcirculation, 951, 954
effect of sympathetic nerve stimulation, 954
Vasomotor system
vasomotion in microvascular control, 273–274
vasomotor nerves in control of microcirculation and blood-tissue exchange, 672–673
Veins
see also Venules
flow studies by Poiseuille in 1830, 3
Venous pressure
changes in, adjustments of capillary filtration rate after, 392–396
elevation of, responses of microcirculation and blood-tissue exchange to, 648
low pressures, fluid balance and capillary pressure in tissues at, 390–392
studies by Poiseuille in 1830, 3
Venules
postcapillary venule junctions, regulation of, 131–136
ultrastructural organization of, 73–78
muscular venules, 75–78
pericytic (postcapillary) venules, 73–75
Vitreous body
properties and movements, 1020

Water
movement through capillary walls, evidence for an exclusive water channel, 400
permeability through capillaries, 431
permeability through endothelial cell membrane of microvascular wall, 81–91
tracer-transient analysis of blood-tissue exchange in heart, 790–792
transfer across blood-brain barrier, 977–979
Wing
bat wing, architecture of microcirculation of, 27–29
Wound healing
capillary growth in, 194–198
healing and regeneration of muscle wounds, 195–197
healing in cornea, 198
healing of skin wounds and grafts, 197–198
observations in implanted rabbit ear chamber, 194–195